INTERPRETING ENGINEERING DRAWINGS

Fourth Canadian Edition

INTERPRETING ENGINEERING DRAWINGS

Fourth Canadian Edition

Cecil H. Jensen

NELSON
THOMSON LEARNING

Australia • Canada • Mexico • Singapore • Spain • United Kingdom • United States

NELSON
THOMSON LEARNING

Interpreting Engineering Drawings
Fourth Canadian Edition

by Cecil H. Jensen

Editorial Director and Publisher:
Evelyn Veitch

Acquisitions Editor:
Edward Ikeda

Marketing Manager:
Jim Rozsa

Senior Project Editor:
Karina TenVeldhuis

Managing Production Editor:
Susan Calvert

Production Coordinator:
Hedy Sellers

Proofreader:
Claudia Kutchukian

Art Director:
Angela Cluer

Cover Design:
Katherine Strain

Compositor:
Susan Calverley

Printer:
Webcom

Printed and bound in Canada
3 4 04

For more information contact Nelson Thomson Learning, 1120 Birchmount Road, Scarborough, Ontario, M1K 5G4. Or you can visit our Internet site at http://www.nelson.com

National Library of Canada Cataloguing in Publication Data

Jensen, C. H. (Cecil Howard), 1925–
Interpreting engineering drawings

4th Canadian ed.
Includes bibliographical references and index.
ISBN 0-17-616998-9

1. Engineering drawings. I. Title.

T351.5J46 2001 604.2'5
C2001-902777-X

354 9706

1-800-423-0563

CANADA 800-268-2222

CONTENTS

Preface xi
About the Author .xiii
Acknowledgments xiv

Unit 1 1

Bases for Interpreting Drawings 1
Visible Lines 3
Lettering on Drawings 3
Sketching 3
Third-Angle Projection 3
ISO Projection Symbol 6
Title Block 7
Assignments
A-1 . . . . .Sketching Missing Views 9
A-2 . . . . .Sketching Three Views 10
A-3 . . . . .Sketching Pictorial Views 11

Unit 2 12

Working Drawings 12
Dimensioning 12
Linear Units of Measurement 14
SI (Metric) Units of Measurement 15
Choice of Dimensions 16
Basic Rules for Dimensioning 16
Information Shown on Assignment Drawings .17
References 17
Assignments
A-4M . . .Corner Block 18
A-5 . . . . .Step Bracket 19
A-6 . . . . .Counter Clamp Bar 20
A-7 . . . . .Dimensioning 21

Unit 3 22

The Drafting Office 22
Drawing Reproduction 23
Abbreviations Used on Drawings 25
Hidden Lines 25
Assignments
A-8 . . . . .Matching Drawings-1 26
A-9 . . . . .Matching Drawings-2 27
A-10 . . . .Feed Hopper 29
A-11 . . . .Sketching Three Views 30

Unit 4 31

Inclined Surfaces 31
Measurement of Angles 31
Assignments
A-12 . . . .Sketching Three Views 34
A-13 . . . .Sketching Missing Views 35
A-14 . . . .Adapter 36
A-15M . .Guide Block 37
A-16 . . . .Base Plate 38

Unit 5 39

Circular Features 39
Centre Lines 39
Dimensioning of Cylindrical Features 40
Dimensioning of Cylindrical Holes 40
Repetitive Features and Dimensions 40
Drilling, Reaming, and Boring 40
Identifying Similarly Sized Features 42
Rounds and Fillets 42
References 42
Assignments
A-17 . . . .Sketching Circular Features . .43
A-18 . . . .Coupling 45
A-19 . . . .Sketching Missing Views 46

Unit 6 47

Drawing to Scale 47
Inch and Foot Scales 49

SI (Metric Scales) 49
Machine Slots 49
Symmetrical Outlines 50
Reference Dimensions 50
Assignments
A-20 . . . .Reading Scales 52
A-21 . . . .Measuring with Scales 53
A-22 . . . .Compound Rest Slide 55

Unit 7 56

Machining Symbols 56
Not-to-Scale Dimensions 57
Drawing Revisions 58
Break Lines 59
References 59
Assignment
A-23M . .Offset Bracket 61

Unit 8 62

Sectional Views .62
Types of Sections 64
Countersinks, Counterbores, and Spotfaces . .66
Intersection of Unfinished Surfaces 67
Assignments
A-24 . . . .Sketching Full Sections 69
A-25 . . . .Slide Bracket 71
A-26M . .Base Plate 73
A-27 . . . .Sketching Half Sections 74

Unit 9 75

Chamfers 75
Undercuts 75
Tapers 75
Knurls 76
Reference 76
Assignments
A-28 . . . .Handle 78
A-29M . .Indicator Rod 79

Unit 10 80

Selection of Views 80
One- and Two-View Drawings 80
Multiple-Detail Drawings 80
Assignments
A-30 . . . .Centring Connector Details . .83
A-31M . .Link .84

Unit 11 85

Surface Texture .85
Surface Texture Symbol 88
Surface Texture Ratings 88
Control Requirements 89
References 90
Assignments
A-32 . . . .Sketch Missing Views 93
A-33 . . . .Hanger Details 95

Unit 12 96

Tolerances and Allowances 96
Definitions 96
Tolerancing Methods 97
References 99
Assignments
A-34 . . . .Inch Tolerances and Allowances 101
A-35M . . .Millimetre Tolerances and Allowances 103

Unit 13 104

Inch Fits 104
Description of Fits 104
Standard Inch Fits 106
References 108
Assignment
A-36 . . . .Inch Fits Basic Hole System .109

Unit 14 110

Metric Fits 110
Reference 112
Assignments
A-37M . . .Metric Fits Basic Hole System .115
A-38M . .Bracket 117
A-39M . .Swivel 118

Unit 15 119

Threaded Fasteners 119
Threaded Assemblies 119
Threaded Holes 120
Inch Threads 120
Right- and Left-Handed Threads 122
Metric Threads 122
References 124
Assignments
A-40 . . . .Shaft Intermediate Support . .125
A-41M . .Drive Support Details 127

A-42 . . . .Housing Details 129
A-43M . .V-Block Assembly 130

Unit 16 131

Revolved and Removed Sections 131
References 131
Assignments
A-44 . . . .Terminal Block 133
A-45 . . . .Shaft Supports 135

Unit 17 136

Keys 136
Setscrews 137
Flats 138
Bosses and Pads 138
Dimension Origin Symbol 138
Rectangular Coordinate Dimensioning without Dimension Lines 139
Rectangular Coordinate Dimensioning in Tabular Form .139
References 139
Assignments
A-46M . .Terminal Stud 141
A-47 . . . .Rack Details 143
A-48 . . . .Support Bracket 145

Unit 18 146

Primary Auxiliary Views 146
References 146
Assignments
A-49 . . . .Inclined Stop 149
A-50 . . . .Gear Box 150

Unit 19 151

Secondary Auxiliary Views 151
References 152
Assignments
A-51 . . . .Identifying Oblique Surfaces . .153
A-52 . . . .Hexagon Bar Support 155
A-53 . . . .Completing Oblique Surfaces .156

Unit 20 157

Development Drawings 157
Joints, Seams, and Edges 157
Sheet Metal Sizes 157
Straight Line Development 157
Stampings 160
Assignments
A-54 . . . .Letter Box 162
A-55M . .Bracket 163

Unit 21 164

Arrangement of Views 164
Assignments
A-56 . . . .Index Pedestal 167
A-57 . . . .Mounting Plate 168
A-58M . .Contact Arm 169

Unit 22 170

Piping 170
Piping Drawings 172
Pipe Drawing Symbols 174
Reference 177
Assignments
A-59 . . . .Engine Starting Air System . .179
A-60 . . . .Boiler Room 181

Unit 23 182

Bearings 182
Plain Bearings .182
Premounted Bearings 184
References 184
Assignments
A-61M . .Adjustable Shaft Support . . .185
A-62 . . . .Corner Bracket 187

Unit 24 188

Manufacturing Materials 188
Steel 188
Plastics 190
Rubber 191
Assignments
A-63M . .Crossbar 193
A-64 . . . .Oil Chute 195
A-65M . .Parallel Clamp Details 196
A-66M . .Caster Assembly 197

Unit 25 198

Castings 198
Cast Irons 200
Casting Design .201
Cored Castings 203
Machining Lugs 203
Surface Coatings 204
References 204
Assignments
A-67 . . . .Offset Bracket 205
A-68 . . . .Trip Box 207
A-69 . . . .Auxiliary Pump Base 209
A-70M . .Slide Valve 210

Unit 26 211

Chain Dimensioning 211
Base Line Dimensioning 211
References 211
Assignments
A-71 . . . .Interlock Base 215
A-72M . .Contactor 216

Unit 27 217

Alignment of Parts and Holes 217
Partial Views 218
Naming of Views for Spark Adjuster 219
Drill Sizes 219
References 219
Assignments
A-73 . . . .Spark Adjuster 221
A-74 . . . .Control Bracket 223

Unit 28 224

Broken-out and Partial Sections 224
Webs in Section 224
Ribs in Section 224
Spokes in Section 226
References 226
Assignments
A-75M . .Raise Block 229
A-76 . . . .Coil Frame 231

Unit 29 232

Pin Fasteners 232
Section through Shafts, Pins, and Keys 236
Arrangement of Views of Drawing A-77M 236
References 236
Assignments
A-77M . .Spider 239
A-78 . . . .Hood 241

Unit 30 242

Drawings for Numerical Control 242
Dimensioning for Numerical Control 242
Dimensioning for Two-Axis Coordinate System 242
Assignments
A-79 . . . .Cover Plate 245
A-80M . .Terminal Board 246

Unit 31 247

Assembly Drawings 247
Bill of Material (Items List) 249
Swivels and Universal Joints 250
Reference 250
Assignments
A-81 . . . .Universal Trolley 253
A-82M . .Parallel Clamp Assembly 255

Unit 32 256

Structural Steel Shapes 256
Phantom Outlines 257
Conical Washers 258
References 258
Assignment
A-83 . . . .Four-Wheel Trolley 261

Unit 33 262

Welding Drawings 262
Welding Symbols 262
Fillet Welds 265
References 267
Assignments
A-84 . . . .Fillet Welds 269
A-85 . . . .Shaft Support 270

Unit 34 271

Groove Welds 271
Supplementary Symbols 273
References 275
Assignments
A-86 . . . .Base Skid 277
A-87 . . . .Groove Welds 278

Unit 35 279

Other Basic Welds 279
References 285
Assignments
A-88 . . . .Base Assembly 287
A-89 . . . .Plug, Slot, and Spot Welds 288
A-90 . . . .Seam and Flange Welds 289

Unit 36 290

Gears 290
Spur Gears 291
Reference 295
Assignments
A-91 . . . .Spur Gear 297
A-92 . . . .Spur Gear Calculations 298

Unit 37 299

Bevel Gears .299
Reference .299
Assignment
A-93 . . . .Mitre Gear .303

Unit 38 304

Gear Trains .304
Assignments
A-94 . . . .Motor Drive Assembly .307
A-95 . . . .Gear Train Calculations .308

Unit 39 309

Cams .309
Assignments
A-96 . . . .Cylindrical Feeder Cam .313
A-97 . . . .Plate Cam .314

Unit 40 315

Antifriction Bearings .315
Retaining Rings .317
O-Ring Seals .317
Clutches .317
Belt Drives .317
References .321
Assignment
A-98 . . . .Power Drive .323

Unit 41 324

Ratchet Wheels .324
Assignment
A-99 . . . .Winch .327

Unit 42 328

Modern Engineering Tolerancing .328
Geometric Tolerancing .330
Feature Control Frame .330
Form Tolerances .333
Straightness .333
Straightness Controlling Surface Elements .333
References .336
Assignment
A-100 . . .Straightness Tolerance Controlling Surface Elements .339

Unit 43 340

Straightness of a Feature of Size .340
Feature of Size Definitions .340
Material Condition Symbols .342
Examples .342
Maximum Material Condition (MMC) .343
Regardless of Feature Size (RFS) .344
Least Material Condition (LMC) .344
Straightness of a Feature of Size .345
References .349
Assignment
A-101 . .Straightness of a Feature of Size .351

Unit 44 352

Form Tolerances .352
Flatness .352
Circularity .353
Cylindricity .354
References .355
Assignment
A-102 . . .Form Tolerances .357

Unit 45 358

Datums and the Three-Plane Concept .358
Datums for Geometric Tolerancing .358
Three-Plane System .358
Uneven Surfaces .359
Datum Feature Symbol .361
References .365
Assignments
A-103 . . .Datums .367
A-104M .Axle .369

Unit 46 370

Orientation Tolerancing for Flat Surfaces .370
Orientation Tolerancing for Flat Surfaces .372
References .373
Assignments
A-105 . . .Stand .375
A-106M .Cut-Off Stand .377

Unit 47 378

Orientation Tolerancing for Features of Size .378
Internal Cylindrical Features .381
External Cylindrical Features .384
References .386
Assignment
A-107 . . .Orientation Tolerancing for Features of Size .389

Unit 48 390

Datum Targets .390
Datum-Target Symbol .390
References .394
Assignment
A-108 . . .Bearing Housing .397

Unit 49 398

Tolerancing of Features by Position .398
Tolerancing Methods .398
Coordinate Tolerancing .399
Advantages of Coordinate Tolerancing .402
Disadvantages of Coordinate Tolerancing .402
Positional Tolerancing .402
Material Condition Basis .402
Positional Tolerancing for Circular Features .404
Advantages of Positional Tolerancing .408
References .409
Assignment
A-109 . . .Positional Tolerancing .413

Unit 50 414

Selection of Datum Features for Positional Tolerancing .414
Long Holes .414
Circular Datums .415
Multiple Hole Datums .415
References .415
Assignment
A-110 . . .Datum Selection for Positional Tolerancing .418

Unit 51 419

Profile Tolerances .419
Profile of a Line .419
Profile of a Surface .422
References .424
Assignment
A-111 . . .Profile Tolerancing .427

Unit 52 428

Runout Tolerances .428
Circular Runout .428
Total Runout .430
Establishing Datums .431
References .433
Assignments
A-112 Runout Tolerances .435
A-113 Housing .437
A-114M End Plate .438

APPENDIX 439

Table 1 Chart for Converting Inch Dimensions to Millimetres .439
Table 2 Abbreviations and Symbols Used on Technical Drawings .440
Table 3 Number and Letter Size Drills .441
Table 4 Metric Twist Drill Sizes .442
Table 5 Unified and American (Inch) Threads .443
Table 6 Metric Threads .444
Table 7 Common Cap Screws .445
Table 8 Hexagon-Head Bolts and Cap Screws .446
Table 9 Setscrews .447
Table 10 Hexagon-Head Nuts .448
Table 11 Hex Flange Nuts .449
Table 12 Common Washer Sizes .450
Table 13 Square and Flat Stock Keys .452
Table 14 Woodruff Keys .452
Table 15 American Standard Wrought Steel Pipe .453
Table 16 Sheet Metal Gauges and Thicknesses .454
Table 17 Running and Sliding Fits (Values in Thousandths of an Inch) .455
Table 18 Locational Clearance Fits (Values in Thousandths of an Inch) .456
Table 19 Locational Transition Fits (Values in Thousandths of an Inch) .457
Table 20 Locational Interference Fits (Values in Thousandths of an Inch) .458
Table 21 Force and Shrink Fits (Values in Thousandths of an Inch) .459
Table 22 Preferred Hole Basis Metric Fits Description .460
Table 23 Preferred Shaft Basis Metric Fits Description .461
Table 24 Preferred Hole Basis Metric Fits (Values in Millimetres) .462
Table 25 Preferred Shaft Basis Metric Fits (Values in Millimetres) .464
Table 26 Metric Conversion Tables .466

INDEX 467

PREFACE

The Fourth Canadian Edition of *Interpreting Engineering Drawings* builds on the success of previous editions in preparing students for careers in modern, technology-intensive industry. Now, more than ever, people entering industry, or those in industry who seek to upgrade their knowledge and skills, require educational materials that reflect the current state of technology.

This trend toward more efficient worldwide communication makes this text a very valuable asset when training personnel to participate and compete in the world marketplace of the new millennium.

Interpreting Engineering Drawings is the only blueprint reading text designed to provide customized drawing interpretation courses for each and every student. This text was designed to contain far more information than what is normally required for any traditional program. This was intentionally done. The text provides the instructor with the opportunity of selecting units of instruction that would best suit the needs of the students in that particular area or industry. The first part of the text covers information that is essential to all courses. The latter part of the text contains units that are more specialized. They are selected on the basis of providing the necessary range of topics to ensure that readers who conscientiously study and practise will know how to interpret the engineering drawings used in their community.

The features that have made the text such a valuable learning resource in previous editions have been retained in the new edition. The topics build progressively from simple to complex. Numerous examples and illustrations are provided to show the applications of each concept described. Colour is used extensively in the text to draw attention to important concepts and changes of state from one part or location to another. Tables are provided to summarize useful data for future reference. Similar topics are organized into discrete units of moderate length, followed by immediate application by way of assignments. Each assignment drawing contains questions that require the student to follow a logical thought process to arrive at the answer. Many questions require the application of basic mathematics to arrive at solutions. The appendix contains 26 tables of machining data, which serve as a ready reference for the solution of text problems as well as for on-the-job use.

The text consistently uses drafting practices based on the latest standards. In recognition of the fact that certain industries require the use of the metric system of measurement, the principles of metric measurement are introduced early in the text, and selected assignments throughout the text are dimensioned in metric units. In the appendix, standard parts are shown in both inch and millimetre sizes, and standard metric fits are included.

FEATURES OF THE FOURTH CANADIAN EDITION

- **The adoption of the latest CSA and ASME drawing standards.** The ISO datum symbol, along with other new symbols, is used and explained.
- **Manufacturing materials.** A new unit on manufacturing materials has been added. It includes plastics and rubber, in addition to the traditional iron and steel specifications.
- **Drawings for numerical control.** This new unit explains how to dimension for a two-coordinate system.
- **Increase in assignments.** Twelve new assignments, designed to broaden and reinforce basic concepts, have been added.
- **Using manufacturer's catalogues and tables.** Many new questions, designed for using the standard purchased items, the tap drill and fit charts, have been added.
- **Pictorials.** Pictorials, which will help the student to better visualize the part, have been added to several drawing assignments.

An Instructor's Guide accompanies the text and contains answers and solutions to all questions, problems, and sketching exercises in the unit assignments. Tests and solutions are also included to evaluate the student's progress.

ABOUT THE AUTHOR

Cecil H. Jensen, now retired, held the position of Technical Director at the McLaughlin Collegiate and Vocational Institute, Oshawa, Ontario, Canada, and has more than twenty-seven years of teaching experience in mechanical drafting. He was an active member of the Canadian Standards Association (CSA) Committee on Technical Drawings. Mr. Jensen has represented Canada at international (ISO) conferences on engineering drawing standards, which took place in Oslo, Norway, and Paris, France. He also represented Canada on the ANSI Y14.5M Committee on Dimensioning and Tolerancing. He is the successful author of numerous texts, including *Drafting Fundamentals, Engineering Drawing and Design, Geometric Dimensioning, Tolerancing for Engineering and Manufacturing Tolerancing, Computer-Aided Engineering Drawing,* and *Home Planning and Design*. Before he began teaching, Mr. Jensen spent several years in industrial design. He was also the supervisor of evening courses and was responsible for teaching selected courses for the General Motors Corporation apprentices in Oshawa, Canada.

ACKNOWLEDGMENTS

The author would like to thank and acknowledge the many professionals who reviewed the manuscript, helping us publish this textbook. The technical edit was performed by Connie Dotson, Newport Corporation.

A special acknowledgment is due to the following instructors who reviewed the chapters in detail:

Gerald Cavanaugh, Schoolcraft College, Livonia, MI

Dale Howser, Milwaukee Area Technical College, Milwaukee, WI

Jim Johnson, Lorain County Community College, Elyria, OH

UNIT 1

BASES FOR INTERPRETING DRAWINGS

Commonly Used Descriptive Terms

When looking at objects, we normally see them as three-dimensional: as having width, depth, and height; or length, width, and height. The choice of terms used depends on the shape and proportions of the object.

Spherical shapes, such as a basketball, would be described as having a certain *diameter* (one term).

Cylindrical shapes, such as a baseball bat, would have *diameter* and *length*. However, a hockey puck would have *diameter* and *thickness* (two terms).

Objects that are not spherical or cylindrical require *three* terms to describe their overall shape. The terms used for a car would probably be *length, width,* and *height;* for a filing cabinet—width, *height,* and *depth* even though the longest measurement (length) could be the width, height, or depth; for a sheet of drawing paper—*length, width,* and *thickness.* The terms used are interchangeable according to the *proportions* of the object being described, and the *position* it is in when being viewed. For example, a telephone pole lying on the ground would be described as having *diameter* and *length,* but when placed in a vertical position, its dimensions would be *diameter* and *height.*

In order to avoid confusion, distances from left to right are referred to as width, distances from front to back as depth, and vertical distances (except when very small in proportion to the others) as height.

The Need for Standardization

Engineering drawings are more complicated and require a set of rules, terms, and symbols that everyone can understand and use. A drawing showing a part may be drawn in Toronto, the part made in Vancouver, and then the part sent to Hamilton for assembly. If this is to be successfully accomplished, the drawing must have only one interpretation.

Most countries set up standards committees to accomplish this feat. These committees must decide on factors such as the best methods of representation, dimensioning, and tolerancing, and the adopting of drawing symbols. If only one interpretation of a drawing is to be met, then the rules must be followed and interpreted correctly.

In Canada, drawing standards are established by the *Canadian Standards Association* (CSA) and in the United States, by the *American Society of Mechanical Engineers* (ASME). Members of these committees are part of the worldwide committee on standardization, known as the *International Organization for Standardization* (ISO).

The drawings and information shown throughout this text are based on CSA drawing standards. In some areas of drawing practice, such as in simplified drafting, national standards have not yet been established. The author has, in such cases, adopted the practices used by leading industries in Canada and the United States.

Engineering or *technical drawings* furnish a description of the shape and size of an object. Other information necessary for the construction of the object is given in a way that renders it readily recognizable to anyone familiar with engineering drawings.

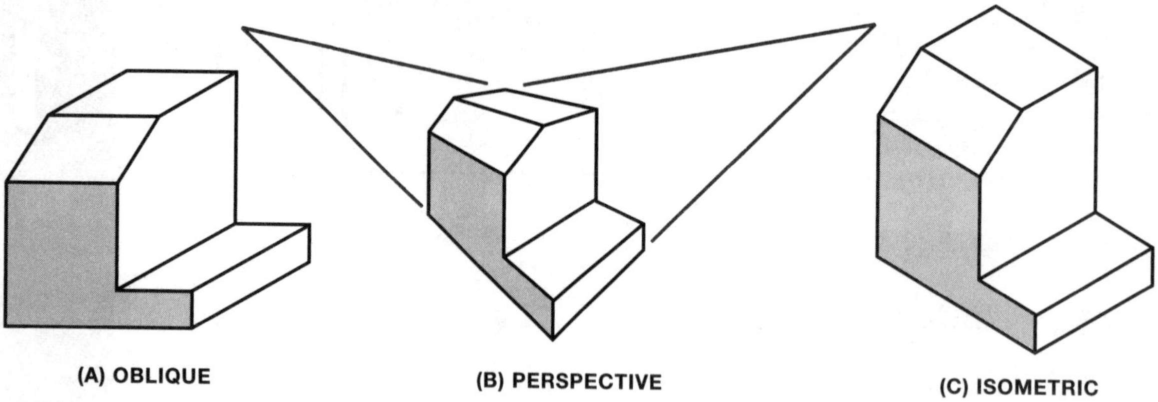
(A) OBLIQUE
(B) PERSPECTIVE
(C) ISOMETRIC

FIGURE 1–1 ■ Pictorial drawings

Pictorial drawings are similar to photographs, because they show objects as they would appear to the eye of the observer, Figure 1–1. Such drawings, however, are not often used for technical designs because interior features and complicated detail are easier to understand and dimension on orthographic drawings. The drawings used in industry must clearly show the exact shape of objects. This usually cannot be accomplished in just one pictorial view, because many details of the object may be hidden or not clearly shown when the object is viewed from only one side.

For this reason, the drafter must show a number of views of the object as seen from different directions. These views, referred to as front view, top view, right-side view, and so forth, are systematically arranged on the drawing sheet and projected from one another, Figure 1–2. This type of projection is called *orthographic projection.* The ability to understand and visualize an object from these views is essential in the interpretation of engineering drawings.

The principles of orthographic projection can be applied in four angles, or systems: first-, second-, third-, and fourth-angle projection. However, only two

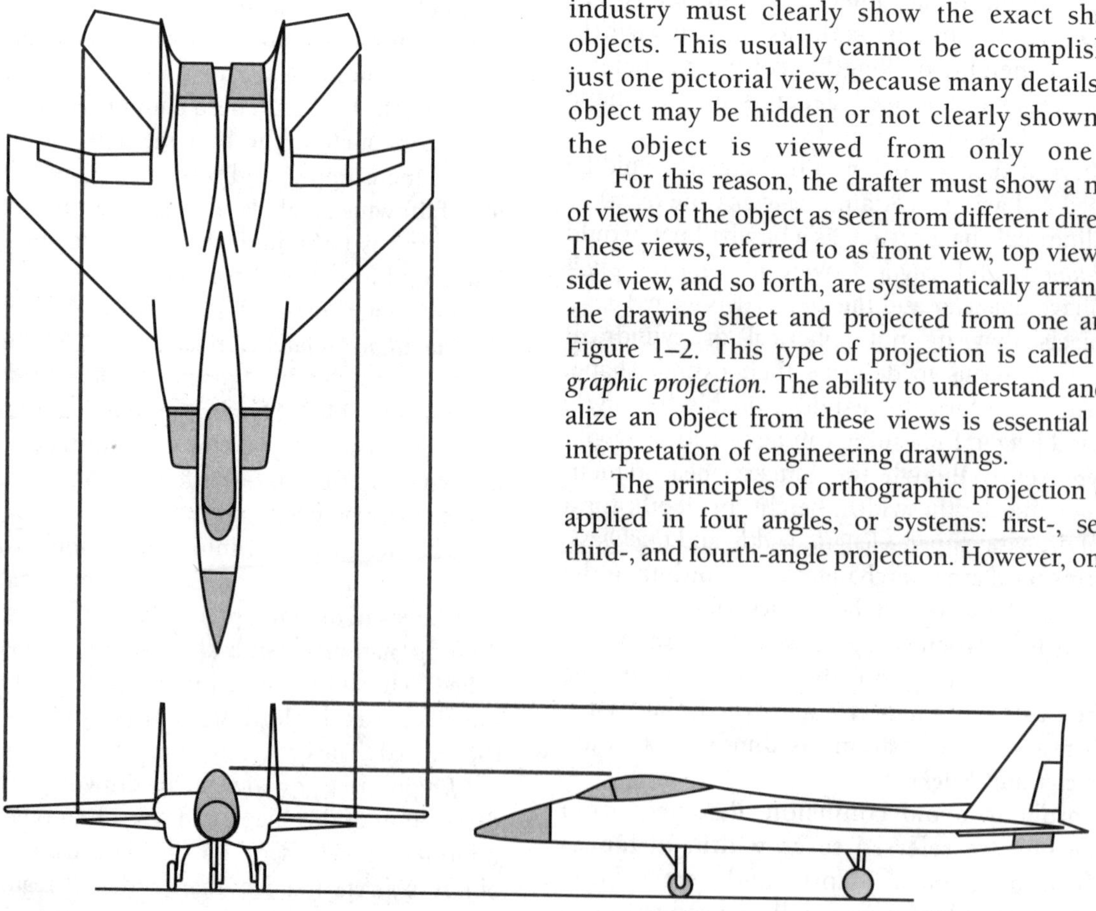

FIGURE 1–2 ■ Systematic arrangement of views

systems, first- and third-angle projection, are used. *Third-angle projection* is used in Canada, the United States, and many other countries. *First-angle projection* is used mainly in Europe. Because world trade has brought about the exchange of both engineering drawings and products, drafters are now called upon to communicate in both types of orthographic projection, as well as pictorial representations.

VISIBLE LINES

A thick solid line is used to indicate the visible edges and corners of an object. Visible lines should stand out clearly in contrast to other lines, making the general shape of the object apparent to the eye.

LETTERING ON DRAWINGS

The most important requirements for lettering used on engineering drawings are legibility and reproducibility. These requirements are best met by the style of lettering known as standard uppercase Gothic, as shown in Figure 1–3. Vertical lettering is preferred, but sloping style may be used, though never on the same drawing as vertical lettering. Suitable lettering size for notes and dimensions is .10 inch (in.). Larger characters are used for drawing titles and numbers. They are also used where it may be necessary to bring some part of the drawing to the attention of the reader.

A B C D E F G H I J K L M N O P
Q R S T U V W X Y Z
1 2 3 4 5 6 7 8 9 0
VERTICAL

A B C D E F G H I J K L M N O P
Q R S T U V W X Y Z
1 2 3 4 5 6 7 8 9 0
SLOPED

FIGURE 1–3 ■ Lettering for drawings

SKETCHING

Sketching is a necessary part of the course of interpreting technical drawings because the skilled technician in the shop is frequently called upon to sketch and explain points to other people. Sketching also helps to develop a good sense of proportion and accuracy of observation. The most common types of sketching paper are shown in Figure 1–4. Each square on the paper may represent .10 in., .25 in., 1.00 in., one foot (ft.), or 10 mm of actual object length. Figure 1–4 illustrates the use of graph paper for sketching (A) orthographic projection, and (B) pictorial drawings. Figure 1–5 shows some simple objects drawn in orthographic projection.

THIRD-ANGLE PROJECTION

The third-angle system of projection is used almost exclusively on mechanical engineering drawings in North America because it permits each

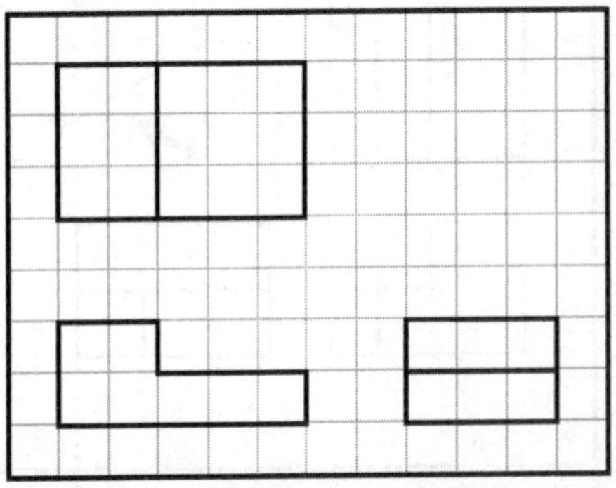

(A) COORDINATE SKETCHING PAPER USED FOR SKETCHING ORTHOGRAPHIC PROJECTION

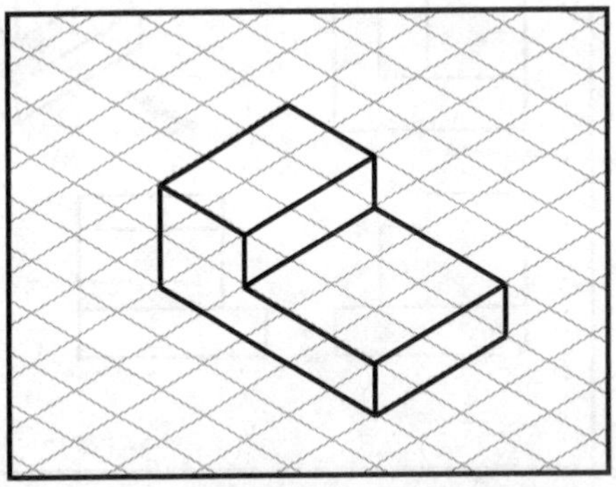

(B) ISOMETRIC SKETCHING PAPER USED FOR SKETCHING PICTORIAL DRAWINGS

FIGURE 1–4 ■ Sketching paper

feature of the object to be drawn in true proportion and without distortion along all dimensions.

Three views are usually sufficient to describe the shape of an object. The views most commonly used are the front, top, and right side, Figure 1-6(A). In third-angle projection the object may be assumed to be enclosed in a glass box, Figure 1–6(B). A view of the object drawn on each side of the box represents

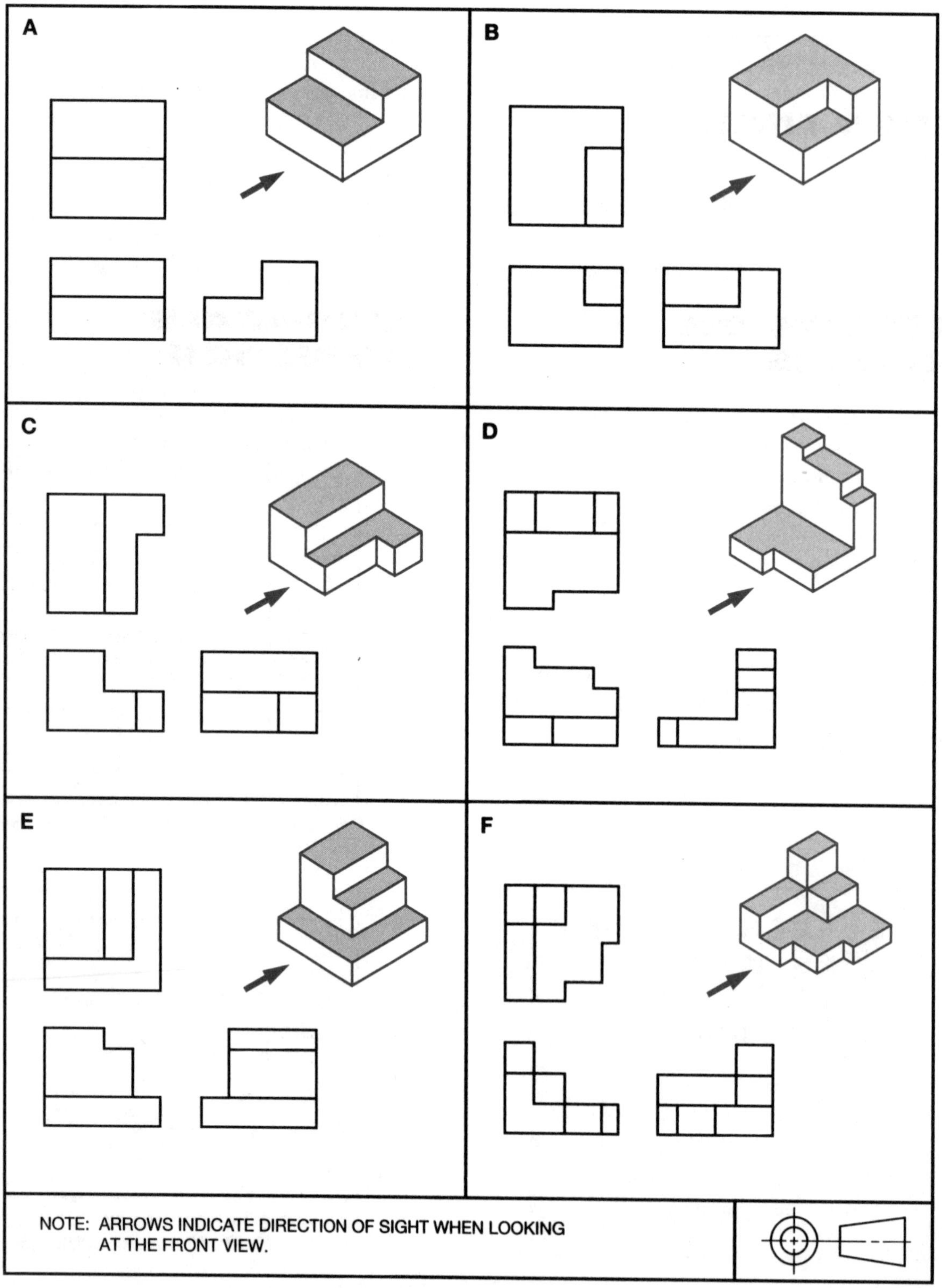
A
B
C
D
E
F
NOTE: ARROWS INDICATE DIRECTION OF SIGHT WHEN LOOKING AT THE FRONT VIEW.

FIGURE 1–5 ■ Illustrations of simple objects drawn in orthographic projection that which is seen when looking perpendicularly at each face of the box. If the box were unfolded as if hinged around the front face, the desired orthographic projection would result, Figure 1–6(C) and (D). These views are identified by names as shown. With reference to the front view:

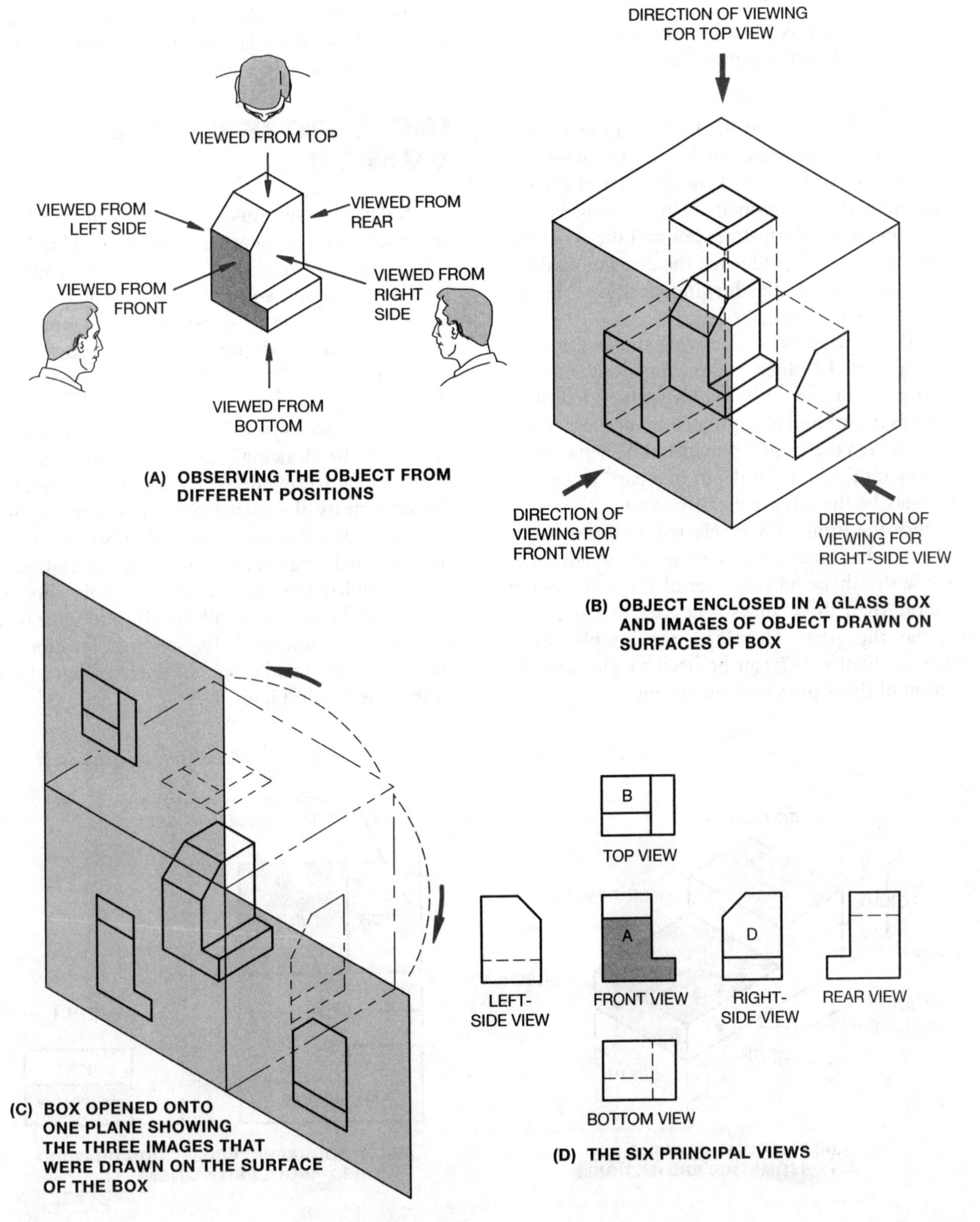
VIEWED FROM TOP
VIEWED FROM LEFT SIDE
VIEWED FROM REAR
VIEWED FROM FRONT
VIEWED FROM RIGHT SIDE
VIEWED FROM BOTTOM
(A) OBSERVING THE OBJECT FROM DIFFERENT POSITIONS
DIRECTION OF VIEWING FOR TOP VIEW
DIRECTION OF VIEWING FOR FRONT VIEW
DIRECTION OF VIEWING FOR RIGHT-SIDE VIEW
(B) OBJECT ENCLOSED IN A GLASS BOX AND IMAGES OF OBJECT DRAWN ON SURFACES OF BOX
(C) BOX OPENED ONTO ONE PLANE SHOWING THE THREE IMAGES THAT WERE DRAWN ON THE SURFACE OF THE BOX
B
TOP VIEW
A
D
LEFT-SIDE VIEW
FRONT VIEW
RIGHT-SIDE VIEW
REAR VIEW
BOTTOM VIEW
(D) THE SIX PRINCIPAL VIEWS

FIGURE 1–6 ■ Third-angle orthographic projection

- The top view is placed above.
- The bottom view is placed underneath.
- The left view is placed on the left.
- The right view is placed on the right.
- The rear view is placed at the extreme left or right, whichever is convenient.

Before a drawing is made the drafter must decide on the number of views necessary to adequately show the part, and which of the six sides of the part would make the best principal (front) view. Factors such as the most informative view and the avoidance of hidden lines help influence the decision making. The front view of the drawing need not be the "front" of the finished part.

The front view on the drawing shows the width and height of the object. As previously mentioned, the term *length* should be avoided when describing the views in orthographic projection, because it normally refers to the longest dimension. When describing the width, height, or depth of a part, any one of these may be the longest measurement.

Once the front view is selected, the next step is to decide what other views are required to adequately show the shape and features of the part. Seldom are more than three views necessary to completely describe the part. Therefore, the simple object shown in Figure 1–7 can be used to illustrate the position of these principal dimensions.

In Figure 1–7 the object is shown in (A) pictorial form, and (B) orthographic projection. The orthographic drawing uses each view to represent the exact shape and size of the object and the relationship of the three views to one another. This principle of projection is used in all mechanical drawings. The isometric drawing shows the relationship of the front, top, and right-side surfaces in a single view.

ISO PROJECTION SYMBOL

Today, two systems of orthographic projection are used on engineering drawings. Third-angle orthographic projection is used by many countries, including Canada and the United States, and thus is used in this text. Most European and Asian countries have adopted first-angle projection, which places the views in opposite positions to third-angle projection.

Because two types of projection (arrangement of views on the drawing), first- and third-angle, are used on engineering drawings, and because each has the same units of measurement, it is necessary to be able to identify the type of projection. The International Organization for Standardization has recommended that one of the symbols shown in Figure 1–8 be shown on all drawings to indicate the type of projection used. Its preferred location is in the lower right-hand corner of the drawing, adjacent to the title block, Figure 1–9.

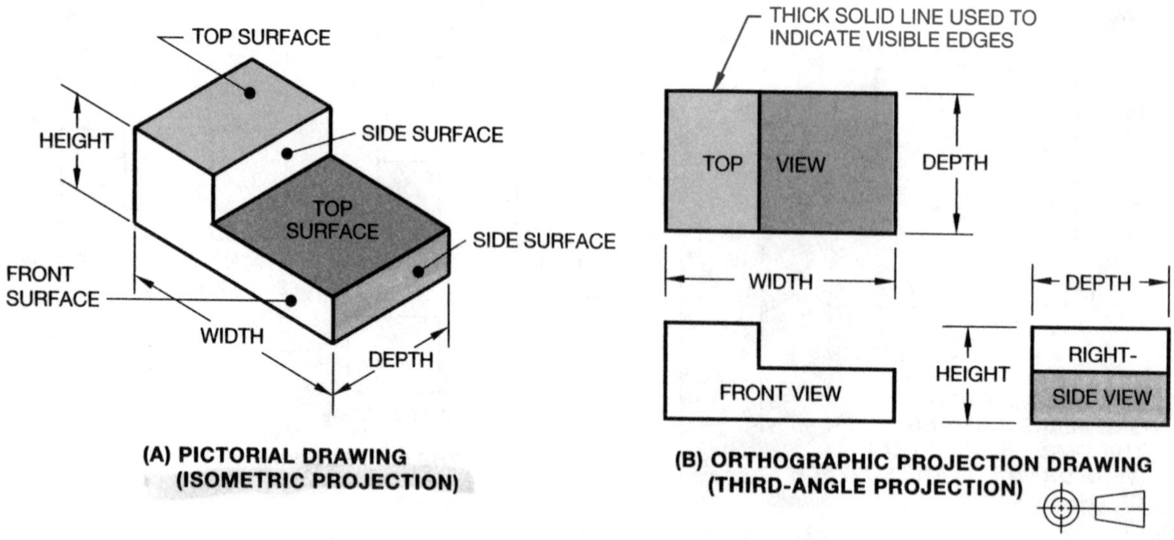

FIGURE 1–7 ■ A simple object shown in (A) pictorial form, and (B) orthographic projection

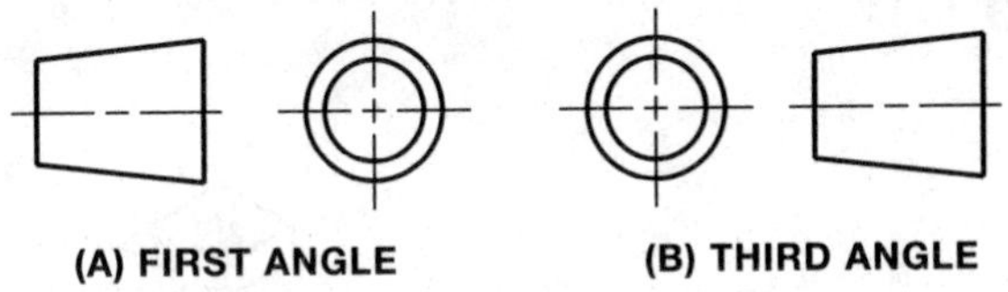
(A) FIRST ANGLE
(B) THIRD ANGLE

FIGURE 1–8 ■ ISO projection symbols

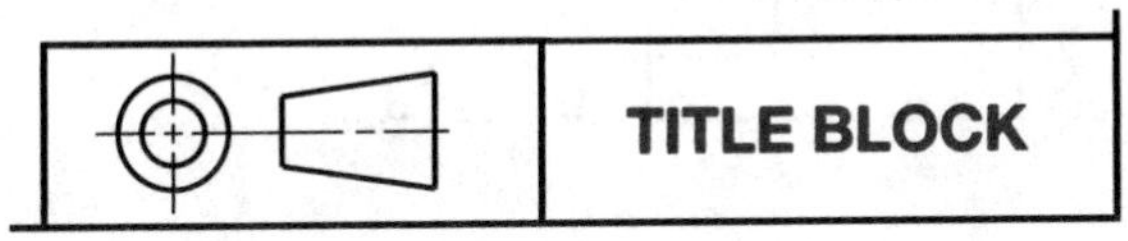
TITLE BLOCK

FIGURE 1–9 ■ The ISO symbol is located adjacent to the title block on the drawing.

TITLE BLOCK

All drawings will have some form of title block, usually placed in the lower right-hand corner. A title block may contain such information as the

- name of the part
- name of the drafter
- order number
- name of the drawing checker
- date
- drawing number
- material to be used
- scale size used

MITER LINE EXAMPLE HERE.

A

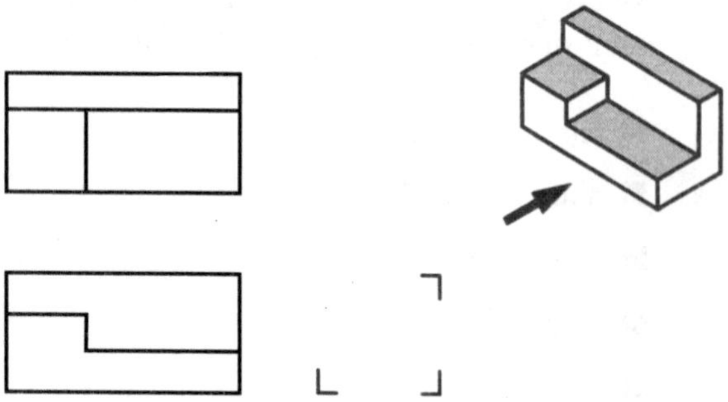

B

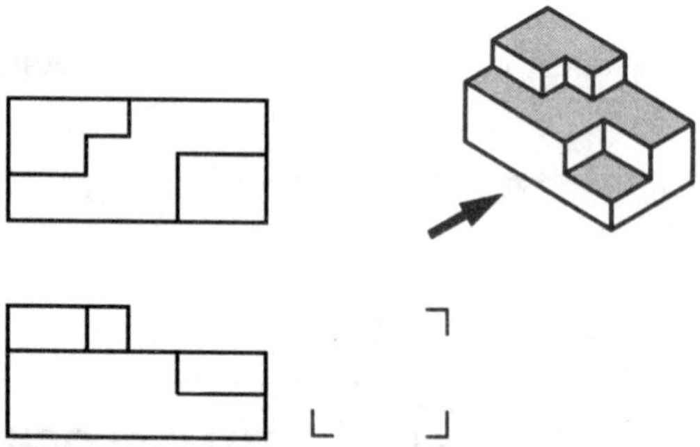

E

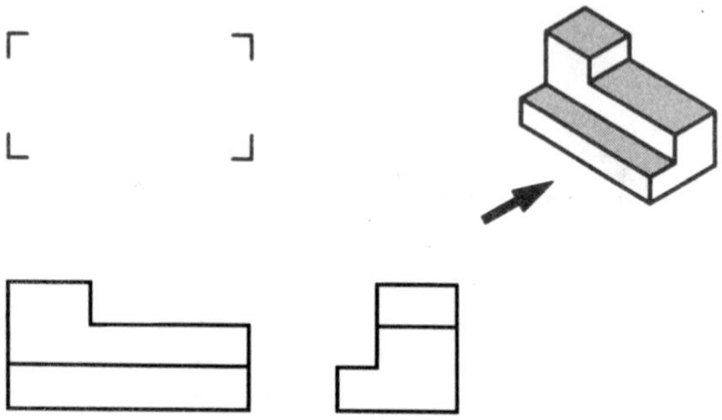

F

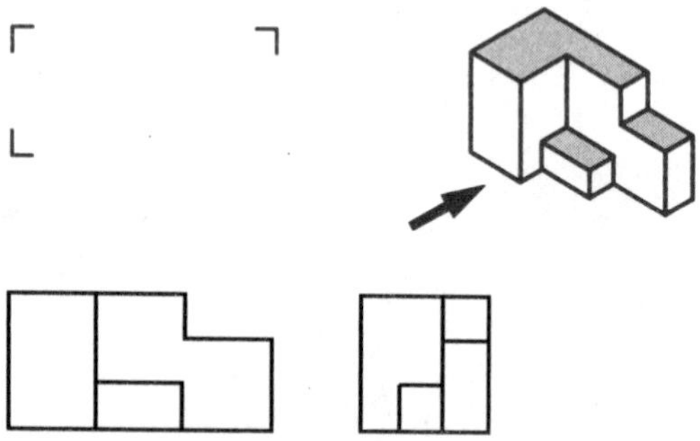

J

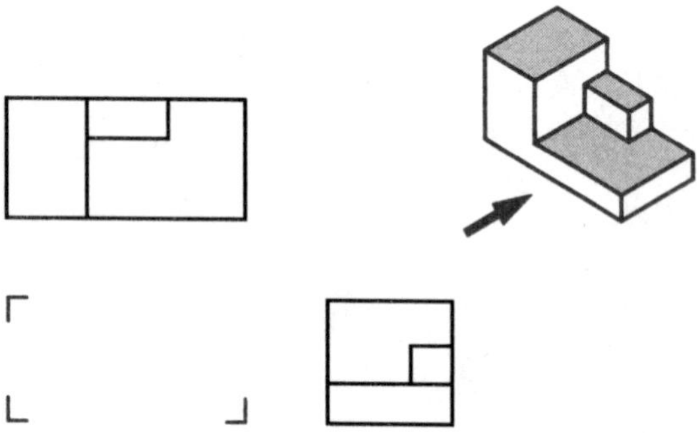

K

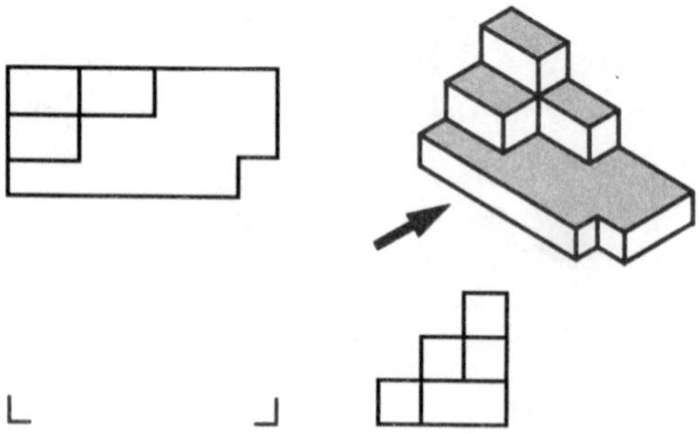

ASSIGNMENT: SKETCH THE MISSING VIEWS. THE OTHER TWO VIEWS ARE COMPLETE.

C

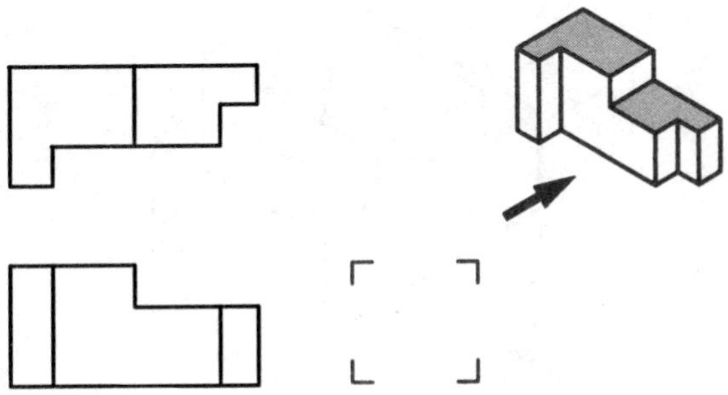

D

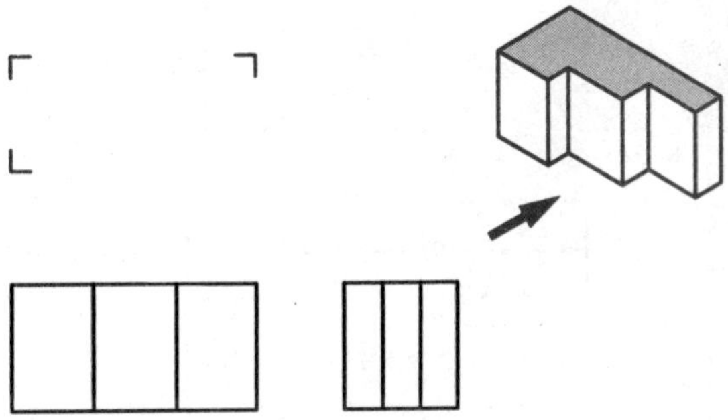

G

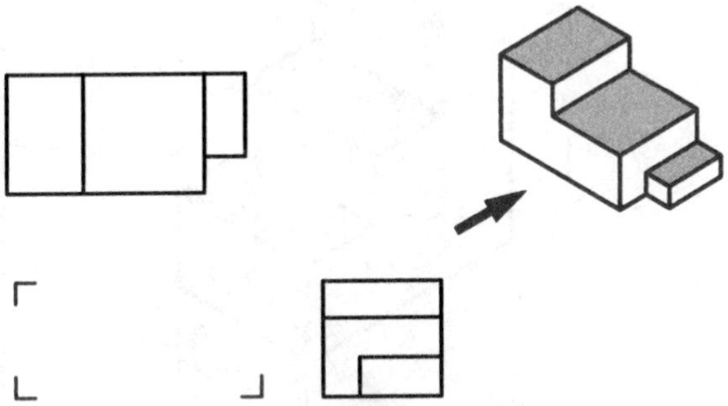

H

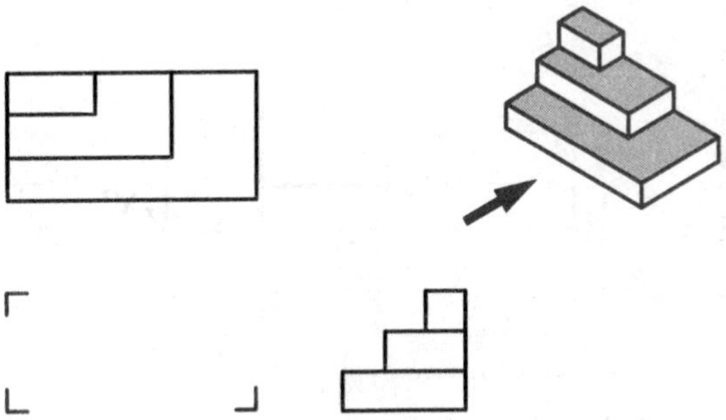

L

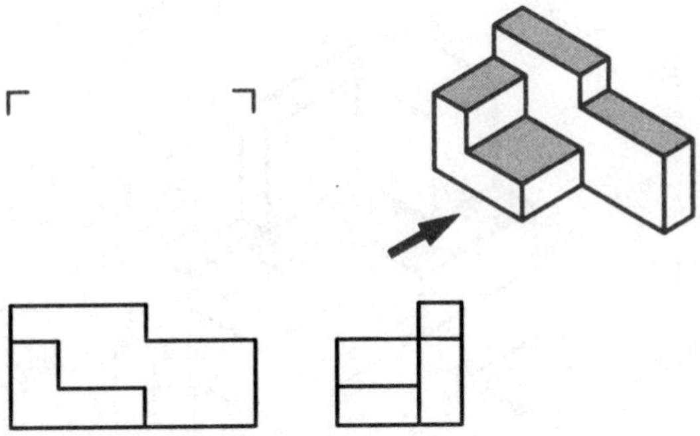

M

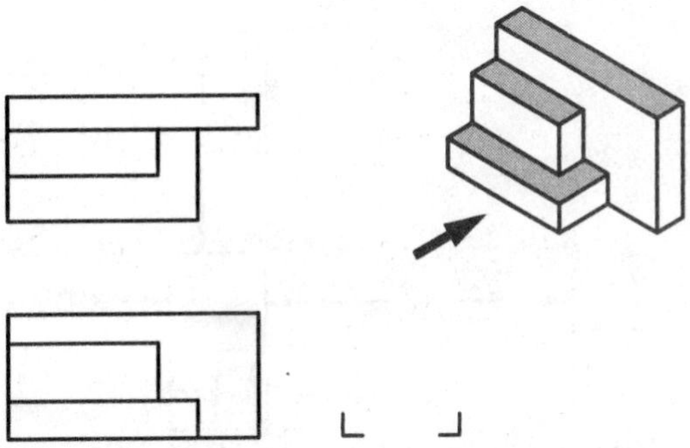

SKETCHING MISSING VIEWS

A-1

A

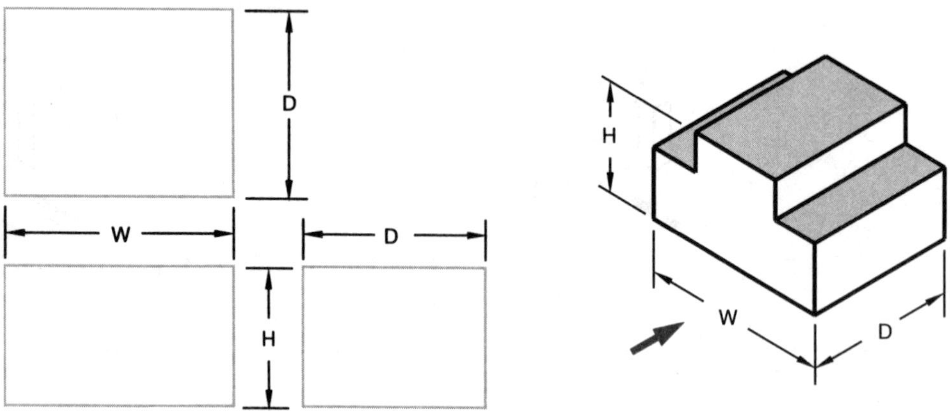

B

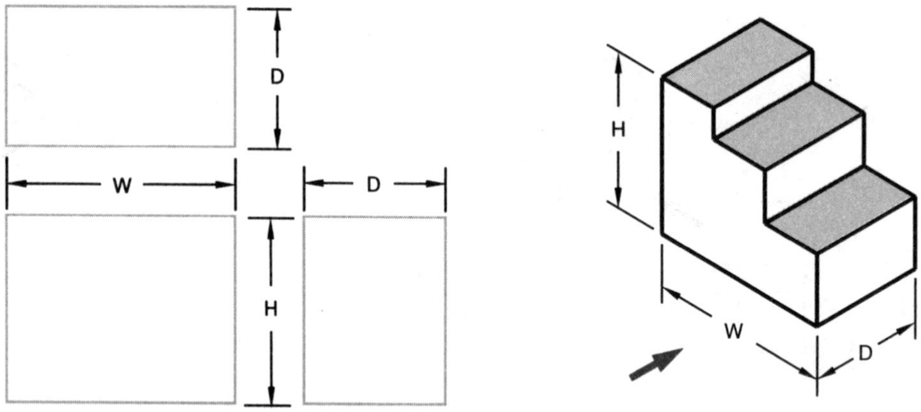

C

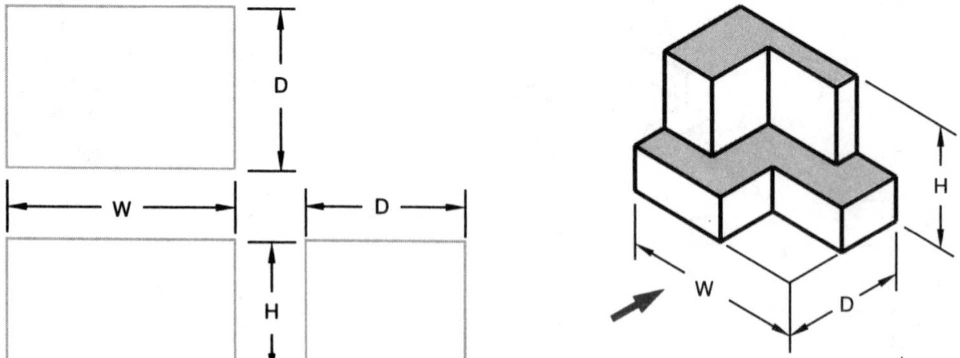

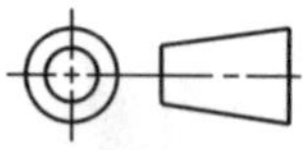

ASSIGNMENT: SKETCH IN THE TOP, FRONT, AND SIDE VIEWS USING THIRD-ANGLE PROJECTION.
NOTE: ARROW INDICATES DIRECTION OF FRONT VIEW.

SKETCHING THREE VIEWS	A-2

A

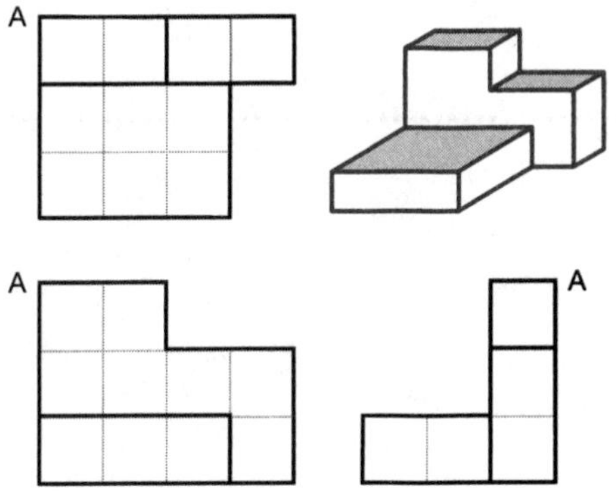

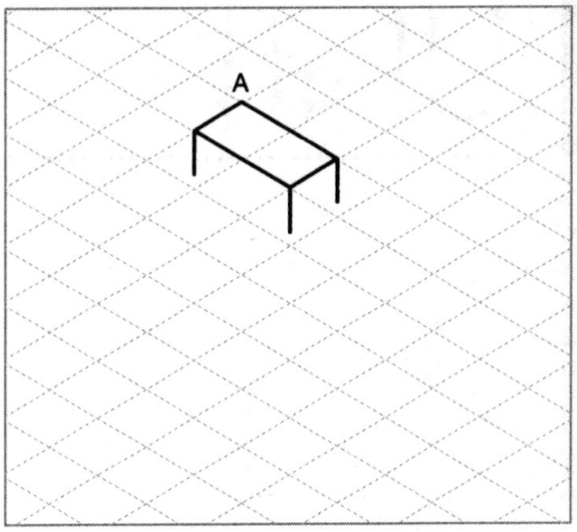

B

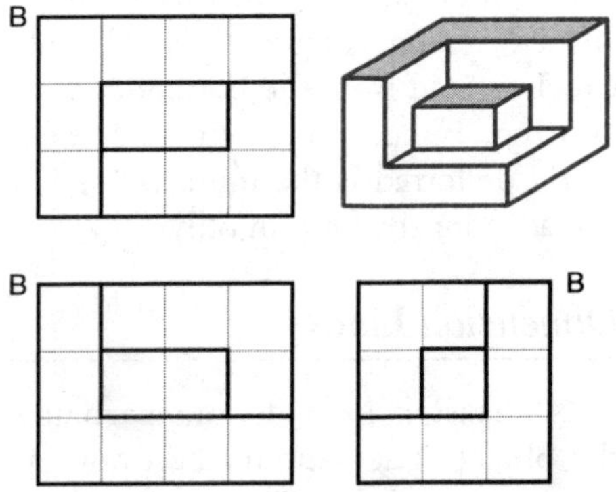

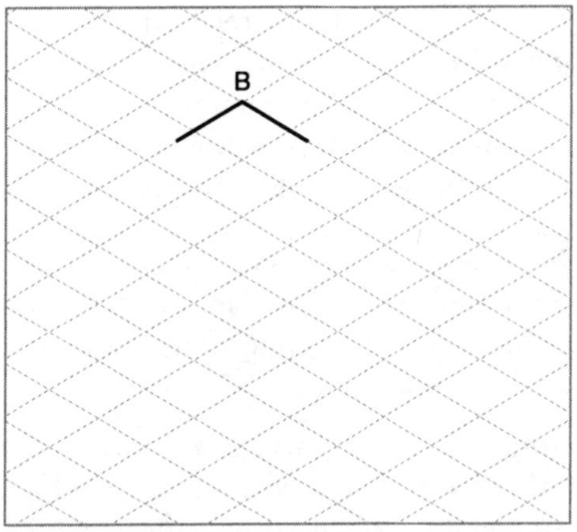

C

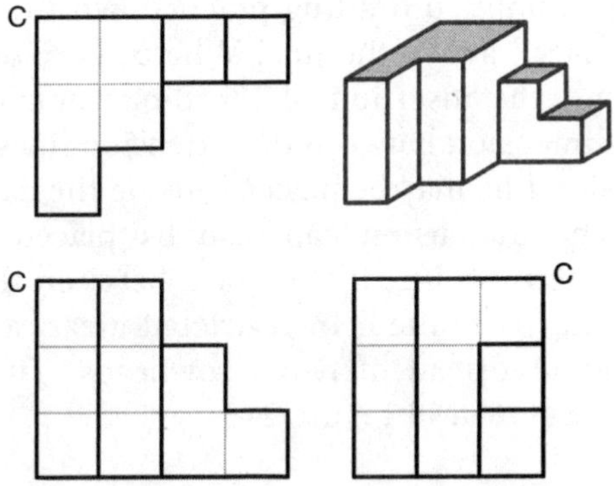

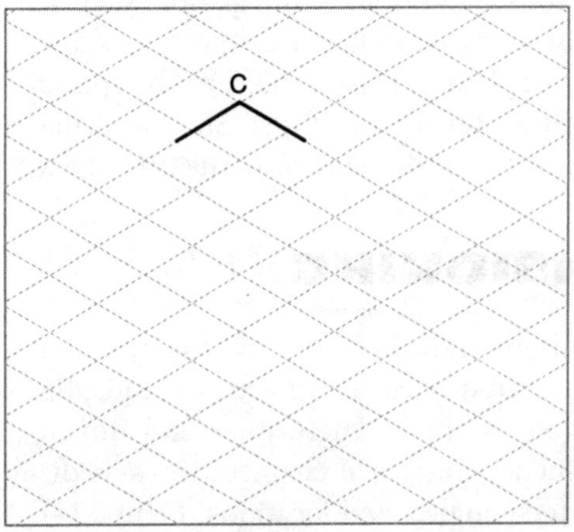

ASSIGNMENT:
COMPLETE THE PICTORIAL DRAWINGS. USE THE SAME NUMBER OF SQUARES AS SHOWN FOR THE WIDTH, HEIGHT, AND DEPTH.

	SKETCHING PICTORIAL VIEWS	A-3

2 UNIT

WORKING DRAWINGS

A *working drawing,* sometimes referred to as a *detail* or *assembly drawing,* contains the complete information for the construction of an object or the assembly of a product. The information found on this drawing may be classified under three headings:

- **Shape.** The description of the shape of all objects is indicated by the number and type of views and lines selected to completely show or describe the form of an object.
- **Dimensioning.** The description of the size and location of the shape of an object is indicated by lines and numerals used to specify the dimensions of an object.
- **Specifications.** Additional information such as general notes, material, heat treatment, machine finish, and applied finish are indicated by special entries written on the drawings. Such information is found on the drawing or in the title block.

DIMENSIONING

Dimensions are indicated on drawings by extension lines, dimension lines, leaders, arrowheads, figures, notes, and symbols. These lines and dimensions define such geometrical characteristics as distances, diameters, angles, and locations, Figure 2–1. The lines used in dimensioning are thin in contrast to the outline of the object. The dimension must be clear and concise, permitting only one interpretation. In general, each surface, line, or point is located by only one set of dimensions. Exceptions to these rules are the two types of rectangular coordinate dimensioning discussed in Unit 17.

Placement of Dimensions

The two methods of dimensioning most commonly used are the *unidirectional system* and the *aligned system,* Figure 2–2. The aligned system, which is read from the bottom and right side of the drawing, is becoming outdated. The method currently preferred is the unidirectional system, which is read from the bottom only.

Dimension Lines

Dimension lines denote particular sections of the object. They should be drawn parallel to the section they define. Dimension lines terminate in arrowheads, which touch an extension line and are broken in order to allow the insertion of the dimension. Unbroken lines are sometimes used as a simplified drafting practice, with the dimension placed above the line. Where space does not permit the insertion of the dimension line and the dimension between the extension lines, the dimension line may be placed outside the extension line. The dimension can also be placed outside the extension line if the space between the extension lines is limited. In restricted areas, a dot may be used instead of two arrowheads. These methods are shown in Figure 2–3.

Extension Lines

Extension lines denote the points or surfaces between which a dimension applies. They extend from object lines and are drawn perpendicular to the dimension lines (as shown in Figures 2–1 and 2–2). A small gap (.03 to .06 in.) is left between the extension line and the outline to which it refers.

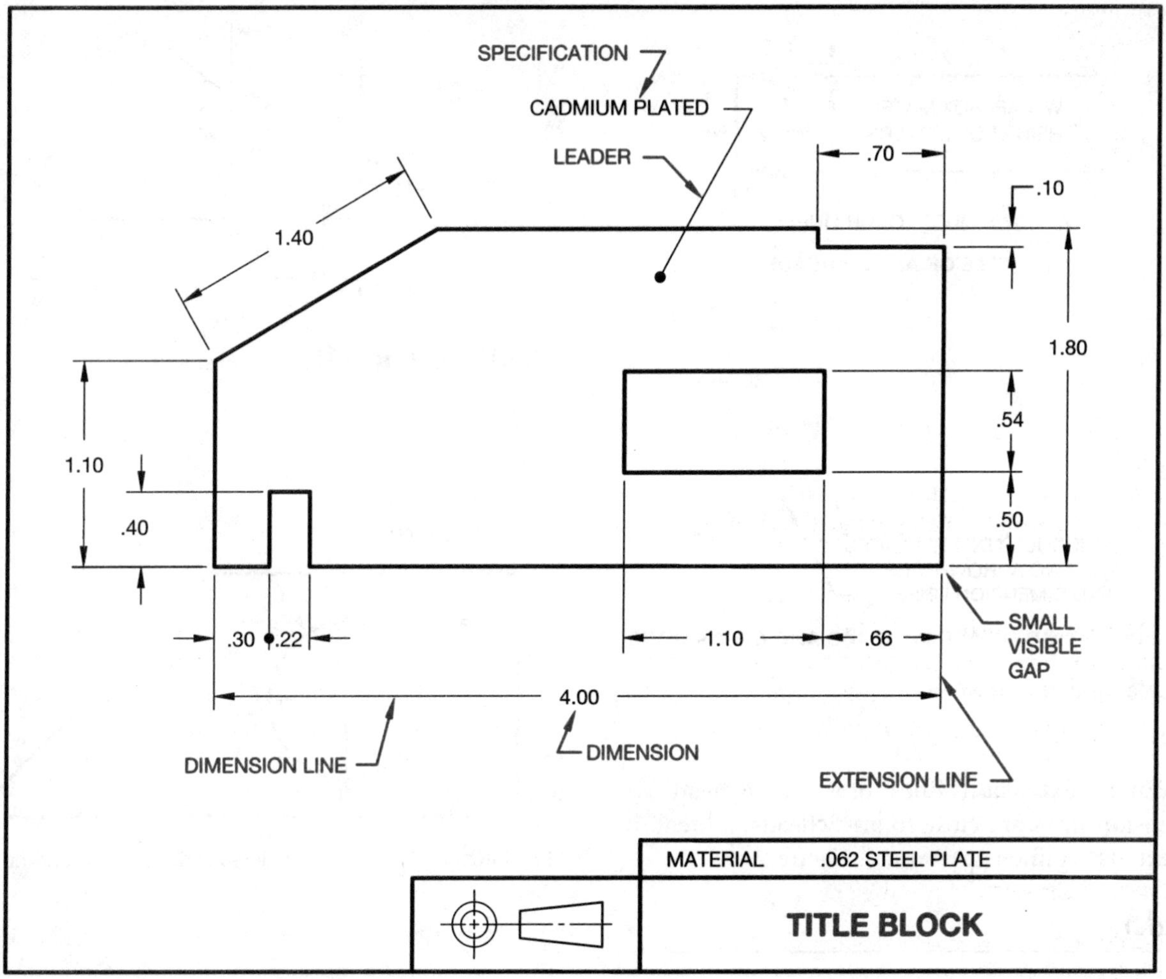

FIGURE 2–1 ■ Basic dimensioning elements

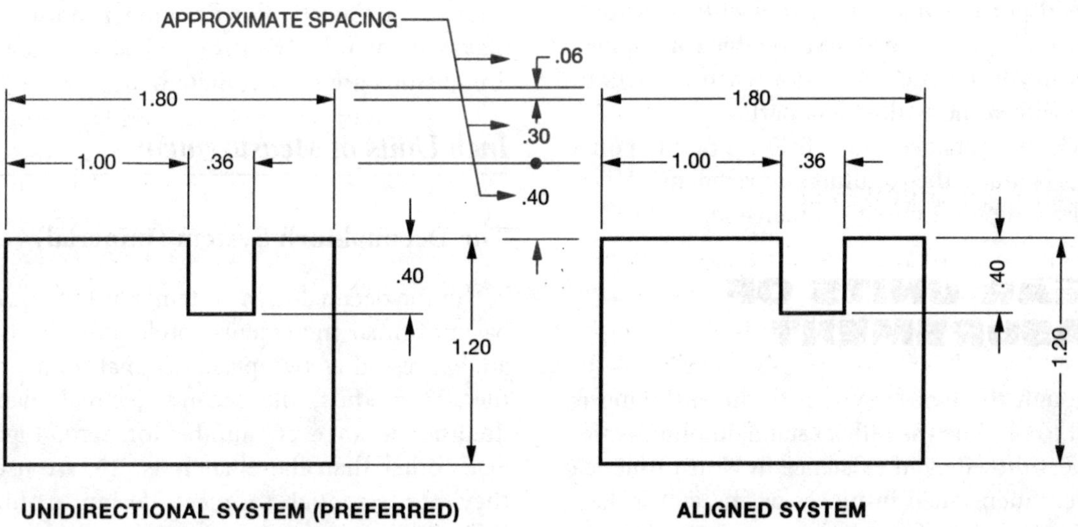

FIGURE 2–2 ■ Dimensioning systems

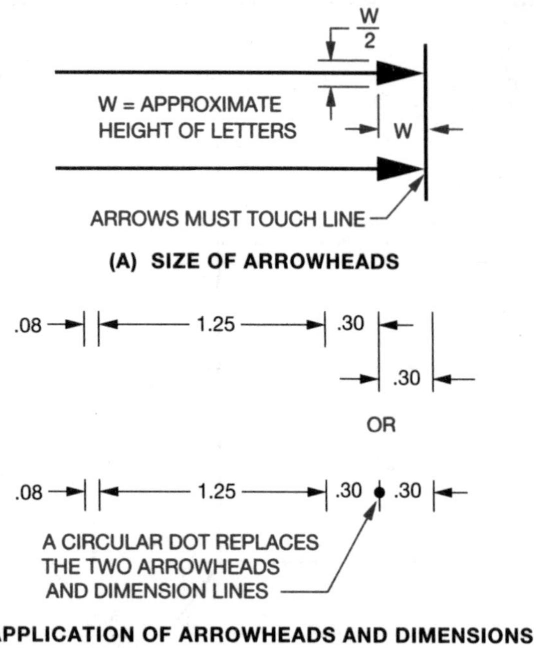

FIGURE 2–3 ■ Arrowheads

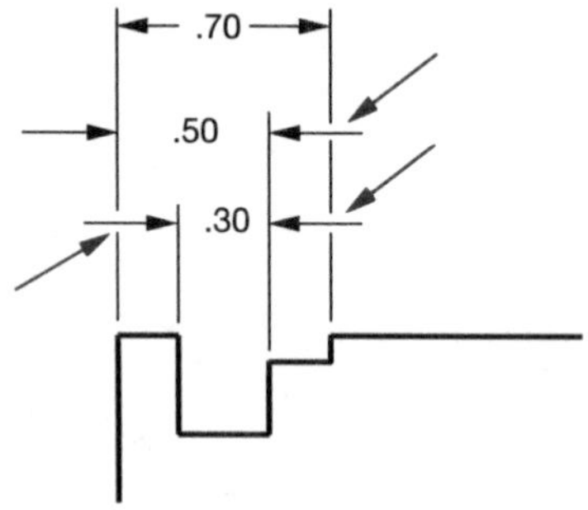

FIGURE 2–4 ■ Breaks in extension lines

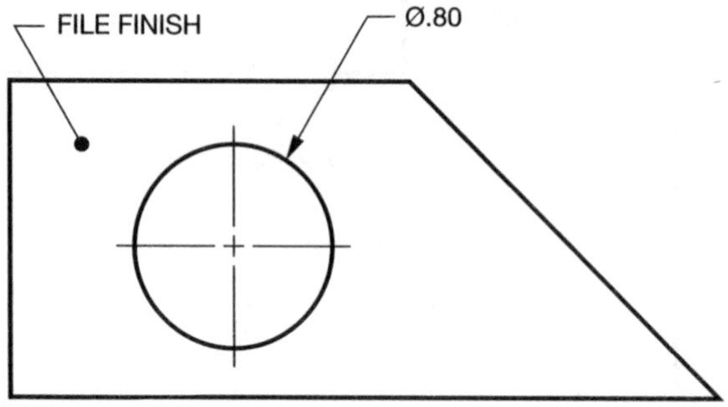

FIGURE 2–5 ■ Using leaders for dimensions and notes

Where extension lines cross arrowheads or dimension lines are close to arrowheads, a break in the extension line is permitted, Figure 2–4.

Leaders

Leaders are used to direct dimensions or notes to the surface or points to which they apply, Figure 2–5. A leader consists of a line with or without short horizontal bars adjacent to the note or dimension, and an inclined portion that terminates with an arrowhead touching the line or point to which it applies. A leader may terminate with a dot when it refers to a surface within the outline of a part.

NOTE: If by chance a dimension is omitted on a drawing, contact the drafting department. *Never* scale a drawing for a missing dimension.

LINEAR UNITS OF MEASUREMENT

Although the metric system of dimensioning is expected to become the official standard of measurement, most drawings in existence in North America today are dimensioned in inches or feet and inches. For this reason, drafters and persons involved in reading engineering drawings should be familiar with all the dimensioning systems they may encounter.

The dimensions used in this book are primarily decimal inch. However, metric dimensions are used very frequently. When metric units of measurement are used, the drawing prominently displays the word METRIC and a note stating the dimensions are in millimetres.

Inch Units of Measurement

The Decimal-inch System (Imperial)

In the decimal-inch system, parts are designed in basic decimal increments, preferably .02 inch, and are expressed as two-place decimal numbers. Using the .02 module, the second decimal place (hundredths) is an even number or zero, Figure 2–6. Sizes other than these, such as .25, are used when they are essential to meet design requirements. When greater accuracy is required, sizes are expressed as three- or four-place decimal numbers such as 1.875 or 4.5625.

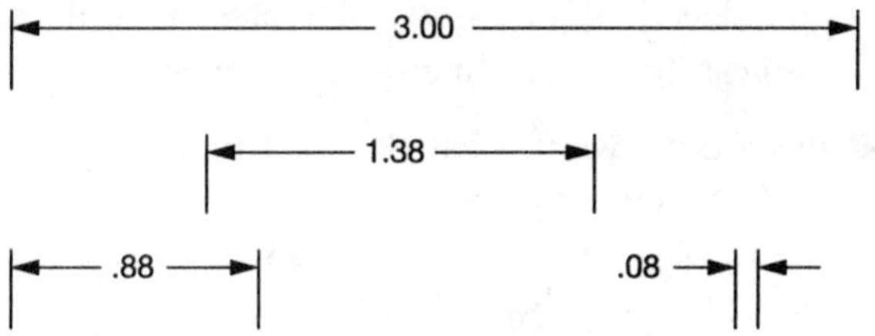

FIGURE 2–6 ■ Decimal-inch dimensioning

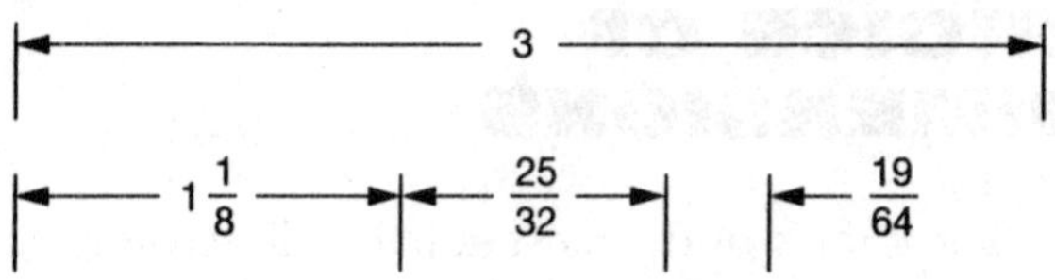

FIGURE 2–7 ■ Fractional-inch dimensioning

The Fractional-inch System

In this system, sizes are expressed in common fractions, the smallest division being 64ths, Figure 2–7. Sizes other than common fractions are expressed as decimals.

The Feet and Inches System

This system is used in architectural drawings and for large structural and installation drawings. Dimensions greater than 12 inches are given in feet and inches, with parts of an inch given as common fractions. Inch marks are not used, and a zero is added to indicate no full inches. A dash mark is placed between the foot and inch values, Figure 2–8.

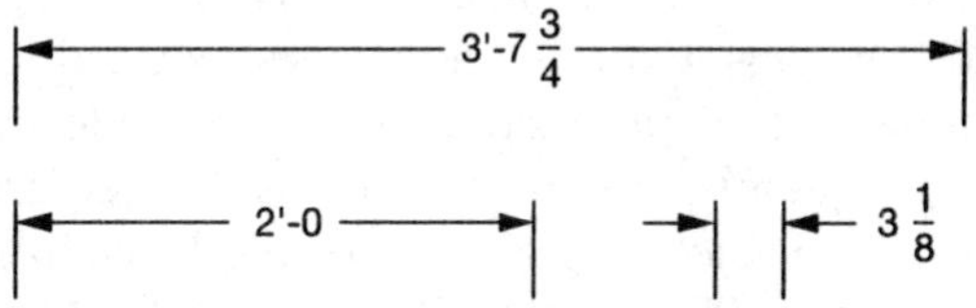

FIGURE 2–8 ■ Feet and inch dimensioning

SI (METRIC) UNITS OF MEASUREMENT

The standard metric units on engineering drawings are the millimetre for linear measure and the micrometre for surface roughness. For architectural drawings metre and millimetre units are used, Figure 2–9.

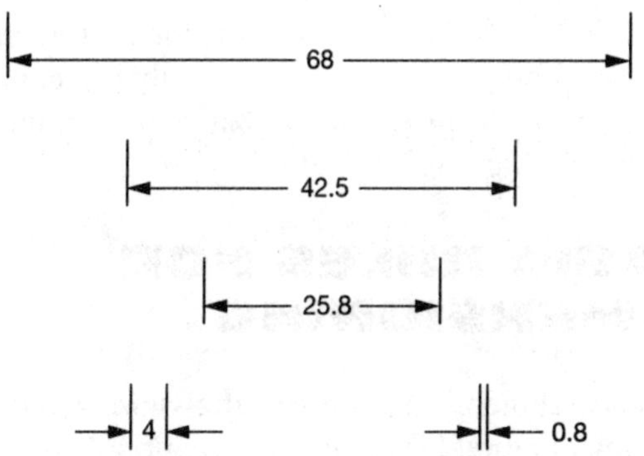

FIGURE 2–9 ■ Metric (millimetre) dimensioning

In metric dimensioning, as in decimal-inch dimensioning, numerals to the right of the decimal point indicate the degree of precision.

Whole dimensions do not require a zero to the right of the decimal point.

2 not 2.0
10 not 10.0

A millimetre value of less than 1 is shown with a zero to the left of the decimal point.

0.2 not .2 or .20
0.26 not .26

Commas should not be used to separate groups of three numbers in metric values. A space should be used in place of the comma.

32 541 not 32,541
2.562 826 6 not 2.5628266

Identification

A metric drawing should include a general note, such as UNLESS OTHERWISE SPECIFIED, DIMENSIONS ARE IN MILLIMETRES. In addition, a metric drawing should be identified by the word METRIC prominently displayed near the title block.

CHOICE OF DIMENSIONS

The choice of the most suitable dimensions and dimensioning methods depends, to some extent, on whether the drawings are intended for unit production or mass production.

Unit production refers to applications in which each part is to be made separately, using general-purpose tools and machines. Details on custom-built machines, jigs, fixtures, and gauges required for the manufacture of production parts are made in this way. Frequently, only one of each part is required.

Mass production refers to parts produced in quantity, for which special tooling is usually provided. Most part drawings for manufactured products are considered to be for mass-produced parts.

Functional dimensioning should be expressed directly on the drawing, especially for mass-produced parts. This will result in the selection of datum features on the basis of function and assembly. For unit-produced parts, it is generally preferable to select datum features on the basis of manufacture and machining, Figure 2–10.

BASIC RULES FOR DIMENSIONING

- Place dimensions between the views when possible, Figure 2–11(A).
- Place the dimension line for the shortest width, height, and depth nearest the outline of the object, Figure 2–11(B). Parallel dimension lines are placed in order of their size, making the longest dimension line the outermost line.
- Place dimensions near the view that best shows the characteristic contour or shape of the object, Figure 2–11(C). In following this rule, dimensions will not always be between views.

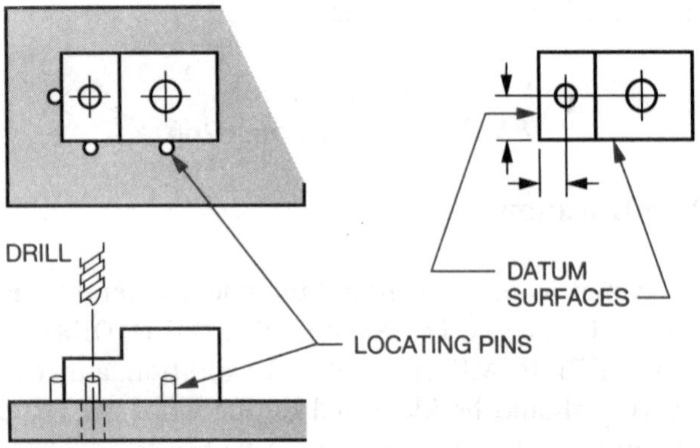

FIGURE 2–10 ■ Selection of datum surfaces for dimensioning

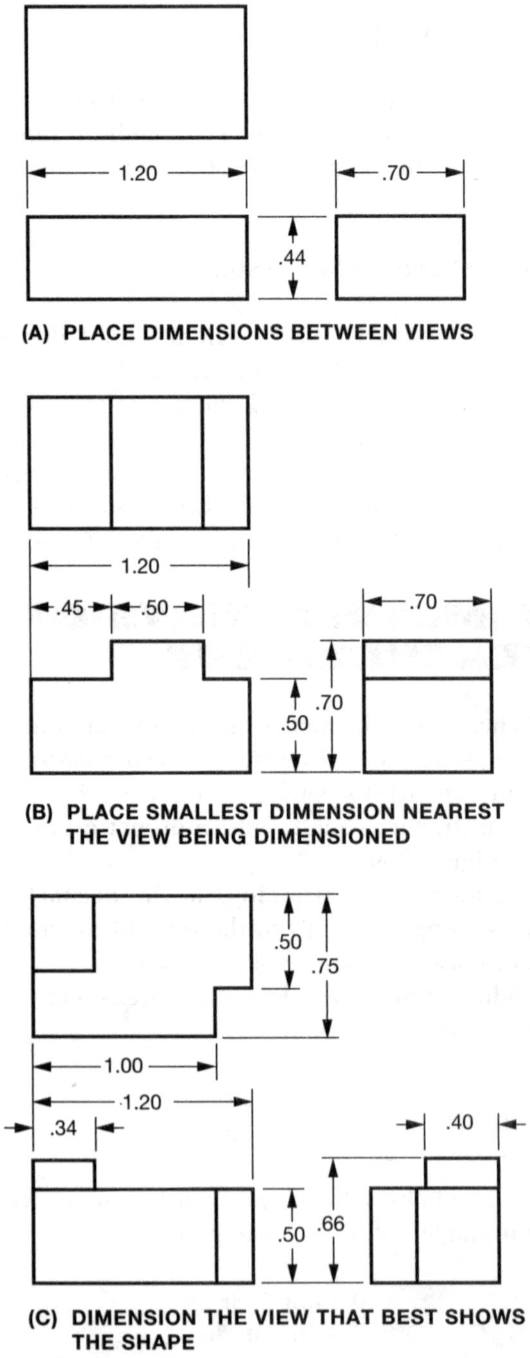

FIGURE 2–11 ■ Basic dimensioning rules

- On large drawings, dimensions can be placed on the view to improve clarity.
- Use only one system of dimensions, either the unidirectional or the aligned, on any one drawing.

INFORMATION SHOWN ON ASSIGNMENT DRAWINGS

Circled numbers and letters shown in colour are used to identify lines, distances, and surfaces on the drawing assignments so that questions may be asked about these features. To simplify the drawings, the actual working drawing is drawn in black. The information used in the developing of interpreting technical drawings is shown in colour and would not appear on working drawings found in industry.

REFERENCES

CAN/CSA-B78.2-M91 Dimensioning and Tolerancing of Technical Drawings

ASME Y14.5M-1994 Dimensioning and Tolerancing

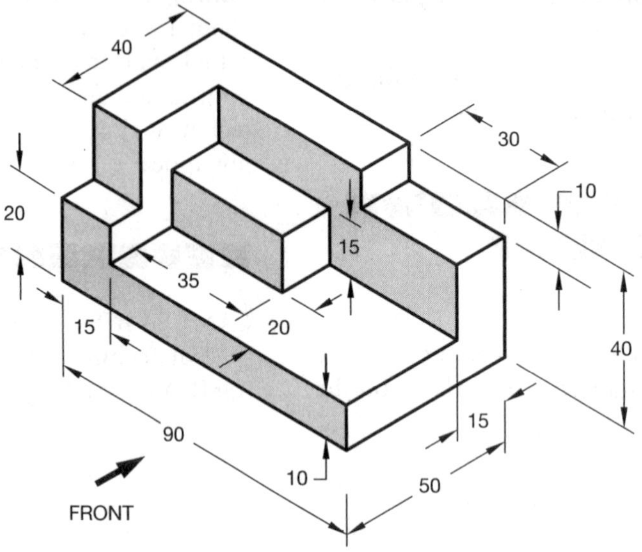

10 mm SQUARES (1 mm GRID)

BOTTOM LEFT CORNER OF FRONT VIEW

METRIC
DIMENSIONS IN MILLIMETRES

ASSIGNMENT: SKETCH THE TOP, FRONT, AND RIGHT-SIDE VIEWS USING THIRD-ANGLE PROJECTION. FULL SCALE. ALLOW 10 mm BETWEEN VIEWS.

CORNER BLOCK	A-4M

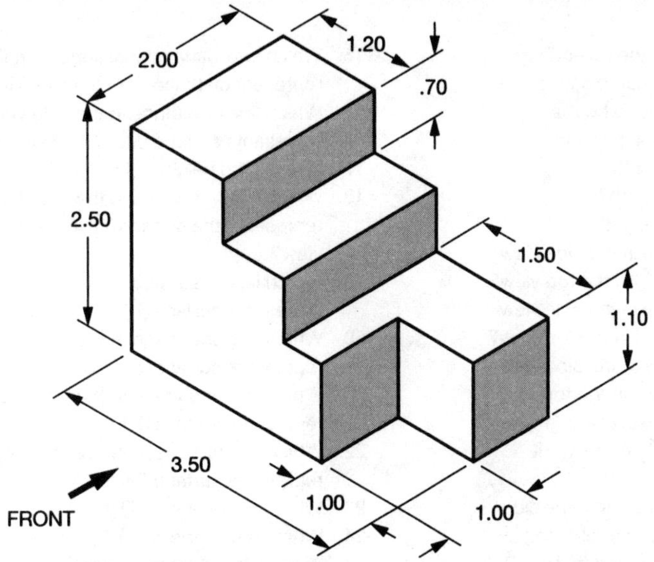
2.00
1.20
.70
2.50
1.50
1.10
3.50
1.00
1.00
FRONT

BOTTOM LEFT CORNER OF FRONT VIEW

.50 INCH SQUARES (.10 IN. GRID)

ASSIGNMENT: SKETCH THE TOP, FRONT, AND RIGHT-SIDE VIEWS USING THIRD-ANGLE PROJECTION. FULL SCALE. ALLOW .5 IN. BETWEEN VIEWS.

STEP BRACKET	A-5

QUESTIONS

1. What is the name of the object?
2. What is the drawing number?
3. How many pieces are to be made?
4. Of what material is the part made?
5. What is the overall width?
6. What is the overall depth?
7. What is the overall height?
8. Which line or surface in the side view represents surface Ⓕ in the top view?
9. Which line or surface in the side view represents surface Ⓔ in the top view?
10. Which line or surface in the side view represents surface Ⓖ in the top view?
11. Which line or surface in the side view represents surface Ⓛ of the front view?
12. What is the vertical height in the side view from the surface represented by line Ⓟ to that represented by line Ⓠ ?
13. What is the height of the step in the side view from the bottom of the part to the surface represented by surface Ⓔ ?
14. Which two-dimensional (letters) in the top view represent distance V in the side view?
15. Which two-dimensional (letters) in the top view represent distance W in the side view?
16. Which line or surface in the side view represents surface Ⓜ in the front view?
17. What is the height of line Ⓝ ?
18. Which line or surface in the front view represents the surface Ⓡ in the side view?
19. Which line or surface in the top view represents surface Ⓛ ?
20. Which line or surface in the front view represents surface Ⓕ ?
21. Which line or surface in the front view represents surface Ⓔ ?
22. Which line or surface in the top view represents surface Ⓜ ?
23. What type of line is Ⓣ ?
24. What type of line is Ⓨ ?
25. What units of measurement are used on this drawing?
26. Calculate dimensions B, C, D, and W.

ANSWERS

1. ____________
2. ____________
3. ____________
4. ____________
5. ____________
6. ____________
7. ____________
8. ____________
9. ____________
10. ____________
11. ____________
12. ____________
13. ____________
14. ____________
15. ____________
16. ____________
17. ____________
18. ____________
19. ____________
20. ____________
21. ____________
22. ____________
23. ____________
24. ____________
25. ____________
26. B ____________
C ____________
D ____________
W ____________

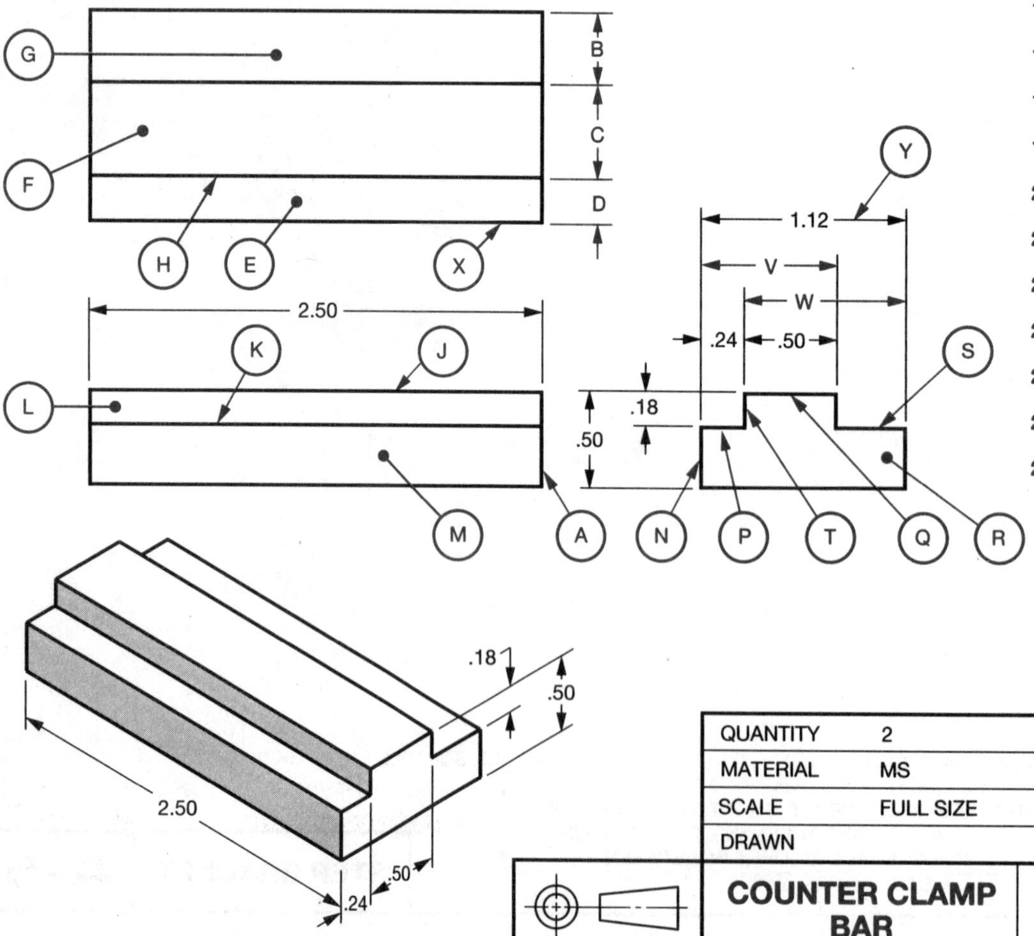

QUANTITY	2	
MATERIAL	MS	
SCALE	FULL SIZE	
DRAWN		DATE
COUNTER CLAMP BAR		A-6

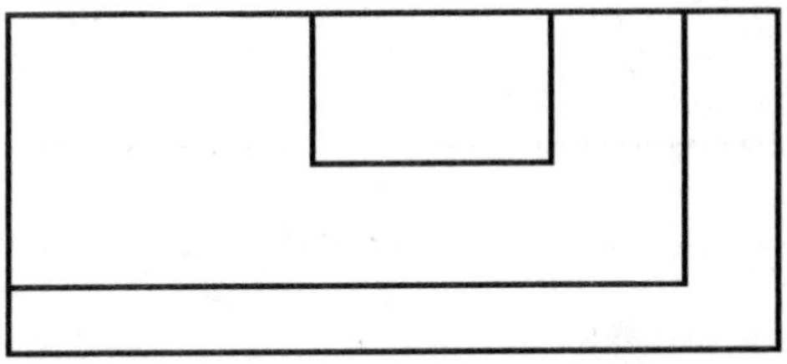

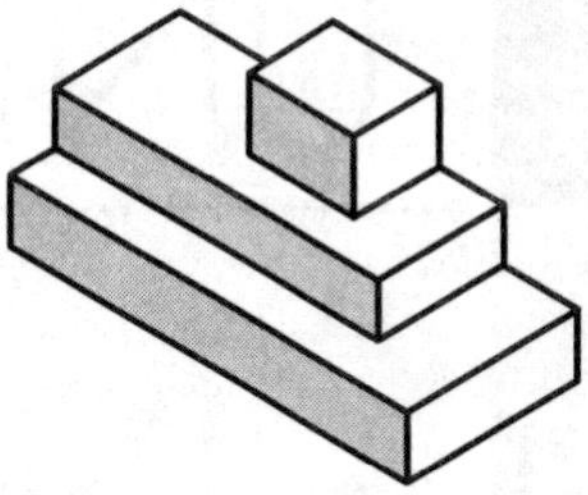

INCH DRAWING
DIMENSION TO THE NEAREST .02 INCH

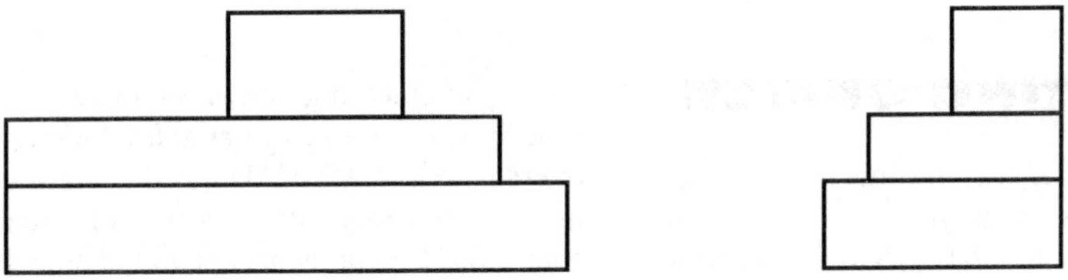

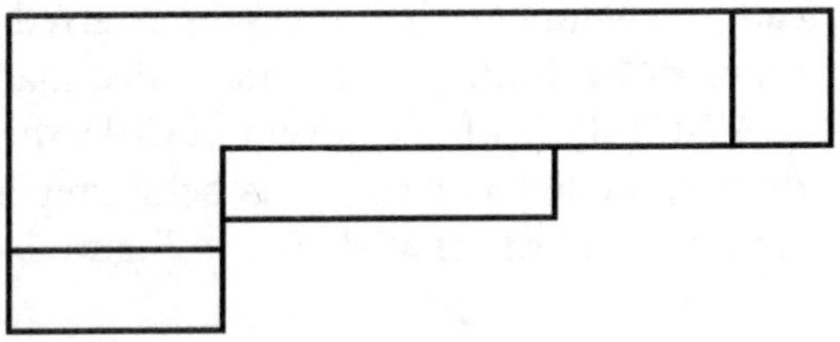

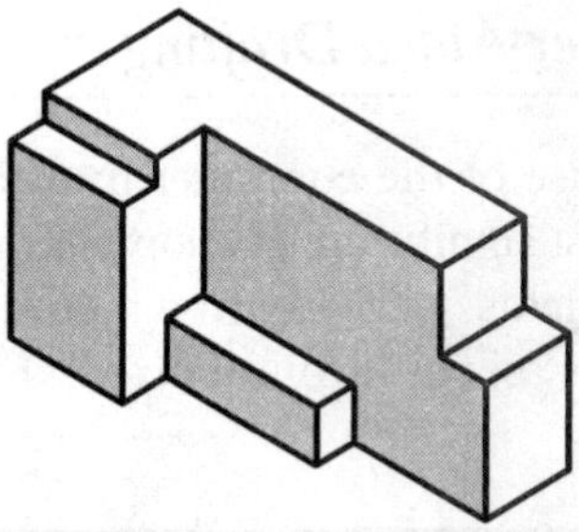

METRIC DRAWING
DIMENSION TO THE NEAREST MILLIMETRE

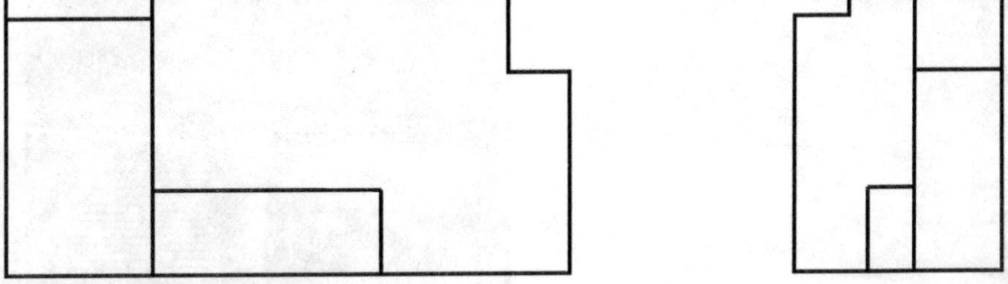

ASSIGNMENT: FOLLOW THE DIMENSIONING PRACTICE OUTLINED IN UNIT 2 TO ADD DIMENSIONS TO THE ABOVE DRAWING, FULL SCALE.

DIMENSIONING	**A-7**

3 UNIT

THE DRAFTING OFFICE

The drafting office is the starting point for all engineering work. Its product, the engineering drawing, is the main method of communication among all people concerned with the design and manufacture of parts.

Computer-Aided Drafting

The use of the computer in design and drafting is the most significant development to occur recently in these fields. The way in which drawings are prepared has been revolutionized, Figure 3–1. Producing engineering drawings on a computer is a process known as *computer-aided drafting,* commonly referred to as *CAD.* CAD has many advantages over manual drafting. Some major advantages are the ability to (1) rapidly access and change information on drawings; (2) cross-reference related information in an easy manner; (3) increase productivity in the drafting room; and (4) make three-dimensional modelling economically possible.

If information is to be sent directly to the fabricating machinery, the process is referred to as computer-aided drafting–computer-aided manufacturing *(CAD-CAM).* With the advent of CAD, the traditional drafting table has been, or is being, replaced with a station similar to that shown in Figure 3–2.

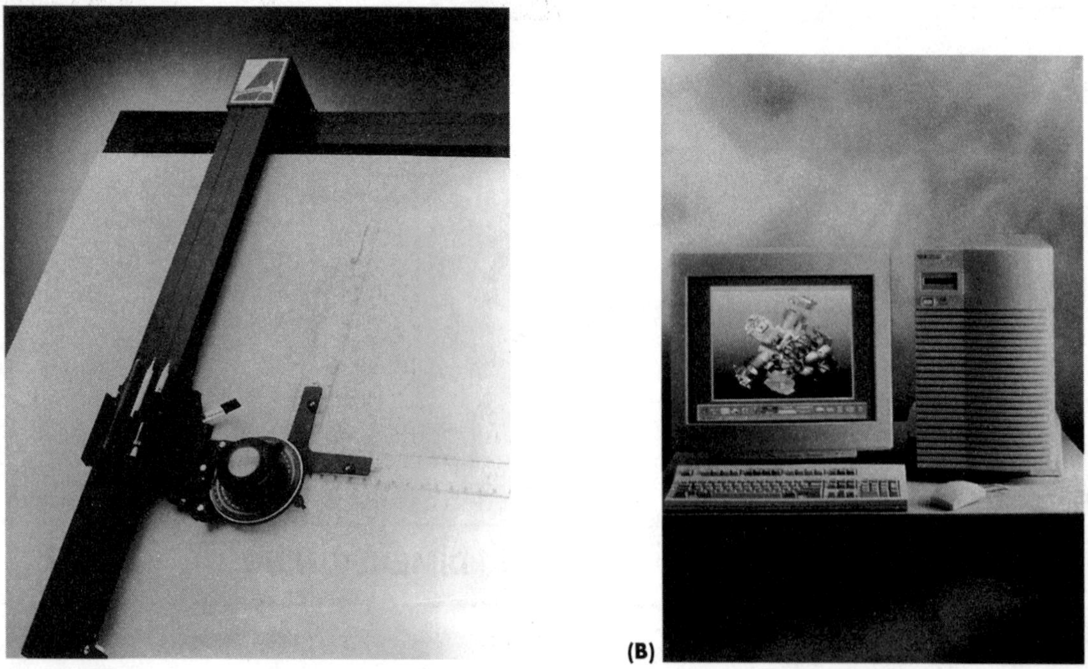

(A) **(B)**

FIGURE 3–1 ■ Manual drafting and CAD workstations. *(A) Courtesy Alvin & Co., (B) Courtesy Hewlett-Packard Co.*

FIGURE 3–2 ■ A CAD workstation. *Courtesy Hewlett-Packard Co.*

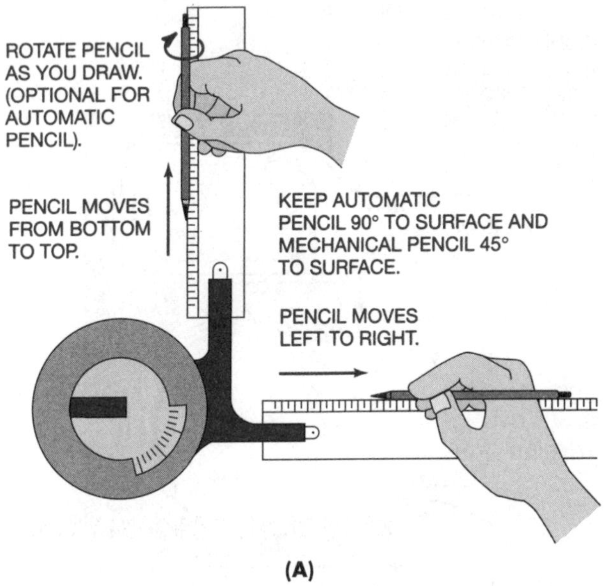

FIGURE 3–3 ■ Skill requirements for manual and computer-aided drafting. (A) Manual drafting (B) Computer-aided drafting *Courtesy Baystate Technologies Inc.*

Whether preparing manual (traditional) or automated (computer-aided) drawings, the drafter must be familiar with the principles of drafting. Only the skill requirements and drafting equipment are different, Figure 3–3. With manual drafting, skills in drawing lines and lettering are mandatory. With automated drafting, skills in drawing lines and lettering are not as critical. A cathode-ray terminal, a processing unit, a digitizer, and a plotter replace the manual drafting equipment.

A CAD system by itself cannot create. A drafter must create the drawing, and thus a strong design and drafting background remains essential.

DRAWING REPRODUCTION

The original drawings made by the drafter are kept in the engineering department at all times. Copies or prints of the originals are sent to the shop. For many years the most popular reproduction method was the blueprint. The demand for a faster and more versatile type of reproduction during World War II led to the introduction of the diazo process (whiteprints) of duplicating drawings, Figure 3–4.

Today, the demand for more economical and versatile methods of reproducing drawings and the expense of maintaining filing systems have brought about the introduction of new methods of reproducing drawings, two of which are *microfilming* and *photoreproduction*.

The use of microfilm has been steadily increasing in recent years. Microfilm has a 35-mm image set into an aperture card, Figure 3–5. Using this technique, the drawing may also be stored on a roll of 35-mm film.

Microfilm enables the drawing to be stored in a fraction of the floor space needed for filing the full-sized paper originals. It can be referenced on the screen of a reader or, if a print is required, microfilm can be enlarged and reproduced on a reader-printer, Figure 3–6.

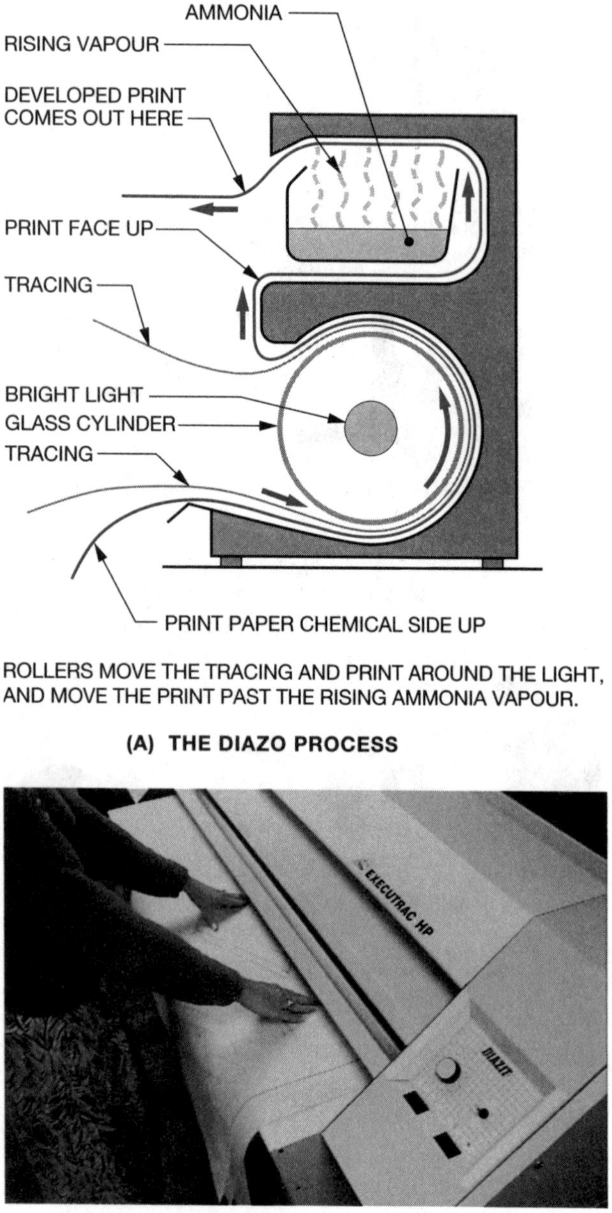
AMMONIA
RISING VAPOUR
DEVELOPED PRINT COMES OUT HERE
PRINT FACE UP
TRACING
BRIGHT LIGHT
GLASS CYLINDER
TRACING
PRINT PAPER CHEMICAL SIDE UP
ROLLERS MOVE THE TRACING AND PRINT AROUND THE LIGHT, AND MOVE THE PRINT PAST THE RISING AMMONIA VAPOUR.
(A) THE DIAZO PROCESS
EXECUTRAC HP

(B) A WHITEPRINT DIAZO MACHINE IN USE.

FIGURE 3–4 ■ The diazo method of reproduction. (B) A whiteprint diazo machine in use. *Courtesy Ozalid Corporation*

Photoreproduction is one of the newest and most versatile methods for reproducing engineering drawings, Figure 3–7. One such printer offers, in addition to full-scale printing, reduction settings by which a drawing, or part of a drawing, can be reduced in size. Drawing reductions allow significant advantages: less paper consumption, lower handling and mailing costs, and smaller filing-space requirements.

FIGURE 3–5 ■ Aperture cards

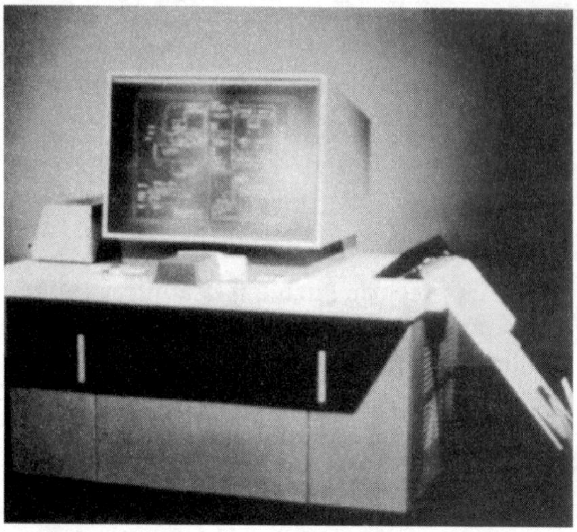

FIGURE 3–6 ■ Reader-printer for microfilm

FIGURE 3–7 ■ Inkjet printer. *Courtesy CalComp*

Another advantage is that because the drawing is photographed and prints or tracings can be made from the original work, the drafter can draw on practically any type of paper. However, in industrial practice, drawings are usually done on translucent sheets.

Because photoreproduction utilizes photography, it is suitable for scissors and paste-up drafting. This technique allows the drafter to incorporate previously printed or drawn material into his or her own work.

ABBREVIATIONS USED ON DRAWINGS

Abbreviations and symbols are used on drawings to conserve time and space, but only when their meaning is perfectly understood. A few of the more common abbreviations and symbols are shown in Table 2 of the Appendix. A complete set of abbreviations for drawing use may be found in CSA Z85-1983, "Abbreviations for Scientific and Engineering Terms."

HIDDEN LINES

Most objects drawn in engineering offices are complicated and contain many surfaces and edges. Many features, such as lines and holes, cannot be seen when viewed from the outside of the piece. These hidden edges are shown on the drawings by a *hidden line,* a series of short dashes. The length of the dashes varies slightly in relationship to the size of the drawing. Hidden lines are usually required on the drawing to help show the true shape of the object but may be omitted when not required to preserve the clarity of the drawing.

Hidden lines should always start and end with a dash except when such a dash would form a continuation of a visible detail line. Dashes should always join at corners. Illustrations of these hidden-line techniques are shown in Figure 3–8.

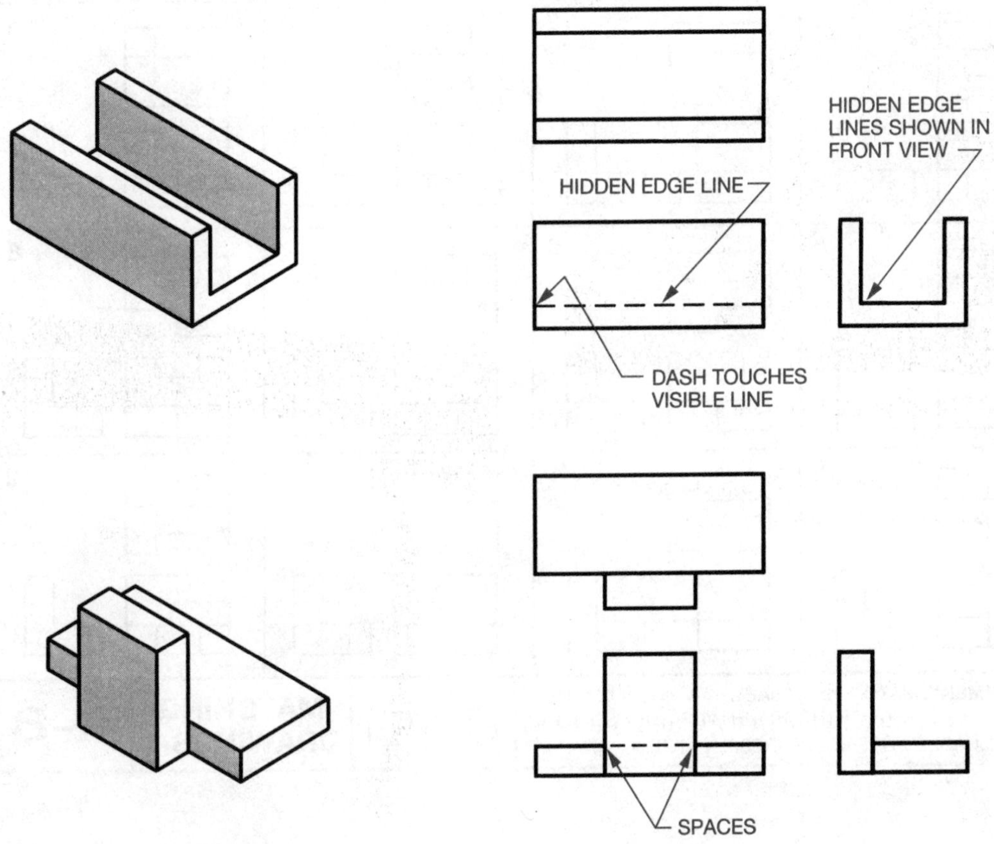

FIGURE 3–8 ■ Hidden lines

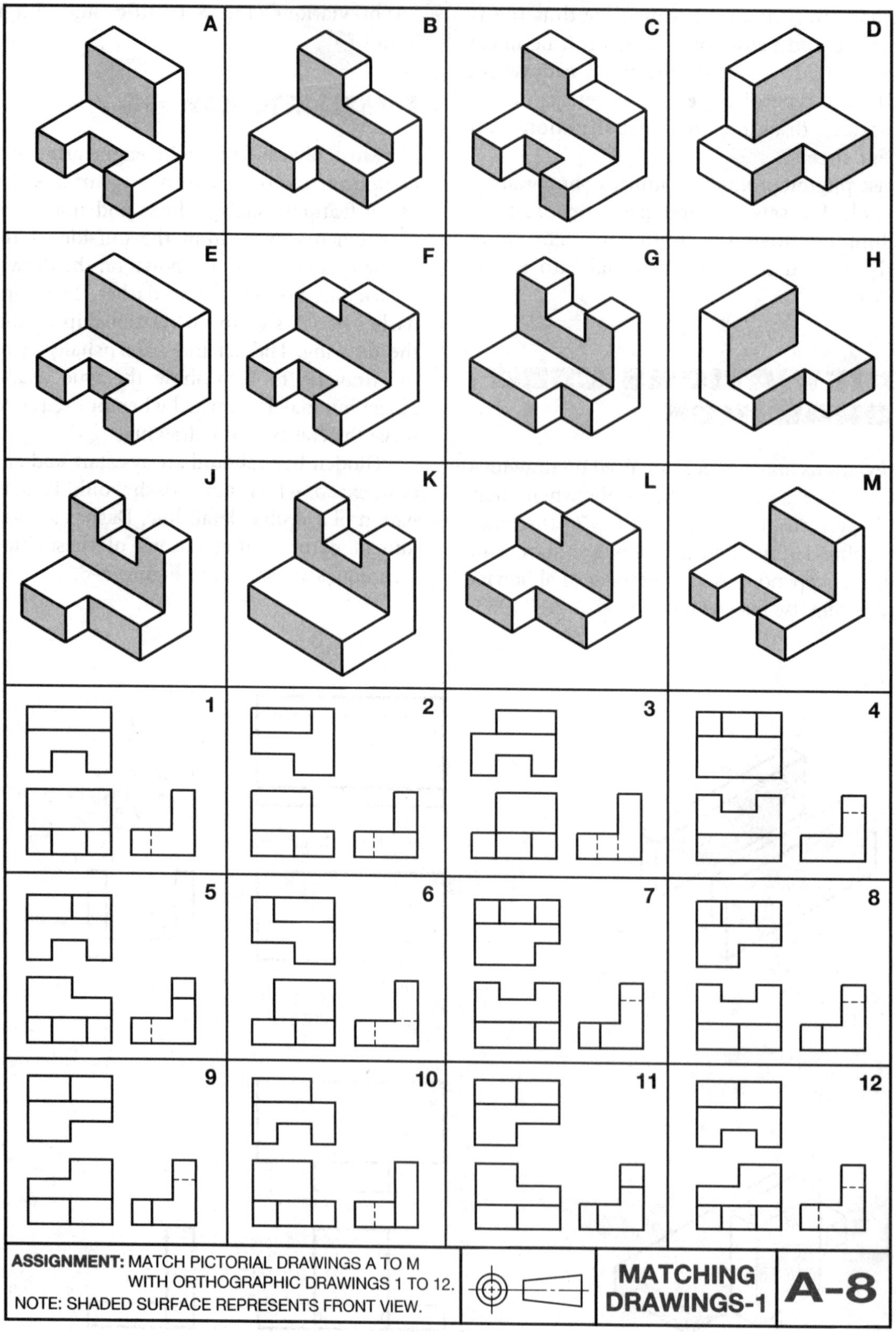

ASSIGNMENT: MATCH PICTORIAL DRAWINGS A TO M WITH ORTHOGRAPHIC DRAWINGS 1 TO 12.

NOTE: SHADED SURFACE REPRESENTS FRONT VIEW.

MATCHING DRAWINGS-1

A-8

N
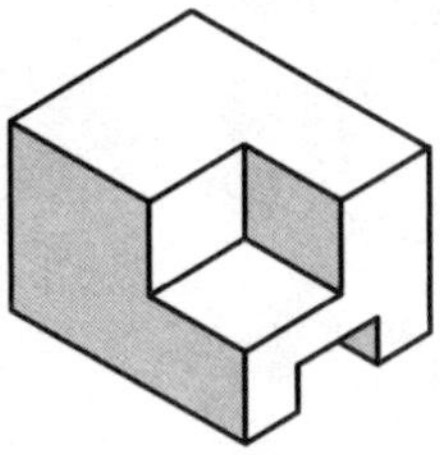
O
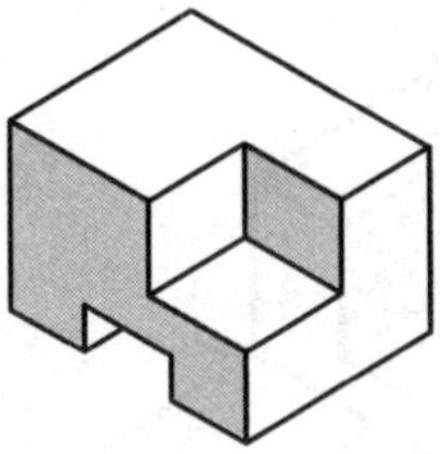
P

Q

R
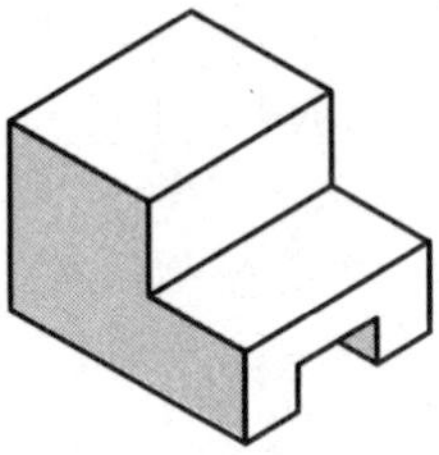
S
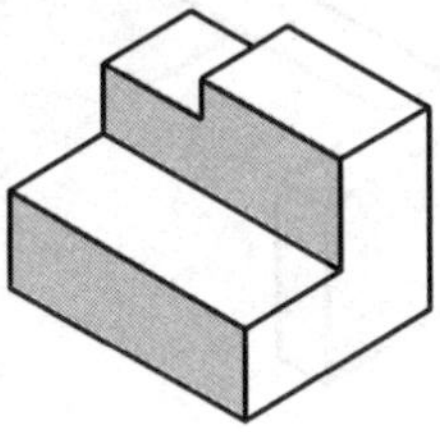
T
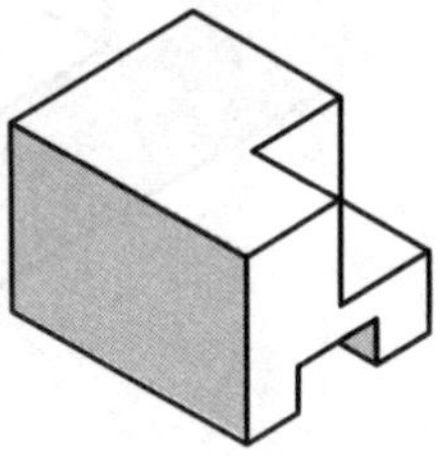
U

V
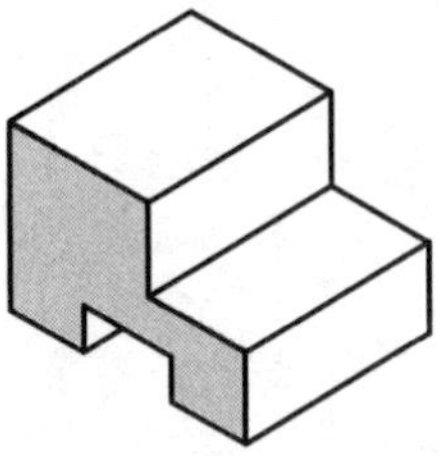
W
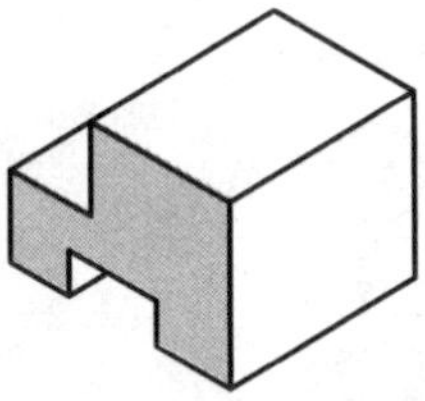
X
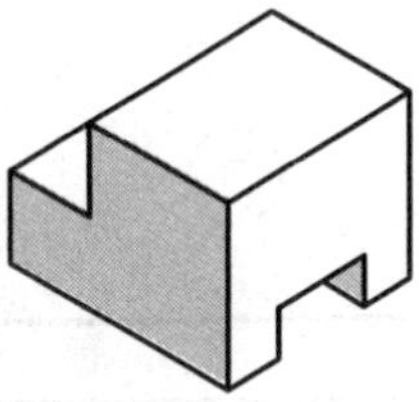
Y
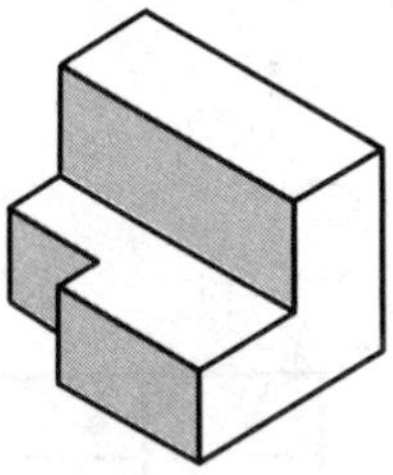
13
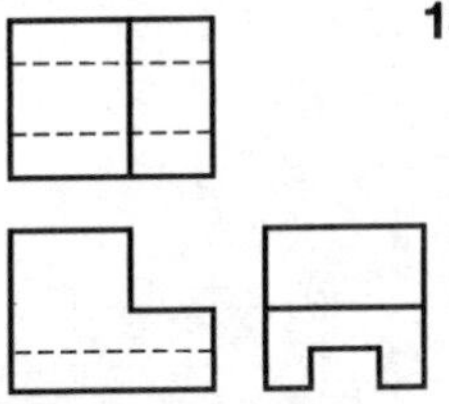
14
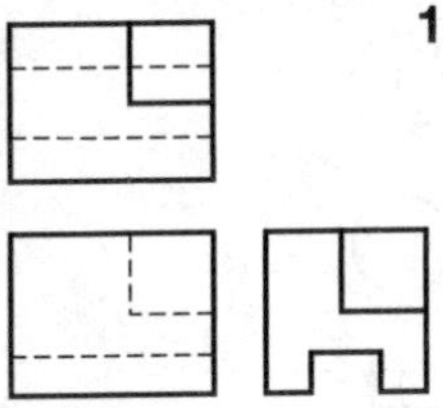
15
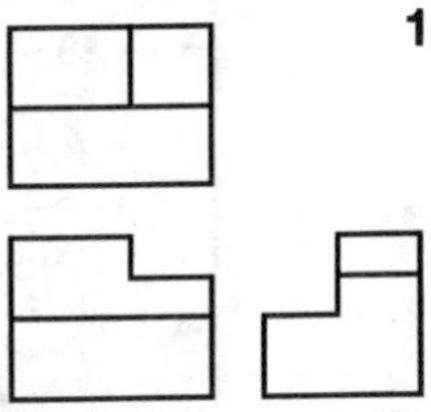
16
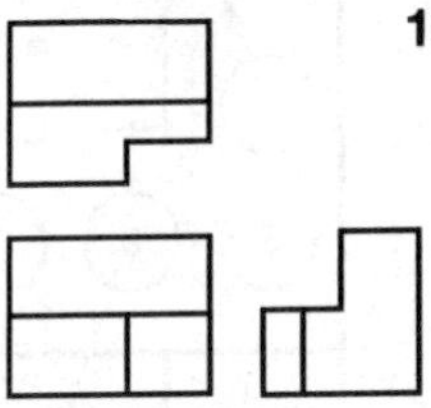
17
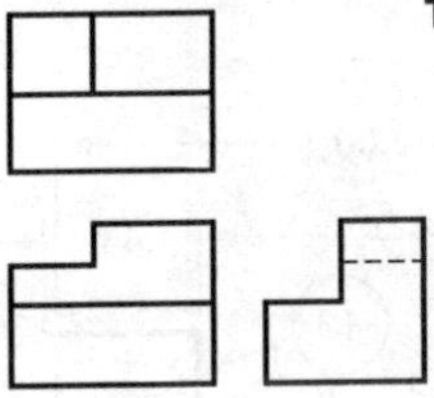
18
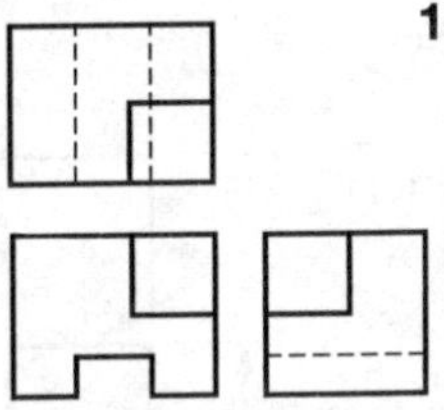
19
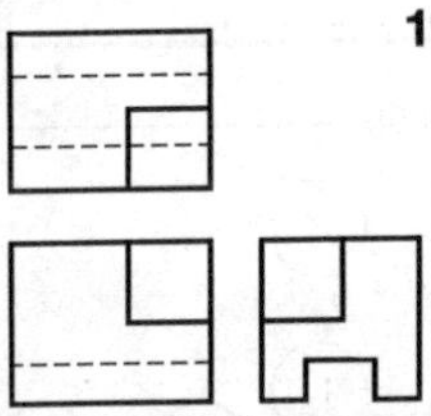
20
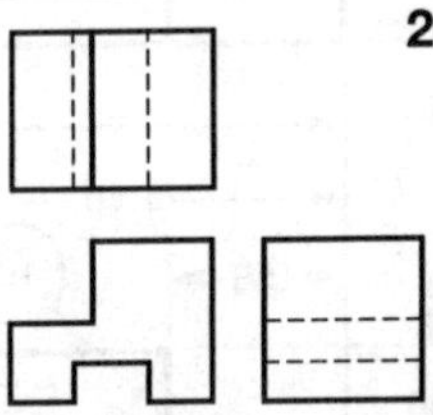
21
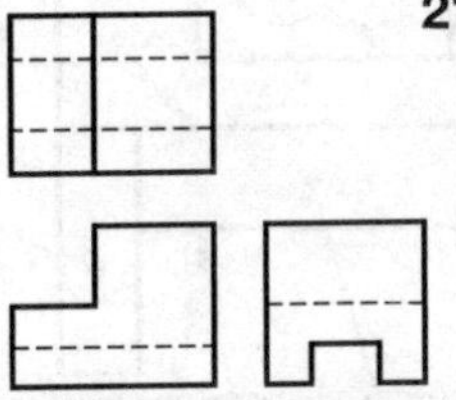
22
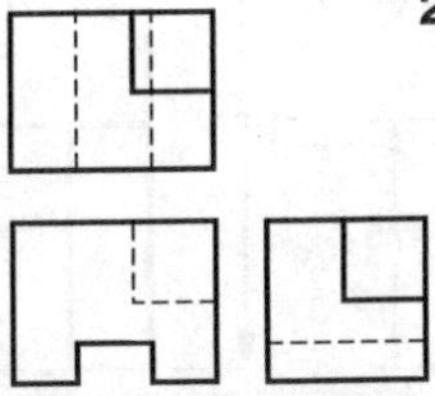
23
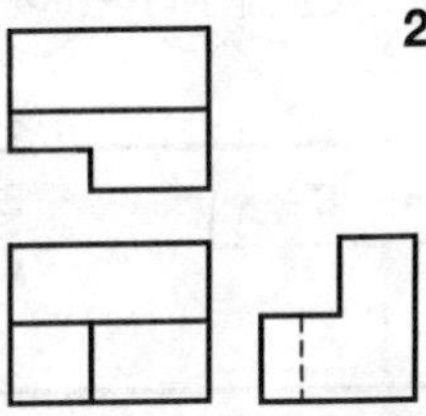
24
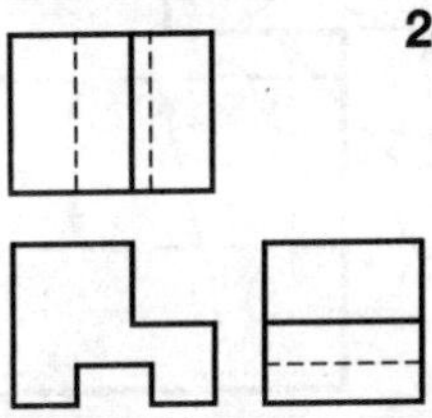

ASSIGNMENT: MATCH PICTORIAL DRAWINGS N TO Y WITH ORTHOGRAPHIC DRAWINGS 13 TO 24.

NOTE: SHADED SURFACE REPRESENTS FRONT VIEW.

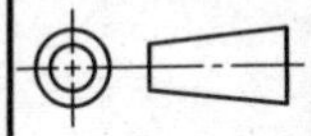

MATCHING DRAWINGS-2

A-9

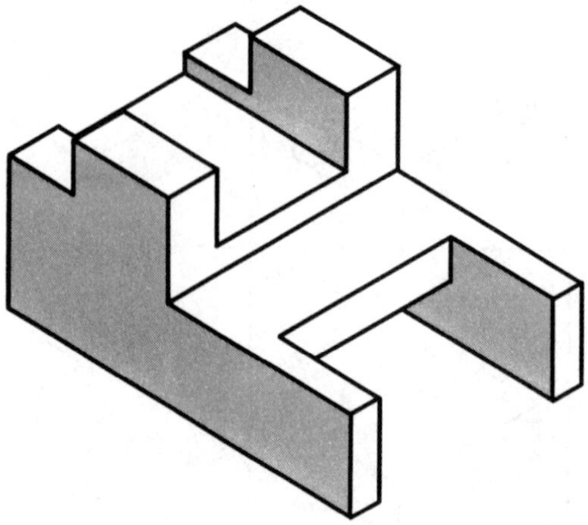

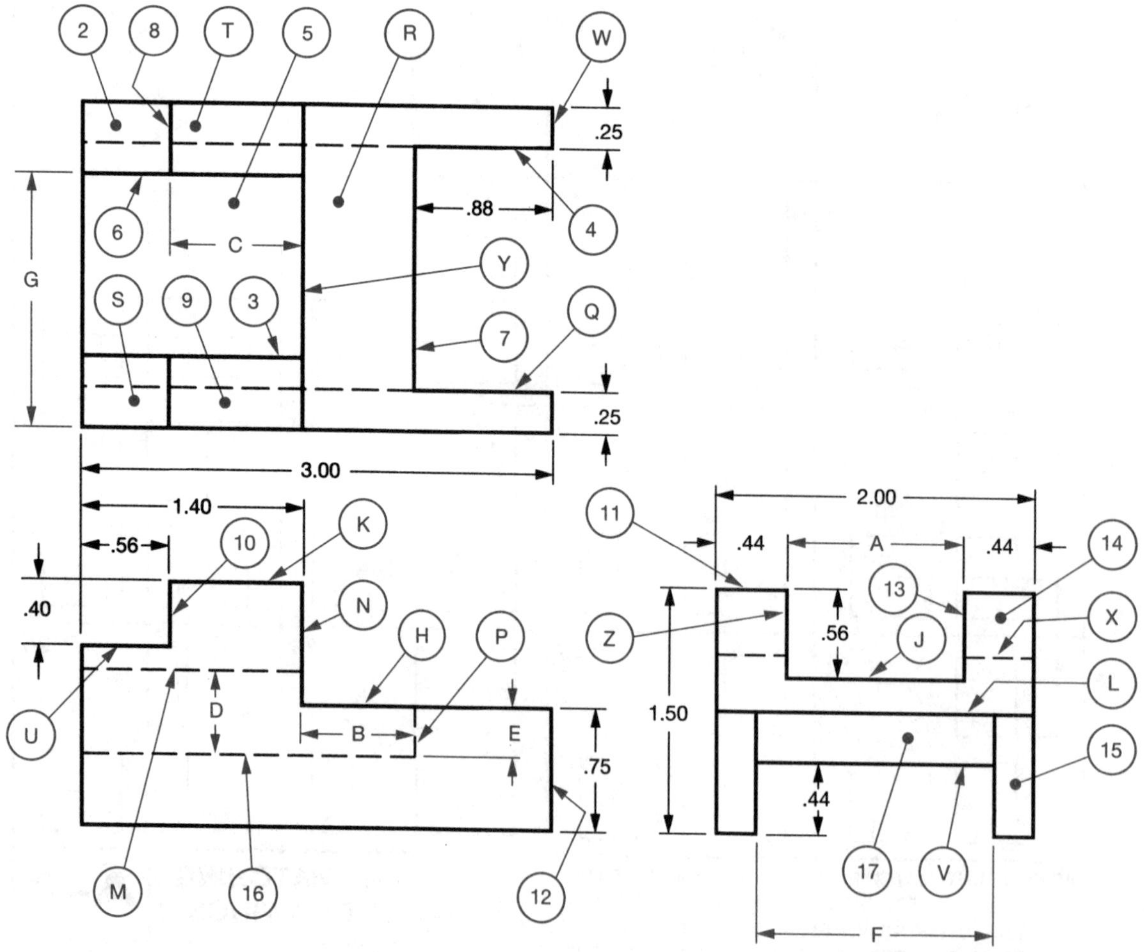
2
8
T
5
R
W
.25
4
.88
6
C
G
Y
S
9
3
Q
7
.25
3.00
1.40
.56
10
K
.40
N
H
P
U
D
B
E
.75
M
16
12
11
2.00
.44
A
.44
14
13
Z
.56
J
X
L
1.50
15
.44
17
V
F

QUESTIONS

1. What is the object?
2. What is the drawing number?
3. How many castings are required?
4. What material is the part made of?
5. What is the overall width?
6. What is the overall height?
7. What is the overall depth?
8. Calculate distances A through G.
9. Which line in the top view represents surface (P) ?
10. Which line in the side view represents surface (5) ?
11. Which line in the side view represents surface (R) ?
12. Which surface in the top view does line (K) in the front view represent?
13. Which surface in the top view does line (M) in the front view represent?
14. Which line in the side view represents the same surface represented by line (M) of the front view?
15. What kind, or type of line, is line (M) ?
16. Which front-view line does line (X) in the side view represent?
17. Which front-view line does line (Y) in the top view represent?
18. Which line in the front view does the surface (15) in the side view represent?
19. Which front-view line represents surface (R) in the top view?
20. Which surface in the side view represents line (N) of the front view?
21. Which line in the side view represents surface (2) ?
22. Which surface in the side view does line (P) represent?
23. Which surface in the top view does line (11) represent?
24. Which line in the side view does line (3) in the top view represent?
25. Which line in the side view does line (16) in the front view represent?
26. Which surface in the side view does line (W) represent?

ANSWERS

1. ______
2. ______
3. ______
4. ______
5. ______
6. ______
7. ______
8. A ______
   B ______
   C ______
   D ______
   E ______
   F ______
   G ______
9. ______
10. ______
11. ______
12. ______
13. ______
14. ______
15. ______
16. ______
17. ______
18. ______
19. ______
20. ______
21. ______
22. ______
23. ______
24. ______
25. ______
26. ______

QUANTITY	875	
MATERIAL	MALLEABLE IRON	
SCALE	NOT TO SCALE	
DRAWN		DATE
FEED HOPPER		A-10

1

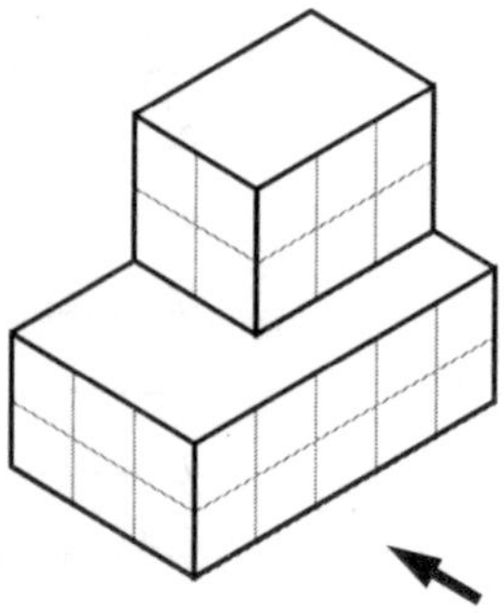

2

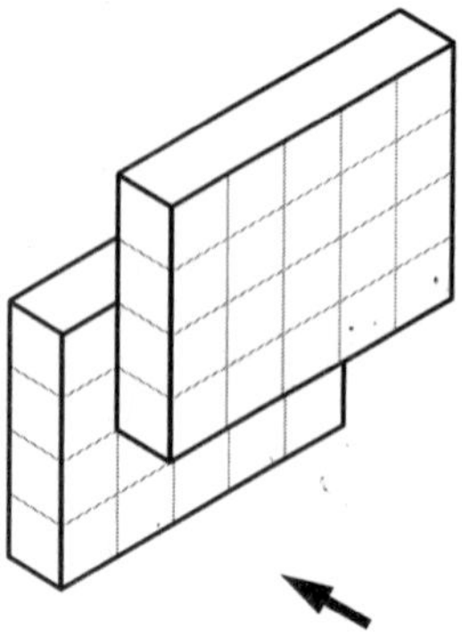

3

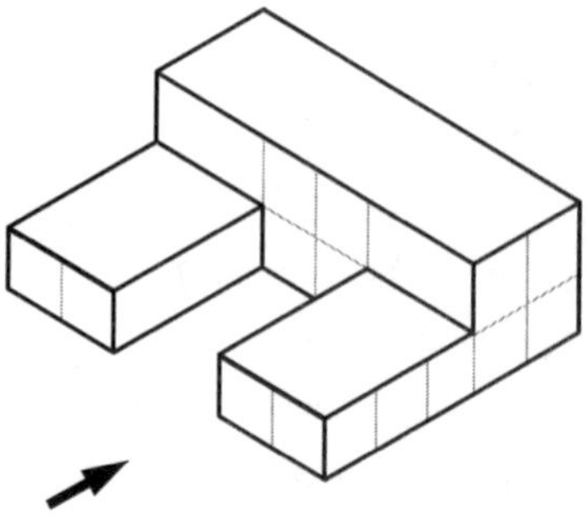

4

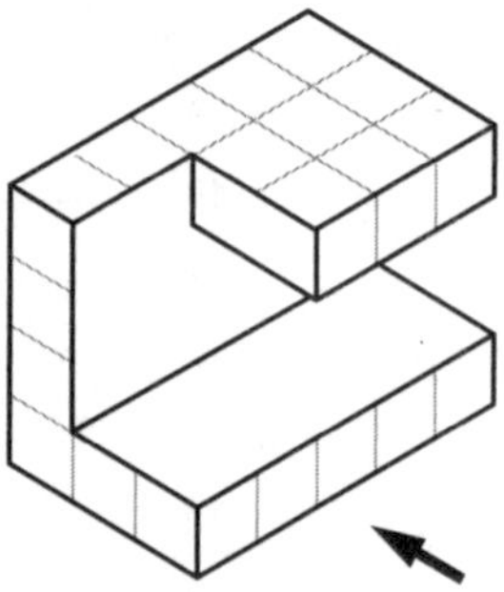

5

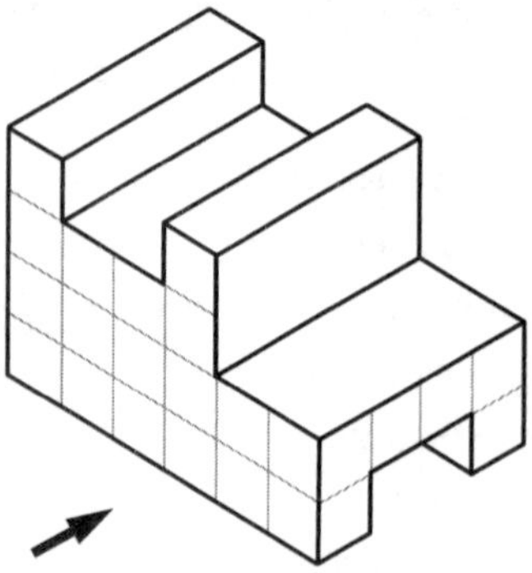

6

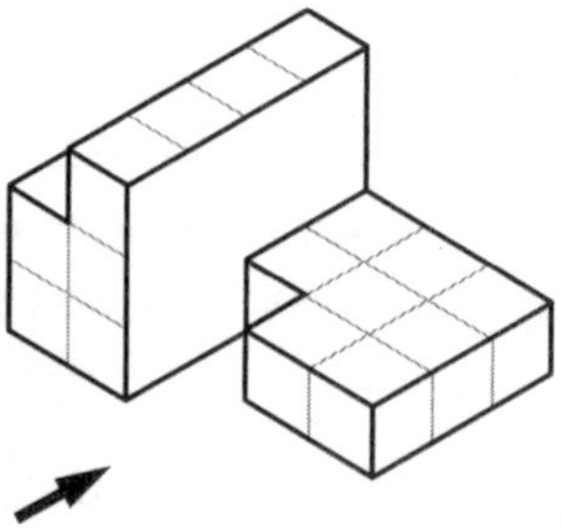

7

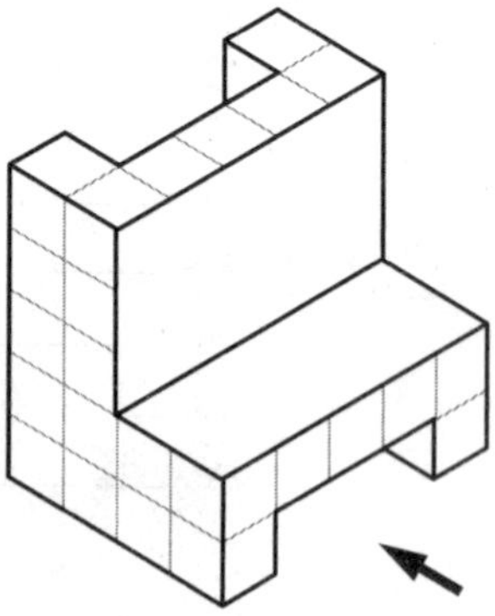

8

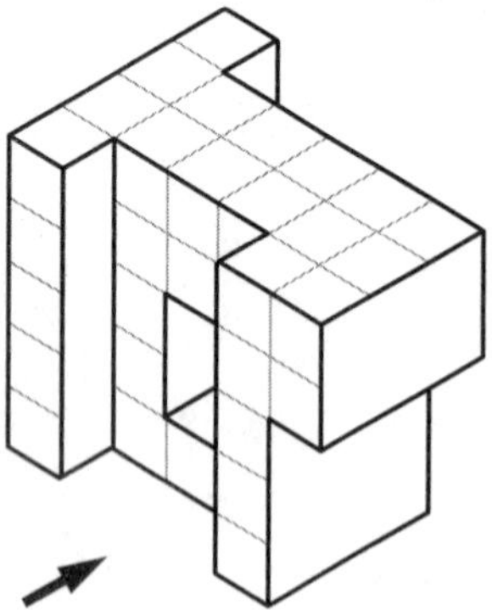

9

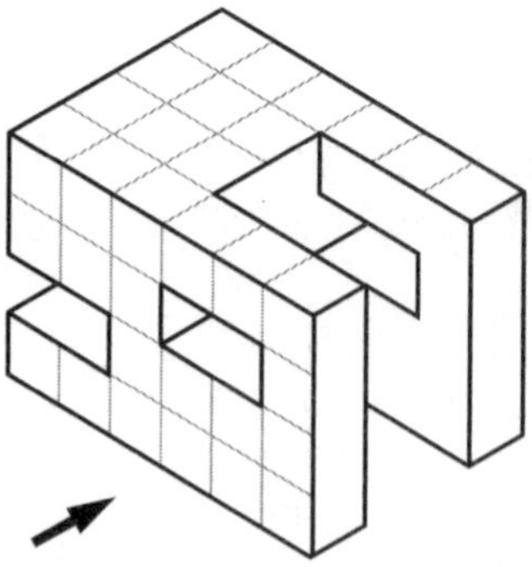

ASSIGNMENT: ON GRAPH PAPER SKETCH THE TOP, FRONT, AND RIGHT-SIDE VIEWS OF THE OBJECTS SHOWN. SHOW ALL HIDDEN LINES. THE ARROW POINTS TO THE FRONT VIEW. USE THIRD-ANGLE ORTHOGRAPHIC PROJECTION.

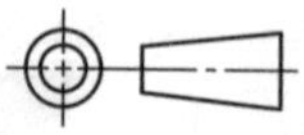

SKETCHING THREE VIEWS

A-11

UNIT 4

INCLINED SURFACES

If the surfaces of an object lie in either a horizontal or vertical position, the surfaces appear in their true shape in one of the three views, and these surfaces appear as a line in the other two views.

When a surface is sloped or inclined in only one direction, that surface is not seen in its true shape in the top, front, or side views. It is, however, seen in two views as a distorted surface. On the third view it appears as a line.

The true length of surfaces A and B in Figure 4–1 is seen in the front view only. In the top and side views, only the width of surfaces A and B appears in its true size. The length of these surfaces is foreshortened.

Where an inclined surface has important features that must be shown clearly and without distortion, an auxiliary or helper view must be used. These views are discussed in detail later in the book.

MEASUREMENT OF ANGLES

Some objects do not have all their features positioned in such a way that all surfaces can be in the horizontal and vertical planes at the same time. The design of the part may require that some of the lines in the drawing be shown in a direction other than horizontal or vertical. This will necessitate that some lines be drawn at an angle.

The amount of this divergence, or obliqueness, of lines may be indicated by either an offset dimension or an angle dimension, as shown in Figure 4–2.

Angle dimensions may be expressed in degrees and decimal parts of a degree. They may also be expressed in degrees, minutes, and seconds. The former method is now preferred.

The symbols for degrees (°), minutes (′), and seconds (″) are included with the appropriate values. For example, 2°; 30°; 28°10′; 0°15′; 27°13′15″; 0°0′30″; 0.25°; 30°0′0″; ± 0°2′30″; and 2° ± 0.5° are all correct forms.

Illustrations of simple objects having inclined surfaces appear in Figure 4–3.

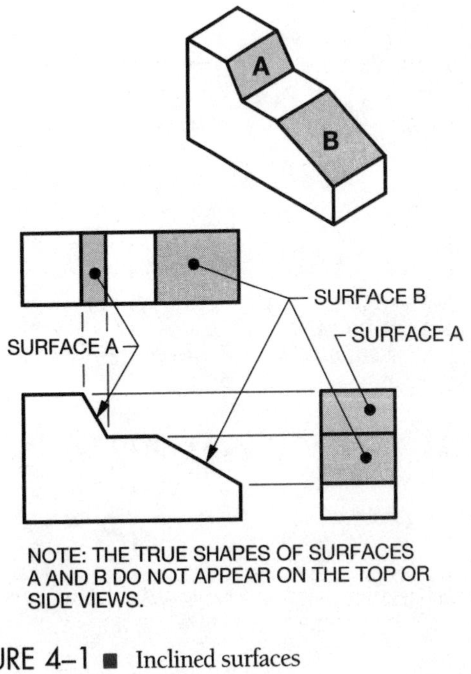
A
B
SURFACE B
SURFACE A
SURFACE A

NOTE: THE TRUE SHAPES OF SURFACES A AND B DO NOT APPEAR ON THE TOP OR SIDE VIEWS.

FIGURE 4–1 ■ Inclined surfaces

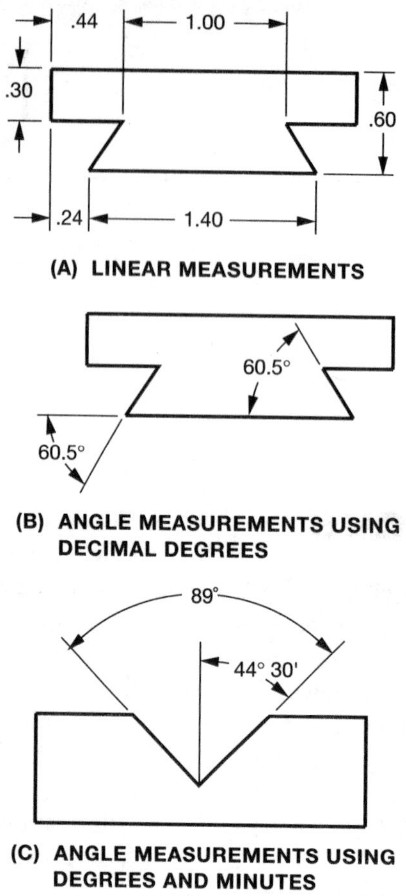
.44
1.00
.30
.60
.24
1.40
(A) LINEAR MEASUREMENTS
60.5°
60.5°
(B) ANGLE MEASUREMENTS USING DECIMAL DEGREES
89°
44° 30'
(C) ANGLE MEASUREMENTS USING DEGREES AND MINUTES

FIGURE 4–2 ■ Dimensioning angles

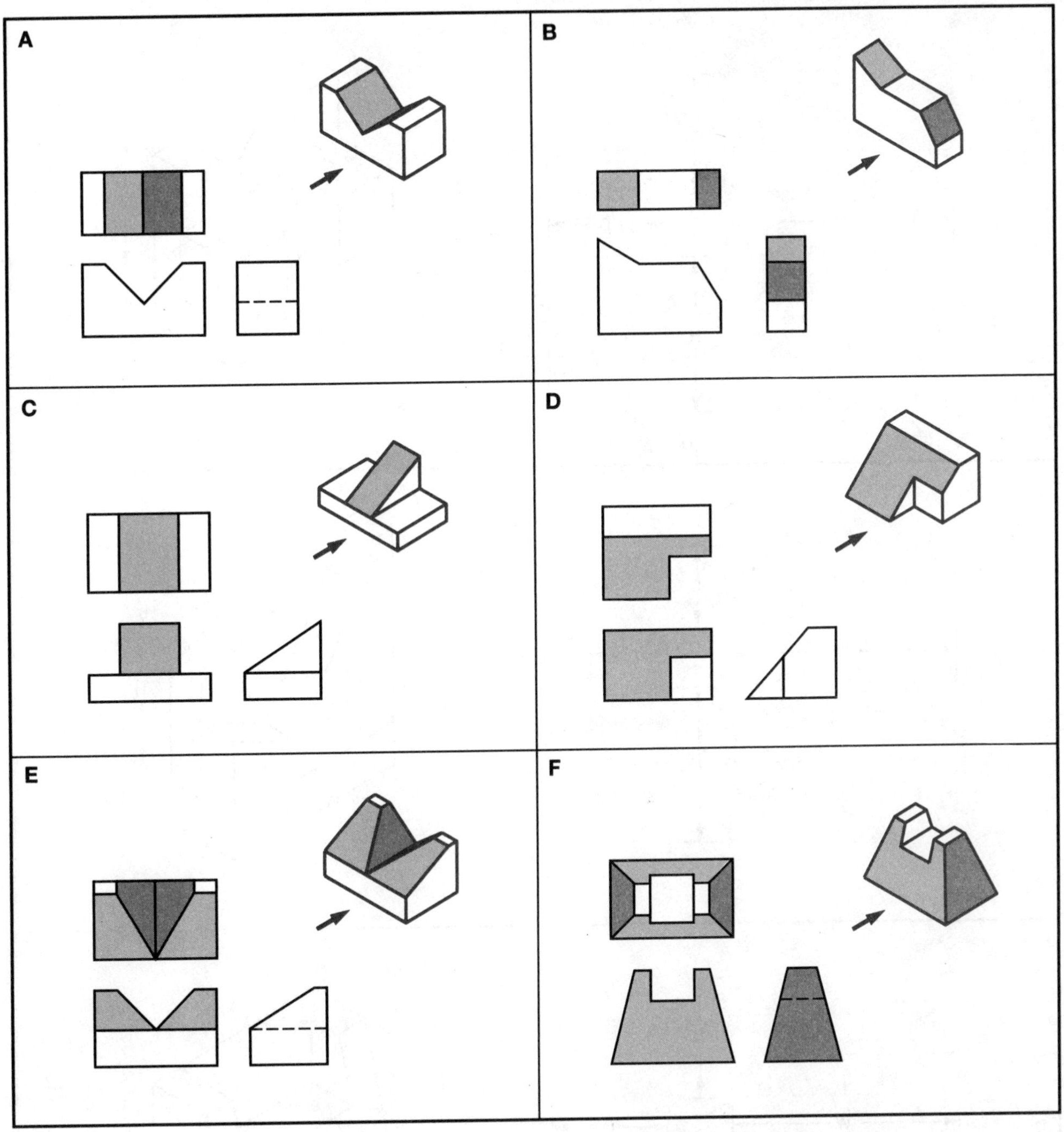

NOTE: ARROWS INDICATE DIRECTION OF SIGHT WHEN LOOKING AT FRONT VIEW.

FIGURE 4–3 ■ Illustrations of simple objects having inclined surfaces

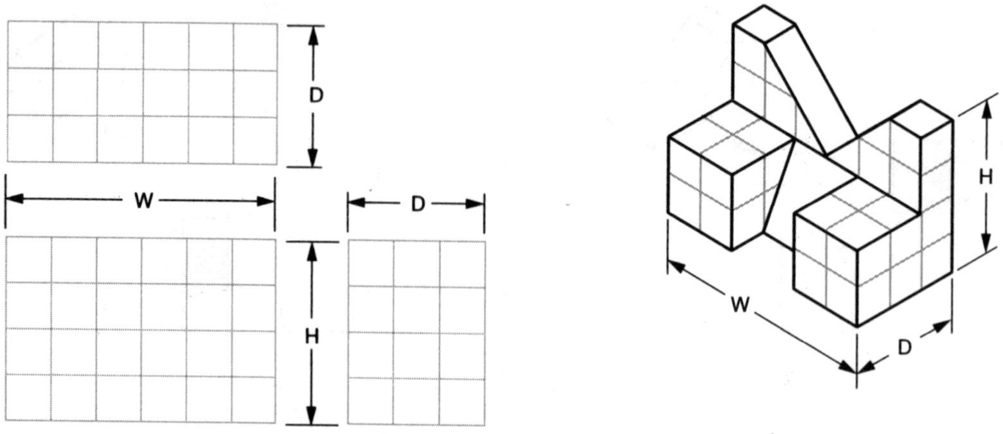

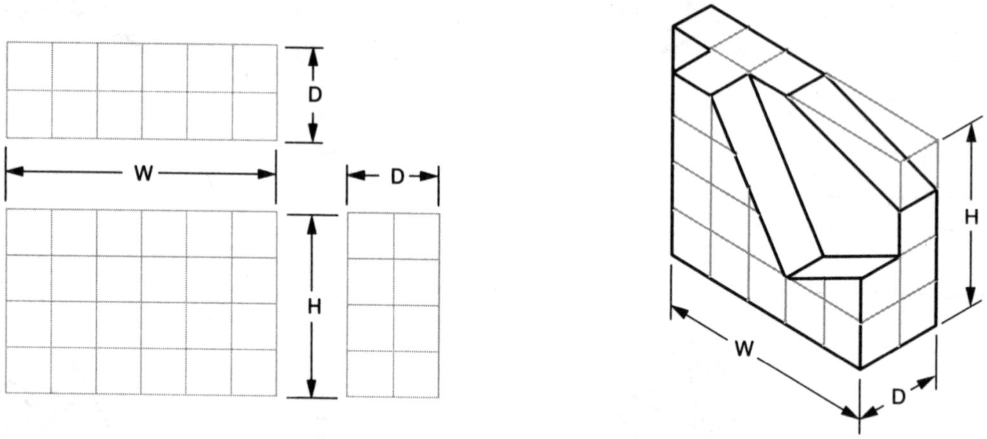

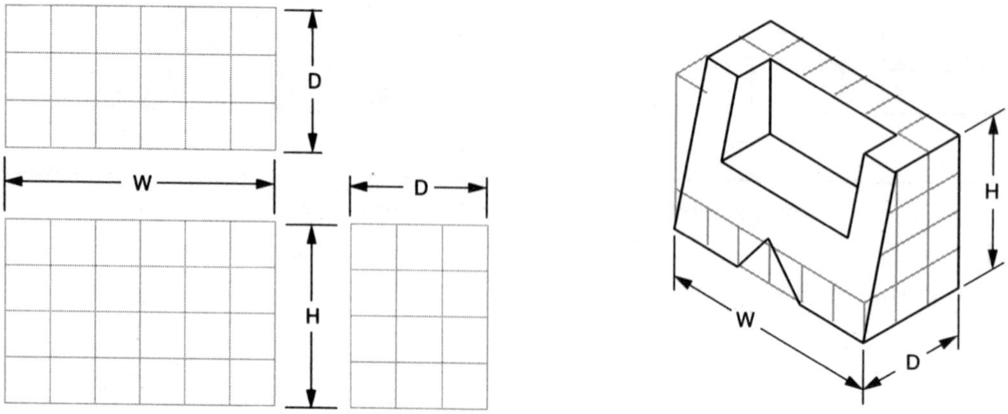

ASSIGNMENT: SKETCH THE TOP, FRONT, AND SIDE VIEWS OF THE OBJECT SHOWN.

	SKETCHING THREE VIEWS	**A-12**

A

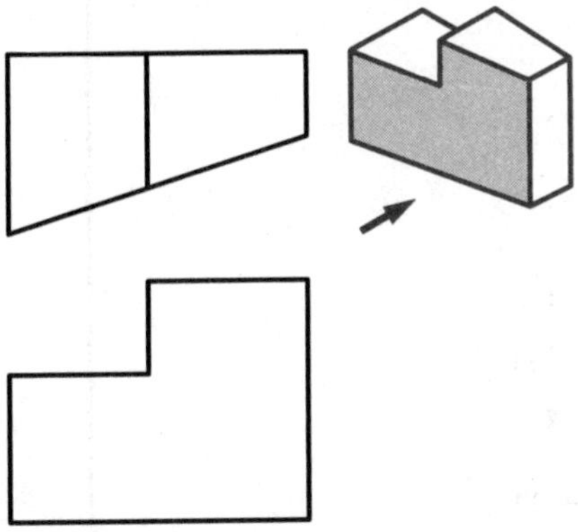

B

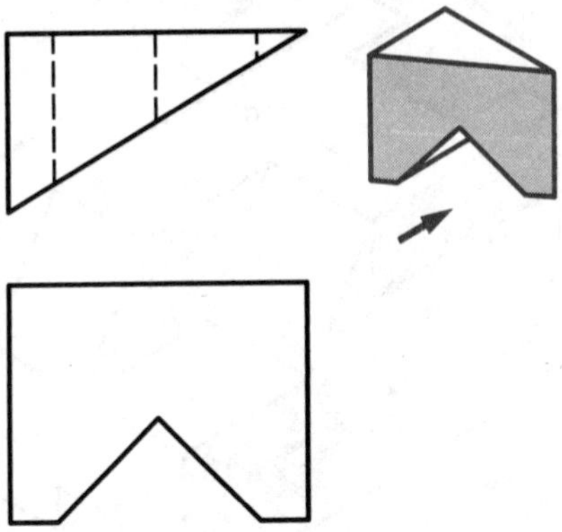

C

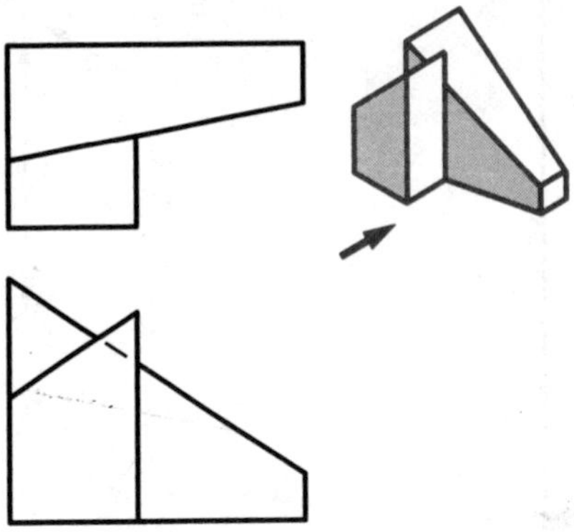

SKETCH THE RIGHT-SIDE VIEWS. THE TOP AND FRONT VIEWS ARE COMPLETE.

D

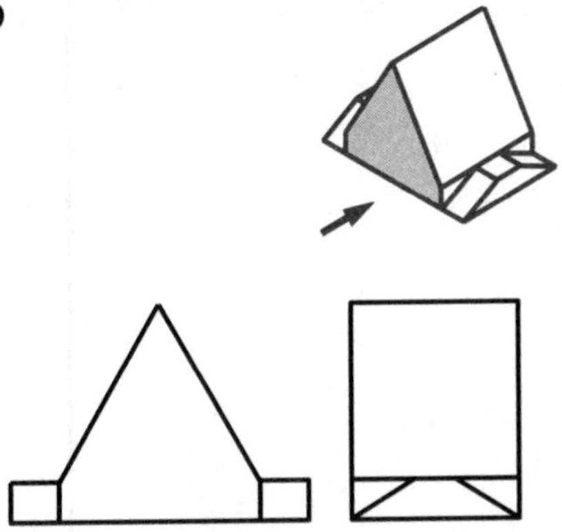

E

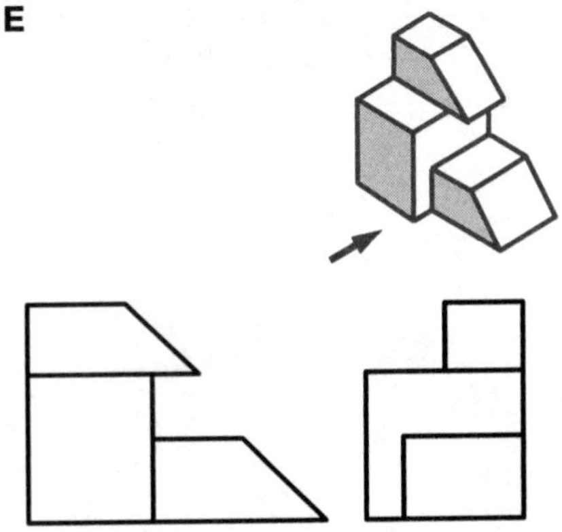

F

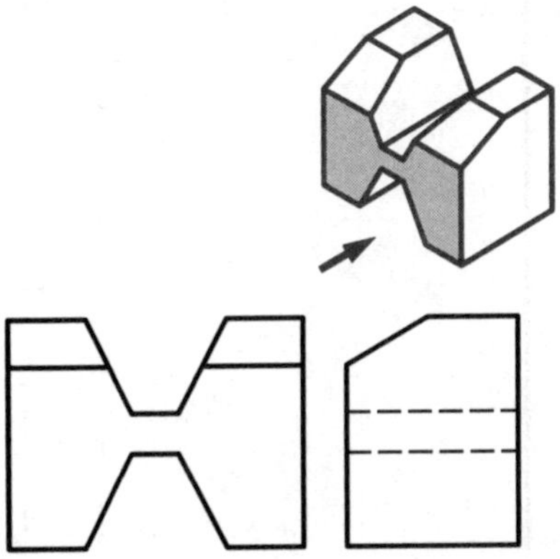

SKETCH THE TOP VIEWS. THE FRONT AND RIGHT-SIDE VIEWS ARE COMPLETE.

G

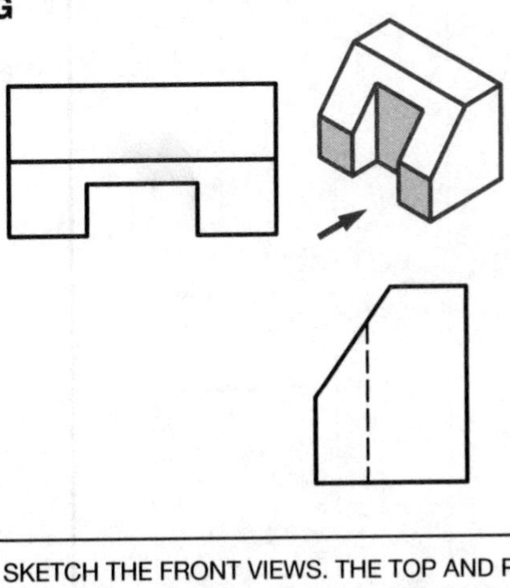

H

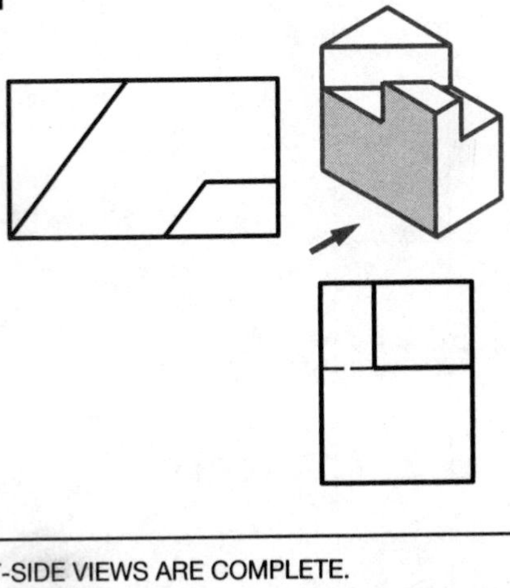

J

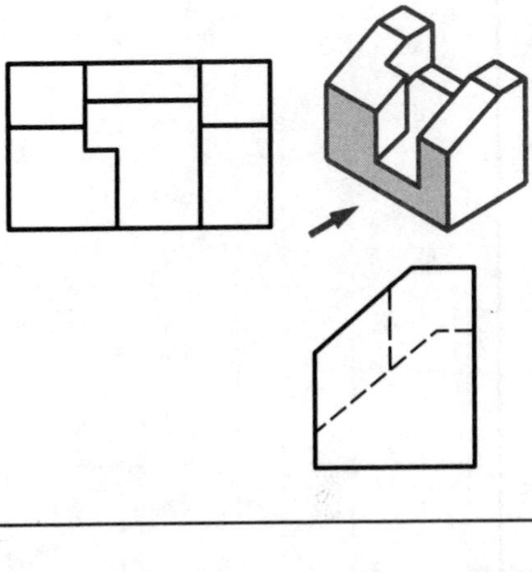

SKETCH THE FRONT VIEWS. THE TOP AND RIGHT-SIDE VIEWS ARE COMPLETE.

ASSIGNMENT: SKETCH THE MISSING VIEWS. ALL OBJECTS HAVE SLOPING SURFACES.

SKETCHING MISSING VIEWS

A-13

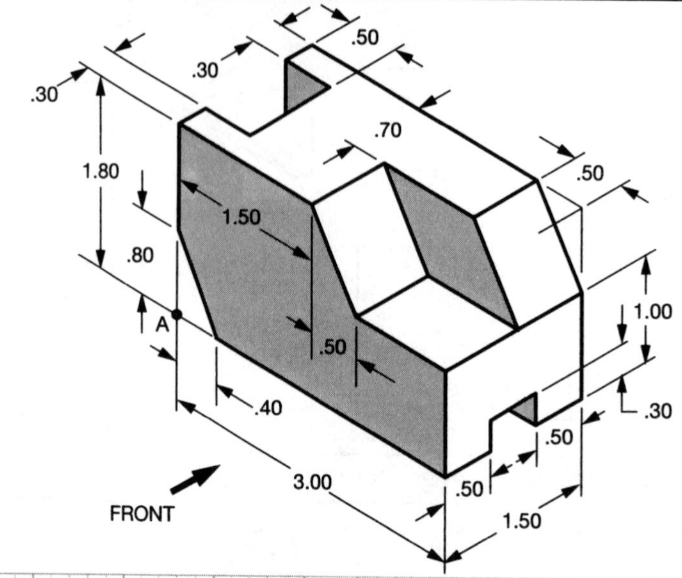

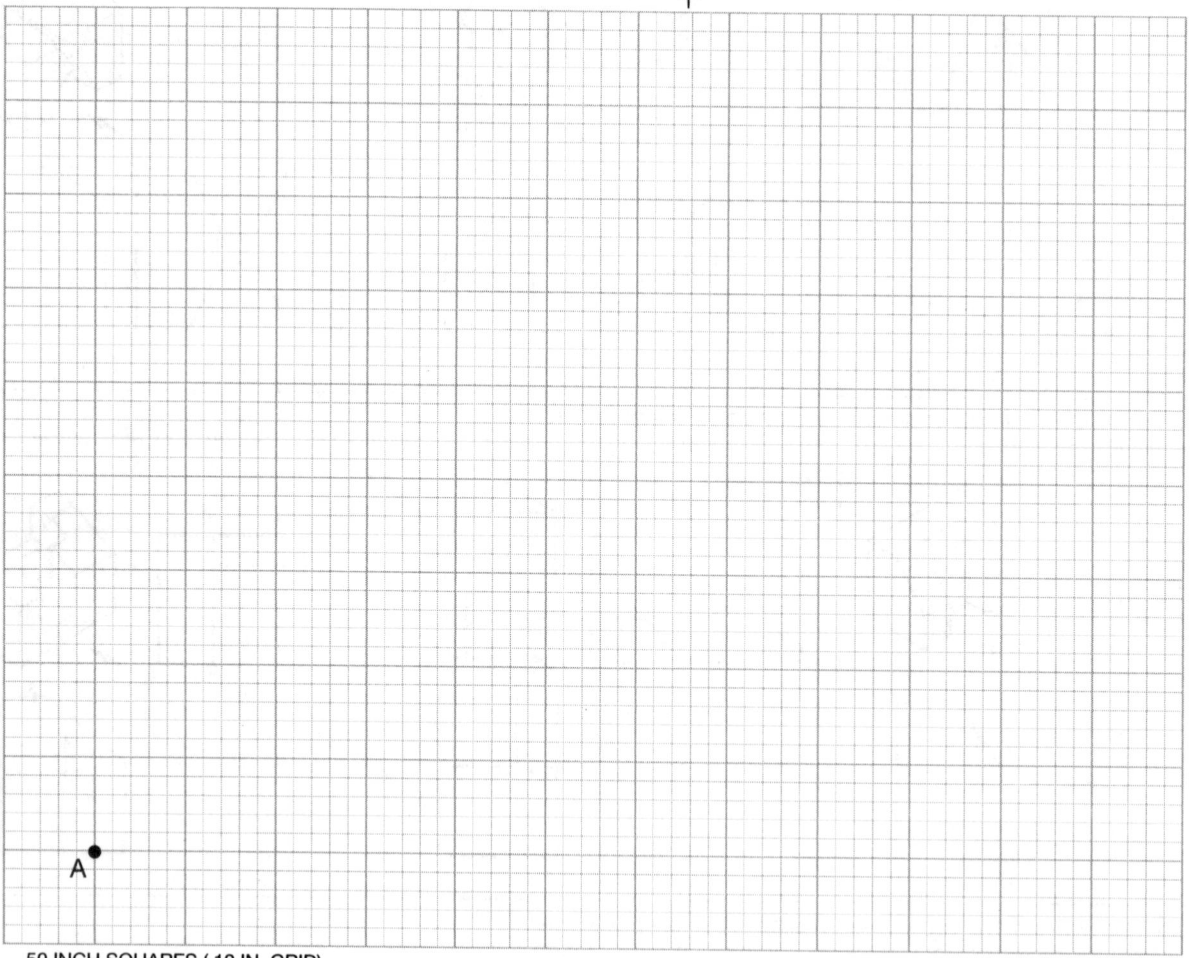

.50 INCH SQUARES (.10 IN. GRID)

ASSIGNMENT: SKETCH THE TOP, FRONT, AND RIGHT-SIDE VIEWS USING THIRD-ANGLE PROJECTION AND DIMENSION. SCALE FULL SIZE. ALLOW ONE INCH BETWEEN VIEWS.

ADAPTER	**A-14**

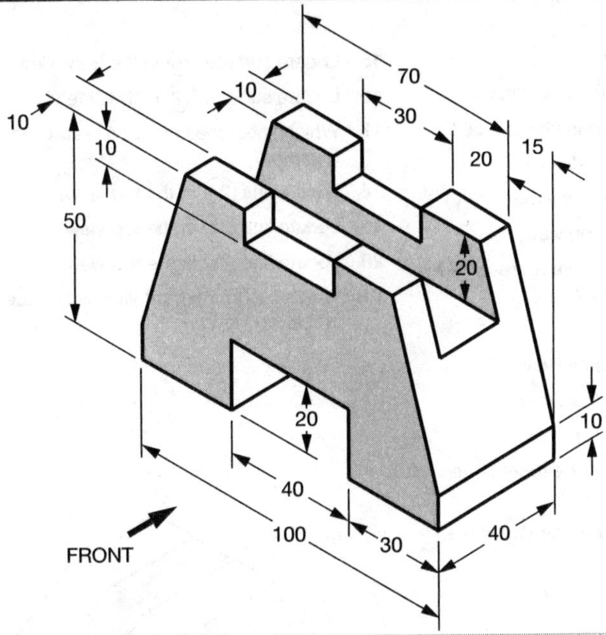

10 mm SQUARES (1 mm GRID)

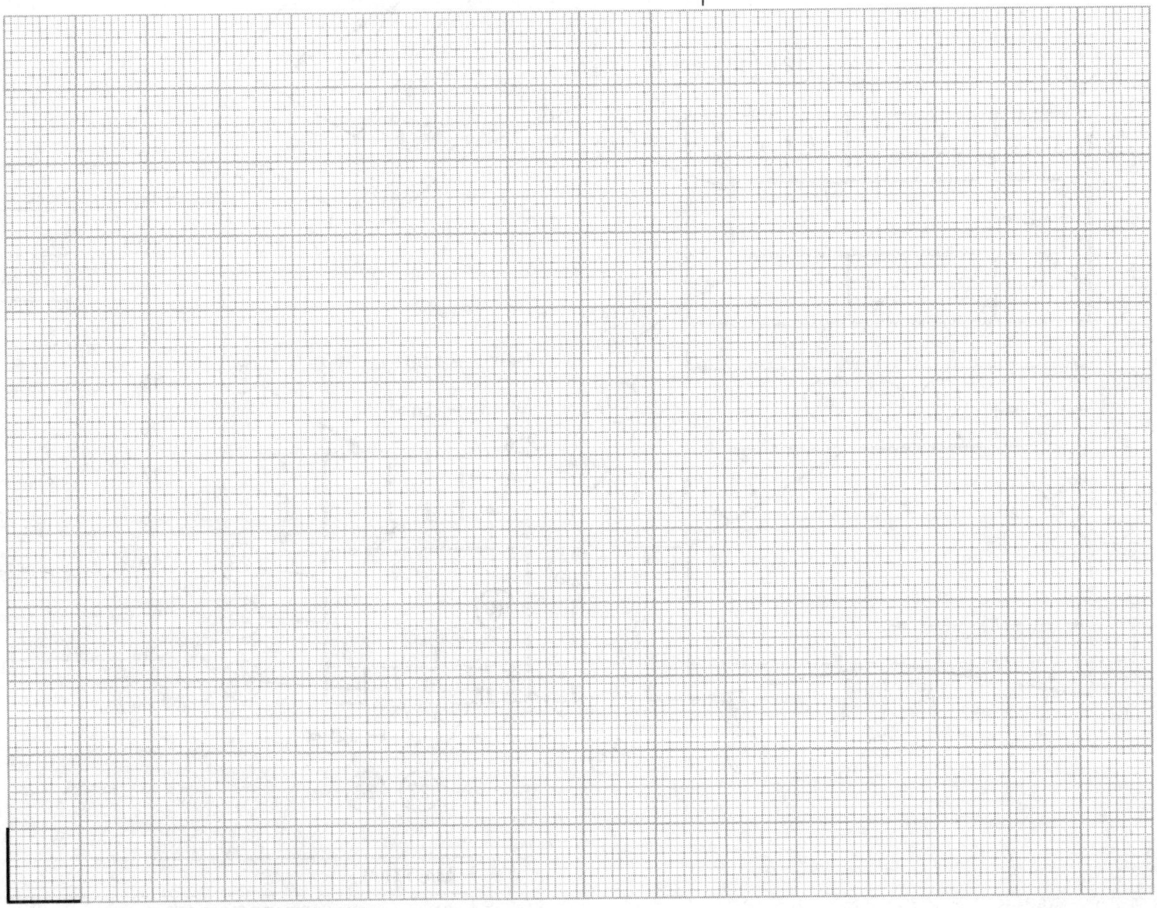

BOTTOM LEFT CORNER OF FRONT VIEW

METRIC
DIMENSIONS IN MILLIMETRES

ASSIGNMENT: SKETCH THE TOP, FRONT, AND RIGHT-SIDE VIEWS USING THIRD-ANGLE PROJECTION AND DIMENSION. SCALE FULL SIZE. ALLOW 20 mm BETWEEN VIEWS.

GUIDE BLOCK	A-15M

QUESTIONS

1. Calculate distances A to G.
2. At what angle is line (6) to the vertical?
3. At what angle is line (7) to the horizontal?
4. Locate surface (6) in the side view.
5. Locate surface (1) in the side view.
6. Locate surface (6) in the top view.
7. Which lines in the side view are represented by line (2) in the front view?
8. Locate (18) in the top view.
9. Locate surface (9) in the side view.
10. Locate surface (12) in the front view.
11. Locate surface (3) in the top view.
12. Which lines in the side view are represented by point (4) in the front view?
13. Which line in the side view is line (16) in the top view?
14. Locate surface (10) in the side view.
15. Locate surface (10) in the front view.
16. Locate surface (12) in the side view.
17. Which lines does point (4) represent in the top view?
18. Locate line (24) in the top view.
19. Locate line (28) in the top view.
20. Locate line (25) in the top view.
21. Which line in the front view is surface (9) in the top view?

ANSWERS

1. A ______
   B ______
   C ______
   D ______
   E ______
   F ______
   G ______
2. ______
3. ______
4. ______
5. ______
6. ______
7. ______
8. ______
9. ______
10. ______
11. ______
12. ______
13. ______
14. ______
15. ______
16. ______
17. ______
18. ______
19. ______
20. ______
21. ______

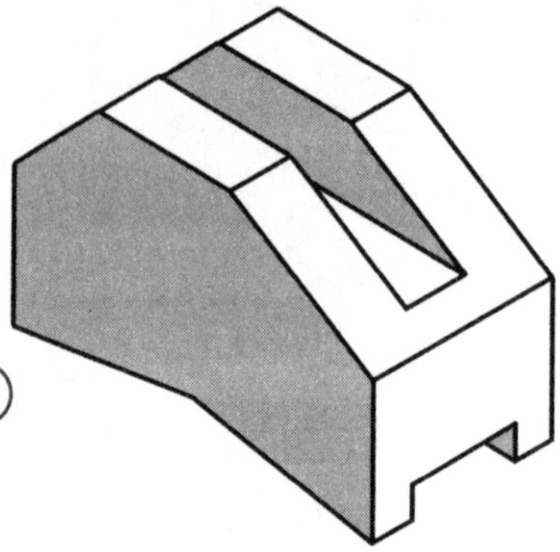

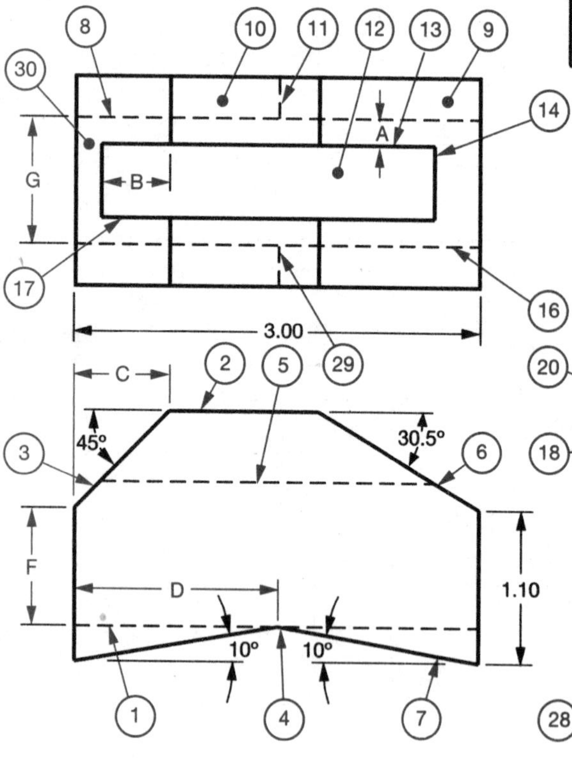

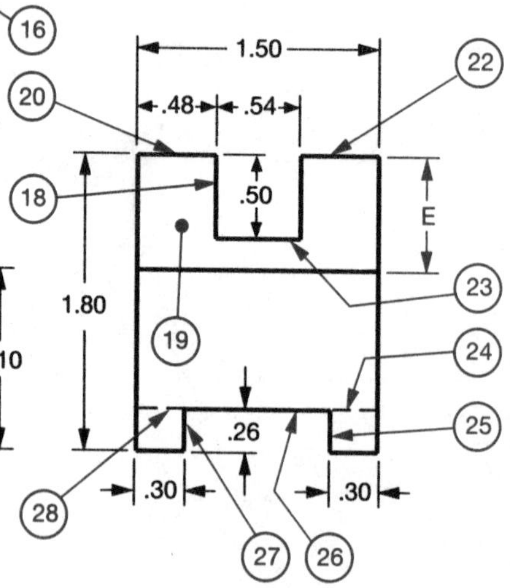

MATERIAL	MS		
SCALE	NOT TO SCALE		
DRAWN		DATE	
	BASE PLATE		**A-16**

UNIT 5

CIRCULAR FEATURES

Typical parts with circular features are illustrated in Figure 5–1. Note that the circular feature appears circular in one view only and that no line is used to indicate where a curved surface joins a flat surface. Hidden circles, like hidden flat surfaces, are represented on drawings by a hidden line. Often only two views are required to show the shape of the part, as shown in Figures 5–1(E) and (F).

CENTRE LINES

A *centre line* is drawn as a thin broken line of alternating long and short dashes. Centre lines may be used to indicate centre points, axes of cylindrical parts, and axes of symmetry. Solid centre lines are often used as a simplified drafting practice; however, the interrupted line is preferred. Centre lines should project for a short distance beyond the outline of the part or feature to which they refer. They may be

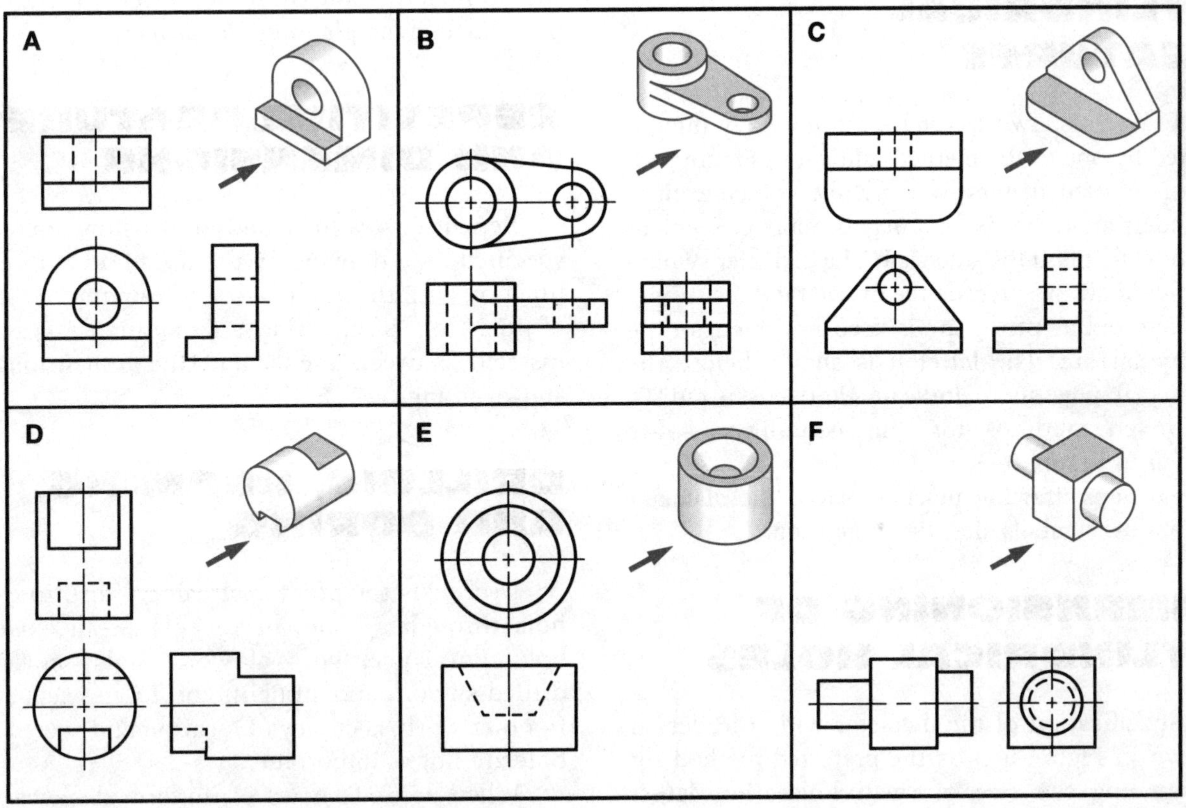

FIGURE 5–1 ■ Illustrations of simple objects having circular features

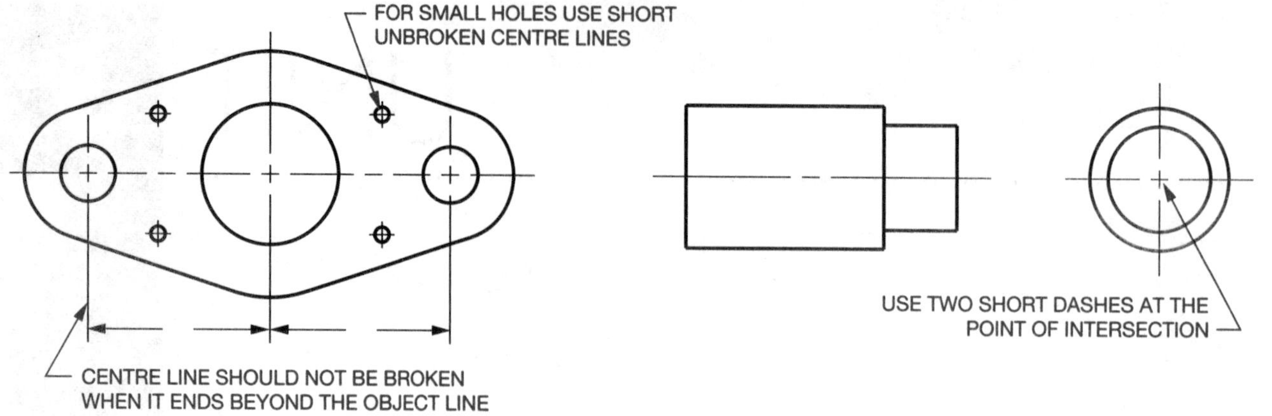

FIGURE 5–2 ■ Centre line application

lengthened for use as extension lines for dimensioning purposes; in this case the extended portion is not broken.

In end views of circular features, the point of intersection of two centre lines is shown by two intersecting short dashes. However, for very small circles a solid unbroken line is recommended. These techniques are shown in Figure 5–2.

DIMENSIONING OF CYLINDRICAL FEATURES

Features shown as circles are normally dimensioned by one of the methods shown in Figure 5–3. Where the diameters of a number of concentric cylinders are to be given, it may be more convenient to show them on the side view. The diameter symbol ∅ should always precede the diametral dimension.

The radius of the arc is used in dimensioning a circular arc. The letter R is shown before the radius dimension to indicate that it is a radius. Approved methods for dimensioning arcs are shown in Figure 5–4.

Previous drawing practice placed the diameter and radius symbols after the dimension.

DIMENSIONING OF CYLINDRICAL HOLES

Specification of the diameter with a leader, as shown in Figure 5–5, is the preferred method for designating the size of small holes. For larger diameters, use one of the methods illustrated in Figure 5–3. When the leader is used, the symbol ∅ precedes the size of the hole. The note end of the leader terminates in a short horizontal bar. When two or more holes of the same size are required, the number of holes is specified. If a blind hole is required, the depth of the hole is included in the dimensioning note; otherwise, it is assumed that all holes shown are through holes. Terms such as *drill, ream, bore,* and so forth should be avoided on drawings. The method of producing the hole should be left to the discretion of either the shop personnel or the planning department.

REPETITIVE FEATURES AND DIMENSIONS

Repetitive features and dimensions may be specified on a drawing by the use of an × in conjunction with the numeral to indicate the "number of times" or "places" they are required. A space is inserted between the × and the dimension, as shown in Figure 5–6.

DRILLING, REAMING, AND BORING

Drilling is the process of using a drill to cut a hole through a solid, or to enlarge an existing hole. For some types of work, holes must be drilled smooth and straight, and to an exact size. In other work, accuracy of location and size of the hole are not as important.

When accurate holes of uniform diameter are required, they are first drilled slightly undersize and

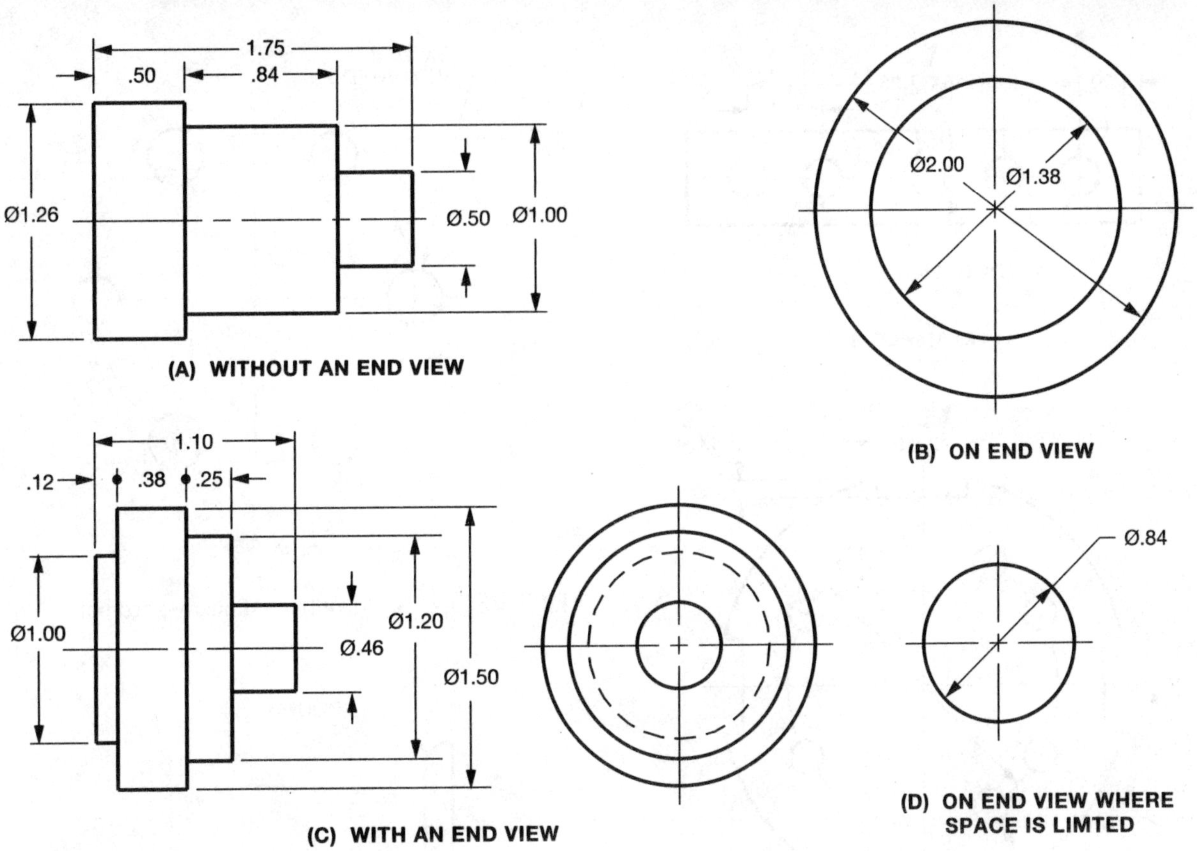

FIGURE 5–3 ■ Dimensioning diameters

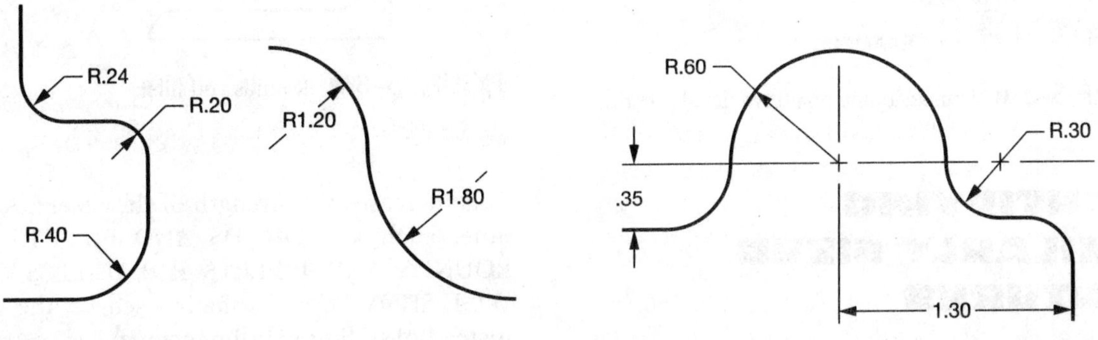

FIGURE 5–4 ■ Dimensioning radii

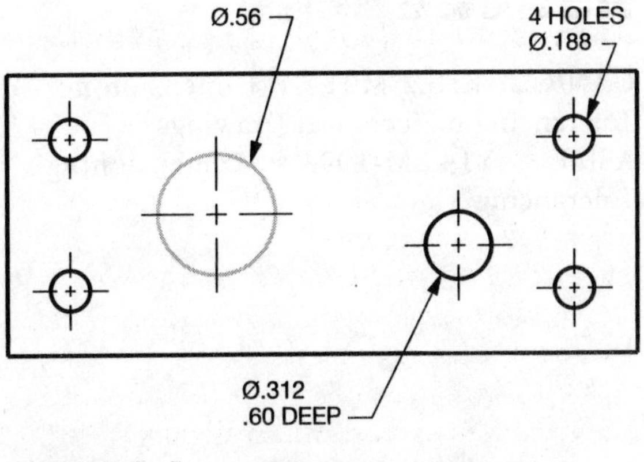

FIGURE 5–5 ■ Dimensioning cylindrical holes

then reamed. *Reaming* is the process of sizing a hole to a given diameter with a reamer in order to produce a hole that is round, smooth, and straight.

Boring is one of the more dependable methods of producing holes that are round and concentric. The term *boring* refers to enlarging a hole by means of a boring tool. The use of reaming is limited to the sizes of available reamers. However, holes may be bored to any size desired.

The degree of accuracy to which a hole is to be machined is specified on the drawing.

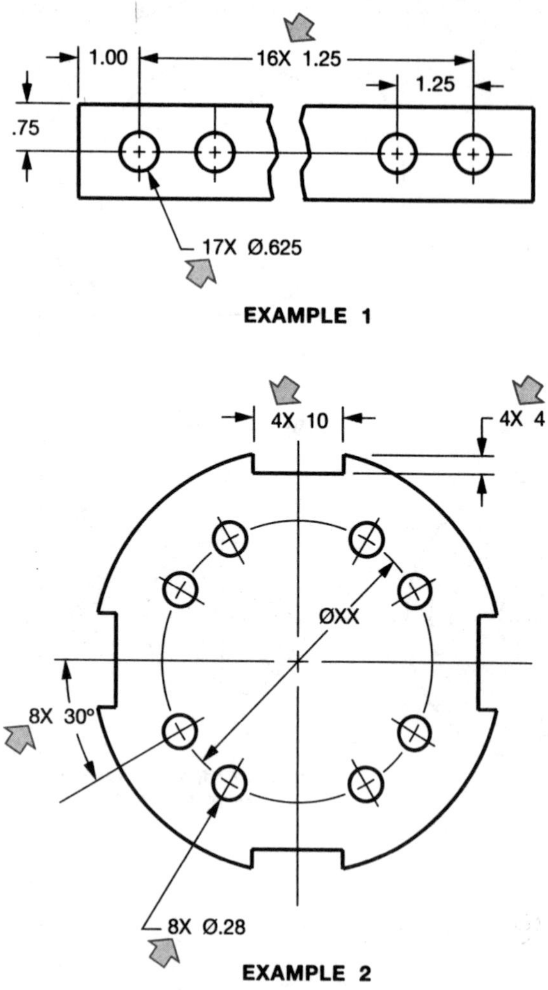

FIGURE 5–6 ■ Dimensioning repetitive detail

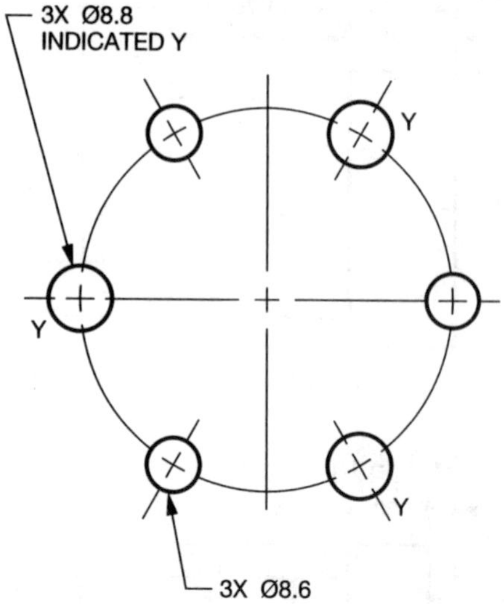

FIGURE 5–7 ■ Identifying similarly sized holes

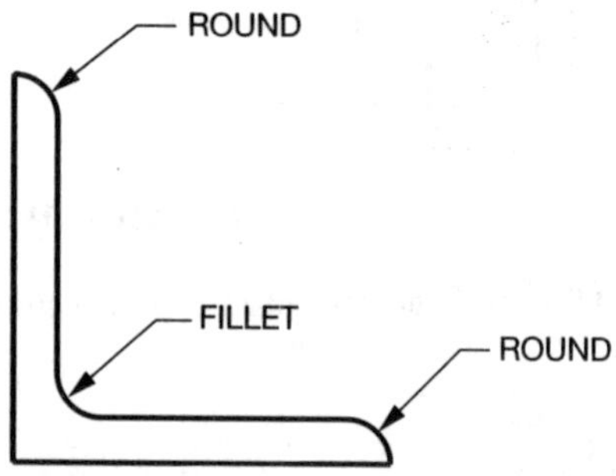

FIGURE 5–8 ■ Rounds and fillets

IDENTIFYING SIMILARLY SIZED FEATURES

Where many similarly sized holes or features appear on a part, some form of identification may be desirable in order to ensure the legibility of the drawing, Figure 5–7.

ROUNDS AND FILLETS

A round, or radius, or chamfer is put on the outside of a piece to improve its appearance and to avoid forming a sharp edge that might chip off under a sharp blow or cause interference. It is also a safety feature. A fillet is additional metal allowed in the inner intersection of two surfaces, Figure 5–8. This increases the strength of the object. A general note, such as ROUNDS AND FILLETS R10 or ROUNDS AND FILLETS R10 UNLESS OTHERWISE SHOWN, is normally used on the drawing instead of individual dimensions.

REFERENCES

CAN/CSA-B78.2-M91 Dimensioning and Tolerancing of Technical Drawings
ASME Y14.5M-1994 Dimensioning and Tolerancing

A

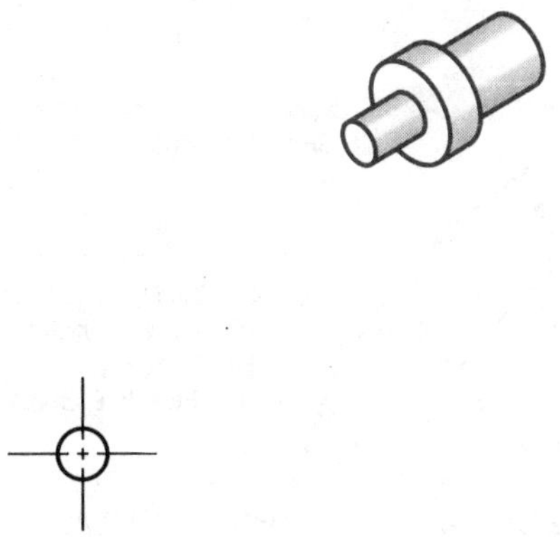

B

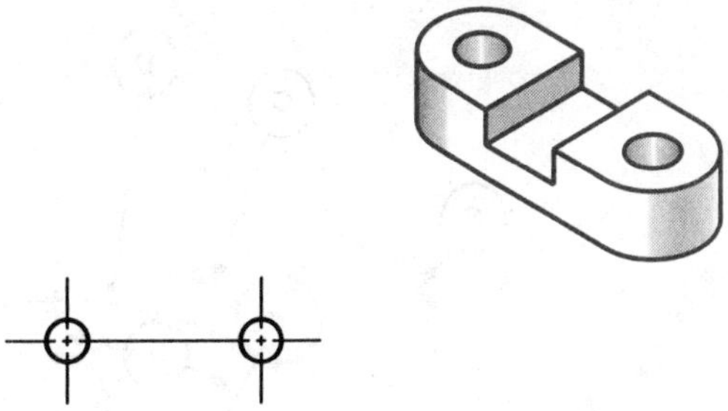

C

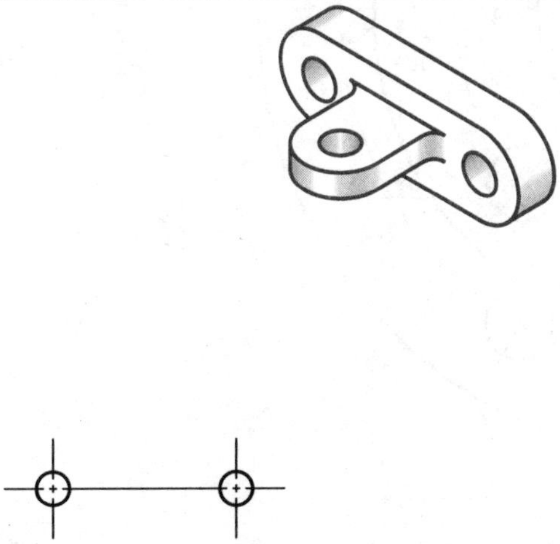

D

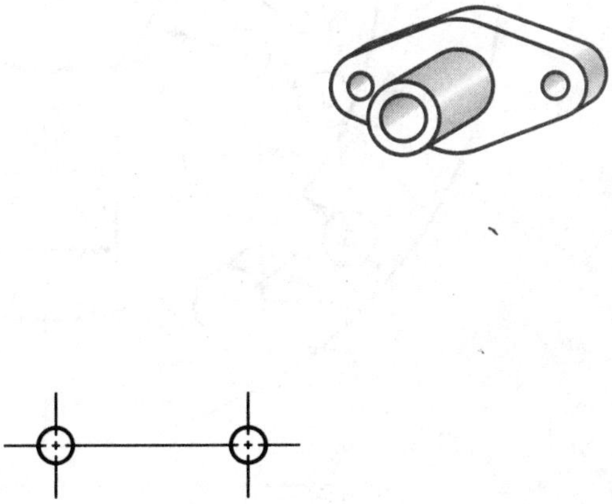

E

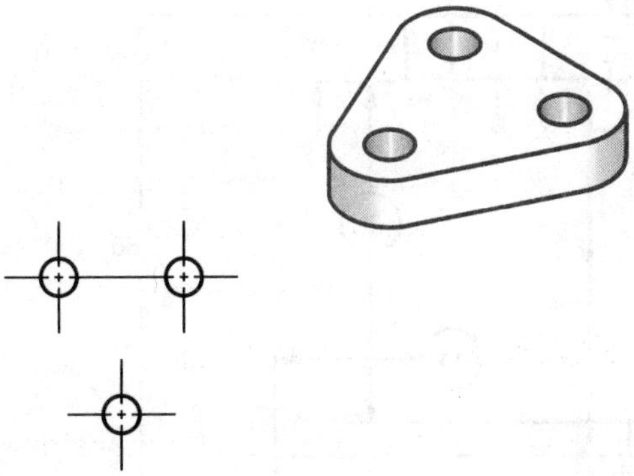

F

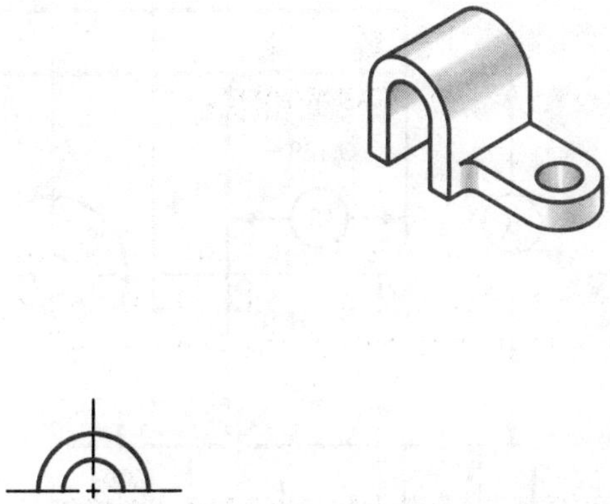

ASSIGNMENT:
SKETCH IN THE ORTHOGRAPHIC VIEWS OF THE OBJECTS SHOWN. USE YOUR JUDGMENT FOR NUMBER AND SELECTION OF VIEWS.

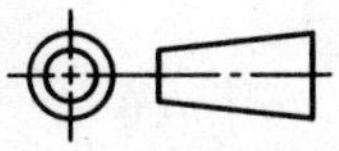

SKETCHING CIRCULAR FEATURES

A-17

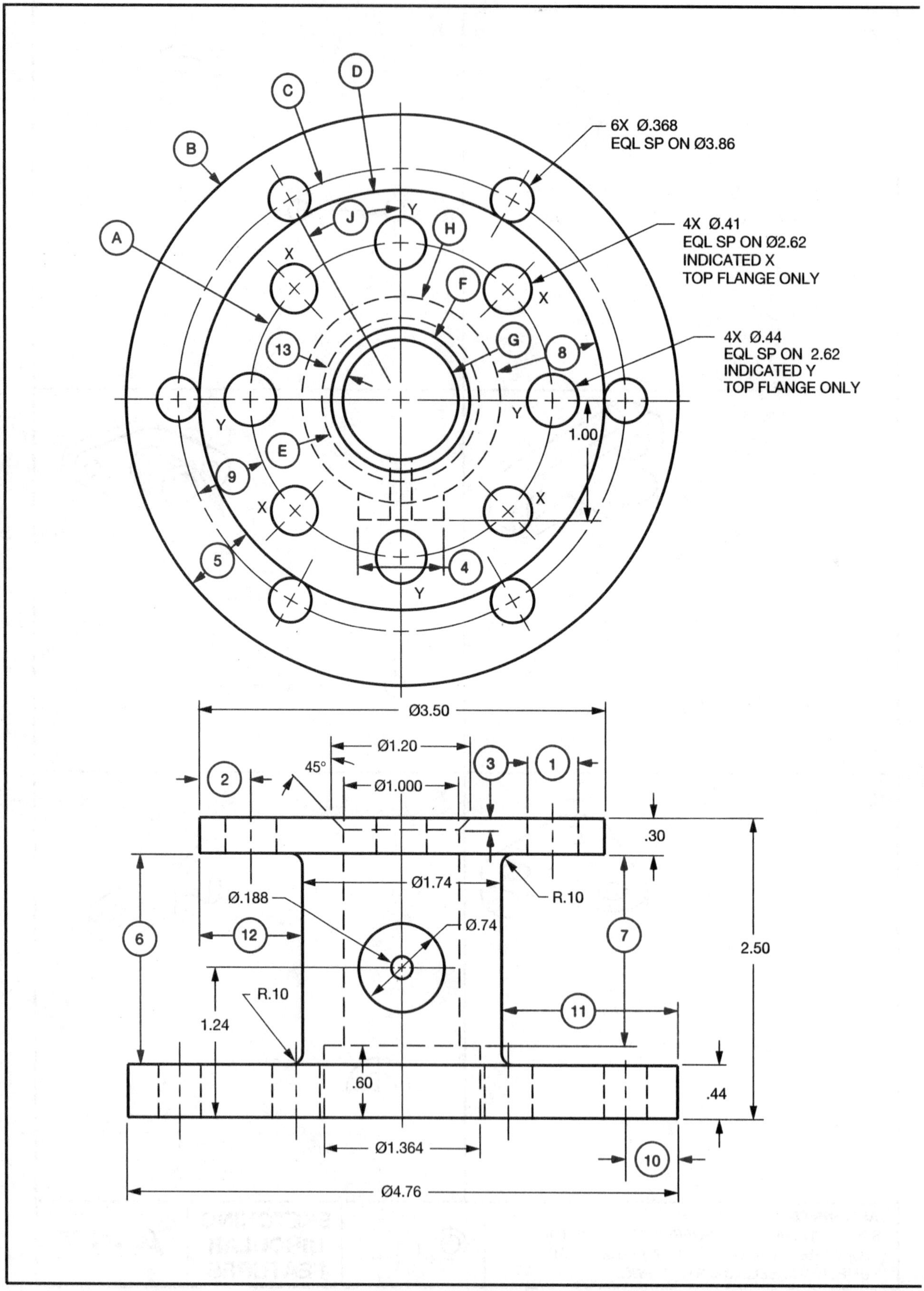
6X Ø.368
EQL SP ON Ø3.86
4X Ø.41
EQL SP ON Ø2.62
INDICATED X
TOP FLANGE ONLY
4X Ø.44
EQL SP ON 2.62
INDICATED Y
TOP FLANGE ONLY
A
B
C
D
E
F
G
H
J
X
Y
1.00
Ø3.50
Ø1.20
Ø1.000
45°
.30
Ø1.74
R.10
Ø.188
Ø.74
2.50
R.10
1.24
.60
.44
Ø1.364
Ø4.76
1
2
3
4
5
6
7
8
9
10
11
12
13

QUESTIONS

1. What are the diameters of circles (A) to (H)?
2. How many holes are in the bottom surface?
3. How many holes are in the top surface?
4. How deep is the Ø1.000 hole from the top of the coupling?
5. What is angle (J)?
6. How thick is the largest flange?
7. What size bolts would be used for the Y holes located on the top flange? Allow approximately .06 total clearance. (Refer to the bolt sizes in the Appendix.)
8. What size bolts would be used for the bottom flange? Allow approximately .06 total clearance. (Refer to the bolt sizes in the Appendix.)
9. Calculate distances (1) to (13).

ANSWERS

1. A ________
   B ________
   C ________
   D ________
   E ________
   F ________
   G ________
   H ________
2. ________
3. ________
4. ________
5. ________
6. ________
7. ________
8. ________

9. 1 ________
   2 ________
   3 ________
   4 ________
   5 ________
   6 ________
   7 ________
   8 ________
   9 ________
   10 ________
   11 ________
   12 ________
   13 ________

MATERIAL	GREY IRON	
SCALE	NOT TO SCALE	
DRAWN		DATE
COUPLING		A-18

A

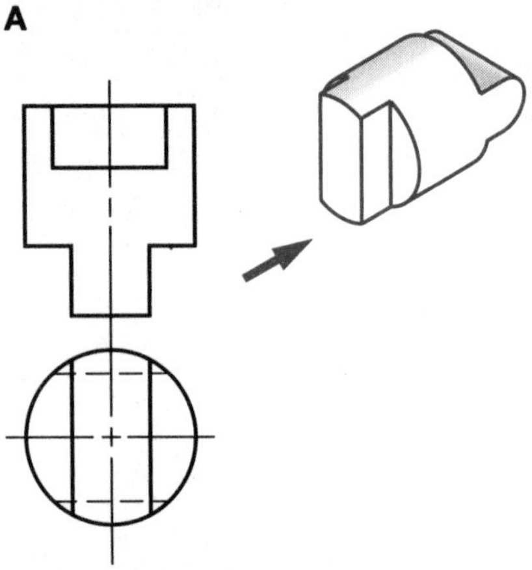

B

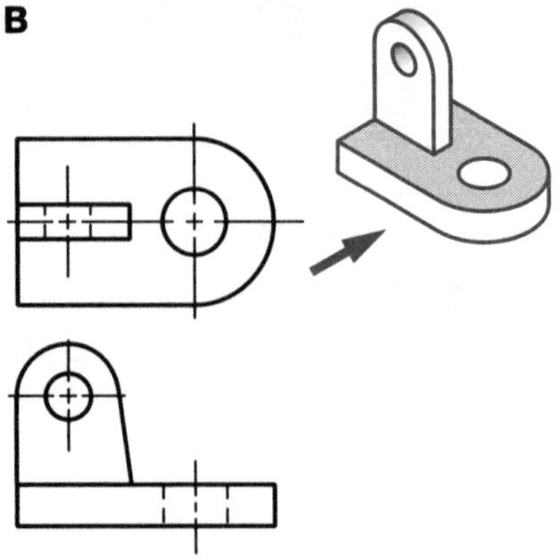

C

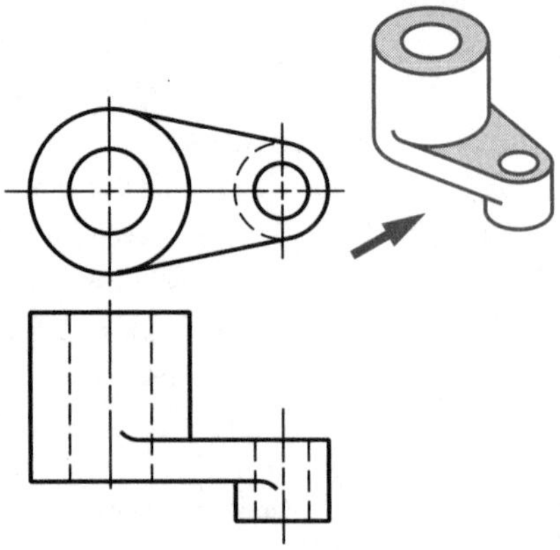

SKETCH THE RIGHT-SIDE VIEW. THE TOP AND FRONT VIEWS ARE COMPLETE.

D

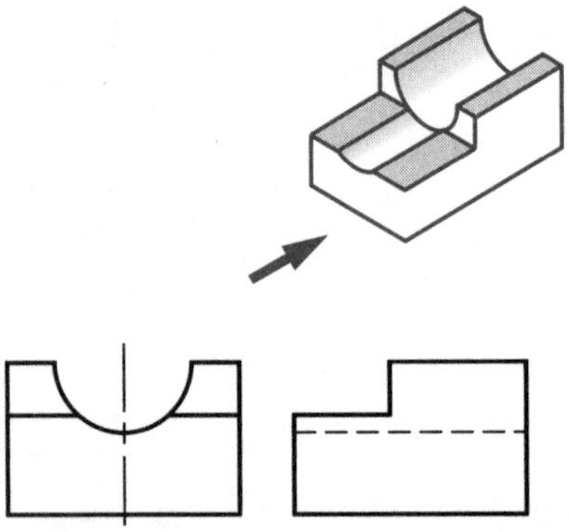

E

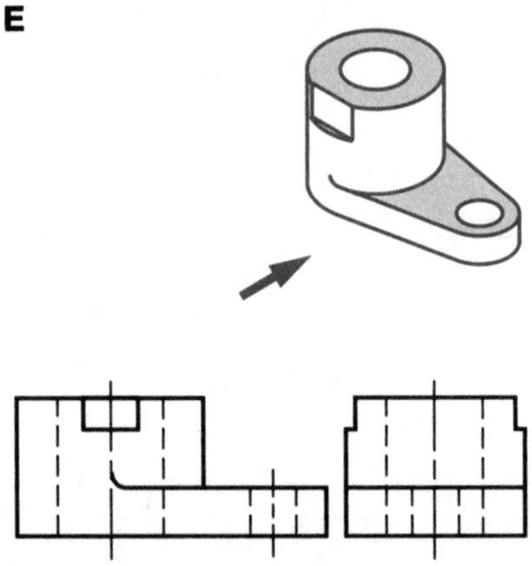

F

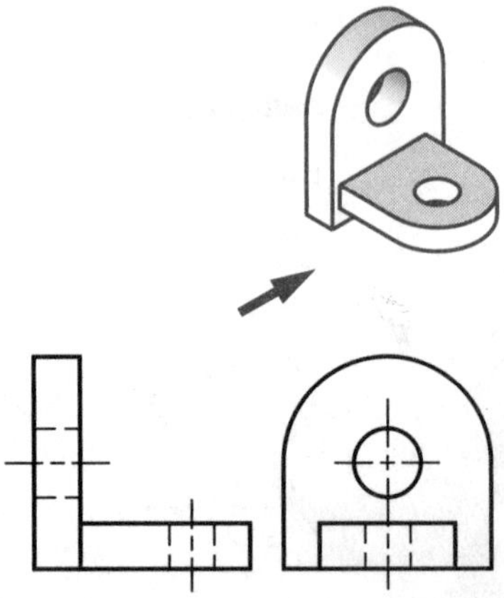

SKETCH THE TOP VIEW. THE FRONT AND RIGHT-SIDE VIEWS ARE COMPLETE.

G

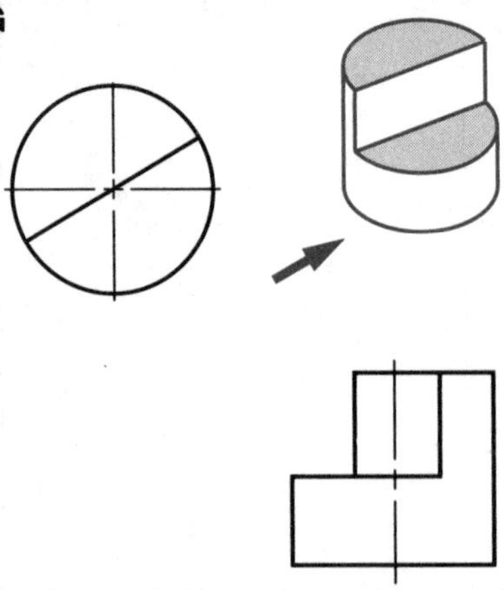

H

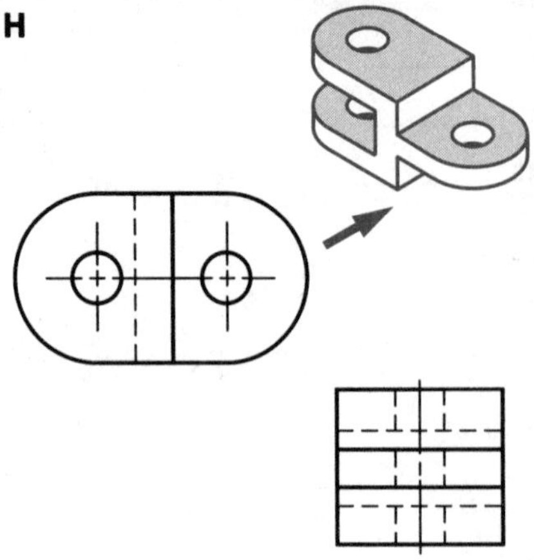

J

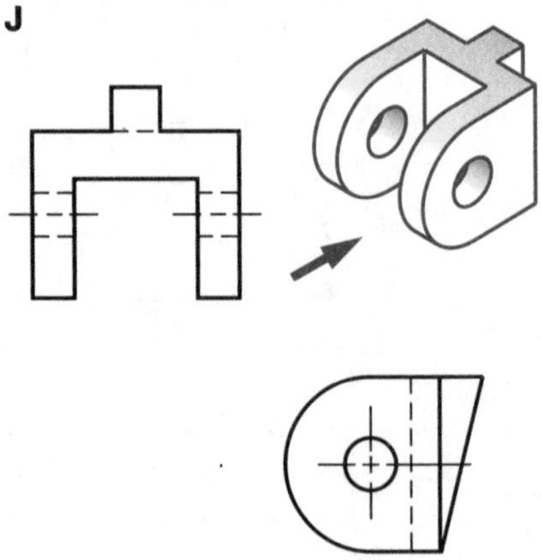

SKETCH THE FRONT VIEW. THE TOP AND RIGHT-SIDE VIEWS ARE COMPLETE.

OBJECTS HAVING CIRCULAR FEATURES.

ASSIGNMENT: SKETCH THE MISSING VIEWS.

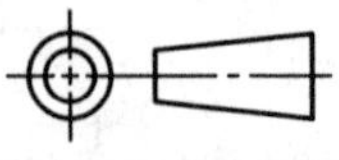

SKETCHING MISSING VIEWS

A-19

UNIT 6

DRAWING TO SCALE

When objects are drawn at their actual size, the drawing is called *full scale* or *scale 1:1*. Many objects, however, including buildings, ships, and airplanes, are too large to be drawn full scale. Therefore, they must be drawn to a *reduced scale*. An example would be the drawing of a house to a scale of 1:48 (1/4" = 1 foot) in the inch-foot scale.

Frequently, small objects, such as watch parts, are drawn larger than their actual size in order to clearly define their shapes. This is called drawing to an *enlarged scale*. The minute hand of a wristwatch, for example, could be drawn to scale 4:1.

Many mechanical parts are drawn to half scale, 1:2, and quarter scale, 1:4. Notice that the scale of the drawing is expressed in the form of a ratio. The left side of the ratio represents a unit of measurement of the size drawn. The right side represents the measurement of the actual object. Thus, 1 unit of measurement on the drawing equals 4 units of measurement on the actual object. Many of the common scale ratios are shown in Figure 6–1.

Drafting scales are constructed with a variety of combined scale ratios marked on their surfaces. This combination of scale ratios spares the drafter the inconvenience of calculating the size to be drawn when working to a scale other than full size. The more common drafting scales are shown in Figure 6–2.

TYPE OF SCALE		ENLARGED SCALE	SIZE AS	REDUCED SCALE
INCH SCALES	DECIMAL-INCH SCALE	10:1 4:1 2:1	1:1	1:2 1:3 1:4
INCH SCALES	FRACTIONAL-INCH SCALE		1:1	1:2 1:4 3:4
INCH SCALES	CIVIL ENGINEER'S SCALE		1:1	1:20 1:30 1:40 1:50 1:60
FOOT SCALES			1:1	$\frac{1}{8}$" = 1 FOOT $\frac{1}{4}$" = 1 FOOT 1" = 1 FOOT 3" = 1 FOOT
METRIC SCALES (MILLIMETRES)		100:1 50:1 20:1 10:1 5:1 2:1	1:1	1:2 1:5 1:10 1:20 1:50 1:100

FIGURE 6–1 ■ Common scale ratios used on drawings

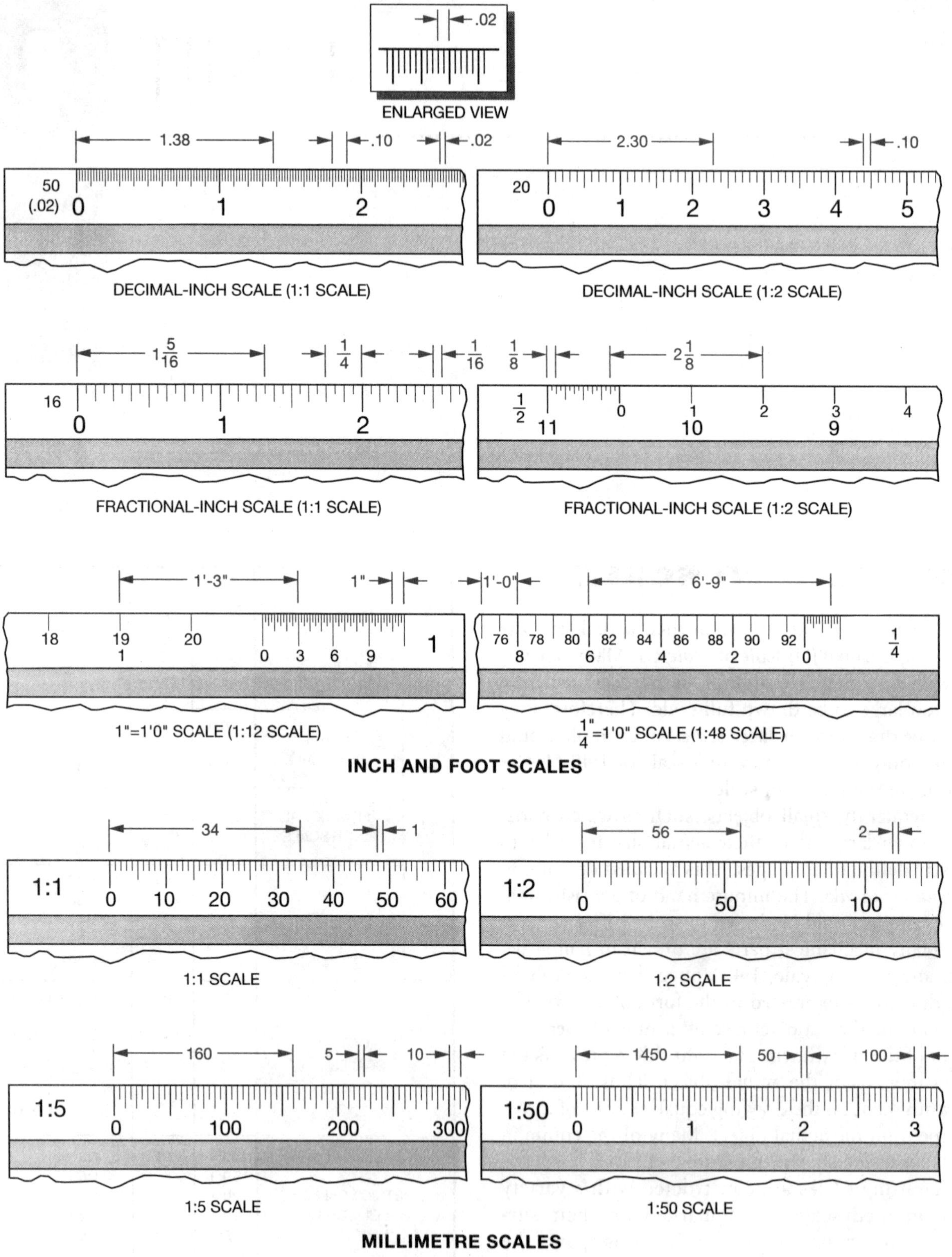

FIGURE 6–2 ■ Drafting scales

INCH AND FOOT SCALES

The Inch Scales

There are three types of scales showing values that are equal to 1 inch. They are the *decimal-inch scale,* the *fractional-inch scale,* and the *civil engineer's scale.*

The civil engineer's scale has divisions of 10, 20, 30, 40, 50, 60, and 80 parts to the inch.

On fractional-inch scales, multipliers or divisors of 2, 4, 8, and 16 are used, offering such scales as full size, half size, quarter size, and so forth.

The Foot Scales

Foot scales are used mostly in architectural work. The main difference between foot and inch scales is that in the foot scale each major division represents a foot, not an inch, and the end units are subdivided into inches or parts of an inch. The more common scales are the 1/8 inch = 1 foot; 1/4 inch = 1 foot; 1 inch = 1 foot; and 3 inches = 1 foot.

SI (METRIC SCALES)

Scale multipliers and divisors of 2, 5, and 10 are recommended, resulting in the scales shown in Figures 6–1 and 6–2.

MACHINE SLOTS

Slots are used chiefly in machines to hold parts together. The two principal types are *T slots* and *dovetails,* Figure 6–3.

A dovetail is a groove or slide whose sides are cut on an angle. This forms an interlocking joint between two pieces, enabling the slot to resist pulling apart in any direction other than along the lines of the dovetail slide itself.

The dovetail is commonly used in the design of slides, including lathe cross slides, milling machine table slides, and other sliding parts.

The two parts of a dovetail slide are shown in Figure 6–3.

When dovetail parts are to be machined to a given width, they may be gauged by using accurately sized cylindrical rods or wires.

Dovetails are usually dimensioned as in Figure 6–4. The dimensions limit the boundaries within which the machinist works.

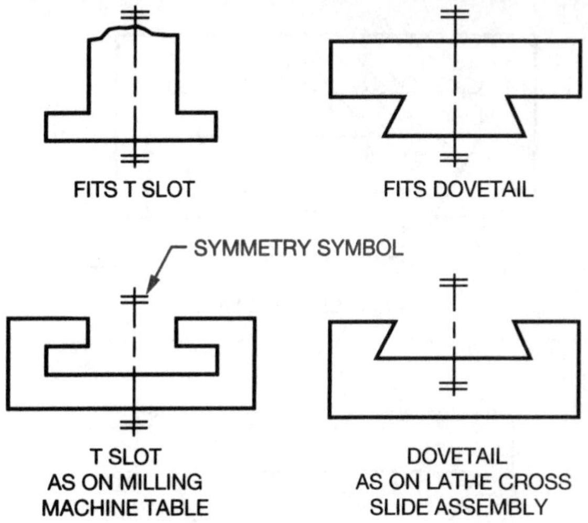
FITS T SLOT
FITS DOVETAIL
SYMMETRY SYMBOL
T SLOT
AS ON MILLING
MACHINE TABLE
DOVETAIL
AS ON LATHE CROSS
SLIDE ASSEMBLY

FIGURE 6–3 ■ Typical machine slots

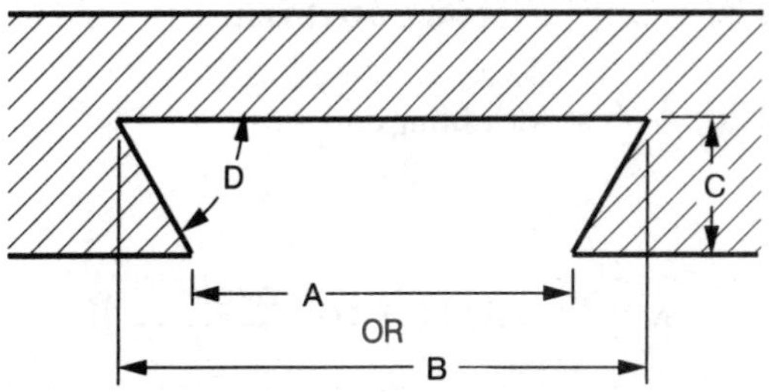
D
C
A
OR
B

FIGURE 6–4 ■ Dimensions for dovetail

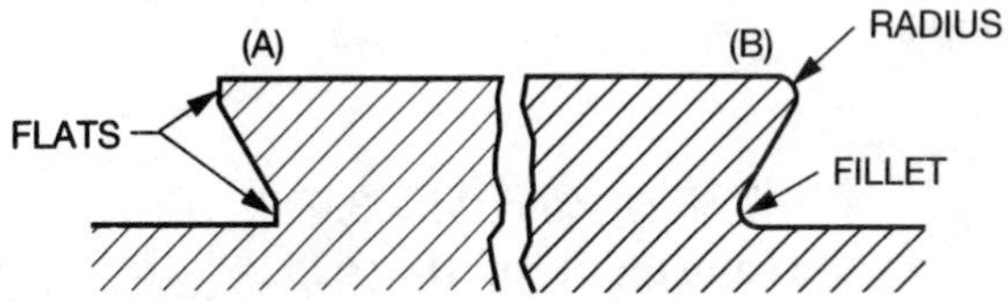
(A)
(B)
RADIUS
FLATS
FILLET

FIGURE 6–5 ■ Corners used on large dovetails

The edges of a dovetail are usually broken to remove the sharp corners. On large dovetails the external and internal corners are often machined as shown in Figure 6–5 as at (A) or (B).

Measuring Dovetails

Female dovetails may be measured by placing two accurate rods of known diameter against the sides and bottom of the dovetail as shown in Figure 6–6. The distance **R** is then measured and checked against the computed value of **R** as found by the following formula:

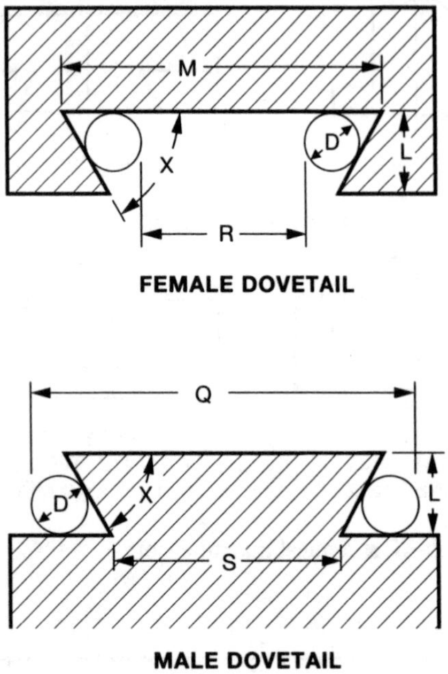

FIGURE 6–6 ■ Measuring dovetails

$$R = M - [D\,(1 + \cot \frac{\text{angle } X}{2})]$$

Note: Diameter D should be slightly less than distance L.

Example:

Given:

Distance **M** = 3.000"
Diameter of rod **D** = .625"
Degrees in angle **X** = 55°

Then:

R = 3.000 – .625 (1 + 1.921)
Combining: R = 3.000 – 1.826
R = 1.174"

Male dovetails may also be measured in a similar manner by placing two accurate rods of known diameter against the sides and bottom of the dovetail. The distance Q over the rods is measured and then checked against the computed value of Q as found by the following formula:

$$Q = D\,(1 + \cot \frac{\text{angle } X}{2}) + S$$

Example:

Given: Distance S = 2.000"
Diameter of Rod **D** = .625"
Degrees in angle **X** = 55°

Then: Q = .625 (1 + 1.921) + 2
Combining: Q = (.625 × 2.921) + 2
Q = 3.826"

Common slots produced by the milling machine are shown in Figure 6–7.

SYMMETRICAL OUTLINES

Symmetrical outlines or features may be indicated on a drawing by means of the symmetry symbol shown in Figure 6–3. Two thick parallel lines are placed on the centre lines above and below the feature. The use of this symbol means the part or feature is symmetrical about the centre line or feature.

REFERENCE DIMENSIONS

When a reference dimension is shown on a drawing for information only and is not used for the manufacture of the part, it must be clearly labelled. The approved method for indicating reference dimensions on a drawing is the enclosure of the dimensions inside parentheses, Figure 6–8. Previously, reference dimensions were indicated by placing the abbreviation REF after or below the dimension.

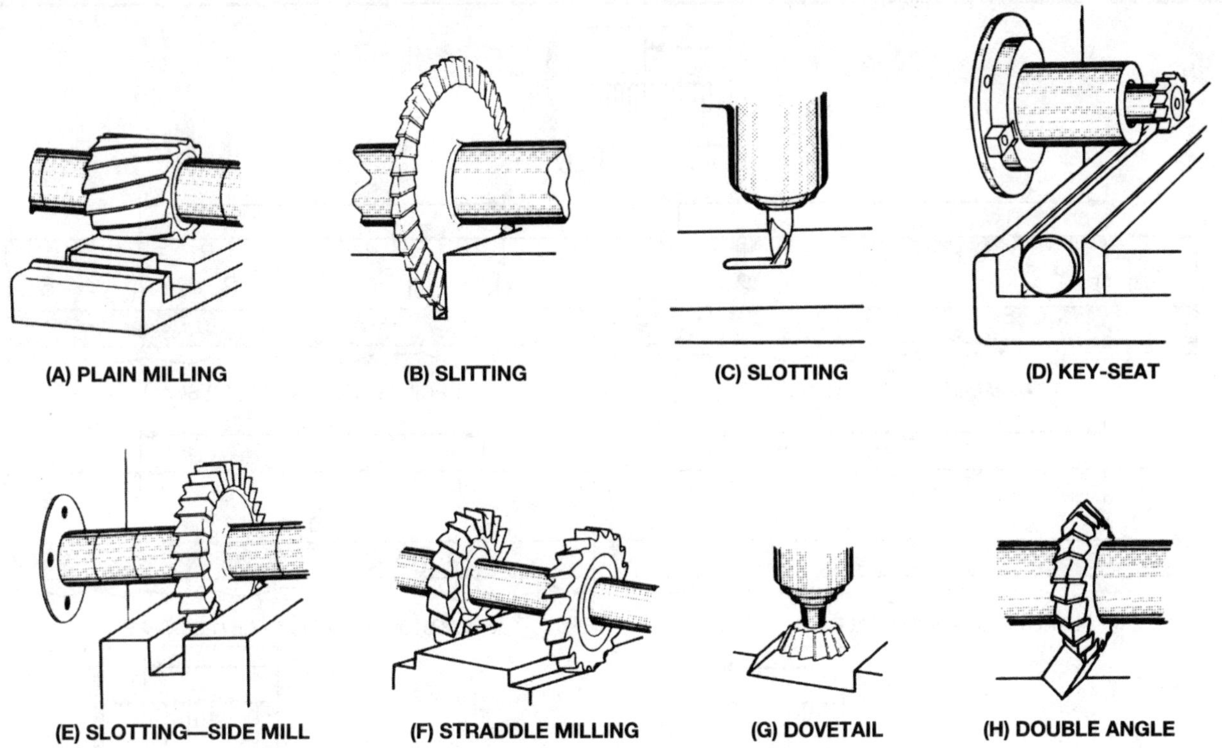
(A) PLAIN MILLING
(B) SLITTING
(C) SLOTTING
(D) KEY-SEAT
(E) SLOTTING—SIDE MILL
(F) STRADDLE MILLING
(G) DOVETAIL
(H) DOUBLE ANGLE

FIGURE 6–7 ■ Common milling machine operations

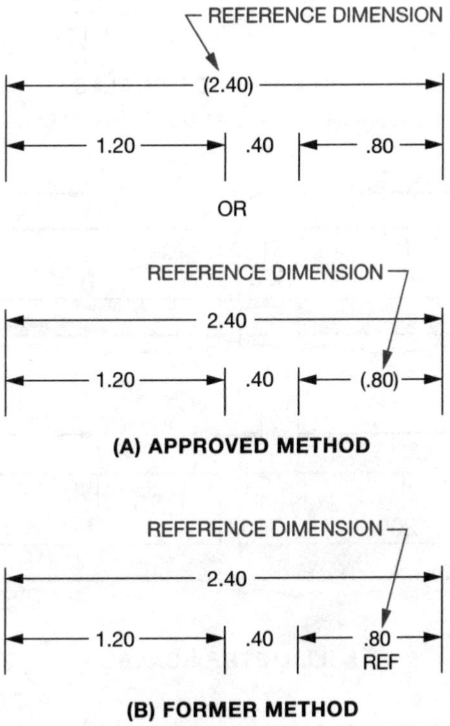
REFERENCE DIMENSION
(2.40)
1.20
.40
.80
OR
REFERENCE DIMENSION
2.40
1.20
.40
(.80)
(A) APPROVED METHOD
REFERENCE DIMENSION
2.40
1.20
.40
.80
REF
(B) FORMER METHOD

FIGURE 6–8 ■ Reference dimensions

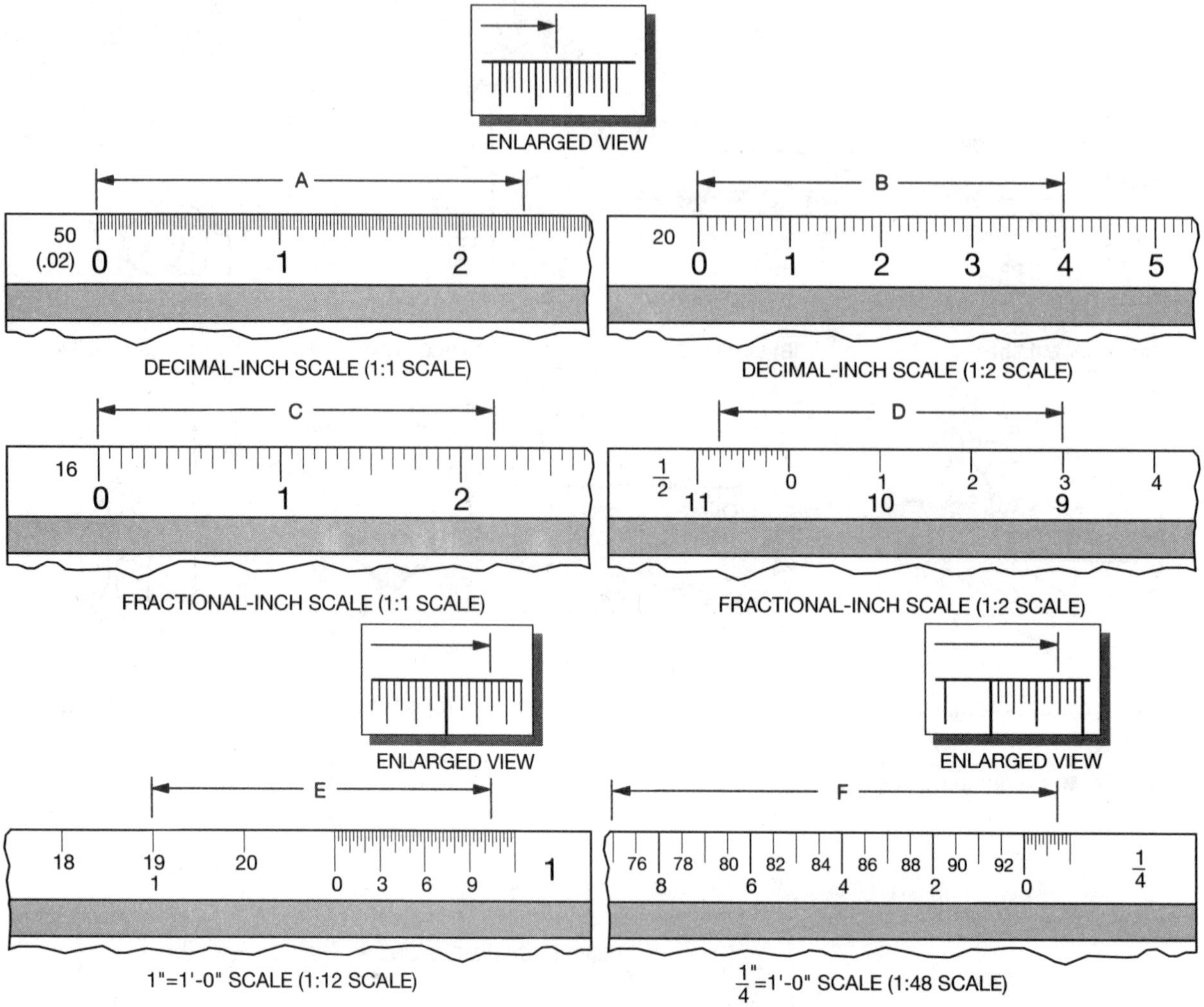
ENLARGED VIEW
A
B
50
(.02) 0 1 2
20
0 1 2 3 4 5
DECIMAL-INCH SCALE (1:1 SCALE)
DECIMAL-INCH SCALE (1:2 SCALE)
C
D
16
0 1 2
1/2
11 0 1 10 2 3 9 4
FRACTIONAL-INCH SCALE (1:1 SCALE)
FRACTIONAL-INCH SCALE (1:2 SCALE)
ENLARGED VIEW
ENLARGED VIEW
E
F
18 19 1 20 0 3 6 9 1
76 8 78 80 6 82 84 4 86 88 2 90 92 0 1/4
1"=1'-0" SCALE (1:12 SCALE)
1"/4=1'-0" SCALE (1:48 SCALE)

INCH AND FOOT SCALES

NOTE: FOR MEASUREMENTS A, E, AND F REFER TO ENLARGED VIEWS.

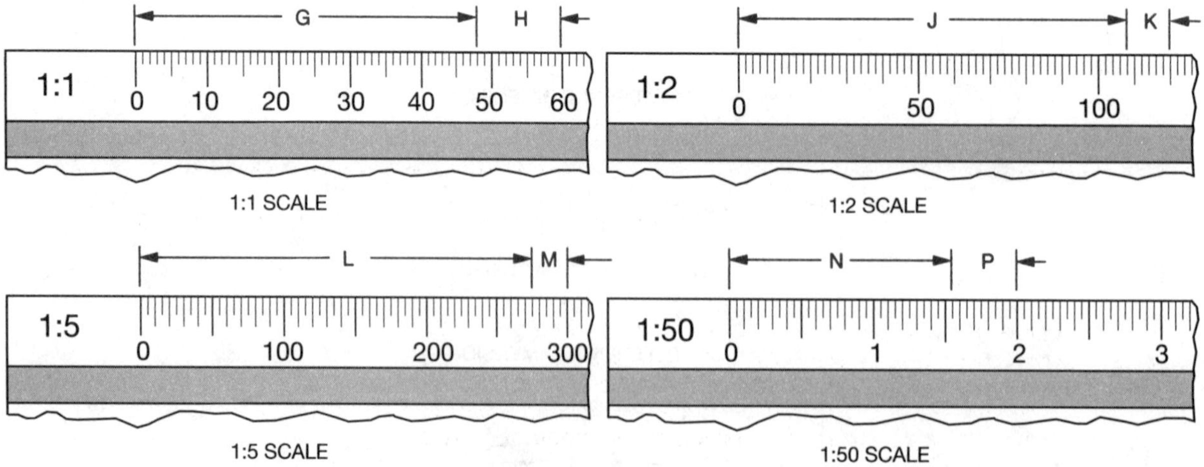
G
H
J
K
1:1
0 10 20 30 40 50 60
1:2
0 50 100
1:1 SCALE
1:2 SCALE
L
M
N
P
1:5
0 100 200 300
1:50
0 1 2 3
1:5 SCALE
1:50 SCALE

MILLIMETRE SCALES

ASSIGNMENT: DETERMINE DISTANCES A TO P.

READING SCALES	A-20

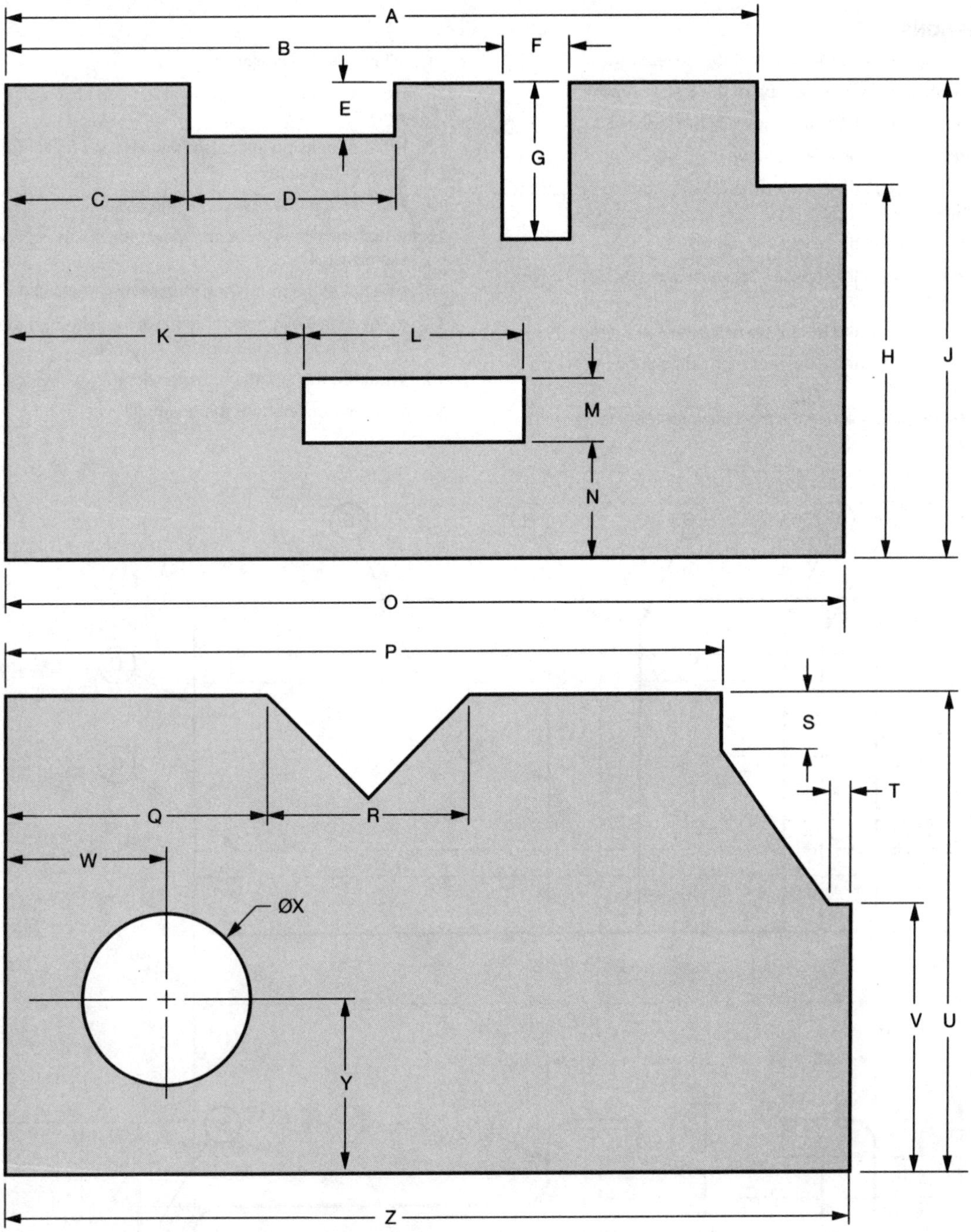

ASSIGNMENT:

INCH AND FOOT SCALES
- USING THE SCALE 1:1 MEASURE THE DISTANCES A TO E.
- USING THE SCALE 1:2 MEASURE THE DISTANCES F TO K.
- USING THE SCALE 3" = 1 FOOT MEASURE THE DISTANCES L TO P.
- USING THE SCALE 1" = 1 FOOT MEASURE THE DISTANCES Q TO U.
- USING THE SCALE 1/4" = 1 FOOT MEASURE THE DISTANCES V TO Z.

METRIC SCALES
- USING THE SCALE 1:1 MEASURE THE DISTANCES A TO K.
- USING THE SCALE 1:2 MEASURE THE DISTANCES L TO U.
- USING THE SCALE 1:5 MEASURE THE DISTANCES V TO Z.

MEASURING WITH SCALES	A-21

QUESTIONS

1. In which view is the shape of the dovetail shown?
2. In which view is the shape of the T slot shown?
3. How many rounds are shown in the top view?
4. In which view is a fillet shown?
5. Which line in the top view represents surface (R) of the side view?
6. Which line in the front view represents surface (R)?
7. Which line in the top view represents surface (L) of the side view?
8. Which line in the front view represents surface (L)?
9. Which line in the side view represents surface (A) on the top view?
10. Which dimension in the front view represents the width of surface (A)?
11. What type of lines are (B), (J), and (K)?
12. How far apart are the two hidden edge lines on the side view?
13. What dimension indicates how far line (J) is from the base of the slide?
14. How wide is the opening in the dovetail?
15. Which two lines in the top view indicate the opening of the dovetail?
16. At what angle to the horizontal is the dovetail cut?
17. In the side view, how far is the lower left edge of the dovetail from the left side of the piece?
18. What are the lengths of dimensions Y, V, and X?
19. What is the height of the dovetail?

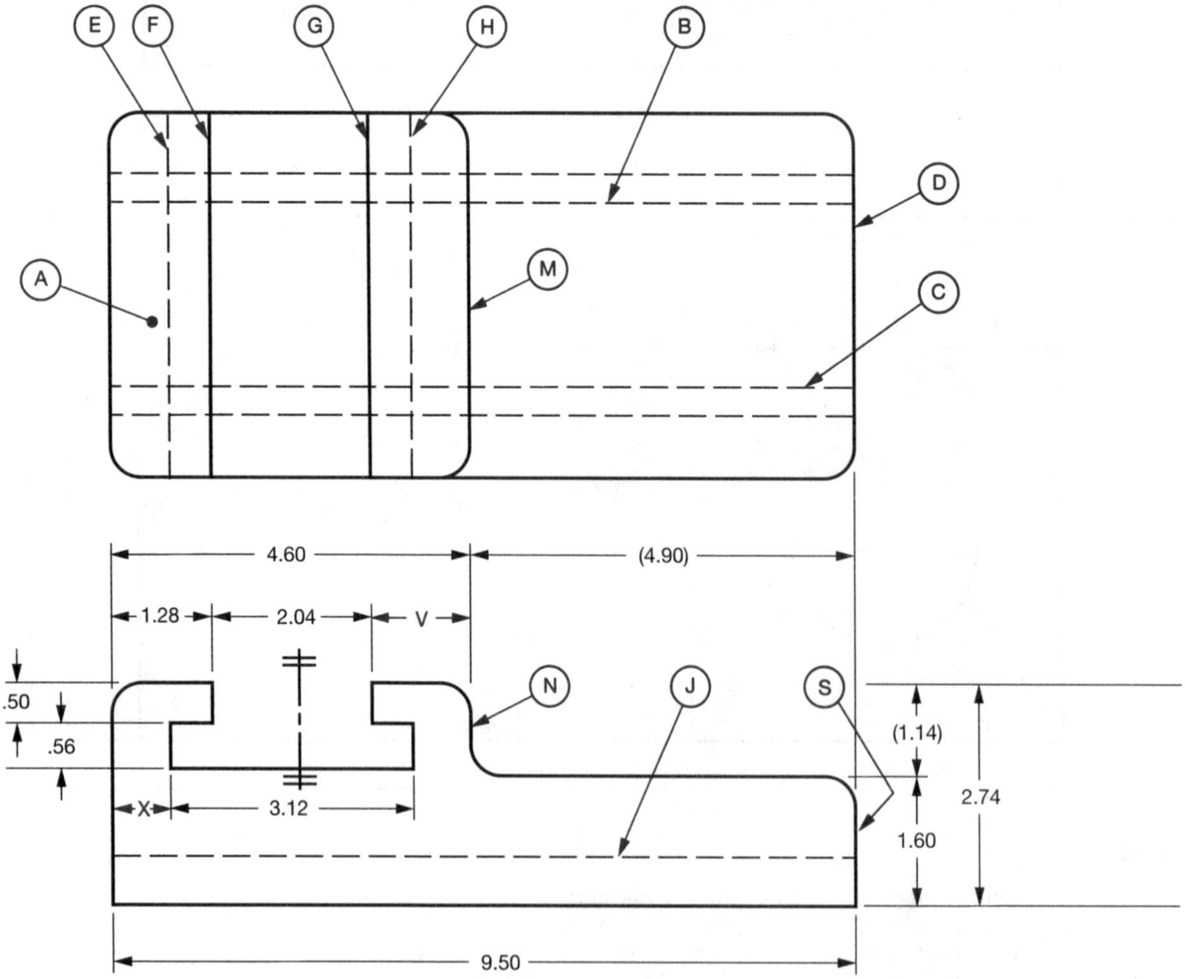

20. How much material remains between the surface represented by line (Q) and the top of the dovetail after the cut has been taken?
21. What is the vertical distance from the surface represented by line (Q) to that represented by line (T)?
22. Which dimension represents the distance between lines (F) and (G)?
23. What is the overall height of the T slot?
24. What is the distance between the bottom of the T slot and the top of the dovetail?
25. What is the width of the bottom of the T slot?
26. What is the height of the opening of the bottom of the T slot?
27. What is the horizontal distance from line (N) to line (S)?
28. What is the unit of measurement for the angles shown?
29. How many reference dimensions are shown on the drawing?
30. What is the size of the largest reference dimension?

ANSWERS

1. ______
2. ______
3. ______
4. ______
5. ______
6. ______
7. ______
8. ______
9. ______
10. ______
11. B ______
J ______
K ______
12. ______
13. ______
14. ______
15. ______
16. ______
17. ______
18. Y ______
V ______
X ______
19. ______
20. ______
21. ______
22. ______
23. ______
24. ______
25. ______
26. ______
27. ______
28. ______
29. ______
30. ______

ROUNDS AND FILLETS R.38

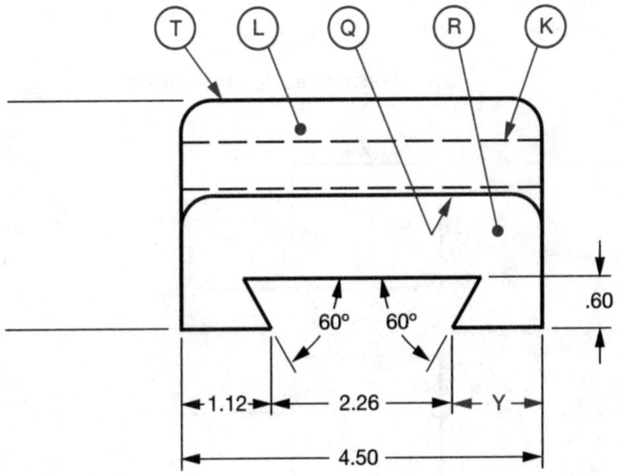

MATERIAL	GREY IRON	
SCALE	NOT TO SCALE	
DRAWN		DATE
COMPOUND REST SLIDE		**A-22**

7 UNIT

MACHINING SYMBOLS

When preparing working drawings of parts to be cast or forged, the drafter must indicate part surfaces that require machining or finishing. This requirement is indicated by adding a machining allowance symbol to the surface or surfaces that must be finished by the removal of material, Figure 7–1. Figure 7–2 shows the current machining symbol and those that were formerly used on drawings. This information is essential in order to alert the patternmaker and diemaker to provide extra metal on the casting or forging to allow for the finishing process. Depending on the material to be cast or forged, between .04 and .10 inch is usually allowed on small castings and forgings for each surface that requires finishing, Figure 7–3.

Like dimensions, machining symbols are not duplicated on the drawing. They should be used on the same view as the dimensions that give the size or location of the surfaces. The symbol is placed on the line representing the surface or on a leader or an extension line locating the surface. The symbol and the inscription should be oriented so they may be read from the bottom or right-hand side of the drawing.

Where all the surfaces are to be machined, a general note, such as FINISH ALL OVER (FAO), may be used and the symbols on the drawings omitted.

The outdated machining symbols shown in Figure 7–2(B) are found on many drawings in use

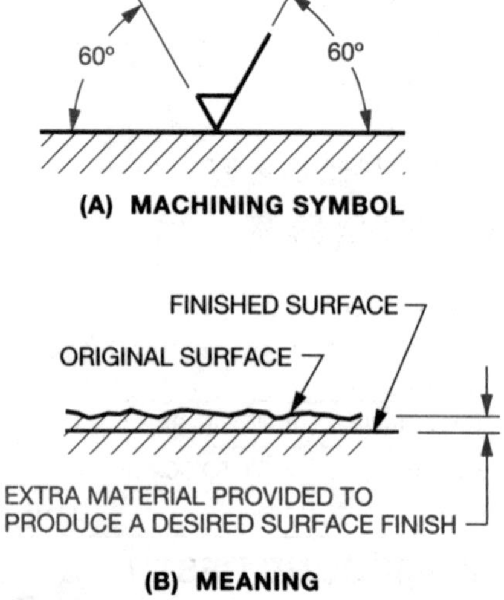

60°
60°
(A) MACHINING SYMBOL
FINISHED SURFACE
ORIGINAL SURFACE
EXTRA MATERIAL PROVIDED TO
PRODUCE A DESIRED SURFACE FINISH
(B) MEANING

FIGURE 7–1 ■ Machining symbol

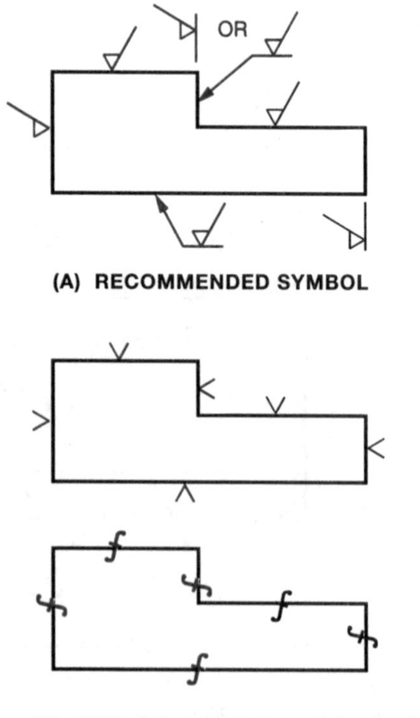

OR
(A) RECOMMENDED SYMBOL
(B) FORMER MACHINING SYMBOLS

FIGURE 7–2 ■ Application of machining symbols

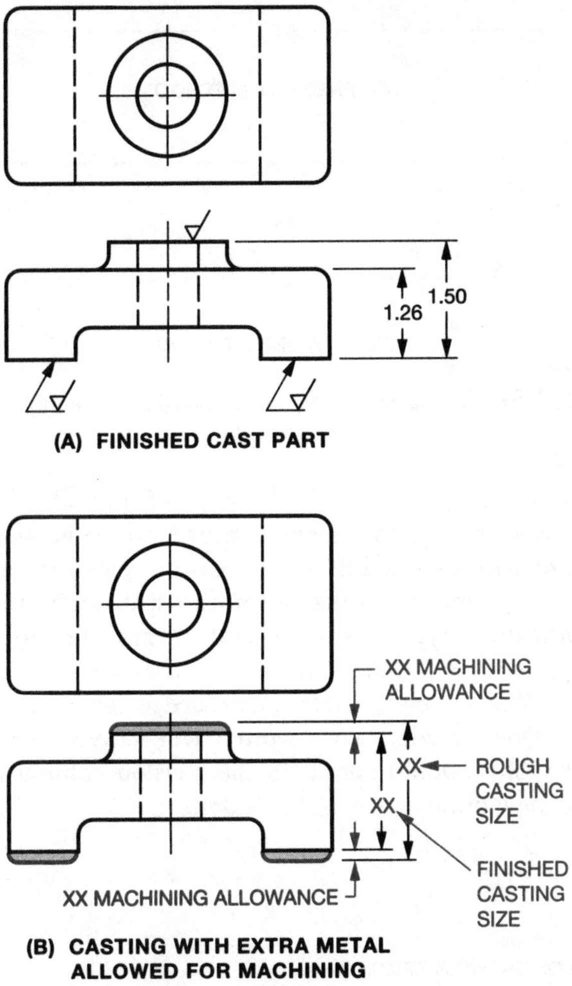

FIGURE 7–3 ■ Allowances for machining

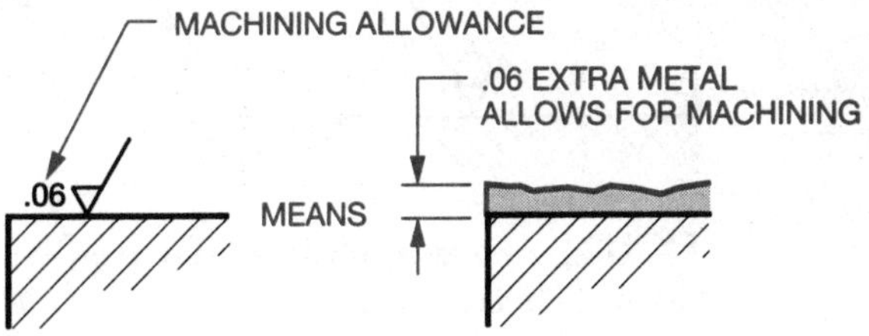

FIGURE 7–4 ■ Indicating the value of the machining allowance

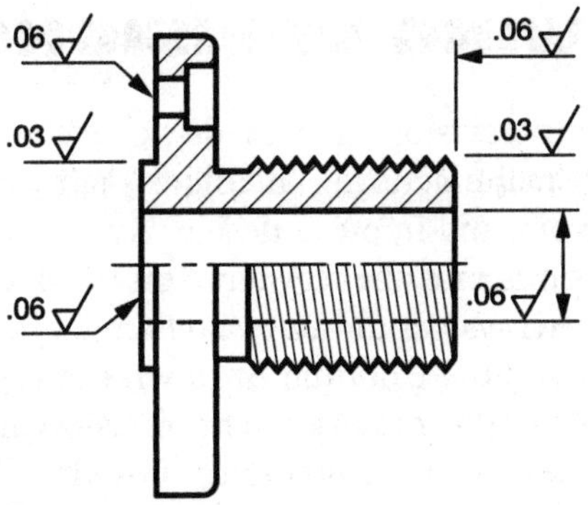

FIGURE 7–5 ■ The value of the machining allowance as shown on the drawing

today. When called upon to make changes or revisions on a drawing already in existence, a drafter must adhere to the drawing conventions shown on that drawing.

The machining symbol does not indicate surface-finish quality. The surface texture symbol, which is defined and discussed in Unit 11, is used to signify the desired surface-finish quality.

Indicating Machining Allowance

When the value of the machining allowance must be specified, it is indicated to the left of the symbol, Figures 7–4 and 7–5. This value is expressed in inches or millimetres depending on which units of measurement are used on the drawing.

Removal of Material Prohibited

A surface from which the removal of material is prohibited is indicated by the symbol shown in Figure 7–6. This symbol indicates that a surface must be left the way it is affected by a preceding manufacturing process, regardless of the removal of material or other changes. This machining symbol is part of the surface texture symbol described in Unit 11.

NOT-TO-SCALE DIMENSIONS

When a dimension on a drawing is altered, making it not to scale, a straight freehand line is drawn below the dimension to indicate that the dimension is not drawn to scale, Figure 7–7(A).

This is a change from earlier methods of indicating not-to-scale dimensions. Formerly, a wavy line below the dimension or the letters NTS beside the

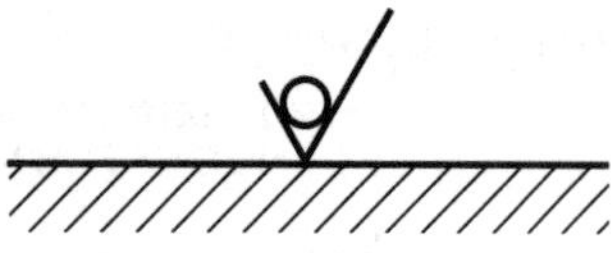

FIGURE 7–6 ■ Symbol for removal of material not permitted

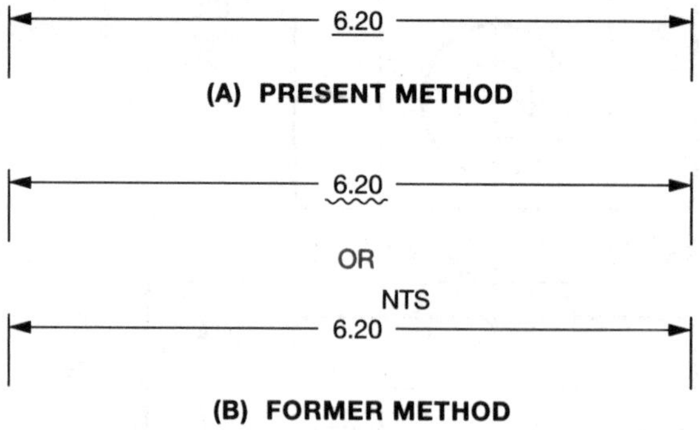

FIGURE 7–7 ■ Indicating dimensions that are not to scale

dimension were used to indicate not-to-scale dimensions, Figure 7–7(B).

DRAWING REVISIONS

Drawing revisions are made to accommodate improved manufacturing methods, reduce costs, correct errors, and improve design. A clear record of these revisions must be registered on the drawing.

All drawings should carry a change or revision table located at the bottom or down the top right-hand side of the drawing. The revision number, enclosed in a circle or triangle, should be located near the revised dimension for easy identification, Figure 7–8(A). The revision block should include a revision number or symbol, the date, the drafter's name or initials, and approval of the change. Should the drawing revision cause a dimension or dimensions to be different from the scale indicated, the dimensions that are not to scale should be indicated. Typical revision tables are shown in Figures 7–8(B) and (C).

When many revisions are needed, a new drawing is often made. The words REDRAWN AND REVISED should appear in the revision column of the new drawing when this is done.

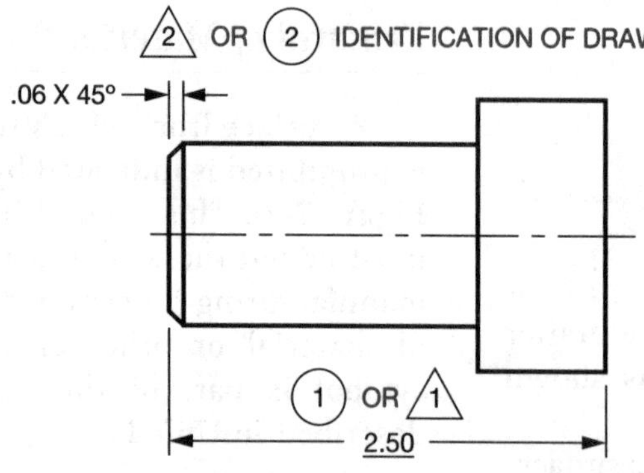

(A) DRAWING REVISIONS

REVISIONS			
Rev.	Description	Date	Approved
1	LENGTH WAS 2.40	JAN. 6/00	J. CAMPBELL
2	CHAMFER ADDED	MAR. 3/00	D. ARNOLD

(B) TYPICAL VERTICAL REVISION BLOCK (SIZE MAY VARY)

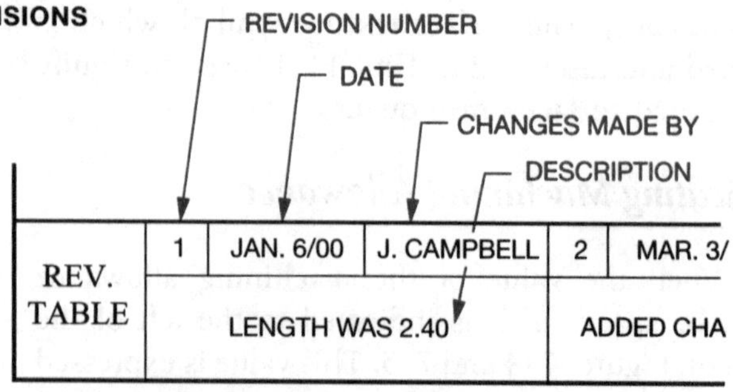

(C) TYPICAL HORIZONTAL REVISION BLOCK (SIZE MAY VARY)

FIGURE 7–8 ■ Drawing revisions

After a revision to a drawing is made, a new set of prints of that drawing is distributed to the appropriate departments and the prints of the original drawing are destroyed.

BREAK LINES

Break lines, as shown in Figure 7–9, are used to shorten the view of long uniform sections. They are also used when only a partial view is required. Such lines are used on both detail and assembly drawings. The thin line with freehand zigzags is recommended for long breaks, and the jagged line for wood parts. The special breaks shown for cylindrical and tubular parts are useful when an end view is not shown; otherwise, the thick break line is adequate.

REFERENCES

CAN3-B95-1962 (R1996) Surface Texture
ASME Y14.36M-1996 Surface Texture Symbols

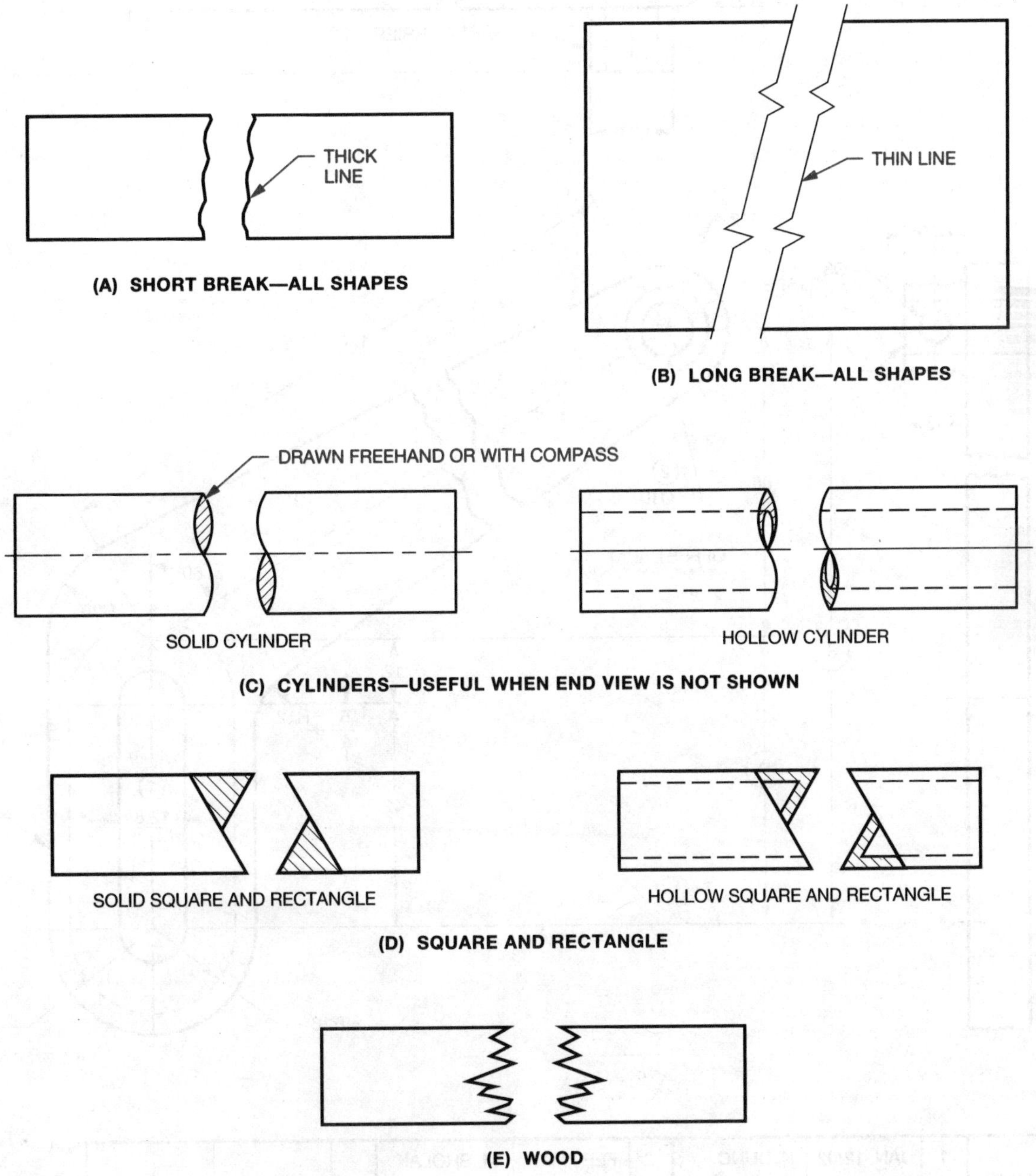
THICK LINE
(A) SHORT BREAK—ALL SHAPES
THIN LINE
(B) LONG BREAK—ALL SHAPES
DRAWN FREEHAND OR WITH COMPASS
SOLID CYLINDER
HOLLOW CYLINDER
(C) CYLINDERS—USEFUL WHEN END VIEW IS NOT SHOWN
SOLID SQUARE AND RECTANGLE
HOLLOW SQUARE AND RECTANGLE
(D) SQUARE AND RECTANGLE
(E) WOOD

FIGURE 7–9 ■ Conventional break lines

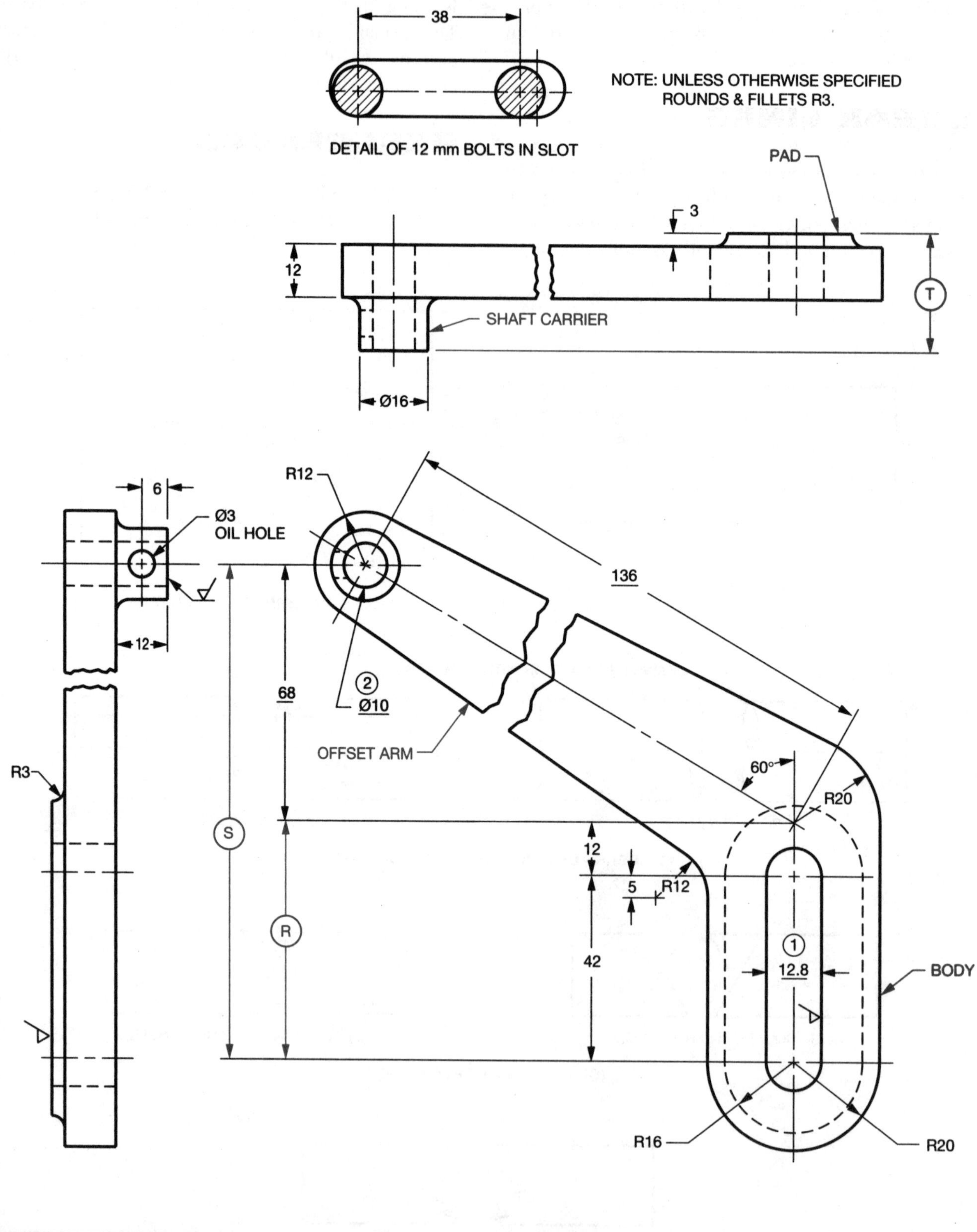
38
DETAIL OF 12 mm BOLTS IN SLOT
NOTE: UNLESS OTHERWISE SPECIFIED
ROUNDS & FILLETS R3.
PAD
3
12
T
SHAFT CARRIER
Ø16
R12
6
Ø3
OIL HOLE
136
12
68
② Ø10
OFFSET ARM
R3
S
60°
R20
12
5
R12
R
42
① 12.8
BODY
R16
R20

REVISIONS	1	JAN. 12/02	K. DUNC	2	FEB. 3/00	M. SHOLAK		
	SLOT WIDTH WAS 16			HOLE WAS Ø8				

QUESTIONS

1. At what angle is the offset arm to the body of the piece?
2. What is the centre-to-centre measurement of the length of the offset arm?
3. Which radius forms the upper end of the offset arm?
4. Which radii form the lower end of the offset arm where it joins the body?
5. What is the width of the bolt slot in the body of the brackt?
6. What is the centre-to-centre length of this slot?
7. What was the slot width before revision?
8. Which radii forms the ends of the pad?
9. What is the overall length of this pad?
10. What is the overall width of this pad?
11. What is the radii of the fillet between the pad and the body?
12. What is the diameter of the shaft carrier body?
13. What is the diameter of the shaft carrier hole?
14. What is the distance from the face of the shaft carrier to the face of the pad?
15. What is the radii of the inside fillet between the arm and the body of the piece?
16. If M12 bolts are used in holding the bracket to the machine base, what is the clearance on each side of the slot?
17. If the centre-to-centre distance of the two M12 bolts that fit the slot is 38 mm, how much play is there lengthwise in the slot?
18. What size oil hole is in the shaft carrier?
19. How far is the centre of the oil hole from the face of the shaft carrier?
20. How thick is the combined body and pad?
21. Calculate distances (R), (S), and (T).
22. The hole in the shaft carrier was revised. What is the difference in size between the new and old hole?
23. How many dimensions are not to scale?
24. If 2 mm is allowed for each surface to be machined, what would be the overall thickness of the orininal casting?

ANSWERS

1. ________
2. ________
3. ________
4. ________
5. ________
6. ________
7. ________
8. ________
9. ________
10. ________
11. ________
12. ________
13. ________
14. ________
15. ________
16. ________
17. ________
18. ________
19. ________
20. ________

21. R ________
S ________
T ________

22. ________
23. ________
24. ________

METRIC
DIMENSIONS IN MILLIMETRES

MATERIAL	MI	
SCALE	1:1	
DRAWN		DATE
OFFSET BRACKET		**A-23M**

8 UNIT

SECTIONAL VIEWS

Sectional views, commonly called *sections,* are used to show interior detail too complicated to be shown clearly and dimensioned by outside views and hidden lines. A sectional view is obtained by supposing the nearest part of the object has been cut or broken away on an imaginary cutting plane. The exposed or cut surfaces are identified by section lining or crosshatching. Hidden lines and details behind the cutting-plane line are usually omitted unless they are required for clarity. It should be understood that only in the sectional view is any part of the object shown as having been removed.

A sectional view frequently replaces one of the regular views. For example, a regular front view is replaced by a front view in section, as shown in Figure 8–1.

The Cutting-Plane Line

A *cutting-plane line* indicates where the imaginary cutting takes place. The position of the cutting plane is indicated, when necessary, on a view of the object or assembly by a cutting-plane line, as shown in Figure 8–2. The ends of the cutting-plane line are bent at 90 degrees and terminated by arrowheads to indicate the direction of sight for viewing the section. Cutting planes are not shown on sectional views. The cutting-plane line may be omitted when it corresponds to the centre line of the part or when only one sectional view appears on a drawing.

If two or more sections appear on the same drawing, the cutting-plane lines are identified by two identical large, single-stroke, Gothic letters. One letter is placed at each end of the line. Sectional view subtitles are given when identification letters are used and appear directly below the view, incorporating the letters at each end of the

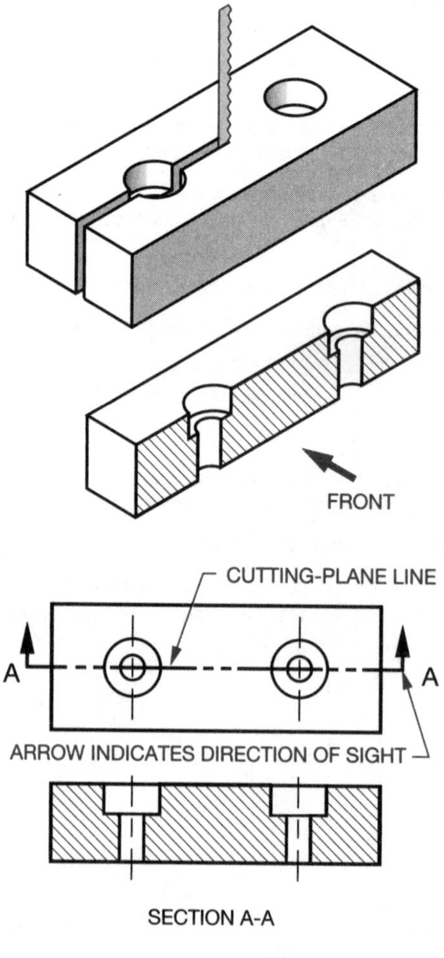

FIGURE 8–1 ■ A section drawing

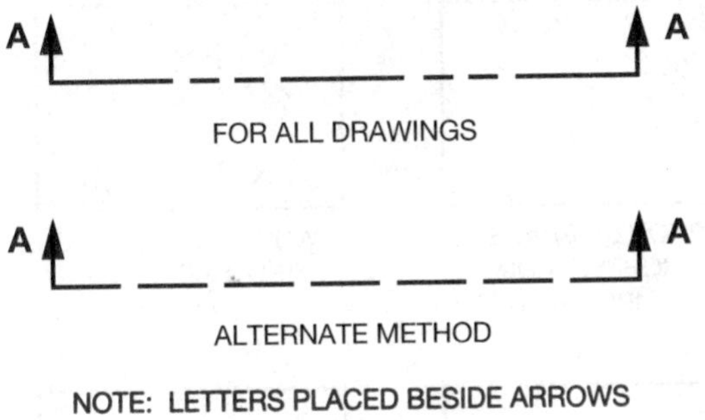
A
A
FOR ALL DRAWINGS
A
A
ALTERNATE METHOD
NOTE: LETTERS PLACED BESIDE ARROWS

FIGURE 8–2 ■ Cutting-plane lines

cutting-plane line, thus: SECTION A-A or, abbreviated, SECT A-A. See Assignment A-26M.

Section Lining

Section lining indicates the surface that has been cut and makes it stand out clearly. Section lines usually consist of thin parallel lines, Figure 8–3, drawn at an angle of approximately 45 degrees to the principal edges or axis of the part.

Because the exact material specifications for a part are usually given elsewhere, the general use section lining, Figure 8–4, is recommended for general use.

When it is desirable to indicate differences in materials, other symbolic section lines are used, such as those shown in Figure 8–4. If the part shape would cause section lines to be parallel or nearly parallel to one of the sides or features of the part, an angle other than 45 degrees is chosen.

The spacing of the hatching lines is uniform to give a good appearance to the drawing. The pitch, or distance, between lines varies from .06 to .18 inch, depending on the size of the area to be sectioned. Section lining is similar in direction and spacing in all sections of a single component.

Wood and concrete are the only two materials usually shown symbolically. When wood symbols are used, the direction of the grain is shown.

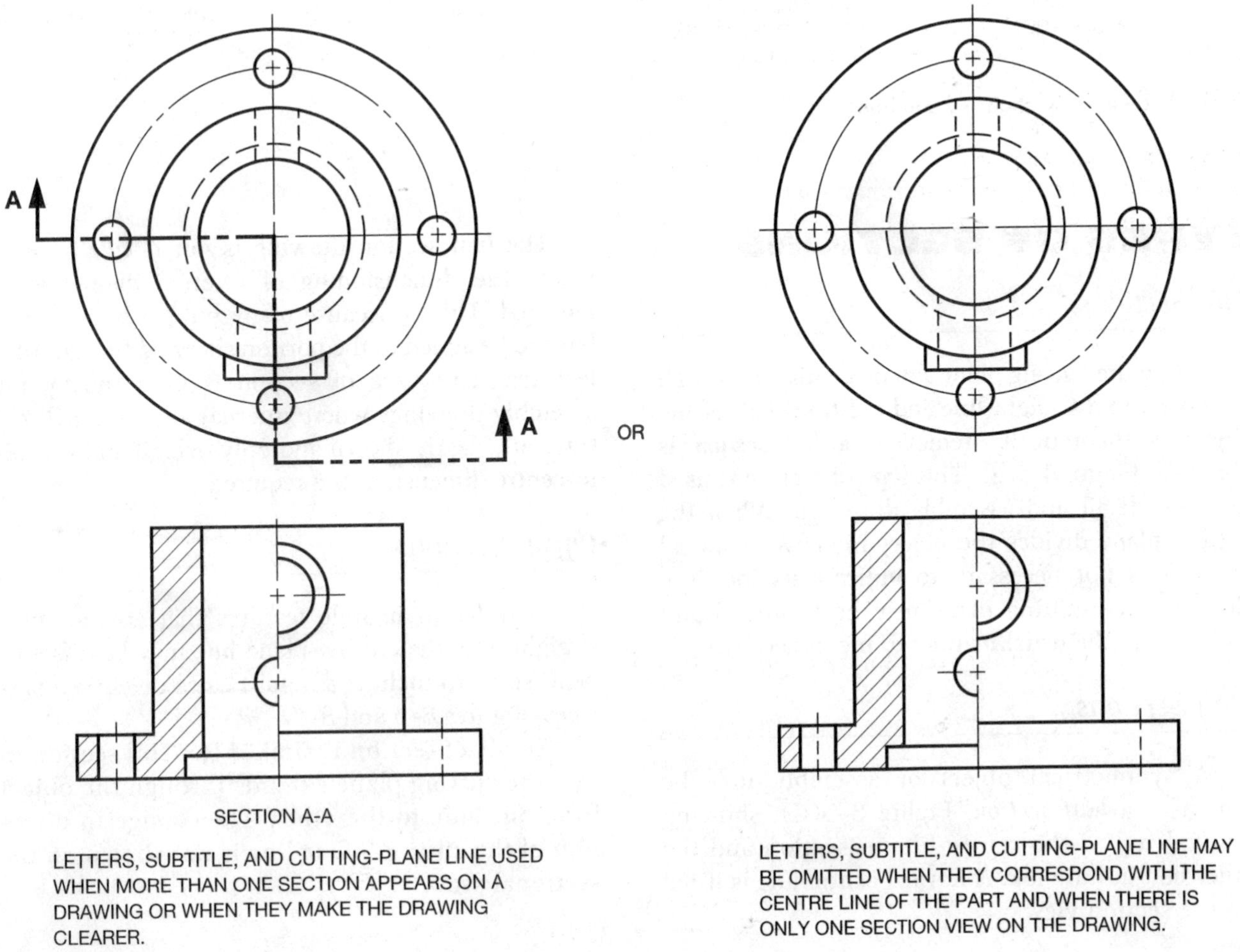
A
A
OR
SECTION A-A
LETTERS, SUBTITLE, AND CUTTING-PLANE LINE USED WHEN MORE THAN ONE SECTION APPEARS ON A DRAWING OR WHEN THEY MAKE THE DRAWING CLEARER.
LETTERS, SUBTITLE, AND CUTTING-PLANE LINE MAY BE OMITTED WHEN THEY CORRESPOND WITH THE CENTRE LINE OF THE PART AND WHEN THERE IS ONLY ONE SECTION VIEW ON THE DRAWING.

FIGURE 8–3 ■ Identification of cutting plane and sectional views

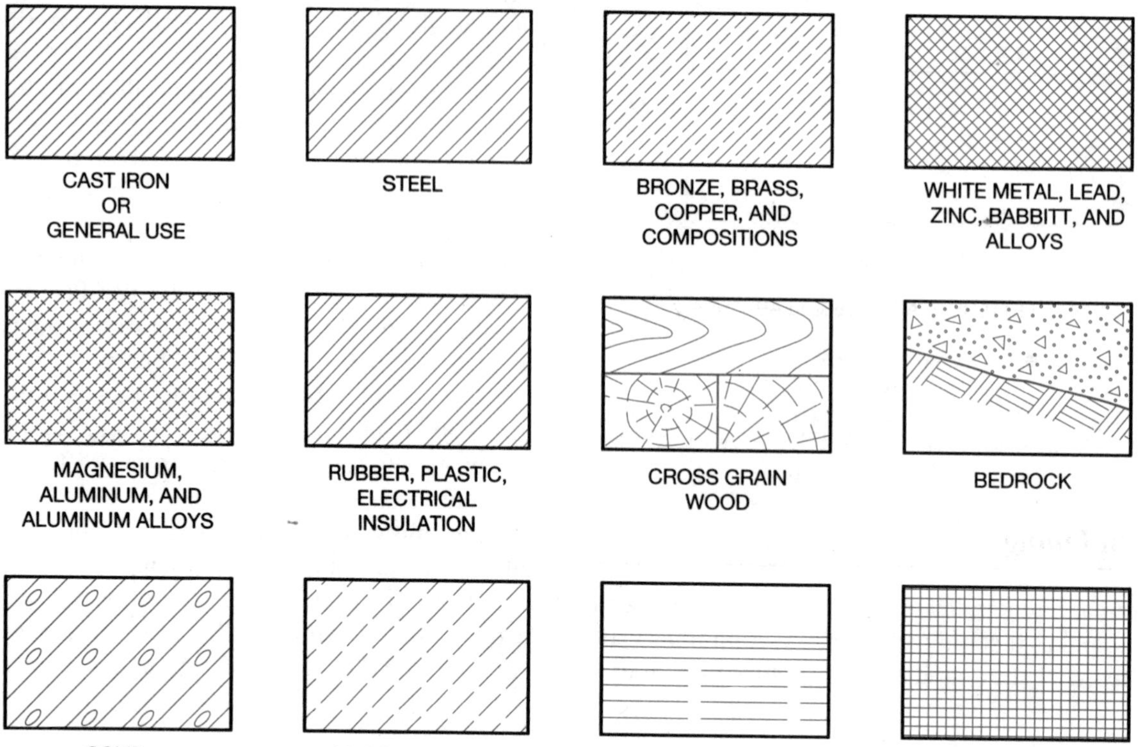
CAST IRON
OR
GENERAL USE
STEEL
BRONZE, BRASS,
COPPER, AND
COMPOSITIONS
WHITE METAL, LEAD,
ZINC, BABBITT, AND
ALLOYS
MAGNESIUM,
ALUMINUM, AND
ALUMINUM ALLOYS
RUBBER, PLASTIC,
ELECTRICAL
INSULATION
CROSS GRAIN
WOOD
BEDROCK
SOLID
INSULATION
MARBLE, SLATE,
GLASS, PORCELAIN,
ETC.
LIQUIDS
ELECTRIC WINDINGS
AND CABLES

FIGURE 8–4 ■ Symbolic section lining

TYPES OF SECTIONS

Full Sections

When the cutting plane extends entirely through the object in a straight line and the front half of the object is theoretically removed, a *full section* is obtained, Figure 8–5(B). This type of section is used for both detail and assembly drawings. When the cutting plane divides the object into two identical parts, it is not necessary to indicate its location. However, the cutting plane may be identified and indicated in the usual manner to increase clarity.

Half Sections

A symmetrical object or assembly may be drawn as a *half section,* Figure 8–5(C), showing one half up to the centre line in section and the other half in full view. A normal centre line is listed on the section view.

The half section drawing is not normally used where the dimensioning of internal diameters is required. This is because many hidden lines would have to be added to the portion showing the external features. This type of section is used mostly for assembly drawings where internal and external features are clearly shown and only overall and centre-to-centre dimensions are required.

Offset Sections

In order to include features that are not in a straight line, the cutting-plane line may be offset or bent, so as to include several planes or curved surfaces, Figures 8–6 and 8–7.

An offset section is similar to a full section in that the cutting plane extends through the object from one side to the other. The change in direction of the cutting-plane line is not shown on the sectional view.

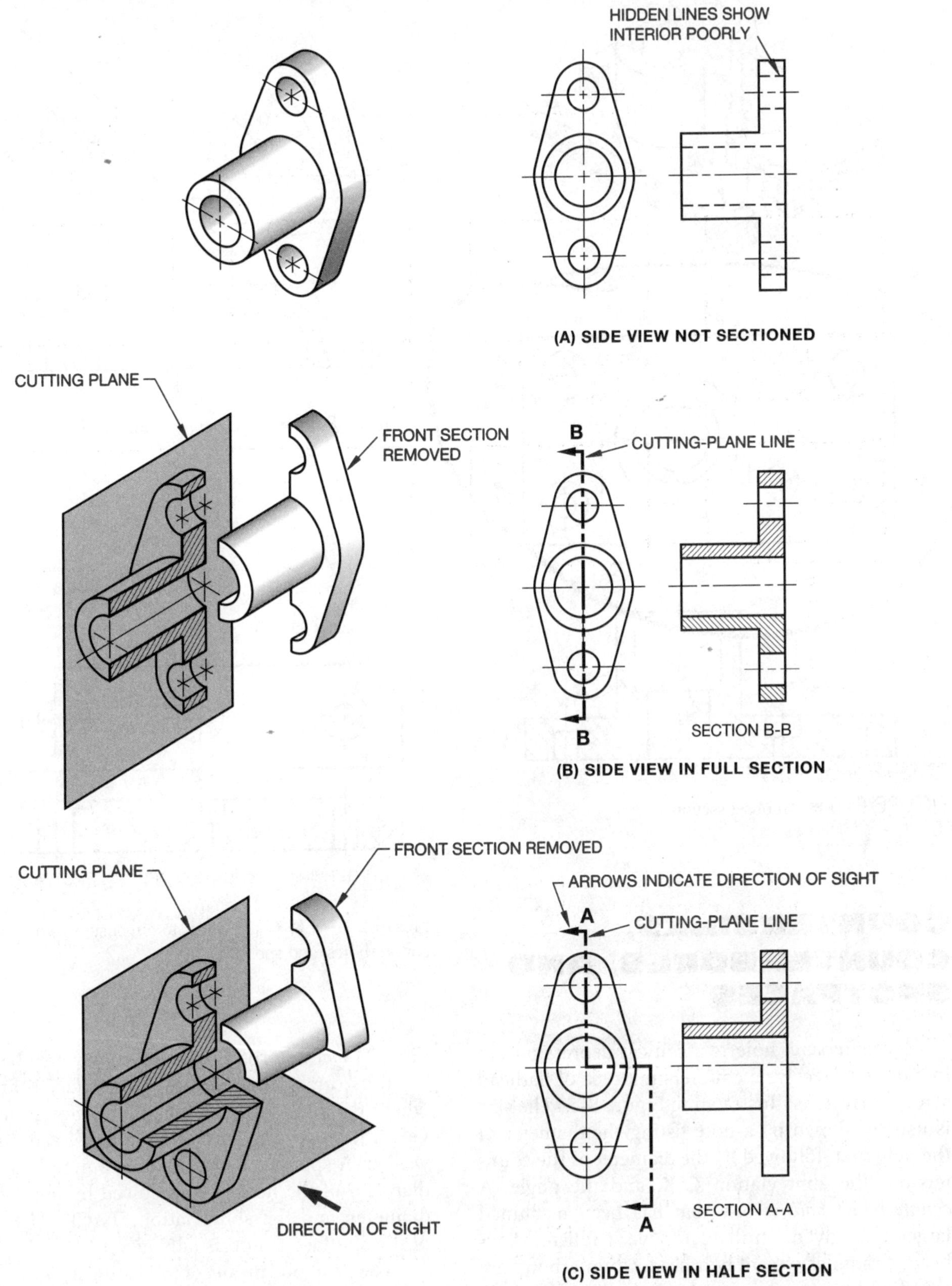
HIDDEN LINES SHOW INTERIOR POORLY
(A) SIDE VIEW NOT SECTIONED
CUTTING PLANE
FRONT SECTION REMOVED
B
CUTTING-PLANE LINE
B
SECTION B-B
(B) SIDE VIEW IN FULL SECTION
FRONT SECTION REMOVED
CUTTING PLANE
ARROWS INDICATE DIRECTION OF SIGHT
A
CUTTING-PLANE LINE
DIRECTION OF SIGHT
SECTION A-A
A
(C) SIDE VIEW IN HALF SECTION

FIGURE 8–5 ■ Full and half sections

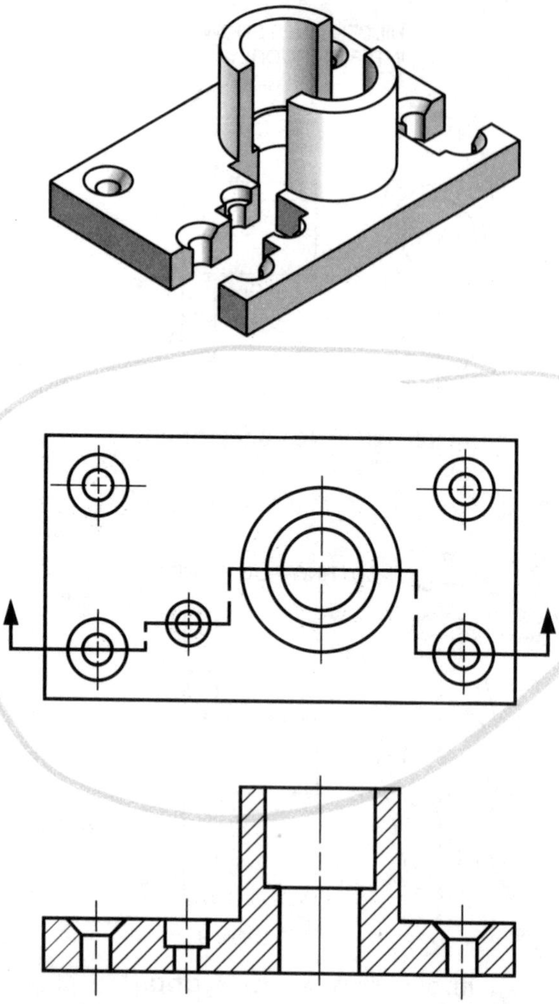

FIGURE 8–6 ■ An offset section

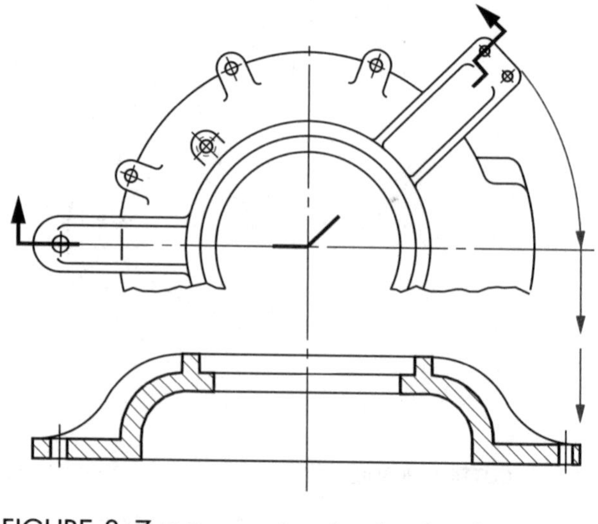

FIGURE 8–7 ■ Bent cutting-plane line for offset sections

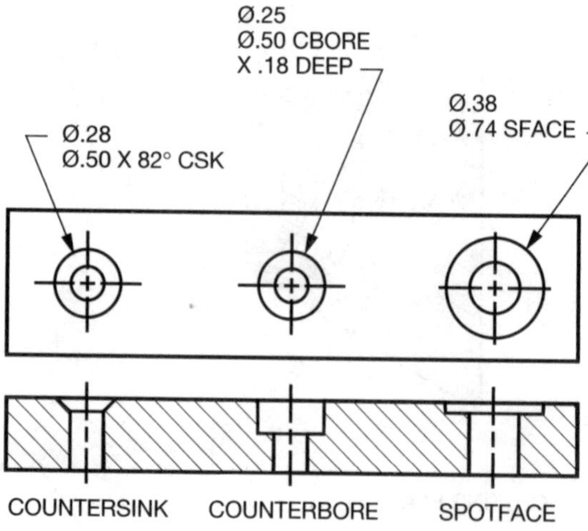

FIGURE 8–8 ■ Using words to dimension countersinks, counterbores, and spotfaces

COUNTERSINKS, COUNTERBORES, AND SPOTFACES

A *countersunk* hole is a conical depression cut in a piece to receive a countersunk type of flathead screw or rivet, as illustrated in Figure 8–8. The size is usually shown by a note listing the diameter of the hole first, followed by the diameter of the countersink, the abbreviation CSK, and the angle, A *counterbored hole* is one that has been machined larger to a given depth to receive a fillister, hex-head, or similar type of bolt head. Counterbores are specified by a note giving the diameter of the hole first, followed by the counterbore diameter, the abbreviation CBORE, and the depth of the counterbore. The counterbore and depth may also be indicated by direct dimensioning. A *spotface* is an area where the surface is machined just enough to provide a level seating surface for a bolt head, nut, or washer. A spotface is specified by a note listing the diameter of the hole first, followed by the spotface diameter, and the abbreviation SFACE. The depth of the spotface is not usually given.

The symbolic means of indicating a countersink, a counterbore or spotface, and the depth of a feature are shown in Figure 8–9. In each case, the symbol precedes the dimension.

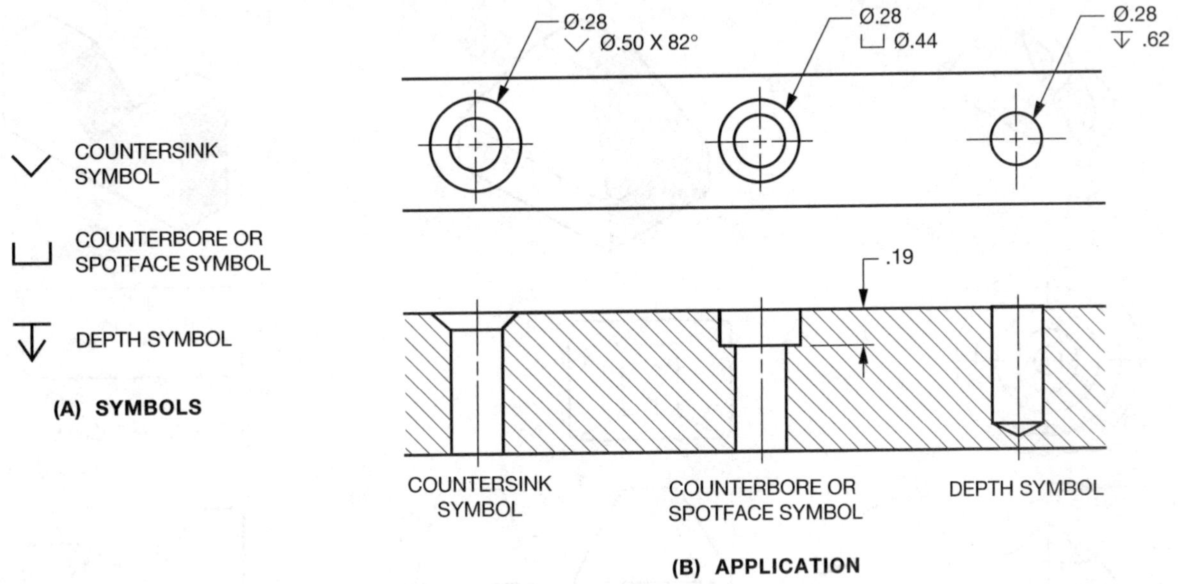

FIGURE 8–9 ■ Using symbols to indicate shape and depth of holes

INTERSECTION OF UNFINISHED SURFACES

The intersection of unfinished surfaces that are rounded or filleted at the point of theoretical intersection is indicated by a line coinciding with the theoretical point of intersection. The need for this convention is shown by the examples in Figure 8–10. For a large radius, Figure 8–10(C), no line is drawn.

Members such as ribs and arms that blend into other features end in curves called *runouts*.

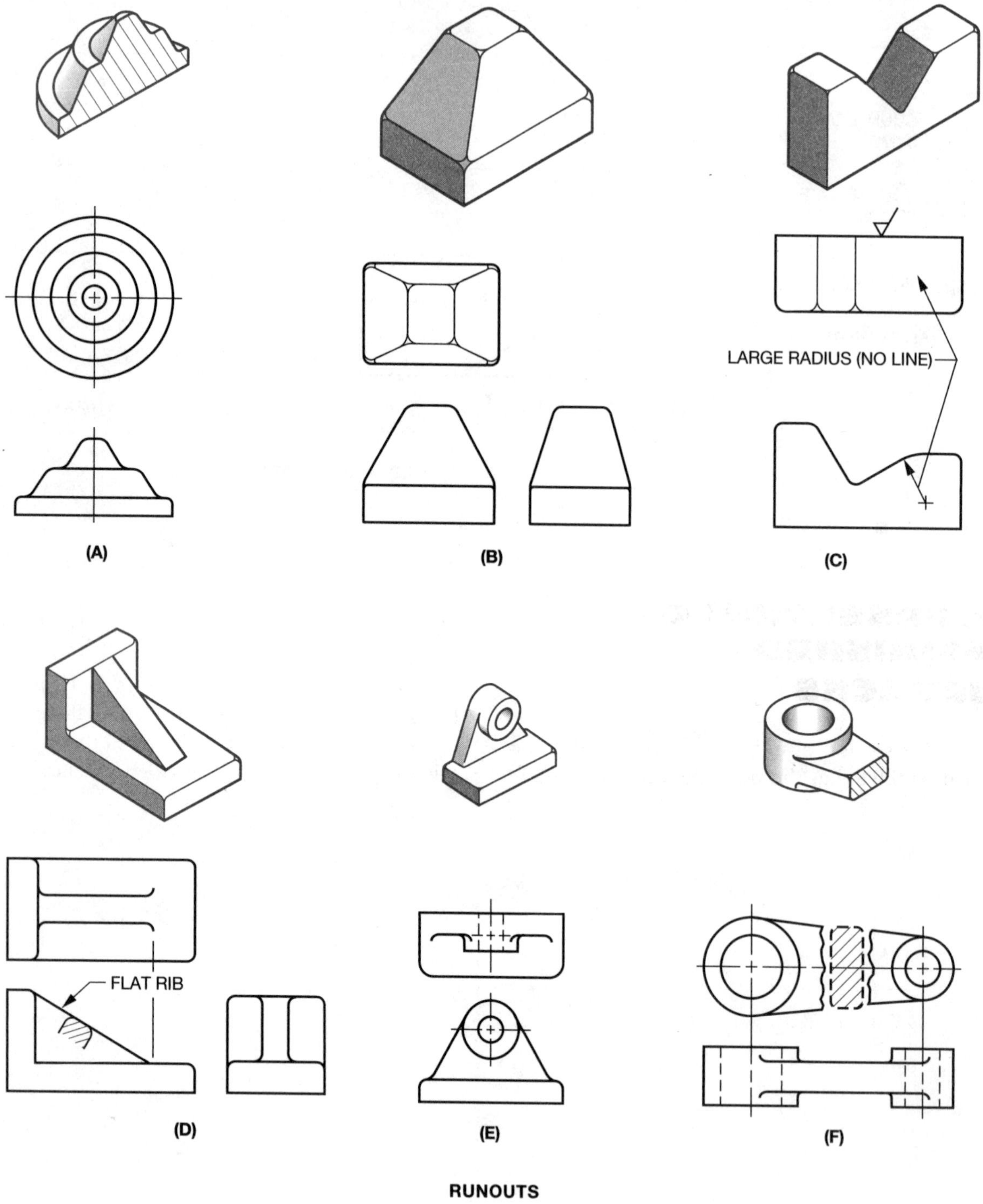
LARGE RADIUS (NO LINE)
(A)
(B)
(C)
FLAT RIB
(D)
(E)
(F)
RUNOUTS

FIGURE 8–10 ■ Rounded and filleted intersections

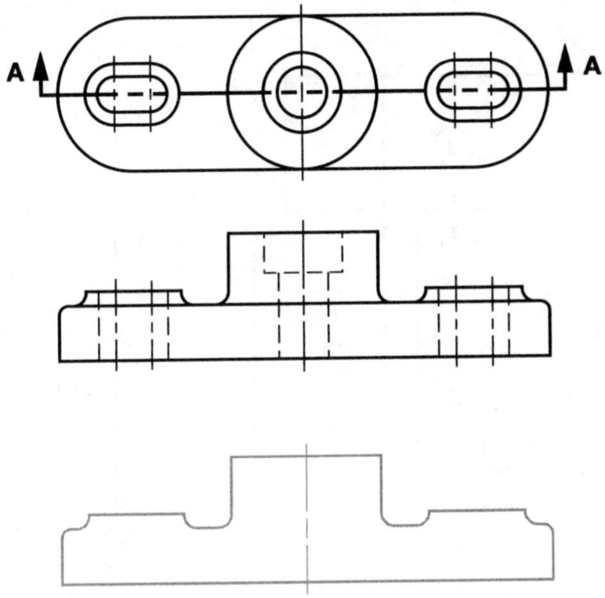

SKETCH SECTION A-A HERE.

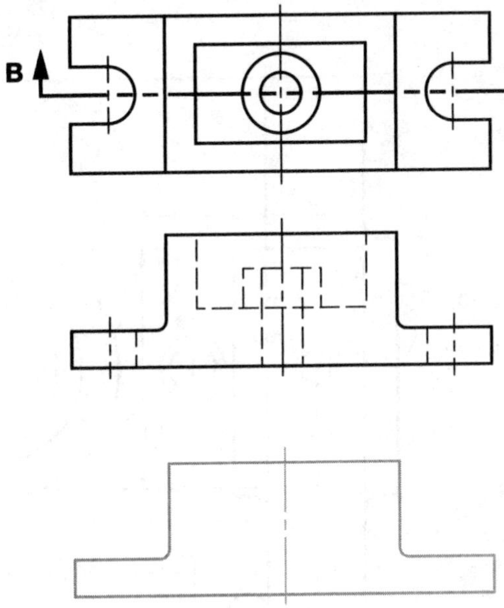

SKETCH SECTION B-B HERE.

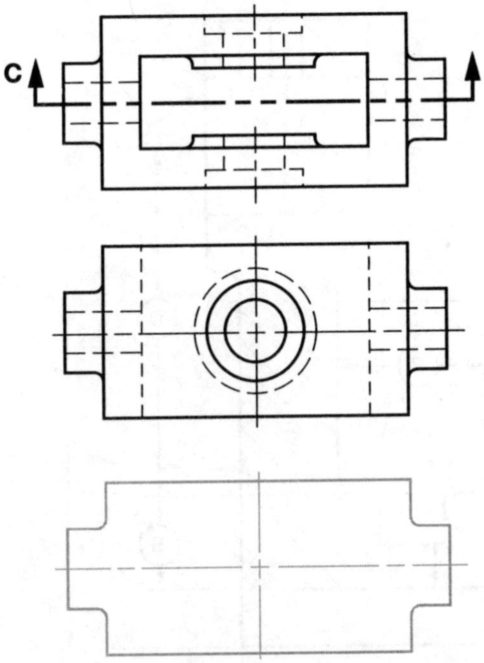

SKETCH SECTION C-C HERE.

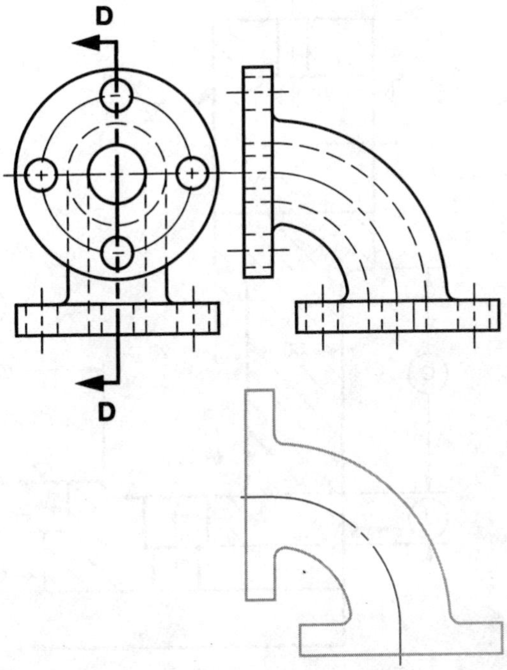

SKETCH SECTION D-D HERE.

ASSIGNMENT: SKETCH THE FOUR FULL SECTIONAL VIEWS IN THE SPACES SHOWN.		**SKETCHING FULL SECTIONS**	**A-24**

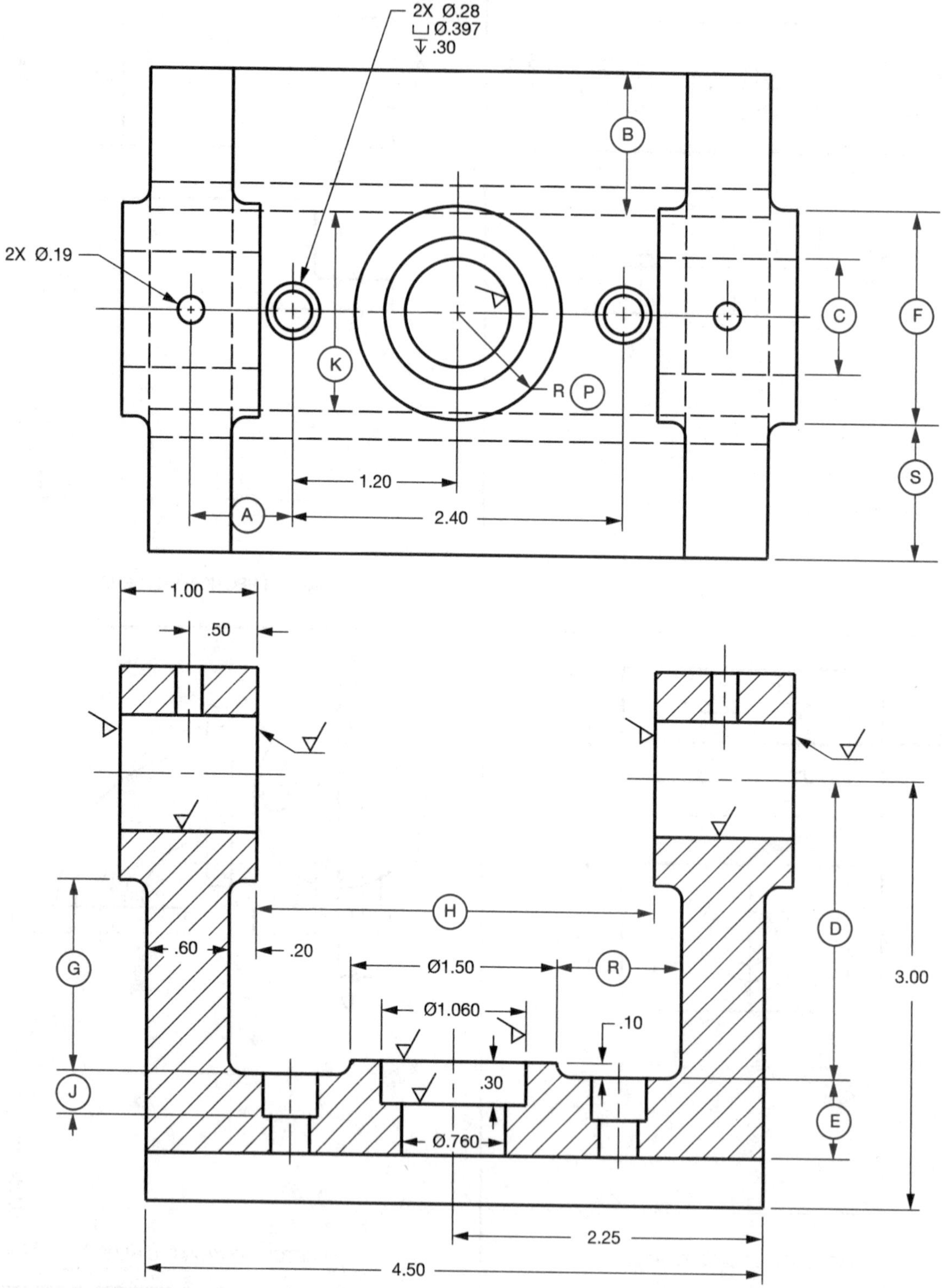
2X Ø.28
⌴ Ø.397
↧ .30
2X Ø.19
B
C
F
K
R P
S
1.20
A
2.40
1.00
.50
G
.60
.20
H
Ø1.50
R
Ø1.060
.10
D
3.00
J
.30
E
Ø.760
2.25
4.50

REVISIONS	1	MAR. 7/02	A. HEINEN
	Ø1.50 WAS Ø1.56		

√ ARE .30√ UNLESS OTHERWISE SPECIFIED

QUESTIONS

1. What is the overall width?
2. What is the overall height?
3. What is the centre-to-centre distance of the Ø.19 holes?
4. If .03 is allowed for each surface requiring finishing, calculate the width of the casting before machining.
5. At what angle to the vertical is the dovetail slot?
6. How many different surfaces require finishing?
7. Which type of lines in the top view represent the dovetail?
8. What was the original size of the Ø1.50?
9. How wide is the opening in the dovetail?
10. How high is the dovetail?
11. When was the Ø1.50 dimension altered?
12. How many reference dimensions are shown?
13. Calculate the distances (A) to (S).
14. What is the (A) size and (B) type of cap screw required to fasten the slide bracket to its mating part?

ANSWERS

1. ________
2. ________
3. ________
4. ________
5. ________
6. ________
7. ________
8. ________
9. ________
10. ________
11. ________
12. ________
13. A ________
B ________
C ________
D ________
E ________
F ________
G ________
H ________
J ________
K ________
L ________
M ________
N ________
P ________
Q ________
R ________
S ________
14. A ________
B ________

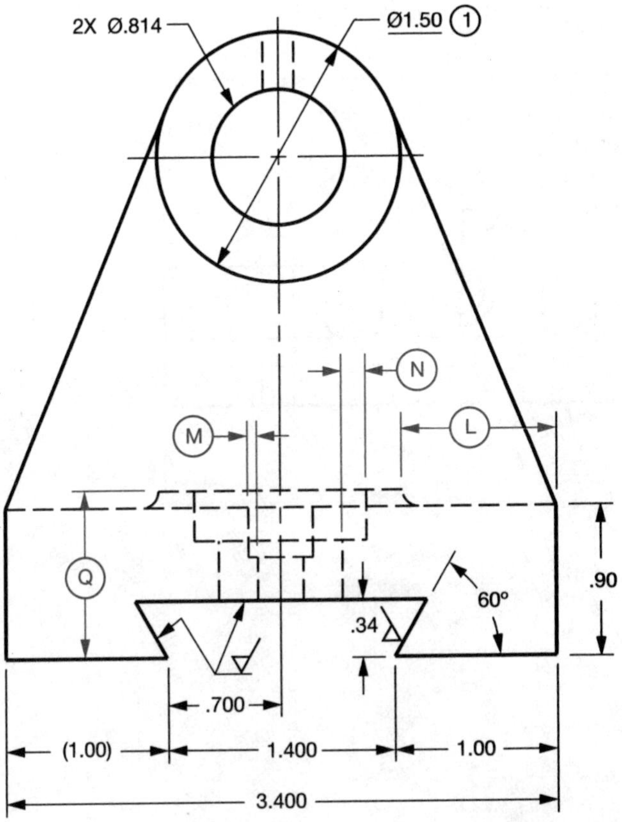

ROUNDS AND FILLETS R.10

MATERIAL	GREY IRON	
SCALE	NOT TO SCALE	
DRAWN		DATE
SLIDE BRACKET		A-25

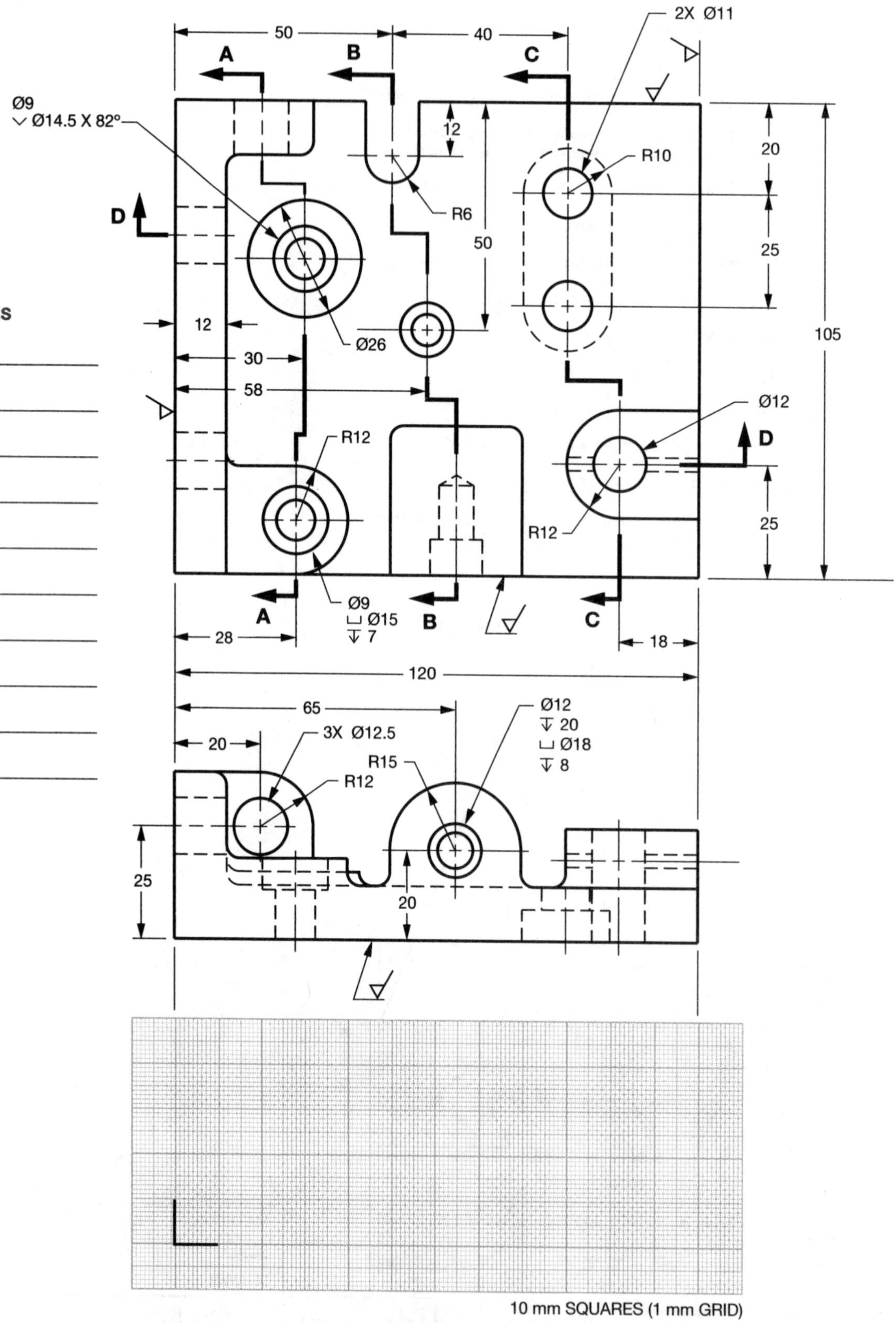
2X Ø11
50
40
A
B
C
Ø9
⌵ Ø14.5 X 82°
12
R10
20
R6
D
50
25
Ø26
105
12
30
58
Ø12
D
R12
25
R12
Ø9
⌴ Ø15
↧ 7
A
B
C
28
18
120
65
Ø12
↧ 20
⌴ Ø18
↧ 8
20
3X Ø12.5
R15
R12
25
20
10 mm SQUARES (1 mm GRID)

ANSWERS

1. ____________
2. ____________
3. ____________
4. ____________
5. A ____________
   B ____________
   C ____________
6. A ____________
   B ____________
7. ____________

SECTION D-D

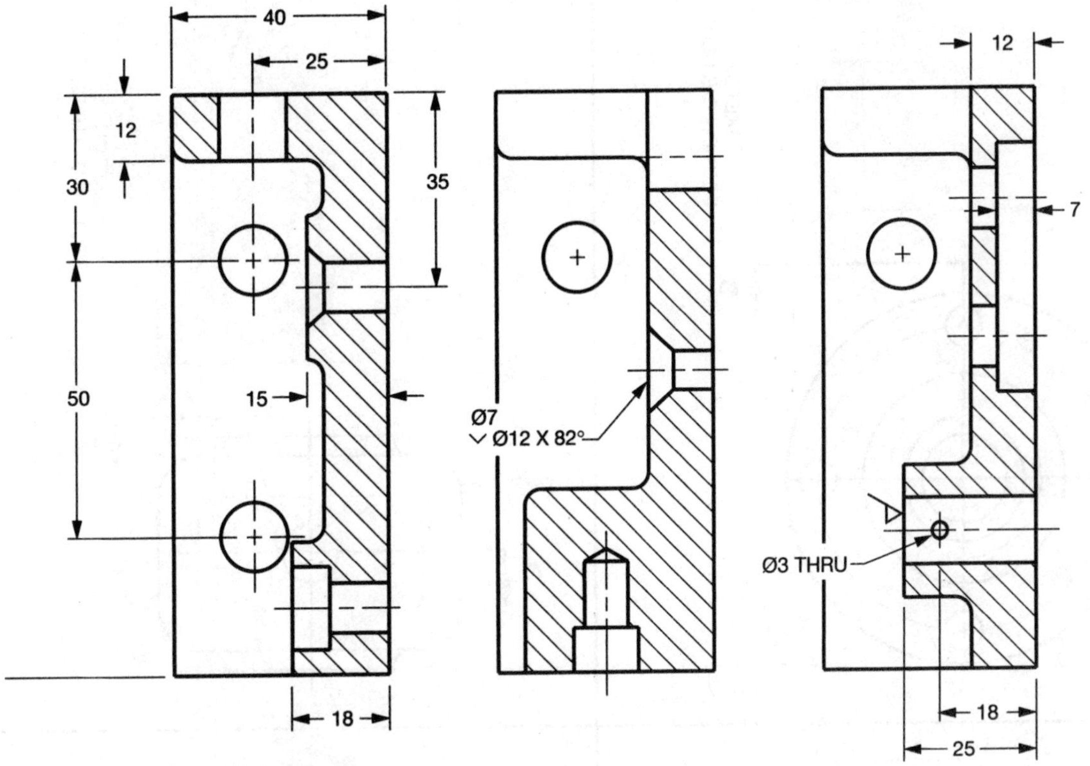

SECTION A-A **SECTION B-B** **SECTION C-C**

ROUNDS AND FILLETS R3

√ SHOWN TO BE 2√

QUESTIONS

1. What type of sectional view is used?
2. How many surfaces require finishing?
3. What is the total number of holes in the part?
   Note: A THRU hole is considered one hole.
4. How many countersunk holes are there?
5. What was the (A) width, (B) height, and (C) depth of the casting before finishing?
6. With reference to the counterbored hole, what is the (A) size and (B) type of cap screw required if the head of the cap screw must not protrude above the surface of the part? Refer to Table 7 of the Appendix.
7. What is the total number of offsets used on the cutting-plane lines?

ASSIGNMENT:
ON THE GRID PROVIDED SKETCH OFFSET SECTION D-D HAVING THE CUTTING-PLANE PASS THROUGH THE CENTRES OF THE COUNTERSUNK HOLES.

METRIC
NOTE: DIMENSIONS IN MILLIMETRES

MATERIAL MALLEABLE IRON	
SCALE	
DRAWN	DATE
BASE PLATE	**A-26M**

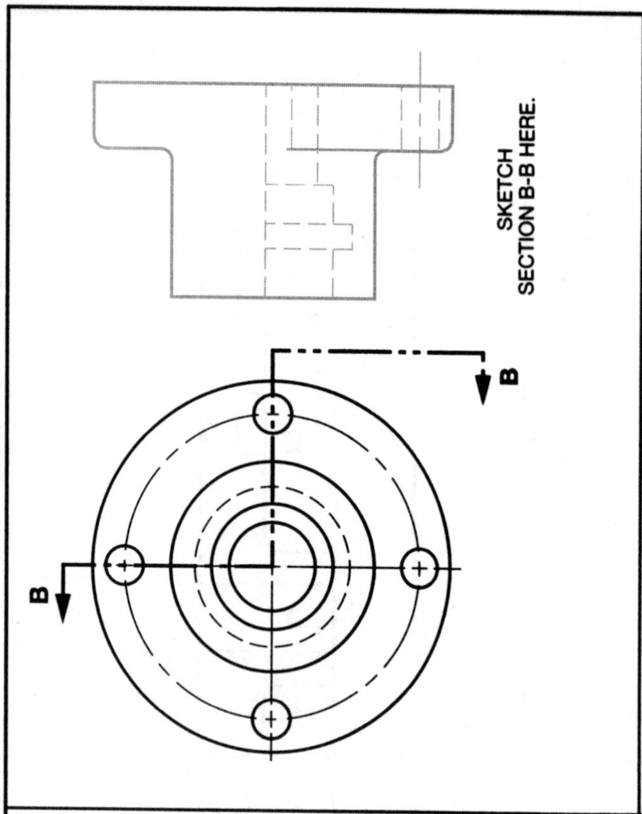
SKETCH
SECTION B-B HERE.
B
B

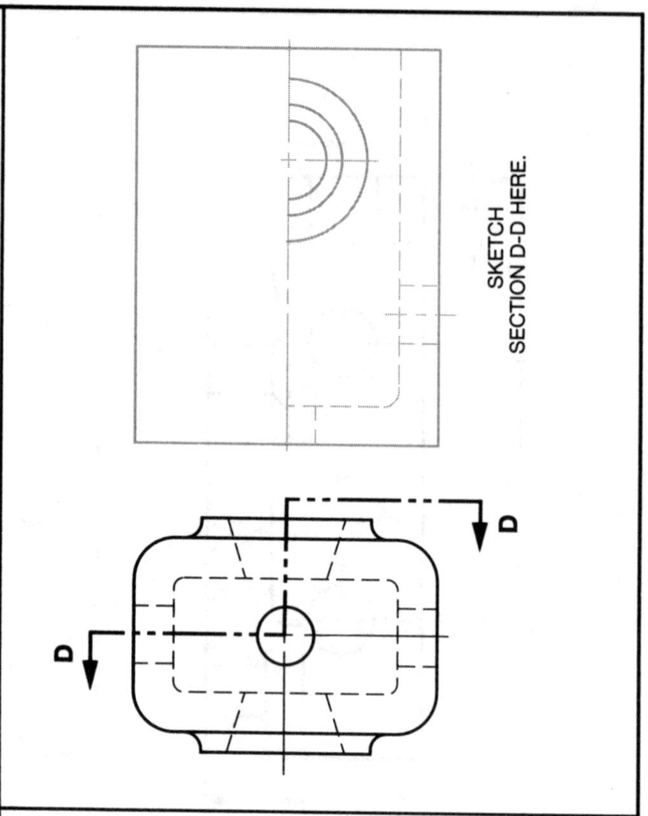
SKETCH
SECTION D-D HERE.
D
D

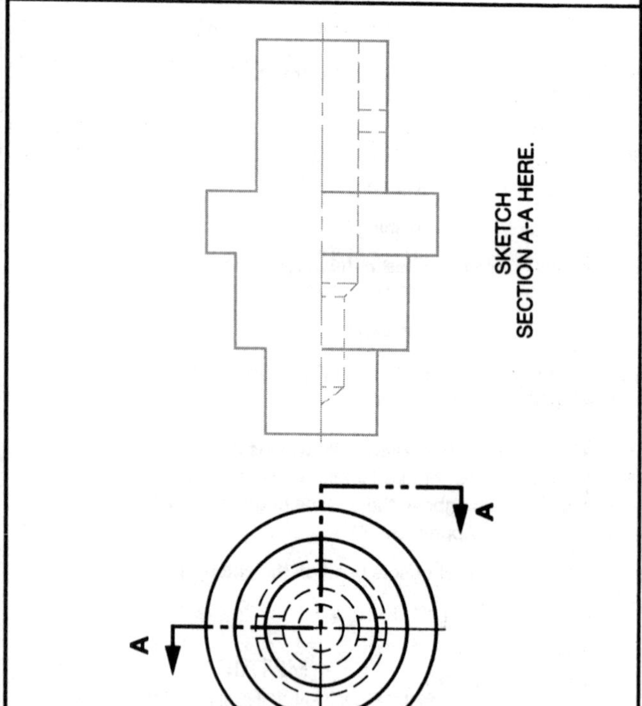
SKETCH
SECTION A-A HERE.
A
A

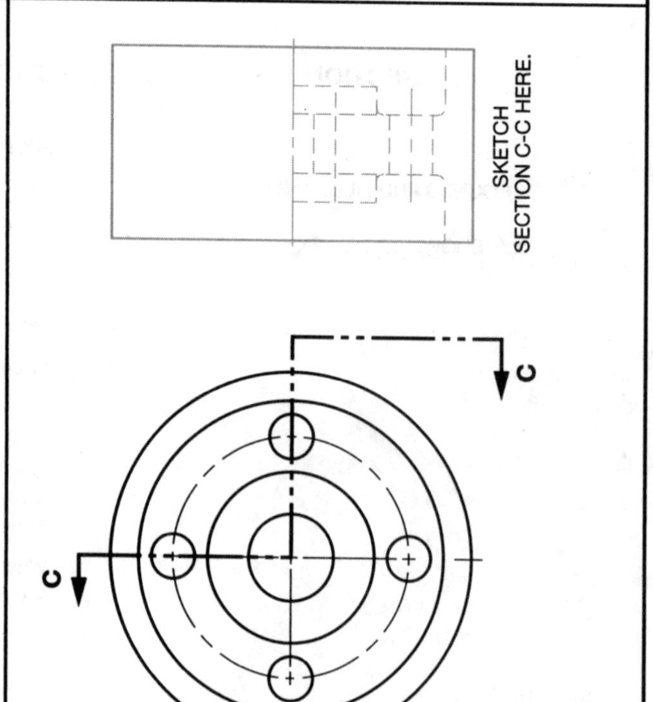
SKETCH
SECTION C-C HERE.
C
C

ASSIGNMENT: SKETCH THE FOUR HALF SECTION VIEWS IN THE SPACES SHOWN.		**SKETCHING HALF SECTIONS**	**A-27**

UNIT 9

CHAMFERS

The process of *chamfering*, that is, cutting away the inside or outside corner of an object, is done to facilitate assembly, Figure 9–1. The recommended method of dimensioning a chamfer is to give an angle and the linear length, or an angle and a diameter. For angles of 45 degrees only, a note form may be used. This method is permissible only with 45-degree angles because the size may apply to either the longitudinal or radial dimension. Chamfers are never measured along the angular surface.

UNDERCUTS

The operation of *undercutting*, also referred to as *necking*, is the cutting of a recess in a diameter. Undercuts permit two parts to join, Figure 9–1. Undercutting is indicated on a drawing by a note listing the width first and then the diameter. If the radius is shown at the bottom of the undercut, it is assumed that the radius will be equal to half the width unless specified differently and the diameter will apply to the centre of the undercut. Where the size of the neck is unimportant, the dimension may be omitted from the drawing.

TAPERS

A taper is the ratio of the difference in diameters of two sections (perpendicular to the axis of a cone to the distances between these two sections).

Conical Tapers

Tapered shanks are used on many small tools such as drills, reamers, counterbores, and spotfaces to hold them accurately in the machine spindle. Conical taper means the difference in diameter or width in a given length. There are many standard tapers; the Morse taper and the Brown and Sharpe taper are the most common.

The following dimensions may be used in suitable combinations, to define the size and form of tapered features:

- the diameter (or width) at one end of the tapered feature
- the length of the tapered feature
- the rate of taper
- the included angle
- the taper ratio

In dimensioning a taper by means of taper ratio, the conical taper symbol should precede the ratio figures, and the vertical leg of the symbol is always shown to the left, Figure 9–2.

Flat Tapers

Flat tapers (slopes) are used as locking devices such as taper keys and adjusting shims. The methods recommended for dimensioning flat tapers are

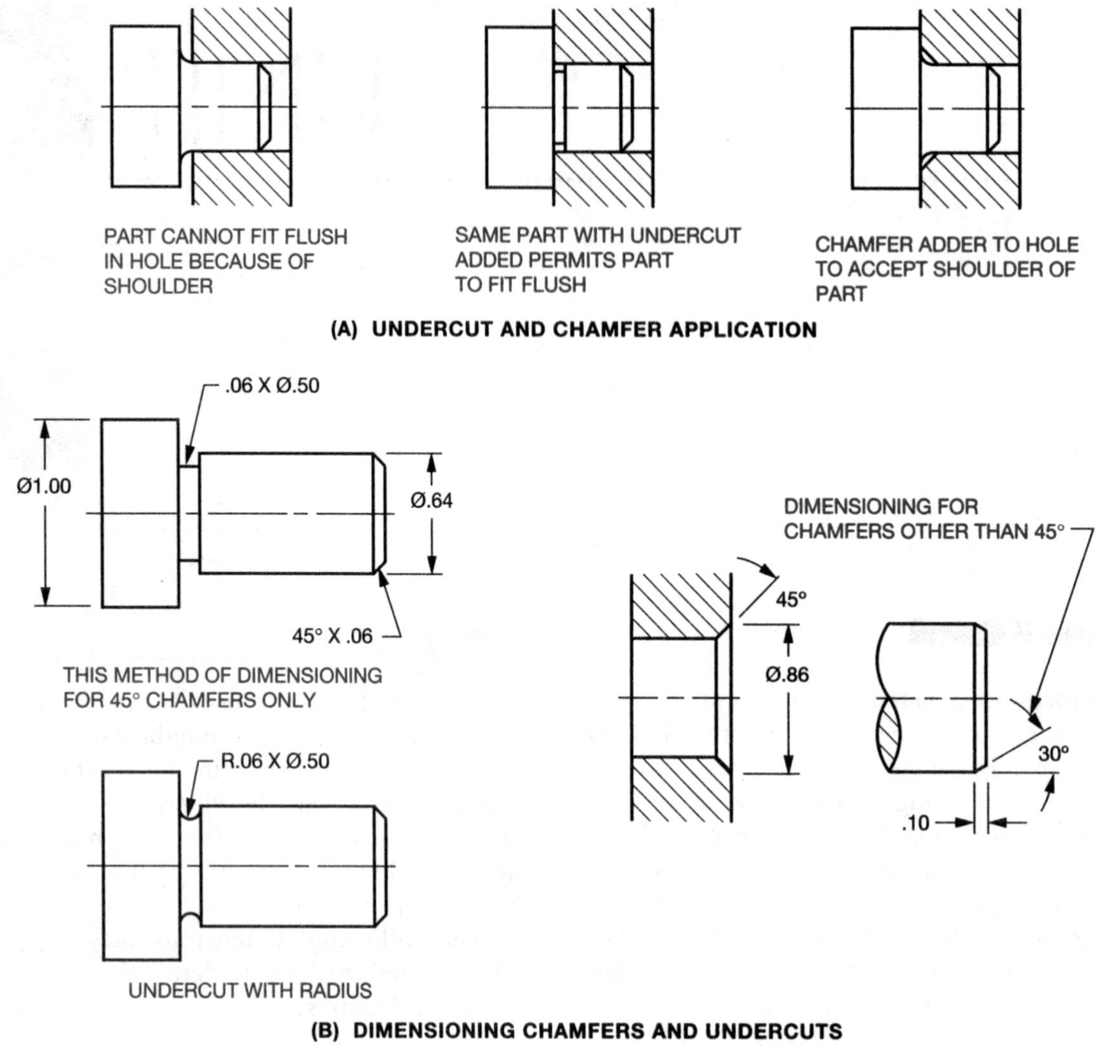
PART CANNOT FIT FLUSH IN HOLE BECAUSE OF SHOULDER
SAME PART WITH UNDERCUT ADDED PERMITS PART TO FIT FLUSH
CHAMFER ADDER TO HOLE TO ACCEPT SHOULDER OF PART
(A) UNDERCUT AND CHAMFER APPLICATION
.06 X Ø.50
Ø1.00
Ø.64
45° X .06
THIS METHOD OF DIMENSIONING FOR 45° CHAMFERS ONLY
R.06 X Ø.50
UNDERCUT WITH RADIUS
DIMENSIONING FOR CHAMFERS OTHER THAN 45°
45°
Ø.86
30°
.10
(B) DIMENSIONING CHAMFERS AND UNDERCUTS

FIGURE 9–1 ■ Chamfers and undercuts

shown in Figure 9–3. The flat taper symbol should precede the ratio figures, and the vertical leg of the symbol is always shown to the left.

KNURLS

Knurling is the machining of a surface to create uniform depressions. Knurling permits a better grip. Knurling is shown on drawings as either a straight or diamond pattern. The pitch of the knurl may be specified. It is unnecessary to hatch in the whole area to be knurled if enough is shown to clearly indicate the pattern. Knurls are specified on the drawing by a note calling for the type and pitch. The length and diameter of the knurl are shown as dimensions, Figure 9–4.

REFERENCE

CAN/CSA-B78.2-M91 Dimensioning and Tolerancing of Technical Drawings

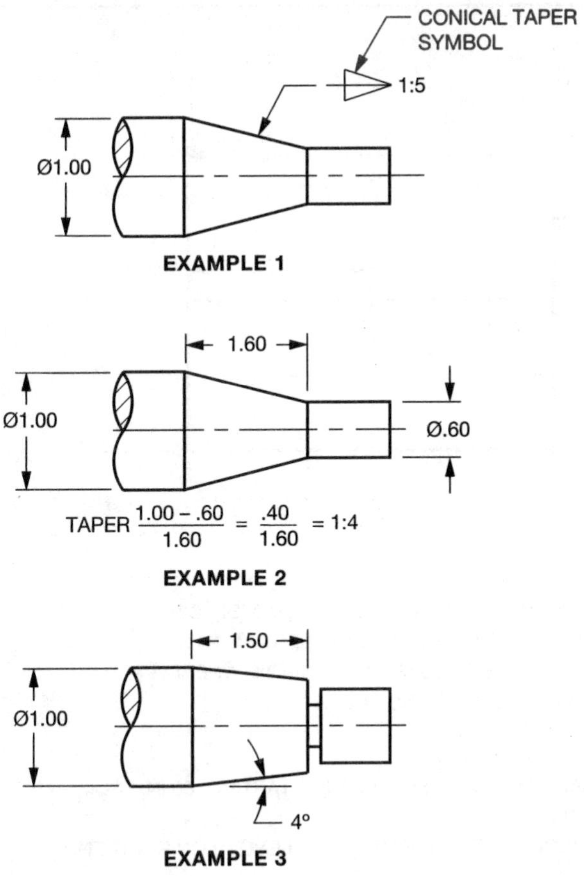

FIGURE 9–2 ■ Dimensioning conical tapers

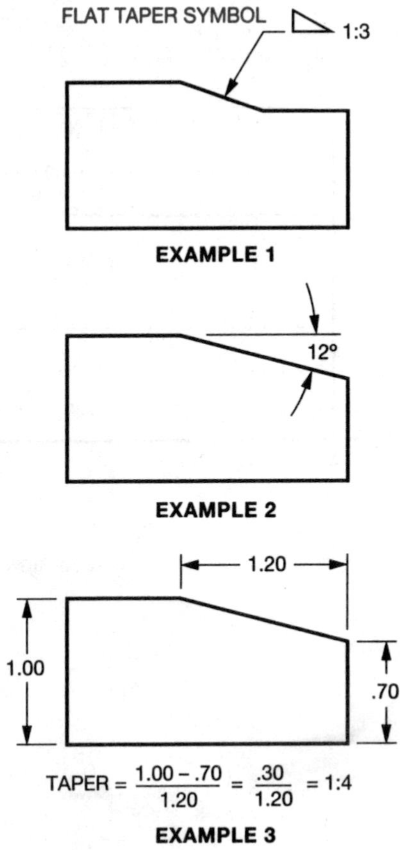

FIGURE 9–3 ■ Dimensioning flat tapers (slopes)

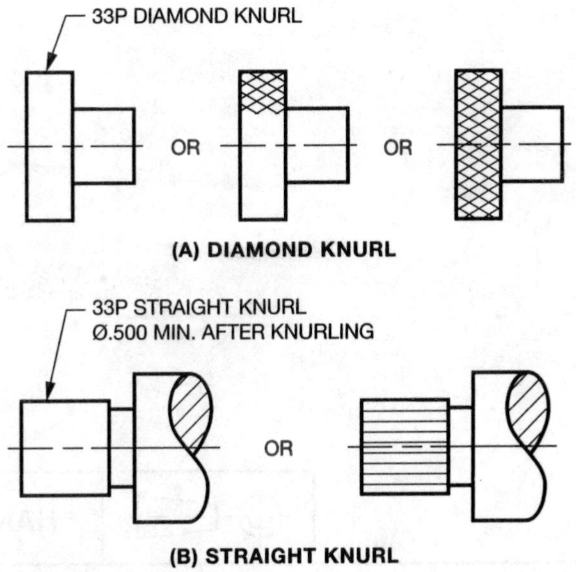

FIGURE 9–4 ■ Knurling

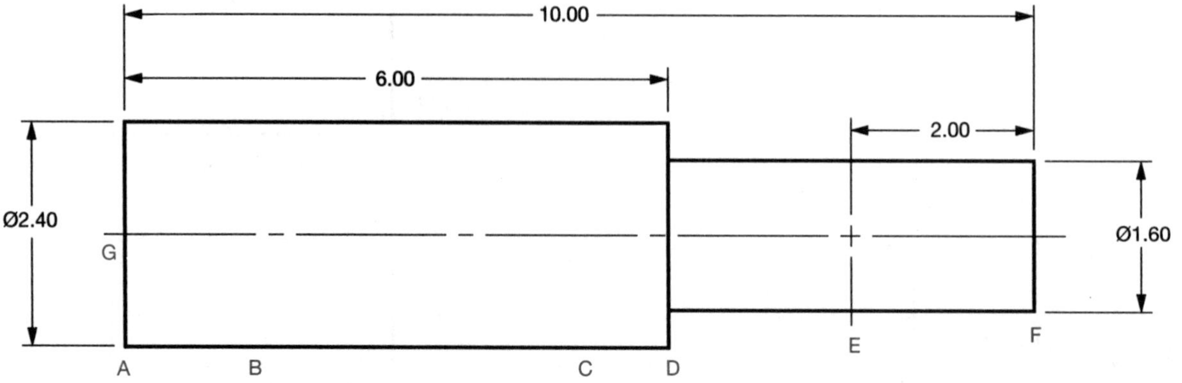

ASSIGNMENT: REDRAW THE HANDLE ON THE GRID SHOWN BELOW. SCALE IS 1:2. THE FOLLOWING FEATURES ARE TO BE ADDED AND DIMENSIONED USING SYMBOLS WHEREVER POSSIBLE AT THE LOCATIONS SHOWN:

A. 45° X .20 CHAMFER
B. 33P DIAMOND KNURL FOR 1.20 IN. STARTING .80 IN. FROM LEFT END
C. 0.1:1 CIRCULAR TAPER FOR 1.20 IN. LENGTH ON RIGHT END OF Ø2.40
D. .20 X Ø1.40 UNDERCUT ON Ø1.60
E. Ø.20 X .50 DEEP, 4 HOLES EQUALLY SPACED
F. 30° X .30 CHAMFER, THE .30 DIMENSION TAKEN HORIZONTALLY ALONG THE SHAFT
G. Ø.60 HOLE, 1.50 DEEP

1.00 IN. SQUARES (.20 IN. GRID)

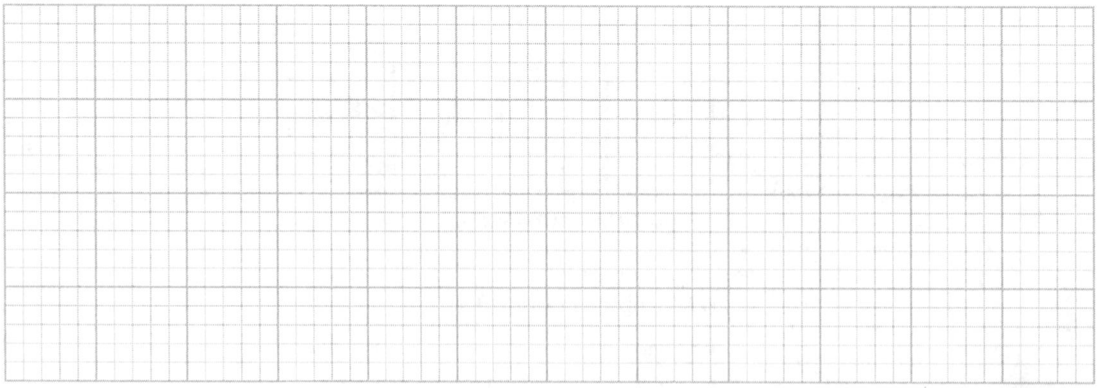

	HANDLE	A-28

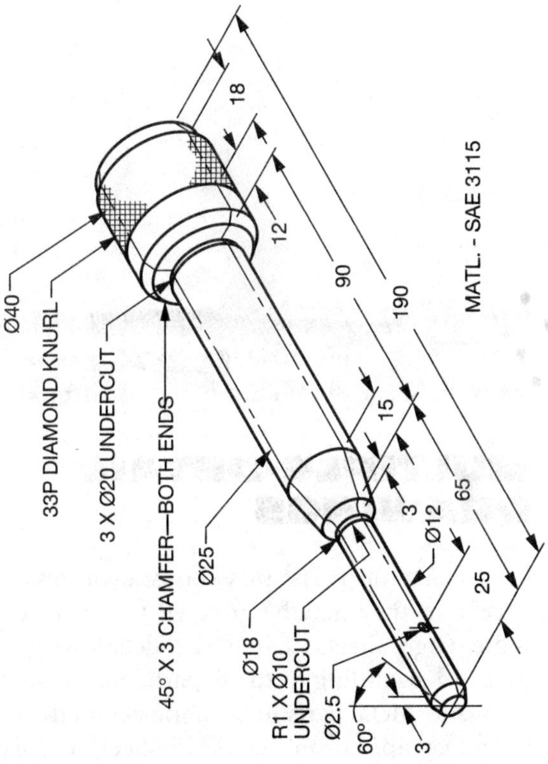
Ø40
33P DIAMOND KNURL
3 X Ø20 UNDERCUT
45° X 3 CHAMFER—BOTH ENDS
Ø25
Ø18
R1 X Ø10 UNDERCUT
Ø2.5
60°
3
18
12
90
190
15
3
Ø12
65
25
MATL. - SAE 3115

10 mm SQUARES (1 mm GRID)

ASSIGNMENT: ON THE GRID PROVIDED DRAW A ONE-VIEW DRAWING, COMPLETE WITH DIMENSIONS, OF THE INDICATOR ROD. USE A CONVENTIONAL BREAK ON THE 25 DIAMETER TO SHORTEN THE LENGTH OF THE VIEW.

METRIC
DIMENSIONS IN MILLIMETRES

	INDICATOR ROD	**A-29M**

10 UNIT

SELECTION OF VIEWS

ONE- AND TWO-VIEW DRAWINGS

Except for complex objects of irregular shapes, it is seldom necessary to draw more than three views, and for simple parts one- or two-view drawings will often suffice.

In one-view drawings the third dimension is expressed by a note or by symbols or abbreviations, such as ∅, □, HEX ACR FLT, R, Figure 10–1 and Table 2 of the Appendix. The symmetry symbol shown at the ends of the centre line indicates that the part is symmetrical. Frequently, the drafter will decide that only two views are necessary to explain the shape of an object fully, Figure 10–2. One or two views usually show the shape of cylindrical objects adequately.

MULTIPLE-DETAIL DRAWINGS

Details of parts may be shown on separate sheets, or they may be grouped together on one or more large sheets. Often the details of parts are grouped according to the department in which they are made. Metal parts to be fabricated in the machine shop may appear on one detail sheet, whereas parts to be made in the wood shop may be grouped on another. Figure 10–3 shows several details used in the assembly of a drafting compass.

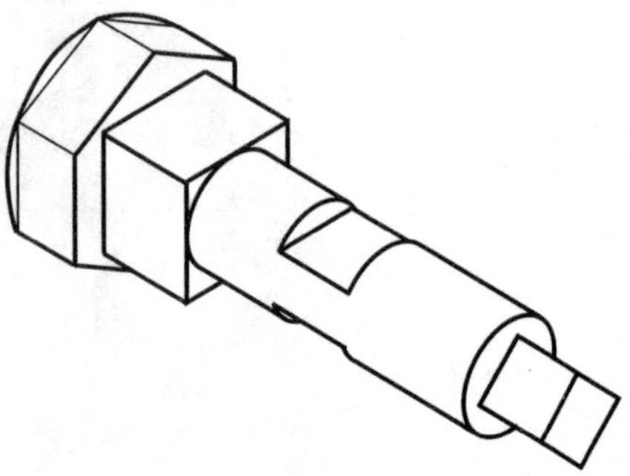

(A) THE PART

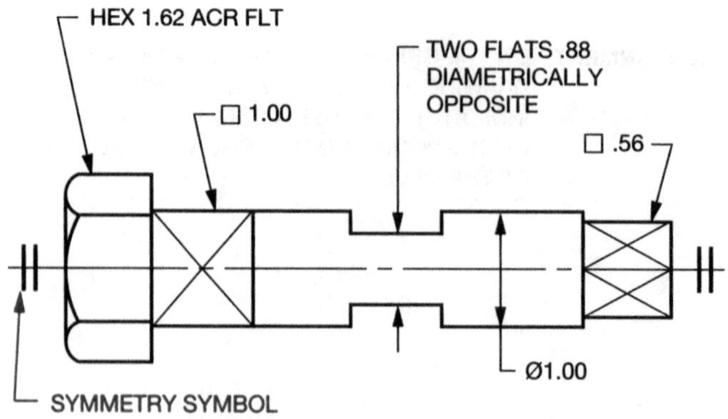
HEX 1.62 ACR FLT
TWO FLATS .88
DIAMETRICALLY
OPPOSITE
□ 1.00
□ .56
Ø1.00
SYMMETRY SYMBOL

(B) ONE-VIEW DRAWING OF THE PART

FIGURE 10–1 ■ Words and symbols used to identify shapes and sizes

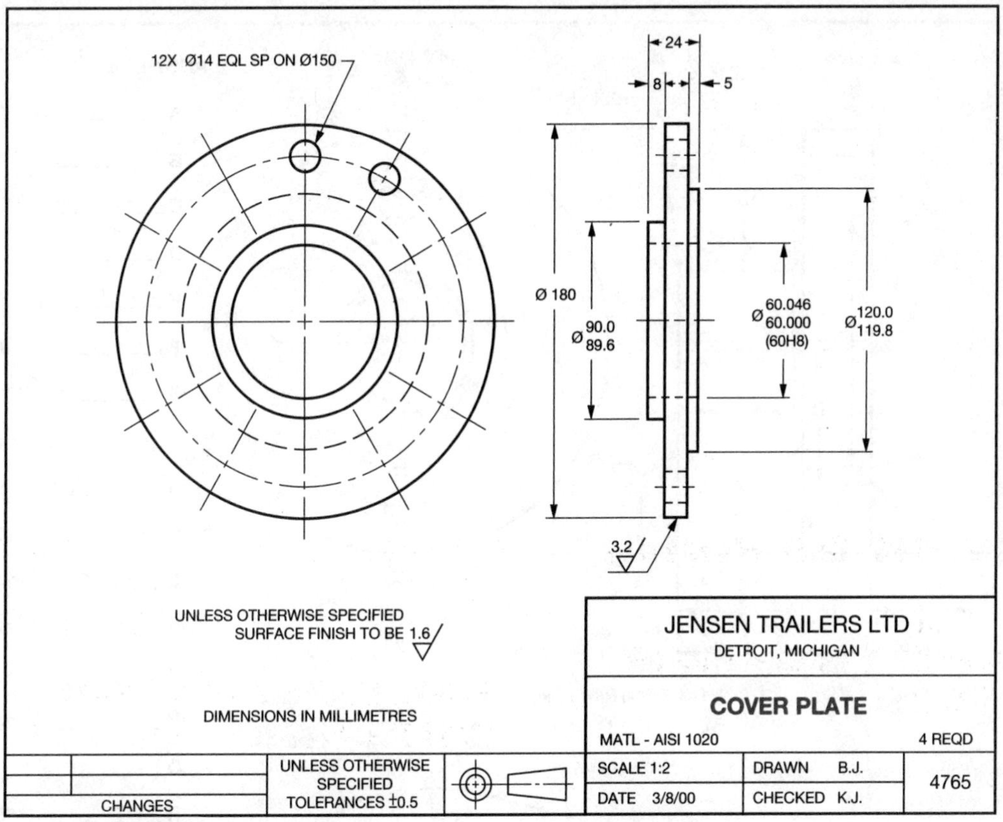

FIGURE 10–2 ■ Two-view drawing

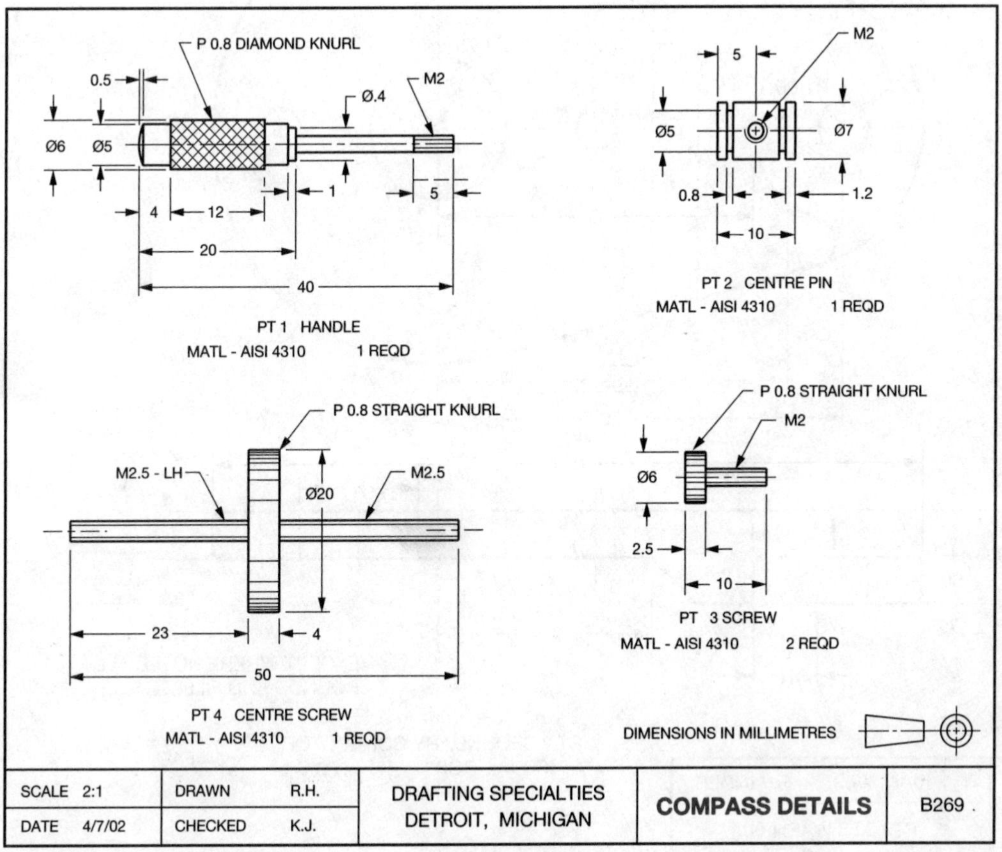

FIGURE 10–3 ■ Detail drawing containing several parts

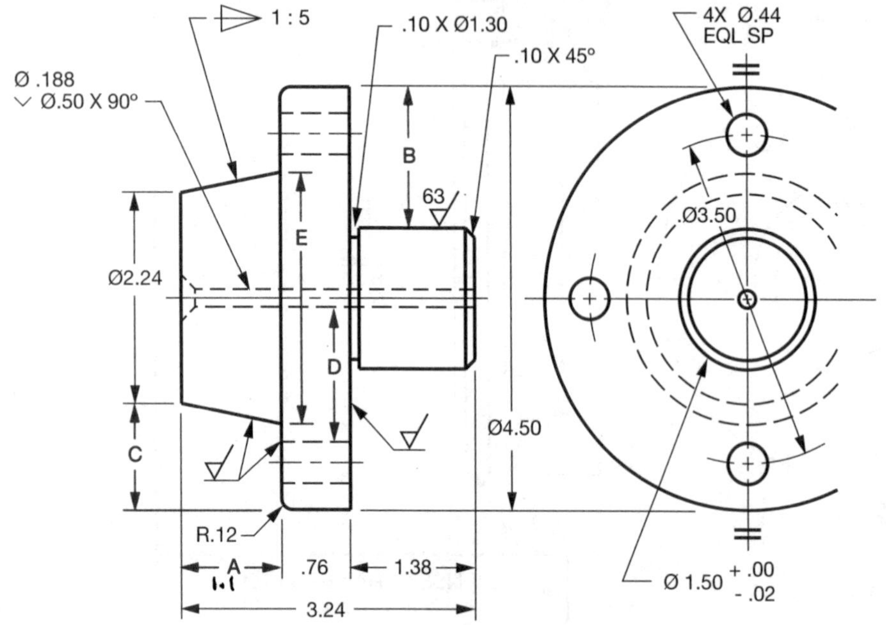

PT. 1 CENTRING SHAFT
MATL - COP QTY - 1

ANSWERS

1. A	________	2.	________
B	________	3.	________
C	________	4.	________
D	________		________
E	2.46	5.	________
F	________	6.	________
G	________	7.	________
H	________	8.	________
J	________	9.	________
K	________	10.	________
L	________	11.	________
M	________	12.	________
N	________	13.	________
P	________	14.	________
Q	________		________
R	________	15.	________
		16.	________
		17.	________
		18.	________

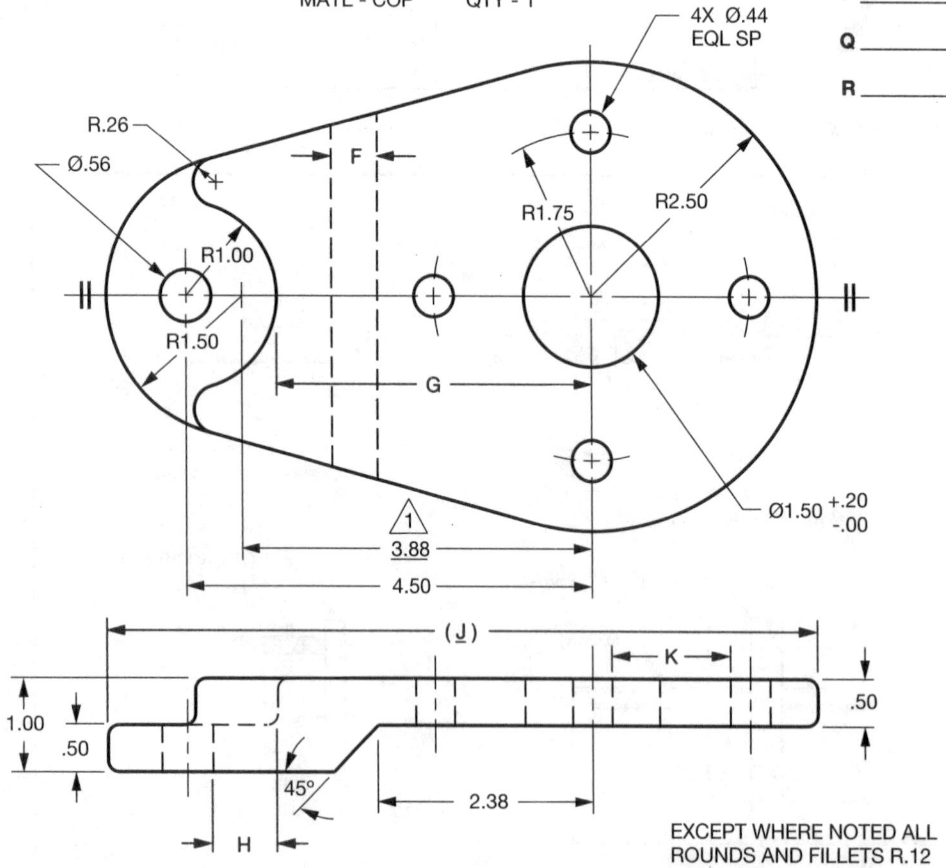

EXCEPT WHERE NOTED ALL ROUNDS AND FILLETS R.12

PT.2 SECONDARY CONNECTOR
MATERIAL-COP QTY-1

√ FAO

REVISIONS	1	JAN. 7/02	R. LINDER
	PT2 3.88 WAS 4.00		

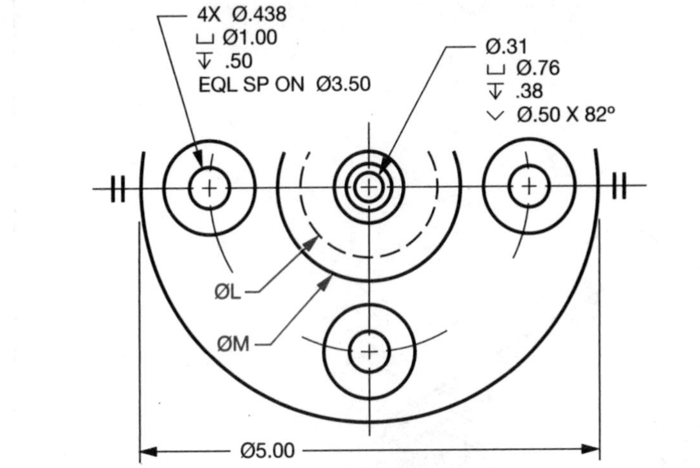
4X Ø.438
⌴ Ø1.00
↧ .50
EQL SP ON Ø3.50
Ø.31
⌴ Ø.76
↧ .38
⌵ Ø.50 X 82°
ØL
ØM
Ø5.00

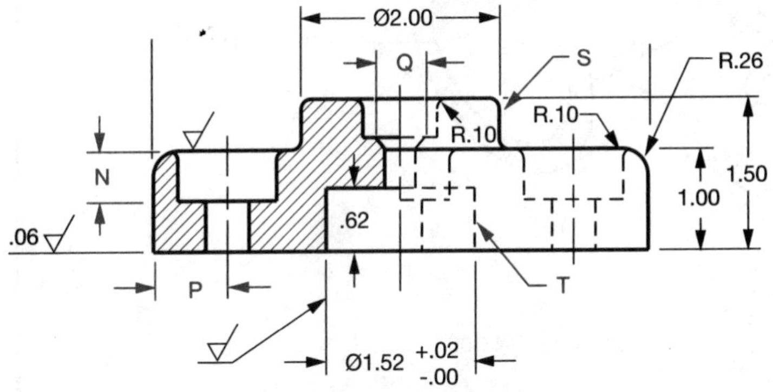
Ø2.00
Q
S
R.26
R.10
R.10
N
1.50
1.00
.62
.06
P
T
Ø1.52 +.02 -.00

PT. 3 PRESSURE NUT
MATL - COP QTY-1

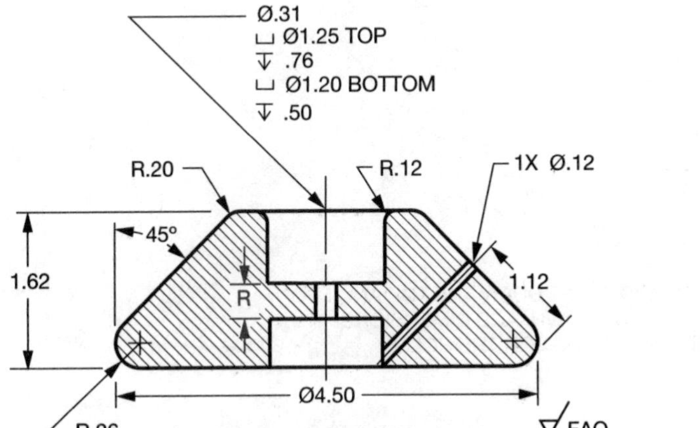
Ø.31
⌴ Ø1.25 TOP
↧ .76
⌴ Ø1.20 BOTTOM
↧ .50
R.20
R.12
1X Ø.12
45°
1.62
R
1.12
Ø4.50
R.26
FAO
HIGH POLISH

PT. 4 CORONA NUT
MATL - COP QTY 1

QUESTIONS

1. Calculate dimensions A to R. Use nominal sizes. There is no I or O.

Refer to Part 1

2. What is the length of the Ø1.50 shaft? Do not include the undercut or chamfer.
3. What is the length of the Ø.188 hole excluding the countersink?
4. Give two reasons why only part of the end view is drawn.
5. What is the diameter of the undercut?

Refer to Part 2

6. What does FAO mean?
7. What does the line under the 3.88 dimension indicate?
8. What does the abbreviation COP mean?
9. What do the parentheses around dimension J indicate?
10. What is the size of the fillets?

Refer to Part 3

11. How much machining allowance is provided for the bottom of the part?
12. What line in the front view represents line L in the top view?
13. What line in the top view represents line S in the front view?
14. What are the limits of the diameter of the counterbore in the bottom of the part?
15. What type of section view is shown?

Refer to Part 4

16. What is the diameter of the counterbore where the Ø.12 hole terminates?
17. What is the distance between the centre points of the .26 radii?
18. What type of section view is shown?

.50 INCH SQUARES (.10 IN. GRID)

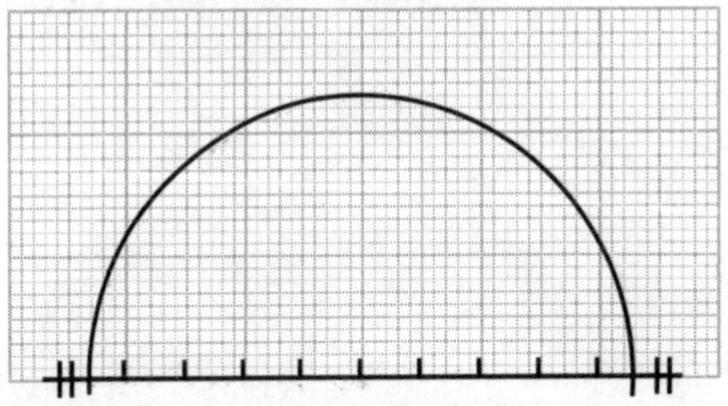

COMPLETE THE PARTIAL TOP VIEW OF PART 4

ASSIGNMENT: ON THE GRID PROVIDED, COMPLETE THE HALF TOP VIEW OF PART 4.

SCALE NTS
DRAWN
DATE

CENTRING CONNECTOR DETAILS

A-30

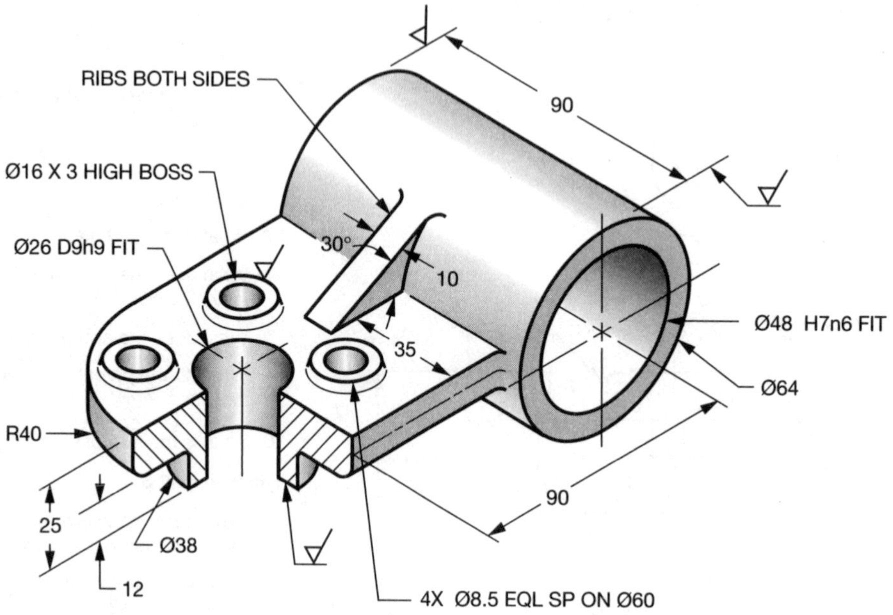
RIBS BOTH SIDES
Ø16 X 3 HIGH BOSS
Ø26 D9h9 FIT
30°
10
35
90
90
Ø48 H7n6 FIT
Ø64
R40
25
12
Ø38
4X Ø8.5 EQL SP ON Ø60

MATL - CAST STEEL

ROUNDS AND FILLETS R3

ASSIGNMENT: ON A METRIC GRID SHEET DRAW THE TOP AND FRONT VIEWS OF THE LINK SHOWN. ADD DIMENSIONS. SHOW LIMIT DIMENSIONS FOR THE HOLES.

METRIC DIMENSIONS IN MILLIMETRES	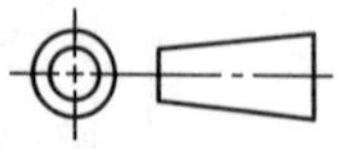	LINK	A-31M

UNIT 11

SURFACE TEXTURE

The development of modern, high-speed machines has resulted in higher loadings and faster moving parts. To withstand these more severe operating conditions with minimum friction and wear, a particular surface texture is often essential. This requires the designer to accurately describe the needed texture (sometimes called *finish*) to the persons who are actually making the parts.

Rarely are entire machines designed and manufactured in one plant. They are usually designed in one location, manufactured in another, and perhaps assembled in a third.

All surface finish control begins in the drafting room. The designer is responsible for specifying the correct surface finish for maximum performance and service life at the lowest cost. In selecting the required surface finish for any particular part, the designer bases the decision on past experience with similar parts, field service data, and engineering tests. Many factors influence the designer's choice. These factors include the function of the parts, the type of loading, the speed and direction of movement, and the operating conditions. Also considered are such factors as the physical characteristics of both materials on contact, whether the part is subjected to stress reversals, the type and amount of lubricant, contaminants, and temperature.

The two principal reasons for surface finish control are friction reduction and the control of wear.

Whenever a lubricating film must be maintained between two moving parts, the surface irregularities must be small enough to prevent penetrating the oil film under even the most severe operating conditions. Such parts as bearings, journals, cylinder bores, piston pins, bushings, pad bearings, helical and worm gears, seal surfaces, and machine ways are objects where this condition must be fulfilled.

Surface finish is also important to the wear service of certain pieces subject to dry friction, such as machine tool bits, threading dies, stamping dies, rolls, clutch plates, and brake drums.

Smooth finishes are essential on certain high-precision pieces. In mechanisms such as injectors and high-pressure cylinders, smoothness and lack of waviness are essential to accuracy and pressure-retaining ability. Smooth finishes are also used on micrometer anvils, gauges, and gauge blocks, and other items.

Smoothness is often important for the visual appeal of the finished product. For this reason, surface finish is controlled on such articles as rolls, extrusion dies, and precision casting dies.

For gears and other parts, surface finish control may be necessary to ensure quiet operation.

In cases where boundary lubrication exists or where surfaces are not compatible (for example, two hard surfaces running together), a certain amount of roughness or character of surface will assist in lubrication.

To meet the requirements for effective control of surface quality under diversified conditions, there is a system for accurately describing the surface.

Surfaces are usually very complex in character. Only the height, width, and direction of surface irregularities are covered in this section, because these are of practical importance in specific applications.

Surface Texture Definitions

The following terms relating to surface texture are illustrated in Figure 11–1.

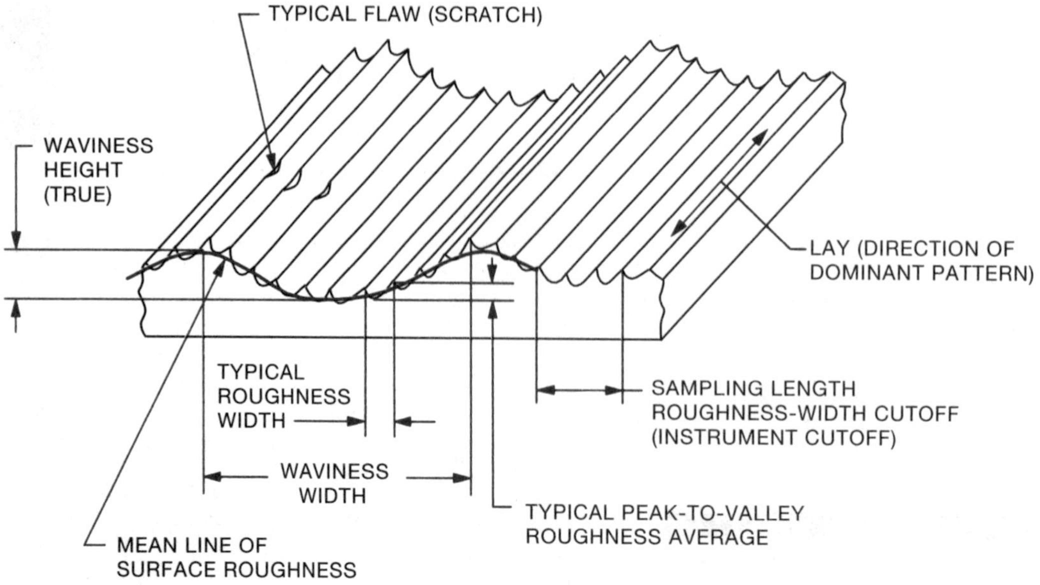

FIGURE 11–1 ■ Surface texture characteristics

Microinch (μin)

A microinch is one millionth of an inch (.000001 inch). For written specifications or reference to surface roughness requirements, microinches may be abbreviated as μin.

Micrometre (μm)

A micrometre is one millionth of a metre (0.000 001 metre.) For written specifications or reference to surface roughness requirements, micrometres may be abbreviated as μm.

Roughness

Roughness consists of the finer irregularities in the surface texture usually including those irregularities, which result from the inherent action of the production process. These include traverse feed marks and other irregularities within the limits of the roughness-width cutoff.

Roughness Average (R_a)

Roughness average is expressed in microinches, micrometres, or roughness grade numbers N1 to N12. The "N" series of roughness grade numbers is often used in lieu of the roughness average values to avoid misinterpretation when drawings are exchanged internationally.

Roughness Width

Roughness width is the distance parallel to the nominal surface between successive peaks or ridges that constitute the predominant pattern of the roughness. Roughness width is rated in inches or millimetres.

Roughness-Width Cutoff

The greatest spacing of repetitive surface irregularities to be included in the measurement of average roughness height is the roughness-width cutoff. Roughness-width cutoff is rated in inches or millimetres and must always be greater than the roughness width in order to obtain the total roughness height rating.

Waviness

Waviness is the usually widely spaced component of surface texture and is generally spaced farther apart than the roughness-width cutoff. Waviness may result from machine or work deflections, vibration, chatter, heat treatment, or warping strains. Roughness may be considered superimposed on a wavy surface. Although waviness is not currently in ISO standards, it is included as part of the surface texture symbol to follow present industrial practices in North America.

Lay

The direction of the predominant surface pattern, which is ordinarily determined by the production method used, is the lay. Symbols for the lay are shown in Figure 11–2.

Flaws

Flaws are surface irregularities occurring at one place or at relatively infrequent or widely varying intervals. Flaws include cracks, blow holes, checks, ridges, scratches, and so forth. Unless otherwise

SYMBOL	DESCRIPTION	EXAMPLE
=	LAY PARALLEL TO THE LINE REPRESENTING THE SURFACE TO WHICH THE SYMBOL IS APPLIED	 DIRECTION OF TOOL MARKS
⊥	LAY PERPENDICULAR TO THE LINE REPRESENTING THE SURFACE TO WHICH THE SYMBOL IS APPLIED	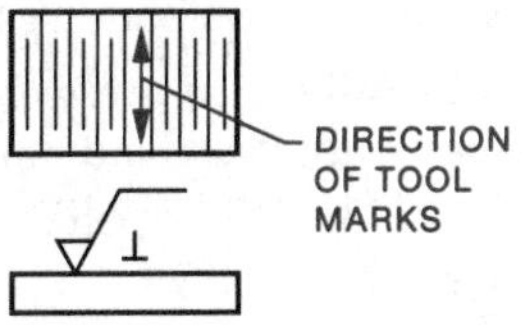 DIRECTION OF TOOL MARKS
X	LAY ANGULAR IN BOTH DIRECTIONS TO THE LINE REPRESENTING THE SURFACE TO WHICH THE SYMBOL IS APPLIED	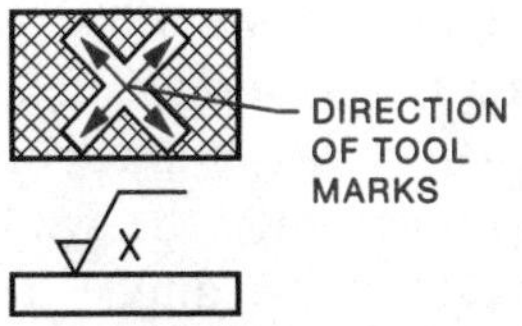 DIRECTION OF TOOL MARKS X
M	LAY MULTIDIRECTIONAL	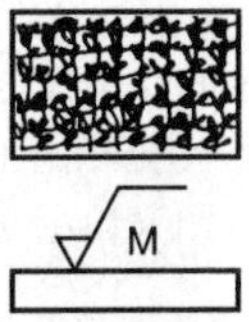 M
C	LAY APPROXIMATELY CIRCULAR RELATIVE TO THE CENTRE OF THE SURFACE TO WHICH THE SYMBOL IS APPLIED	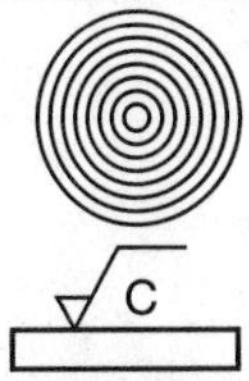 C
R	LAY APPROXIMATELY RADIAL RELATIVE TO THE CENTRE OF THE SURFACE TO WHICH THE SYMBOL IS APPLIED	 R
P	LAY NONDIRECTIONAL, PITTED, OR PROTUBERANT	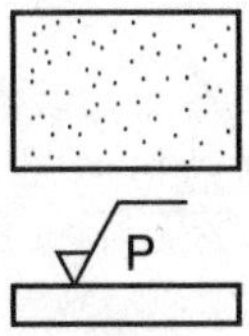 P

FIGURE 11–2 ■ Lay symbols

specified, the effect of flaws is not included in the roughness height measurements.

SURFACE TEXTURE SYMBOL

The surface texture symbol, Figure 11–3, denotes surface characteristics on the drawing. Roughness, waviness, and lay are controlled by waviness ratings applying the desired values to the surface texture symbol, Figure 11–4, or in a general note. The two methods may be used together. The point of the symbol should be on the line indicating the surface, on an extension line from the surface, or on a leader pointing either to the surface or to extension line, Figure 11–5. To be readable from the bottom, the symbol is placed in an upright position when notes or numbers are used. This means the long leg and extension line will be on the right. The symbol applies to the entire surface, unless otherwise specified.

This symbol is the same symbol (machining symbol) that was described in Unit 7. As well as identifying which surfaces require machining, other surface characteristics are defined by this symbol.

Like dimensions, the symbol for the same surface should not be duplicated on other views. It should be placed on the view with the dimensions showing size or location of the surfaces. Surface texture symbols designate surface texture characteristics, which include machining of surfaces. The method of indicating machine finishes on surfaces is covered in Unit 7.

Where all the surfaces are to be machined, a general note such as FAO (finish all over) or ✓ ALL OVER may be used and the symbols on the part may be omitted.

SURFACE TEXTURE RATINGS

Roughness average, which is measured in microinches, micrometres, or roughness grade numbers, is shown to the left of the long leg of the symbol, Figure 11–4. The specification of only one rating indicates the maximum value; any lesser value is acceptable. Specifying two ratings indicates the minimum and maximum values. Anything within that range is acceptable. The maximum value is placed over the minimum.

Waviness height ratings are indicated in inches or millimetres and positioned as shown in Figure 11–4. Any lesser value is acceptable.

Waviness spacing ratings are indicated in inches or millimetres and positioned as shown in Figure 11–4. Any lesser value is acceptable.

Lay symbols, indicating the directional pattern of the surface texture, are shown in Figure 11–2. The symbol is on the right of the long leg of the symbol.

Roughness sampling length ratings are given in inches or millimetres and are located below the horizontal extension. Unless otherwise specified, roughness-width cutoff is .03 in. (0.8 mm).

See Figure 11–5 for an application of roughness values and wariness ratings.

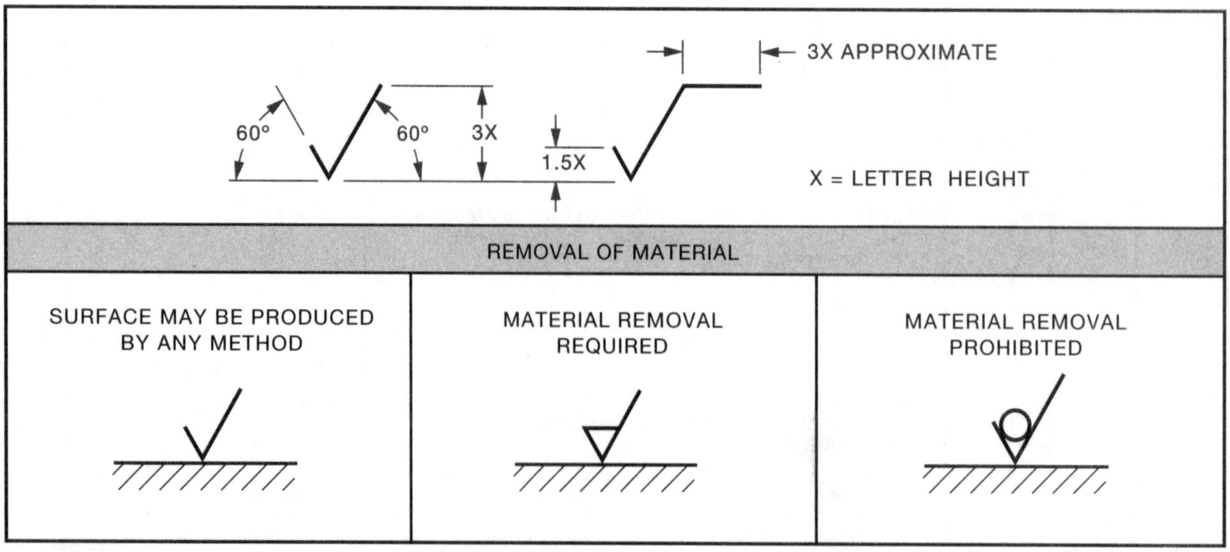

FIGURE 11–3 ■ Basic surface texture symbol

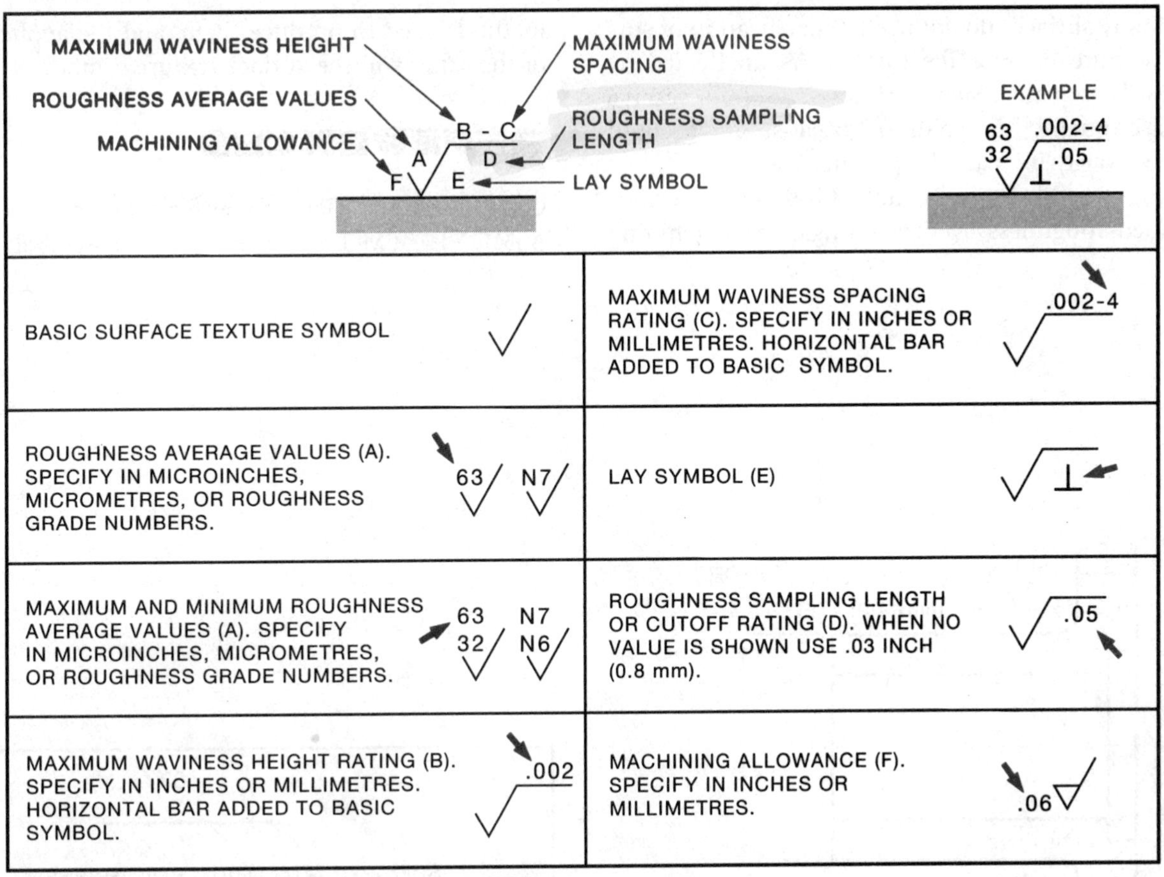

NOTE: WAVINESS IS NOT USED IN ISO STANDARDS.

FIGURE 11–4 ■ Location of ratings and symbols on surface texture symbol

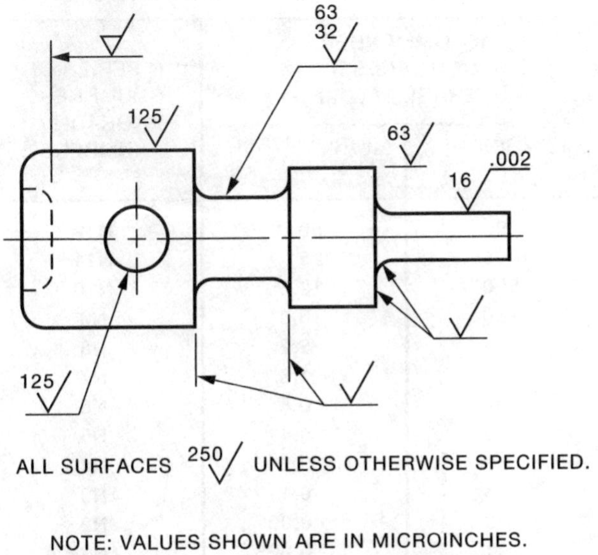

FIGURE 11–5 ■ Application of roughness values and waviness ratings

Notes

Usually, a note is used where a given roughness requirement applies to either the whole part or the major portion, or before or after plating. Examples are shown in Figure 11–6.

CONTROL REQUIREMENTS

Surface texture control should be specified for surfaces where texture is a functional requirement. For example, most surfaces that have contact with a mating part have a certain texture requirement, especially for roughness. The drawing should reflect the texture necessary for optimum part function without depending on the variables of machining practices.

Many surfaces do not need a specification of surface texture because the function is unaffected by the surface quality. Such surfaces should not receive surface quality designations because they could unnecessarily increase the product cost.

Figures 11–7, 11–8, and 11–9 show recommended roughness average ratings, the machining methods used to produce them, and the application of the ratings to the surface texture symbol.

REFERENCES

CAN3-B95-1962 (R1996) Surface Texture
ASME Y14.36M-1996 Surface Texture Symbols

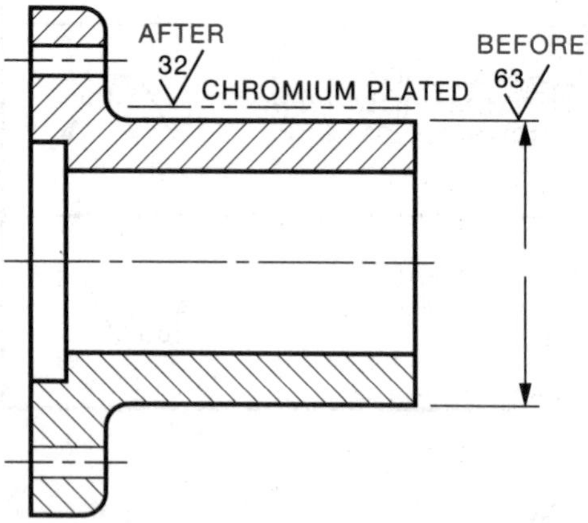

(A) INDICATING SURFACE TEXTURE BEFORE AND AFTER PLATING

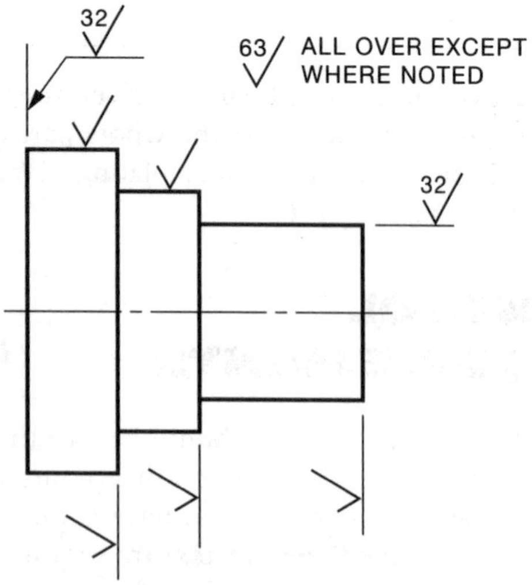

(B) A GENERAL NOTE BESIDE PART

FIGURE 11–6 ■ The use of notes with surface texture symbol

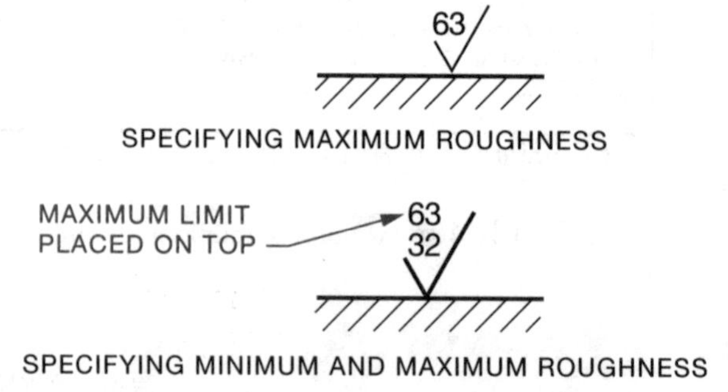

VALUES SHOWN ARE IN MICROINCHES

RECOMMENDED ROUGHNESS AVERAGE VALUES		N SERIES OF ROUGHNESS GRADE NUMBERS
MICROINCHES μin.	MICROMETRES μm	
2000	50	N12
1000	25	N11
500	12.5	N10
250	6.3	N9
125	3.2	N8
63	1.6	N7
32	0.8	N6
16	0.4	N5
8	0.2	N4
4	0.1	N3
2	0.05	N2
1	0.025	N1

FIGURE 11–7 ■ Recommended roughness average ratings

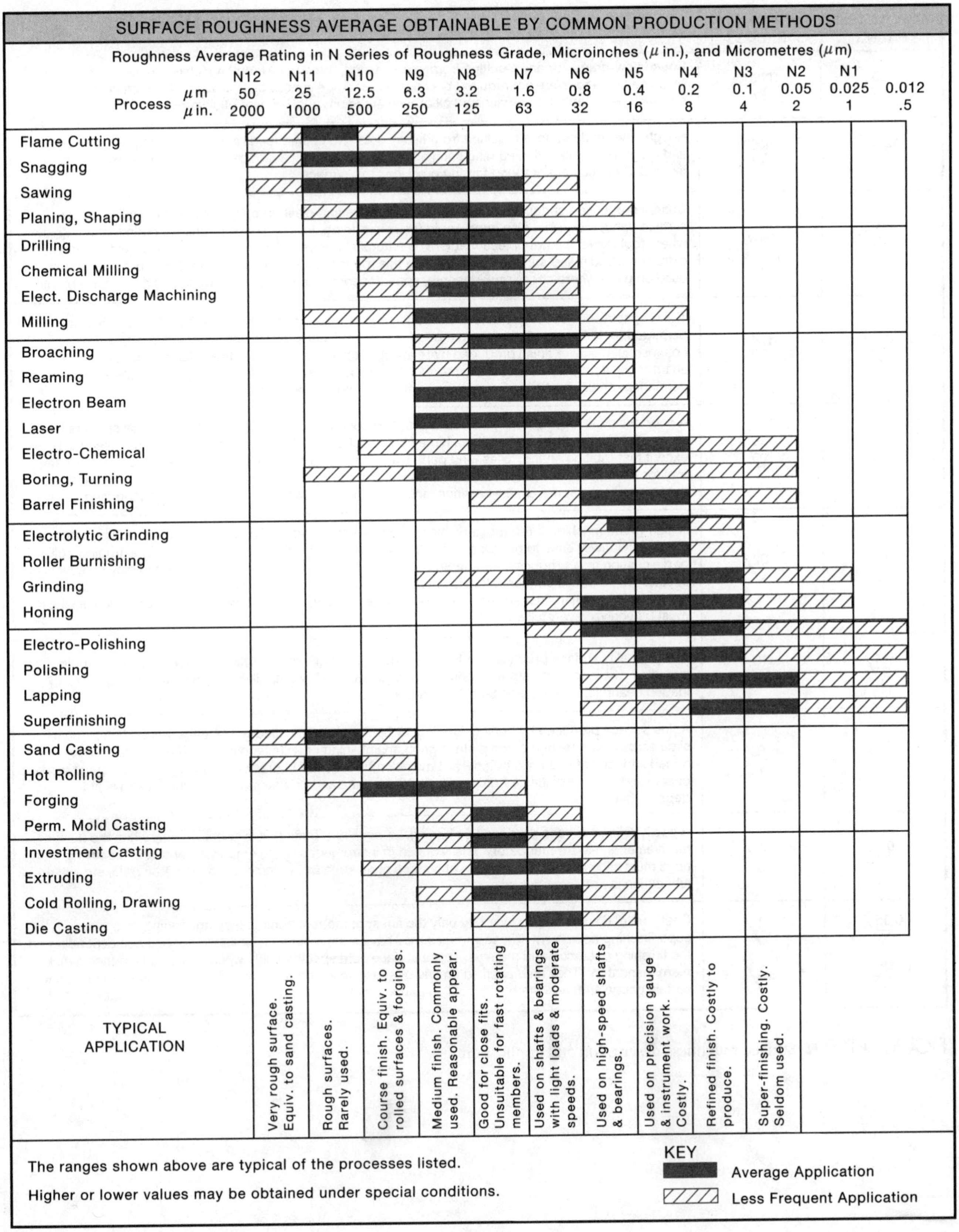

FIGURE 11–8 ■ Surface roughness range for common production methods

MICROMETRES RATING	MICROINCHES RATING	APPLICATION
25	1000	Rough, low-grade surface resulting from sand casting, torch or saw cutting, chipping, or rough forging. Machine operations are not required because appearance is not objectionable. This surface, rarely specified, is suitable for unmachined clearance areas on rough construction items.
12.5	500	Rough, low-grade surface resulting from heavy cuts and coarse feeds in milling, turning, shaping, boring, and rough filing, disc grinding, and snagging. It is suitable for clearance areas on machinery, jigs, and fixtures. Sand casting or rough forging produces this surface.
6.3	250	Coarse production surface, for unimportant clearance and cleanup operation resulting from coarse surface grind, rough file, disc grind, rapid feeds in turning, milling, shaping, drilling, boring, grinding, etc., where tool marks are not objectionable. The natural surfaces of forgings, permanent mould castings, extrusions, and rolled surfaces also produce this roughness. It can be produced economically and is used on parts where stress requirements, appearance, and conditions of operations and design permit.
3.2	125	The roughest surface recommended for parts subject to loads, vibration, and high stress. It is also permitted for bearing surfaces when motion is slow and loads light or infrequent. It is a medium commercial machine finish produced by relatively high speeds and fine feeds taking light cuts with sharp tools. It may be economically produced on lathes, milling machines, shapers, grinders, etc., or on permanent mould castings, die castings, extrusions, and rolled surfaces.
1.6	63	A good machine finish produced under controlled conditions using relatively high speeds and fine feeds to take light cuts with sharp cuttings. It may be specified for close fits and used for all stressed parts, except fast rotating shafts, axles, and parts subject to severe vibration or extreme tension. It is satisfactory for bearing surfaces when motion is slow and loads light or infrequent. It may also be obtained on extrusions, rolled surfaces, die castings, and permanent mould castings when rigidly controlled.
0.8	32	A high-grade machine finish requiring close control when produced by lathes, shapers, milling machines, etc., but relatively easy to produce by centreless, cylindrical, or surface grinders. Also, extruding, rolling, or die casting may produce a comparable surface when rigidly controlled. This surface may be specified in parts where stress concentration is present. It is used for bearings when motion is not continuous and loads are light. When finer finishes are specified, production costs rise rapidly; therefore, such finishes must be analyzed carefully.
0.4	16	A high-quality surface produced by fine cylindrical grinding, emery buffing, coarse honing, or lapping, it is specified where smoothness is of primary importance, such as rapidly rotating shaft bearings, heavily loaded bearings, and extreme tension members.
0.2	8	A fine surface produced by honing, lapping, or buffing. It is specified where packings and rings must slide across the direction of the surface grain, maintaining or withstanding pressures, or for interior honed surfaces of hydraulic cylinders. It may also be required in precision gauges and instrument work, or sensitive value surfaces, or on rapidly rotating shafts and on bearings where lubrication is not dependable.
0.1	4	A costly refined surface produced by honing, lapping, and buffing. It is specified only when the design requirements make it mandatory. It is required in instrument work, gauge work, and where packing and rings must slide across the direction of surface grain such as on chrome-plated piston rods, etc. where lubrication is not dependable.
0.05 0.025	2 1	Costly refined surfaces produced by only the finest of modern honing, lapping, buffing, and superfinishing equipment. These surfaces may have a satin or highly polished appearance depending on the finishing operation and material. These surfaces are specified only when design requirements make them mandatory. They are specified on fine or sensitive instrument parts or other laboratory items, and certain gauge surfaces, such as precision gauge blocks.

FIGURE 11–9 ■ Surface roughness description and application

A

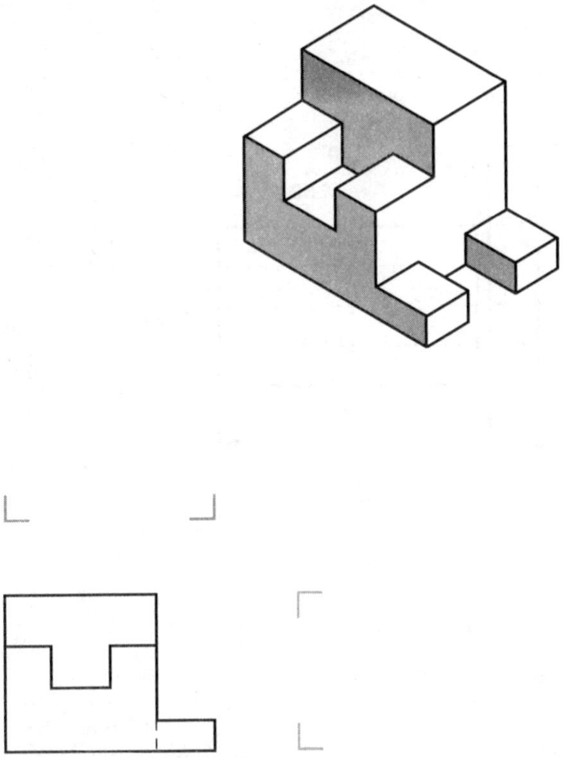

B

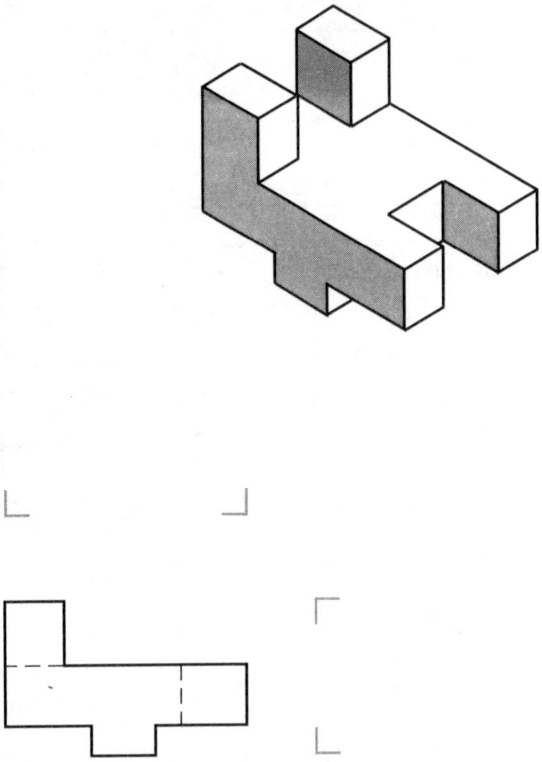

C

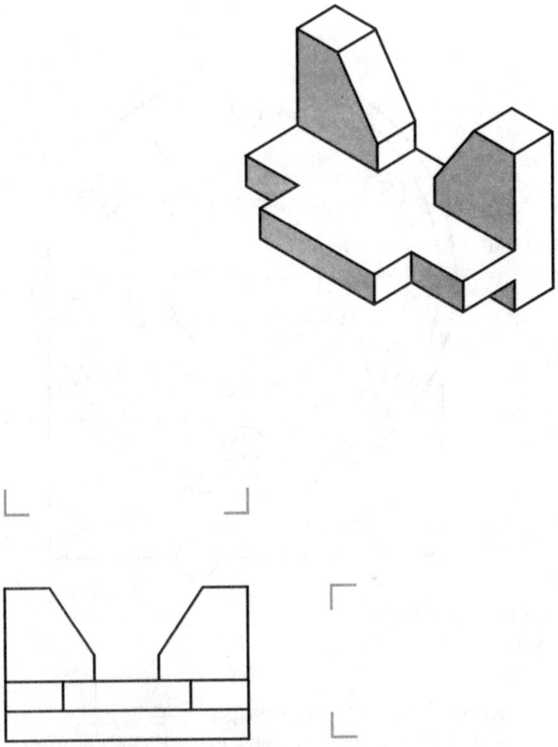

D

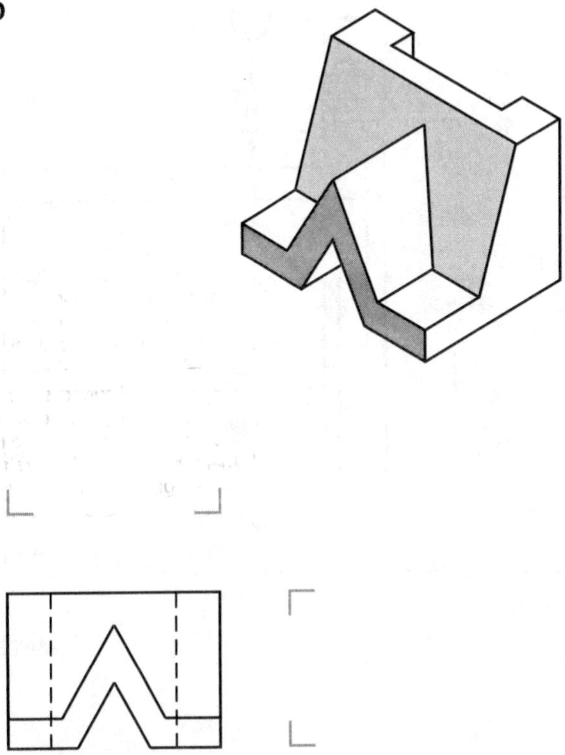

ASSIGNMENT: DRAW THE TWO MISSING VIEWS AS INDICATED ON THE DRAWINGS. SHOW ALL HIDDEN LINES.

SKETCH MISSING VIEWS

A-32

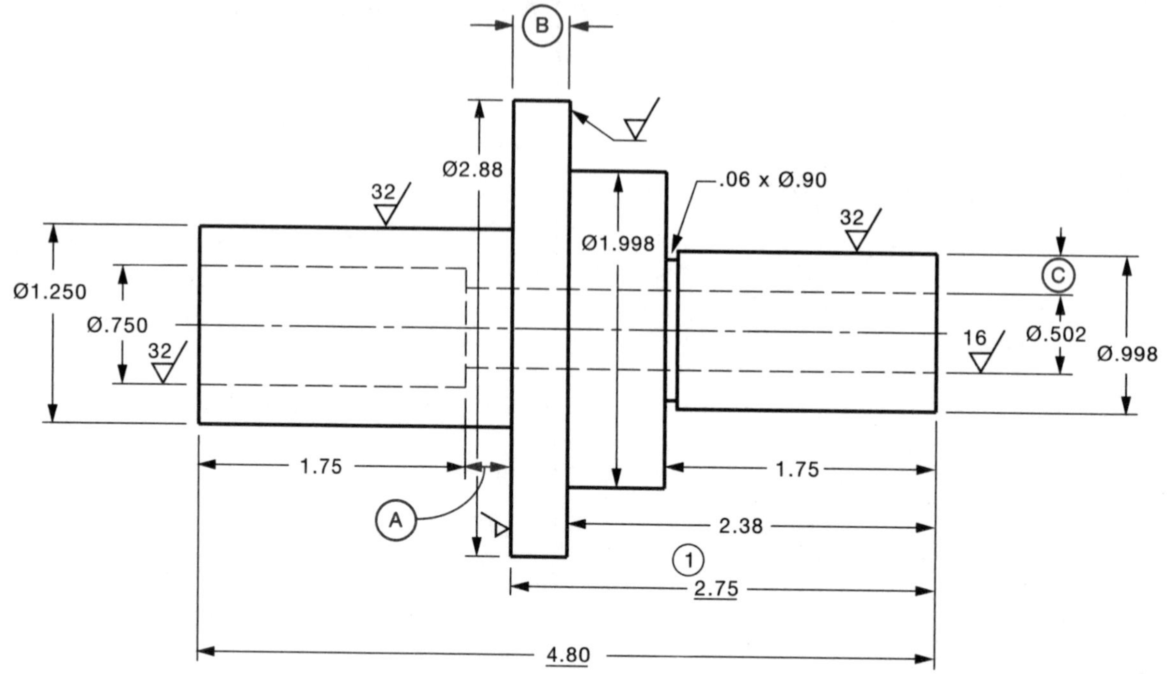

PT 1 LOWER SHAFT
MATERIAL-CRS, 2 REQD

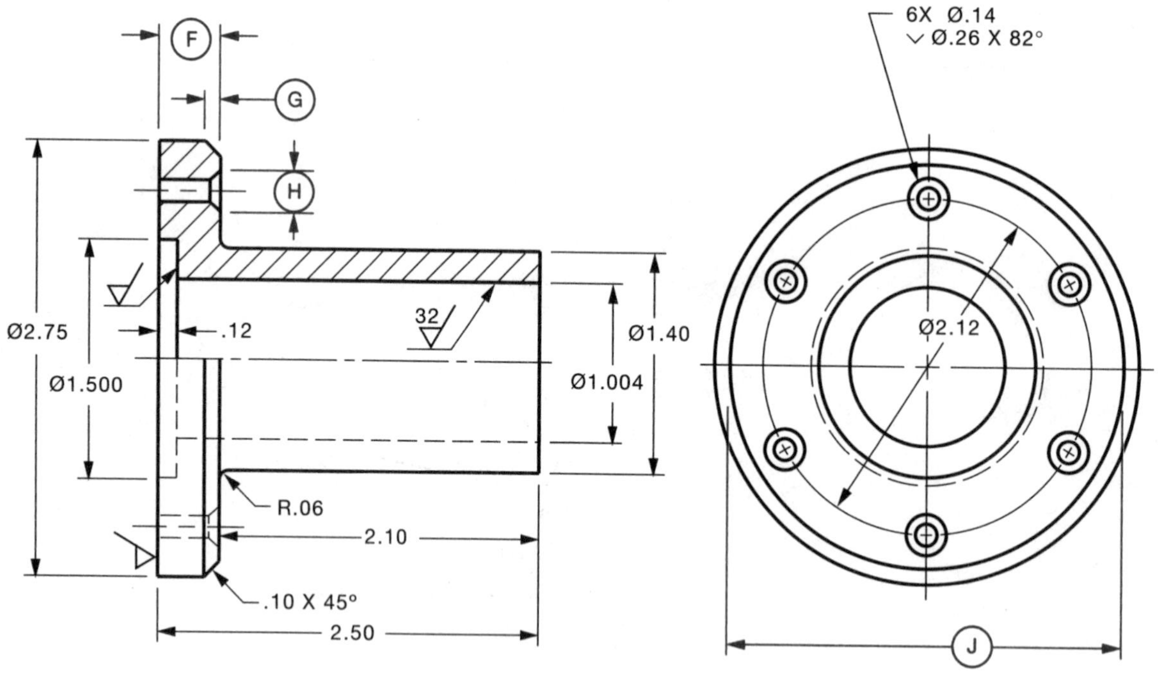

PT 3 CAM SUPPORT
MATERIAL - ALUMINUM, 2 REQD

NOTE: UNLESS OTHERWISE SPECIFIED:
—TOLERANCES ON TWO-PLACE DIMENSIONS ±.02
—TOLERANCES ON THREE-PLACE DIMENSIONS ±.001
63 ✓ EXCEPT WHERE NOTED

REVISIONS	1	JAN. 12/02	A. HEINEN
	LENGTH WAS 2.80		

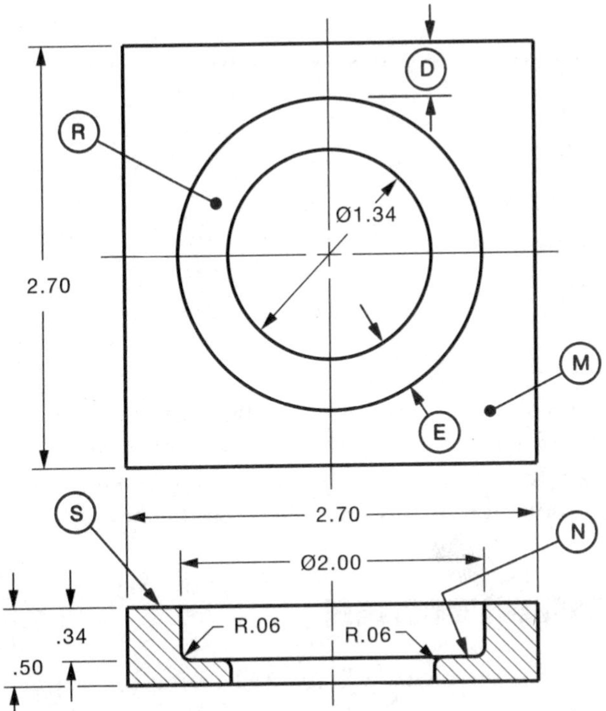
D
R
Ø1.34
2.70
M
E
S
2.70
N
Ø2.00
.34
R.06
R.06
.50

PT 2 WASHER
MATERIAL-MS. 4 REQD. FAO

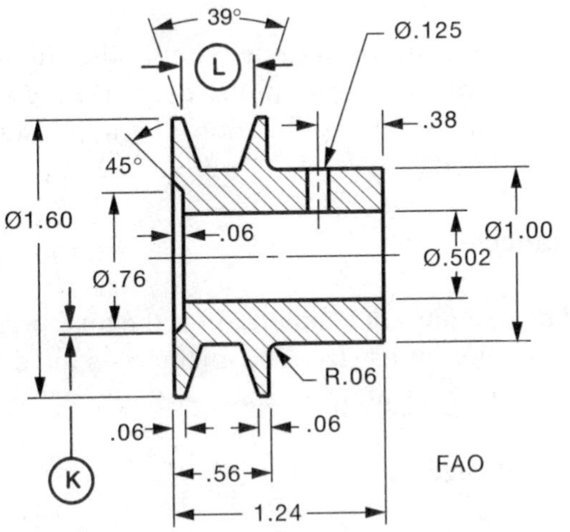
39°
L
Ø.125
.38
45°
Ø1.60
.06
Ø1.00
Ø.502
Ø.76
R.06
.06
.06
K
.56
1.24
FAO

PT 4 V-BELT PULLEY
MATERIAL-CRS, 4 REQD

QUESTIONS

1. Calculate dimensions (A) to (L).

Referring to Figure 11–8, what production methods would be suitable to produce the surface texture of

2. Ø.502 hole in Part 1?
3. Ø1.250 on Part 1?
4. Ø1.004 hole in Part 3?
5. How many dimensions indicate that the dimension is not drawn to scale?

Refer to Part 1

6. What is the length of the Ø.998 portion?
7. What was the original length of the 2.75 dimension?
8. How many hidden circles would be seen if the right end view were drawn?

Refer to Part 2

9. Which surface does (R) represent in the front view?
10. Which surface does (S) represent in the top view?
11. If the part that passes through the washer is Ø1.30, what is the clearance per side between the two parts?
12. How many fillets are required?

Refer to Part 3

13. How many degrees apart on the Ø2.12 are the Ø.14 holes?
14. Is the centre line of the countersunk holes in the centre of the flange?
15. What operation is performed to allow the head of the mounting screws to rest flush with the flange?
16. What type of section view is shown?
17. What is the amount and degree of chamfer?
18. What is the (A) size and (B) type of cap screw required to mount the cam support to its mating parts?

Refer to Part 4

19. How deep is the Ø.125 hole?
20. How deep is the belt groove?
21. What does FAO mean?
22. What type of section view is shown?

ANSWERS

1. A ______
B ______
C ______
D ______
E ______
F ______
G ______
H ______
J ______
K ______
L ______
2. ______
3. ______
4. ______
5. ______
6. ______
7. ______
8. ______
9. ______
10. ______
11. ______
12. ______
13. ______
14. ______
15. ______
16. ______
17. ______
18. A ______
B ______
19. ______
20. ______
21. ______
22. ______

SCALE NOT TO SCALE		
DRAWN		DATE
	HANGER DETAILS	**A-33**

12 UNIT

TOLERANCES AND ALLOWANCES

The history of engineering drawing as a means of communicating engineering information spans a period of 6000 years. It seems inconceivable that such an elementary practice as the tolerancing of dimensions, which is taken for granted today, was introduced for the first time about 80 years ago.

Apparently, engineers and workers realized only gradually that exact dimensions and shapes could not be attained in the shaping of physical objects. The skilled handicrafters of the past took pride in the ability to work to exact dimensions. This meant that objects were dimensioned more accurately than they could be measured. The use of modern measuring instruments would have shown the deviations from the sizes that were called exact.

It was soon realized that variations in the sizes of parts had always been present, that such variations could be restricted but not avoided, and that slight variation in the size that a part was originally intended to have could be tolerated without impairment of its correct functioning. It became evident that interchangeable parts need not be identical parts, but rather it would be sufficient if the significant sizes that controlled their fits lay between definite limits. Therefore, the problem of interchangeable manufacture developed from the making of parts to a supposedly exact size to the holding of parts between two limiting sizes lying so close together that any intermediate size would be acceptable.

The concept of limits means essentially that a precisely defined basic condition (expressed by one numerical value or specification) is replaced by two limiting conditions. Any result lying between these two limits is acceptable. A workable scheme of interchangeable manufacture that is indispensable to mass production methods had been established.

DEFINITIONS

In order to calculate limits and tolerances, the following definitions should be clearly understood.

Basic Size

The basic size of a dimension is the theoretical size from which the limits for that dimension are derived, by the application of the allowance and tolerance.

Tolerances

The tolerance of a dimension is the total permissible variation in its size. The tolerance is the difference between the limits of size.

Limits of Size

The limits of size are the maximum and minimum sizes permitted for a specific dimension.

Allowance

An allowance is the intentional difference in size of mating parts. It is the minimum clearance (positive allowance) or maximum interference (negative allowance) between such parts. Fits between parts is covered in Units 13 and 14.

All dimensions on a drawing have tolerances. Some dimensions must be more exact than other dimensions and consequently have smaller tolerances.

When dimensions require a greater accuracy than the general note provides, individual tolerances or limits must be shown for those dimensions.

Where limits dimensions are used and where either the maximum or the minimum dimension has digits to the right of the decimal point, the other value should have the zeros added so that both limits of size are expressed to the same number of decimal places.

When limit dimensions are used for diameter or radial features and the dimensions are placed one above the other, only one diameter or radius symbol is used and located at midheight.

Where one limit alone is important and where any variations away from that limit in the other direction may be permitted, the MAX (maximum) or MIN (minimum) can be specified. Examples are depth of holes, corner radii, and chamfers. Figures 12–1 and 12–2 show applications of limit dimensioning.

TOLERANCING METHODS

Dimensional tolerances are expressed in one of two ways: limit dimensioning or plus and minus tolerancing.

Limit Dimensioning

In the limiting dimensioning method, only the maximum and minimum dimensions are specified, Figure 12–1. When placed above each other, the larger dimension is placed on top. When shown with a leader and placed in one line, the smaller size is shown first. A small dash separates the two dimensions. When limit dimensions are used for diameter or radial features, the Ø or R symbol is centred midway between the two limits, Figure 12–1(A). These rules apply to both inch and metric drawings.

Plus and Minus Tolerancing

In this method the dimension of the specified size is given first and is followed by a plus and minus tolerance expression. The tolerance can be bilateral or unilateral, Figure 12–3.

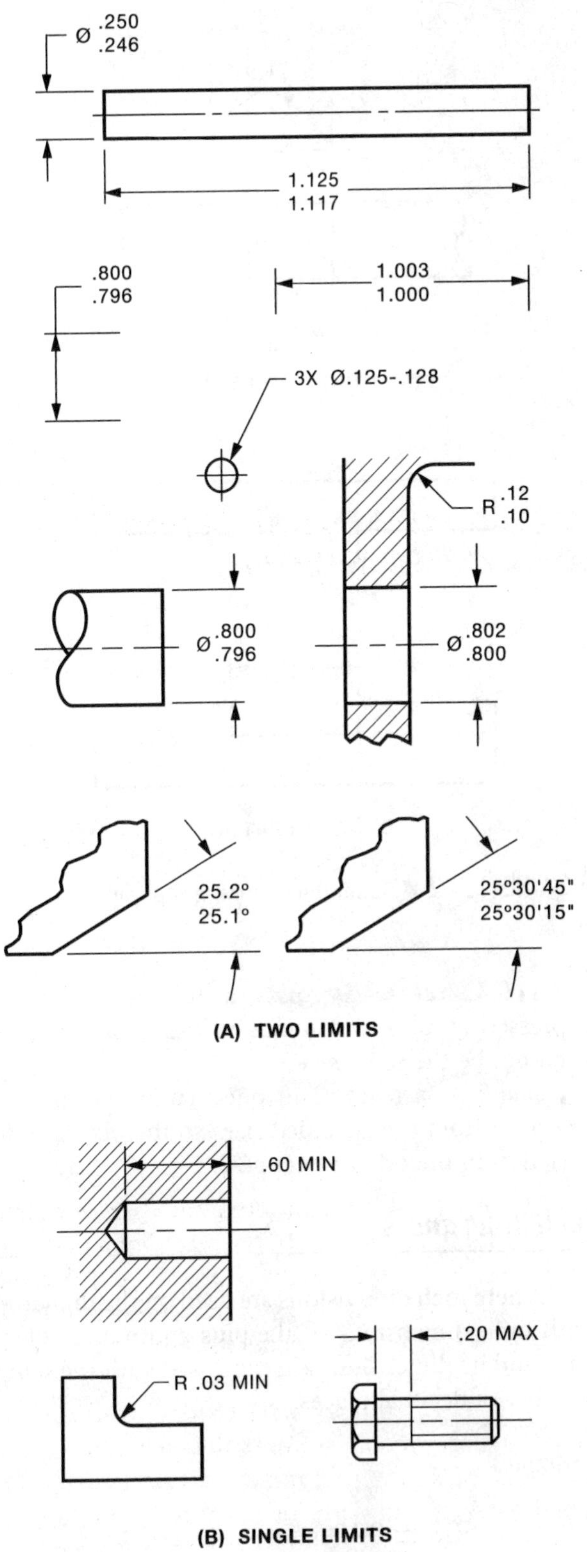

FIGURE 12–1 ■ Limit dimensioning

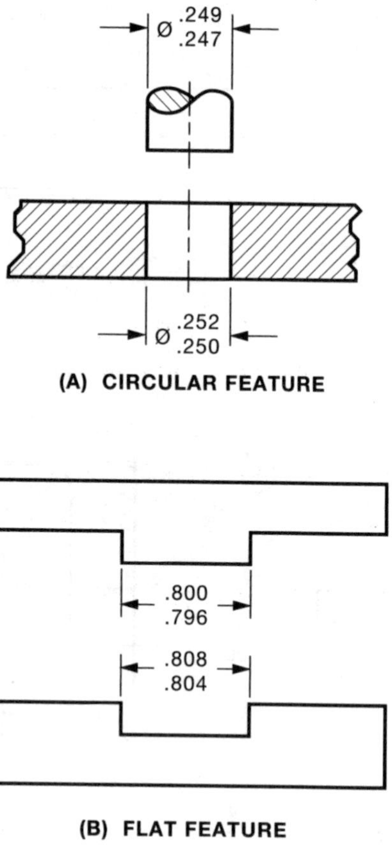

FIGURE 12–2 ■ Limit dimensioning application

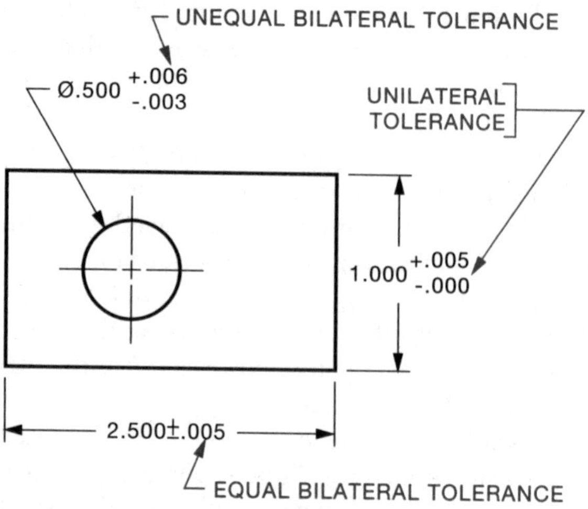

FIGURE 12–3 ■ Plus and minus tolerancing

A *bilateral tolerance* is a tolerance that is expressed as plus and minus values. These values need not be the same size.

A *unilateral tolerance* is one that applies in one direction from the specified size, so the permissible variation in the other direction is zero.

Inch Tolerances

Where inch dimensions are used on the drawing, both limit dimensions or the plus and minus tolerance and its dimensions are expressed with the same number of decimal places.

Examples

$.500 \pm .005$ not $.50 \pm .005$

$.500 \pm ^{.005}_{.000}$ not $.500 \pm ^{.005}_{.0}$

$25.0 \pm .2$ not $25 \pm .2$

General tolerance notes greatly simplify the drawing. The following examples illustrate the variety of application in this system. The values given in the examples are typical only:

EXCEPT WHERE STATED OTHERWISE,
TOLERANCE ON DIMENSIONS ±.005

EXCEPT WHERE STATED OTHERWISE,
TOLERANCES ON FINISHED DIMENSIONS
TO BE AS FOLLOWS:

DIMENSION	TOLERANCE
UP TO 3.00	.01
OVER 3.00 TO 12.00	.02
OVER 12.00 TO 24.00	.04
OVER 24.00	.06

UNLESS OTHERWISE SPECIFIED
±.005 TOLERANCE ON MACHINED DIMENSIONS
±.04 TOLERANCE ON CAST DIMENSIONS
ANGULAR TOLERANCE ±30′

Millimetre Tolerances

Where millimetre dimensions are used on the drawings, the following apply:

A. The dimension and its tolerance need not be expressed to the same number of decimal places.

Example

15 ± 0.5 not 15.0 ± 0.5

B. Where unilateral tolerancing is used and either the plus or minus value is nil, a single zero is shown without a plus or minus sign.

Example

$32^{\ 0}_{-0.02}$ or $32^{+0.02}_{\ 0}$

C. Where bilateral tolerancing is used, both the plus and the minus values have the same number of decimal places, using zeros where necessary.

Example

$32^{+0.25}_{-0.10}$ not $32^{+0.25}_{-0.1}$

REFERENCES

CAN/CSA-B78.2-M91 Dimensioning and Tolerancing of Technical Drawings

ASME Y14.5M-1994 Dimensioning and Tolerancing

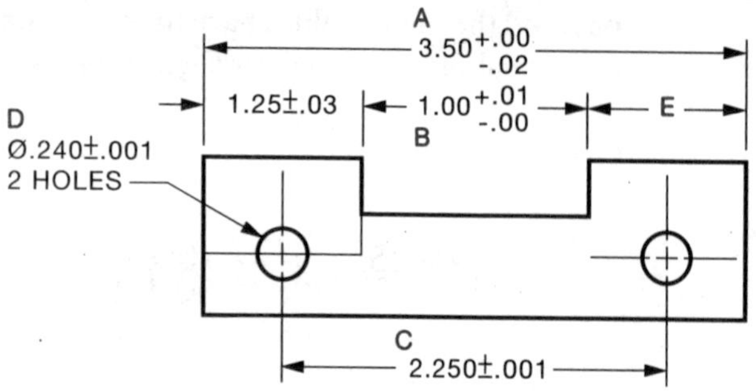

QUESTIONS - Calculate the following:

1. A dim — (A) Basic Size (B) Tolerance (C) Max. Limit (D) Min. Limit
2. B dim — (A) Basic Size (B) Tolerance (C) Max. Limit (D) Min. Limit
3. C dim — (A) Basic Size (B) Tolerance (C) Max. Limit (D) Min. Limit
4. D dim — (A) Basic Size (B) Tolerance (C) Max. Limit (D) Min. Limit
5. E dim — (A) Max. Size (B) Min. Size

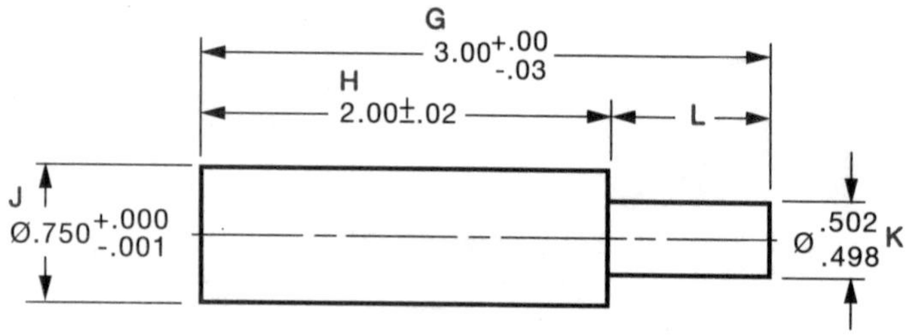

QUESTIONS - Calculate the following:

6. G dim — (A) Basic Size (B) Tolerance (C) Max. Limit (D) Min. Limit
7. H dim — (A) Basic Size (B) Tolerance (C) Max. Limit (D) Min. Limit
8. J dim — (A) Basic Size (B) Tolerance (C) Max. Limit (D) Min. Limit
9. K dim — (A) Basic Size (B) Tolerance (C) Max. Limit (D) Min. Limit
10. L dim — (A) Max. Size (B) Min. Size

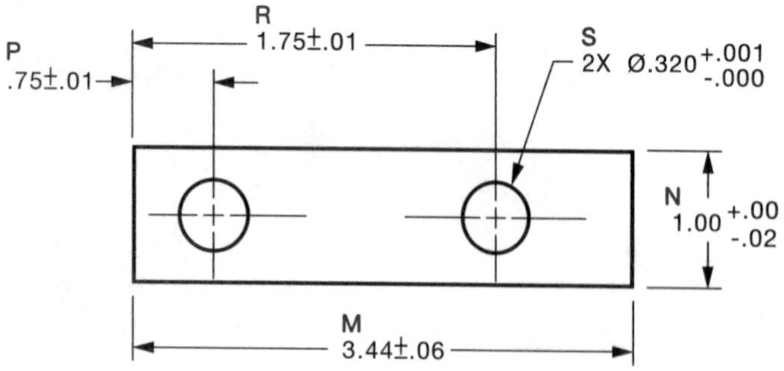

QUESTIONS - Calculate the following:

11. M dim — (A) Basic Size (B) Tolerance (C) Max. Limit (D) Min. Limit
12. N dim — (A) Basic Size (B) Tolerance (C) Max. Limit (D) Min. Limit
13. P dim — (A) Basic Size (B) Tolerance (C) Max. Limit (D) Min. Limit
14. R dim — (A) Basic Size (B) Tolerance (C) Max. Limit (D) Min. Limit
15. S dim — (A) Max. Size (B) Min. Size

ANSWERS

1. A ____________
B ____________
C ____________
D ____________
2. A ____________
B ____________
C ____________
D ____________
3. A ____________
B ____________
C ____________
D ____________
4. A ____________
B ____________
C ____________
D ____________
5. A ____________
B ____________
6. A ____________
B ____________
C ____________
D ____________
7. A ____________
B ____________
C ____________
D ____________
8. A ____________
B ____________
C ____________
D ____________
9. A ____________
B ____________
C ____________
D ____________
10. A ____________
B ____________
11. A ____________
B ____________
C ____________
D ____________
12. A ____________
B ____________
C ____________
D ____________
13. A ____________
B ____________
C ____________
D ____________
14. A ____________
B ____________
C ____________
D ____________
15. A ____________
B ____________

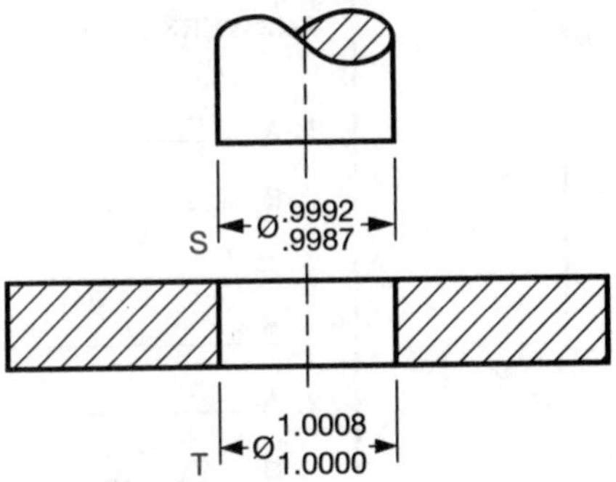

ANSWERS

16. ____________
17. ____________
18. ____________
19. ____________

QUESTIONS

16. What is the tolerance on the shaft (S)?
17. What is the tolerance on the hole (T)?
18. What is the minimum clearance between the parts?
19. What is the maximum clearance between the parts?

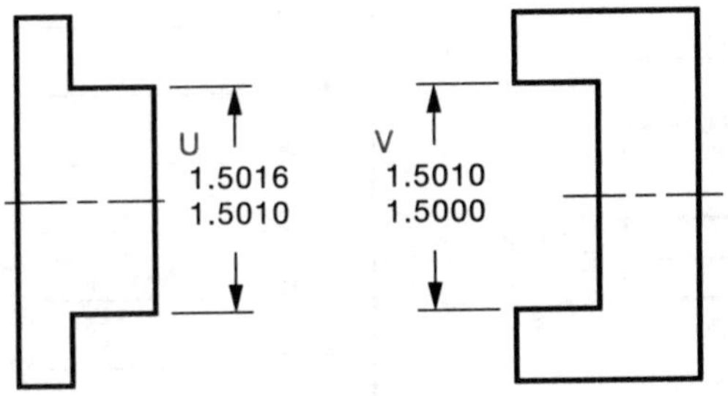

20. ____________
21. ____________
22. ____________
23. ____________

QUESTIONS

20. What is the tolerance on the part (U)?
21. What is the tolerance on the slot (V)?
22. What is the minimum interference between the parts?
23. What is the maximum interference between the parts?

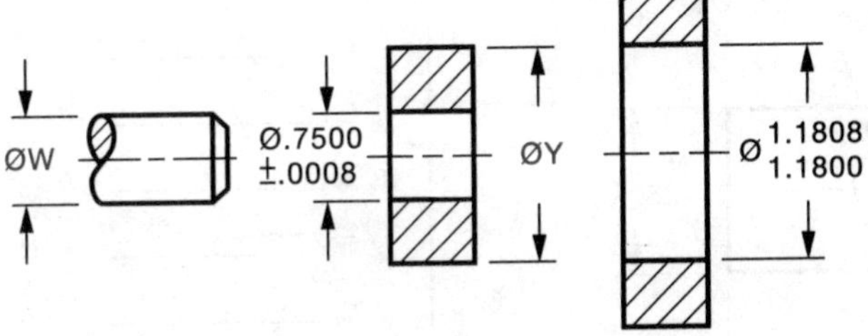

24. Max. ____________
Min. ____________
25. Max. ____________
Min. ____________

QUESTIONS - Calculate the following:

24. Dimension of shaft (W) to have a tolerance of .0014 and a minimum clearance of .0006.
25. Dimension of bushing (Y) to have a tolerance of .0006 and a minimum interference of zero.

NOTE: ONLY THE DIMENSIONS PERTAINING TO THE QUESTIONS ARE GIVEN ON THE DRAWINGS.

INCH TOLERANCES AND ALLOWANCES	A-34

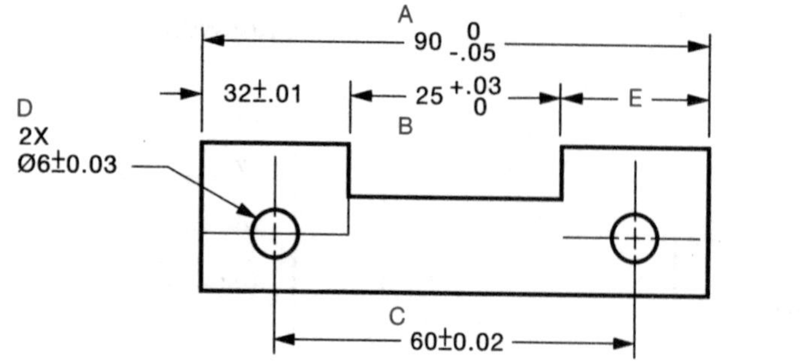

QUESTIONS - Calculate the following:

1. A dim — (A) Basic Size (B) Tolerance (C) Max. Limit (D) Min. Limit
2. B dim — (A) Basic Size (B) Tolerance (C) Max. Limit (D) Min. Limit
3. C dim — (A) Basic Size (B) Tolerance (C) Max. Limit (D) Min. Limit
4. D dim — (A) Basic Size (B) Tolerance (C) Max. Limit (D) Min. Limit
5. E dim — (A) Max. Size (B) Min. Size

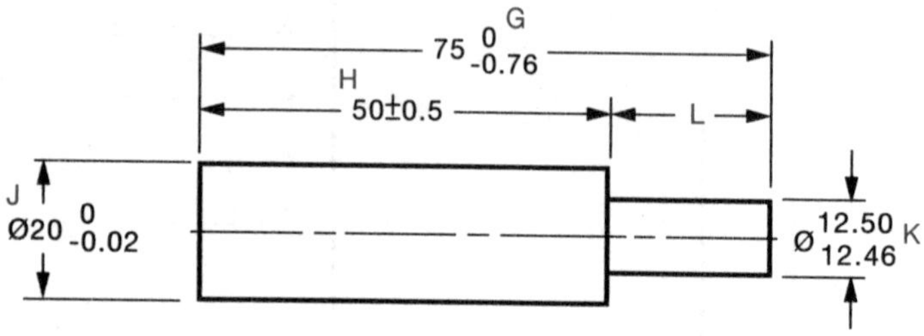

QUESTIONS - Calculate the following:

6. G dim — (A) Basic Size (B) Tolerance (C) Max. Limit (D) Min. Limit
7. H dim — (A) Basic Size (B) Tolerance (C) Max. Limit (D) Min. Limit
8. J dim — (A) Basic Size (B) Tolerance (C) Max. Limit (D) Min. Limit
9. K dim — (A) Basic Size (B) Tolerance (C) Max. Limit (D) Min. Limit
10. L dim — (A) Max. Size (B) Min. Size

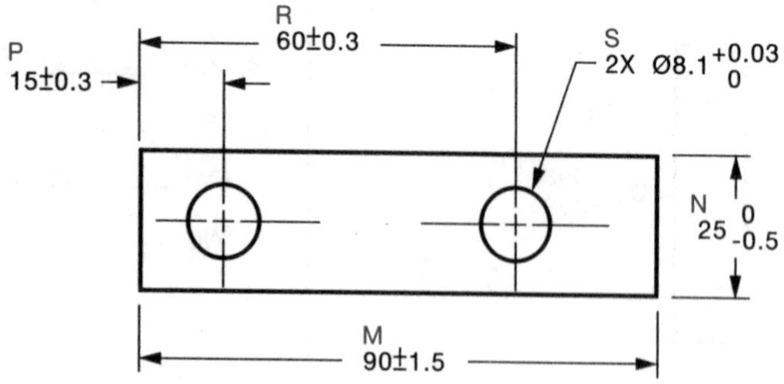

QUESTIONS - Calculate the following:

11. M dim — (A) Basic Size (B) Tolerance (C) Max. Limit (D) Min. Limit
12. N dim — (A) Basic Size (B) Tolerance (C) Max. Limit (D) Min. Limit
13. P dim — (A) Basic Size (B) Tolerance (C) Max. Limit (D) Min. Limit
14. R dim — (A) Basic Size (B) Tolerance (C) Max. Limit (D) Min. Limit
15. S dim — (A) Max. Size (B) Min. Size

ANSWERS

1. A ______ B ______ C ______ D ______
2. A ______ B ______ C ______ D ______
3. A ______ B ______ C ______ D ______
4. A ______ B ______ C ______ D ______
5. A ______ B ______
6. A ______ B ______ C ______ D ______
7. A ______ B ______ C ______ D ______
8. A ______ B ______ C ______ D ______
9. A ______ B ______ C ______ D ______
10. A ______ B ______
11. A ______ B ______ C ______ D ______
12. A ______ B ______ C ______ D ______
13. A ______ B ______ C ______ D ______
14. A ______ B ______ C ______ D ______
15. A ______ B ______

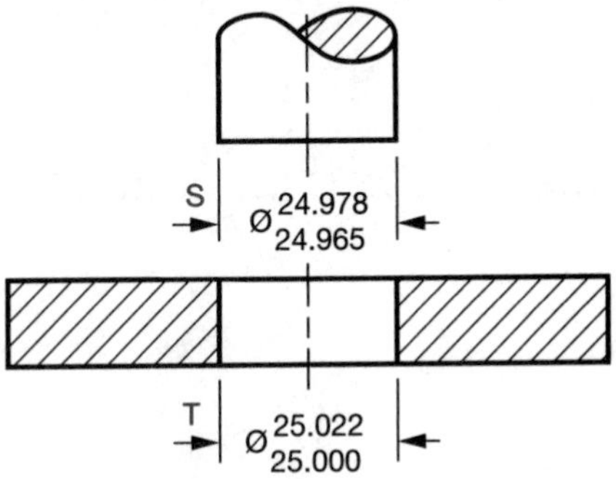

QUESTIONS

16. What is the tolerance on the shaft (S)?
17. What is the tolerance on the hole (T)?
18. What is the minimum clearance between parts?
19. What is the maximum clearance between parts?

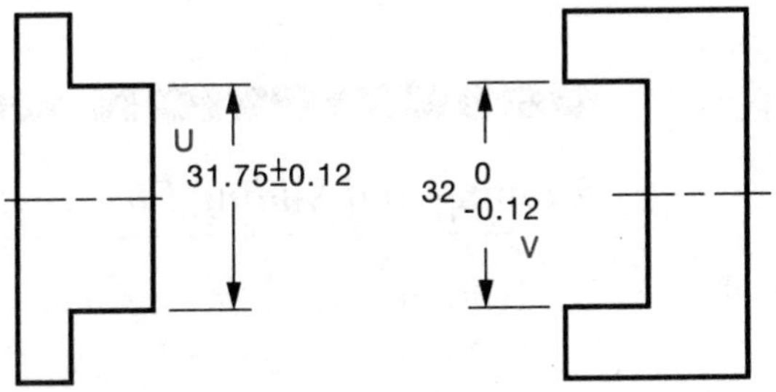

QUESTIONS

20. What is the tolerance on the part (U)?
21. What is the tolerance on the slot (V)?
22. What is the minimum clearance between parts?
23. What is the maximum clearance between parts?

19.05 − .02 = 19.03 − .015 =

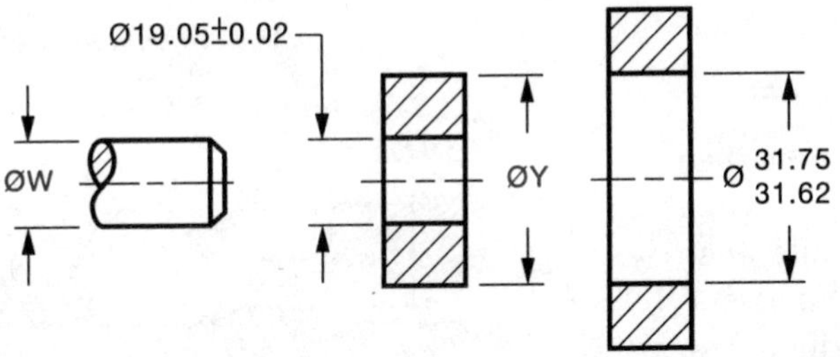

QUESTIONS - Calculate the following:

24. Dimension of shaft (W) to have a tolerance of 0.036 and a minimum clearance of 0.015.
25. Dimension of bushing (Y) to have a tolerance of 0.016 and a minimum interference of zero.

ANSWERS

16. ______
17. ______
18. ______
19. ______
20. ______
21. ______
22. ______
23. ______
24. Max. 19.015
    Min. 18.979
25. Max. ______
    Min. ______

METRIC
DIMENSIONS ARE IN MILLIMETRES

NOTE: ONLY THE DIMENSIONS PERTAINING TO THE QUESTIONS ARE GIVEN ON THE DRAWINGS.

MILLIMETRE TOLERANCES AND ALLOWANCES

A-35M

13 UNIT

INCH FITS

Fit is the general term used to signify the range of tightness or looseness resulting from the application of a specific combination of allowances and tolerances in the design of mating parts. Fits are of three general types: clearance, interference, and transition. Figures 13–1 and 13–2 illustrate the three types of fits.

Clearance Fits

Clearance fits have limits of size prescribed so a clearance always results when mating parts are assembled. Clearance fits are intended for accurate assembly of parts and bearings. The parts can be assembled by hand because the hole is always larger than the shaft.

Interference Fits

Interference fits have limits of size so prescribed that an interference always results when mating parts are assembled. The hole is always smaller than the shaft. Interference fits are for permanent assemblies of parts that require rigidity and alignment, such as dowel pins and bearings in castings. Parts are usually pressed together using an arbor press.

Transition Fits

Transition fits have limits of size indicating that either a clearance or an interference may result when mating parts are assembled. Transition fits are a compromise between clearance and interference fits. They are used for applications where accurate location is important, but either a small amount of clearance or interference is permissible.

DESCRIPTION OF FITS

Running and Sliding Fits

These fits, for which tolerances and clearances are given in Table 17 of the Appendix, represent a special type of clearance fit. These are intended to provide a similar running performance, with suitable lubrication allowance, throughout the range of sizes.

Locational Fits

Locational fits are intended to determine only the location of the mating parts; they may provide

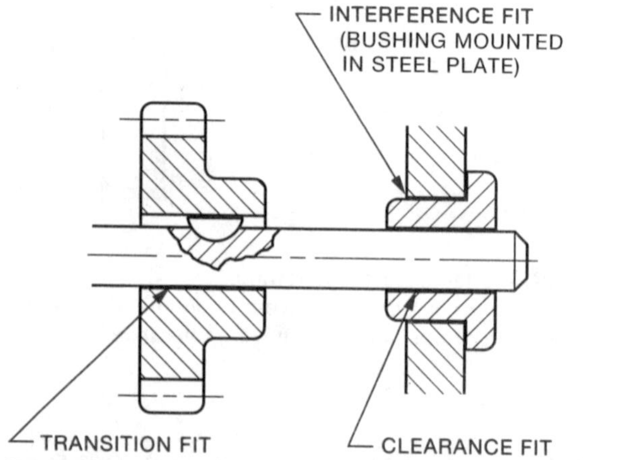
INTERFERENCE FIT
(BUSHING MOUNTED
IN STEEL PLATE)
TRANSITION FIT
(GEAR HELD IN SHAFT)
CLEARANCE FIT
(SHAFT ROTATING IN BUSHING)

FIGURE 13–1 ■ Application of types of fits

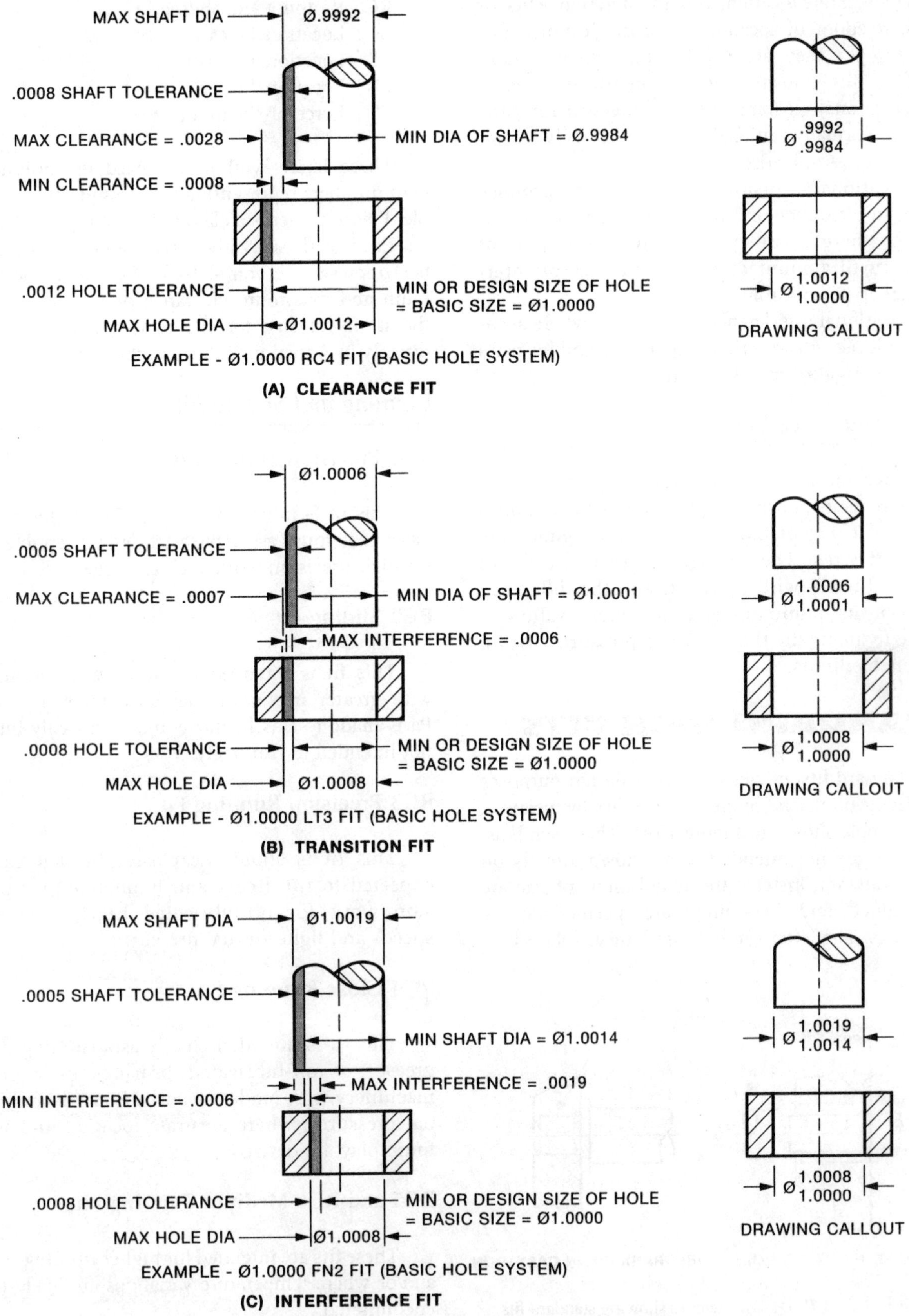
MAX SHAFT DIA
Ø.9992
.0008 SHAFT TOLERANCE
MAX CLEARANCE = .0028
MIN DIA OF SHAFT = Ø.9984
MIN CLEARANCE = .0008
.0012 HOLE TOLERANCE
MIN OR DESIGN SIZE OF HOLE = BASIC SIZE = Ø1.0000
MAX HOLE DIA
Ø1.0012
Ø .9992 .9984
Ø 1.0012 1.0000
DRAWING CALLOUT
EXAMPLE - Ø1.0000 RC4 FIT (BASIC HOLE SYSTEM)
(A) CLEARANCE FIT
Ø1.0006
.0005 SHAFT TOLERANCE
MAX CLEARANCE = .0007
MIN DIA OF SHAFT = Ø1.0001
MAX INTERFERENCE = .0006
.0008 HOLE TOLERANCE
MIN OR DESIGN SIZE OF HOLE = BASIC SIZE = Ø1.0000
MAX HOLE DIA
Ø1.0008
Ø 1.0006 1.0001
Ø 1.0008 1.0000
DRAWING CALLOUT
EXAMPLE - Ø1.0000 LT3 FIT (BASIC HOLE SYSTEM)
(B) TRANSITION FIT
MAX SHAFT DIA
Ø1.0019
.0005 SHAFT TOLERANCE
MIN SHAFT DIA = Ø1.0014
MAX INTERFERENCE = .0019
MIN INTERFERENCE = .0006
.0008 HOLE TOLERANCE
MIN OR DESIGN SIZE OF HOLE = BASIC SIZE = Ø1.0000
MAX HOLE DIA
Ø1.0008
Ø 1.0019 1.0014
Ø 1.0008 1.0000
DRAWING CALLOUT
EXAMPLE - Ø1.0000 FN2 FIT (BASIC HOLE SYSTEM)
(C) INTERFERENCE FIT

FIGURE 13–2 ■ Types and examples of inch fits

rigid or accurate location, as with interference fits, or some freedom of location, as with clearance fits. Accordingly, they are divided into three groups: clearance fits, transition fits, and interference fits.

Locational clearance fits are intended for parts that are normally stationary but can be freely assembled or disassembled.

Locational transition fits are a compromise between clearance and interference fits for application where accuracy of location is important but a small amount of either clearance or interference is permissible.

Locational interference fits are used where accuracy of location is of prime importance and for parts requiring rigidity and alignment.

Drive and Force Fits

Drive and force fits constitute a special type of interference fit, normally characterized by maintenance of constant bore pressures throughout the range of sizes. The interference therefore varies almost directly with diameter, and the difference between its minimum and maximum values is small to maintain the resulting pressures within reasonable limits.

STANDARD INCH FITS

Standard fits are designated for design purposes in specifications and on design sketches by means of the symbols shown in Figure 13–3. These symbols, however, are not intended to be shown directly on shop drawings; instead, the actual limits of size are determined, and these limits are specified on the drawings. The letter symbols used are as follows:

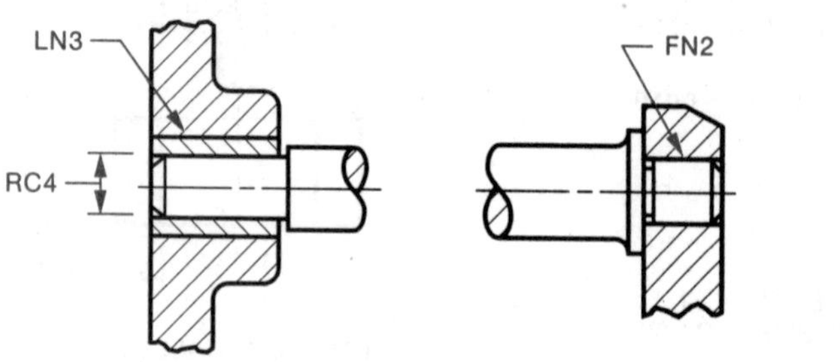

(A) SHAFT IN BUSHED HOLE (B) CRANK PIN IN CAST IRON

FIGURE 13–3 ■ Design sketches showing standard fits

RC Running and sliding fit
LC Locational clearance fit
LT Locational transition fit
LN Locational interference fit
FN Force or shrink fit

These letter symbols are used in conjunction with numbers representing the class of fit; for example, FN4 represents a class 4, force fit.

Each of these symbols (two letters and a number) represents a complete fit, for which the minimum and maximum clearance or interference and the limits of size for the mating parts are given directly in Appendix Tables 17 through 21.

Running and Sliding Fits

RC1 Precision Sliding Fit

This fit is intended for the accurate location of parts that must assemble without perceptible play for high-precision work such as gauges.

RC2 Sliding Fit

This fit is intended for accurate location, but with greater maximum clearance than class RC1. Parts made to this fit move and turn easily but are not intended to run freely.

RC3 Precision Running Fit

This fit is about the closest fit that can be expected to run freely, and is intended for precision work for oil-lubricated bearings at slow speeds and light journal pressures.

RC4 Close Running Fit

This fit is intended chiefly as a running fit for grease- or oil-lubricated bearings on accurate machinery with moderate surface speeds and journal pressures, where accurate location and minimum play are desired.

RC5 and RC6 Medium Running Fits

These fits are intended for higher running speeds and/or where temperature variations are likely to be encountered.

RC7 Free Running Fit

This fit is intended for use where accuracy is not essential, and/or where large temperature variations are likely to be encountered.

RC8 and RC9 Loose Running Fits

These fits are intended for use where materials made to commercial tolerances are involved, such as cold-rolled shafting, tubing, etc.

Locational Clearance Fits

Locational clearance fits are intended for parts that are normally stationary but can be freely assembled or disassembled. These are classified as follows:

LC1 to LC4

These fits have a minimum zero clearance, but in practice the probability is that the fit will always have a clearance.

LC5 and LC6

These fits have a small minimum clearance intended for close location fits for non-running parts.

LC7 and LC11

These fits have progressively larger clearances and tolerances, and are useful for various loose clearances for assembly of bolts and similar parts.

Locational Transition Fits

Locational transition fits are a compromise between clearance and interference fits or for application where accuracy of location is important, but either a small amount of clearance or interference is permissible. These are classified as follows:

LT1 and LT2

These fits average a slight clearance, giving a light push fit.

LT3 and LT4

These fits average virtually no clearance, and are for use where some interference can be tolerated. These are sometimes referred to as an easy keying fit, and are used for shaft keys and ball race fits. Assembly is generally by pressure or hammer blows.

LT5 and LT6

These fits average a slight interference, although appreciable assembly force will be required.

Locational Interference Fits

Locational interference fits are used where accuracy of location is of prime importance, and for parts requiring rigidity and alignment with no special requirements for bore pressure. These are classified as follows:

LN1 and LN2

These are light press fits, with very small minimum interference, suitable for parts such as dowel pins, which are assembled with an arbor press in steel, cast iron, or brass. Parts can normally be dismantled and reassembled.

LN3

This is suitable as a heavy press fit in steel and brass, or a light press fit in more elastic materials and light alloys.

LN4 to LN6

While LN4 can be used for permanent assembly of steel parts, these fits are primarily intended as press fits for soft materials.

Force or Shrink Fits

Force or shrink fits constitute a special type of interference fit. The interference varies almost directly with diameter, and the difference between its minimum and maximum values is small to maintain the resulting pressures within reasonable limits. These fits are classified as follows:

FN1 Light Drive Fit

Requires light assembly pressure and produces more or less permanent assemblies. It is suitable for thin sections or long fits, or in cast-iron external members.

FN2 Medium Drive Fit

Suitable for heavier steel parts, or as a shrink fit on light sections.

FN3 Heavy Drive Fit

Suitable for heavier steel parts, or as a shrink fit in medium sections.

FN4 and FN5 Force Fits

Suitable for parts that can be highly stressed.

Basic Hole System

In the basic hole system, which is recommended for general use, the basic size will be the design size for the hole, and the tolerance will be plus. The design size for the shaft will be the basic size minus the minimum clearance, or plus the maximum interference, and the tolerance will be minus, as given in the tables in the Appendix. For example (see Table 17), for a 1-in. RC7 fit, values of +.0020, .0025, and –.0012 are given; hence, tolerances will be

Hole Ø1.0000 $^{+.0020}_{-.0000}$

Shaft Ø.9975 $^{+.0000}_{-.0012}$

Basic Shaft System

Fits are sometimes required on a basic shaft system, especially in cases where two or more fits are required on the same shaft. This is designated for design purposes by a letter S following the fit symbol; for example, RC7S.

Tolerances for holes and shafts are identical with those for a basic hole system, but the basic size becomes the design size for the shaft, and the design size for the hole is found by adding the minimum clearance or subtracting the maximum interference from the basic size.

For example, for a 1-in. RC7S fit, values of +.0020, .0025, and –.0012 are given; therefore, tolerances will be

Hole Ø1.0025 $^{+.0020}_{-.0000}$

Shaft Ø1.000 $^{+.0000}_{-.0012}$

Additional examples of how to use the inch fits are shown in Tables 17 to 21 in the Appendix.

REFERENCES

CSA-B97.3-1970 (R1992) Standard Fits for Mating Parts, Inch Sizes

CAN/CSA-B78.2-M91 Dimensioning and Tolerancing of Technical Drawings

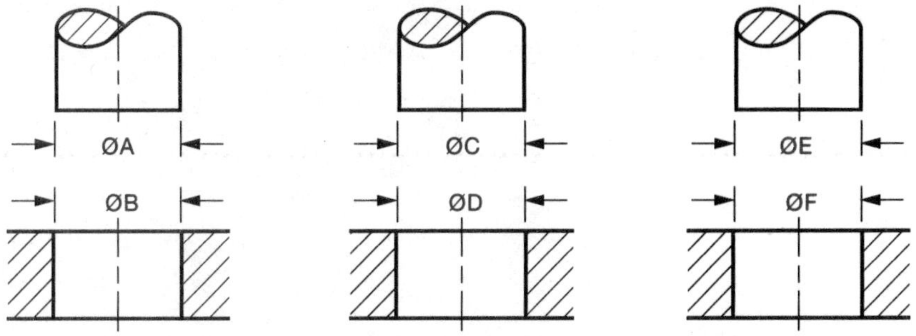

Ø.625 RC2 | Ø1.000 RC4 | Ø1.500RC8

RUNNING AND SLIDING FITS

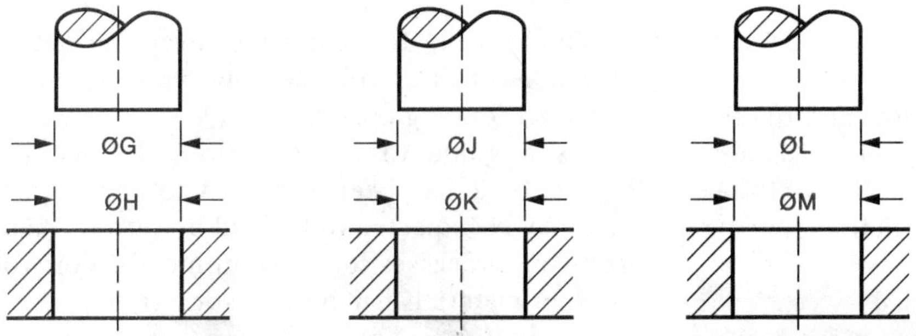

Ø.625 LC5 | Ø1.125 LT3 | Ø1.375 LN2

LOCATIONAL FITS

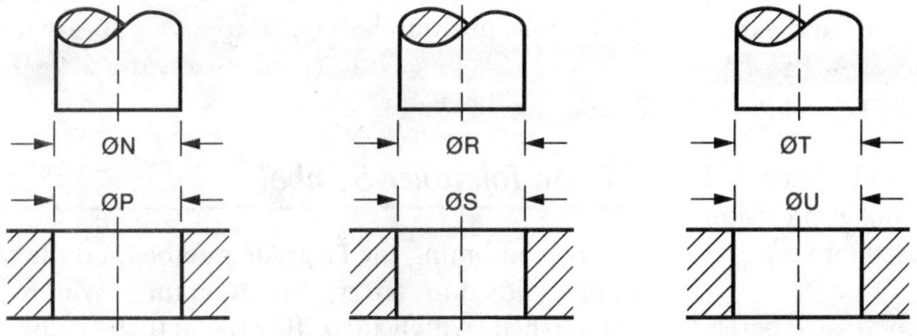

Ø.875 FN1 | Ø1.250 FN2 | Ø1.750 FN4

FORCE OR SHRINK FITS

ANSWERS

A LIMITS .62475
.62445

B LIMITS .625
.6254

MIN CLEAR. .00025

MAX CLEAR. .00095

C LIMITS ______

D LIMITS ______

MIN CLEAR. ______

MAX CLEAR. ______

E LIMITS ______

F LIMITS ______

MIN CLEAR. ______

MAX CLEAR. ______

G LIMITS ______

H LIMITS ______

MIN CLEAR. ______

MAX CLEAR. ______

J LIMITS ______

K LIMITS ______

MAX INTERF. ______

MAX CLEAR. ______

N LIMITS ______

P LIMITS ______

MAX INTERF. ______

MIN INTERF. ______

R LIMITS ______

S LIMITS ______

MAX INTERF. ______

MIN INTERF. ______

T LIMITS ______

U LIMITS ______

MAX INTERF. ______

MIN INTERF. ______

L LIMITS ______

M LIMITS ______

MAX INTERF. ______

MAX CLEAR. ______

ASSIGNMENT: COMPLETE THE MISSING INFORMATION FOR THE FITS SHOWN.

INCH FITS BASIC HOLE SYSTEM

A-36

14 UNIT

METRIC FITS

The ISO (metric) system of limits and fits for mating parts is approved and adopted for general use in Canada and the United States. It establishes the designation symbols used to define specific dimensional limits on drawings.

The general terms "hole" and "shaft" can also be taken as referring to the space containing or contained by two parallel faces of any part, such as the width of a slot or the thickness of a key.

An "International Tolerance Guide" establishes the magnitude of the tolerance zone or the amount of part size variation allowed for internal and external dimensions alike. The smaller the grade number, the smaller the tolerance zone. For general applications of IT grades, see Figure 14–1.

Grades 1 to 4 are very precise grades intended primarily for gauge making and similar precision work, although grade 4 can also be used for very precise production work.

Grades 5 to 16 represent a progressive series suitable for cutting operations, such as turning, boring, grinding, milling, and sawing. Grade 5 is the most precise grade, obtainable by fine grinding and lapping, while grade 16 is the coarsest grade for rough sawing and machining.

Grades 12 to 16 are intended for manufacturing operations such as cold heading, pressing, rolling, and other forming operations.

As a guide to the selection of tolerances, Figure 14–2 has been prepared to show grades that may be expected to be held by various manufacturing processes for work in metals. For work in other materials, such as plastics, it may be necessary to use coarser tolerance grades for the same process.

A fundamental deviation establishes the position of the tolerance zone with respect to the basic size. Fundamental deviations are expressed by "tolerance position letters." Capital letters are used for internal dimensions, and lowercase letters for external dimensions.

Metric Tolerance Symbol

By combining the IT grade number and the tolerance position letter, the tolerance symbol is established, which identifies the actual maximum and minimum limits of the part. The toleranced sizes are thus defined by the basic size of the part followed by the symbol composed of a letter and number, Figure 14–3.

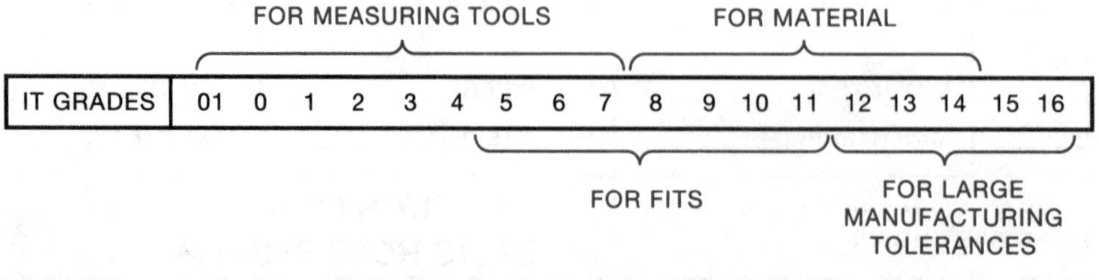

FIGURE 14–1 ■ Application of international tolerance (IT) grades

Hole basis fits have a fundamental deviation of "H" on the hole, and shaft basis fits have a fundamental deviation of "h" on the shaft. Normally, the hole basis system is preferred.

Fit Symbol

A fit is indicated by the basic size common to both components, followed by a symbol corresponding

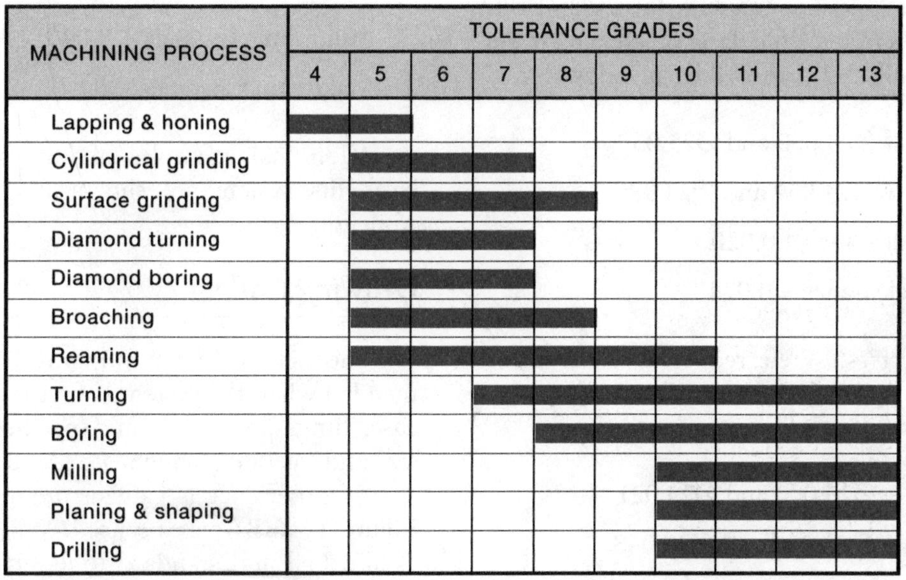

FIGURE 14–2 ■ Tolerancing grades for machining processes

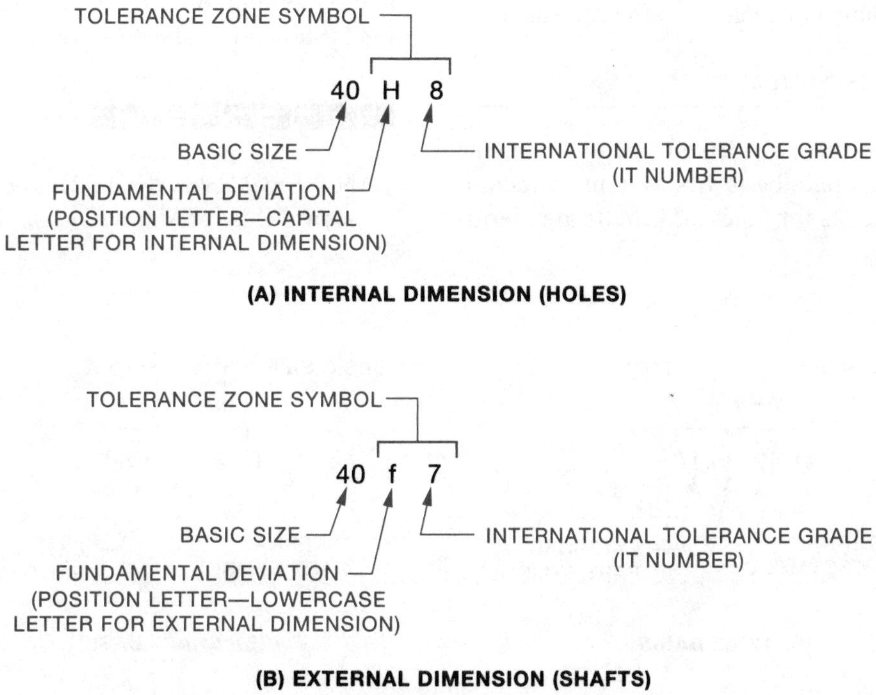

FIGURE 14–3 ■ Tolerance symbol (hole basis fit)

to each component, with the internal part symbol preceding the external part symbol, Figure 14–4.

Figure 14–5 shows examples of three common fits.

Hole Basis Fits System

In the hole basis fits system (see Tables 22 and 24 of the Appendix) the basic size will be the minimum size of the hole. For example, for a Ø25 H8/f7 fit, which is a Preferred Hole Basis Clearance Fit, the limits for the hole and shaft will be as follows:

Hole limits = Ø25.000 and Ø25.033

Shaft limits = Ø24.959 and Ø24.980

Minimum clearance = 0.020

Maximum clearance = 0.074

If a Ø25 H7/s6 Preferred Hole Basis Interference Fit is required, the limits for the hole and shaft will be as follows:

Hole limits = Ø25.000 and Ø25.021

Shaft limits = Ø25.035 and Ø25.048

Minimum interference = −0.014

Maximum interference = −0.048

Additional examples of how to use the hole basis fits system are shown in Table 24 of the Appendix.

Shaft Basis Fits System

Where more than two fits are required on the same shaft, the shaft basis fits system is recommended. Tolerances for holes and shafts are identical with those for a basic hole system; however, the basic size becomes the maximum shaft size. For example, for a Ø16 C11/h11 fit, which is a Preferred Shaft Basis Clearance Fit, the limits for the hole and shaft will be as follows:

Hole limits = Ø16.095 and Ø16.205

Shaft limits = Ø15.890 and Ø16.000

Minimum clearance = 0.095

Maximum clearance = 0.315

Additional examples of how to use the shaft basis fits system are shown in Table 25 of the Appendix.

Drawing Callout

The method shown in Figure 14–6(A) is recommended when the system is first introduced. In this case, limit dimensions are specified and the basic size and tolerance symbol are identified as reference.

As experience is gained, the method shown in Figure 14–6(B) may be used. When the system is established and standard tools, gauges, and stock materials are available with size and symbol identification, the method shown in Figure 14–6(C) may be used.

This would result in a clearance between 0.020 and 0.074 mm. A description of the preferred metric fits is shown in Tables 22 and 23 of the Appendix.

REFERENCE

CAN-B97.3-M1982 (R1992) Tolerances and Standard Fits for Mating Parts, Metric Sizes

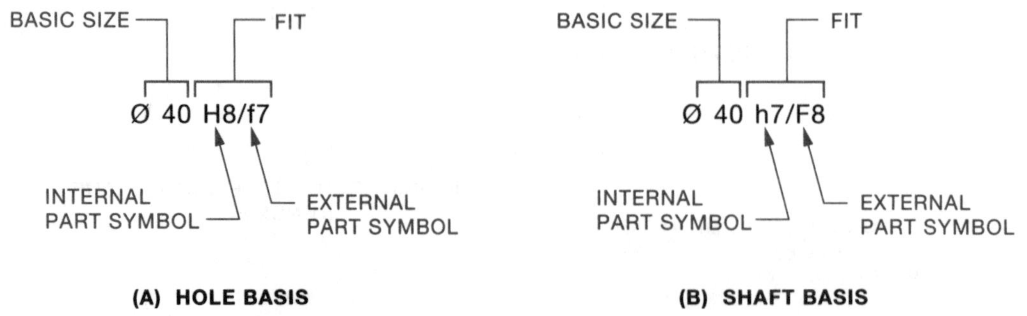

FIGURE 14–4 ■ Fit symbol

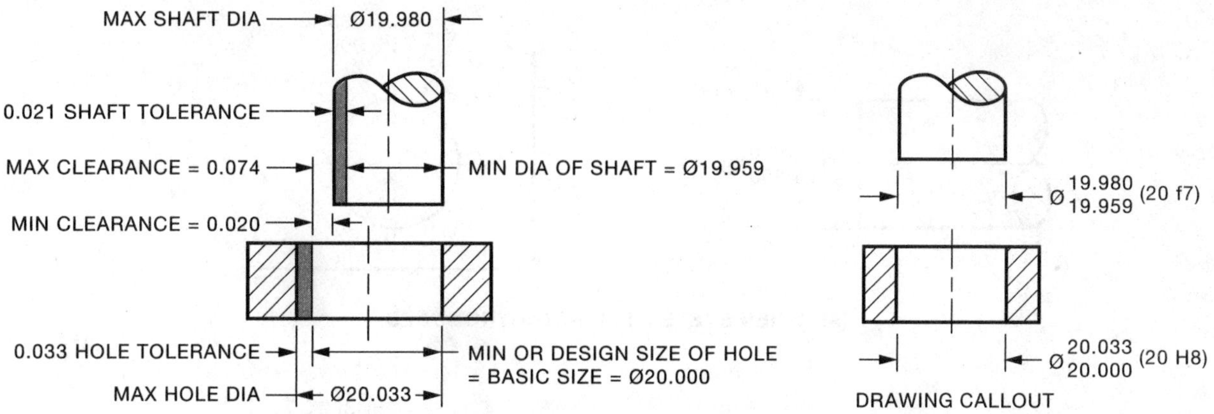

EXAMPLE—H8/f7 PREFERRED HOLE BASIS FIT FOR A Ø20 HOLE (SEE APPENDIX, TABLE 24)

(A) CLEARANCE FIT

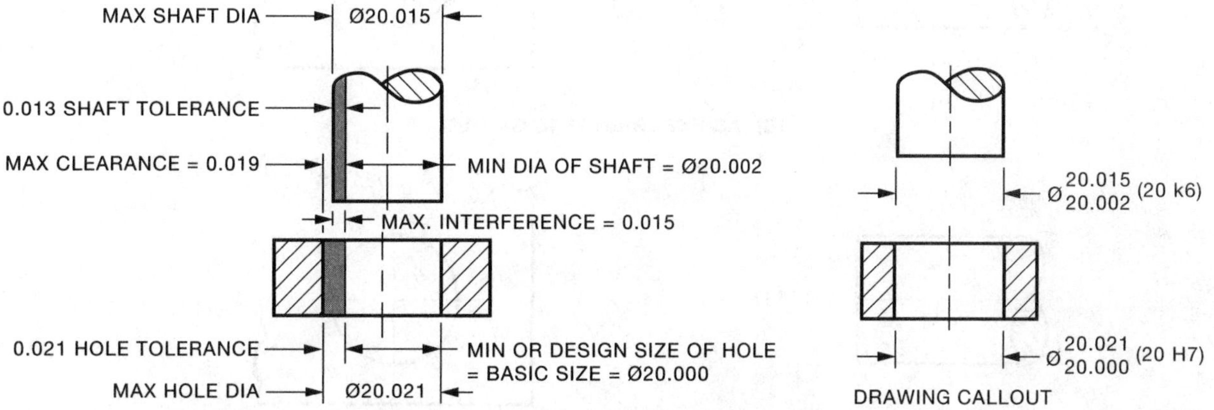

EXAMPLE—H7/k6 PREFERRED HOLE BASIS FIT FOR A Ø20 HOLE (SEE APPENDIX, TABLE 24)

(B) TRANSITION FIT

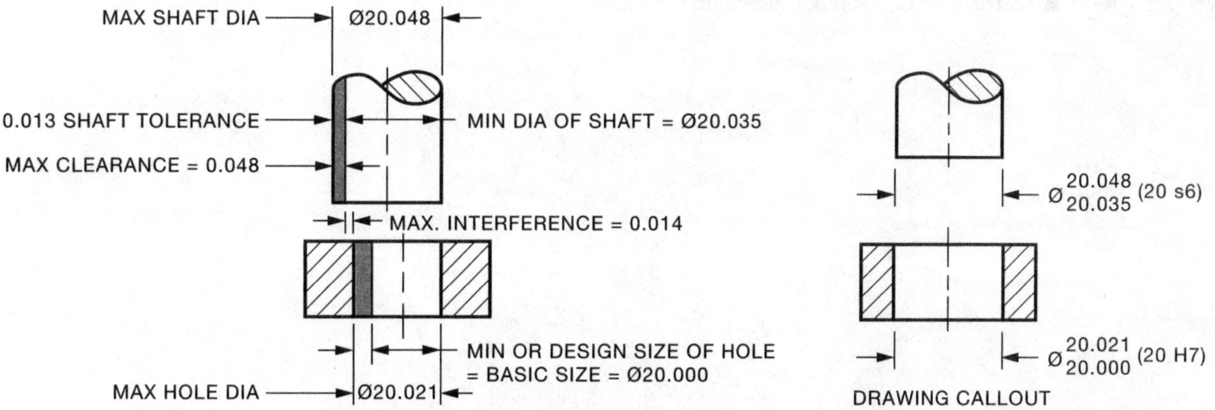

EXAMPLE—H7/s6 PREFERRED HOLE BASIS FIT FOR A Ø20 HOLE (SEE APPENDIX, TABLE 24)

(C) INTERFERENCE FIT

FIGURE 14–5 ■ Types and examples of millimetre fits

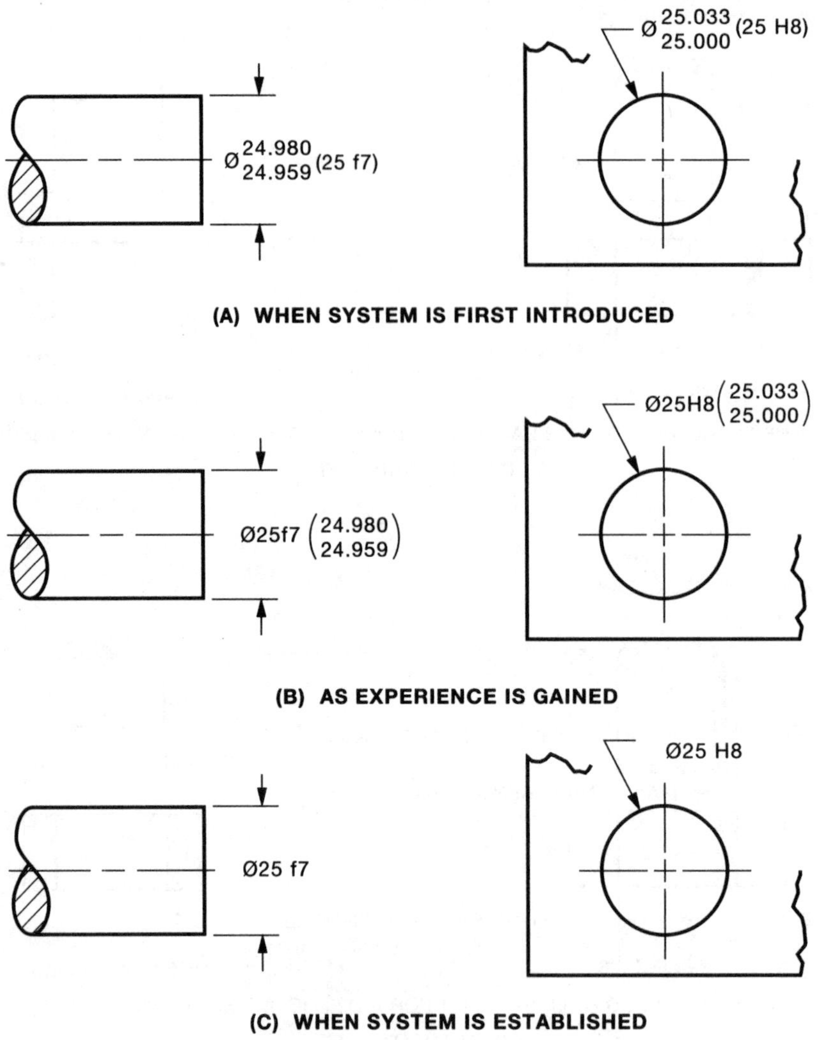
Ø 24.980 / 24.959 (25 f7)
Ø 25.033 / 25.000 (25 H8)
(A) WHEN SYSTEM IS FIRST INTRODUCED
Ø25f7 (24.980 / 24.959)
Ø25H8 (25.033 / 25.000)
(B) AS EXPERIENCE IS GAINED
Ø25 f7
Ø25 H8
(C) WHEN SYSTEM IS ESTABLISHED

FIGURE 14–6 ■ Metric tolerance symbol shown on drawings

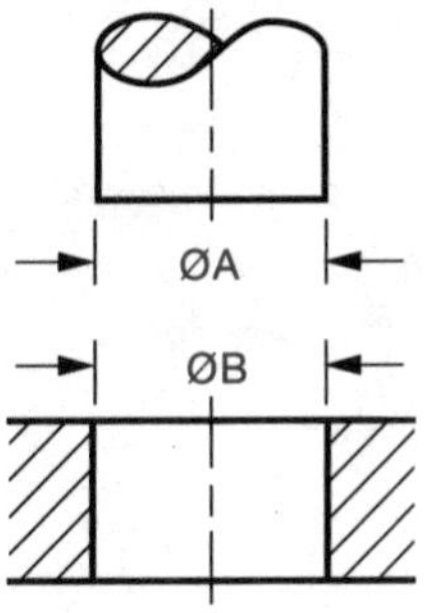

Ø16 H7/g6

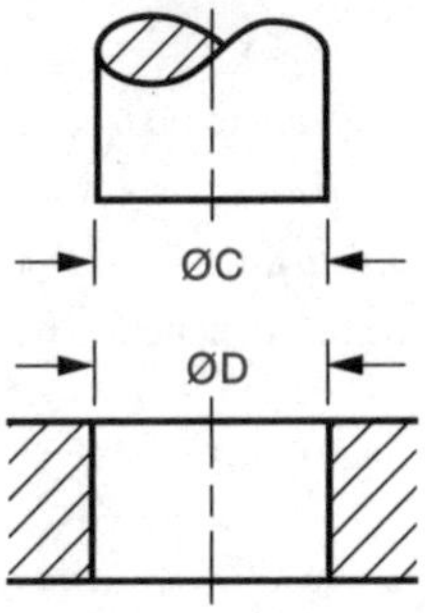

Ø25 H9/d9

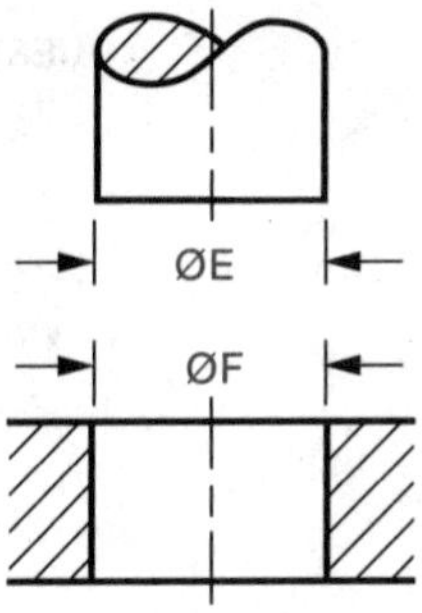

Ø40 H11/c11

RUNNING AND SLIDING FITS

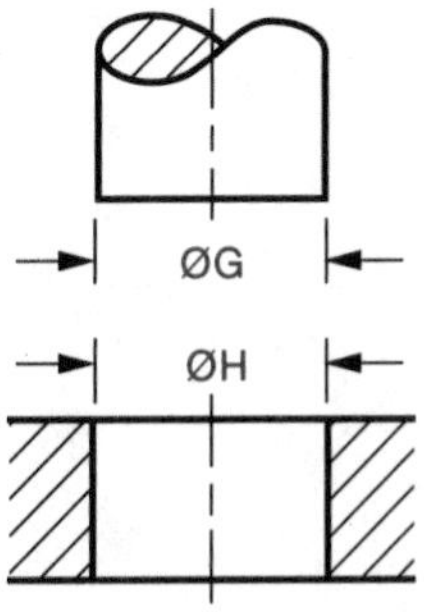

Ø20 H7/h6

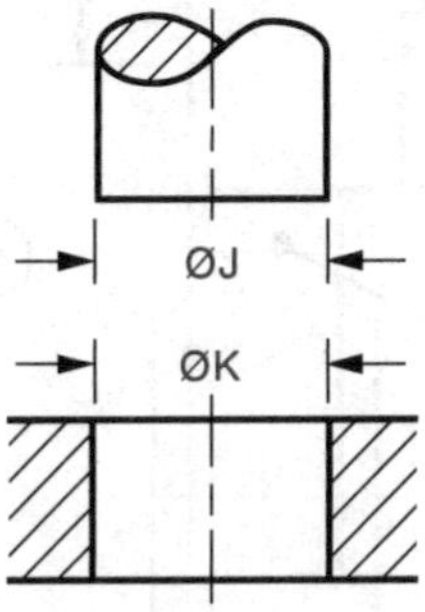

Ø30 H7/k6

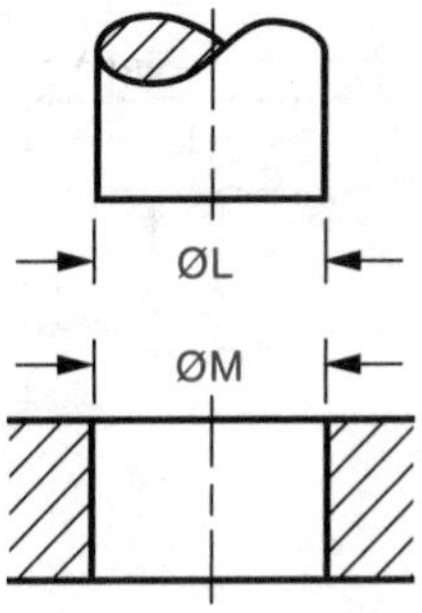

Ø45 H7/p6

LOCATIONAL FITS

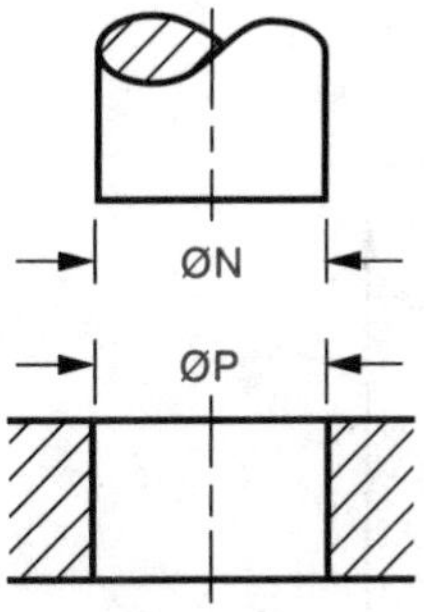

Ø16 H7/s6

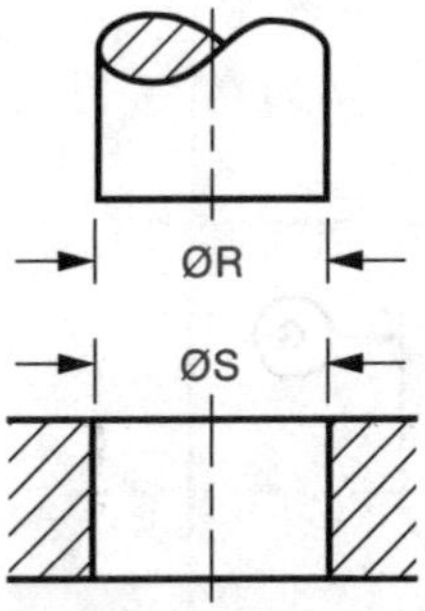

Ø25 H7/u6

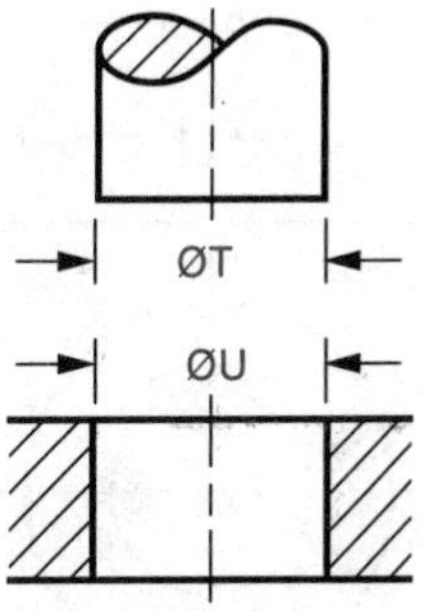

Ø40 H7/n6

FORCE OR SHRINK FITS FITS

ANSWERS

A LIMITS ____________
____

B LIMITS ____________
____

MIN CLEAR. ____________

MAX CLEAR. ____________

C LIMITS ____________
____

D LIMITS ____________
____

MIN CLEAR. ____________

MAX CLEAR. ____________

E LIMITS ____________
____

F LIMITS ____________
____

MIN CLEAR. ____________

MAX CLEAR. ____________

G LIMITS ____________
____

H LIMITS ____________
____

MIN CLEAR. ____________

MAX CLEAR. ____________

J LIMITS ____________
____

K LIMITS ____________
____

MAX INTERF. ____________

MAX CLEAR. ____________

N LIMITS ____________
____

P LIMITS ____________
____

MIN INTERF. ____________

MAX INTERF. ____________

R LIMITS ____________
____

S LIMITS ____________
____

MIN INTERF. ____________

MAX INTERF. ____________

T LIMITS ____________
____

U LIMITS ____________
____

MIN INTERF. ____________

MAX INTERF. ____________

L LIMITS ____________
____

M LIMITS ____________
____

MAX INTERF. ____________

MAX INTERF. ____________

ASSIGNMENT: COMPLETE THE MISSING INFORMATION FOR THE FITS SHOWN.

METRIC FITS
BASIC HOLE SYSTEM

A-37M

NOTE: EXCEPT WHERE NOTED
TOLERANCES ON DIMENSIONS ±0.5
6.3 EXCEPT WHERE NOTED

ROUNDS AND FILLETS R5

QUESTIONS

1. How many surfaces are to be finished?
2. Except where noted otherwise, what is the tolerance on all dimensions?
3. What is the tolerance on the Ø12.000-12.018 holes?
4. What are the limit dimensions for the 40.64 dimension shown on the side view?

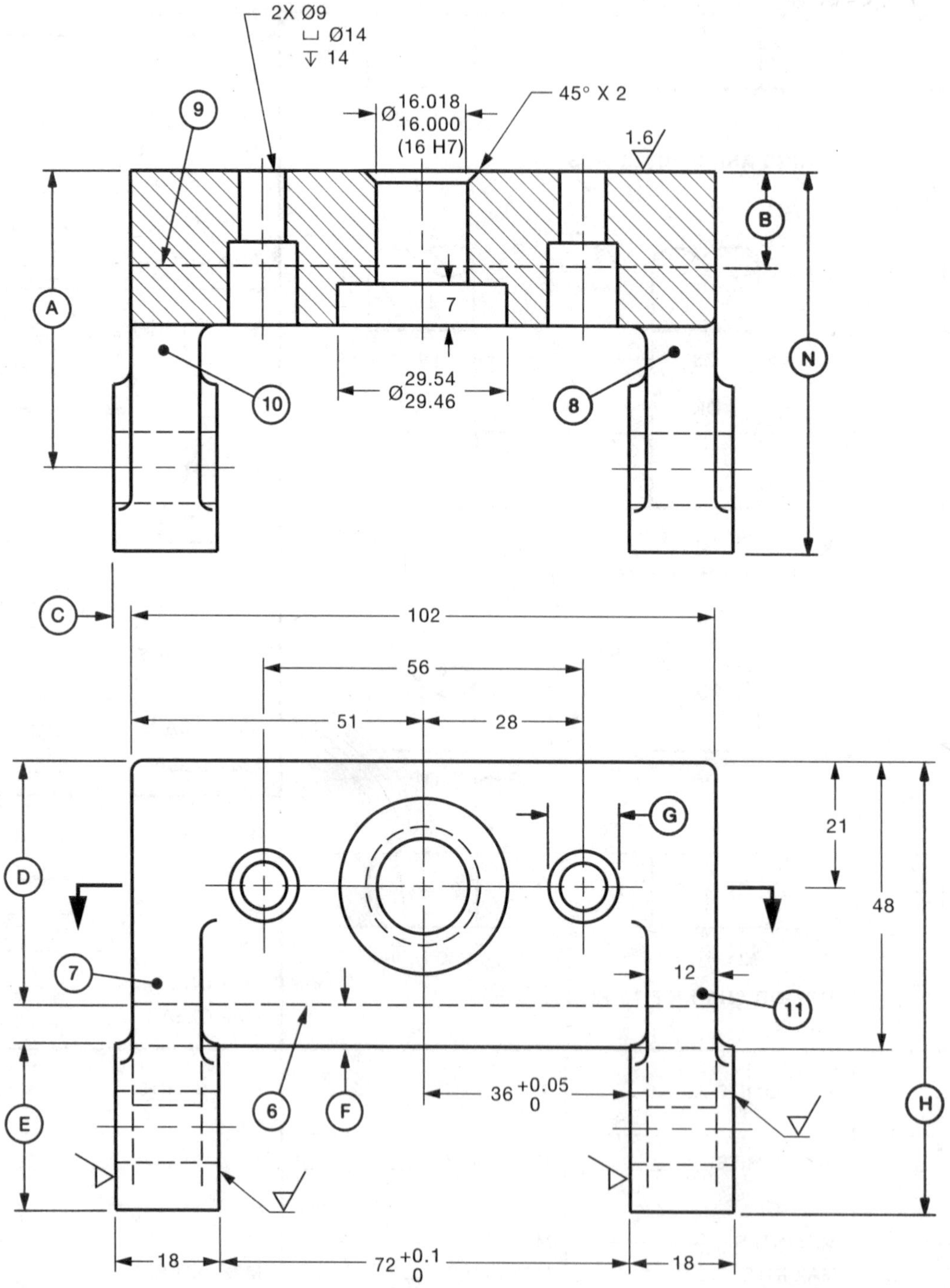

5. What are the limit dimensions for the 26 dimension shown in the side view?
6. What is the maximum distance permissible between the centres of the Ø9 hole?
7. Express the Ø12.000-12.018 holes as a plus-and-minus tolerance dimension.
8. How many surfaces require a 6.3∇ finish?
9. What are the limit dimensions for the 7 dimension shown in the top view?
10. Locate surface (4) in the top view.
11. How many bosses are there?
12. Locate line (3) in the top view.
13. Locate line (6) in the side view.
14. Which surface in the front view indicates line (4) in the side view?
15. Calculate distances (A) to (N).
16. What is the (A) size and (B) type of cap screw used to fasten the bracket?
17. Can standard lockwashers be used with the cap screws?
18. What type of tolerance is shown on the (A) 40.64 vertical dimension and (B) 72 horizontal dimension?
19. What type of sectional view is used?

ANSWERS

1. ______
2. ______
3. ______
4. ______
5. ______
6. ______
7. ______
8. ______
9. ______
10. ______
11. ______
12. ______
13. ______
14. ______

15. A ______
B ______
C ______
D ______
E ______
F ______
G ______
H ______
J ______
K ______
L ______
M ______
N ______

16. A ______
B ______

17. ______

18. A ______
B ______

19. ______

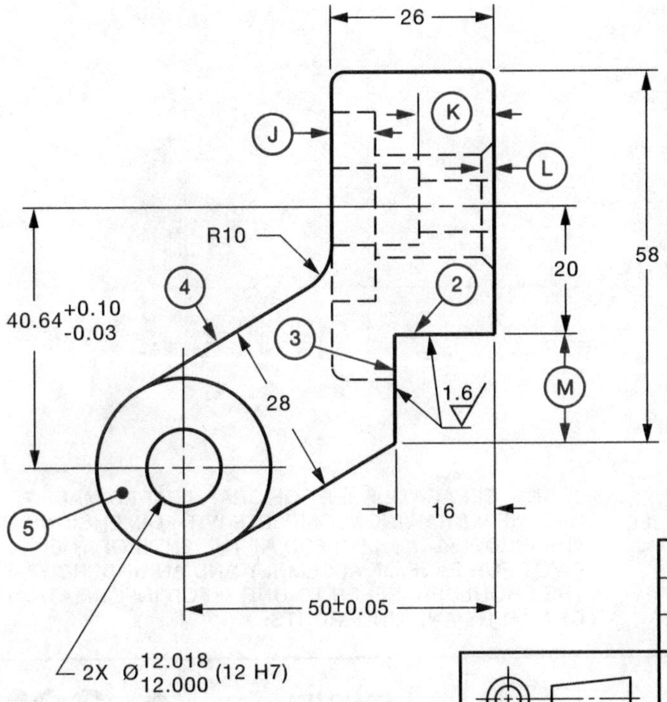

METRIC
DIMENSIONS ARE IN MILLIMETRES

MATERIAL	GI	
SCALE	NOT TO SCALE	
DRAWN		DATE
BRACKET		A-38M

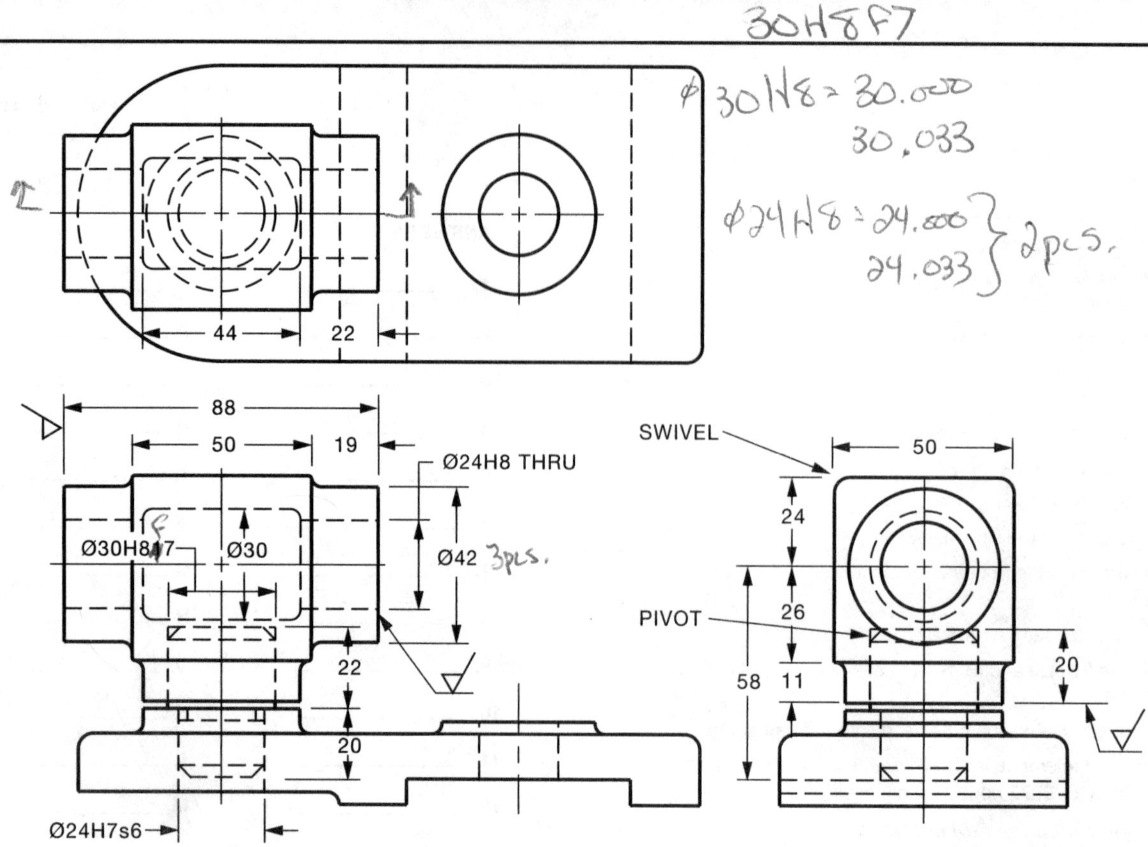

10 mm SQUARES (1 mm GRID)

ASSIGNMENT:

1. SKETCH A FULL SECTION FRONT VIEW OF THE SWIVEL SHOWN IN ASSEMBLY. DIMENSION AND SHOW THE HOLE SIZES AS LIMITS.

2. ON A SEPARATE SHEET OF GRAPH PAPER MAKE A ONE-VIEW DRAWING, COMPLETE WITH DIMENSIONS OF THE PIVOT. ADD CHAMFERS AT THE ENDS OF THE PIVOT FOR EASE OF ASSEMBLY AND AN UNDERCUT AT THE SHOULDER. REFER TO UNIT 9 FOR INFORMATION ON CHAMFERS AND UNDERCUTS.

METRIC

DIMENSIONS ARE IN MILLIMETRES

	SWIVEL	**A-39M**

UNIT 15

THREADED FASTENERS

Fastening devices are vital to most phases of industry. They are used in assembling manufactured products, in the machines and devices used in the manufacturing processes, and in the construction of all types of buildings.

There are two basic types of fasteners: semi-permanent and removable. Rivets are semi-permanent fasteners; bolts, screws, studs, nuts, pins, and keys are removable fasteners. With the progress of industry, fastening devices have become standardized. A thorough knowledge of the design and graphic representation of the common fasteners is essential for interpreting engineering drawings, Figure 15–1.

Thread Representation

True representation of a screw thread is seldom provided on working drawings because of the time involved and the drawing cost. Three types of conventions are generally used for screw thread representation: detailed, schematic, and simplified representation. Simplified representation is used whenever it will clearly indicate the requirements. Sche-matic and detailed representations require more drafting time, but they are sometimes used to avoid confusion with other parallel lines or to more clearly portray particular aspects of threads. One method is generally used within any one drawing. When required, however, all three methods may be used. Canadian (ISO) and American (ASME) thread representation vary slightly, Figures 15–2 and 15–3.

THREADED ASSEMBLIES

Any of the thread conventions shown here may be used for assemblies of threaded parts, and two or more methods may be used on the same drawing, Figures 15–2 and 15–3. In sectional views, the externally threaded part is always shown covering the internally threaded part, Figure 15–4.

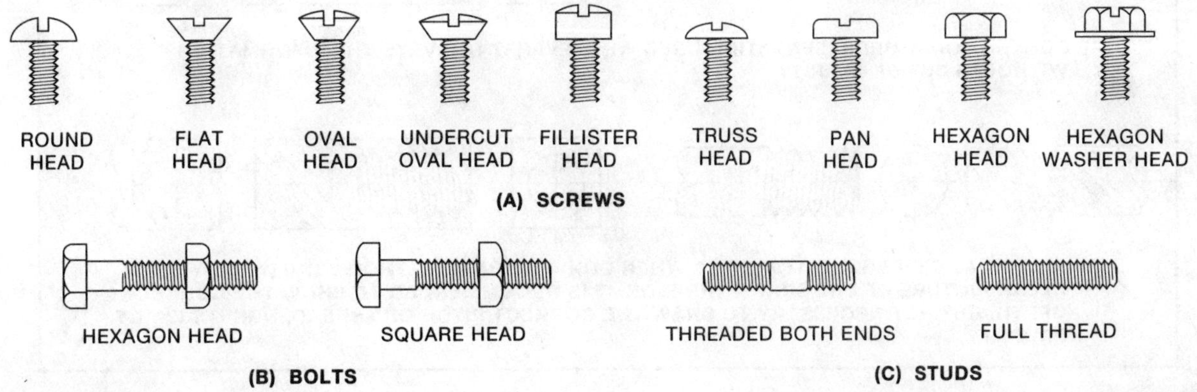

ROUND HEAD
FLAT HEAD
OVAL HEAD
UNDERCUT OVAL HEAD
FILLISTER HEAD
TRUSS HEAD
PAN HEAD
HEXAGON HEAD
HEXAGON WASHER HEAD
(A) SCREWS
HEXAGON HEAD
SQUARE HEAD
(B) BOLTS
THREADED BOTH ENDS
FULL THREAD
(C) STUDS

FIGURE 15–1 ■ Threaded fasteners

Thread Standards

With the progress and growth of industry, there is a growing need for uniform, interchangeable, threaded fasteners. Aside from the threaded forms previously mentioned, the pitch of the thread and the major diameters are factors affecting standards.

THREADED HOLES

When a small threaded hole is required on a part, a common method of producing it is to drill a hole (tap drill size), then add threads to the hole by means of a threading tool called a tap. The tap drill size is not specified on the drawing. For a blind hole, the drilled hole is made a little deeper than the depth required for the threads. The tap drill sizes for inch and metric threads are shown in Tables 5 and 6 of the Appendix.

INCH THREADS

Until 1976, nearly all threaded assemblies in North America were designed using inch-sized threads. In this system the pitch is equal to the distance between corresponding points on adjacent threads and is expressed as

$$\text{Pitch} = \frac{1}{\text{Number of threads per inch}}$$

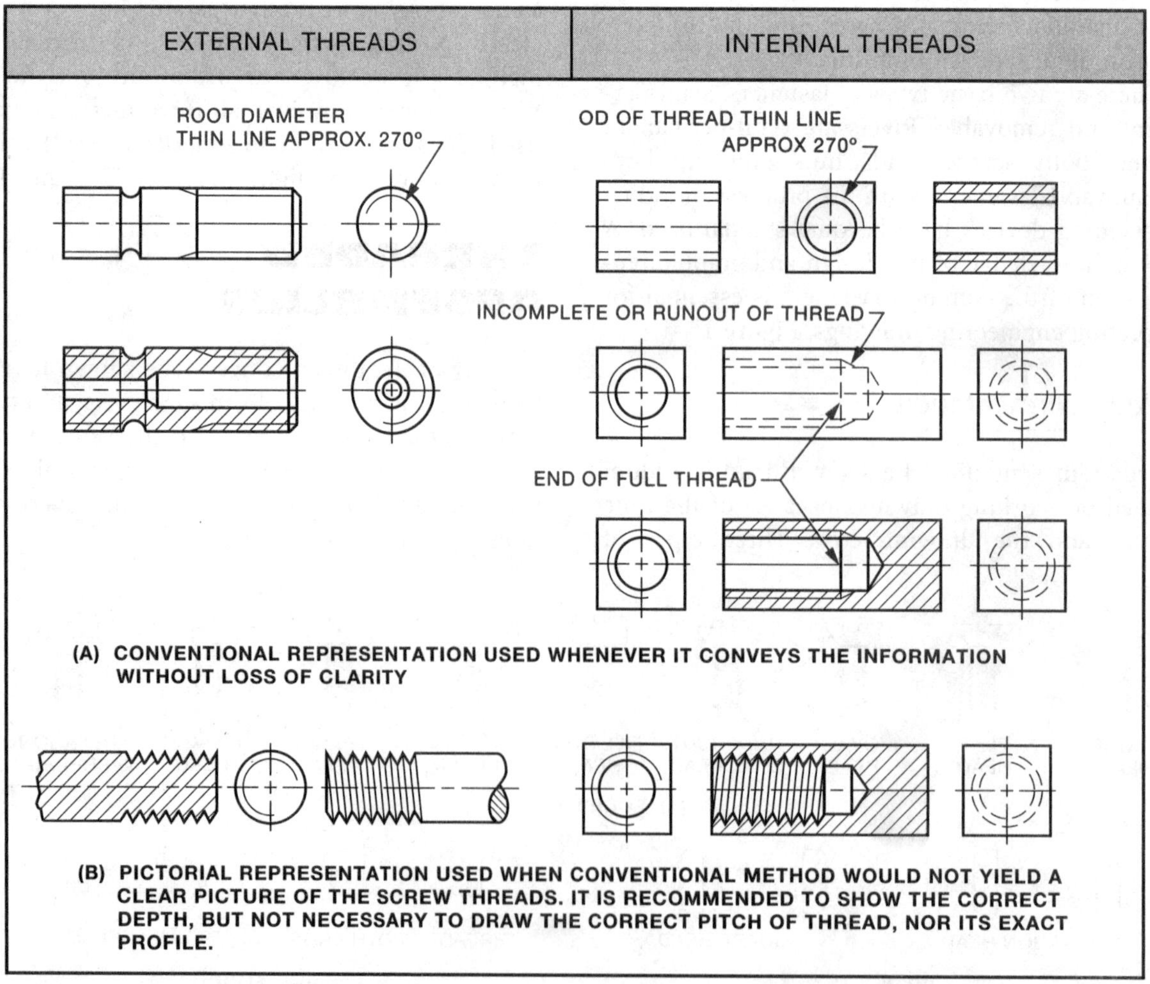

FIGURE 15–2 ■ Standard thread conventions (Canadian and ISO)

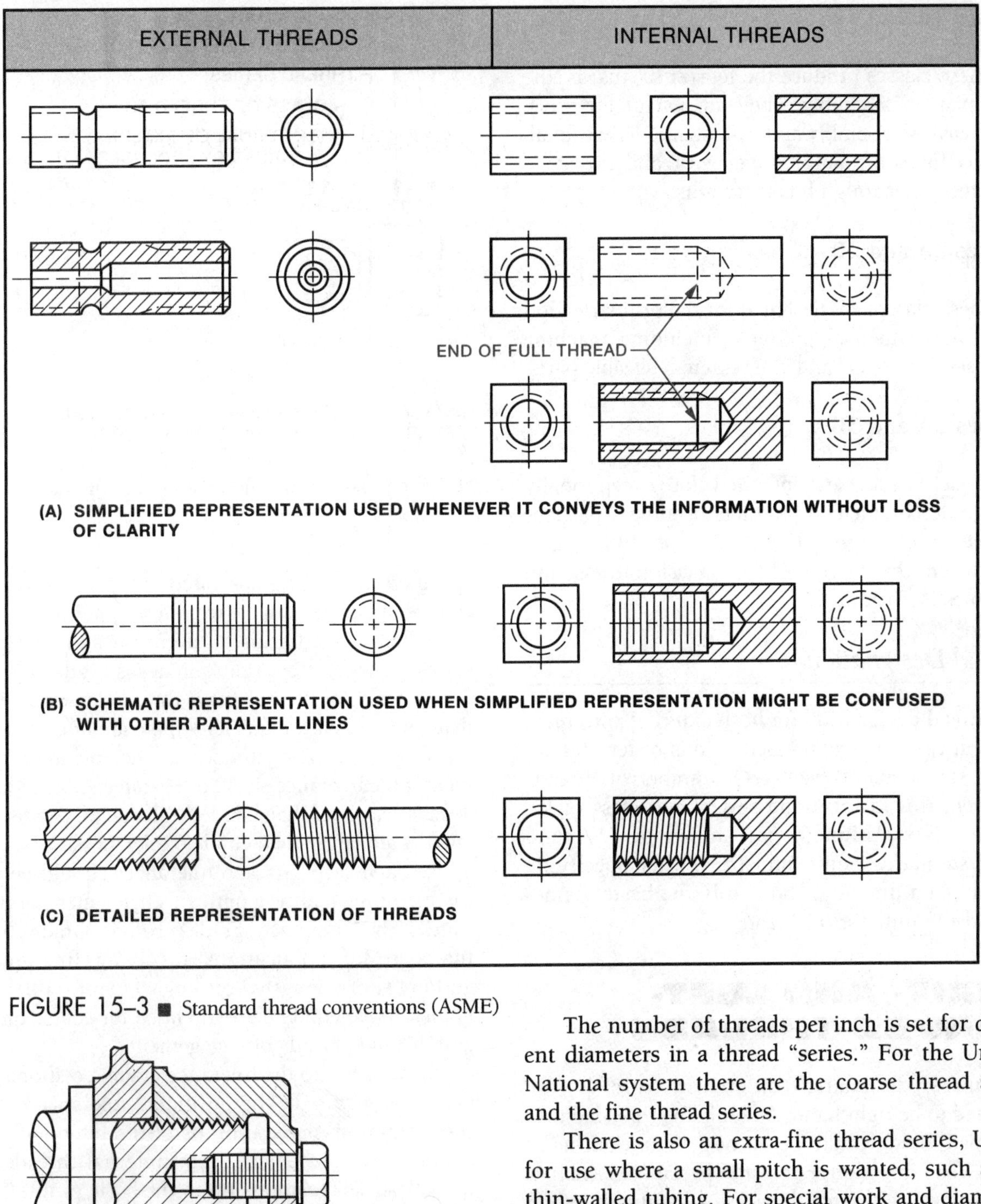
EXTERNAL THREADS
INTERNAL THREADS
END OF FULL THREAD
(A) SIMPLIFIED REPRESENTATION USED WHENEVER IT CONVEYS THE INFORMATION WITHOUT LOSS OF CLARITY
(B) SCHEMATIC REPRESENTATION USED WHEN SIMPLIFIED REPRESENTATION MIGHT BE CONFUSED WITH OTHER PARALLEL LINES
(C) DETAILED REPRESENTATION OF THREADS

FIGURE 15–3 ■ Standard thread conventions (ASME)

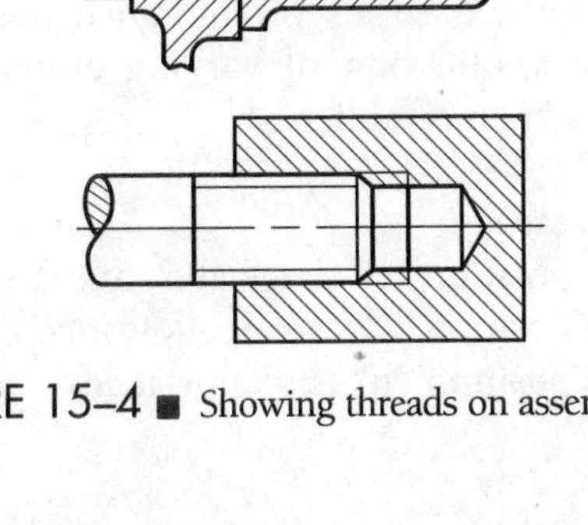

FIGURE 15–4 ■ Showing threads on assembly drawings

The number of threads per inch is set for different diameters in a thread "series." For the Unified National system there are the coarse thread series and the fine thread series.

There is also an extra-fine thread series, UNEF, for use where a small pitch is wanted, such as on thin-walled tubing. For special work and diameters larger than those specified in the coarse and fine series, the Unified Thread system has three series that allow the same number of threads per inch regardless of the diameter. These are the 8-thread series, the 12-thread series, and the 16-thread series.

Three classes of external thread (Classes 1A, 2A, and 3A) and three classes of internal thread (Classes 1B, 2B, and 3B) are provided.

The general characteristics and uses of the classes are as follows:

Classes 1A and 1B

These classes produce the loosest fit, that is, the most play in assembly. They are useful for work where ease of assembly and disassembly is essential, such as for some automotive work and for stove bolts and other rough bolts and nuts.

Classes 2A and 2B

These classes are designed for the ordinary good grade of commercial products, including machine screws and fasteners and most interchangeable parts.

Classes 3A and 3B

These classes are intended for exceptionally high-grade commercial products needing a particularly close or snug fit. Classes 3A and 3B are used only when the high cost of precision tools and machines is warranted.

Thread Designation

Thread designation for both external and internal inch threads is expressed in this order: diameter (basic or major diameter), number of threads per inch, thread form and series, and class of fit, Figure 15–5. Although not shown in CSA and ASME standards, some industries, when specifying threads on a drawing, show only the basic diameter and the number of threads.

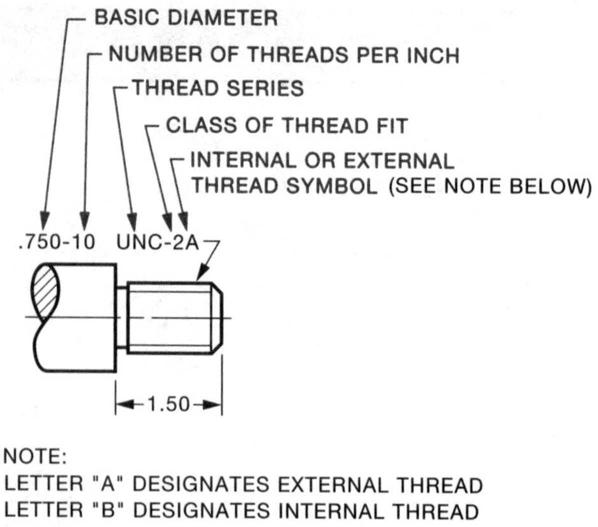

FIGURE 15–5 ■ Specifications for inch threads

RIGHT- AND LEFT-HANDED THREADS

Unless designated differently, threads are assumed to be right hand. A bolt being threaded into a tapped hole would be turned in a right-hand (clockwise) direction. For some special uses, such as turnbuckles, left-hand threads are required. When such a thread is necessary, the letters "LH" are added after the thread designation.

Typical hole and thread callouts are shown in Figure 15–6.

METRIC THREADS

Metric threads are grouped into diameter-pitch combinations differentiated by the pitch applied to specified diameters. The pitch for metric threads is the distance between corresponding points on adjacent teeth. In addition to a coarse and fine pitch series, a series of constant pitches is available.

For each of the two main thread elements—pitch diameter and crest diameter—there are numerous tolerance grades. The number of the tolerance grade reflects the tolerance size. For example: Grade 4 tolerances are smaller than Grade 6 tolerances; Grade 8 tolerances are larger than Grade 6 tolerances.

In each case, Grade 6 tolerances should be used for medium quality length of engagement applications. The tolerance grades below Grade 6 are intended for applications involving fine quality and/or short lengths of engagement. Tolerance grades above Grade 6 are intended for coarse quality and/or long periods of engagement.

In addition to the tolerance grade, positional tolerance is required. The positional tolerance defines the maximum-material limits of the pitch and crest diameters of the external and internal threads and indicates their relationship to the basic profile.

In conformance with current coating (or plating) thickness requirements and the demand for ease of assembly, a series of tolerance positions reflecting the application of varying amounts of allowance has been established.

For External Threads:

Tolerance position "e" (large allowance)
Tolerance position "g" (small allowance)
Tolerance position "h" (no allowance)

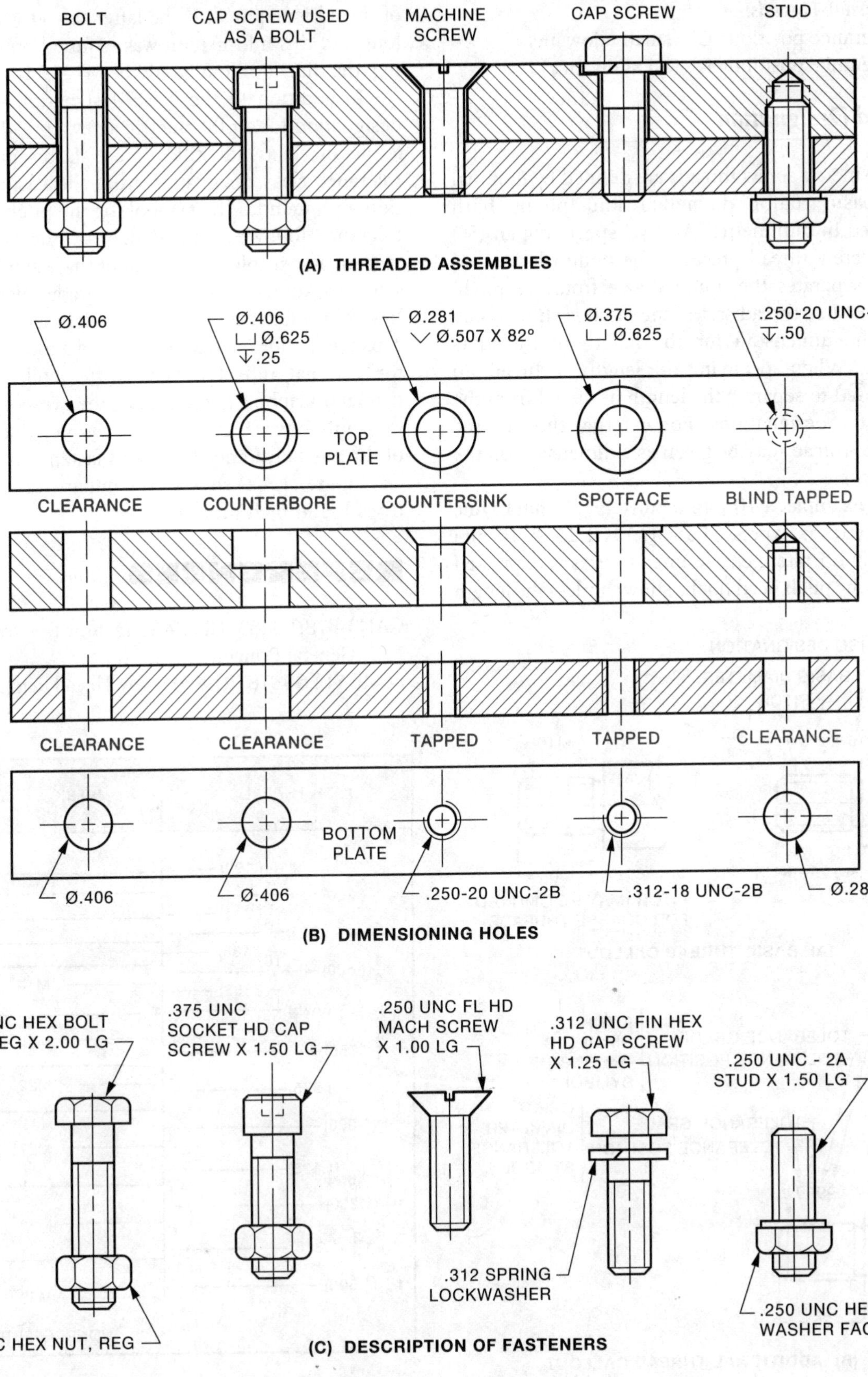
BOLT
CAP SCREW USED AS A BOLT
MACHINE SCREW
CAP SCREW
STUD
(A) THREADED ASSEMBLIES
Ø.406
Ø.406
⌴ Ø.625
↧.25
Ø.281
⌵ Ø.507 X 82°
Ø.375
⌴ Ø.625
.250-20 UNC-2B
↧.50
TOP PLATE
CLEARANCE
COUNTERBORE
COUNTERSINK
SPOTFACE
BLIND TAPPED
CLEARANCE
CLEARANCE
TAPPED
TAPPED
CLEARANCE
BOTTOM PLATE
Ø.406
Ø.406
.250-20 UNC-2B
.312-18 UNC-2B
Ø.281
(B) DIMENSIONING HOLES
.375 UNC HEX BOLT FIN REG X 2.00 LG
.375 UNC SOCKET HD CAP SCREW X 1.50 LG
.250 UNC FL HD MACH SCREW X 1.00 LG
.312 UNC FIN HEX HD CAP SCREW X 1.25 LG
.250 UNC - 2A STUD X 1.50 LG
.312 SPRING LOCKWASHER
375 UNC HEX NUT, REG
.250 UNC HEX NUT, WASHER FACE
(C) DESCRIPTION OF FASTENERS

FIGURE 15–6 ■ Common threaded fasteners

For Internal Threads:

Tolerance position "G" (small allowance)
Tolerance position "H" (no allowance)

Thread Designation

ISO metric screw threads are defined by nominal size (basic major diameter) and pitch, both expressed in millimetres. An "M" specifying an ISO metric screw thread precedes the nominal size and an "X" separates the nominal size from the pitch. For the coarse thread series, the pitch is shown only when the dimension for the length of thread is required. When specifying the length of thread, an "X" is used to separate the length of thread from the rest of the designations. For external threads, the length of thread may be given as a dimension on the drawing.

For example, a 10 mm diameter, 1.25 pitch, fine thread series is expressed as M10 × 1.25. A 10 mm diameter, 1.5 pitch, coarse thread series is expressed as M10; the pitch need not be shown unless the length of thread is required. If the latter thread was 25 mm long and this information was required on the drawing, the thread callout would be M10 × 1.5 × 25.

In addition to the basic designation, complete designation for an ISO metric screw thread includes a tolerance class identification. A dash separates the tolerance class designation from the basic designation and includes the symbol for the pitch diameter tolerance followed immediately by the symbol for crest diameter tolerance. Each of these symbols consists of a numeral indicating the grade tolerance followed by a letter indicating the tolerance position (a capital letter for internal threads and a lowercase letter for external threads). Where the pitch and crest diameter symbols are identical, the symbol is necessary only once. Figure 15–7 illustrates the labelling of threaded clearance holes and fasteners.

Figure 15–8 shows a comparison of metric threads and inch threads.

REFERENCES

CAN3-B78.1-M83 (R1990) Technical Drawings—General Principles
ASME Y14.6-1978 (R1998) Screw Thread Representation

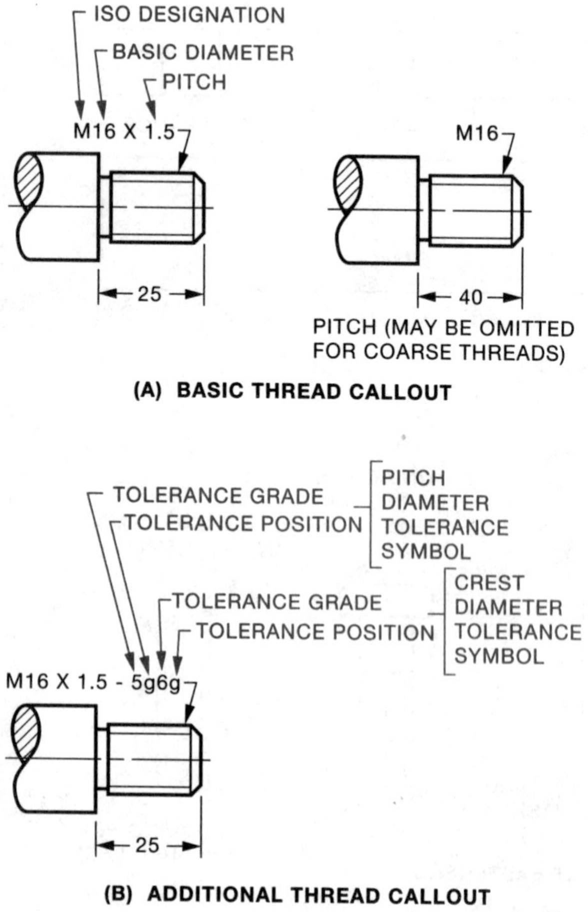

FIGURE 15–7 ■ Specifications for metric threads

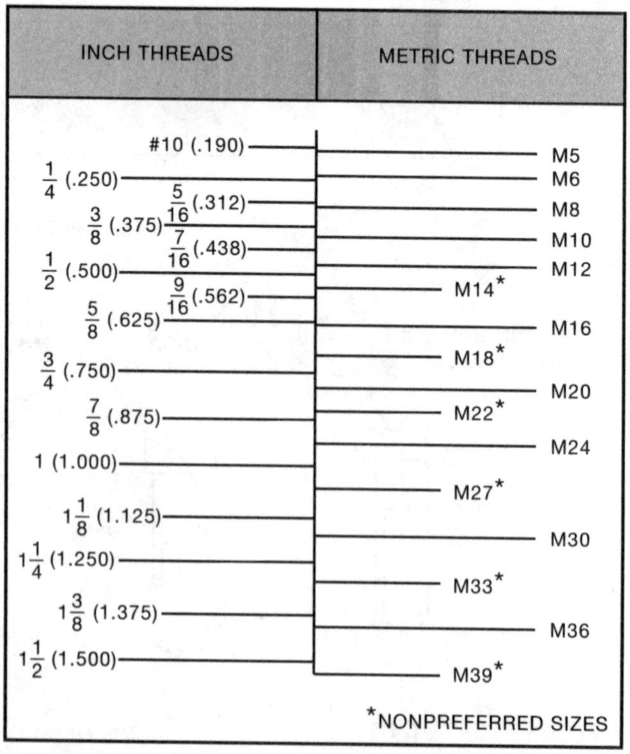

FIGURE 15–8 ■ Size comparison of inch and metric threads

NOTE: ROUNDS AND FILLETS R.25 EXCEPT WHERE OTHERWISE NOTED.

√ TO BE 125√

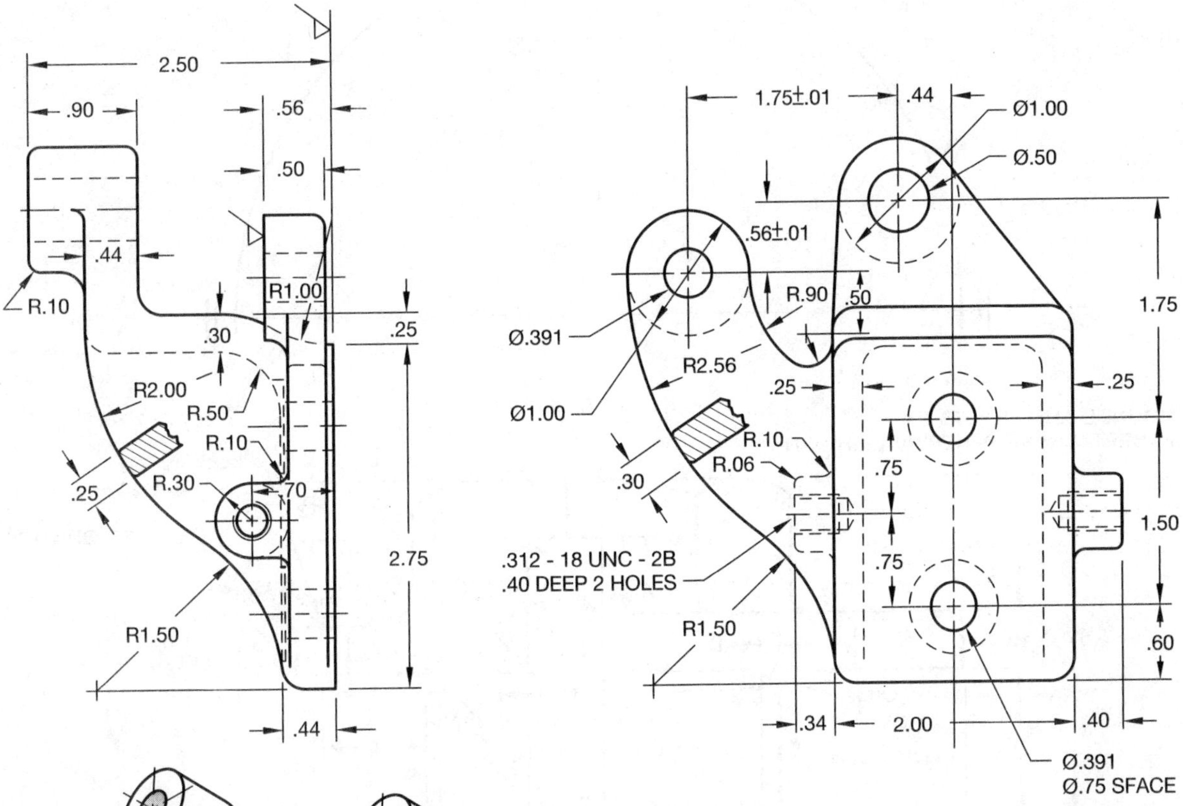
2.50
.90
.56
.50
.44
R.10
R1.00
.30
.25
R2.00
R.50
R.10
.25
R.30
.70
2.75
R1.50
.44
1.75±.01
.44
Ø1.00
Ø.50
.56±.01
R.90
.50
1.75
Ø.391
R2.56
.25
.25
Ø1.00
R.10
R.06
.30
.75
1.50
.312 - 18 UNC - 2B
.40 DEEP 2 HOLES
.75
R1.50
.60
.34
2.00
.40
Ø.391
Ø.75 SFACE

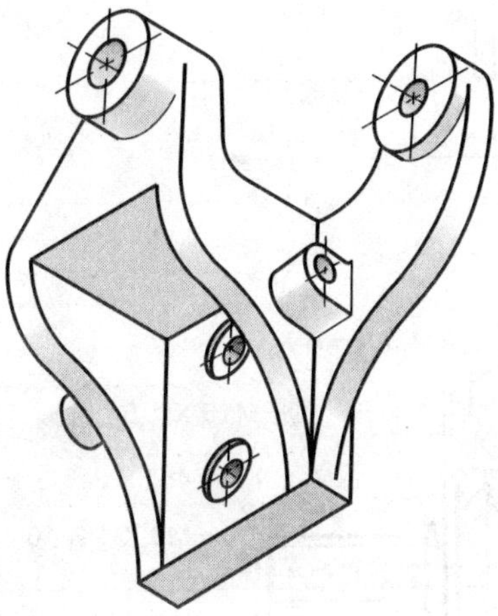

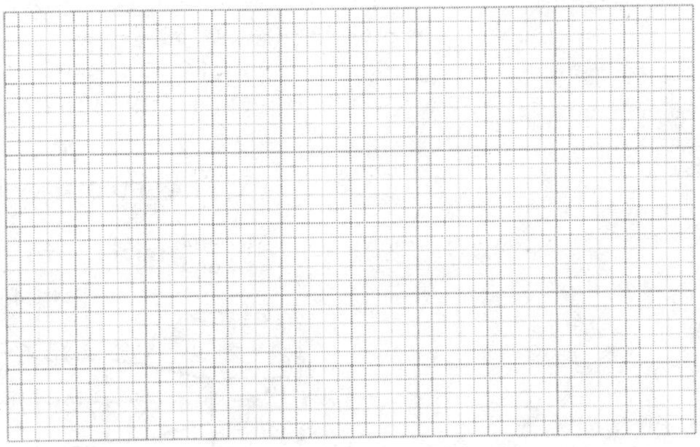

1.00 INCH SQUARES (.10 IN. GRID)

ASSIGNMENT: MAKE A FREEHAND SKETCH ON THE GRAPH SECTION PROVIDED, SHOWING THE BOTTOM VIEW OF THE SHAFT INTERMEDIATE SUPPORT. IF CERTAIN DIMENSIONS CAN BE SHOWN BETTER ON THE BOTTOM VIEW, DUPLICATE THEM.

MATERIAL GI	
SCALE	
DRAWN	DATE
SHAFT INTERMEDIATE SUPPORT	**A-40**

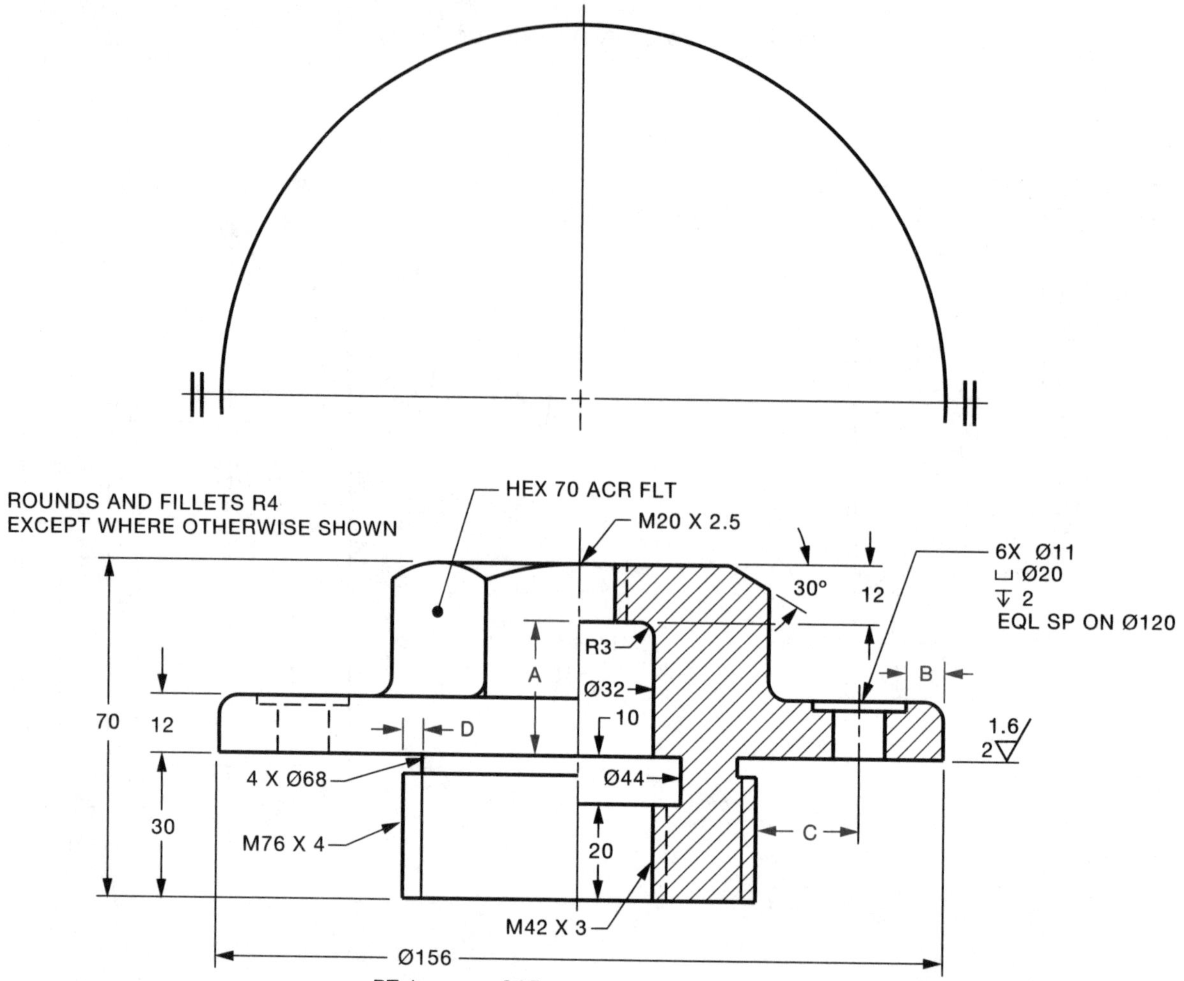
ROUNDS AND FILLETS R4
EXCEPT WHERE OTHERWISE SHOWN
HEX 70 ACR FLT
M20 X 2.5
30°
12
6X Ø11
⌴ Ø20
↧ 2
EQL SP ON Ø120
R3
A
Ø32
B
70
12
10
D
1.6
2
4 X Ø68
Ø44
30
C
M76 X 4
20
M42 X 3
Ø156

PT 1 CAP
MATL - GI 4 REQD

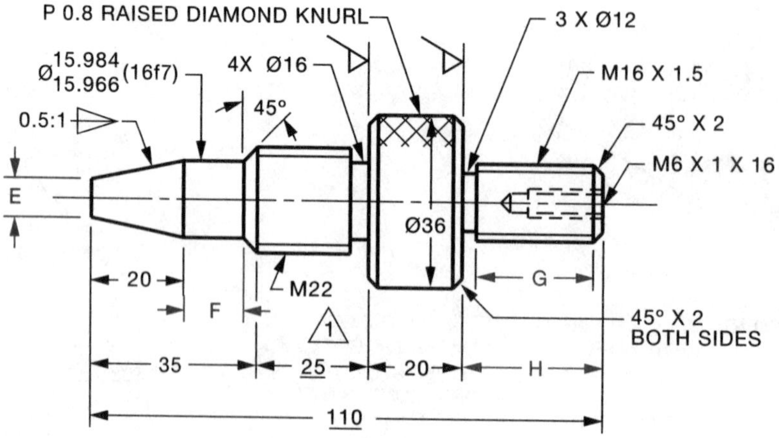
P 0.8 RAISED DIAMOND KNURL
3 X Ø12
Ø15.984 15.966 (16f7)
4X Ø16
M16 X 1.5
0.5:1
45°
45° X 2
M6 X 1 X 16
E
Ø36
20
M22
G
F
1
45° X 2
BOTH SIDES
35
25
20
H
110

PT 2 CONNECTOR
MATL - MS 6 REQD

REVISIONS	1	MAY 27/02	R. HINES
	25 IN PT 2 WAS 30		

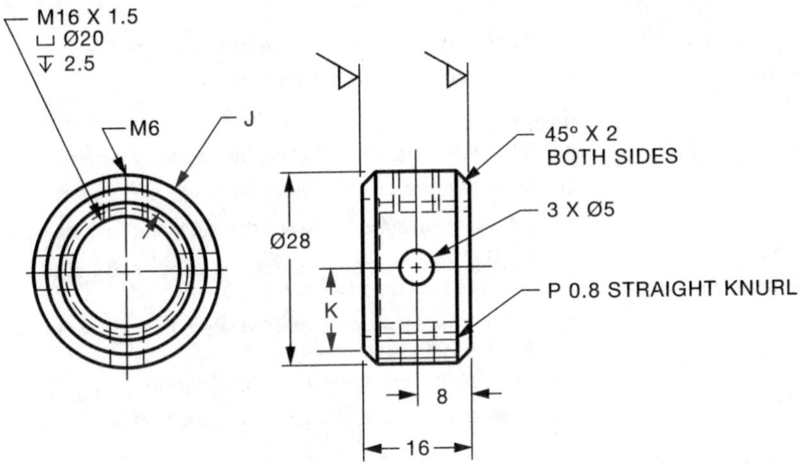
M16 X 1.5
⌴ Ø20
↧ 2.5
M6
J
45° X 2
BOTH SIDES
3 X Ø5
Ø28
K
P 0.8 STRAIGHT KNURL
8
16

PT 3 NUT
MATL - BRASS 12 REQD

NOTE: UNLESS OTHERWISE SHOWN:
—TOLERANCES ON DIMENSIONS ±0.5
—TOLERANCES ON ANGLES ±30'

SURFACES ✓ TO BE 3.2✓

ANSWERS

1. A ______
   B ______
   C ______
   D ______
   E ______
   F ______
   G ______
   H ______
   J ______
   K ______
2. ______
3. ______
4. ______
5. ______
6. ______
7. ______
8. ______
9. ______
10. ______
11. ______
12. ______
13. ______
14. ______
15. ______
16. ______
17. ______
18. ______
19. ______
20. A ______
    B ______

QUESTIONS

1. Calculate dimensions A to K.

Refer to Part 1

2. How many holes are in the part?
3. How many external threads are on the part?
4. How many internal threads are in the part?
5. What is the pitch for the M20 thread?
6. How many complete threads are on the M20 hole?
7. How many complete threads are on the M42 section?
8. What is the diameter of the spotface?
9. What is the angle between the Ø11 holes?
10. How much extra metal was provided on the surface that required machining?

Refer to Part 2

11. What is the pitch of the internal thread?
12. What is the pitch on the M22 thread?
13. What provides for better gripping when rotating the part?
14. How many undercuts are shown?
15. How many chamfers are required?

Refer to Part 3

16. How many holes are in the part?
17. What is the depth of the counterbore?
18. How many full threads has the M16 hole?
19. What surface finish is required for the sides of the knurled portion?
20. What are the tap drill sizes required for the (A) M6 and (B) M16 threaded holes?

METRIC
DIMENSIONS ARE IN MILLIMETRES

ASSIGNMENT: SKETCH THE TOP HALF OF PART 1 IN THE SPACE PROVIDED.

DRIVE SUPPORT DETAILS

A-41M

QUESTIONS

1. Calculate dimensions Ⓐ to Ⓙ.
2. How many threaded holes or shafts are shown?
3. How many chamfers are shown?
4. How many necks are shown?
5. How many surfaces require finishing?

Refer to Part 1

6. What are the limit sizes for the Ø.64 dimension?
7. What operation provides better gripping when turning the clamping nut?
8. What is the tap drill size?
9. Is the thread right hand or left hand?
10. What is the depth of the threads?

Refer to Part 2

11. What is the length of the thread?
12. Is the thread pitch fine or coarse?
13. What heat treatment does the part undergo?
14. How many threads are there in a 1-in. length?

Refer to Part 3

15. What is the maximum permissible width of the part?
16. What size thread is cut on the underside of the piece?
17. What is the distance between the last thread and the flange?
18. What is the tolerance on the centre-to-centre distance between the tapped holes?
19. What is the smallest diameter to which the hole through the stuffing box can be made?
20. What are the limits of the Ø2.000 dimension?
21. What is the tap drill size for the threaded holes?

NOTE: EXCEPT WHERE NOTED:
—TOLERANCE ON TWO-PLACE DIMENSIONS ±.02
—TOLERANCE ON THREE-PLACE DIMENSIONS ±.005
—TOLERANCE ON ANGLES ±0.5°

32 ✓ EXCEPT WHERE NOTED

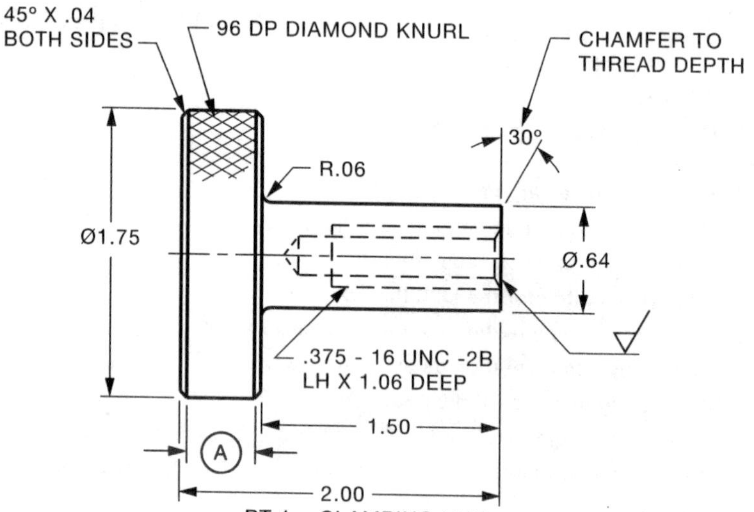

PT 1 CLAMPING NUT
MATL CRS, 16 REQD

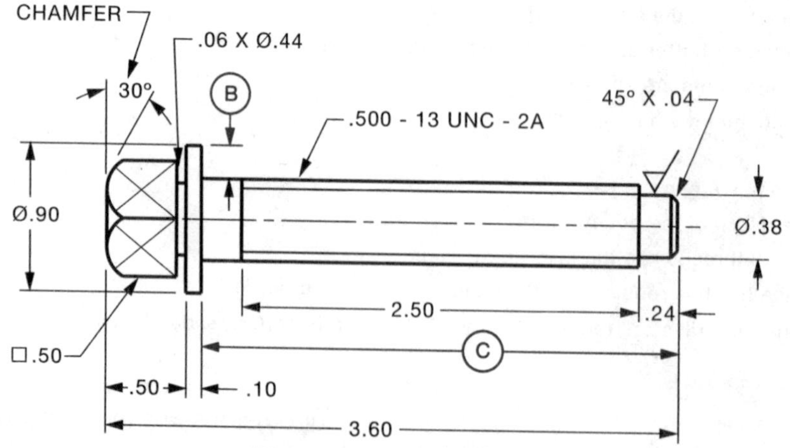

PT 2 ADJUSTING SCREW
MATERIAL CRS CASE HARDEN, 8 REQD

ANSWERS

1. A ______	2. ______	8. ______	15. ______
B ______	3. ______	9. ______	16. ______
C ______	4. ______	10. ______	17. ______
D ______	5. ______	11. ______	18. ______
E ______	6. ______	12. ______	19. ______
F ______	______	13. ______	20. ______
G ______	7. ______	14. ______	21. ______
H ______			
J ______			

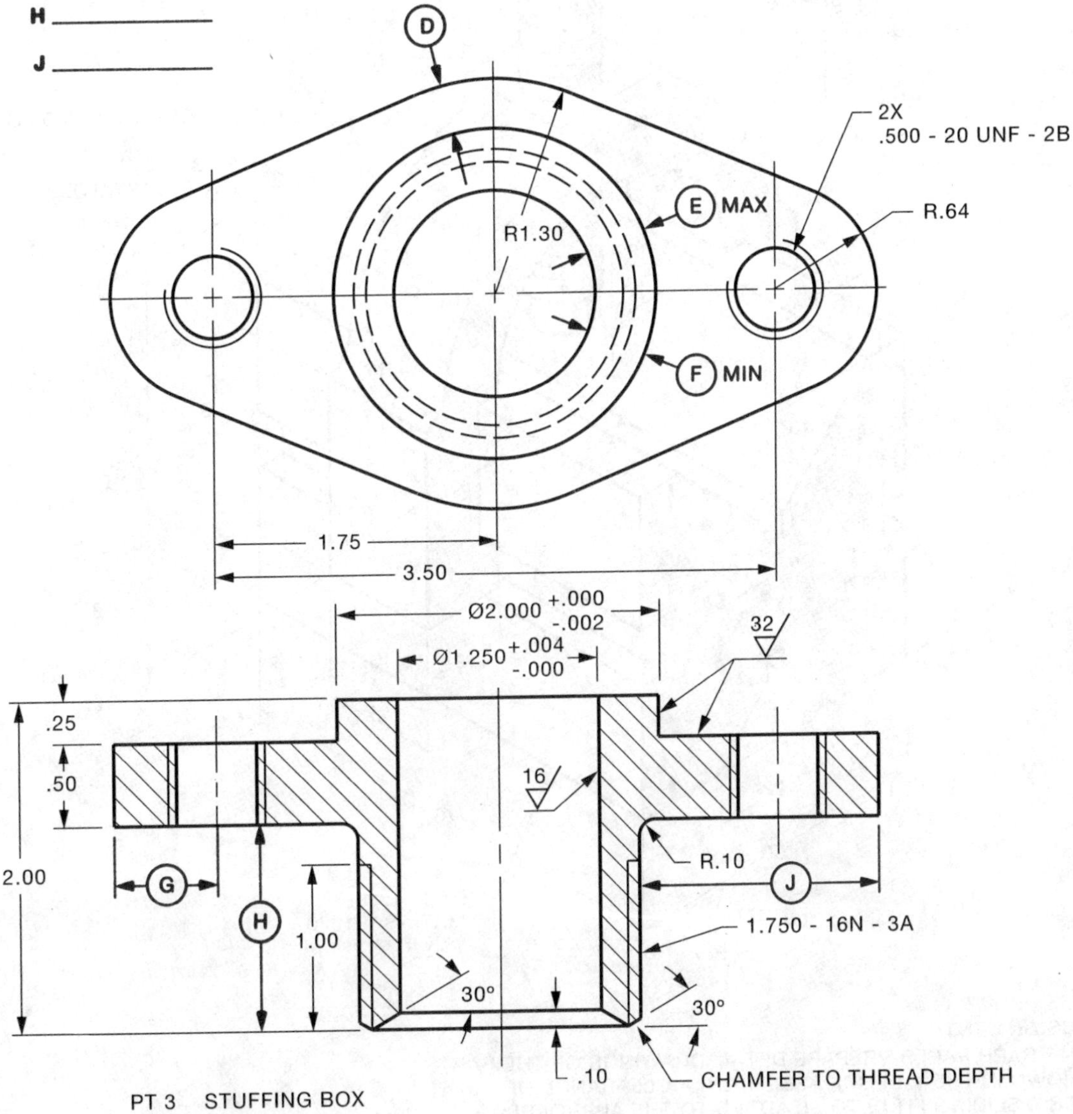

D
2X
.500 - 20 UNF - 2B
E MAX
R.64
R1.30
F MIN
1.75
3.50
Ø2.000 +.000 -.002
Ø1.250 +.004 -.000
32
.25
.50
16
2.00
G
H
1.00
R.10
J
1.750 - 16N - 3A
30°
30°
.10
CHAMFER TO THREAD DEPTH

PT 3 STUFFING BOX
MATL BRONZE, 2 REQD

SCALE NOT TO SCALE	
DRAWN	DATE
HOUSING DETAILS	A-42

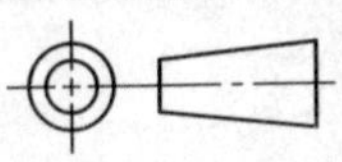

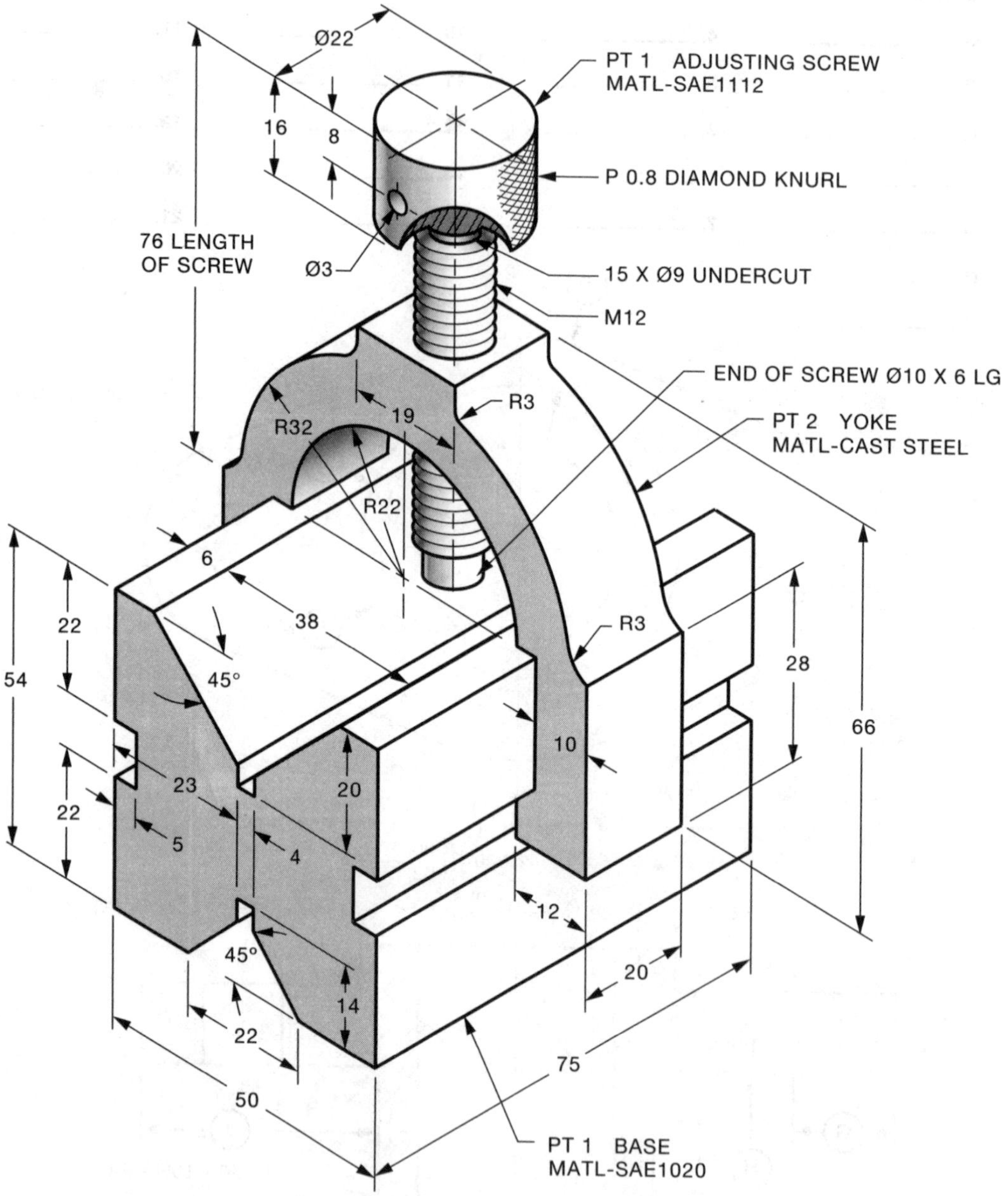
Ø22
PT 1 ADJUSTING SCREW
MATL-SAE1112
16
8
P 0.8 DIAMOND KNURL
76 LENGTH OF SCREW
Ø3
15 X Ø9 UNDERCUT
M12
END OF SCREW Ø10 X 6 LG
R32
19
R3
PT 2 YOKE
MATL-CAST STEEL
R22
6
38
R3
22
54
45°
28
66
10
23
20
22
5
4
12
45°
20
14
22
75
50
PT 1 BASE
MATL-SAE1020

ASSIGNMENT:
ON GRAPH PAPER PREPARE DETAIL DRAWINGS OF THE PARTS SHOWN IN THE V-BLOCK ASSEMBLY. A CLEARANCE OF 1 mm FOR A SLIDING FIT IS TO BE ADDED TO THE APPROPRIATE YOKE DIMENSIONS.

METRIC
DIMENSIONS ARE IN MILLIMETRES

	V-BLOCK ASSEMBLY	A-43M

UNIT 16

REVOLVED AND REMOVED SECTIONS

In Unit 8 you were introduced to full, half, and offset sectional views and how they were shown on drawings. For many drawings only a portion of a complete view needs to be shown in section to improve the clarity of the drawing. Two additional types of sectional views are introduced in this unit.

Revolved and removed sections are used to show the cross-sectional shape of ribs, spokes, or arms when the shape is not obvious in the regular views. End views are often not needed when a revolved section is used.

Revolved Sections

For a *revolved section* a centre line is drawn through the shape on the plane to be described, the part is imagined to be rotated 90 degrees, and the view that would be seen when rotated is superimposed on the view. If the revolved section does not interfere with the view on which it is revolved, then the view is not broken unless it would facilitate clearer dimensioning. When the revolved section interferes or passes through lines on the view on which it is revolved, the view is usually broken. Often the break is used to shorten the length of the object. When superimposed on the view, the outline of the revolved section is a thin continuous line, Figure 16–1.

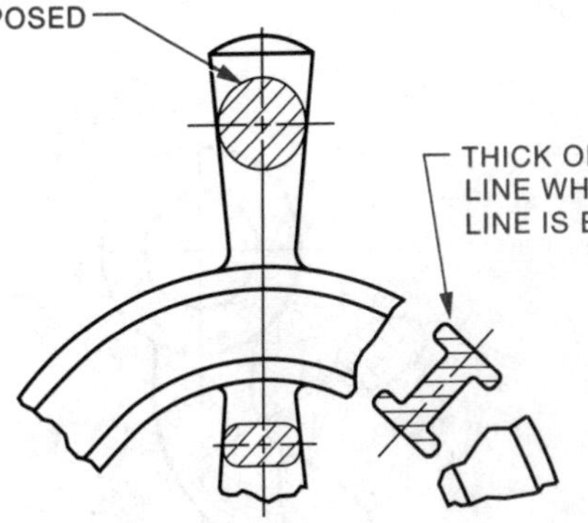
THIN OBJECT
LINE WHEN
SUPERIMPOSED
THICK OBJECT
LINE WHEN
LINE IS BROKEN

FIGURE 16–1 ■ Revolved section

Removed Sections

The *removed section* differs from the revolved section in that the section is removed to an open area on the drawing instead of being drawn directly on the view. Whenever practical, sectional views should be projected perpendicular to the cutting plane and be placed in the normal position for third-angle projection, Figures 16–2, 16–3, 16–4, and 16–5. Frequently, the removed section is drawn to an enlarged scale for clarification and easier dimensioning.

Removed sections of symmetrical parts are placed on the extension of the centre line where possible.

Broken-out and partial sections are explained and illustrated in Unit 28.

REFERENCES

CAN3-B78.1-M83 (R1990) Technical Drawings—General Principles

ASME Y14.3M-1994 Multi and Sectional View Drawings

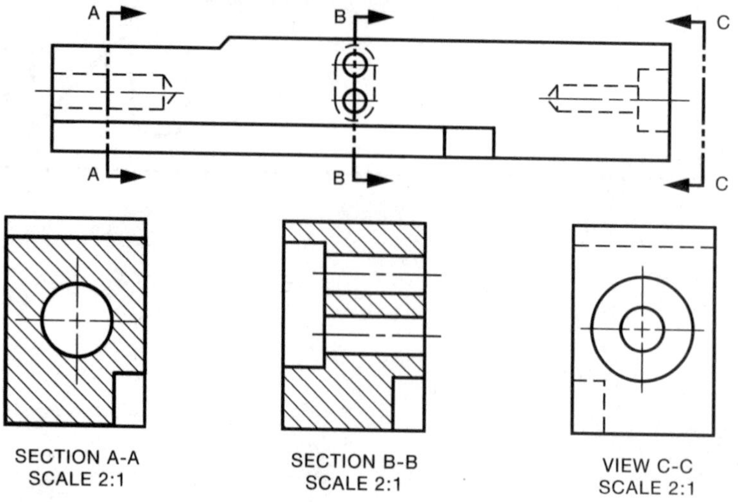
A
A
B
B
C
C
SECTION A-A
SCALE 2:1
SECTION B-B
SCALE 2:1
VIEW C-C
SCALE 2:1

FIGURE 16–2 ■ Removed sections and removed view

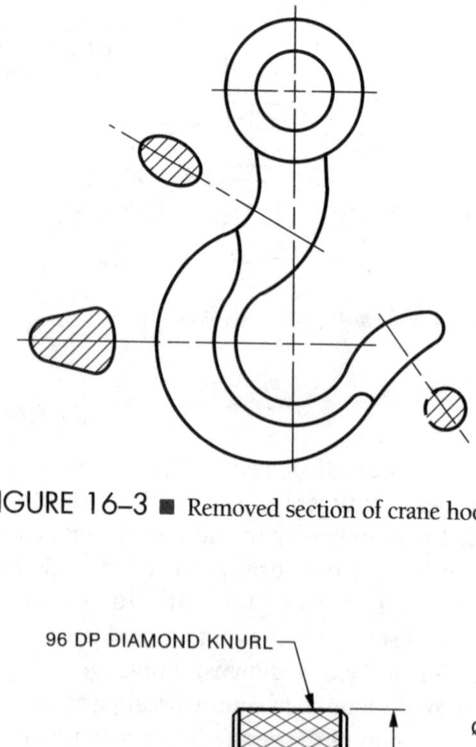

FIGURE 16–3 ■ Removed section of crane hook

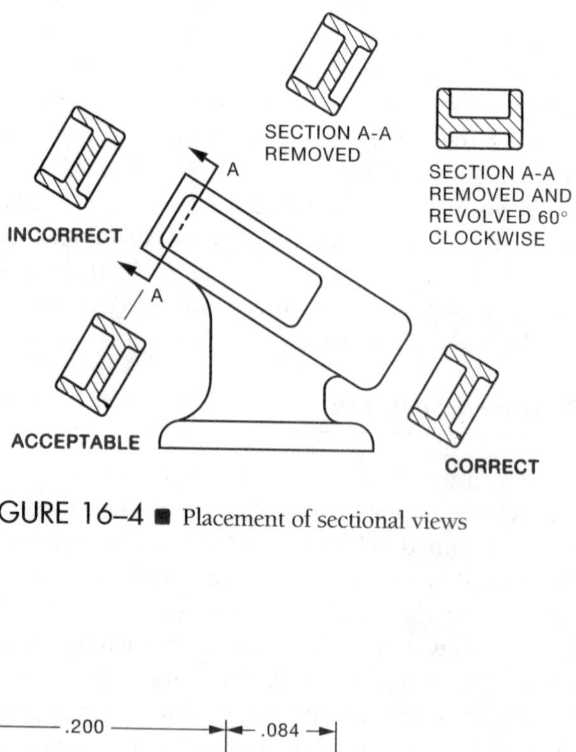
SECTION A-A
REMOVED
SECTION A-A
REMOVED AND
REVOLVED 60°
CLOCKWISE
A
A
INCORRECT
ACCEPTABLE
CORRECT

FIGURE 16–4 ■ Placement of sectional views

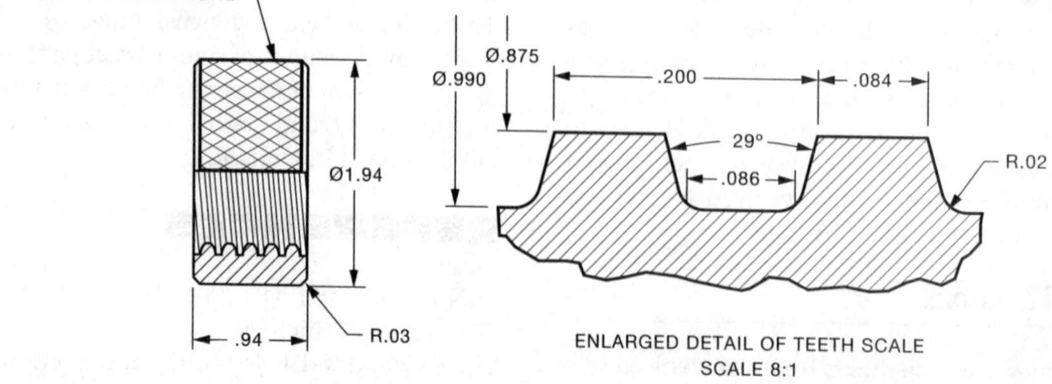
96 DP DIAMOND KNURL
Ø1.94
.94
R.03
Ø.875
Ø.990
.200
.084
29°
.086
R.02
ENLARGED DETAIL OF TEETH SCALE
SCALE 8:1

FIGURE 16–5 ■ Removed section of nut

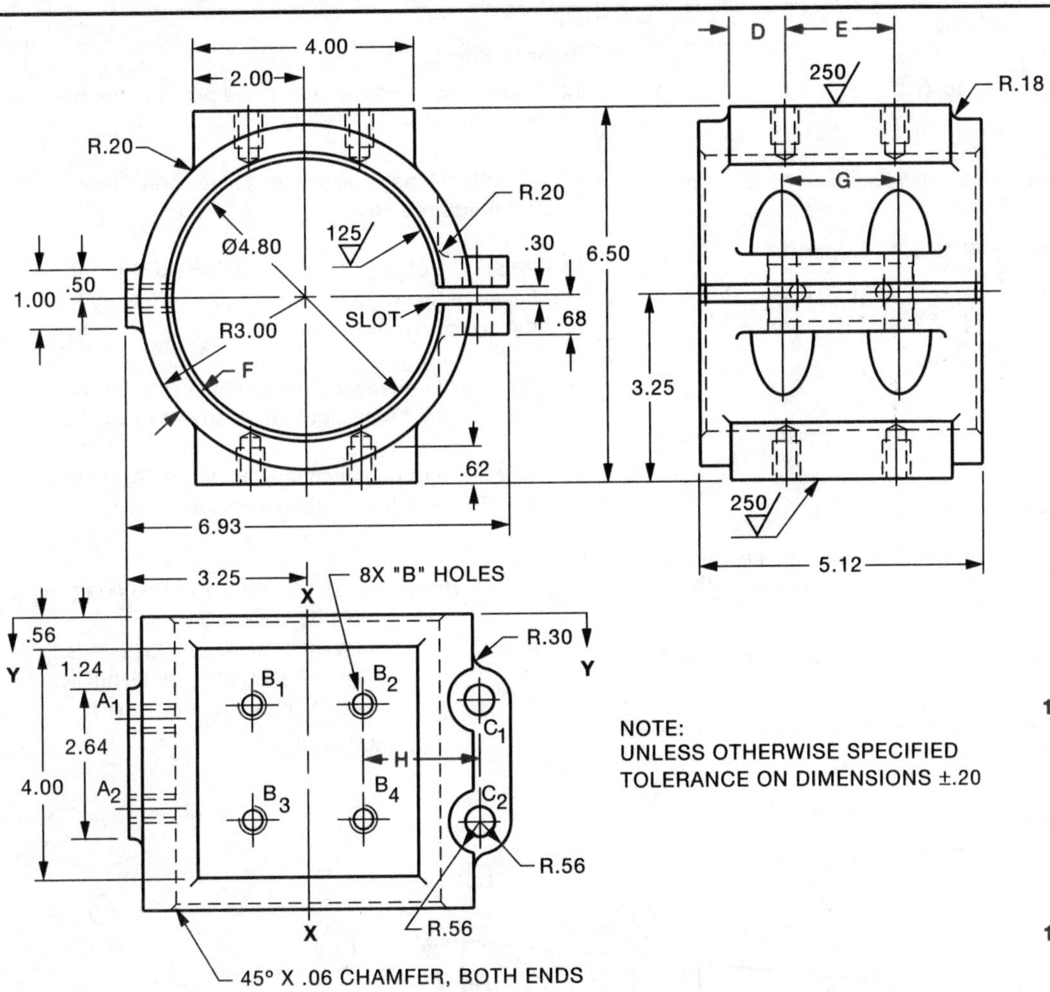

NOTE:
UNLESS OTHERWISE SPECIFIED
TOLERANCE ON DIMENSIONS ±.20

ANSWERS

1. A ______
   B ______
   C ______
2. ______
3. ______
4. ______
5. ______
6. ______
7. ______
8. ______
9. ______
10. D ______
    E ______
    F ______
    G ______
    H ______
11. A ______
    B ______

QUESTIONS

1. What is the centre-to-centre distance between the following?
   (A) the A_1 and A_2 holes
   (B) the B_1 and B_2 holes
   (C) the C_1 and C_2 holes
2. What finish is required on the 4.00 x 4.00 face?
3. How far apart are the two surfaces of the slot?
4. How many surfaces require finishing?
5. What is the depth of the A holes?
6. What is the length of the threading in the B holes?
7. What size bolts would be used in the C holes if .031 clearance is used?
8. How many chamfers are called for?
9. How many tapped holes are there?
10. Calculate distances D, E, F, G, and H.
11. What is the tap drill size required for the (A) #10 and (B) .500 threaded holes?

HOLE	HOLE SIZE	LOCATION	
		X-X	Y-Y
A_1	10-24		1.78
A_2	10-24		3.32
B_1	.500 -13	1.00	1.56
B_2	.500 -13	1.00	1.56
B_3	.500 -13	1.00	3.56
B_4	.500 -13	1.00	3.56
C_1	Ø.531	3.12	1.50
C_2	Ø.531	3.12	3.62

MATERIAL	COPPER	
SCALE	NOT TO SCALE	
DRAWN		DATE
	TERMINAL BLOCK	**A-44**

QUESTIONS

1. Calculate distances (A) to (K).
2. How many surfaces require finishing ?
3. What tolerance is permitted on dimensions that do not specify a certain tolerance?
4. What type of section view is used on part 1?
5. What type of section view is used on part 2?
6. How many holes are there?

Refer to Part 1

7. What is the maximum centre-to-centre distance between the holes?
8. Which surface finish is required?
9. Using the smallest permissible hole size as the basic size, replace the limit dimensions for the larger hole with plus-and-minus tolerances.
10. What is the maximum permissible wall thickness at the larger hole?
11. What would be the minimum permissible wall thickness at the smaller hole?

Refer to Part 2

12. Name two machines that could produce the type of finish required for the slot.
13. What is the nominal size machine screw used in the counterbored holes?
14. What type of cap screw should be used if the heads of these screws must not protrude above the surface of the support?
15. What is the distance between the centre of the counterbored holes and the centre of the slot?
16. What type of tolerance is used on the (A) Ø1.250 hole and (B) 3.250 horizontal dimension?

NOTE: EXCEPT WHERE STATED OTHERWISE:
—TOLERANCES ON
TWO-DECIMAL DIMENSIONS ±.02
THREE-DECIMAL DIMENSIONS ±.005
—ROUNDS AND FILLETS R.10
MACHINE FINISH 32

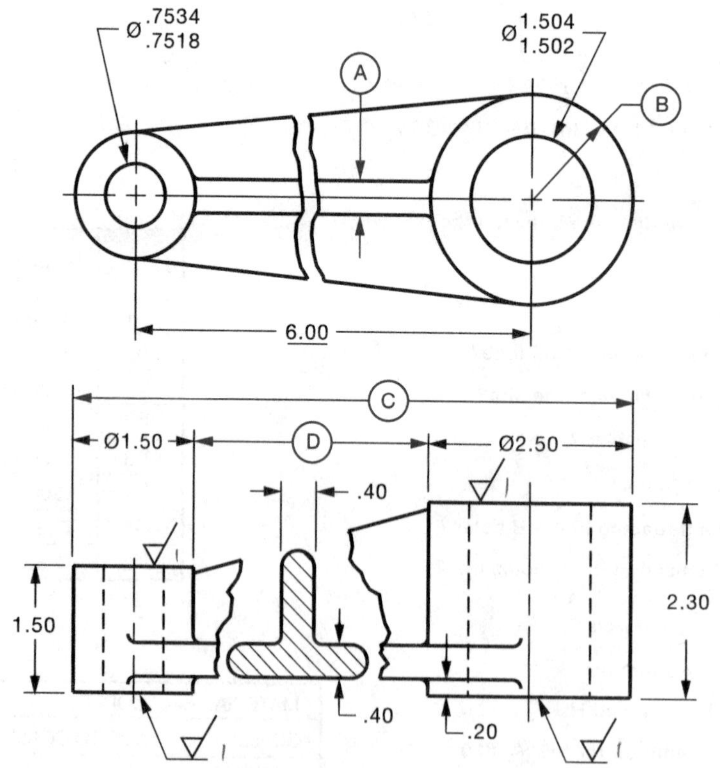

PT 1 SHAFT SUPPORT
MATL-MI

ANSWERS

1. A ______	H ______	6. ______	13. ______
B ______	J ______	7. ______	14. ______
C ______	K ______	8. ______	15. ______
D ______	2. ______	9. ______	16. A ______
E ______	3. ______	10. ______	B ______
F ______	4. ______	11. ______	
G ______	5. ______	12. ______	
		______	

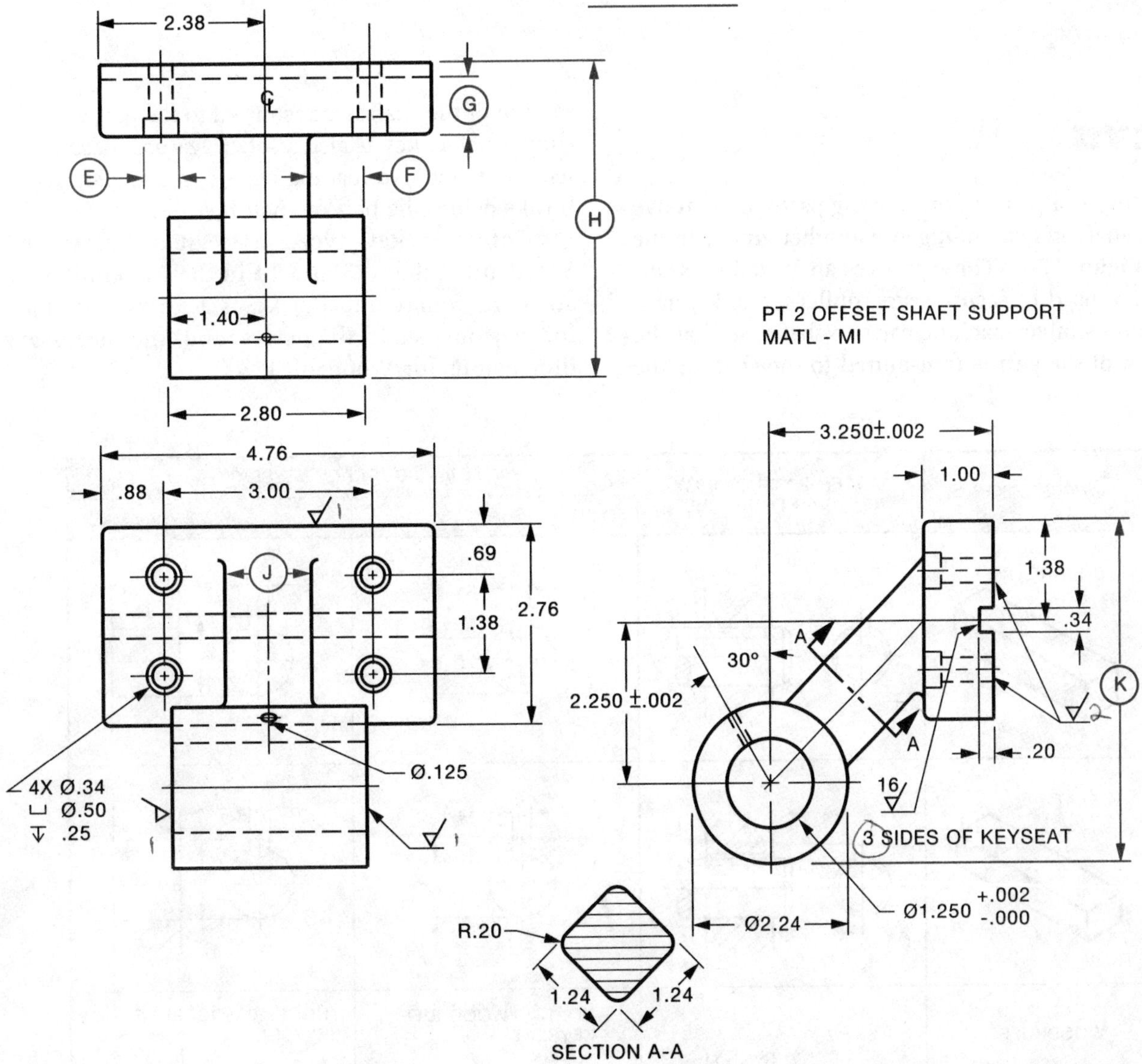

SCALE NOT TO SCALE		
DRAWN		DATE
	SHAFT SUPPORTS	**A-45**

17 UNIT

KEYS

A *key* is a piece of metal lying partly in a groove in the shaft and extending into another groove in the hub, Figure 17–1. These grooves are called *keyseats*. Keys are used to secure gears, pulleys, cranks, handles, and similar machine parts to shafts, so that the motion of the part is transmitted to the shaft or the motion of the shaft is transmitted to the part without slippage. The key is also a safety feature. Because of its size, when overloading occurs, the key shears or breaks before the part or shaft breaks.

Common key types are square, flat, and Woodruff. Tables 13 and 14 in the Appendix give standard square and flat key sizes recommended for various shaft diameters and the necessary dimensions for Woodruff keys.

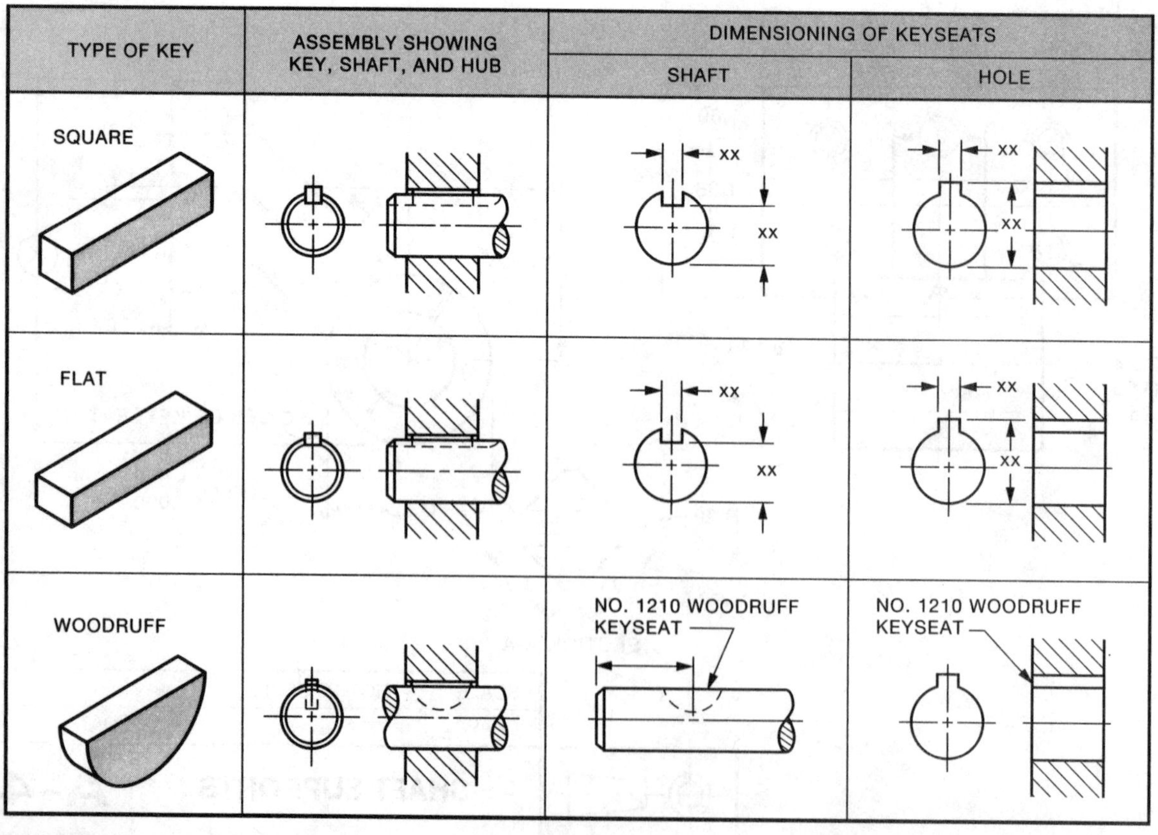

TYPE OF KEY
ASSEMBLY SHOWING KEY, SHAFT, AND HUB
DIMENSIONING OF KEYSEATS
SHAFT
HOLE
SQUARE
XX
XX
XX
XX
FLAT
XX
XX
XX
XX
WOODRUFF
NO. 1210 WOODRUFF KEYSEAT
NO. 1210 WOODRUFF KEYSEAT

FIGURE 17–1 ■ Common keys

The *Woodruff key* is semicircular and fits into a semicircular keyseat in the shaft and a rectangular keyseat in the hub. Woodruff keys currently are available only in inch sizes, and are identified by a three- or four-digit key number. The last two numbers give the nominal diameter in eighths of an inch. The digit or digits preceding the last two digits gives the key width in thirty-secondths of an inch. For example, a No. 1210 Woodruff key indicates a key 12/32 inch wide by 10/8 (1.25) inches in diameter.

Dimensioning of Keyseats

Keyseat dimensions are usually given in limit dimensions to ensure proper fits and are located from the opposite side of the hole or shaft, Figure 17–2. Alternatively, for unit production where the machinist is expected to fit the key into the keyseat, a leader pointing to the keyseat, specifying first the width and then the depth of the keyseat, may be used. See Part 2, Rack Details, drawing A–47.

SETSCREWS

Setscrews are used as semipermanent fasteners to hold a collar, sheave, or gear on a shaft against rotational or translational forces. In contrast to most fastening devices, the setscrew is essentially a compression device. Forces developed by the screw point during tightening produce a strong clamping action that resists relative motion between assembled parts. The basic problem in setscrew selection is finding the best combination of setscrew form, size, and point style providing the required holding power.

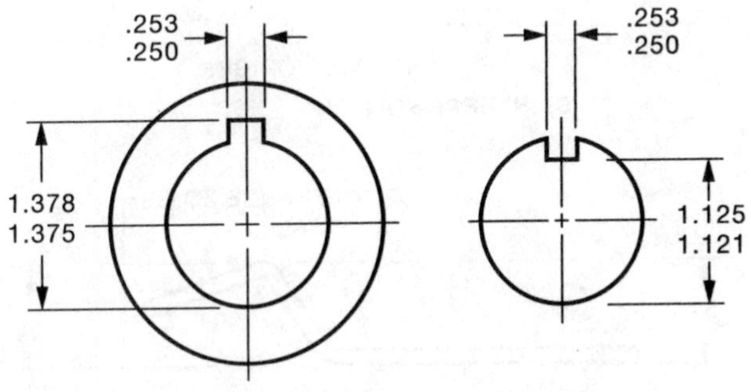

FIGURE 17–2 ■ Dimensioning keyseats

Setscrews are categorized by their forms and the desired point style, Figure 17–3. Each of the standardized setscrew forms is available in a variety of point styles. Selection of a specific form or point is influenced by functional as well as other considerations.

The selection of the type of driver, and thus the setscrew form, is usually determined by factors other than tightening. Despite higher tightening ability, the protrusion of the square head is a major disadvantage. Compactness, weight saving, safety, and appearance may dictate the use of flush-seating socket or slotted headless forms.

The conventional approach to setscrew selection is usually based on a rule-of-thumb procedure: the setscrew diameter should be roughly equal to one-half the shaft diameter. This rule of

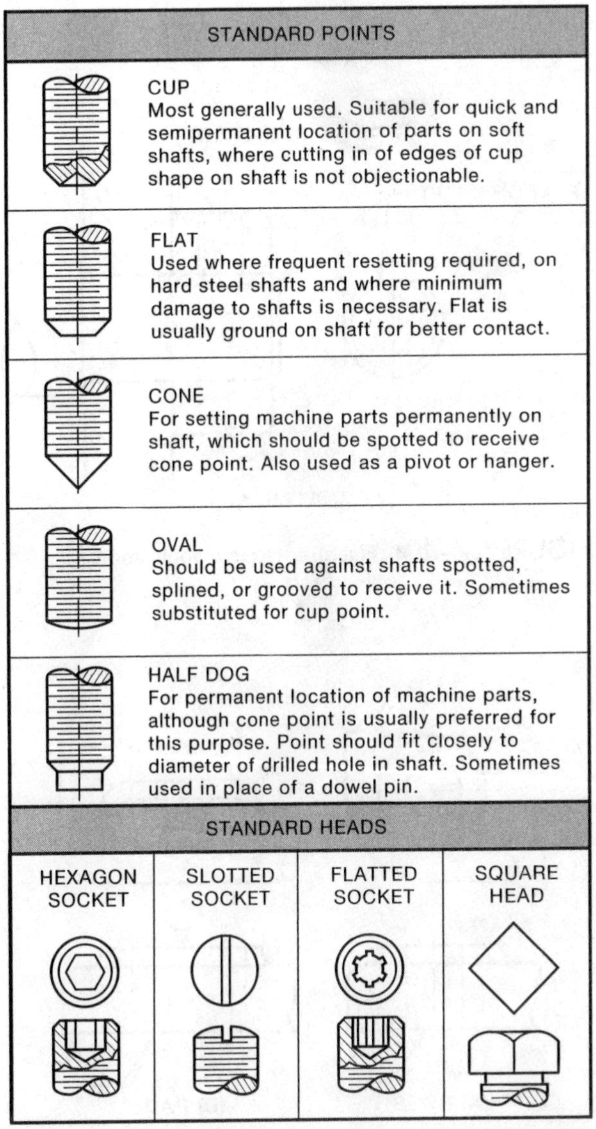

FIGURE 17–3 ■ Setscrews

thumb often gives satisfactory results, but it has a limited range of usefulness. When a setscrew and key are used together, the screw diameter should be equal to the width of the key.

Standard setscrews are shown in Table 9 of the Appendix.

FLATS

A *flat* is a slight depression usually cut on a shaft to serve as a surface on which the end of a setscrew can rest when holding an object in place, Figure 17–4.

BOSSES AND PADS

A *boss* is a relatively small cylindrical projection above the surface of an object. A *pad* is a slight, noncircular projection above the surface of an object, Figure 17–5. Bosses and pads are used to provide additional clearance or strength in the area where they are used and allow machining over a smaller area.

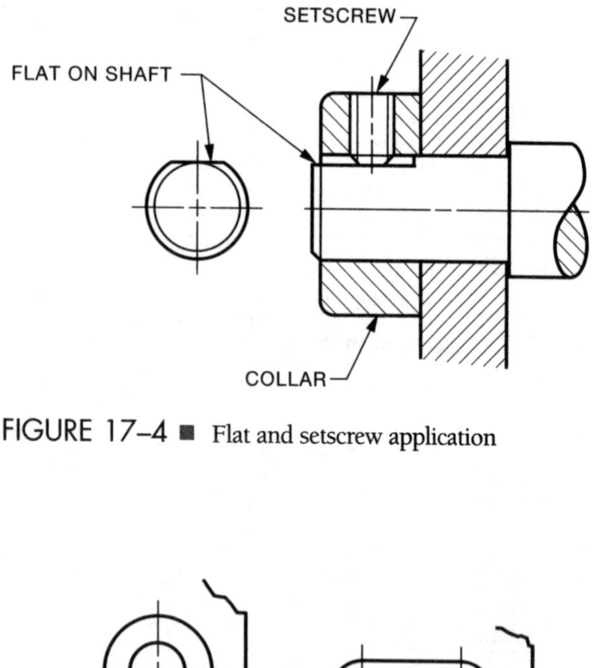

FIGURE 17–4 ■ Flat and setscrew application

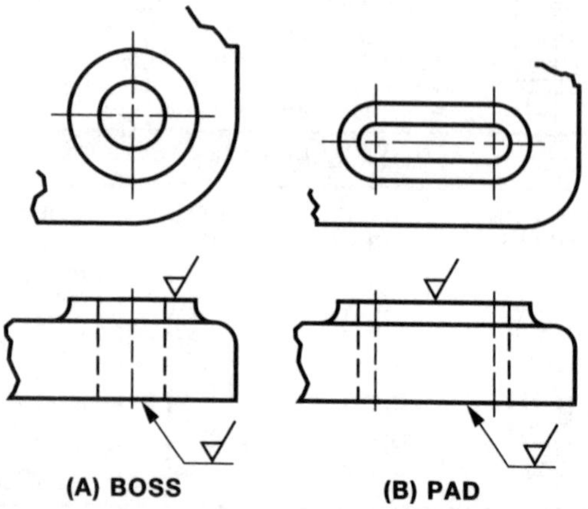

FIGURE 17–5 ■ Bosses and pads

DIMENSION ORIGIN SYMBOL

This symbol is used to indicate that a toleranced dimension between two features originates from one of these features, Figures 17–6 and 17–7.

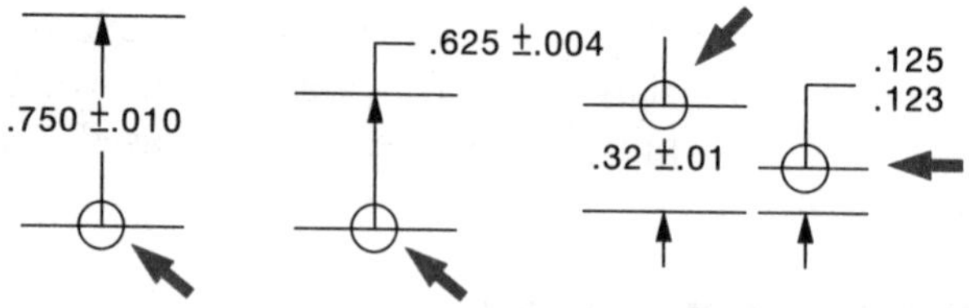

FIGURE 17–6 ■ Dimension origin symbol

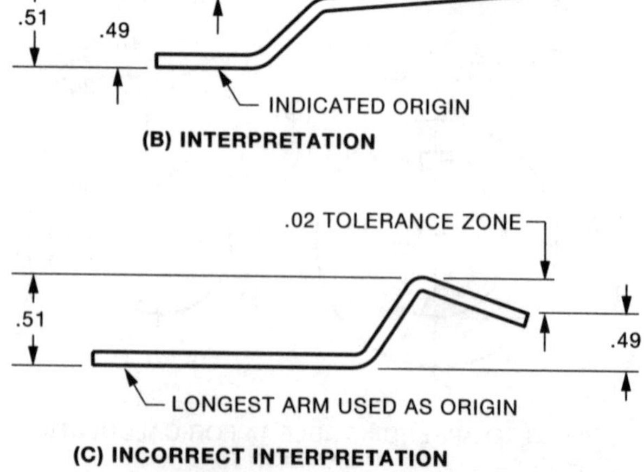

FIGURE 17–7 ■ Relating dimensional limits to an origin

RECTANGULAR COORDINATE DIMENSIONING WITHOUT DIMENSION LINES

To avoid having many dimensions extending away from the object, *rectangular coordinate dimensioning* without dimension lines may be as shown in Figure 17–8. In this system, the "zero" lines are used as reference lines and each of the dimensions shown without arrowheads indicates the distance from the zero line. There is never more than one zero line in each direction.

This type of dimensioning is particularly useful when such features are produced on a general-purpose machine, such as a jig borer, a tape-controlled frill, or a turret-type press. Drawings for numerical control are covered in Unit 30.

RECTANGULAR COORDINATE DIMENSIONING IN TABULAR FORM

When there are many holes or repetitive features, such as in a chassis or a printed circuit board, and where the multitude of centre lines would make a drawing difficult to read, rectangular coordinate dimensioning in tabular form is recommended. In this system each hole or feature is assigned a letter or a letter and numeral subscript. The feature dimensions and the feature location along the X, Y, and Z axes are given in a table as shown in Figure 17–9.

REFERENCES

CAN3-B232-75 (R1996) Keys, Keyseats and Keyways
CAN/CSA-B78.2-M91 Dimensioning and Tolerancing of Technical Drawings

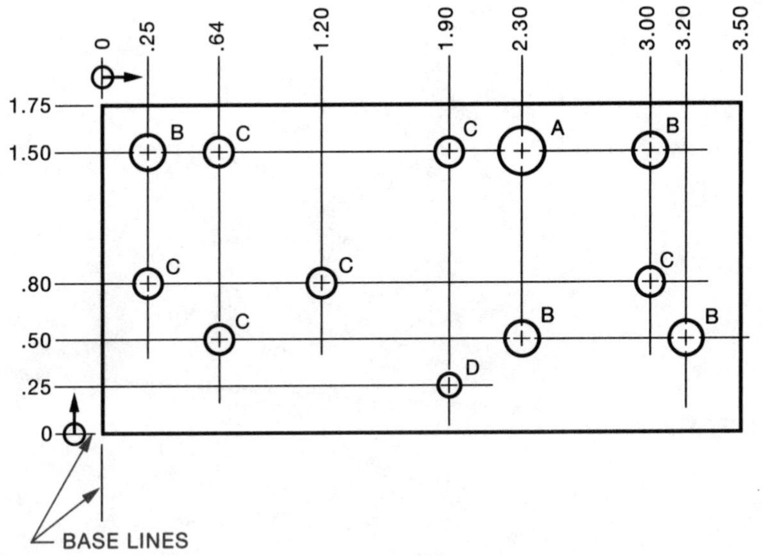

HOLE SYMBOL	HOLE Ø
A	.250
B	.188
C	.156
D	.125

FIGURE 17–8 ■ Rectangular coordinate dimensioning without dimension lines

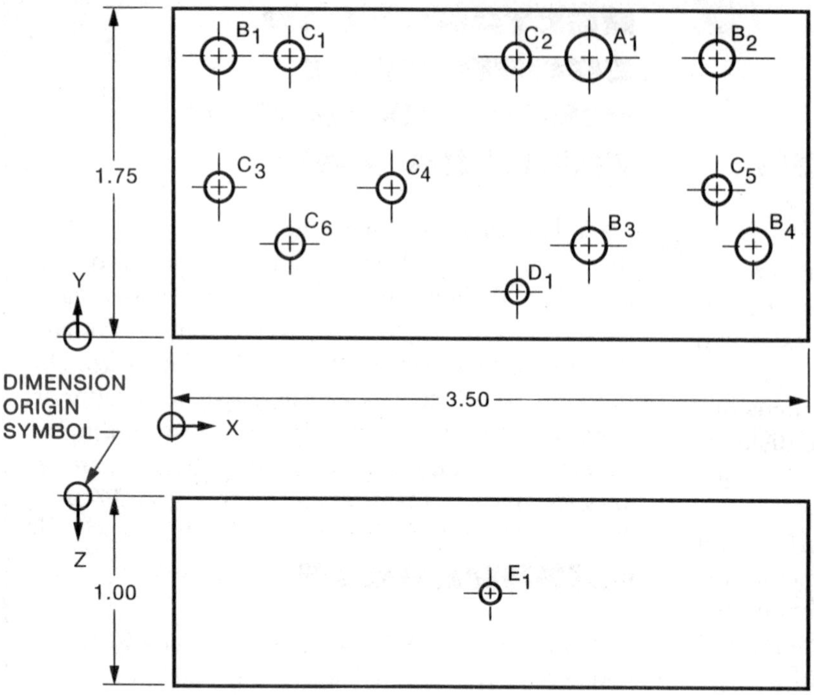

HOLE SYMBOL	Ø HOLE	LOCATION		
		X	Y	Z
A_1	.250	2.30	1.50	.62
B_1	.188	.25	1.50	THRU
B_2	.188	3.00	1.50	THRU
B_3	.188	2.30	.50	THRU
B_4	.188	3.20	.50	THRU
C_1	.156	.64	1.50	THRU
C_2	.156	1.90	1.50	THRU
C_3	.156	.25	.80	THRU
C_4	.156	.120	.80	THRU
C_5	.156	3.00	.80	THRU
C_6	.156	.64	.50	THRU
D_1	.125	1.90	.25	.50
E_1	.109	1.75	1.00	.50

FIGURE 17–9 ■ Rectangular coordinate dimensioning in tabular form

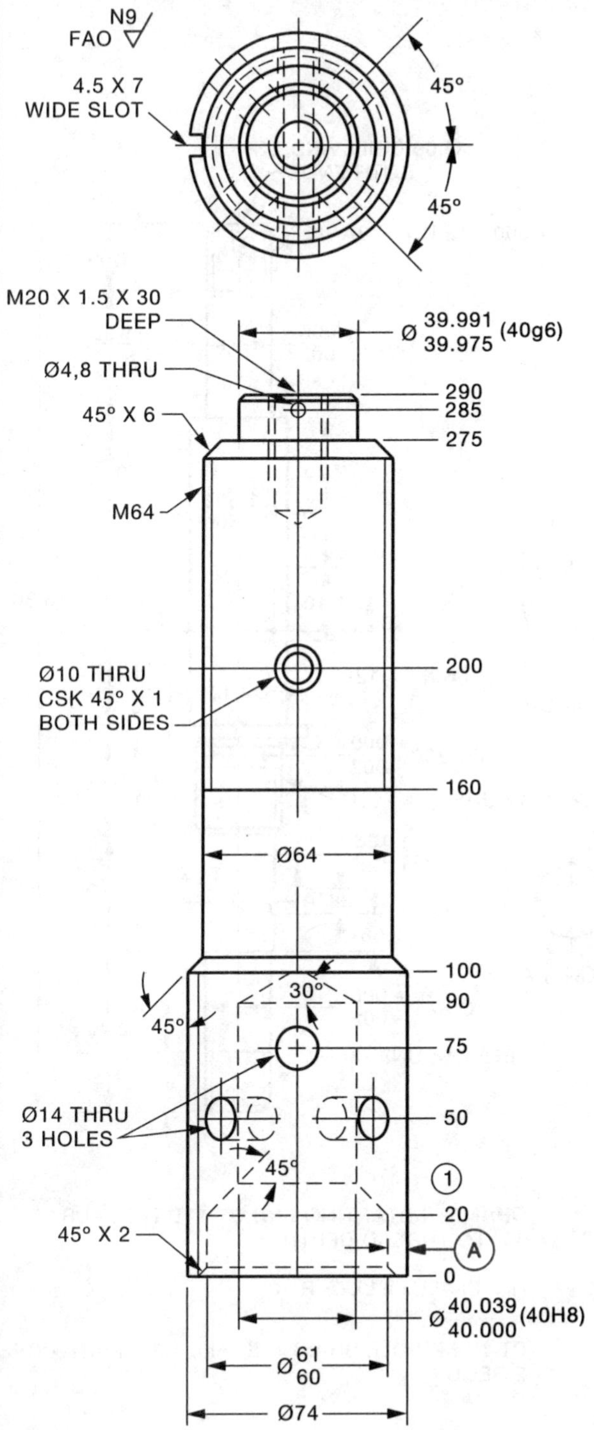

QUESTIONS

1. How long is the Ø64 threaded section?
2. (A.) How deep is the M20 thread?
   (B.) How many full threads are on the tapped hole?
3. How many Ø14 holes are there?
4. What is the maximum thickness of the wall at the Ø14 holes?
5. What series of thread is required for the tapped hole?
6. What is the vertical centre distance between the top Ø14 hole and the Ø4.8 hole?
7. What is the length of the Ø64 unthreaded section?
8. What are the minimum and maximum thicknesses at (A)?
9. What is the maximum overall diameter of the finished stud?
10. What is the tolerance on the largest hole at the bottom of the stud?
11. Give the quality of surface texture in micrometres.
12. What is the angle between the slot and the Ø14 hole located 75 from the base of the stud?

ANSWERS

1. ______________ 7. ______________

2. A ______________ 8. MIN ______________

B ______________ MAX ______________

3. ______________ 9. ______________

4. ______________ 10. ______________

5. ______________ 11. ______________

6. ______________ 12. ______________

NOTE: UNLESS OTHERWISE SPECIFIED
—TOLERANCE ON DIMENSIONS ±0.5
—TOLERANCE ON ANGLES ±0.5

METRIC
DIMENSIONS ARE IN MILLIMETRES

NOTE: HOLES AND THREADS TO BE CLEAN AND BRIGHT

MATERIAL	COPPER	
SCALE	NOT TO SCALE	
DRAWN		DATE

REVISIONS	1	DN. T. FURMAN	CHK. C. JENSEN	TERMINAL STUD	A-46M
		DIMENSION WAS 24	00-06-08		

QUESTIONS

Refer to Part 1

1. What was the original length of the shaft?
2. What symbol is used to indicate that the 1.90 dimension is not to scale?
3. At how many places are threads being cut?
4. Specify for any left-hand threads the thread diameter and the number of threads per inch.
5. What is the pitch for the 1.000 thread?
6. What is the length of that portion of the shaft that includes the (A) .875 thread (include chamfer), (B) 1.250 thread (do not include undercut), and (C) 1.000 thread (include chamfer)?
7. What distance is there between the last thread and the shoulder of the Ø.875 portion of the shaft?
8. How many dimensions have been changed?
9. What type of sectional view is used?
10. What is the largest size to which the Ø1.250 shaft can be turned?
11. What is the minimum permissible size for dimension A ?

Refer to Part 2

12. How many holes are there?
13. What are the overall width and depth dimensions of the base?
14. How many surfaces are to be finished?
15. What is the diameter of the bosses on the base?
16. How wide is the pad on the upright column?
17. What is the depth of the keyseat?
18. How far does the horizontal hole overlap the vertical hole? (Use maximum sizes of holes and minimum centre-to-centre distances.)
19. How much material was added when the change to the bosses was made?
20. Which scale was used on this part?
21. What is the maximum permissible centre-to-centre distance of the two large holes?
22. If limit dimensions (refer to Table 13 M and W of the Appendix) were to replace the keyseat dimensions shown, what would they be?
23. What dimension is indicated as not drawn to scale?

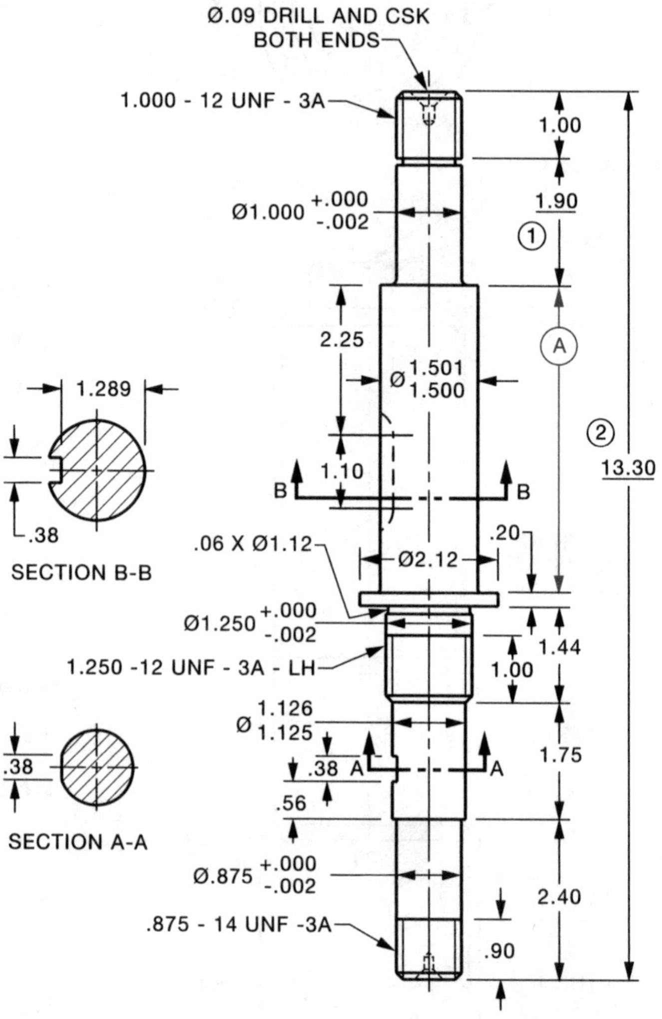

CHAMFER STARTING END OF ALL THREADS 45° TO THREAD DEPTH

NOTE: ALL FILLETS R.10

PT 1 SPINDLE SHAFT, SCALE 1:2, MATL - CRS
2 REQD

REVISIONS	1	02-01-12	R.H.	2	99-08-12	C.J.	3	02-12-15	G.H.
	1.90 WAS 2.00			13.30 WAS 13.40			.80 WAS .75		

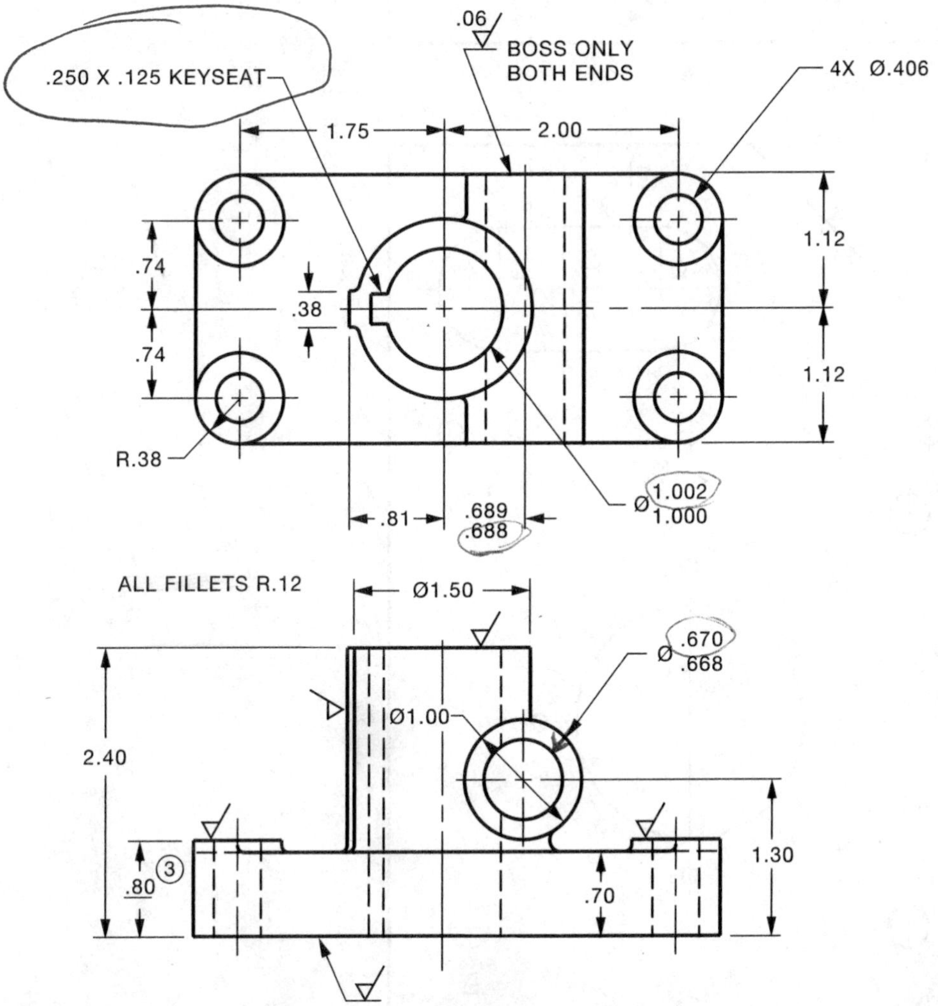
.250 X .125 KEYSEAT
.06
BOSS ONLY
BOTH ENDS
4X Ø.406
1.75
2.00
1.12
1.12
.74
.74
.38
R.38
.81
.689
.688
Ø 1.002
1.000
ALL FILLETS R.12
Ø1.50
Ø .670
.668
Ø1.00
2.40
.80
3
.70
1.30

PT 2 COLUMN BRACKET, SCALE 1:1
MATL - WROUGHT IRON 4 REQD

NOTE: UNLESS OTHERWISE SPECIFIED
TOLERANCE ON DIMENSIONS ±.02

ANSWERS

1. ____
2. ____
3. ____
4. ____
5. ____
6. A ____
   B ____
   C ____
7. ____
8. ____
9. ____
10. ____
11. ____
12. ____
13. W ____
    D ____
14. ____
15. ____
16. ____
17. ____
18. ____
19. ____
20. ____
21. ____
22. W ____
    M ____
23. ____

	SCALE AS SHOWN	
	DRAWN	DATE
	RACK DETAILS	**A-47**

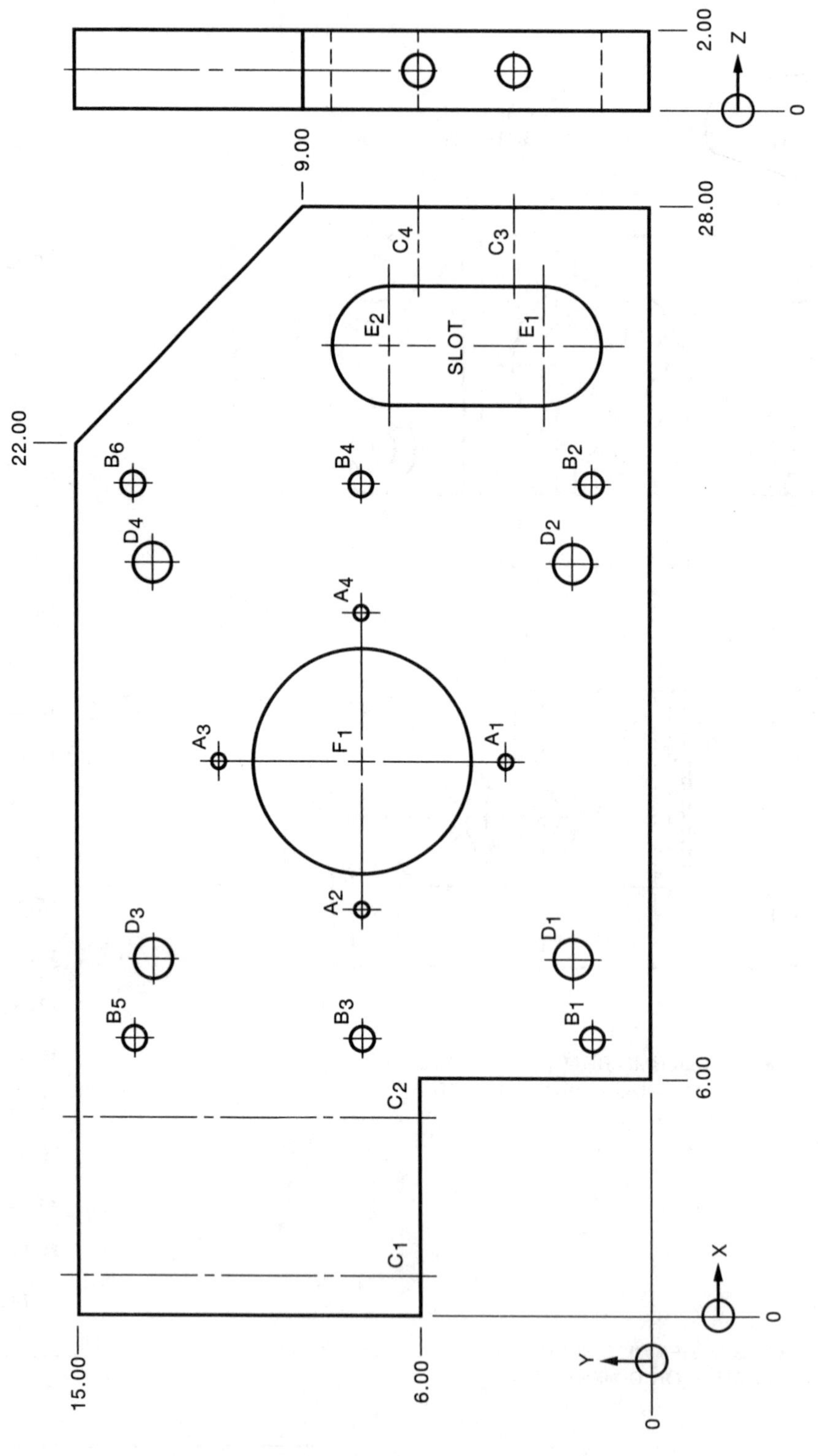

NOTE: TOLERANCE ON LINEAR DIMENSIONS ±.02

QUESTIONS

1. What is the width of the part?
2. What is the height of the part?
3. What are the width and height of the chamfer on the corner?
4. What is the width of slot E?
5. What is the height of slot E?
6. How much wood is left between slot E and the right-hand edge of the part?
7. What are the centre distances between holes?
   (A) B_5 and B_6 (D) D_3 and D_4 (F) C_1 and C_2
   (B) D_2 and D_4 (E) A_1 and A_3 (G) B_3 and A_4
   (C) B_1 and B_5
8. How much wood is left between holes?
   (A) A_1 and E_1 (C) C_1 and C_2
   (B) A_2 and B_3 (D) B_3 and B_4
9. How many places is the origin symbol used?

ANSWERS

1. ____________
2. ____________
3. W ____________
   H ____________
4. ____________
5. ____________
6. ____________
7. A ____________
   B ____________
   C ____________
   D ____________
   E ____________
   F ____________
   G ____________
8. A ____________
   B ____________
   C ____________
   D ____________
9. ____________

HOLE SYMBOL	HOLE DIA.	LOCATION		
		X	Y	Z
A_1	.375	14.00	3.75	
A_2	.375	10.25	7.50	
A_3	.375	14.00	11.25	
A_4	.375	17.75	7.50	
B_1	.625	7.00	1.50	
B_2	.625	21.00	1.50	
B_3	.625	7.00	7.50	
B_4	.625	21.00	7.50	
B_5	.625	7.00	13.50	
B_6	.625	21.00	13.50	
C_1	.812	1.00		1.00
C_2	.812	5.00		1.00
C_3	.812		3.50	1.00
C_4	.812		6.00	1.00
D_1	1.000	9.00	2.00	
D_2	1.000	19.00	2.00	
D_3	1.000	9.00	13.00	
D_4	1.000	19.00	13.00	
E_1	3.000	24.50	2.75	
E_2	3.000	24.50	6.75	
F_1	5.688	14.00	7.50	

NOTE: ALL HOLES THRU UNLESS OTHERWISE SPECIFIED

MATERIAL	DRY MAPLE	
SCALE	NOT TO SCALE	
DRAWN		DATE
	SUPPORT BRACKET	**A-48**

18 UNIT

PRIMARY AUXILIARY VIEWS

Many objects have surfaces that are perpendicular to only one plane of projection. These surfaces are referred to as *inclined sloped surfaces*. In the remaining two orthographic views such surfaces appear to be foreshortened and their true shape is not shown, Figure 18–1. When an inclined surface has important characteristics that should be shown clearly and without distortion, an auxiliary view is used to completely explain the shape of the object.

For example, Figure 18–2 clearly shows why an auxiliary view is required. The circular features on the sloped surface on the front view cannot be seen in their true shape on either the top or side views. The auxiliary view is the only view that shows the actual shape of these features, Figure 18–3. Note that only the sloped surface details are shown. Background detail is often omitted on auxiliary views and regular views to simplify the drawing and avoid confusion. A break line is used to signify the break in an incomplete view. The break line is not required if only the exact surface is drawn for either an auxiliary view or a partial regular view. Dimensions for the detail on the inclined face are placed on the auxiliary view, showing the detail in its true shape.

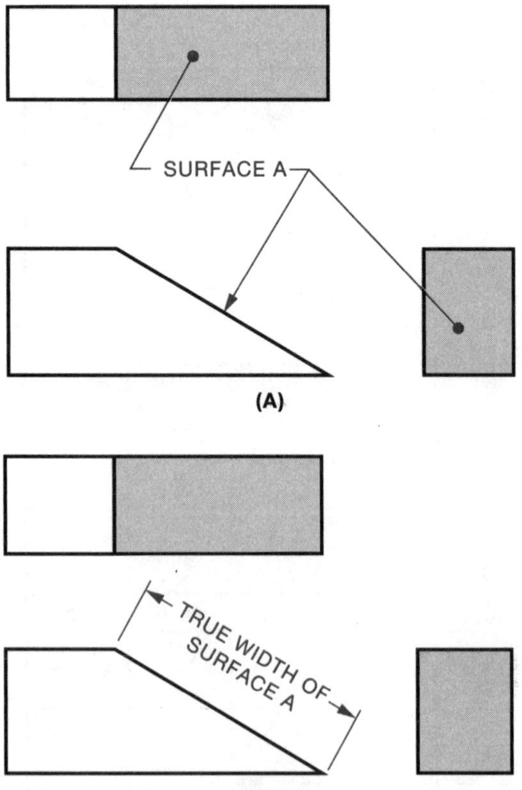

NOTE: SURFACE A IS PERPENDICULAR TO THE FRONT PLANE OF PROJECTION. THEREFORE ONLY THE FRONT VIEW SHOWS THE TRUE WIDTH OF SURFACE A. NO VIEW SHOWS THE TRUE SHAPE OF SURFACE A.

FIGURE 18–1 ■ Object having an inclined surface

REFERENCES

CAN3-B78.1-M83 (R1990) Technical Drawings—General Principles

ASME Y14.3M-1994 Multi and Sectional View Drawings

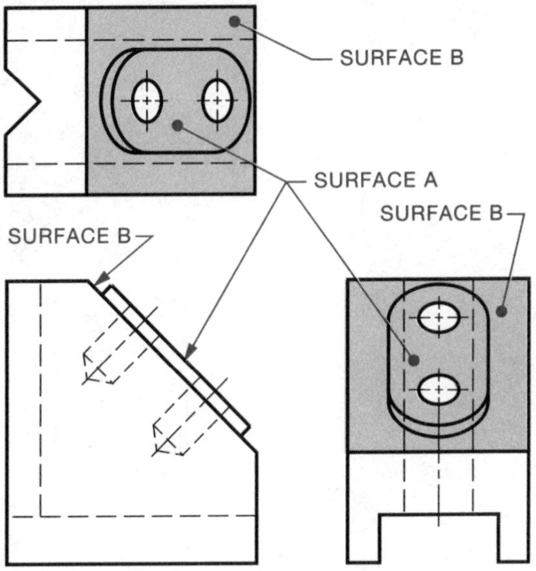
SURFACE B
SURFACE A
SURFACE B
SURFACE B

(A) REGULAR VIEWS DO NOT SHOW TRUE FEATURES OF SURFACES A AND B.

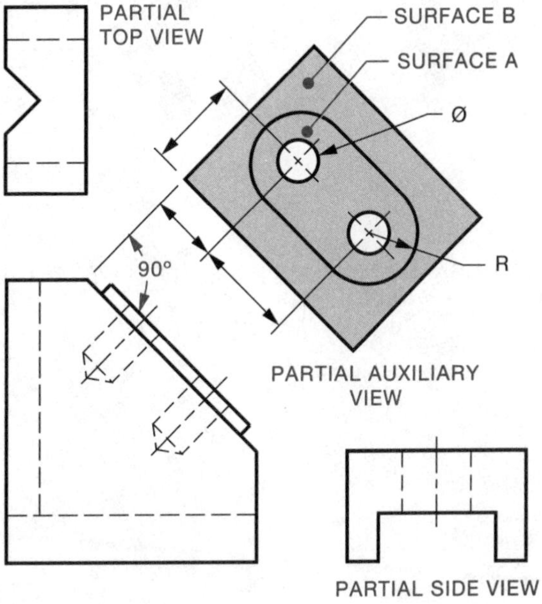
PARTIAL TOP VIEW
SURFACE B
SURFACE A
Ø
R
90°
PARTIAL AUXILIARY VIEW
PARTIAL SIDE VIEW

(B) AUXILIARY VIEW ADDED TO SHOW TRUE FEATURES OF SURFACES A AND B.

FIGURE 18–2 ■ The need for auxiliary views

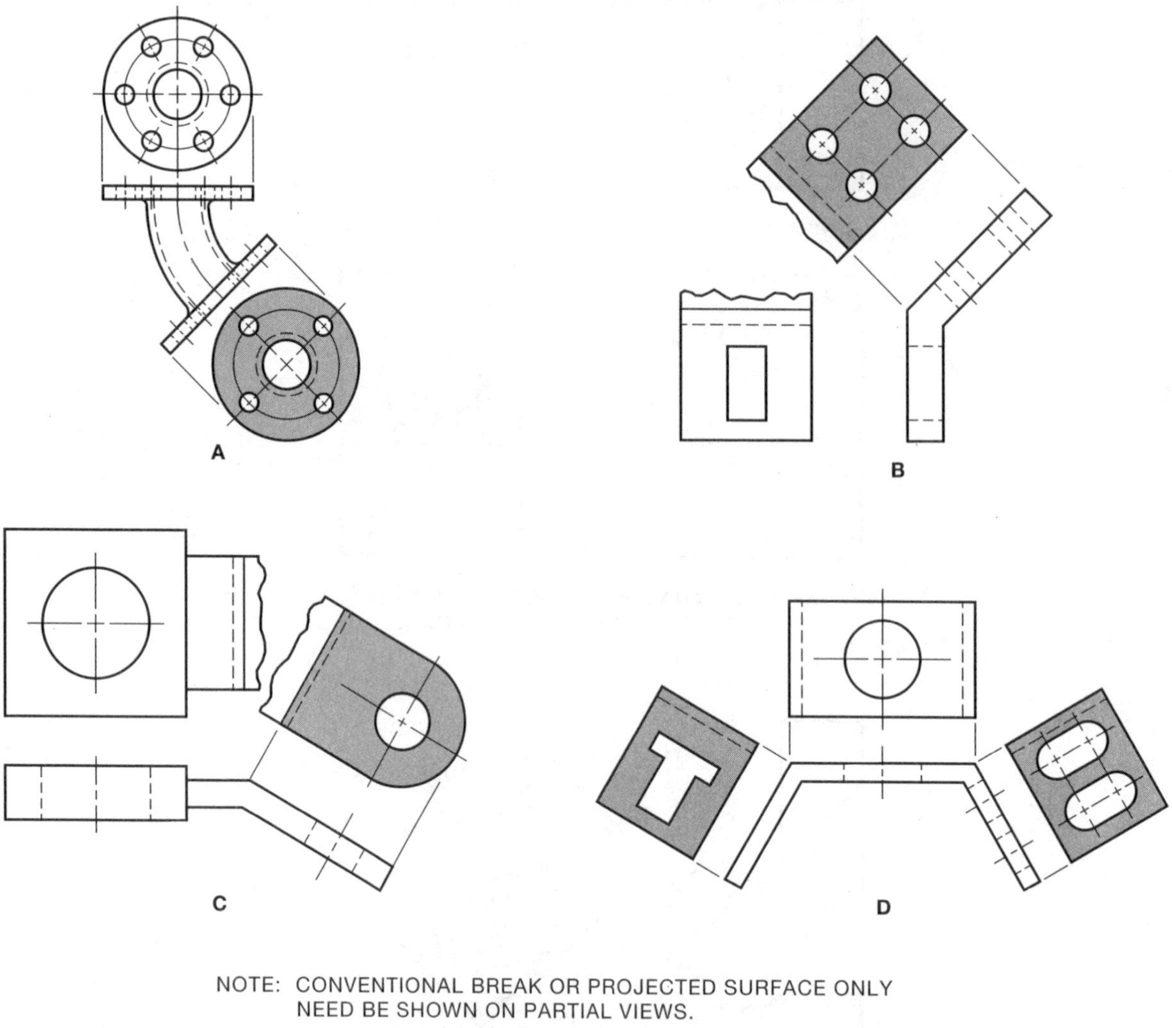
A
B
C
D
NOTE: CONVENTIONAL BREAK OR PROJECTED SURFACE ONLY
NEED BE SHOWN ON PARTIAL VIEWS.

FIGURE 18–3 ■ Examples of auxiliary-view drawings

ASSIGNMENT:
ON THE GRID AREAS PROVIDED, DRAW PARTIAL RIGHT-SIDE AND AUXILIARY VIEWS OF THE INCLINED STOP. THE CENTRES OF THE HOLES ARE LOCATED ON THE GRIDS. PLACE THE APPROPRIATE DIMENSIONS ON THESE VIEWS.

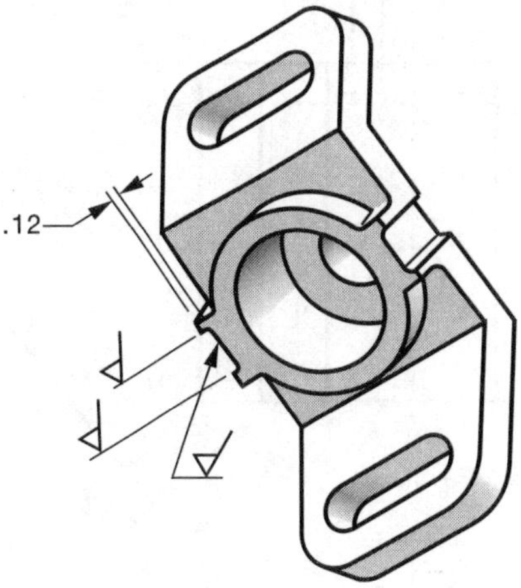

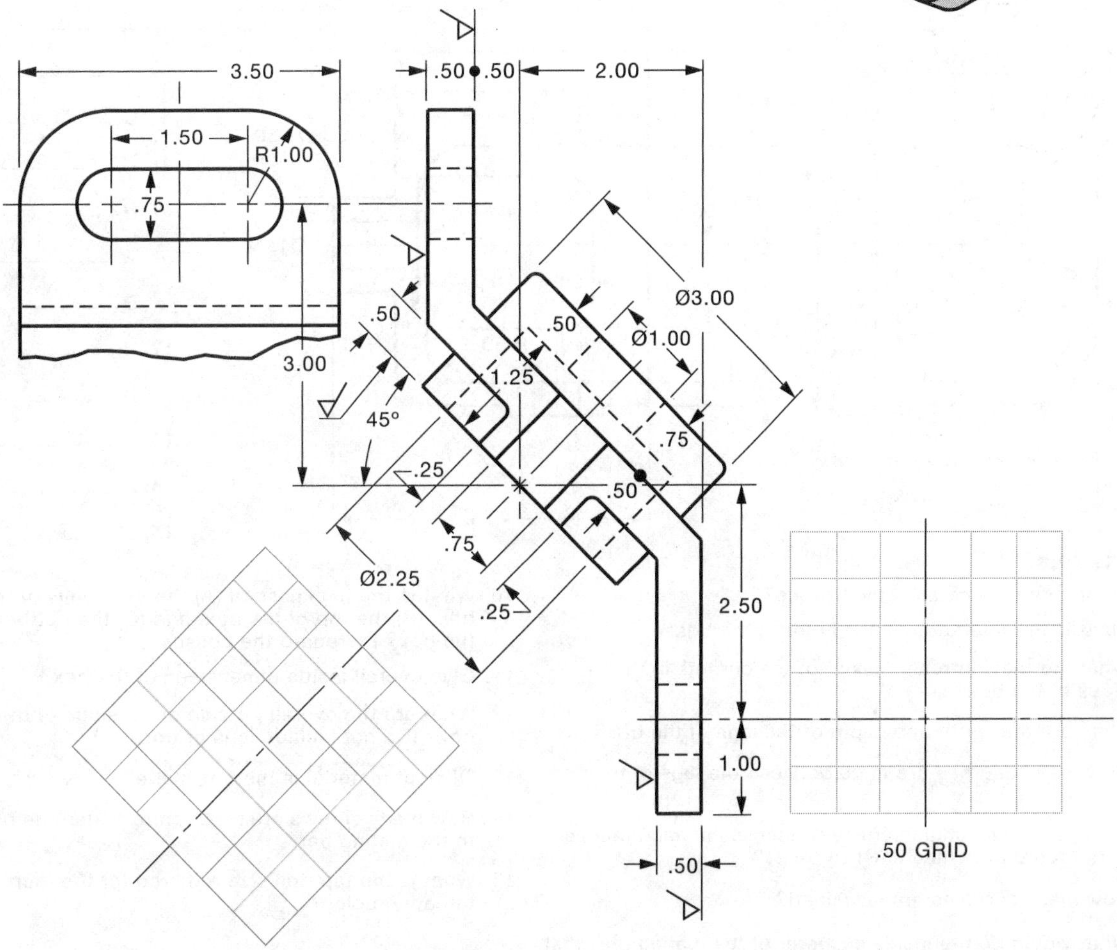

.50 GRID

MATERIAL	GREY IRON		
SCALE	1 : 2		
DRAWN		DATE	
INCLINED STOP		**A-49**	

NOTE: EXCEPT WHERE NOTED:
—ALL ROUNDS AND FILLETS R.10
—ALL √ TO BE 125√
—TOLERANCE ON DIMENSIONS ±.02
—TOLERANCE ON ANGLES ±0.5°

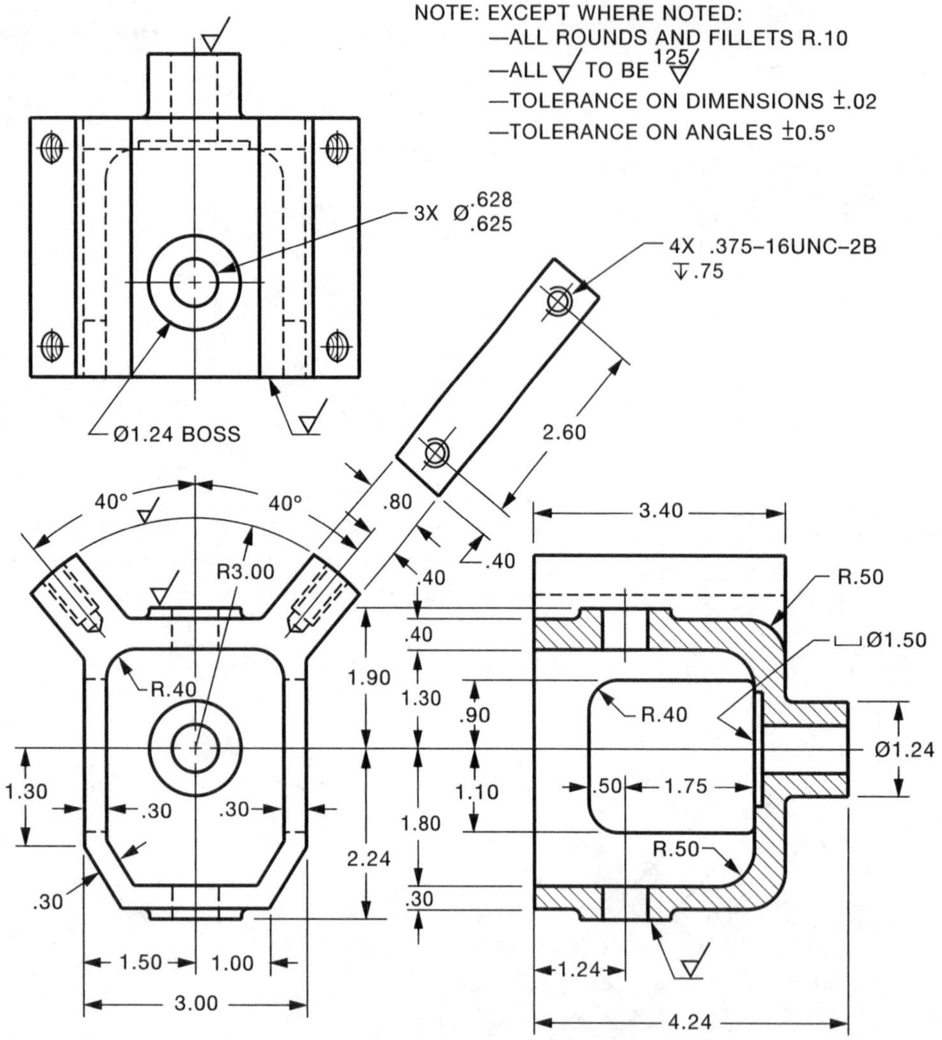
3X Ø.628 .625
Ø1.24 BOSS
4X .375–16UNC–2B
↧.75
2.60
.80
.40
40°
40°
R3.00
R.40
1.90
1.30
.90
1.10
1.80
2.24
.30
1.30
.30
.30
1.50
1.00
3.00
3.40
R.50
⌴Ø1.50
R.40
Ø1.24
.50
1.75
R.50
1.24
4.24

ANSWERS

1. ______
2. ______
3. W ______ H ______
4. W ______ H ______
5. ______
6. ______
7. ______
8. ______
9. ______
10. A ______ B ______ C ______
11. H ______ W ______ D ______
12. H ______ D ______
13. ______
14. ______
15. ______

QUESTIONS

1. What is the diameter of the bosses?
2. What is the tolerance on the holes in the bosses?
3. What are the width and height of the cutouts in the sides of the box?
4. What are the width and depth of the legs of the box?
5. How many degrees are there between the legs of the box?
6. What is the maximum surface roughness in microinches permitted on the machined surfaces?
7. How many surfaces are machined?
8. What would be the inside diameter of the mating part that this box fits into?
9. If the mating part is .44 thick and a lockwasher is used, what diameter and longest standard length of socket head cap screws could be used to fasten the parts together? (See Tables 7 and 12 in the Appendix.) Lengths available in .25 in. increments.
10. What is the thickness of (A) the side walls of the box, (B) the top of the box, and (C) the bottom of the box? Disregard the bosses.
11. Give overall inside dimensions of the box.
12. What are the overall outside dimensions of the box? (Do not include legs or bosses.)
13. Of what material is the box made?
14. How many screws are required to fasten the box to the mating part?
15. What is the tap drill size required for the four threaded holes?

MATERIAL	GREY IRON	
SCALE	NOT TO SCALE	
DRAWN		DATE
	GEAR BOX	A-50

1,8+.3 +1.3+.4   3,8=H

UNIT 19

SECONDARY AUXILIARY VIEWS

As mentioned earlier, auxiliary views show the true lengths of lines and the true shapes of surfaces that cannot be described in the ordinary views.

A primary auxiliary view is drawn by projecting lines from a regular view where the inclined surface appears as an edge.

The auxiliary view in Figure 19–1(A), which shows the true projection and true shape of surface X, is called a *primary auxiliary view* because it is projected directly from the regular front view.

Some surfaces are inclined so that they are not perpendicular to any of the three viewing planes. In this case, they appear as a surface in all three views but never in their true shape. These are referred to as *oblique surfaces,* Figure 19–2.

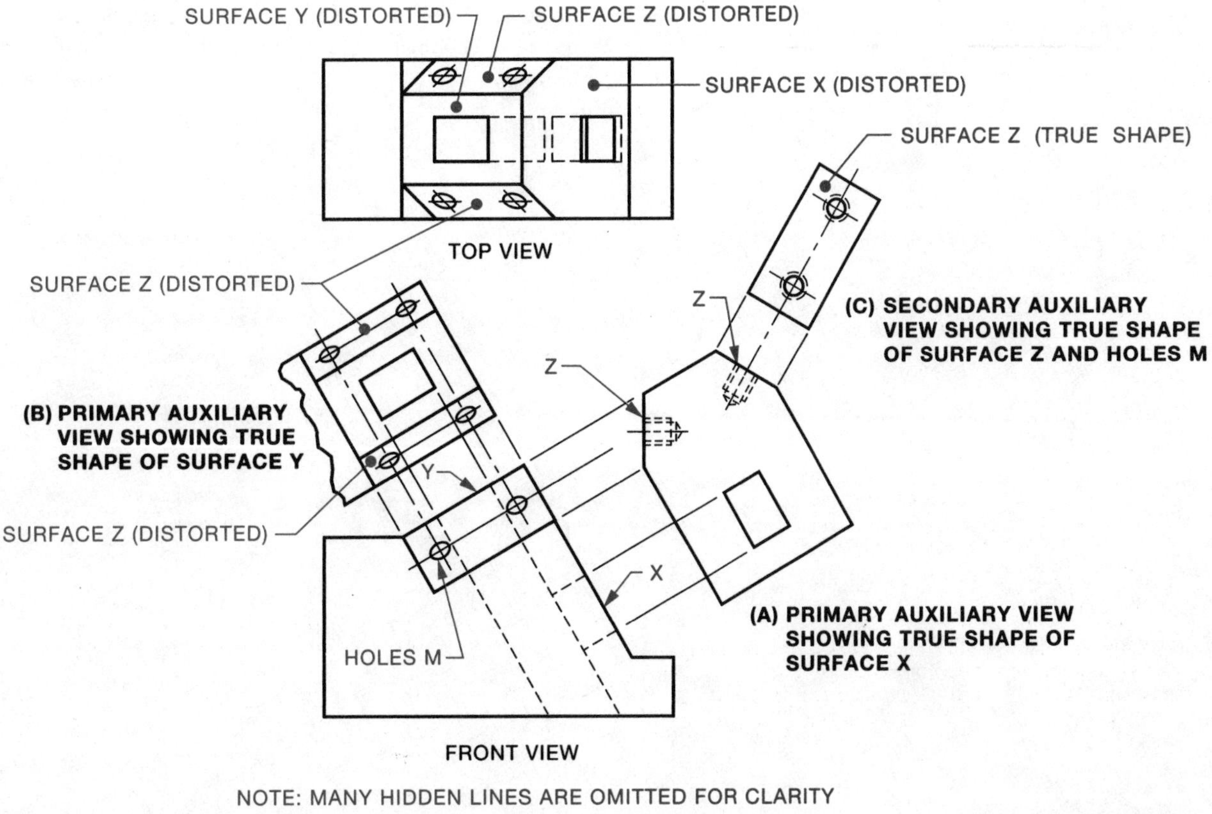
SURFACE Y (DISTORTED)
SURFACE Z (DISTORTED)
SURFACE X (DISTORTED)
SURFACE Z (TRUE SHAPE)
TOP VIEW
SURFACE Z (DISTORTED)
Z
(C) SECONDARY AUXILIARY VIEW SHOWING TRUE SHAPE OF SURFACE Z AND HOLES M
Z
(B) PRIMARY AUXILIARY VIEW SHOWING TRUE SHAPE OF SURFACE Y
Y
SURFACE Z (DISTORTED)
X
HOLES M
(A) PRIMARY AUXILIARY VIEW SHOWING TRUE SHAPE OF SURFACE X
FRONT VIEW
NOTE: MANY HIDDEN LINES ARE OMITTED FOR CLARITY

FIGURE 19–1 ■ Primary and secondary auxiliary views

Because the oblique surface is not perpendicular to the viewing planes, it cannot be parallel to them. Consequently, the surface appears foreshortened in all three views. If a true view is required for this surface, two auxiliary views, a primary and a secondary view, must be drawn.

The chamfered comers **Z** have threaded holes on the oblique surfaces. To show the true shape and location of the threaded holes **M**, a second auxiliary view must be shown, as at (C). This auxiliary view is projected from the first or primary auxiliary view, and is known as a *secondary auxiliary view.* The view at (B) is a primary auxiliary view because it is projected from one of the regular views. Notice that the side view is not drawn because the auxiliary views provide the information usually shown on this view.

REFERENCES

CAN3-B78.1-M83 (R1990) Technical Drawings—General Principles

ASME Y14.3M-1994 Multi and Sectional View Drawings

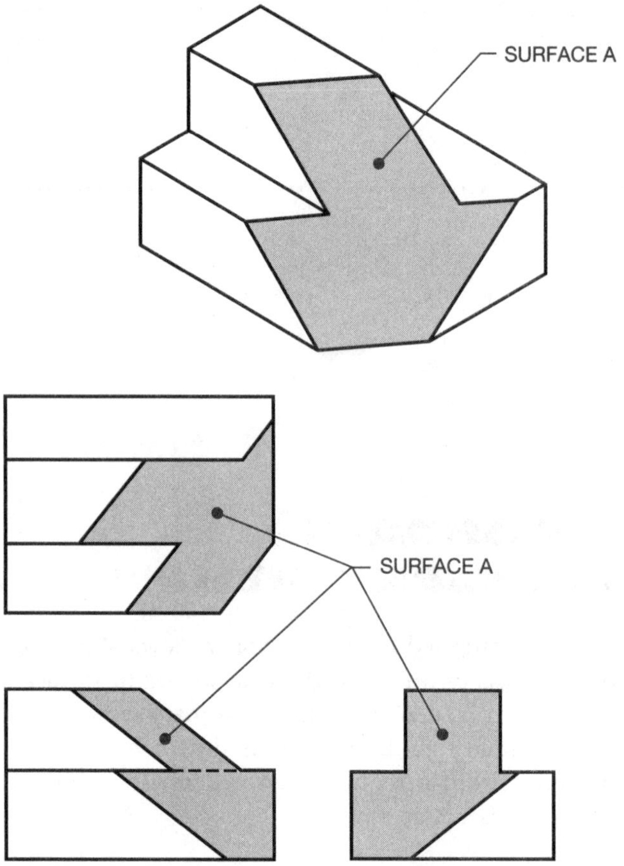

FIGURE 19–2 ■ Surface A is not perpendicular to any of the three viewing planes and is therefore considered oblique.

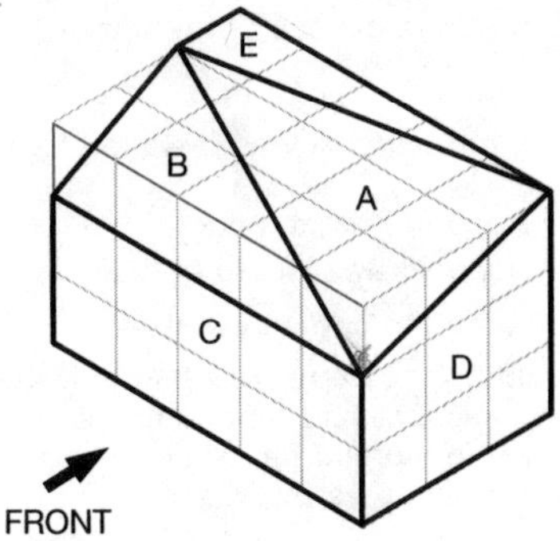

1.

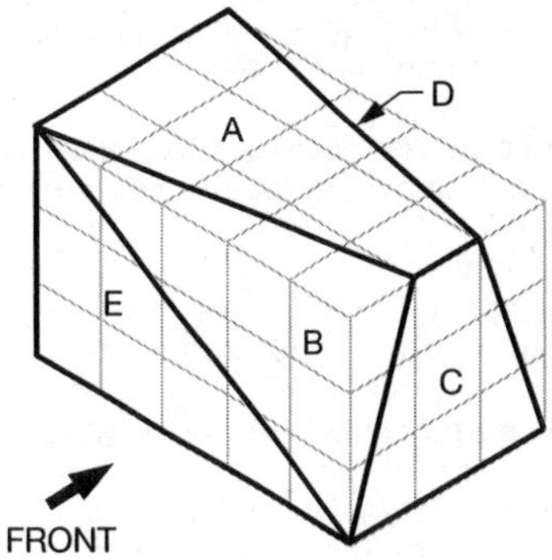

2.

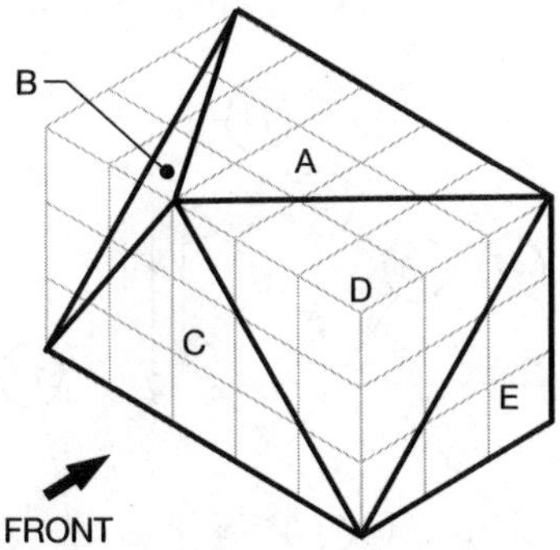

3.

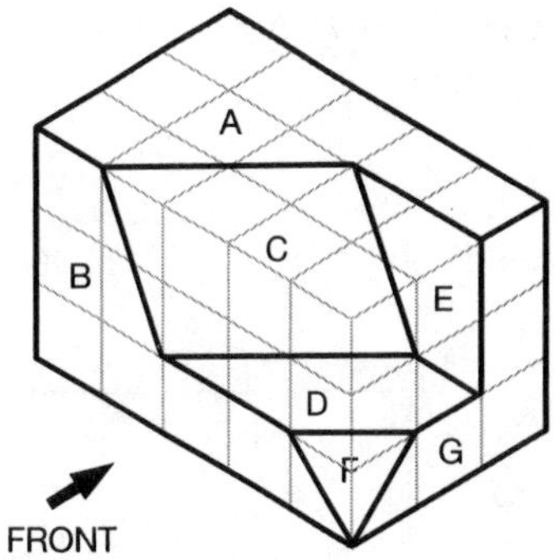

4.

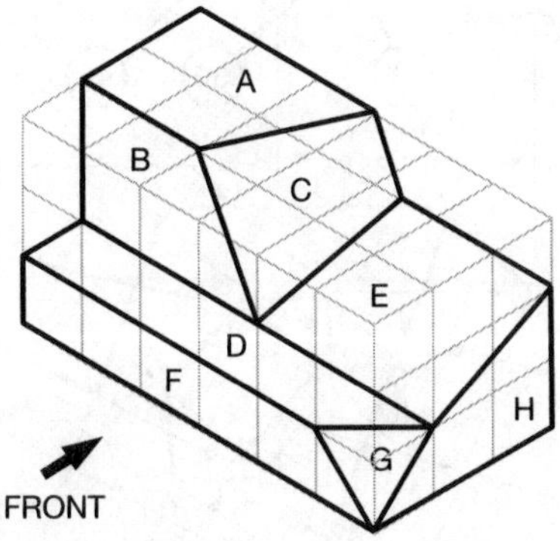

5.

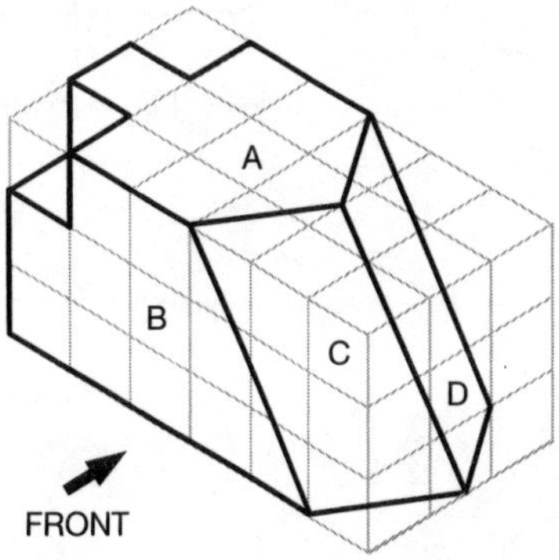

6.

ASSIGNMENT:

USING THE SAME NUMBER OF SQUARES, DRAW ON GRAPH PAPER THE FRONT, TOP, AND SIDE VIEWS. IDENTIFY THE OBLIQUE SURFACES ON THE THREE VIEWS WITH THE APPROPRIATE LETTERS.

IDENTIFYING OBLIQUE SURFACES	A-51

QUESTIONS

1. Which other view(s) show the true height of the .62 dimension shown in the front view?
2. Which other view(s) show the true width of the .60 dimension shown in the primary auxiliary view?
3. What view(s) show the (A) height, (B) depth, and (C) width of the top portion of the support?
4. How many surfaces require finishing?
5. List the surface(s) or feature(s) that are shown in their true shape or size in the primary auxiliary view but are distorted in all other views.
6. List the surface(s) or feature(s) that are shown in their true shape or size in the secondary auxiliary view but are distorted in all other views.
7. What would be the thickness of the base (26) before machining?
8. If the hexagon bar support was fastened to another member,
   (Refer to the Appendix when necessary.)
   (A) How many cap screws would be used?
   (B) What would be the cap screw size?
   (C) What would be the cap screw length if the supporting member had tapped holes that were .80 deep and flat washers were used under the cap screw heads?
   (D) If the cap screws were of the fine thread series, how would you call out these cap screws?
   (E) What would be the I.D. and O.D. of the flat washers used under these cap screws?

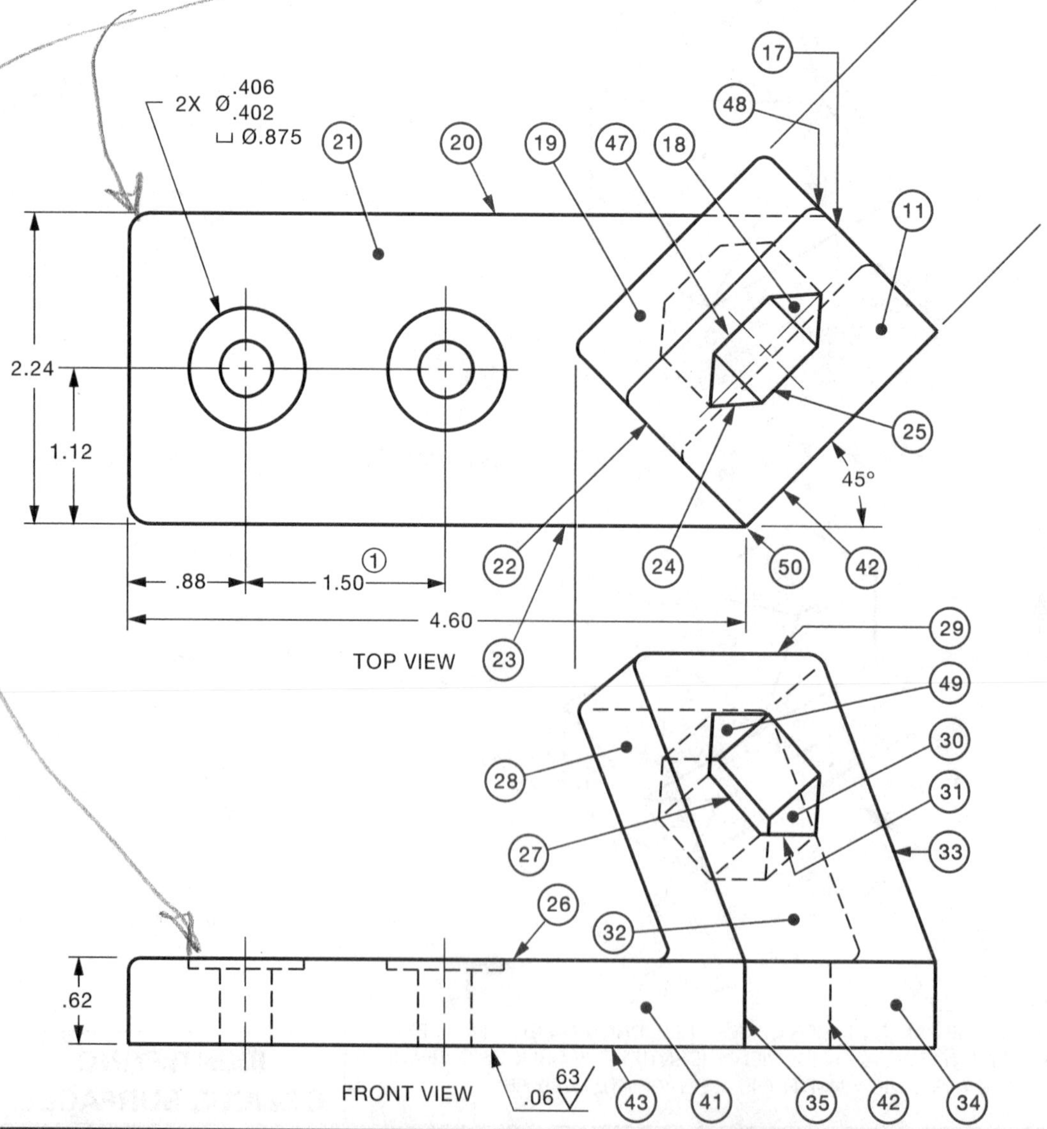

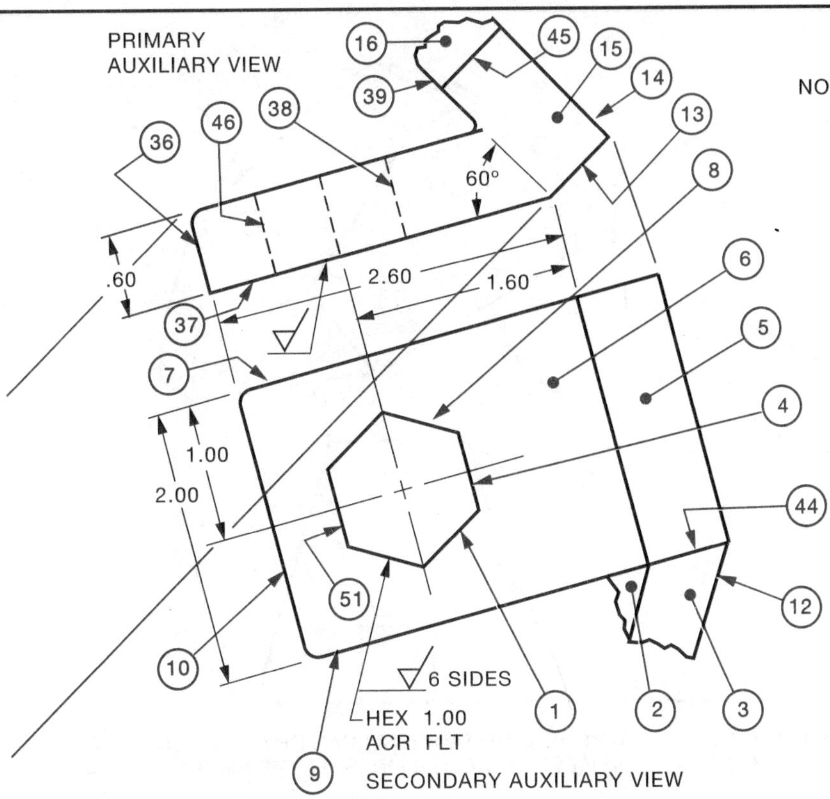

NOTE: UNLESS OTHERWISE SPECIFIED:
—TOLERANCE ON ANGLES ±0.5°
—TOLERANCE ON DIMENSIONS ±.02
—ALL SURFACES SHOWN √HAVE AN N7 FINISH.

ANSWERS

1. ____
2. ____
3. A ____
   B ____
   C ____
4. ____
5. ____
6. ____
7. ____
8. A ____
   B ____
   C ____
   D ____
   E ____

ASSIGNMENT:
IN THE TABLE BELOW, A CERTAIN FEATURE IS SHOWN IN SEVERAL VIEWS. FILL IN THE NUMBER REPRESENTING THE SAME FEATURE IN THE OTHER VIEWS.

Front View	Top View	Primary Auxiliary View	Secondary Auxiliary View
		—	1
	23	—	
26			
		38	
		—	9
—	20		—
33			
	—	14	
			5
	19		
		37	
		—	8
35		—	
42			—
	47		

REVISIONS	1	02-01-23	R. HINES
	1.50 DIM. WAS 1.56		
MATERIAL	GREY IRON		
SCALE			
DRAWN		DATE	
	HEXAGON BAR SUPPORT	A-52	

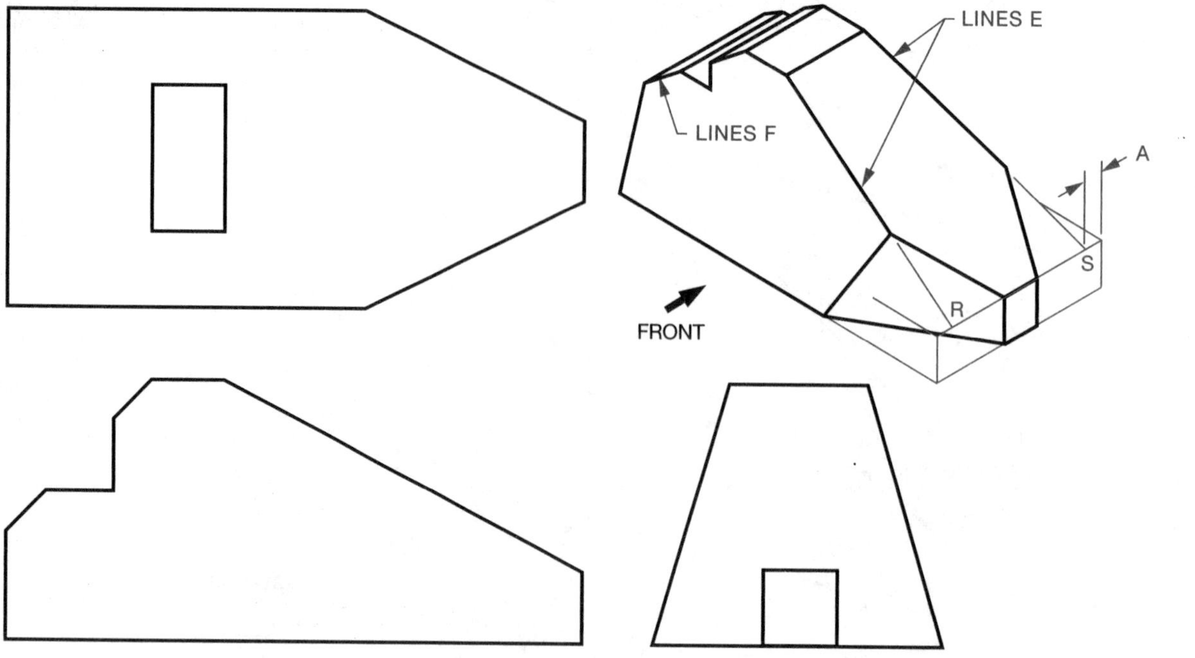
LINES E
LINES F
A
S
R
FRONT

HINT: ESTABLISH POINTS R AND S ON THE TOP VIEW. DISTANCE "A" CAN BE FOUND ON THE SIDE VIEW. DRAW LINES "E" ON THE TOP VIEW. ESTABLISH LINES "F" THE SAME WAY.

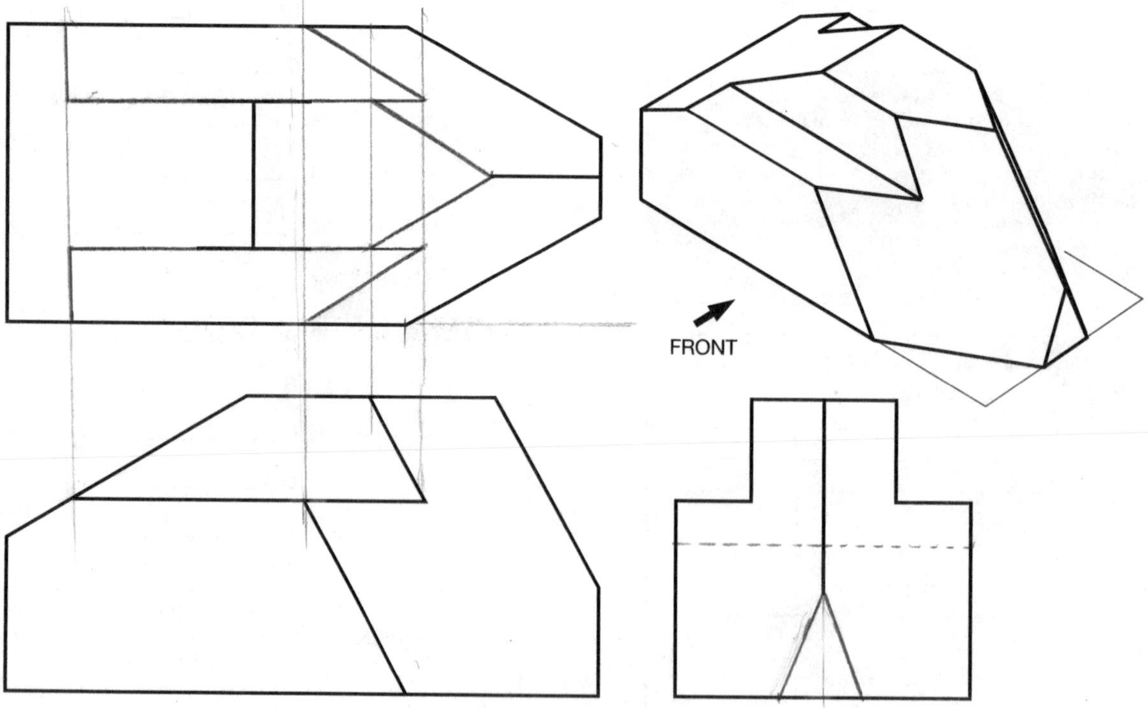
FRONT

HINT: THE FRONT VIEW IS COMPLETE. IDENTIFY THE OBLIQUE SURFACES.

ASSIGNMENT: COMPLETE THE PARTIALLY DRAWN VIEWS, AND USING LETTERS, IDENTIFY THE OBLIQUE SURFACES ON ALL THREE VIEWS.

COMPLETING OBLIQUE SURFACES	A-53

UNIT 20

DEVELOPMENT DRAWINGS

Many objects, such as metal and cardboard boxes, duct work for heating, funnels, and eavestroughing, are made from flat sheet material that is cut so that, when folded, formed, or rolled, it will take the shape of the object. Because a definite shape and size is desired, a regular orthographic drawing of the object is first made; then a development drawing is made to show the complete surface or surfaces laid out in a flat plane, Figure 20–1.

A development drawing is sometimes referred to as a pattern drawing, because the layout, when made of heavy cardboard, metal, or wood, is used as a pattern for tracing out the developed shape on flat material. Such patterns are used extensively in sheet metal shops.

JOINTS, SEAMS, AND EDGES

Additional material is required for assembly and design purposes. When two or more pieces of material or surfaces are joined together, extra material must be provided for the joint or seam. The type of joint or seam for joining metal, Figure 20–2, is dependent on design criteria such as strength, waterproofing, and appearance. Rivets or solder can be added to these joints if required. Exposed edges of metal parts may also be reinforced by the addition of extra material for hemming or for containing a wire. A round metal wastebasket, Figure 20–3, is one example where extra material is provided for the joint, seam, and edge.

SHEET METAL SIZES

Metal thicknesses up to .25 in. (6 mm) are usually designated by a series of gauge numbers. The more common gauges are shown in Table 16 of the Appendix. Metal .25 in. and over is given in inch or millimetre sizes. In calling for the material size of sheet metal developments, customary practice is to give the gauge number, type of gauge, and inch or millimetre equivalent in parentheses followed by the developed width and length, Figure 20–4.

STRAIGHT LINE DEVELOPMENT

This is the term given to the development of an object that has surfaces on a flat plane of projection. The true size of each side of the object is known, and these sides can be laid out in successive order. Figure 20–1 shows the development of a simple rectangular box having a bottom and four sides. Note that in the development of the box, an allowance is made for lap seams at the corners for a folded edge. All lines for each surface are parallel or perpendicular to the other surfaces. The bottom corners of the lap joints are chamfered to facilitate assembly. The fold lines on the development are shown as thin unbroken lines.

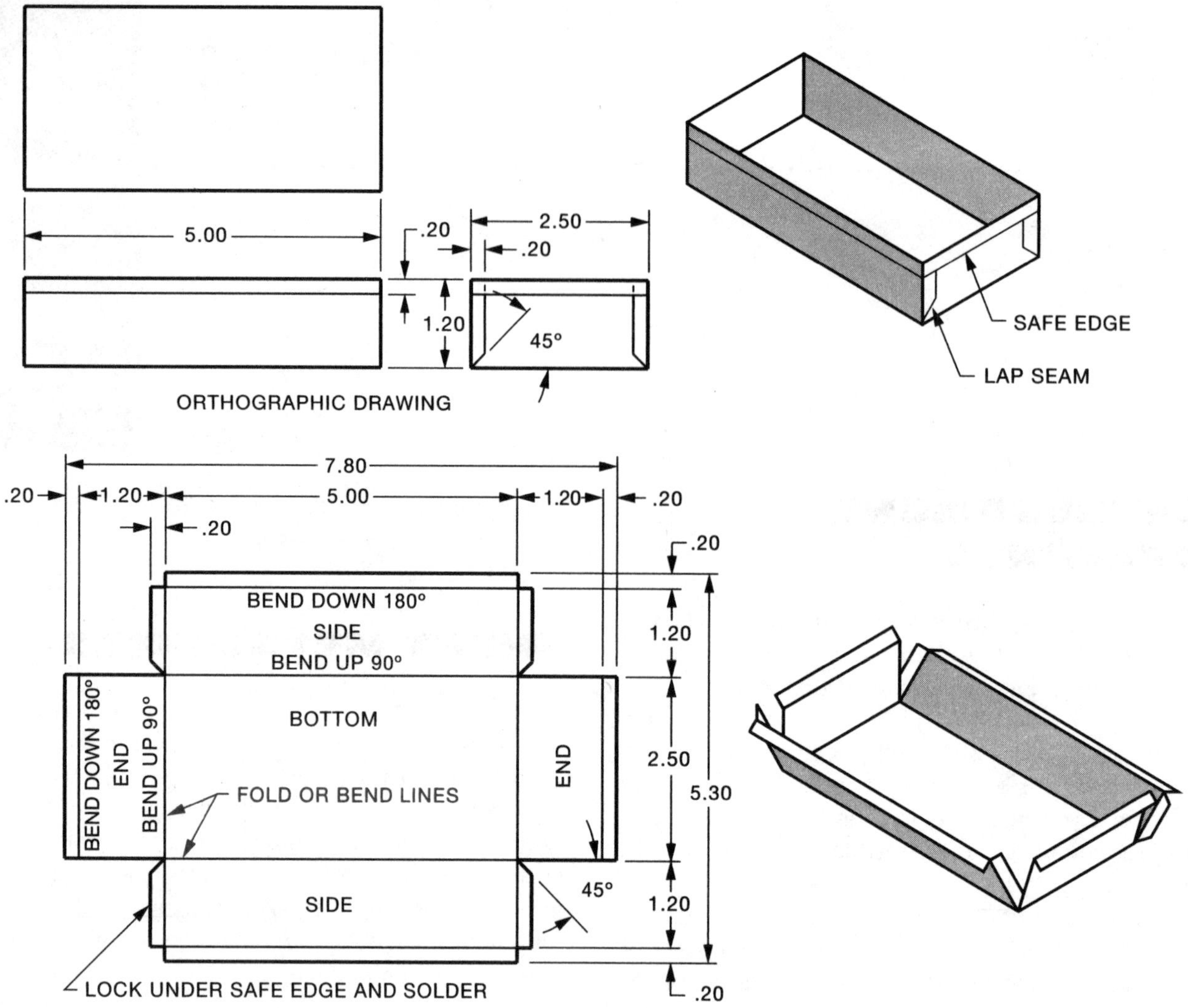
5.00
.20
2.50
.20
1.20
45°
ORTHOGRAPHIC DRAWING
SAFE EDGE
LAP SEAM
7.80
.20
1.20
5.00
1.20
.20
.20
.20
BEND DOWN 180°
SIDE
BEND UP 90°
BEND DOWN 180°
END
BEND UP 90°
BOTTOM
FOLD OR BEND LINES
END
1.20
2.50
5.30
45°
SIDE
1.20
LOCK UNDER SAFE EDGE AND SOLDER
.20

FIGURE 20–1 ■ Development drawing with a complete set of folding instructions

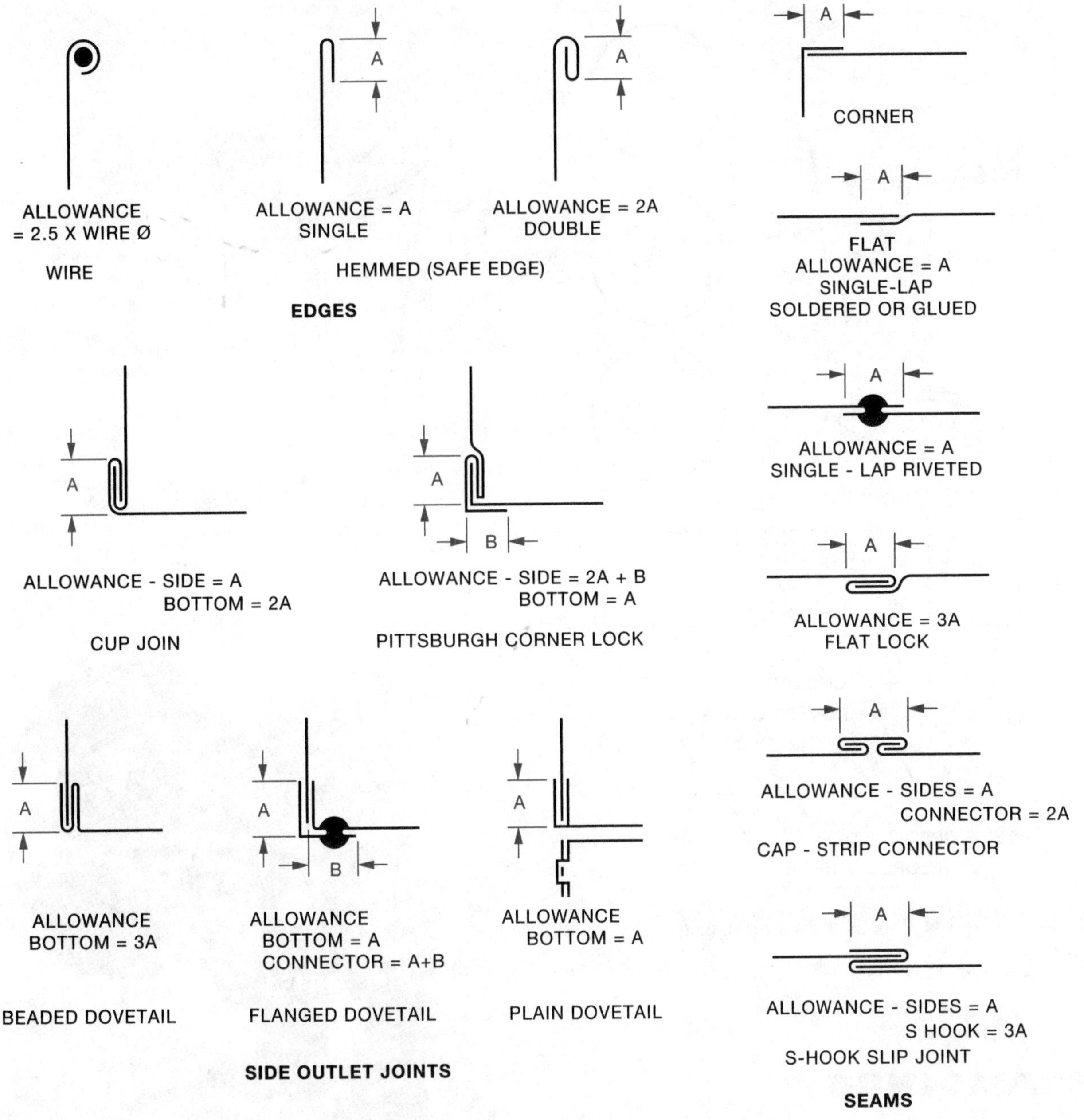
A
A
A
CORNER
A
ALLOWANCE
= 2.5 X WIRE Ø
WIRE
ALLOWANCE = A
SINGLE
ALLOWANCE = 2A
DOUBLE
HEMMED (SAFE EDGE)
EDGES
FLAT
ALLOWANCE = A
SINGLE-LAP
SOLDERED OR GLUED
A
A
A
ALLOWANCE = A
SINGLE - LAP RIVETED
B
ALLOWANCE - SIDE = A
BOTTOM = 2A
CUP JOIN
ALLOWANCE - SIDE = 2A + B
BOTTOM = A
PITTSBURGH CORNER LOCK
A
ALLOWANCE = 3A
FLAT LOCK
A
ALLOWANCE - SIDES = A
CONNECTOR = 2A
CAP - STRIP CONNECTOR
A
A
A
B
ALLOWANCE
BOTTOM = 3A
BEADED DOVETAIL
ALLOWANCE
BOTTOM = A
CONNECTOR = A+B
FLANGED DOVETAIL
ALLOWANCE
BOTTOM = A
PLAIN DOVETAIL
SIDE OUTLET JOINTS
A
ALLOWANCE - SIDES = A
S HOOK = 3A
S-HOOK SLIP JOINT
SEAMS

FIGURE 20–2 ■ Joints, seams, and edges

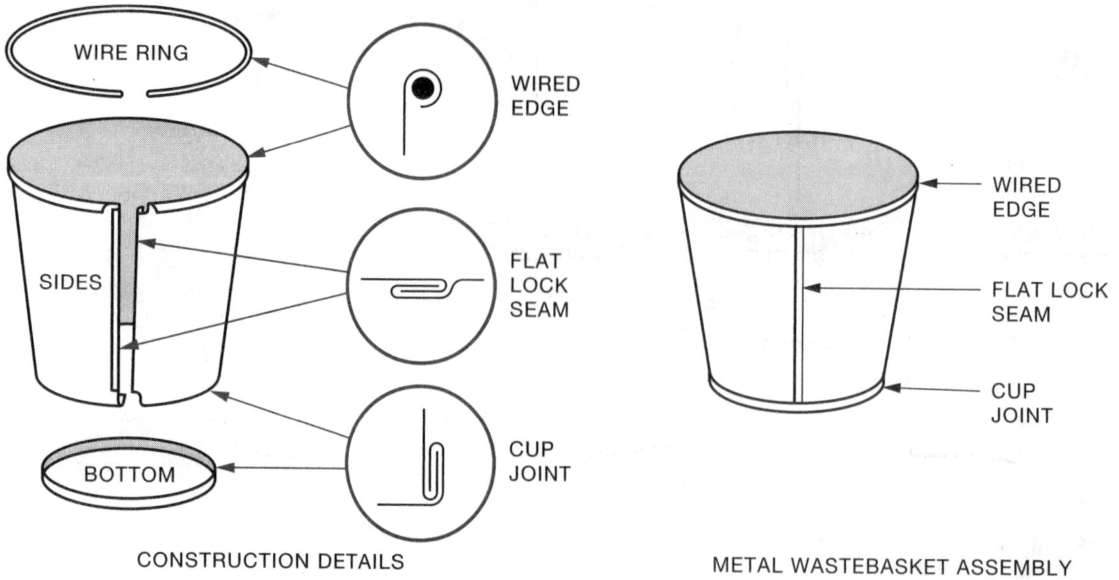

FIGURE 20–3 ■ Wastebasket construction

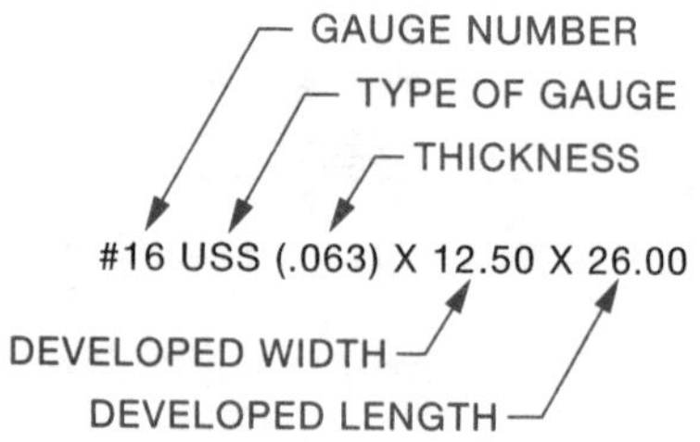

FIGURE 20–4 ■ Callout of sheet metal material

STAMPINGS

Stamping is the art of pressworking sheet metal to change its shape by the use of punches and dies. It may involve punching out a hole or the product itself from a sheet of metal. It may also involve bending or forming, Figures 20–5 and 20–6.

Stamping may be divided into two general classifications: *forming* and *shearing*.

Forming

Forming includes stampings made by forming sheet metal to the shape desired without cutting or shearing the metal. For thicker sheet metal plates, bending allowances must be taken into consideration.

FIGURE 20–5 ■ Punch press used to punch and form metal. *(Courtesy of Whitney Metal Tool Co.)*

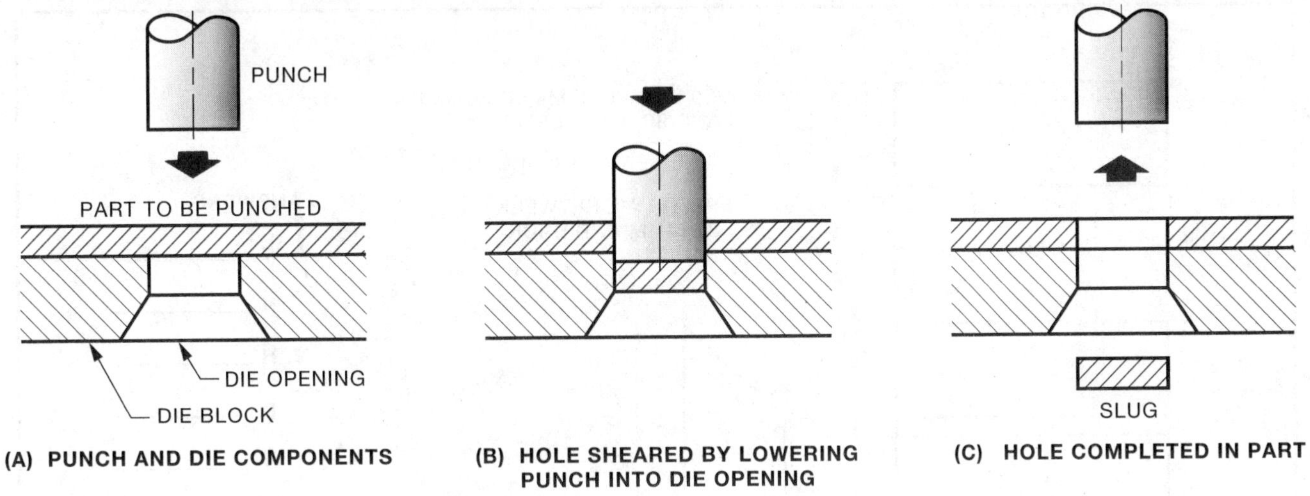
PUNCH
PART TO BE PUNCHED
DIE OPENING
DIE BLOCK
SLUG
(A) PUNCH AND DIE COMPONENTS
(B) HOLE SHEARED BY LOWERING PUNCH INTO DIE OPENING
(C) HOLE COMPLETED IN PART

FIGURE 20–6 ■ Punching a hole in sheet metal

Shearing

Shearing includes stampings made by shearing the sheet metal either to change the outline or to cut holes in the interior of the part. Punching forms a hole or opening in the part.

Height and width dimensions should normally be given to the same side of the metal, either the punch side or the die side. Because larger radii facilitate production, inside radii on stampings should not be less than 1.5 times stock thickness.

The following formula may be used for blank development, Figure 20–7:

$$\text{Total length} = A + B + \text{Bend Allowance}$$

where length for 90° bend =

$$\frac{\pi}{2}(R + .33T \text{ min.}) = 1.57\,(R + .33T \text{ min.})$$

It is not general practice to show the blank development on production drawings.

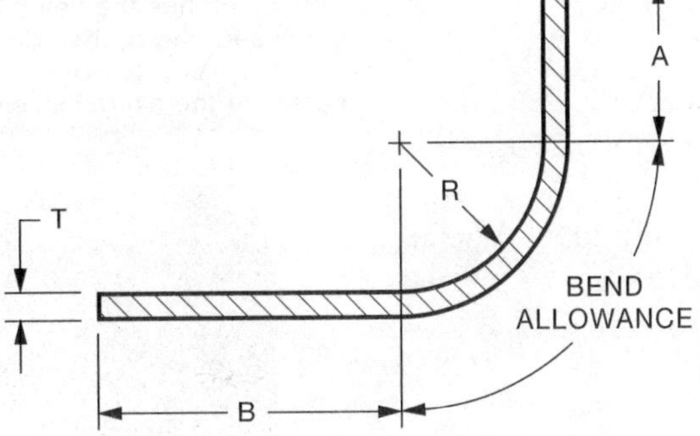
A
R
T
BEND
ALLOWANCE
B

FIGURE 20–7 ■ Dimensions for calculating blank development

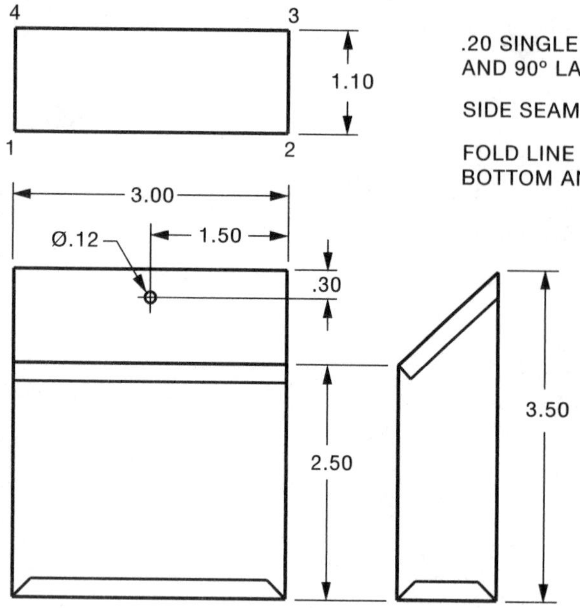

.20 SINGLE HEMMED EDGES
AND 90° LAP SEAMS

SIDE SEAM AT CORNER 1

FOLD LINE BETWEEN
BOTTOM AND BACK

MATERIAL #30 (.012 USS STEEL)

ANSWERS

1. W ________
   H ________
2. H ________
   D ________
3. W ________
4. D ________
   W ________
   H ________
5. ________
6. ________
7. ________

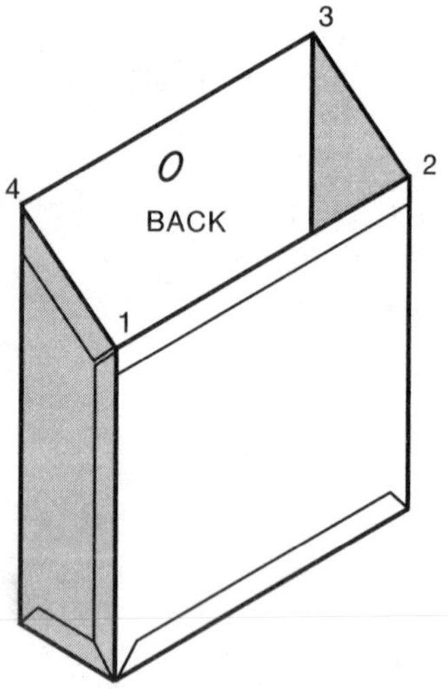

QUESTIONS

1. What are the overall dimensions of the back?
2. What are the overall dimensions of the side?
3. What are the overall dimensions of the bottom?
4. What are the overall dimensions of the front?
5. How much has the width of the development been increased due to the edge of the seam allowance?
6. How much has the height of the development been increased due to the edge of the seam allowance?
7. What are the overall sizes of the development?

ASSIGNMENT:
SKETCH THE DEVELOPMENT OF THE LETTER BOX AND SHOW THE OVERALL DIMENSIONS.

	LETTER BOX	**A-54**

10 mm SQUARES (1 mm GRID)

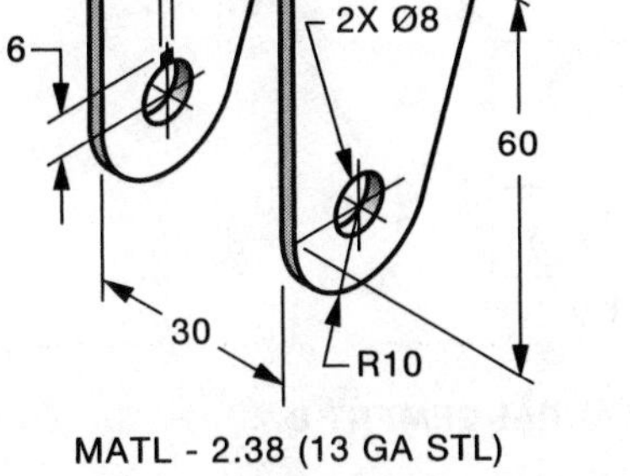

15
Ø14.5
R4
22
44
2.5
6
2X Ø8
60
30
R10

MATL - 2.38 (13 GA STL)

ASSIGNMENT:
ON THE GRID PROVIDED DRAW THE FRONT AND SIDE VIEW, PLUS THE DEVELOPMENT DRAWING OF THE BRACKET BEFORE THE THREE HOLES ARE PRODUCED. THE BRACKET IS PART OF THE WHEEL ASSEMBLY SHOWN ON ASSIGNMENT A-66M.

METRIC
DIMENSIONS ARE IN MILLIMETRES

	BRACKET	**A-55M**

21 UNIT

ARRANGEMENT OF VIEWS

The shape of an object and its complexity influence the possible choices and arrangement of views for that particular object. Because one of the main purposes of making drawings is to furnish the worker with enough information to be able to make the object, only the views that will aid in the interpretation of the drawing should be drawn.

The drafter chooses the view of the object that gives the viewer the clearest idea of the purpose and general contour of the object, and then calls this the front view. This choice of the front view may have no relationship to the actual front of the piece when it is used. The front view does not have to be the actual front of the object itself.

The selection of views to best describe the mounting plate shown in drawing A-57 is shown in Figure 21–1. These views could be called front, right-side, and bottom views as illustrated in Arrangement A. These views could also be designated top, front, and right-side views, as shown in Arrangement B. Note that in Arrangement B the right-side view is projected from the top view and not the front view as shown in Arrangement A. The designation of names is not of major importance. What is important is that these views, in the opinion of the drafter or designer, give the necessary information in the most understandable way.

Once the basic views that best describe the mounting plate have been established, auxiliary (helper) views, when required, are added in order to completely describe the part. The No. 1 auxiliary view is added by projecting it from the front view. This is the only one of the five views that shows this surface and the slotted hole in their true shape. Next the No. 2 auxiliary view is added by projecting it from the top view. This is the only view that shows this surface and the hexagon hole in their true shape.

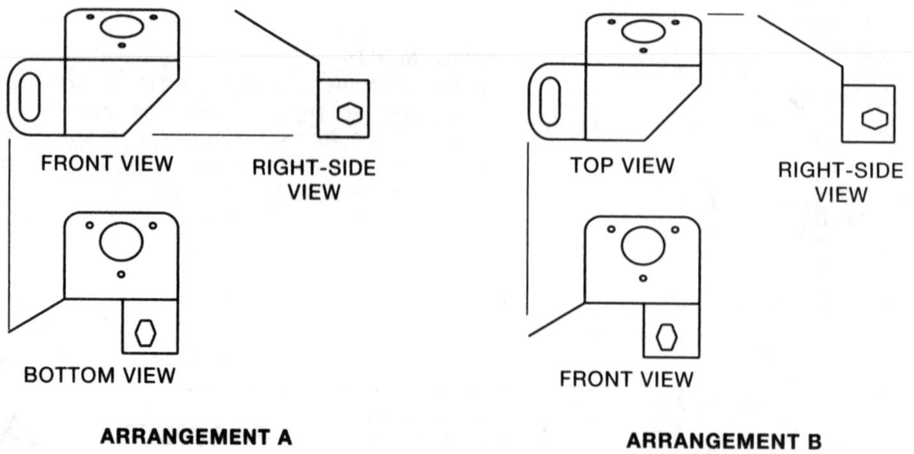

FIGURE 21–1 ■ Naming of views for mounting plate, drawing A-57

Dimensions are then added to the views or surfaces that are not shown distorted.

A variety of arrangements and naming of views to describe the index pedestal in drawing A-56 is shown in Figure 21–2. Arrangements A and B are identical except for the naming of the views. Although Arrangements C and D are acceptable, they are not as easily read.

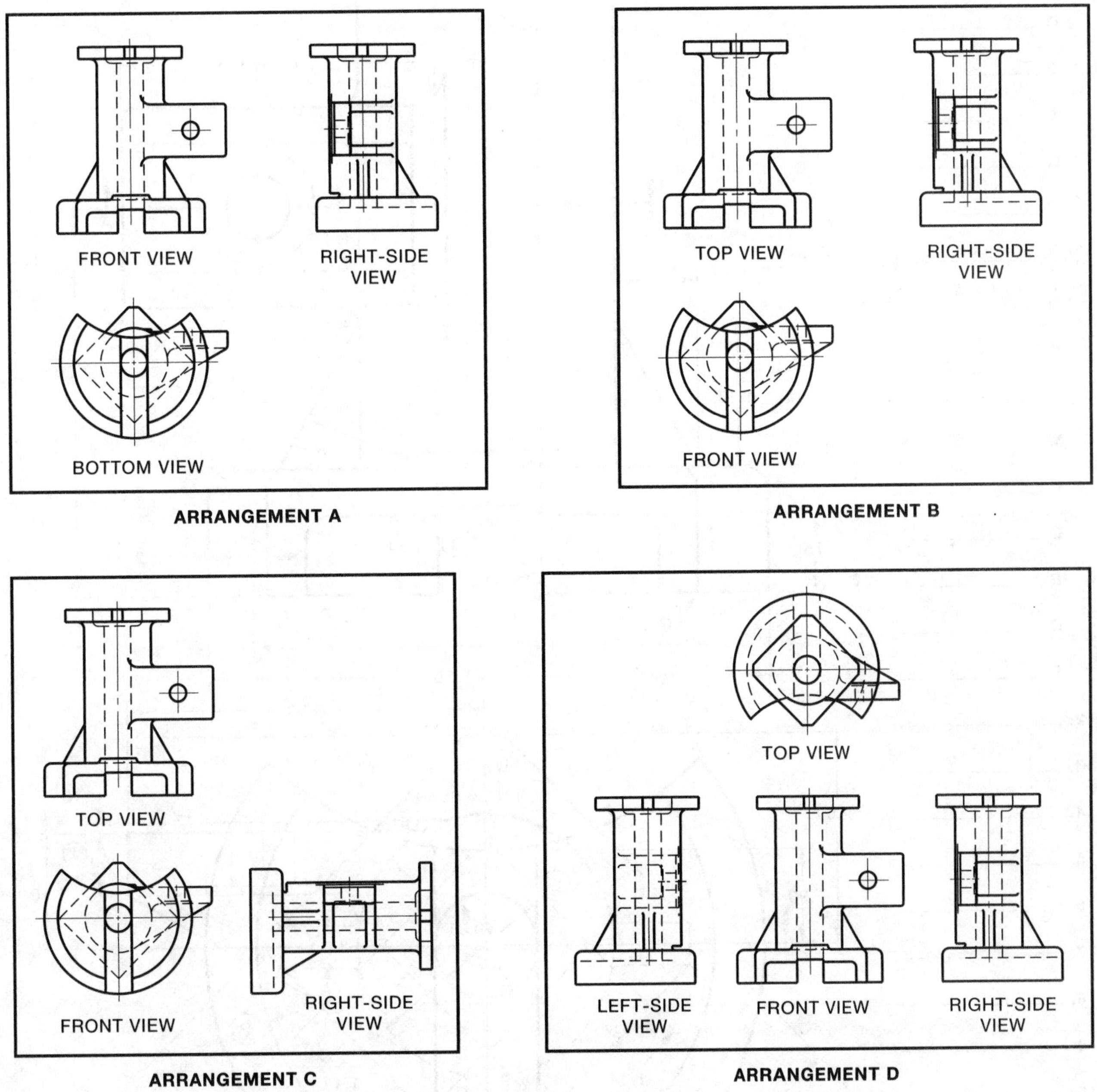

FIGURE 21–2 ■ Arrangements and naming of views for index pedestal, drawing A-56

ANSWERS

1. A ______
   B ______
   C ______
   D ______
   E ______
   F ______
   G ______
   H ______
   I ______
   J ______
   K ______
   L ______
   M ______
   N ______
   O ______
   P ______
   Q ______
   R ______
2. ______
3. ______
4. ______
5. ______
6. ______
7. ______
8. ______
9. ______
10. ______

NOTE: ALL SURFACES SHOWN ✓ TO BE 63✓

REVISIONS	1	02-02-23	F. NEWMAN
	.60 WAS .50		

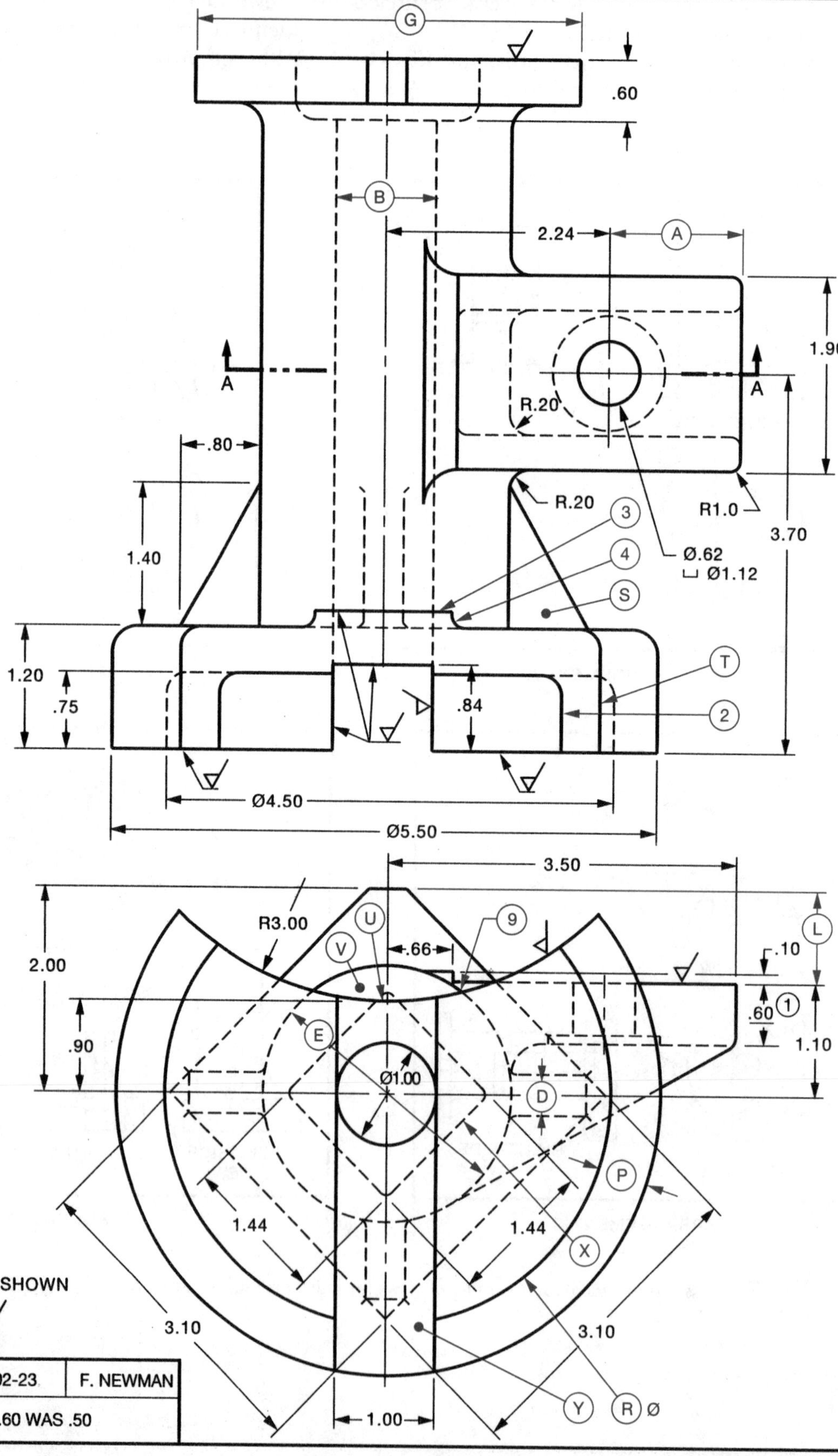

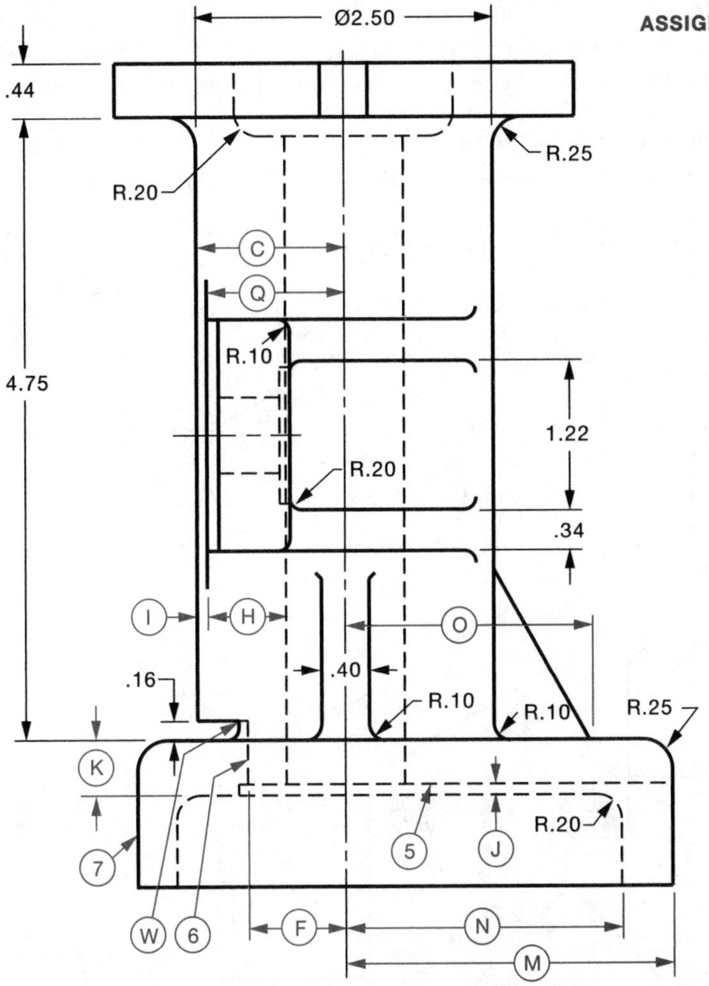

ASSIGNMENT: MAKE A FREEHAND SKETCH OF SECTION A-A IN THE SPACE PROVIDED.

QUESTIONS

1. Determine distances (A) through (R).
2. Which line in the front view does line (7) represent?
3. Which line or surface in the front view represents the surface at (V)?
4. Locate line (4) in the right-side view.
5. Locate line (4) in the bottom view.
6. How deep is the square (X) hole?
7. How many different finished surfaces are indicated?
8. From which point on the bottom view is line (6) projected?
9. Determine overall height of the pedestal.
10. Which line or surface in the right-side view represents surface (Y)?

FRONT VIEW	RIGHT-SIDE VIEW
BOTTOM VIEW	

ARRANGEMENT OF VIEWS

SKETCH PATTERN FOR RIB(S) BELOW

1.00 INCH SQUARES (.20 IN. GRID)

SECTION A-A

MATERIAL	WROUGHT IRON	
SCALE		
DRAWN		DATE
INDEX PEDESTAL		A-56

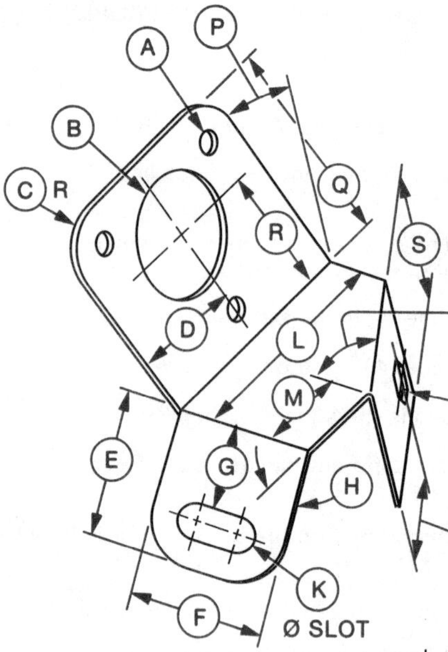
A
P
B
C R
Q
R
S
D
L
N
M
T
ACR
E
G
H
J
K
F
Ø SLOT

QUESTIONS

1. Calculate the dimensions and hole sizes (A) to (T) shown on the pictorial sketch.
2. What would be the overall size of the sheet used to make the part? Sizes to be in .10 inch increments.
3. On which view(s) are the Ø.68 slots shown?
4. Which view(s) show the true shape of the (A) Ø.68 slot, (B) Ø1.30 hole, and (C) .75 hex hole?
5. How would the holes in the part be produced?

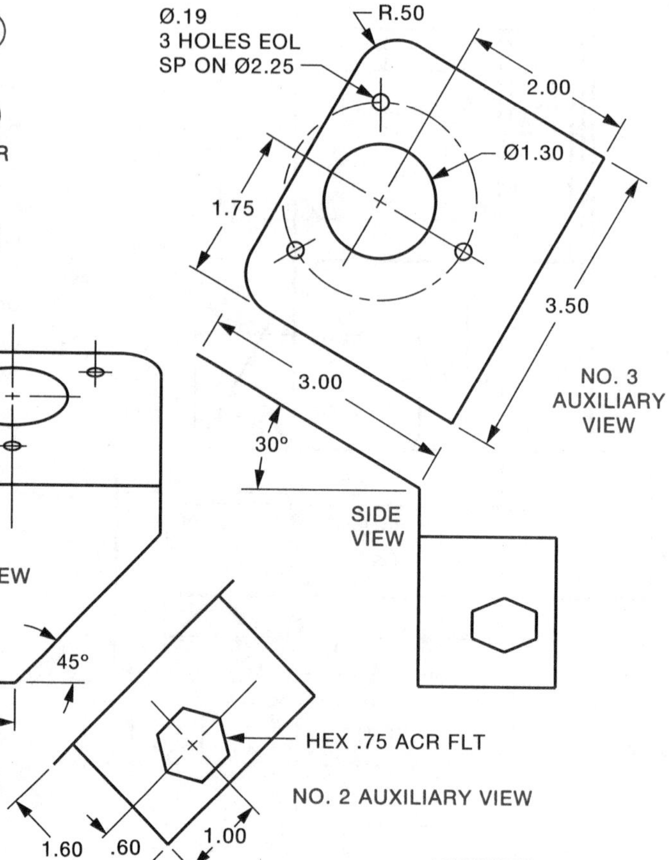
Ø.19
3 HOLES EOL
SP ON Ø2.25
R.50
2.00
Ø1.30
1.75
3.50
3.00
NO. 3
AUXILIARY
VIEW
30°
SIDE
VIEW
TOP VIEW
2.25
45°
1.80
HEX .75 ACR FLT
NO. 2 AUXILIARY VIEW
1.60
.60
1.00

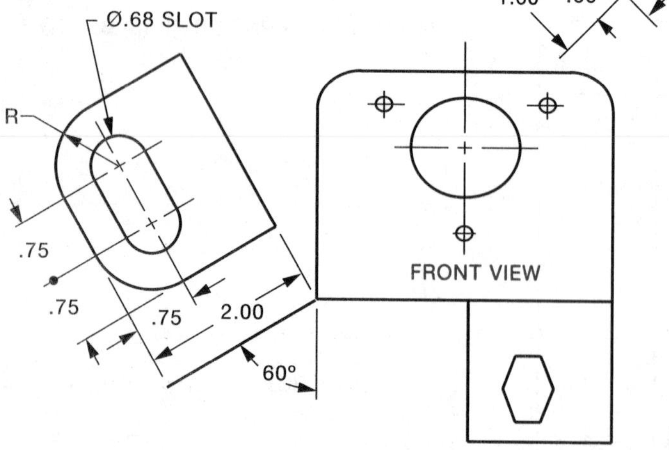
NO. 1 AUXILIARY VIEW
Ø.68 SLOT
R
.75
.75
.75
2.00
60°
FRONT VIEW

ANSWERS

1. A ______	J ______	S ______
B ______	K ______	T ______
C ______	L ______	2. ______
D ______	M ______	3. ______
E ______	N ______	4. A ______
F ______	P ______	B ______
G ______	Q ______	C ______
H ______	R ______	5. ______

MATL - 20 USS (.038) TIN PLATE

	MOUNTING PLATE	A-57

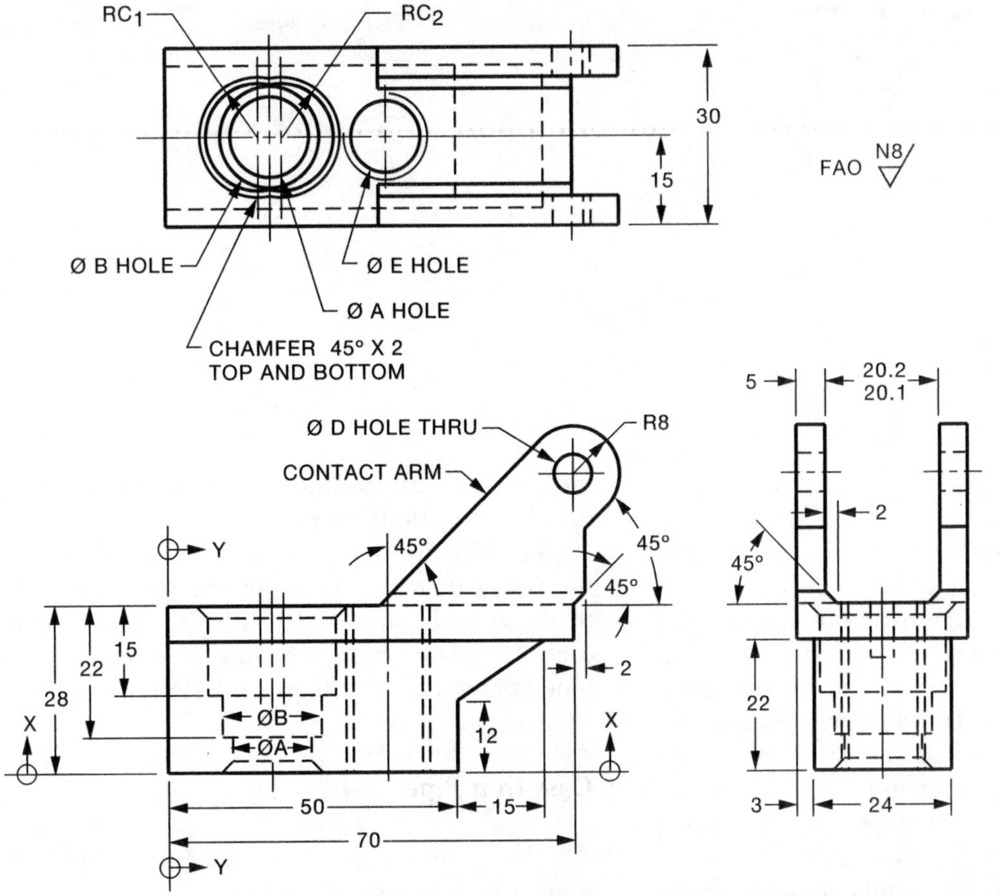
RC1
RC2
30
15
FAO N8
Ø B HOLE
Ø E HOLE
Ø A HOLE
CHAMFER 45° X 2
TOP AND BOTTOM
Ø D HOLE THRU
R8
CONTACT ARM
Y
45°
45°
45°
15
22
28
X
ØB
ØA
12
2
X
50
15
70
Y
5
20.2
20.1
2
45°
22
3
24

ANSWERS

1. ____________
2. ____________
3. ____________
4. ____________
5. ____________
6. ____________
7. ____________
8. ____________
9. ____________
10. ____________
11. ____________
12. ____________
13. ____________
14. ____________
15. ____________

NOTE: UNLESS OTHERWISE SPECIFIED:
—TOLERANCE ON DIMENSIONS ±0.5
—TOLERANCE ON ANGLES ±0.5°

QUESTIONS

1. What is the overall width?
2. What is the overall height?
3. Give the chamfer angle for the C hole.
4. What is the distance from Y-Y to E hole?
5. What is the distance from X-X to D hole?
6. How many complete threads does the tapped hole have?
7. Which thread series is the tapped hole?
8. What is the surface finish in micrometres?
9. How deep is the C counterbore from the top of the surface?
10. How long is the B counterbored hole?
11. Give the distance between the ℄ of C_1 and C_2 radii.
12. What is the nominal thickness of the contact arm at D hole?
13. What is the tolerance on the distance between the contact arms?
14. What is the tolerance on D hole?
15. What is the centre distance between A and E holes?

HOLE SYMBOL	HOLE SIZE	LOCATION	
		X-X	Y-Y
A	Ø13.5		18
B	Ø17		18
C_1	R9		16
C_2	R9		20
D	Ø6.5-6.6	50	70
E	M12 X 1.25		38

METRIC
DIMENSIONS ARE IN MILLIMETRES

MATERIAL	MANGANESE BRONZE		
SCALE	NOT TO SCALE		
DRAWN		DATE	
	CONTACT ARM	A-58M	

22 UNIT

PIPING

Until 100 years ago, water was the only important fluid conveyed from place to place through pipe. Today nearly every conceivable fluid is handled in pipe during its production, processing, transportation, or utilization. During the age of atomic energy and rocket power liquid metals, sodium, and nitrogen have been added to the list of more common fluids such as oil, water, and acids being transported through pipe. Many gases are also being stored and delivered through piping systems.

Pipe is also used for hydraulic and pneumatic mechanisms and used extensively for the controls of machinery and other equipment. Piping is also used as a structural element for columns and handrails.

The nominal size of pipe and the inside diameter, outside diameter, and wall thickness are given in inches.

Kinds of Pipe

Steel and Wrought Iron Pipe

These pipes carry water, steam, oil, and gas and are commonly used under high temperatures and pressures. Standard steel or cast iron pipe is specified by the nominal diameter, which is always less than the actual inner diameter (ID) of the pipe. Until recently, this pipe was available in only three weights—standard, extra strong, and double extra strong, Figure 22–1. In order to use common fittings with these different pipe weights, the outside diameter (OD) of each of the different pipes remained the same. The extra metal was added to the ID to increase the wall thickness of the extra strong and double extra strong pipe.

The demand for a greater variety of pipe for use under increased pressure and temperature led to the introduction of 10 different pipe weights, each designated by a schedule number. Standard pipe is now called schedule 40 pipe. Extra strong pipe is schedule 80.

Cast Iron Pipe

This is often installed underground to carry water, gas, and sewage.

Seamless Brass and Copper Pipe

These pipes are used extensively in plumbing because of their ability to withstand corrosion.

Copper Tubing

This is used in plumbing and heating and where vibration and misalignment are factors, such as in automotive, hydraulic, and pneumatic design.

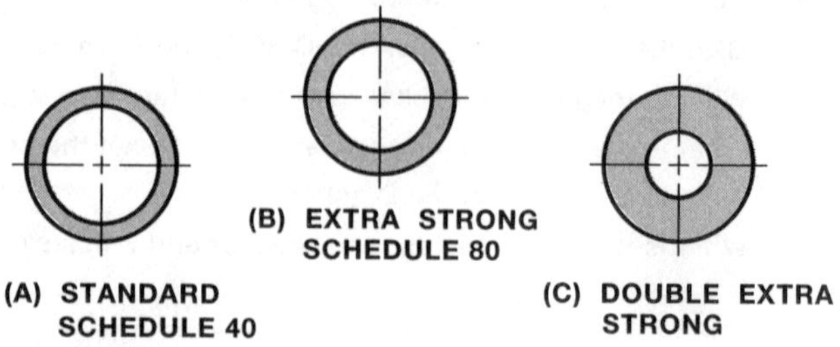
(A) STANDARD SCHEDULE 40
(B) EXTRA STRONG SCHEDULE 80
(C) DOUBLE EXTRA STRONG

FIGURE 22–1 ■ Comparison of wall thicknesses

Plastic Pipe

This pipe or tubing, because of its resistance to corrosion and chemicals, is often used in the chemical industry. It is easily installed. However, it is not recommended where heat or pressure is a factor.

Pipe Joints and Fittings

Parts joined to pipe are called *fittings*. They may be used to change size or direction and to join or provide branch connections. There are three general classes of fittings: screwed, welded, and flanged. Other methods such as soldering, brazing, and gluing are used for cast iron pipe, and copper and plastic tubing.

Pipe fittings are specified by the nominal pipe size, the name of the fitting, and the material. Some fittings—for example, tees, crosses, and elbows—connect different sizes of pipe. These are called *reducing fittings*. Their nominal pipe sizes must be specified. The largest opening of the through run is given first, followed by the opposite end and the outlet. Figure 22–2 illustrates the method of designating sizes of reducing fittings.

Screwed Fittings

Screwed fittings are generally used on small pipe design of 2.50-inch nominal pipe size or less.

There are two types of American Standard Pipe Thread: tapered and straight. The tapered thread is more common. Straight threads are used for special applications.

Tapered threads are designated on drawings as NPT (National Pipe Thread) or whichever standard is used and may be drawn either with or without the taper, Figure 22–3. When drawn in tapered form, the taper is exaggerated. Straight pipe threads are designated on drawings as NPTS and standard thread symbols are used. Pipe threads are assumed to be tapered unless specified otherwise.

Welded Fittings

Welded fittings are used where connections will be permanent and on high pressure and temperature lines. The ends of the pipe and pipe fittings are usually bevelled to accommodate the weld.

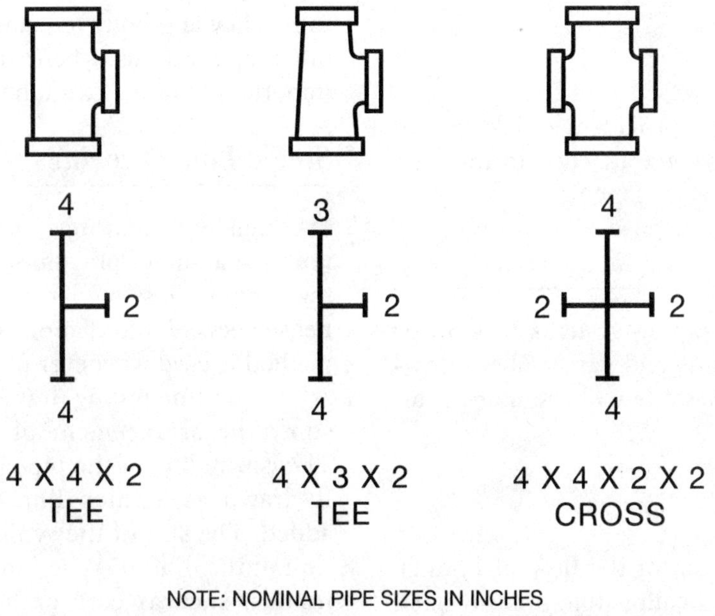

FIGURE 22–2 ■ Order of specifying the openings of reducing fittings

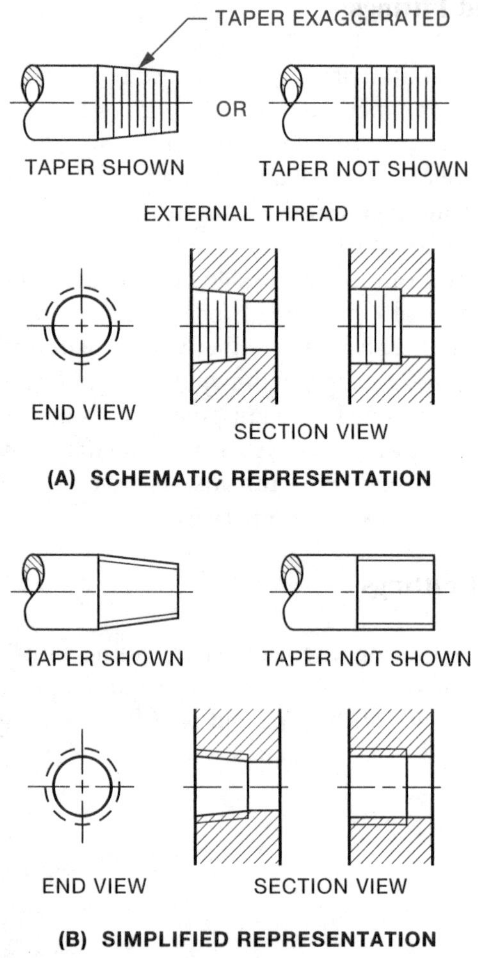

FIGURE 22–3 ■ Pipe thread conventions

Flanged Fittings

Flanged joint fittings provide a quick way to disassemble pipe. Flanges are attached to the pipe ends by welding, screwing, or lapping.

Valves

Valves are used in piping systems to stop or regulate the flow of fluids and gases. The following information describes a few of the more common types.

Gate Valves

These are used to control the flow of liquids. The wedge, or gate, lifts to allow full, unobstructed flow and lowers to stop the flow. They are generally used where operation is infrequent and are not intended for throttling or close control.

Globe Valves

These are used to control the flow of liquids or gases. The design of the globe valve produces two changes in the direction of flow, slightly reducing the pressure in the system. The globe valve is recommended for the control of air, steam, gas, and other compressibles where instantaneous on-and-off operation is essential.

Check Valves

Check valves permit flow in one direction, but check all reverse flow. They are operated by pressure and velocity of line flow alone and have no external means of operation.

PIPING DRAWINGS

Piping drawings show the size and location of pipes, fittings, and valves. Because of the detail required to accurately describe these items, there is a set of symbols to indicate them on drawings.

There are two types of piping drawings in use, single-line and double-line drawings, Figure 22–4. Double-line drawings take longer to draw and are therefore not recommended for production drawings. They are, however, suitable for catalogues and other applications where the appearance is more important than the extra drafting time.

Single-Line Drawings

Single-line drawings, also known as simplified representation, of pipe lines provide substantial savings without loss of clarity or reduction of comprehensiveness of information. Therefore, the simplified method is used whenever possible.

Single-line piping drawings use a single line to show the arrangement of the pipe and fittings. The centre line of the pipe, regardless of pipe size, is drawn as a thick line to which symbols are added. The size of the symbol is left to the discretion of the drafter. When pipe lines carry different liquids, such as cold or hot water, a coded line symbol is often used.

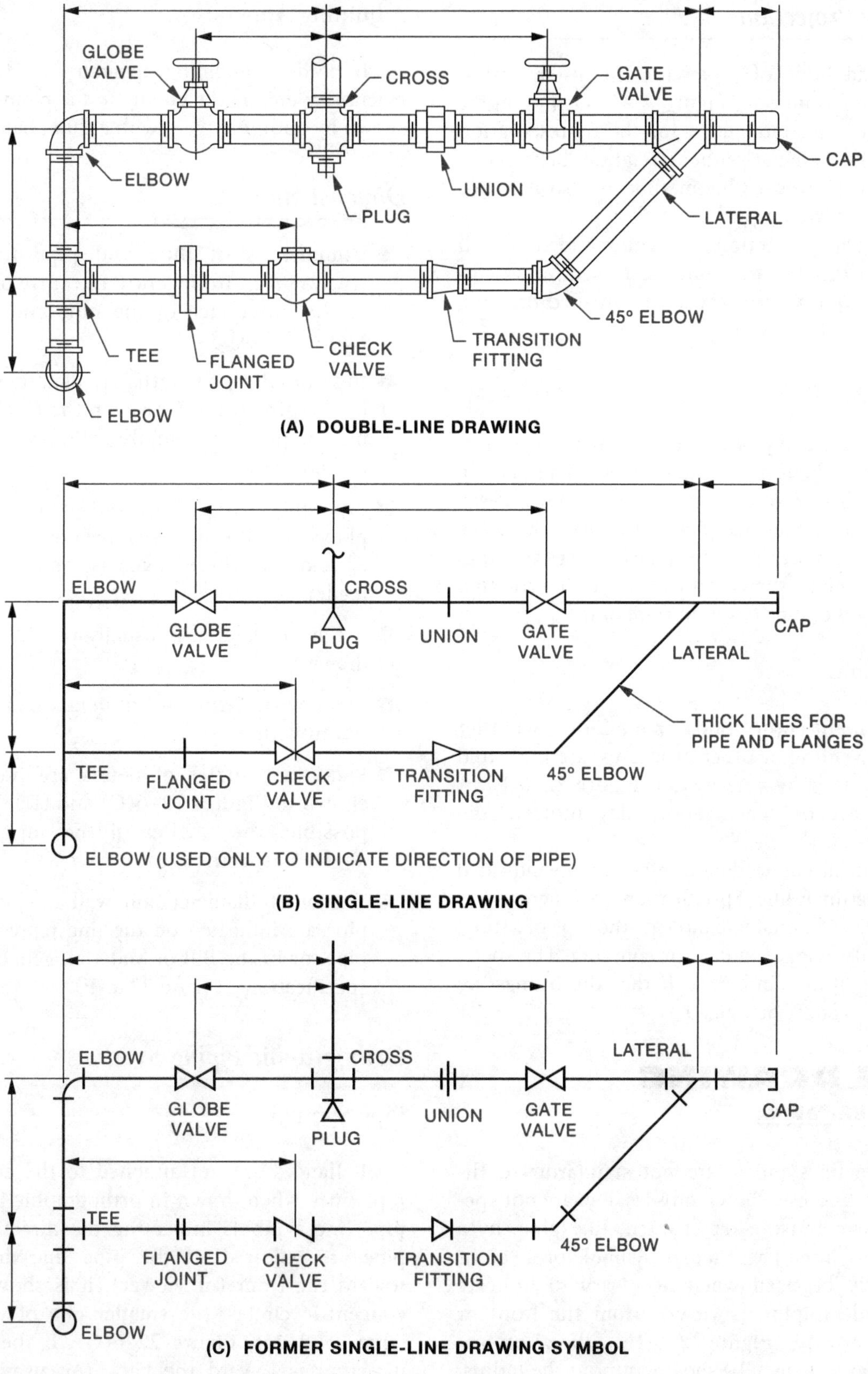

FIGURE 22–4 ■ Piping drawing symbols

Drawing Projection

Two methods of projection are used, orthographic and isometric, Figure 22–5. Orthographic projection is recommended for the representation of single pipes that are either straight or bent in one plane only. However, this method is also used for more complicated pipings.

Isometric projection is recommended for all pipes bent in more than one plane and for assembly and layout work because the finished drawing is easier to understand.

Crossings

The crossing of pipes without connections is usually drawn without interrupting the line representing the hidden line, Figure 22–6(A). But when it is desirable to indicate that one pipe must pass behind the other, the line representing the pipe farthest away from the viewer will be shown with a break or interruption where the other pipe passes in front of it.

Connections

Permanent connections or junctions, whether made by welding or other processes, are indicated on the drawing by a heavy dot, Figure 22–6(F). A general note or specification may indicate the process used.

Detachable connections or junctions are indicated by a single thick line. Specifications, a general note, or the Bill of Material will indicate the type of fitting, for example, flanges, union, or coupling. The specifications will also indicate whether the fittings are flanged, threaded, or welded.

PIPE DRAWING SYMBOLS

If specific symbols are not standardized, fittings such as tees, elbows, crosses, etc. are not specially drawn but are represented, like pipe, by a continuous line. The circular symbol for a tee or elbow may be used when necessary to indicate whether the piping is viewed from the front or back, as shown in Figure 22–6(H). Elbows on isometric drawings may be shown without the radius. However, if this method is used, the direction change of the piping must be shown clearly.

Adjoining Apparatus

If needed, adjoining apparatus, such as tanks, machinery, etc. not belonging to the piping itself, are shown by outlining them with a thin phantom line.

Dimensioning

- Dimensions of pipe and pipe fittings are always given from centre to centre of pipe and to the outer face of the pipe end or flange, Figure 22–6(C).
- Individual pipe lengths are usually cut to suit by the pipe fitter. However, the total length of pipe required is usually called for in the Bill of Material.
- Pipe and fitting sizes and general notes are placed on the drawing beside the part concerned, or where space is restricted, with a leader.
- A Bill of Material is usually provided with the drawing.
- Pipes with bends are dimensioned from vertex to vertex.
- Radii and angles of bends are indicated as shown in Figures 22–6(C) and (D). Whenever possible, the smaller of the supplementary angles is specified.
- The outer diameter and wall thickness of the pipe are indicated on the line representing the pipe, or in the Bill of Material, general note, or specifications, Figure 22–6(E).

Orthographic Piping Symbols

Pipe Symbols

If flanges are not attached to the ends of the pipe lines when drawn in orthographic projection, pipe line symbols indicating the direction of the pipe are required. If the pipe line direction is toward the front (or viewer), it is shown by two concentric circles, the smaller one of which is a large solid dot, Figure 22–6(G). If the pipe line direction is toward the back (or away from the viewer), it will be shown by one solid circle. No extra lines are required on the other views.

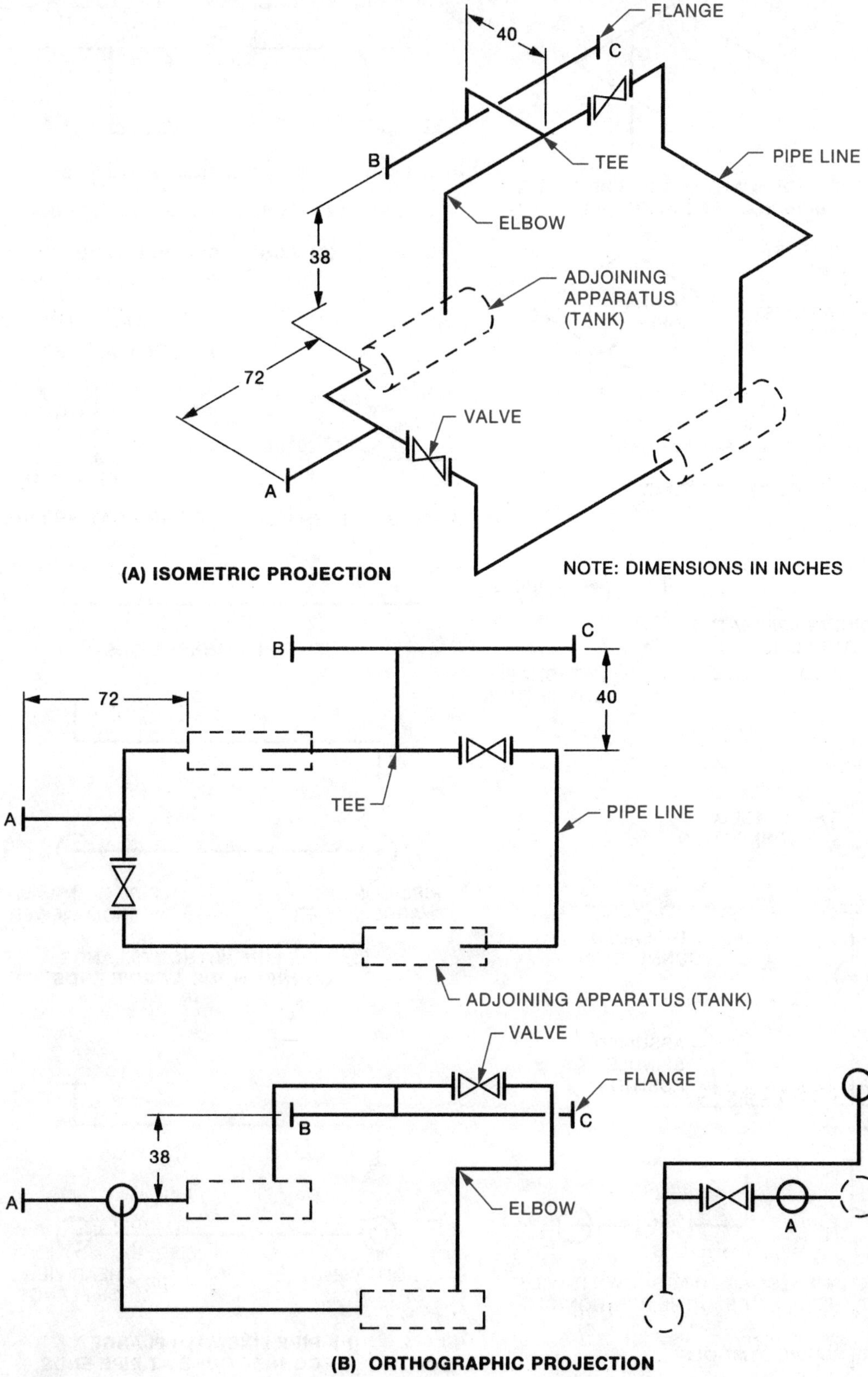

FIGURE 22–5 ■ Single-line piping drawing

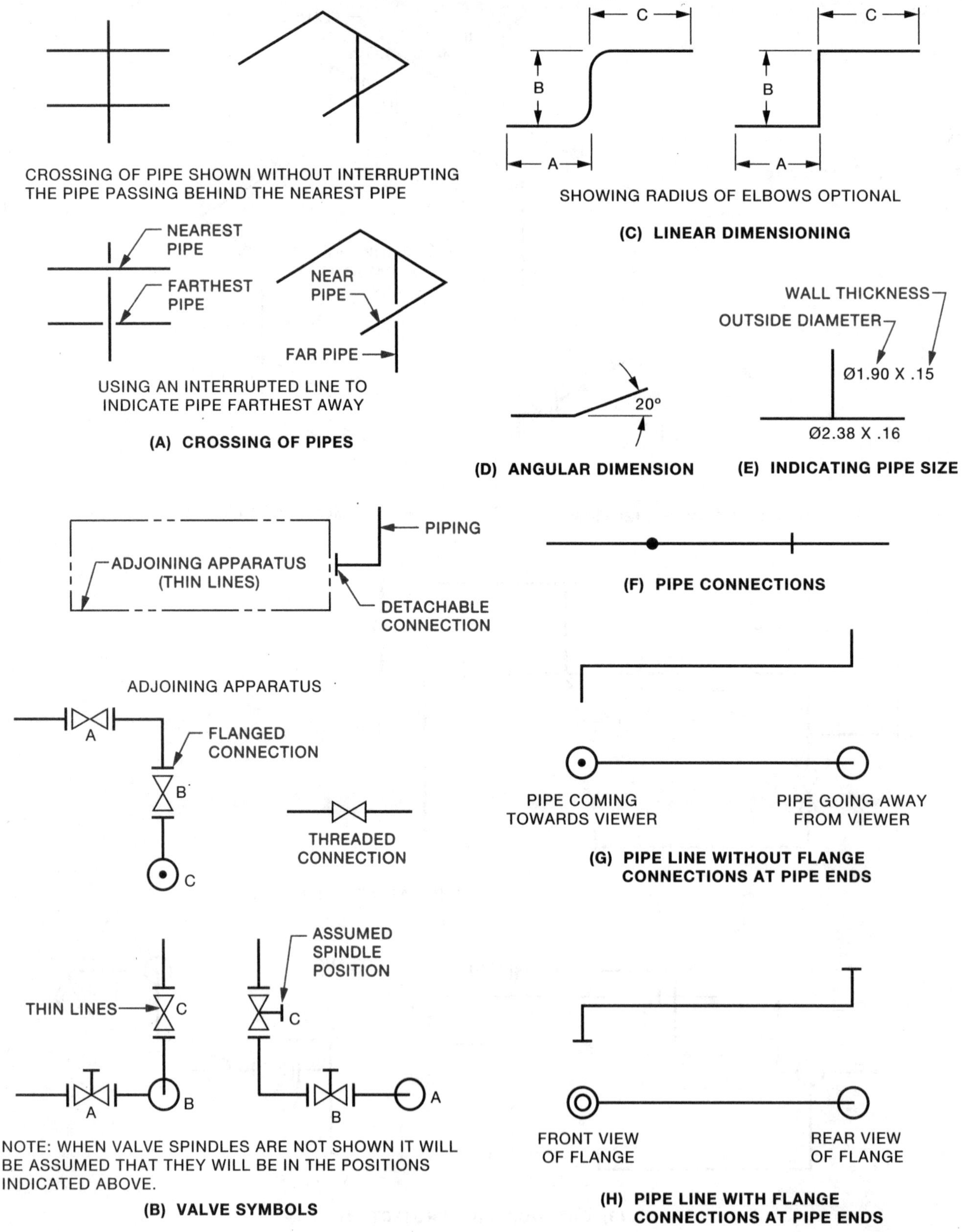
CROSSING OF PIPE SHOWN WITHOUT INTERRUPTING THE PIPE PASSING BEHIND THE NEAREST PIPE
NEAREST PIPE
FARTHEST PIPE
NEAR PIPE
FAR PIPE
USING AN INTERRUPTED LINE TO INDICATE PIPE FARTHEST AWAY
(A) CROSSING OF PIPES
C
B
A
C
B
A
SHOWING RADIUS OF ELBOWS OPTIONAL
(C) LINEAR DIMENSIONING
WALL THICKNESS
OUTSIDE DIAMETER
Ø1.90 X .15
Ø2.38 X .16
20°
(D) ANGULAR DIMENSION
(E) INDICATING PIPE SIZE
PIPING
ADJOINING APPARATUS (THIN LINES)
DETACHABLE CONNECTION
(F) PIPE CONNECTIONS
ADJOINING APPARATUS
A
FLANGED CONNECTION
B
C
THREADED CONNECTION
PIPE COMING TOWARDS VIEWER
PIPE GOING AWAY FROM VIEWER
(G) PIPE LINE WITHOUT FLANGE CONNECTIONS AT PIPE ENDS
ASSUMED SPINDLE POSITION
THIN LINES
C
C
A
B
B
A
NOTE: WHEN VALVE SPINDLES ARE NOT SHOWN IT WILL BE ASSUMED THAT THEY WILL BE IN THE POSITIONS INDICATED ABOVE.
(B) VALVE SYMBOLS
FRONT VIEW OF FLANGE
REAR VIEW OF FLANGE
(H) PIPE LINE WITH FLANGE CONNECTIONS AT PIPE ENDS

FIGURE 22–6 ■ Single-line piping drawing symbols and dimension

Flange Symbols

Irrespective of their type and sizes, flanges are to be represented by

- two concentric circles for the front view
- one circle for the rear view
- a short stroke for the side view

while using lines of equal thickness as chosen for the representation of pipes, Figure 22–6(H).

Valve Symbols

Symbols representing valves are drawn with continuous thin lines (not thick lines as for piping and flanges). The valve spindles should be shown only if it is necessary to define their positions. It will be assumed that unless otherwise indicated, the valve spindle is in the position shown in Figure 22–6(B).

REFERENCE

ASME Y32.2.3-1949 (R1999) Graphic Symbols for Pipe Fittings, Valves and Piping

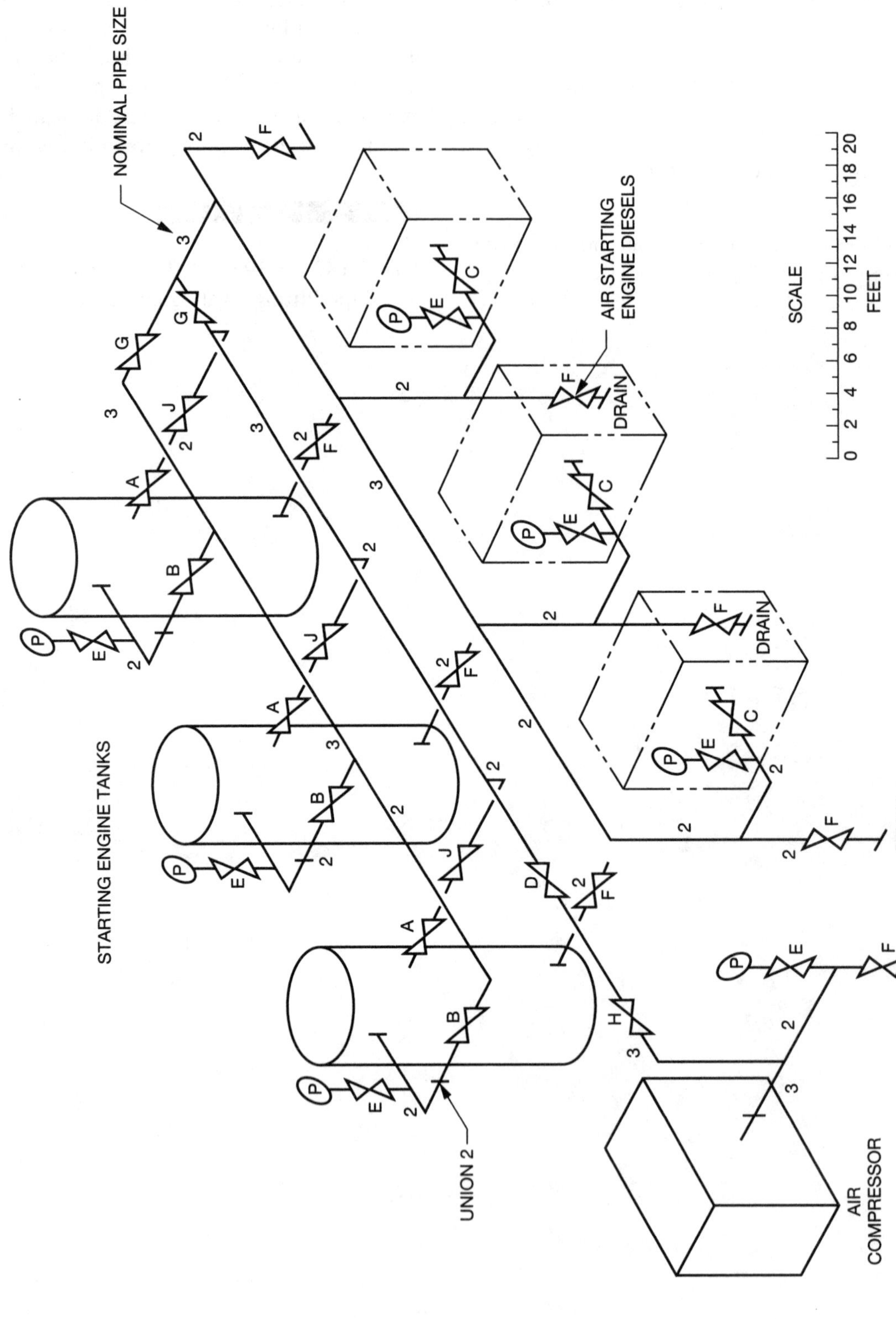
NOMINAL PIPE SIZE
AIR STARTING ENGINE DIESELS
SCALE
0 2 4 6 8 10 12 14 16 18 20
FEET
STARTING ENGINE TANKS
UNION 2
AIR COMPRESSOR
DRAIN

Safety valves are provided for the compressor and the air storage tanks. Check valves are installed on the air storage tank feed lines and the compressor discharge lines to prevent accidental discharge of the tanks.

Piping is arranged so that the compressor will either fill the storage tanks and/or pump directly to the engines. Any of the three storage tanks may be used for starting, and pressure gauges indicate their readiness. The engines are fitted with quick-opening valves to admit air quickly at full pressure and shut it off at the instant rotation is obtained. A bronze globe valve is installed to permit complete shutdown of the engine for repairs, and regulation of the flow of air. Drains are provided at low points to remove condensate from the air storage tanks, lines, and engine feed.

Globe valves are recommended throughout this hookup except on the main shutoff lines where gate valves are used because of infrequent operation.

QUESTIONS (Use scale provided where necessary):

1. What size pipe is used for the main feed line?
2. Disregarding the length of the valves and fittings, what is the total approximate length of
   (A) the 3-inch pipe? (B) the 2-inch pipe?
3. What is the approximate centre line to centre line spacing of the diesel engines?
4. Calculate the approximate number of cubic feet of each of the air tanks.
5. Why are diesel engines used instead of public power supply?
6. What is the purpose of the air compressor?
7. Why is a gate valve used instead of a globe valve in the main line shutoff?
8. State the uses of the following parts:
   (A) valve C (C) gauge P (E) valve D
   (B) valve G (D) valve F (F) valve H

QTY	ITEM	MAT'L	DESCRIPTION	PT NO
				14
				13
				12
				11
				10
				9
				8
				7
				6
				5
				4
				3
				2
				1

ANSWERS

1. ____________
2. A ____________
   B ____________
3. ____________
4. ____________
5. ____________
   ____
6. ____________
   ____
7. ____________

8. A ____________
   ____
   B ____________
   ____
   C ____________
   ____
   D ____________
   ____
   E ____________
   ____
   F ____________

CODE	VALVE	SERVICE
A	BRONZE GLOBE	AIR STORAGE TANK FEED LINES
B	BRONZE GLOBE	AIR STORAGE TANK DISCHARGE LINES
C	BRONZE GLOBE	DIESEL ENGINE SHUTOFF CONTROL
D	BRONZE GLOBE	AIR COMPRESSOR DISCHARGE
E	BRONZE GLOBE	PRESSURE GAUGE SHUTOFF
F	BRONZE GLOBE	DRAIN VALVES
G	SPINDLE GATE	MAIN LINE SHUTOFF
H	BRONZE CHECK	AIR COMPRESSOR CHECK
J	BRONZE CHECK	AIR STORAGE TANK FEED LINES
P	PRESSURE GAUGE	DISCHARGE OR FEED LINES

ASSIGNMENT:
COMPLETE THE BILL OF MATERIAL CALLING FOR ALL VALVES AND FITTINGS.

	SCALE AS SHOWN		
	DRAWN	DATE	
ISOMETRIC PROJECTION	**ENGINE STARTING AIR SYSTEM**		**A-59**

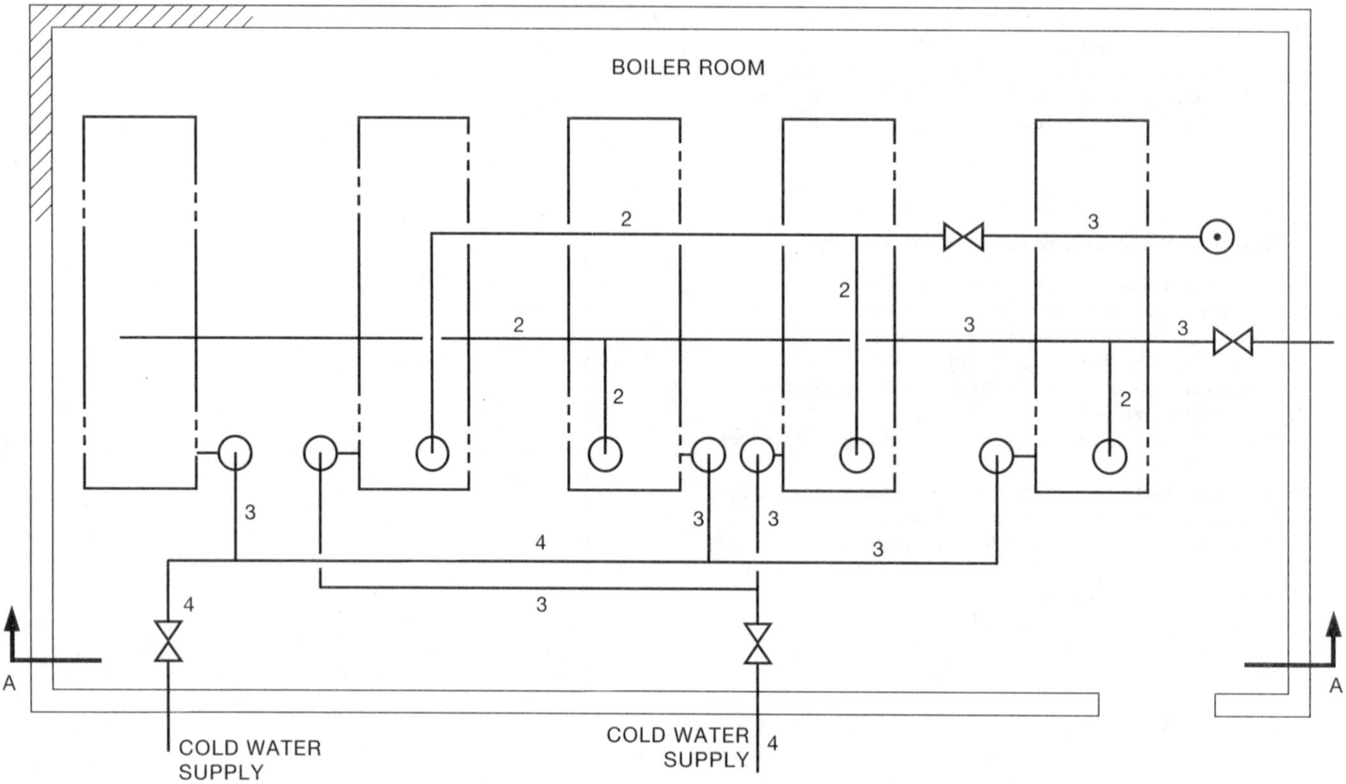
BOILER ROOM
2
3
2
2
3
3
2
2
3
3
3
4
3
4
3
A
A
COLD WATER SUPPLY
COLD WATER SUPPLY
4

PLAN VIEW OF BOILER ROOM

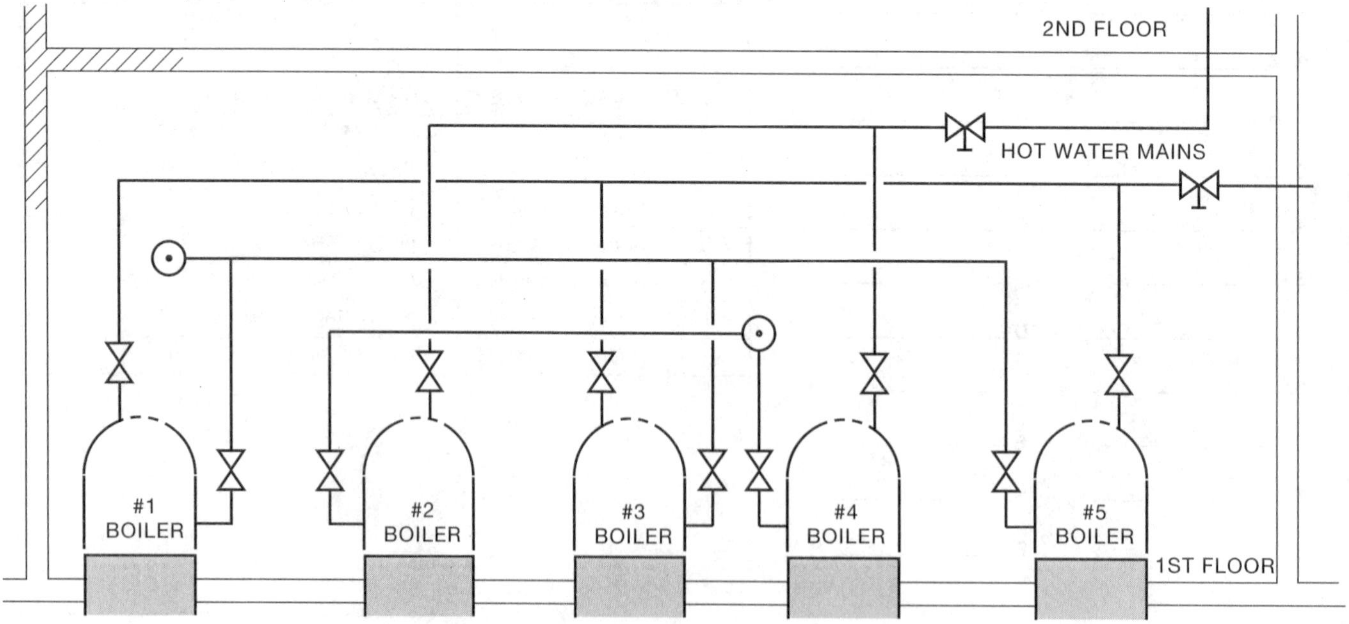
2ND FLOOR
HOT WATER MAINS
#1 BOILER
#2 BOILER
#3 BOILER
#4 BOILER
#5 BOILER
1ST FLOOR

SECTIONAL ELEVATION A-A

ASSIGNMENT:

1. COMPLETE THE ISOMETRIC VIEW OF THE BOILER ROOM PIPING SHOWN IN ORTHOGRAPHIC PROJECTION ON THE OPPOSITE PAGE. IT IS NOT NECESSARY TO SHOW THE WALLS AND FLOORS.

2. ON A SEPARATE SHEET, MAKE UP A BILL OF MATERIAL CALLING FOR ALL VIEWS, FITTINGS, AND PIPE. (GIVE THE TOTAL APPROXIMATE LENGTH OF EACH SIZE OF PIPE.)

3. FROM THE BILL OF MATERIAL, ADD PART NUMBERS TO THE ISOMETRIC DRAWING FOR THE VALVES AND FITTINGS ONLY.

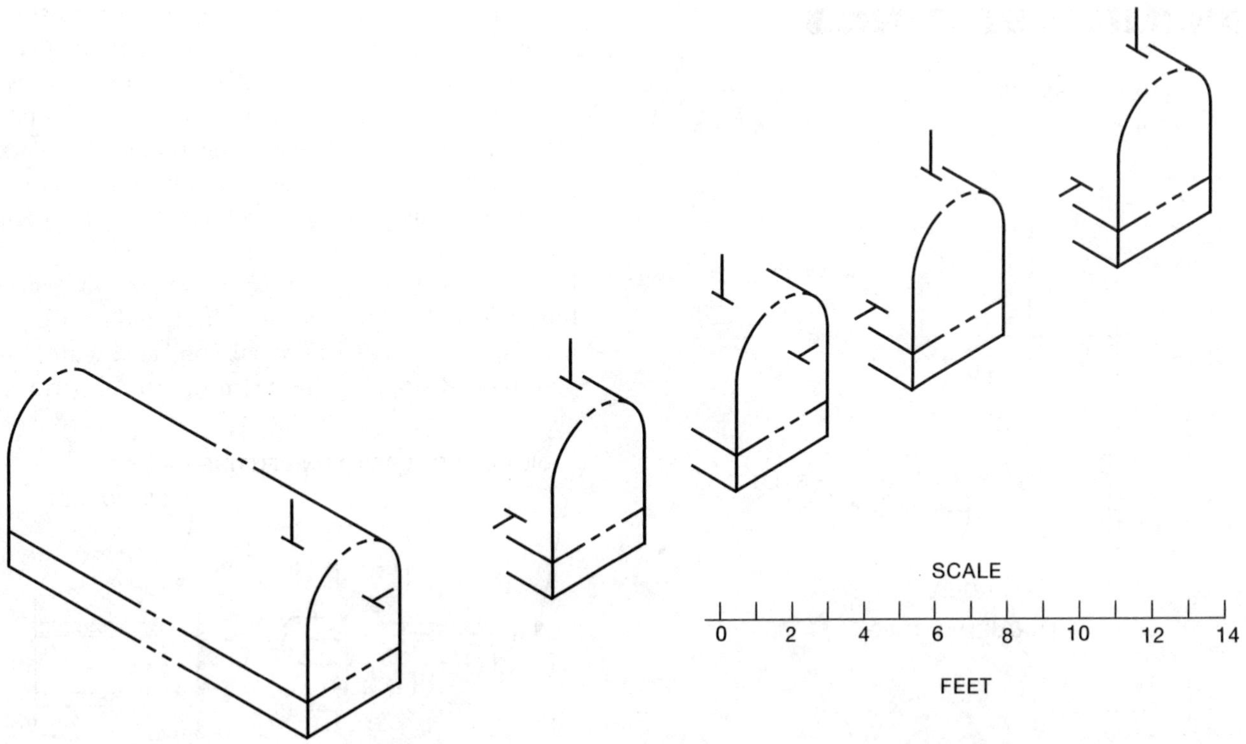
SCALE
0 2 4 6 8 10 12 14
FEET

BOILER #1

SCALE AS SHOWN		
DRAWN		DATE
	BOILER ROOM	A-60

23 UNIT

BEARINGS

All rotating machinery parts are supported by *bearings*. Each bearing type and style has its particular advantages and disadvantages. Bearings are classified into two groups: plain bearings and antifriction bearings.

PLAIN BEARINGS

Plain bearings have many uses. They are available in a variety of shapes and sizes, Figure 23–1.

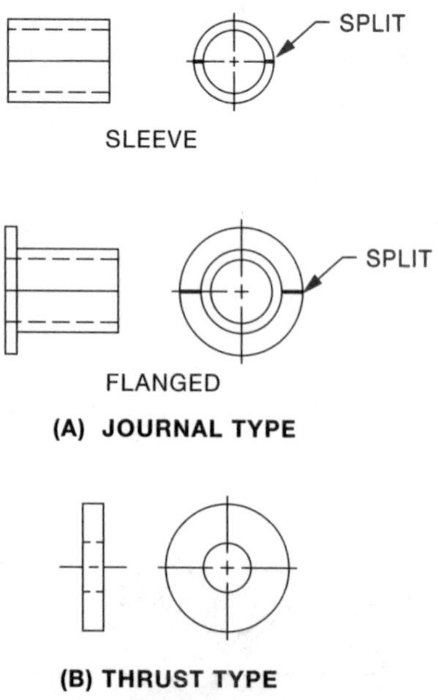
SPLIT
SLEEVE
SPLIT
FLANGED
(A) JOURNAL TYPE
(B) THRUST TYPE

FIGURE 23–1 ■ Plain bearings

Because of their simplicity, plain bearings are versatile. There are several plain bearing categories. The most common are journal (sleeve) bearings and thrust bearings. These are available in a variety of standard sizes and shapes.

Journal or Sleeve Bearings

Journal bearings are the simplest and most economical means of supporting moving parts. *Journal bearings* are usually made of one or two pieces of metal enclosing a shaft. They have no moving parts. The journal is the supporting portion of the shaft.

Speed, mating materials, clearances, temperature, lubrication, and type of loading affect the performance of bearings. The maintenance of an oil film between the bearing surfaces is important. The oil film reduces friction, dissipates heat, and retards wear by minimizing metal-to-metal contact, Figure 23–2. Starting and stopping are the most critical periods of

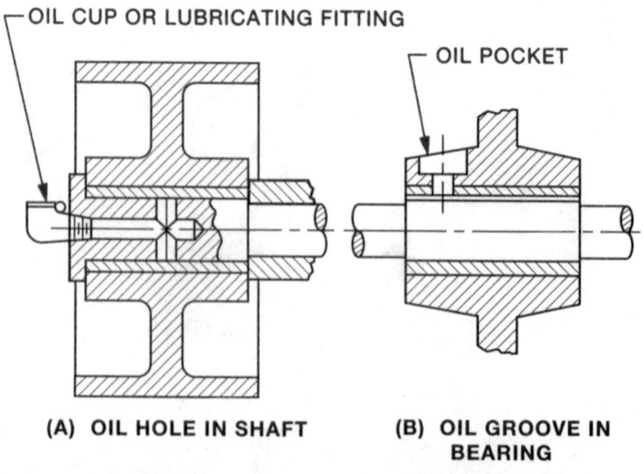
OIL CUP OR LUBRICATING FITTING
OIL POCKET
(A) OIL HOLE IN SHAFT
(B) OIL GROOVE IN BEARING

FIGURE 23–2 ■ Common methods of lubricating journal bearings operation, because the load may cause the bearing surfaces to touch each other.

The shaft should have a smooth finish and be harder than the bearing material. The bearing will perform best with a hard, smooth shaft. For practical reasons, the length of the bearing should be between one and two times the shaft diameter. The outside diameter should be approximately 25 percent larger than the shaft diameter.

Cast bronze and porous bronze are usually used for journal bearings.

Bearings are sometimes split. This design feature facilitates assembly and permits adjustment and replacement of worn parts. Split bearings allow the shaft to be set in one half of the bearing while the other half, or cover, is later secured in position, Figure 23–3.

If the bearings shown in Figure 23–3 are to be made from two parts, they must be fastened together before the hole is bored or reamed. This will facilitate the machining operation and make a perfectly round bearing. For an incorrectly assembled bearing, see Figure 23–4.

One method that gives longer life to the bearing is the insertion of very thin strips of metal between the base and cover halves before boring. These thin strips of varying thickness are called *shims*, Figure 23–5.

When a bearing is shimmed, the same number of pieces of corresponding thickness are used on both sides of the bearing.

As the hole wears, one or more pairs of these shims may be removed for wear compensation.

Thrust Bearings

Plain thrust bearings or thrust washers are available in various materials, including sintered metal, plastic, woven TFE fabric on steel backing, sintered Teflon-bronze-lead on metal backing, aluminum alloy on steel, aluminum alloy, and carbon-graphite.

Antifriction Bearings

Ball, roller, and needle bearings are classified as antifriction bearings as friction has been reduced to a minimum. These are covered in detail in Unit 40.

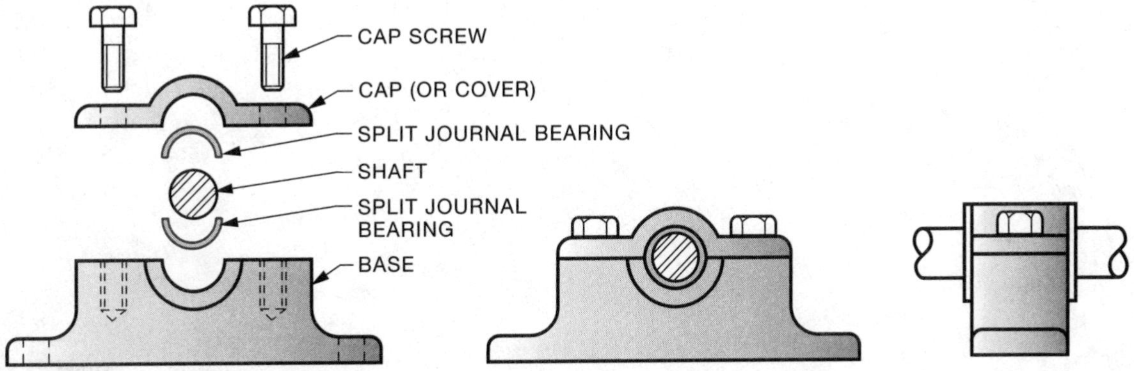
CAP SCREW
CAP (OR COVER)
SPLIT JOURNAL BEARING
SHAFT
SPLIT JOURNAL BEARING
BASE

FIGURE 23–3 ■ Pillow block with split journal bearing

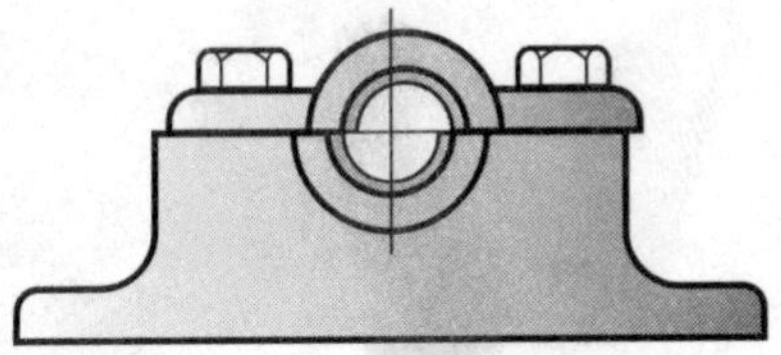

FIGURE 23–4 ■ Bearing halves incorrectly matched

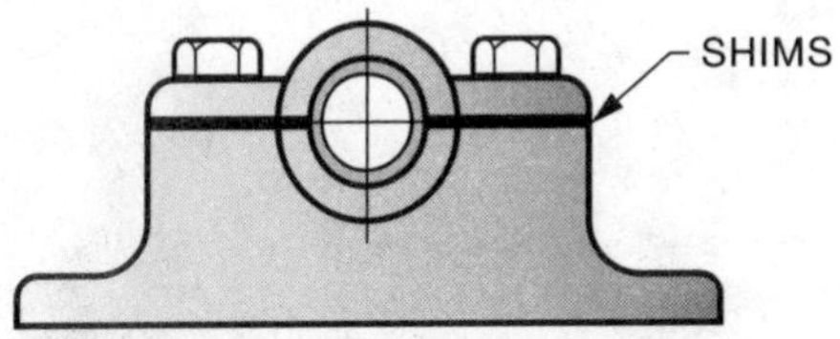
SHIMS

FIGURE 23–5 ■ "Shimmed" bearing

PREMOUNTED BEARINGS

Premounted bearing assemblies consist of a bearing element and a housing, usually assembled to permit convenient adaptation to a machine frame. All components are incorporated within a single unit to ensure proper protection, lubrication, and operation of the bearing. Both plain and roller element bearing units are available in a wide variety of housing design and shaft sizes. An example of an adjustable premounted bearing is shown in Assignment A-61M.

REFERENCES

A.O. De Hart, "Basic Bearing Types," *Machine Design,* 40, No. 14

W.A. Glaeser, "Plain Bearings," *Machine Design,* 40, No. 14

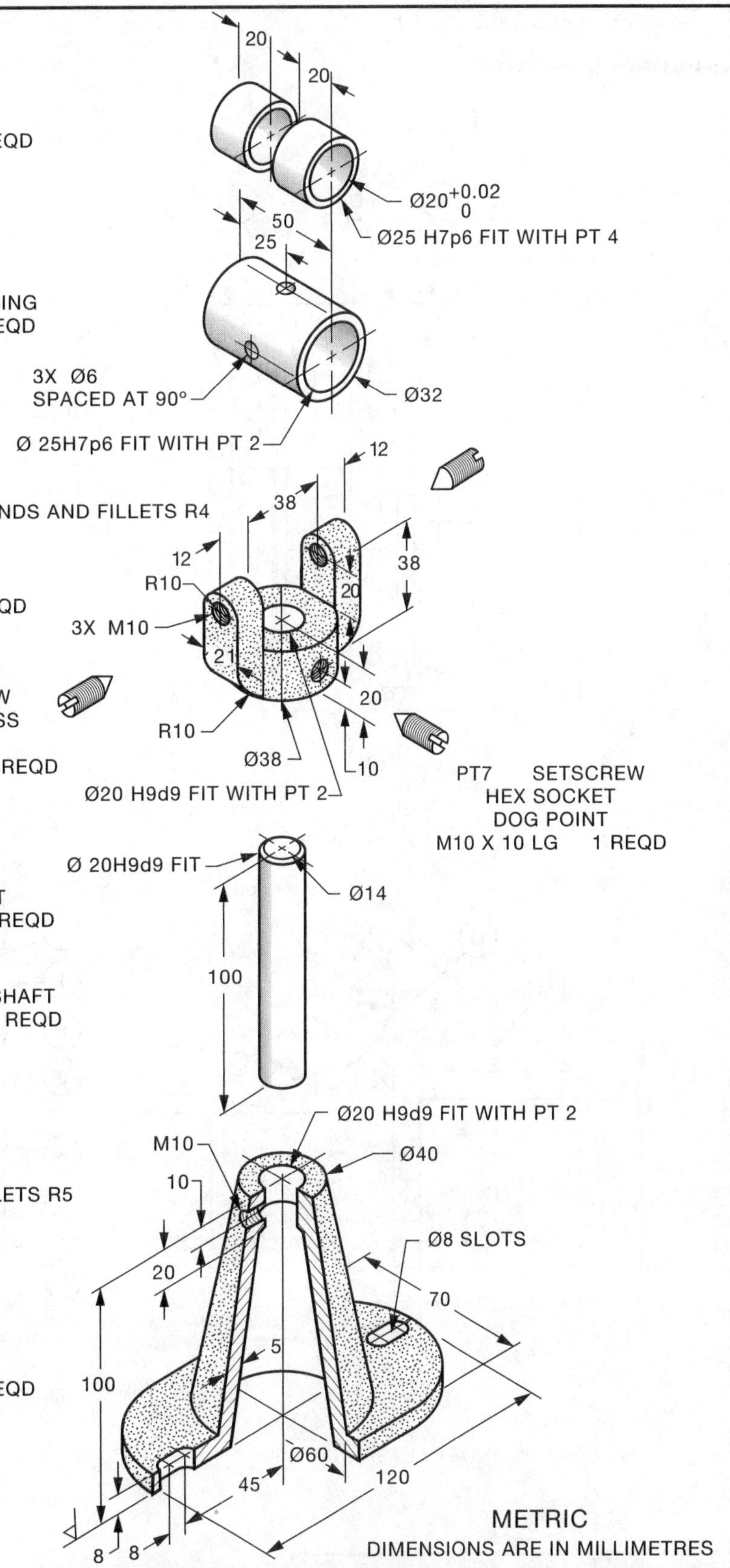
PT 5 BEARING
MATL - BRONZE 2 REQD
20
20
Ø20 +0.02 0
Ø25 H7p6 FIT WITH PT 4
50
25
PT 4 BEARING HOUSING
MATL - STEEL 1 REQD
3X Ø6
SPACED AT 90°
Ø32
Ø 25H7p6 FIT WITH PT 2
12
ROUNDS AND FILLETS R4
38
12
R10
38
PT 3 YOKE
MATL - GI 1 REQD
3X M10
20
21
20
PT 6 SETSCREW
SLOTTED HEADLESS
CONE POINT
M10 X 30 LG 2 REQD
R10
Ø38
10
Ø20 H9d9 FIT WITH PT 2
PT7 SETSCREW
HEX SOCKET
DOG POINT
M10 X 10 LG 1 REQD
Ø 20H9d9 FIT
Ø14
PT8 JAM NUT
HEX HD M10 2 REQD
100
PT 2 VERTICAL SHAFT
MATL - STEEL 1 REQD
Ø20 H9d9 FIT WITH PT 2
M10
Ø40
10
ROUNDS AND FILLETS R5
Ø8 SLOTS
20
70
5
PT 1 BASE
MATL - GI 1 REQD
100
Ø60
45
120
8
8
METRIC
DIMENSIONS ARE IN MILLIMETRES

ASSIGNMENT:

On graph paper, prepare detail drawings of the parts assigned by your instructor from the Adjustable Shaft Support Assembly shown. Show limit dimensions where fits are indicated. Refer to the Appendix for metric fit sizes.

ADJUSTABLE SHAFT SUPPORT

A-61M

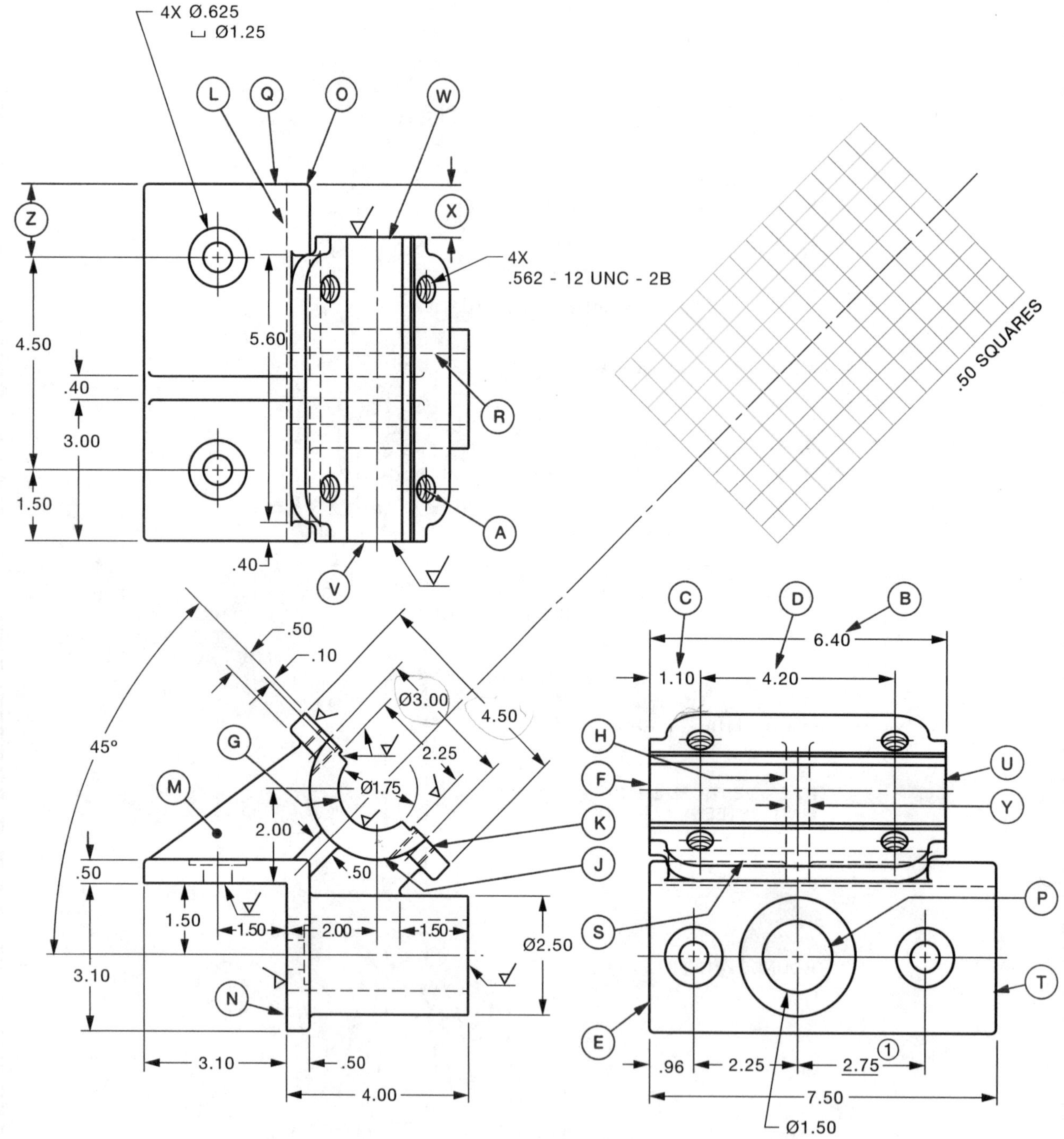
4X Ø.625
⌴ Ø1.25
L
Q
O
W
Z
X
4X
.562 - 12 UNC - 2B
4.50
5.60
.40
3.00
1.50
R
A
.40
V
.50 SQUARES
C
D
B
6.40
1.10
4.20
.50
.10
Ø3.00
4.50
45°
G
2.25
H
U
F
Ø1.75
M
2.00
K
Y
.50
.50
J
P
1.50
1.50
2.00
1.50
Ø2.50
S
3.10
T
N
E
3.10
.50
.96
2.25
2.75 ①
4.00
7.50
Ø1.50

ROUNDS AND FILLETS R.10

REVISIONS	1	20-01-22	B. JENSEN
	2.75 WAS 2.60		

QUESTIONS

1. How many definite finished surfaces are on the casting? (Note: Two or more surfaces could lie on one plane.)
2. What is the size of (P) hole?
3. What size spotface is used on the mounting holes?
4. What are the number and size of the mounting holes?
5. Note that surface (E) is not finished, but surface (F) is to be finished. Allowing .06 in. for finishing, what would be the depth of the rough casting?
6. Would (G) hole be bored before or after bearing cap is assembled?
7. Which line in the side view shows surface (M)?
8. In which view, and by what line, is the surface represented by (N) shown?
9. Which line or surface in the side view shows the projection of point (J)? ~~OMIT THIS?~~
10. Which point or surface in the side view does line (R) represent?
11. Locate surface (T) in the top view.
12. Locate surface (U) in the top view.
13. Locate surface (V) in the side view.
14. What are dimensions (X), (Y), and (Z)?
15. What size is the round (O)?
16. Determine dimension (A) and place it correctly on the sketch of the auxiliary view.
17. Place dimensions (B), (C), and (D) correctly on the sketch of the auxiliary view.
18. What tap drill size is required for the four threaded holes?
19. How many dimensions indicated are not drawn to scale?

B = 6.40 C = 1.10 D = 4.20

ANSWERS

1. 12
2. 1.5
3. 1.25
4. 4 ⌀ .625
5. 7.56
6. AFTER
7. H
8. TOP VIEW, LINE L
9. ~~X~~ S
10. P
11. Q
12. W
13. F
14. X 1.10
    Y .40
    Z 1.50
15. .10
16. 3/4 RAD
18. .484 (31/64)
19. ONE

ASSIGNMENT:

MAKE A FREEHAND SKETCH IN THE GRAPH AREA SHOWN AT LEFT, SHOWING THE AUXILIARY VIEW OF THE SPLIT BEARING SURFACES (K) AND (G). SEE QUESTIONS 16 AND 17.

NOTE: UNLESS OTHERWISE SPECIFIED:

—TOLERANCE ON DIMENSIONS ±.02

—TOLERANCE ON ANGLES ±0.5°

— √ TO BE 63√

MATERIAL	GREY IRON	
SCALE	NOT TO SCALE	
DRAWN		DATE
	CORNER BRACKET	**A-62**

24 UNIT

MANUFACTURING MATERIALS

This unit has been expanded to include many of the manufacturing materials that are now readily available. One of the first decisions a designer must make is the choice of material. The choice is influenced by many factors, such as the end use of the product and the properties of the selected material. Perhaps plastics may be the better choice of material over rubber or metal. Would one choice of metal be better than another? Will the part come in contact with water or chemicals? Is strength a factor? If so, what material will meet the stresses required? What material is in stock or readily obtainable? Is the material the correct choice if a plating or coating is required?

Just as steel composition may vary—tool steel and stainless steel, for example—so do other manufacturing materials. This unit covers some of the commonly used manufacturing materials from which to choose. Cast iron is covered in Unit 25.

STEEL

Carbon steels are the workhorses of product design. They account for over 90 percent of total steel production. More carbon steels are used in product manufacturing than all other metals combined. Far more research is going into carbon steel metallurgy and manufacturing technology than into all other steel mill products. Various technical societies and trade associations have issued the specifications covering the composition of metals. They serve as a selection guide and are a way for the buyer to conveniently specify certain known and recognized requirements. The main technical societies and trade associations concerned with metal identification in Canada and the United States are The Canadian Institute of Steel Construction (CISC), the American Iron and Steel Institute (AISI), and the Society of Automotive Engineers (SAE).

SAE and AISI Systems of Steel Identification

The specifications for steel bar are based on a number code indicating the composition of each type of steel covered. They include both plain carbon and alloy steels. The code is a four-number system. The first two figures indicate the alloy series and the last two figures the carbon content in hundredths of a percent, Figure 24–1. Therefore, the numbering code or symbol XX15 indicates 0.15 of 1 percent carbon.

For example, AISI 4830 is a molybdenum-nickel steel containing 0.2–0.3 percent molybdenum, 3.25–3.75 percent nickel, and 0.3 percent carbon. In addition to the four-number designation, the suffix "H" is used for steels produced to specify hardenability

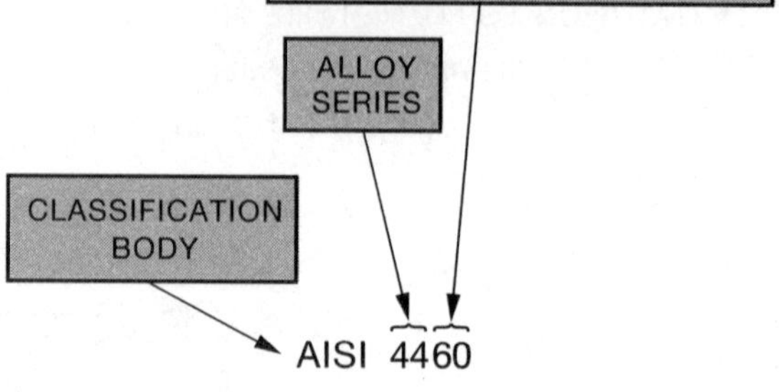

FIGURE 24–1 ■ Steel designation system

limits, and the prefix "E" indicates a steel made by the basic electric-furnace method.

Originally, the second figure indicated the percentage of the major alloying element present. This was true of many of the alloy steels. However, this had to be varied in order to classify all the steels that became available.

Alloying materials are added to steel to improve properties such as strength, hardness, machinability, corrosion resistance, electrical conductivity, and ease of forming. Figure 24–2 lists many types of steel and their uses.

TYPE OF STEEL		AISI SYMBOL	PRINCIPAL PROPERTIES	COMMON USES
CARBON STEELS				
- Nonresulfurized (Basic Carbon Steel)		10XX		
- Plain Carbon		10XX		
- Low Carbon Steel (0.06% to 0.2% Carbon)		1006 to 1020	Toughness and less strength	Chains, rivets, shafts, pressed steel products
- Medium Carbon Steel (0.2% to 0.5% Carbon)		1020 to 1050	Toughness and strength	Gears, axles, machine parts, forgings, bolts, and nuts
- High Carbon Steel (Over 0.5% Carbon)		1050 and over	Less toughness and greater hardness	Saws, drills, knives, razors, finishing tools, music wire
- Resulfurized (Free Cutting)		11XX	Improves machinability	Threads, splines, machined parts
- Phosphorized		12XX	Increases strength and hardness but reduces ductility	
- Manganese Steels		13XX	Improves surface finish	
MOLYBDENUM STEELS				
0.15%–0.30% Mo		40XX	High strength	Axles, forgings, gears, cams, mechanism parts
0.08%–0.35% Mo	0.4%–1.1% Cr	41XX		
1.65%–2.00% NI 0.4%–0.9% Cr	0.2%–0.3% Mo	43XX		
0.45%–0.60% Mo		44XX		
0.7%–2.0% Ni	0.15%–0.30% Mo	46XX		
0.90%–1.2% Ni 0.35%–0.55% Cr	0.15%–0.40% Mo	47XX		
3.25%–3.75% Ni	0.2%– 0.3% Mo	48XX		
CHROMIUM STEELS				
0.3%–0.5% Cr		50XX	Hardness, great strength, and toughness	Gears, shafts, bearings springs, connecting rods
0.70%–1.15%Cr		51XX		
1.00%C	0.90%–1.15% Cr	E51100		
1.00%C	0.90%–1.15% Cr	E52100		
CHROMIUM VANADIUM STEELS				
0.5%–1.1% Cr	0.10%–0.15%V	61XX	Hardness and strength	Punches, piston rods, gears, axles
NICKEL - CHROMIUM - MOLYBDENUM STEELS				
0.4%–0.7%Ni 0.15%–0.25%Mo	0.4%–0.6%Cr	86XX	Rust resistance, hardness, and strength	Food containers, surgical equipment
0.4%–0.7%Ni 0.2%–0.3%Mo	0.4%–0.6%Cr	87XX		
0.4%–0.7%Ni 0.3%–0.4%Mo	0.4%–0.6%Cr	88XX		
SILICON STEELS				
1.8%–2.2% Si		92XX	Springiness and elasticity	Springs

FIGURE 24–2 ■ Designations, uses, and properties of steel

Effect of Alloys on Steel

Carbon

Increasing the carbon content increases the tensile strength and hardness.

Sulphur

When sulphur content is over 0.06 percent the metal tends toward *red shortness* (brittleness in steel when it is red hot). Free cutting steel, for threading and screw machine work, is obtained by increasing sulphur content from about 0.075 to 0.1 percent.

Phosphorus

Phosphorus produces brittleness and general cold shortness. It also strengthens low carbon steel, increases resistance to corrosion, and improves machinability.

Manganese

Manganese is added during the making of steel to prevent red shortness and increase hardenability.

Chromium

Chromium increases hardenability, corrosion resistance, oxidation, and abrasion.

Nickel

Nickel strengthens and toughens ferrite and pearlite steels.

Silicon

Silicon is used as a general-purpose deoxidizer. It strengthens low-alloy steels and increases hardenability.

Copper

Copper is used to increase atmospheric corrosion resistance.

Molybdenum

Molybdenum increases hardenability and coarsening temperature.

Boron

Boron increases hardenability of lower carbon steels and has better machinability than standard alloy steels.

Vanadium

Vanadium elevates coarsening temperatures, increases hardenability, and is a strong deoxidizer.

PLASTICS

Plastics may be defined as nonmetallic materials capable of being formed or molded with the aid of heat, pressure, chemical reactions, or a combination of these.

Plastics are strong, tough, durable materials that solve many problems in machine and equipment design. Metals are hard and rigid. This means they can be machined, to a very close tolerance, into cams, bearings, bushings, and gears that will work smoothly under heavy loads for long periods. Although some come close, no plastic has the hardness or creep resistance of steel, for example. However, metals have many weaknesses that engineering plastics do not. Metals corrode or rust, they must be lubricated, their working surfaces wear readily, they cannot be used as electrical or thermal insulators, they are opaque and noisy, and where they must flex, they fatigue rapidly.

Engineering plastics can be run at low speeds and loads and, without lubrication, are among the world's slipperiest solids, being compared with ice.

Plastics are a family of materials, not a single material. Each material has its special advantage. Being manufactured, plastic raw materials are capable of being combined to give almost any property desired in an end product.

The advantages of plastics are light weight, range of colour, good physical properties, adaptability to mass production methods, and often lower cost. They are usually classified as either *thermoplastic* or *thermosetting*. See Figure 24–3.

Thermoplastics

Thermoplastics soften or liquefy and flow when heat is applied. Removal of the heat causes these materials to set or solidify. They can be reheated or reformed or reused. In this group falls the ABS, acetals, acrylics, celluloses, fluoro carbons, nylons, polyethylene, polystyrene, vinyls, and polycarbonates.

Thermosetting Plastics

Thermosetting plastics undergo an irreversible chemical change when heat is applied or when a catalyst or reactant is added. They become hard, insoluble, and infusible, and they do not soften upon reapplication of heat. Thermosetting plastics include phenolics, amino plastics (melamine and urea), polyesters, epoxies, silicones, alkydes, allylics, and casein.

RUBBER

The use of rubber is advantageous when design considerations involve one or more of the following factors:

- electrical insulation
- vibration isolation
- sealing surfaces
- chemical resistance
- flexibility

BASE RESIN	OUTSTANDING CHARACTERISTICS	TYPICAL APPLICATIONS
THERMOPLASTICS		
ABS	Colourability, toughness	Instrument panels, telephone housings
Acetal	Impact strength, chemical resistance	Replaces zinc or aluminum for castings
Acrylic	Clarity, weather resistance	Windows, lenses, dials, shoe heels, medallions
Cellulosic	Clarity, toughness	Safety glass, film, knobs, bowling balls, electrical parts
Fluorocarbon	Chemical and heat resistance, self-lubrication	Low-pressure bearings, chemical linings, gaskets, bushings
Polyamide (Nylon)	Impact strength, cold flow	Gears, cams, bushings, gaskets, cable clamps, housings, electrical insulation
Polycarbonate	Dimensional stability, clarity, good electrical insulation	Switch housings, terminal blocks
Polyethylene	Ease of forming, chemical resistance	Bottles, toys, underground pipe, electrical insulation, ducts
Polypropylene	Ease of forming, chemical resistance	Bottles, toys, replaces zinc or aluminum for castings
Polystyrene	Ease of forming, transparent	Toys, display and jewellry cases, foamed insulation, refrigerator parts, containers
Polyvinyl Chloride	Flexibility, toughness, chemical resistance	Toys, upholstery, lawn hose, floor tile, electrical insulation, gaskets, ducts
THERMOSETTING PLASTICS		
Epoxy	Room temperature cure, no pressure	Adhesives, coatings, terminal boards, electrical potting, tooling fixtures
Phenol	Dark colours only. Good electrical insulation	Knobs, terminal boards, adhesives, distributor caps and housings
Polyester	Room temperature cure, on pressure	Car bodies, boat hulls, heater ducts
Silicone	Relative constancy of properties over wide temperature range	Terminal boards, electrical moldings
Urea and Melamine	Indoor use. Pastel colours available	Knobs, jars, buttons, dishes, electrical moldings

FIGURE 24–3 ■ Common plastics

Elastomers (rubber-like substances) are derived from either natural or synthetic sources. Rubber can be formed into useful rigid or flexible shapes, usually with the aid of heat, pressure, or both. The most outstanding characteristics of rubber are its low modulus of elasticity and its ability to withstand large deformation and to quickly recover its shape when released.

Rubber parts are produced in either mechanical (solid) or cellular form, depending on the desired performance of the part. They are categorized into two kinds of rubber, natural and synthetic. The synthetic rubbers are further classified into several kinds.

Mechanical Rubber

Mechanical rubber is used in either pressure-molded, cast, or extruded form. Typical parts produced by these methods are tires, belts, and bumpers. Mechanical rubber should be preferred to sponge rubber because of its superior physical properties.

Cellular Rubber

Cellular rubber can be produced with "open" or "closed" cells. Open-cell sponge rubber is made by including a gas-forming chemical compound in the mixture before vulcanization. The heat of the vulcanizing process causes a gas to form in the rubber, making a cellular structure. Typical applications are pads and weather stripping. Foam rubber is a specialized type of open cell.

Both open- and closed-cell sponge rubber is available in block or sheet form that can be cut to size and shape.

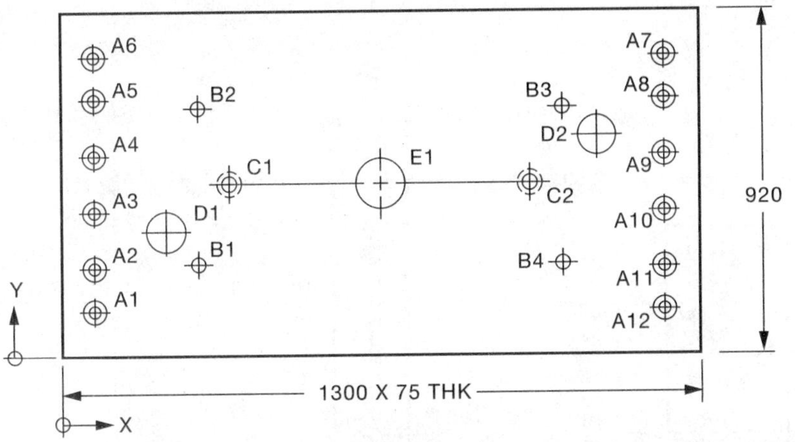

ANSWERS

1. ____________
2. ____________
3. ____________
4. ____________
5. ____________
6. ____________
7. ____________
8. ____________
9. ____________
10. ____________
11. ____________
12. ____________
13. ____________
14. ____________
15. ____________

HOLE	LOCATION		HOLE SIZE
	X	Y	
A1	50	120	12X Ø32
A2	50	235	⌴ Ø64
A3	50	385	↧ 30
A4	50	535	NEAR SIDE ONLY
A5	50	685	
A6	50	800	
A7	1250	800	
A8	1250	685	
A9	1250	535	
A10	1250	385	
A11	1250	235	
A12	1250	120	

HOLE	LOCATION		HOLE SIZE
	X	Y	
B1	280	260	4X Ø16
B2	280	660	
B3	1020	660	
B4	1020	260	
C1	342	460	2X M20
C2	958	460	
D1	210	334	2X Ø $\begin{matrix}80.30\\80.00\end{matrix}$ (80 H7)
D2	1090	586	
E1	650	460	1X Ø $\begin{matrix}100.054\\100.000\end{matrix}$ (100 H8)

NOTE: UNLESS OTHERWISE SPECIFIED, TOLERANCE ON DIMENSIONS ±0.5

QUESTIONS

1. What is the thickness of the material?
2. What type of steel is specified?
3. What indicates that the drawing is not to scale?
4. How many counterbored holes are there?
5. What is the diameter of the CBORE?
6. How many D holes are there?
7. Which letter specifies the Ø100 hole?
8. How many different-sized holes are specified?
9. What is the total number of tapped holes?
10. What is the thread pitch of the C holes?
11. What tolerance is given for the E hole?
12. What is the high limit of the E hole?
13. What is the maximum size for the D holes?
14. Is the E hole on the centre of the part?
15. What is the centre distance between the C holes?

METRIC
DIMENSIONS ARE IN MILLIMETRES

MATERIAL	SAE 1020	
SCALE	NOT TO SCALE	
DRAWN		DATE
CROSSBAR		**A-63M**

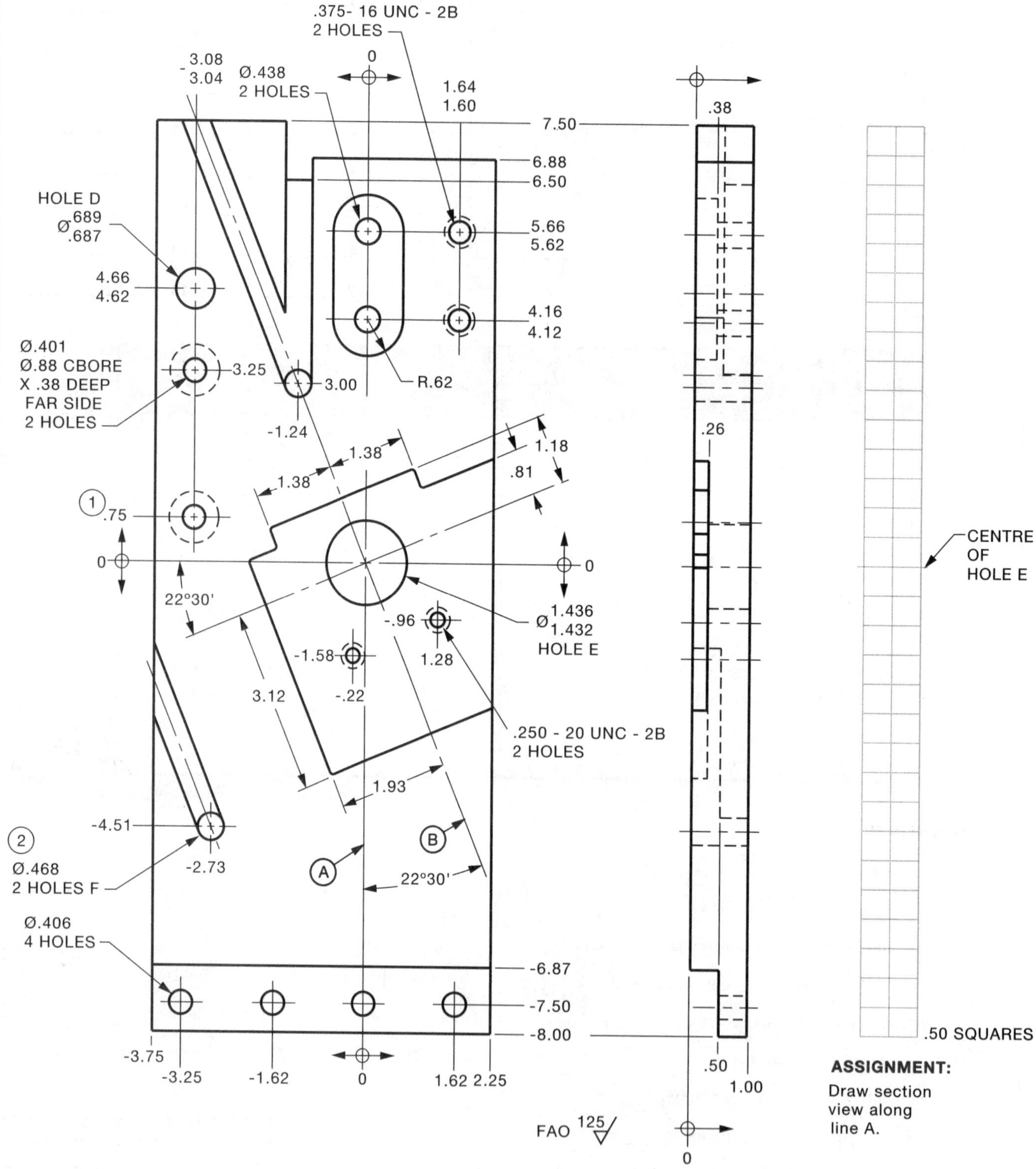
.375- 16 UNC - 2B
2 HOLES
3.08
3.04
Ø.438
2 HOLES
0
1.64
1.60
7.50
.38
6.88
6.50
HOLE D
Ø.689
.687
5.66
5.62
4.66
4.62
4.16
4.12
Ø.401
Ø.88 CBORE
X .38 DEEP
FAR SIDE
2 HOLES
3.25
3.00
R.62
-1.24
.26
1.38
1.18
1.38
.81
1
.75
0
0
22°30'
CENTRE
OF
HOLE E
Ø1.436
1.432
HOLE E
-.96
-1.58
1.28
3.12
-.22
.250 - 20 UNC - 2B
2 HOLES
1.93
-4.51
2
B
-2.73
Ø.468
2 HOLES F
A
22°30'
Ø.406
4 HOLES
-6.87
-7.50
-8.00
.50 SQUARES
-3.75
-3.25
-1.62
0
1.62
2.25
.50
1.00
FAO 125
0

ASSIGNMENT:
Draw section view along line A.

1	02-02-10	B. JENSEN	2	02-03-01	B. JENSEN
	DIMENSION WAS .68			Ø WAS .560	

QUESTIONS

1. What are the overall (A) width, (B) height, and (C) depth of the part?
2. What is the width of the slots that are cut out from the F holes?
3. What is their depth?
4. What class of surface texture is required?
5. What is the depth of the recess adjacent to the (A) E hole and (B) Ø.438 holes?
6. How many degrees are there between line B and the horizontal?
7. What was the size of the F holes before they were changed?
8. What tolerance is required on the E hole?
9. What is the low limit on the E hole?
10. What tolerance is required on the D hole?
11. What is the high limit on the D hole?
12. Determine the maximum vertical centre distance from the D hole to the four Ø.406 holes located at the bottom of the part.
13. Determine the (A) maximum and (B) minimum centre distance between the two .375 tapped holes.
14. Determine the maximum horizontal centre distance between the D hole and the .375 tapped holes.
15. What are the width, height, and depth of the cutout at the bottom of the part?
16. How deep are (A) the Ø.438 holes and (B) the Ø.401 holes?
17. How deep are the .250-20 UNC holes?
18. How many full threads do the .250-20 UNC tapped holes have?
19. What are the main alloys in the material?

ANSWERS

1. A ________
   B ________
   C ________
2. ________
3. ________
4. ________
5. A ________
   B ________
6. ________
7. ________
8. ________
9. ________
10. ________
11. ________
12. ________
13. A ________
    B ________
14. ________
15. W ________
    H ________
    D ________
16. A ________
    B ________
17. ________
18. ________
19. ________
    ____

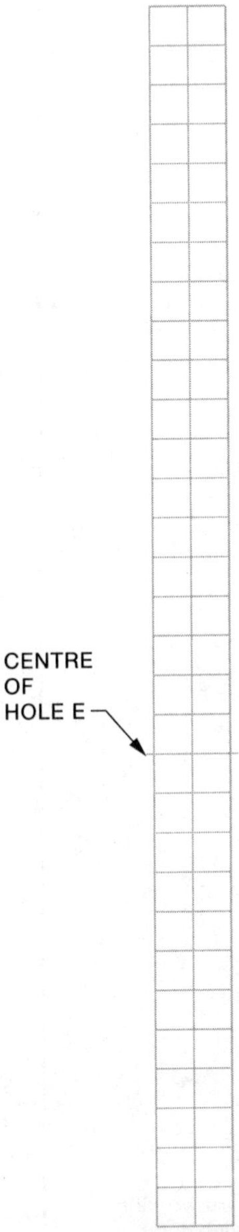

ASSIGNMENT:
Draw section view along line B.

NOTE:

—ALL RADII R.06 UNLESS OTHERWISE SPECIFIED.

—DIMENSIONS ARE TAKEN FROM PLANES DESIGNATED 0-0, AND ARE PARALLEL TO THESE PLANES.

—UNLESS OTHERWISE STATED:
±.02 ON DIMENSIONS
±0.5 ° ON ANGLES

MATERIAL	SAE 4020	
SCALE	NOT TO SCALE	
DRAWN		DATE
	OIL CHUTE	A-64

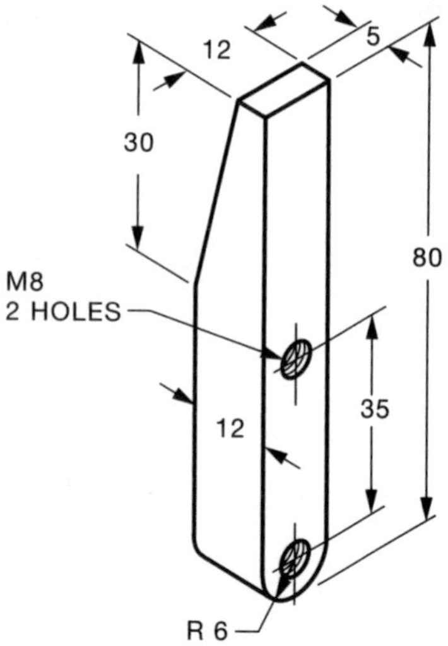
12
5
30
80
M8
2 HOLES
12
35
R 6

PT 1 MOVABLE JAW
1 REQD MATL - SAE 1020

PT 6 CAP SCREW
M3 X 8LG
RD HD 1 REQD

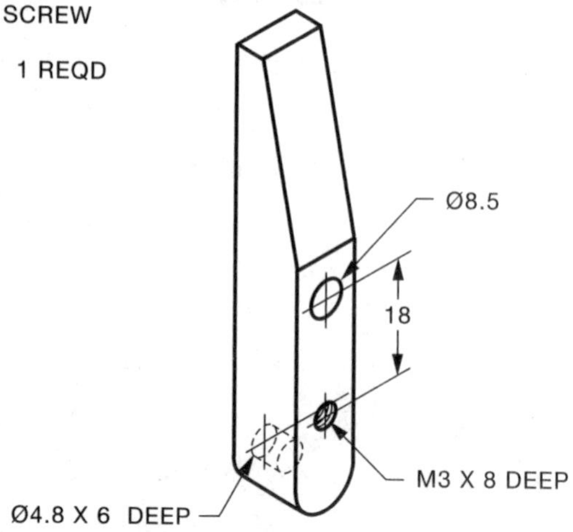
Ø8.5
18
M3 X 8 DEEP
Ø4.8 X 6 DEEP

PT 2 STATIONARY JAW
1 REQD MATL - SAE 1020
AS SHOWN, OTHERWISE SAME AS PART 1.

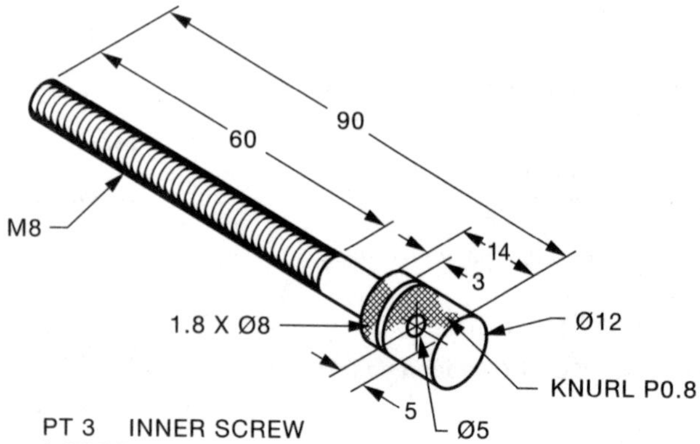
90
60
M8
14
3
1.8 X Ø8
Ø12
KNURL P0.8
5
Ø5

PT 3 INNER SCREW
1 REQD MATL - SAE 1112

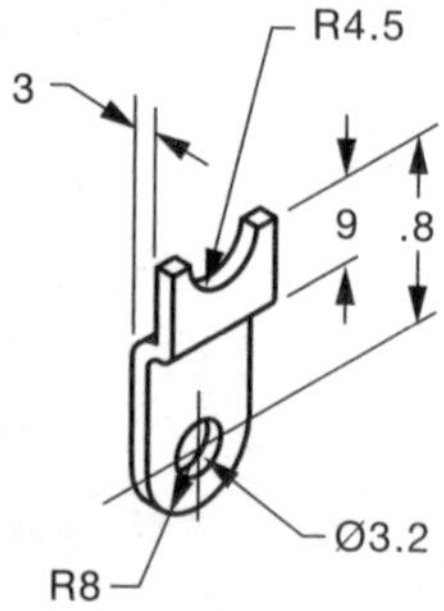
R4.5
3
9
.8
Ø3.2
R8

PT 5 CLIP 1 REQD
MATL - 1.6 (16 USS) STL

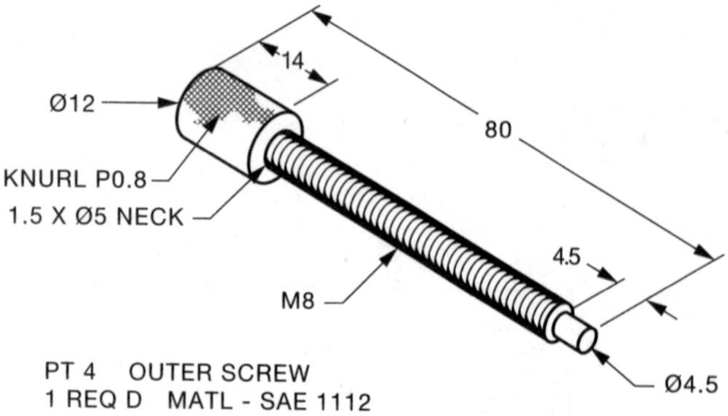
14
Ø12
80
KNURL P0.8
1.5 X Ø5 NECK
4.5
M8
Ø4.5

PT 4 OUTER SCREW
1 REQ D MATL - SAE 1112

ASSIGNMENT:

On metric graph paper prepare working (detail) drawings of the parallel clamp details shown. Use simplified thread conventions (Unit 15) and refer to Unit 10 for the selection of views. Scale 1:1.

METRIC
DIMENSIONS ARE IN MILLIMETRES

	PARALLEL CLAMP DETAILS	**A-65M**

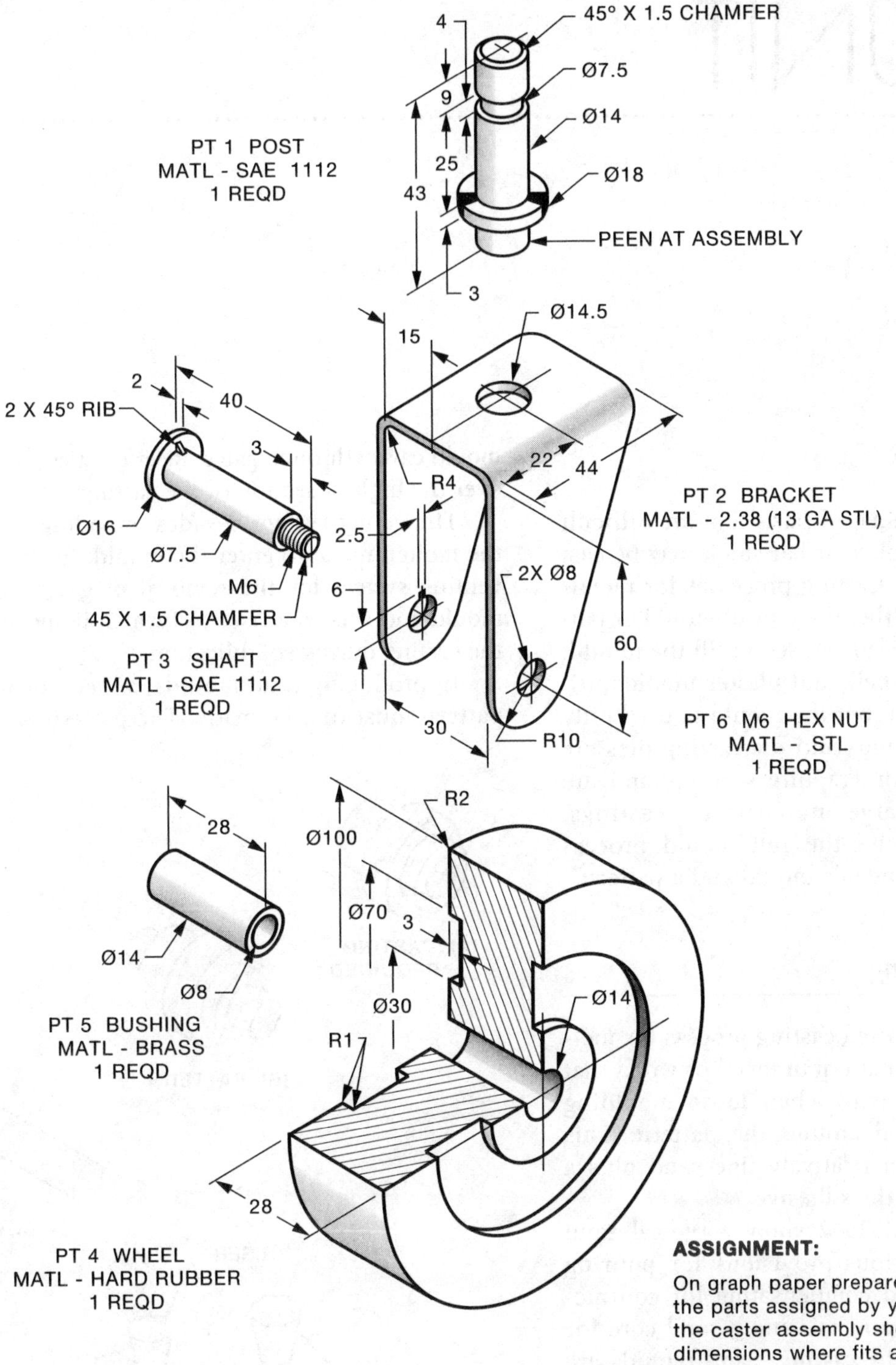
4
45° X 1.5 CHAMFER
Ø7.5
9
Ø14
PT 1 POST
MATL - SAE 1112
1 REQD
25
43
Ø18
PEEN AT ASSEMBLY
3
Ø14.5
15
2
40
2 X 45° RIB
3
22
44
R4
PT 2 BRACKET
MATL - 2.38 (13 GA STL)
1 REQD
Ø16
Ø7.5
2.5
2X Ø8
M6
45 X 1.5 CHAMFER
6
60
PT 3 SHAFT
MATL - SAE 1112
1 REQD
30
R10
PT 6 M6 HEX NUT
MATL - STL
1 REQD
R2
28
Ø100
Ø70
3
Ø14
Ø8
Ø30
Ø14
PT 5 BUSHING
MATL - BRASS
1 REQD
R1
28
PT 4 WHEEL
MATL - HARD RUBBER
1 REQD

ASSIGNMENT:

On graph paper prepare detail drawings of the parts assigned by your instructor from the caster assembly shown. Show limit dimensions where fits are indicated. Refer to the Appendix for metric fit sizes.

METRIC

DIMENSIONS ARE IN MILLIMETRES

	CASTER ASSEMBLY	A-66M

25 UNIT

CASTINGS

Irregular or odd-shaped parts that are difficult to make from metal plate or bar stock may be cast to the desired shape. Casting processes for metals can be classified by either the type of mould or pattern or the pressure of force used to fill the mould. Conventional sand, shell, and plaster moulds utilize a durable pattern, but the mould is used only once. Permanent moulds and die-casting dies are machined in metal or graphite sections and are employed for a large number of castings. Investment casting and the full mould process involve both an expendable mould and a pattern.

Sand Mould Casting

The most widely used casting process for metals uses a permanent pattern of metal or wood that shapes the mould cavity when loose moulding material is compacted around the pattern. This material consists of a relatively fine sand plus a binder that serves as the adhesive.

Figures 25–1 and 25–2 show a typical sand mould, with the various provisions for pouring the molten metal and compensating for contraction of the solidifying metal, and a sand core for forming a cavity in the casting. Sand moulds are prepared in flasks, which consist of two or more sections: bottom (drag), top (cope), and intermediate sections (checks) when required.

The cope and drag are equipped with pins and lugs to ensure the alignment of the flask. Molten metal is poured into the sprue, and connecting runners provide flow channels for the metal to enter the mould cavity through gates. Riser cavities are located over the highest section of the casting.

The gating system, besides providing a way for the molten metal to enter the mould, functions as a venting system for the removal of gases from the mould and acts as a riser to furnish liquid metal to the casting during solidification.

In producing sand moulds, a metal or wooden pattern must first be made. The pattern is slightly

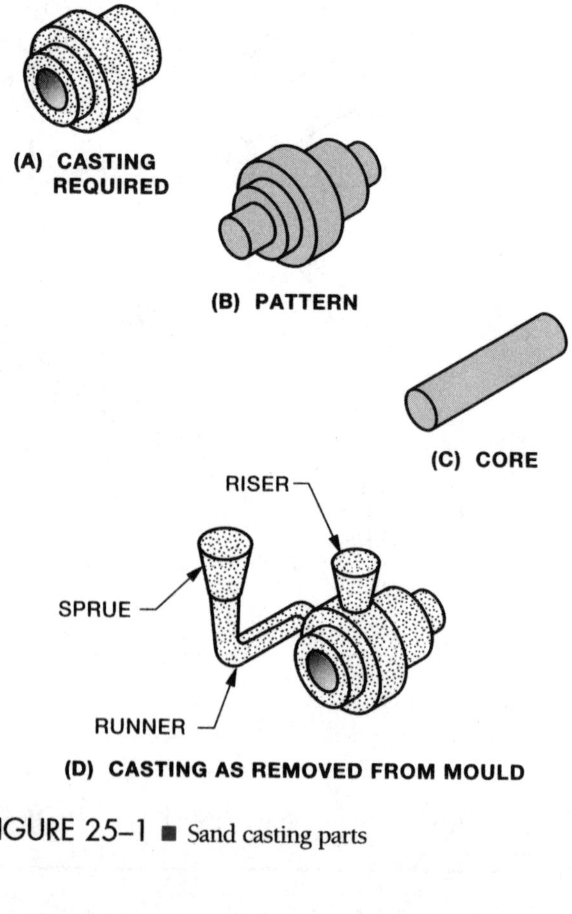
(A) CASTING REQUIRED
(B) PATTERN
(C) CORE
RISER
SPRUE
RUNNER
(D) CASTING AS REMOVED FROM MOULD

FIGURE 25–1 ■ Sand casting parts

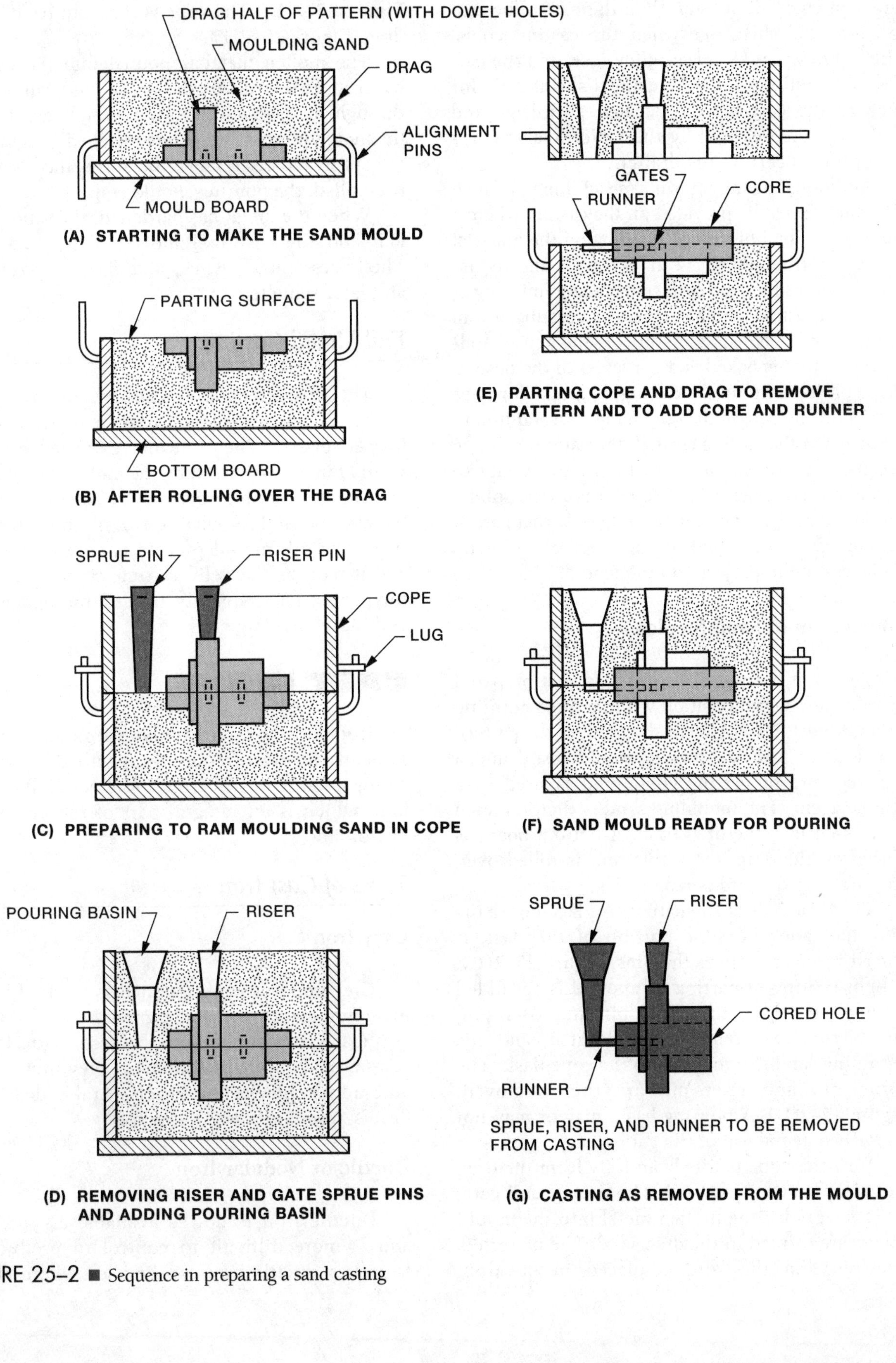
DRAG HALF OF PATTERN (WITH DOWEL HOLES)
MOULDING SAND
DRAG
ALIGNMENT PINS
MOULD BOARD
(A) STARTING TO MAKE THE SAND MOULD
PARTING SURFACE
BOTTOM BOARD
(B) AFTER ROLLING OVER THE DRAG
SPRUE PIN
RISER PIN
COPE
LUG
(C) PREPARING TO RAM MOULDING SAND IN COPE
POURING BASIN
RISER
(D) REMOVING RISER AND GATE SPRUE PINS AND ADDING POURING BASIN
GATES
RUNNER
CORE
(E) PARTING COPE AND DRAG TO REMOVE PATTERN AND TO ADD CORE AND RUNNER
(F) SAND MOULD READY FOR POURING
SPRUE
RISER
CORED HOLE
RUNNER
SPRUE, RISER, AND RUNNER TO BE REMOVED FROM CASTING
(G) CASTING AS REMOVED FROM THE MOULD

FIGURE 25–2 ■ Sequence in preparing a sand casting

larger in every dimension than the part to be cast to allow for shrinkage when the casting cools. This is known as *shrinkage allowance,* and the patternmaker allows for it by using a shrink rule for each of the cast metals. Because shrinkage and draft are taken care of by the patternmaker, they are of no concern to the drafter.

Additional metal, known as machining or finish allowance, must be provided on the casting where a surface is to be finished. Depending on the material being cast, from .06 to .12 in. is usually allowed on small castings for each surface requiring finishing.

When casting a hole or recess in a casting, a core is often used. A core is a mixture of sand and a bonding agent that is baked and hardened to the desired shape of the cavity in the casting, plus an allowance to support the core in the sand mould. In addition to the shape of the casting desired, the pattern must be designed to produce areas in the mould cavity to locate and hold the core. The core must be solidly supported in the mould, permitting only that part of the core that corresponds to the shape of the cavity in the casting to project into the mould.

Preparation of Sand Moulds

The drag portion of the flask is first prepared in an upside-down position with the pins pointing down, Figure 25–2(A). The drag half of the pattern is placed in position on the mould board and a light coating of parting compound is used as a release agent. The moulding sand is then rammed or pressed into the drag flask. A bottom board is placed on the drag, the whole unit is rolled over, and the mould board is removed.

The cope half of the pattern is placed over the drag half and the cope portion of the flask is placed in position over the pins, Figure 25–2(C). A light coating of parting compound is sprinkled throughout. Next, the sprue pin and riser pin, tapered for easy removal, are located, and the moulding sand is rammed into the cope flask. The sprue pin and riser pin are then removed, Figure 25–2(D). A pouring basin may or may not be formed at the top of the gate sprue.

Now the cope is lifted carefully from the drag and the pattern is exposed. The runner and gate, passageways for the molten metal into the mould cavity, are formed in the drag sand. The pattern is removed and the core is placed in position, Figure 25–2(E). The cope is then put back on the drag, Figure 25–2(F).

The molten metal is poured into the pouring basin and runs down the sprue to a runner and through the gate and into the mould cavity. When the mould cavity is filled, the metal will begin to fill the sprue and riser. Once the sprue and riser have been filled, the pouring should stop.

When the metal has hardened, the sand is broken and the casting removed, Figure 25–2(G). The excess metal, gates, and risers are removed and later remelted.

Full Mould Casting

The characteristic feature of the *full mould process* is the use of gasifiable patterns made of foamed plastic. These are not extracted from the mould but are vaporized by the molten metal.

The full mould process is suitable for individual castings and for small series of up to five castings. The full mould process is very economical, and it reduces the delivery time required for prototypes, articles urgently needed for repair jobs, and individual large machine parts.

CAST IRONS

Iron and the large family of iron alloys called steel are the most frequently specified metals. All commercial forms of iron and steel contain carbon, which is an integral part of the metallurgy of iron and steel.

Types of Cast Iron

Grey Iron

Grey iron is a supersaturated solution of carbon in an iron matrix. Generally, grey iron serves well in any machinery applications because of its fatigue resistance. Typical applications of grey iron include automotive blocks, flywheels, brake disks and drums, machine bases, and gears.

Ductile or Nodular Iron

Ductile iron is not as available as grey iron and is more difficult to control in production. However, ductile iron can be used where higher ductility or strength is required than is available in grey iron. Typical applications of ductile iron include crank shafts, heavy-duty gears, and automotive door hinges.

White Iron

White iron is produced by a process called chilling, which prevents graphic carbon from precipitating out. Because of their extreme hardness, white irons are used primarily for applications requiring wear and abrasion resistance such as mill liners and shot-blasting nozzles. Other uses include brick-making equipment, crushers, and pulverizers. The disadvantage of white iron is that it is very brittle.

Malleable Iron

Malleable iron is a white iron that has been converted to a malleable condition. It is commercial cast material that is similar to steel in many respects. It is strong and ductile, has good impact and fatigue properties, and has excellent machining characteristics.

The abbreviations for cast irons and steels found on drawings are shown in Table 2 of the Appendix.

CASTING DESIGN

Simplicity of Moulding from Flat Back Patterns

Simple shapes such as the one shown in Figure 25–3 are very easy to mould. In this case the flat face of the pattern is at the parting line and lies perfectly flat on the moulding board. In this position no moulding sand sifts under the flat surface to interfere with the drawing of the pattern. The simplicity with which flat back patterns of this type may be drawn from the mould is illustrated in Figure 25–3.

Irregular or Odd-Shaped Castings

When a casting is to be made for an odd-shaped piece such as the offset bracket, Figure 25–4, it is necessary to make the pattern for the bracket in one or more parts to facilitate the making of the mould. The difficulties with this are mostly due to the removal of the pattern from the sand mould.

The pattern for the bracket is made in two parts as shown in Figure 25–5. The two adjacent flat surfaces of the divided pattern come together at the parting lines.

Set Cores

In examining the illustration of the offset bracket, note that there are rounded corners. In order to

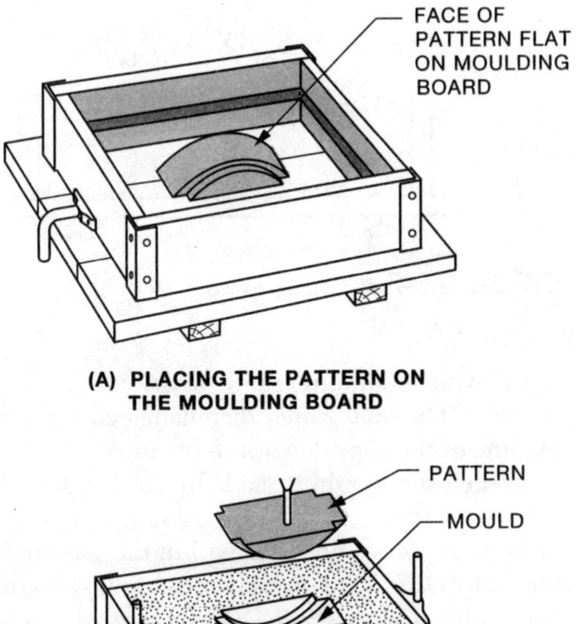

(A) PLACING THE PATTERN ON THE MOULDING BOARD

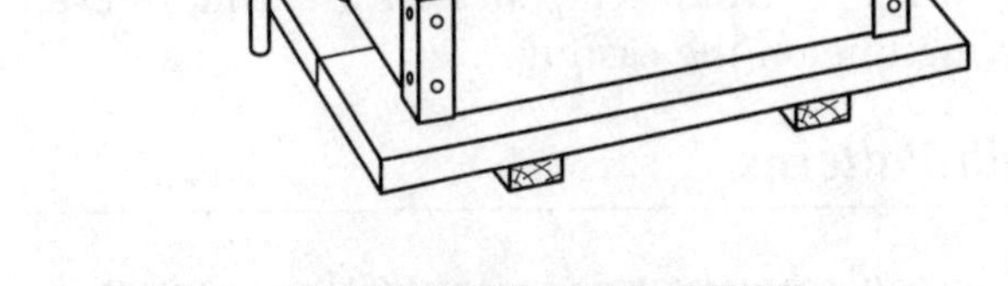

(B) DRAWING THE PATTERN

FIGURE 25–3 ■ Making a mould of a flat back pattern

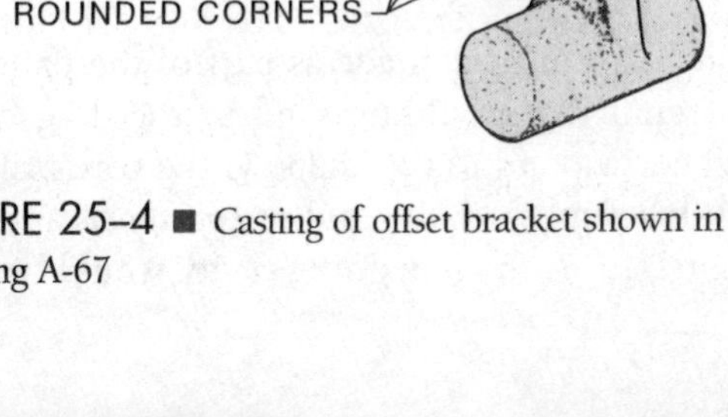

FIGURE 25–4 ■ Casting of offset bracket shown in drawing A-67

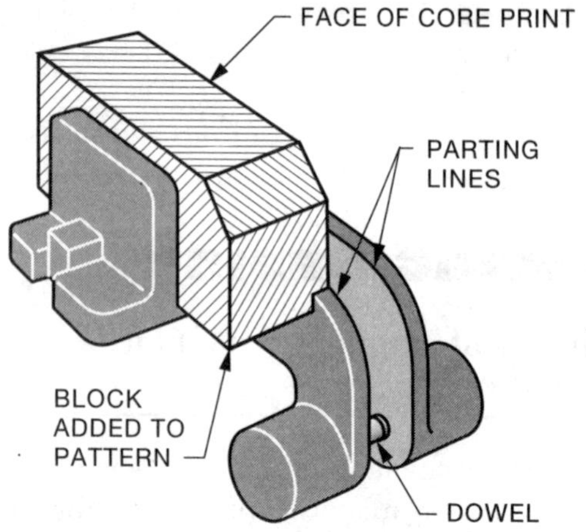

FIGURE 25–5 ■ Two-piece pattern for offset bracket

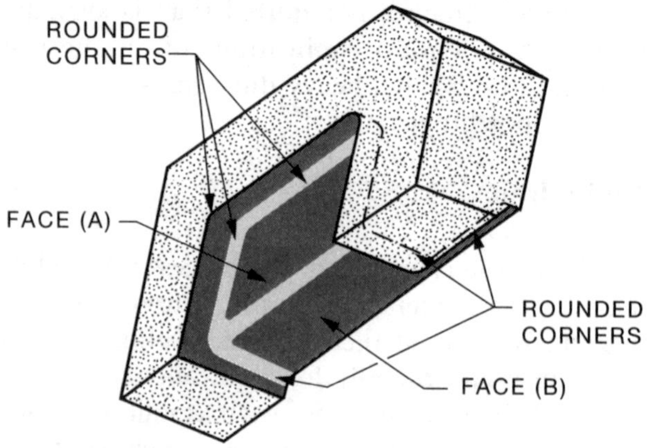

FIGURE 25–6 ■ Set core for offset bracket

make it possible to mould these rounded corners, a block must be added to the pattern for ease in removing it from the mould.

This block, which becomes an integral part of the pattern, also acts as a core print for a *set core* (a core that has been baked hard), Figure 25–6. It is made to conform to the shape of the faces of the casting, including the rounded corners.

The face of the core print also forms the parting line for one side of the two-part pattern. When making the mould for the bracket casting, this face, which corresponds to the flat face of a flat back pattern, is laid on the moulding board with the drag of the flask in position. The sand is then rammed around the pattern.

When the drag is reversed, the cope, or upper part of the flask, is placed in position. The other half of the pattern is then joined with the first part, and the sand is rammed into the cope to flow around that part of the pattern that projects into it.

After the pattern is removed, the set core, which is formed in a core box and baked hard, is set in the impression in the mould made by the core print of the pattern. When poured into the mould, the molten metal fills the cavity made by the pattern and the faces of the set core as shown in Figure 25–6 at **A** and **B** to form the casting.

Coping Down

The core print is made as part of the pattern to avoid removing moulding sand in the drag, which would correspond to the shape of the core print.

If this sand were dug out or *coped out*, as shown in Figure 25–7, the remaining cavity would be again

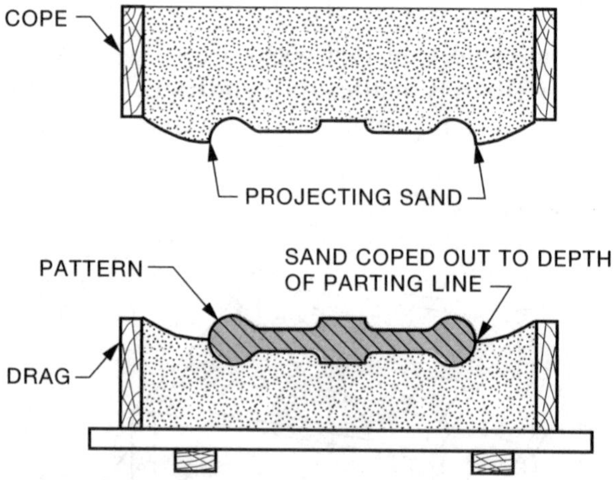

FIGURE 25–7 ■ Coping down

filled with moulding sand when the cope was rammed. The sand would then hang below the parting line of the cope down into the drag.

When the mould is made by coping down, the hanging portion of the cope is supported by soldiers or gaggers embedded within the sand to hold the projecting part in position for subsequent operations, Figure 25–8.

Coping down requires skill and takes time. The set core principle is at times preferred to coping down to avoid delay and ensure a more even parting line on the casting.

Split Patterns

Irregularly shaped patterns that cannot be drawn from the sand are sometimes split so that one half of the pattern may be rammed in the drag

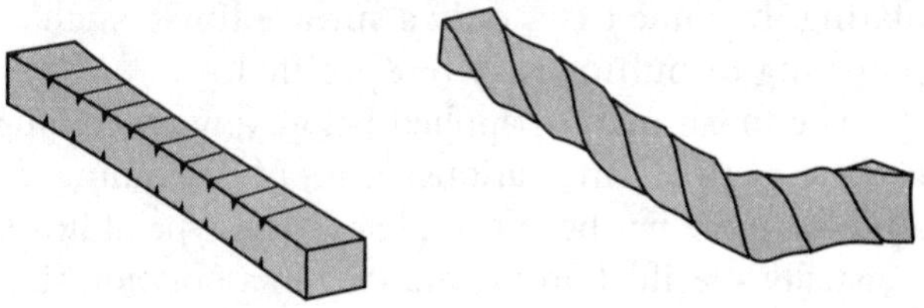

FIGURE 25–8 ■ Soldiers and gaggers

as a simple flat back pattern while the cope half, when placed in position on the drag half, forms the mould in the cope. Patterns of this type are called *split patterns* and do not require coping down to the parting line, which would be necessary if the pattern were made solid.

The pattern for the casting shown in Figure 25–9, when made without a print for a core, can be drawn from the sand only by splitting the pattern on the parting line as illustrated.

The drawing must be examined to determine how the pattern should be constructed. This is important because the parting line must be located in a position that permits the halves of the pattern to be drawn from the sand without interference.

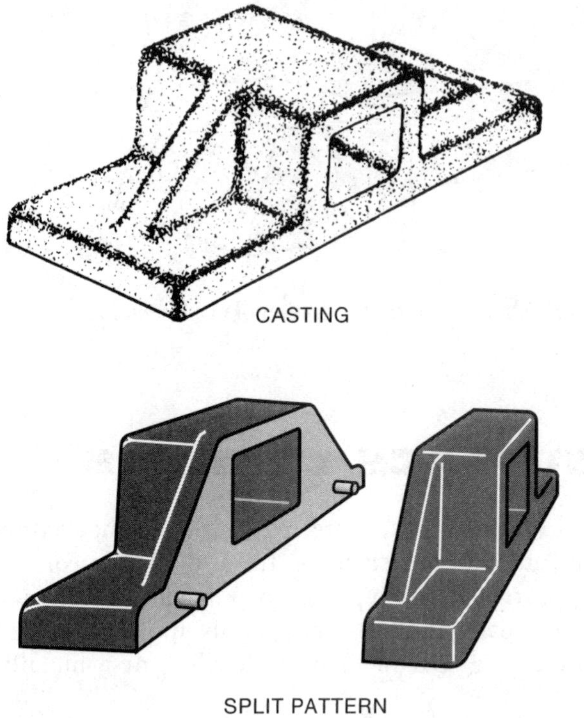
CASTING
SPLIT PATTERN

FIGURE 25–9 ■ Application of split pattern

CORED CASTINGS

Cored castings have certain advantages over solid castings. Where practical, castings are designed with cored holes or openings for economy, appearance, and accessibility to interior surfaces.

Cored openings often improve the appearance of a casting. In most instances, cored castings are more economical than solid castings because of the savings in metal. Although cored castings are lighter, they are designed without sacrificing strength. The openings cast in the part eliminate unnecessary machining.

Hand holes may also be formed by coring in order to provide an opening through which the interior of the casting may be reached. These openings also permit machining an otherwise inaccessible surface of the part as shown in Figure 25–10 and drawing A-69.

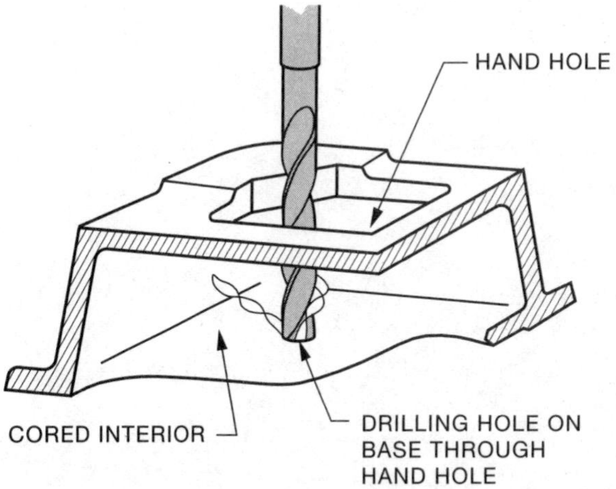
HAND HOLE
CORED INTERIOR
DRILLING HOLE ON BASE THROUGH HAND HOLE

FIGURE 25–10 ■ Section of cored casting

MACHINING LUGS

It is difficult to hold and machine certain parts without using lugs. This is because of the design and nature of certain parts. The lugs are an integral part of the casting. They are sometimes removed to avoid interference with the functioning of the part. Lugs are usually represented in phantom outline.

An example of a machining lug is shown in Figure 25–11. This lug is used to provide a flat surface on the end of the casting for centring and also to give a uniform centre bearing for other machining operations. Both the function of the lug and its appearance determine whether or not it is removed after machining.

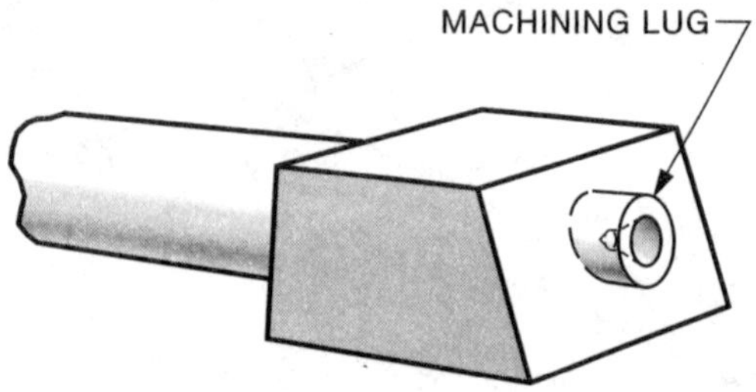

FIGURE 25–11 ■ Application of machining lug

SURFACE COATINGS

Machined parts are frequently finished either to protect the surfaces from oxidation or for appearance. The type of finish depends on the use of the part. The finish commonly applied may be a protective coat of paint or lacquer, or a metallic plating. In some cases only a surface finish such as polishing or buffing may be specified.

The finish may be applied before any machining is done, between the various stages of machining, or after the piece has been completed. The type of finish is usually specified on the drawing in a notation similar to the one indicated on the auxiliary pump base, drawing A-69, which reads CASTING TO BE PAINTED WITH ALUMINUM BEFORE MACHINING.

The decorative finish on the drive housing should be added before machining so that there will be no accidental deposit of paint on the machined surfaces. This will ensure the desired accuracy when assembled with other parts.

REFERENCES

Machine Design, Materials Reference Issue, Mar. 1981
ASME Y14.8M-1996 Castings and Forgings

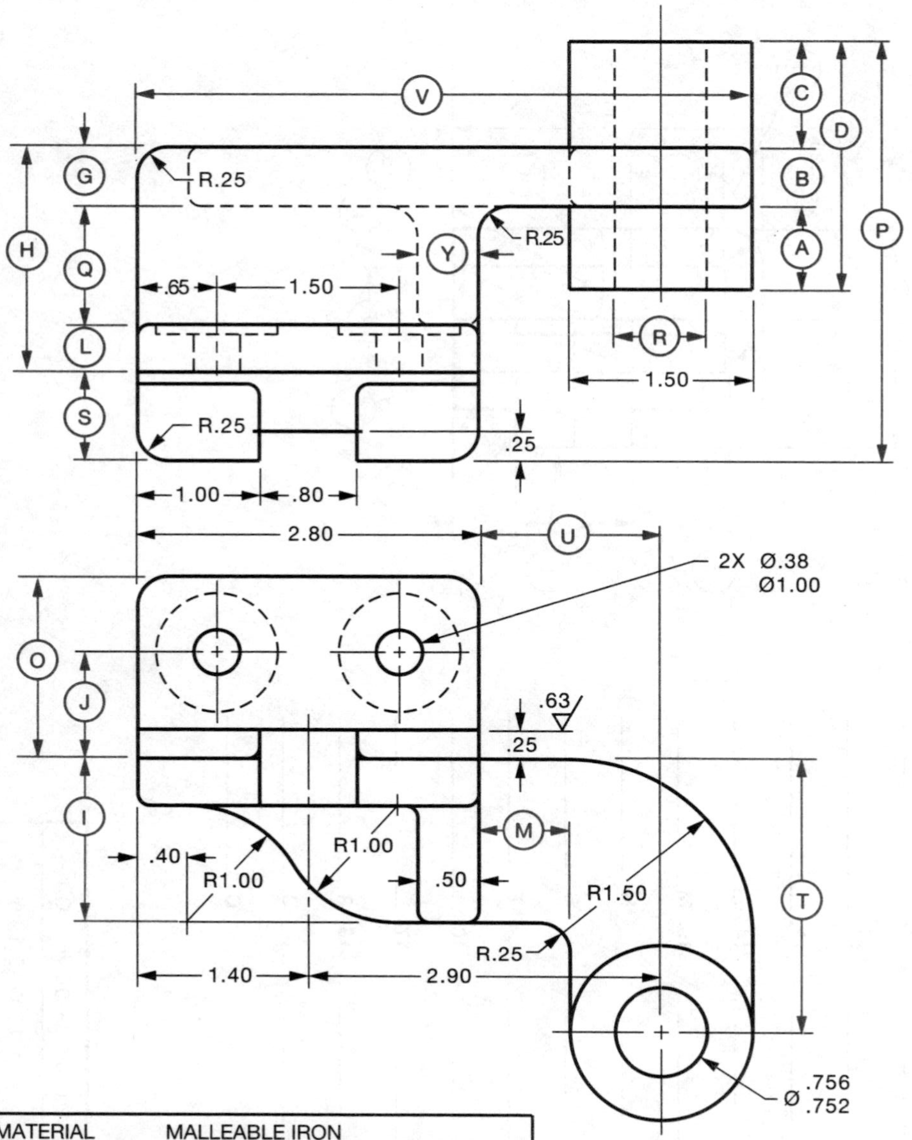

ANSWERS

A. ______	H. ______	O. ______	V. ______
B. ______	I. ______	P. ______	W. ______
C. ______	J. ______	Q. ______	X. ______
D. ______	K. ______	R. ______	Y. ______
E. ______	L. ______	S. ______	Z. ______
F. ______	M. ______	T. ______	
G. ______	N. ______	U. ______	

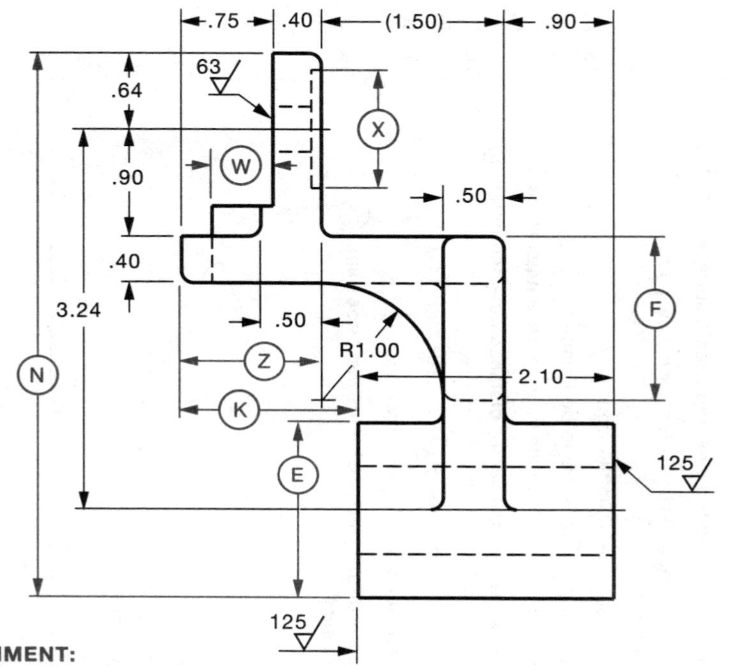

MATERIAL	MALLEABLE IRON	
SCALE	NOT TO SCALE	
DRAWN		DATE

OFFSET BRACKET **A-67**

ASSIGNMENT:
DETERMINE DISTANCES (A) TO (Z)

NOTE: UNLESS OTHERWISE SPECIFIED:
—TOLERANCES ON DIMENSIONS ±.02
—ROUNDS AND FILLETS R.10

QUESTIONS

1. Which line in the top view represents surface (1)?
2. Locate surface (A) in the left-side view and the front view.
3. Locate surface (8) in the front view.
4. How many surfaces are to be finished?
5. Which line in the left-side view represents surface (3)?
6. What is the vertical centre distance between holes (B) and (O) in the front view?
7. Determine distances at (4), (5), (6), and (11).
8. Locate surface (J) in the top view.
9. Which surface of the left-side view does line (14) represent?
10. What point in the front view is represented by line (15)?
11. What is the thickness of boss (E)?
12. Locate surface (G) in the left-side view.
13. Locate point (K) in the top view.
14. Locate surface (D) in the top view.
15. Determine distances at (M), (N), (S), and (T).
16. What point or line in the top view is represented by point (16)?
17. What is the maximum horizontal centre distance between the holes in the front view?
18. What would be the (A) width, (B) height, and (C) depth of the part before machining?

ANSWERS

1. ______
2. L.V. ______
   F.V. ______
3. ______
4. ______
5. ______
6. ______
7. 4 ______
   5 ______
   6 ______
   11 ______
8. ______
9. ______
10. ______
11. ______
12. ______
13. ______
14. ______
15. M ______
    N ______
    S ______
    T ______
16. ______
17. ______
18. A ______
    B ______
    C ______

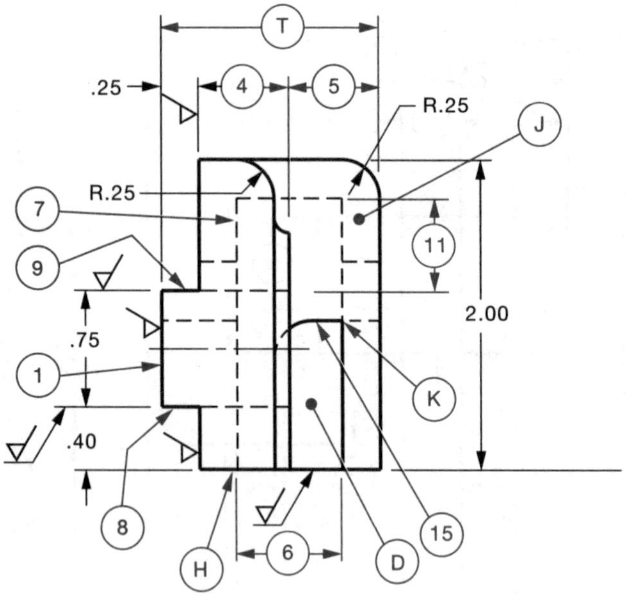

REVISIONS	1	02-03-04	C.J.
	1.15 WAS 1.20		

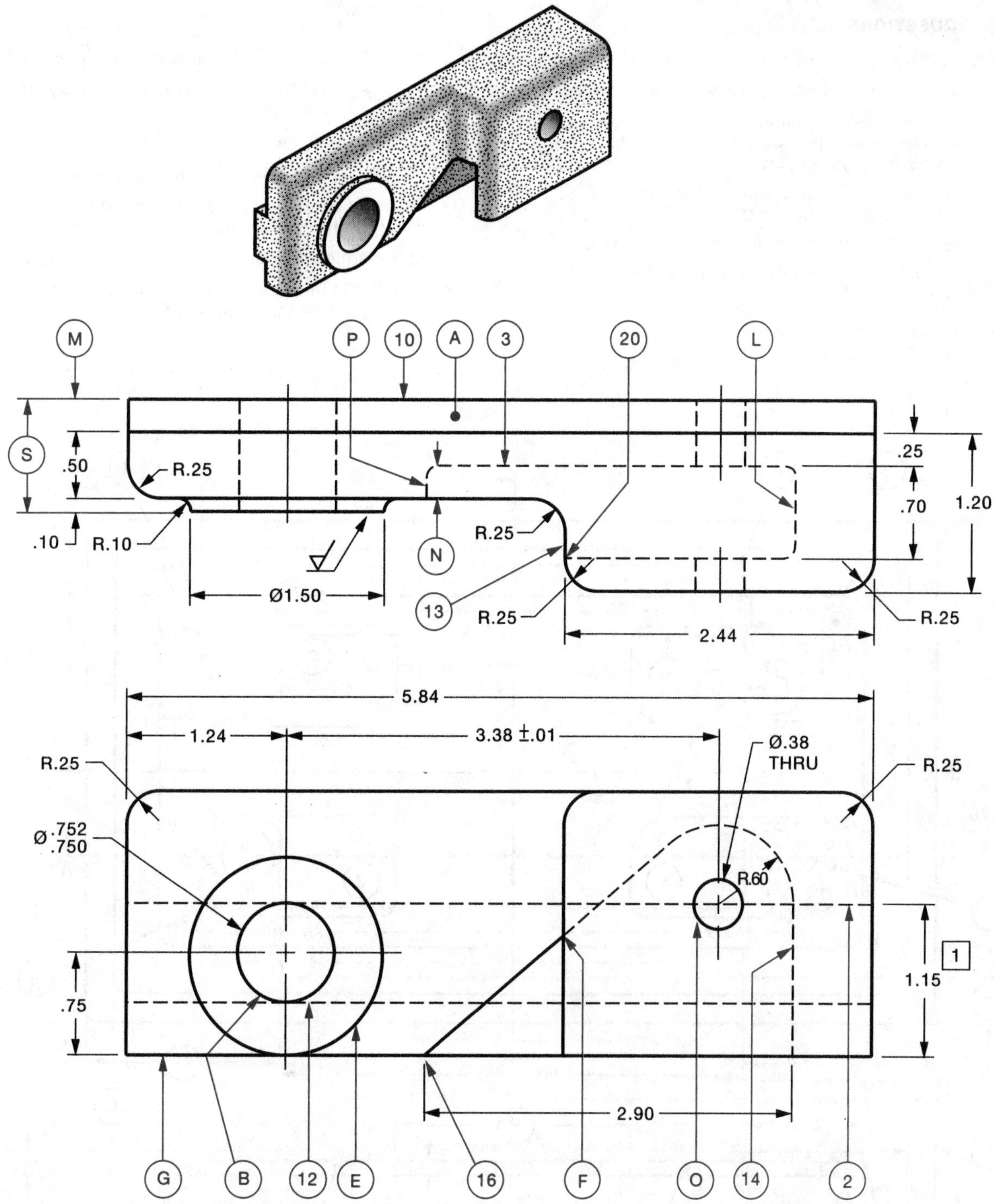

NOTE: UNLESS OTHERWISE SPECIFIED:
- —TOLERANCES ON DIMENSIONS: ±.02
- —.06 125/▽ FINISH WHERE SHOWN AS ▽/
- —ROUNDS AND FILLETS R.10

QUANTITY	500	
MATERIAL	MALLEABLE IRON	
SCALE	NOT TO SCALE	
DRAWN		DATE
	TRIP BOX	A-68

QUESTIONS

1. Of what material is the base made?
2. How many finished surfaces are indicated?
3. Which circled letters on the drawing indicate the spaces that were cored when the casting was made?
4. Locate the surface in the top view that is represented by line ⑥.
5. What is the height of the cored area Ⓧ?
6. What surface finish is used on the top pad?
7. What is the horizontal length of the pad ⑤?
8. What reason might be given for openings Ⓠ Ⓢ, Ⓨ, and Ⓩ?
9. Determine distance Ⓦ.
10. What radius fillet would be used at Ⓡ?
11. What is the total allowance added to the height for machining ?
12. Determine distances Ⓒ through Ⓝ.
13. What is the size of the tap drill required for the four threaded holes ?

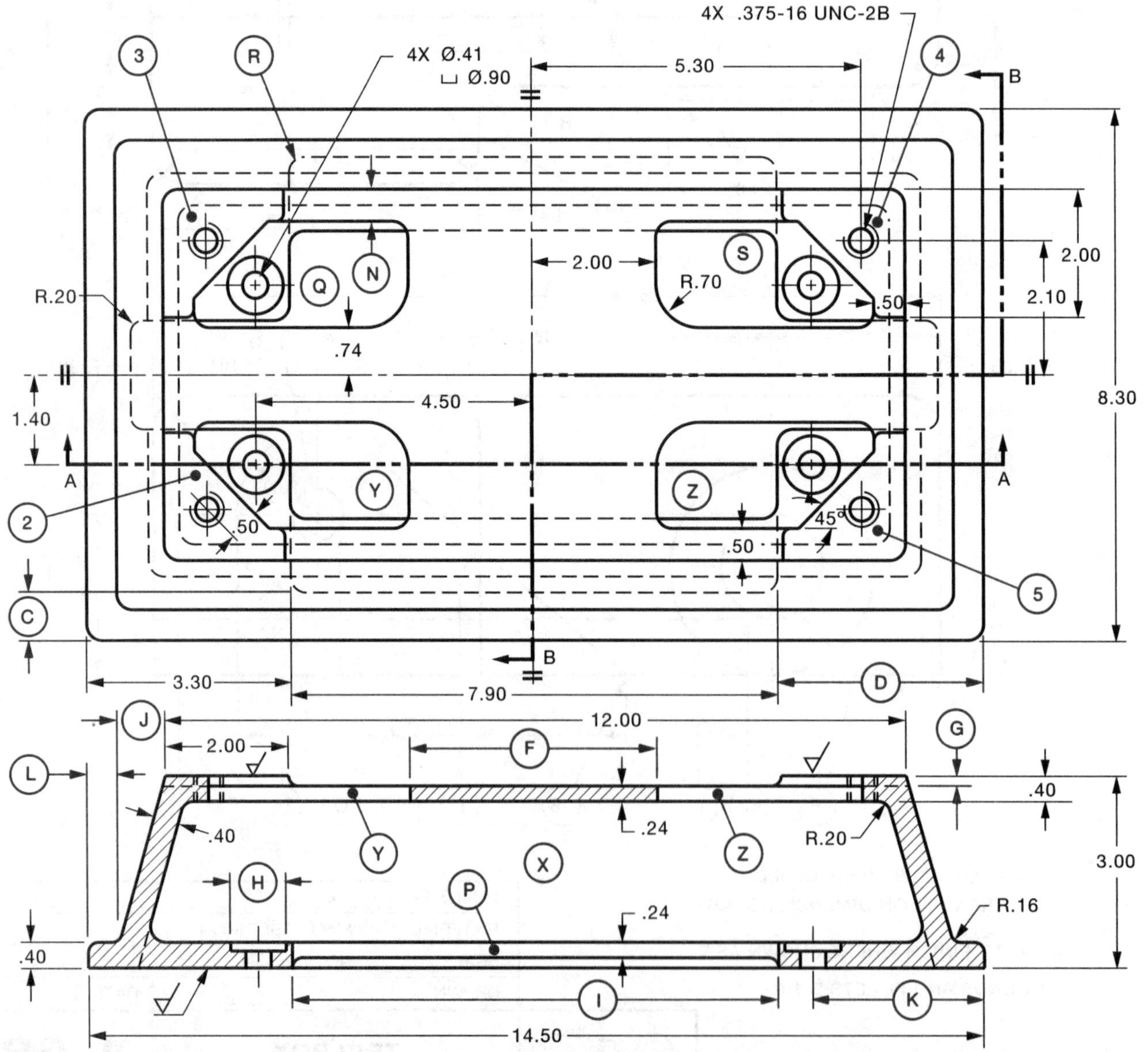

SECTION A-A

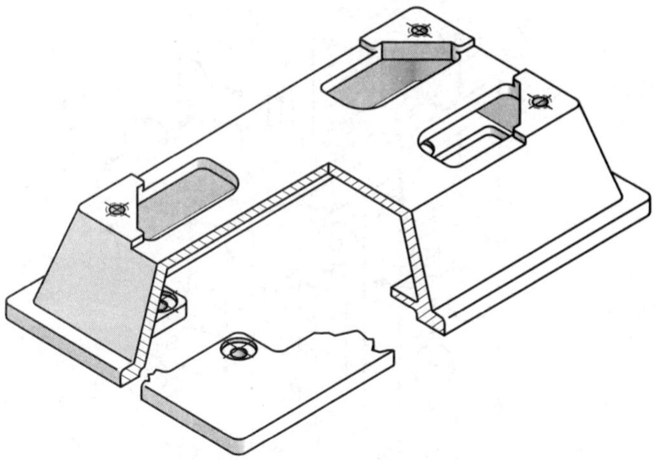

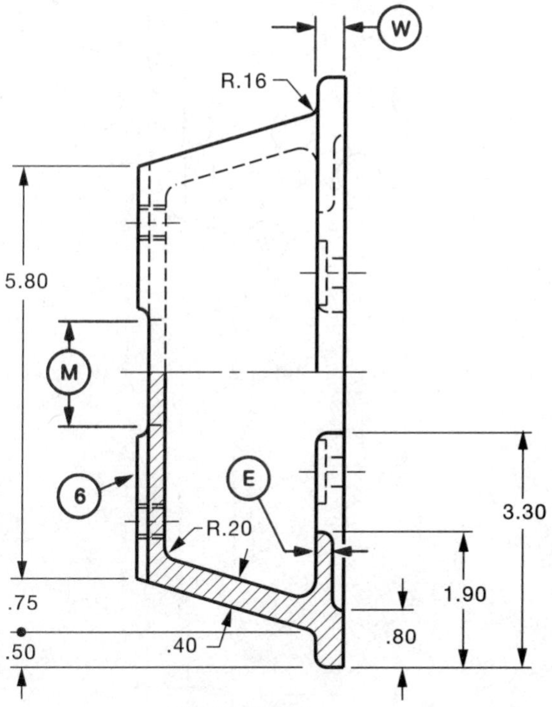
W
R.16
5.80
M
6
E
R.20
3.30
1.90
.75
.50
.40
.80

SECTION B-B

ANSWERS

1. ______
2. ______
3. ______
4. ______
5. ______
6. ______
7. ______
8. ______
9. ______
10. ______
11. ______
12. C ______
D ______
E ______
F ______
G ______
H ______
I ______
J ______
K ______
L ______
M ______
N ______
13. ______

NOTE: UNLESS OTHERWISE SPECIFIED:
- —TOLERANCES ON DIMENSIONS ±.02
- —ROUNDS AND FILLETS R.25
- —FINISHES .06 125/▽
- —CASTING TO BE PAINTED ALUMINUM BEFORE MACHINING

MATERIAL	GREY IRON	
SCALE	NOT TO SCALE	
DRAWN		DATE
	AUXILIARY PUMP BASE	**A-69**

ANSWERS

A. ____________
B. ____________
C. ____________
D. ____________
E. ____________
F. ____________
G. ____________
H. ____________
J. ____________
K. ____________
L. ____________
M. ____________
N. ____________
P. ____________
Q. ____________
R. ____________
S. ____________
T. ____________
U. ____________
V. ____________
W. ____________
X. ____________
Y. ____________
Z. ____________

NOTE:

1. TOLERANCE ON DIMENSIONS ±0.5
2. √ TO BE 1.6√

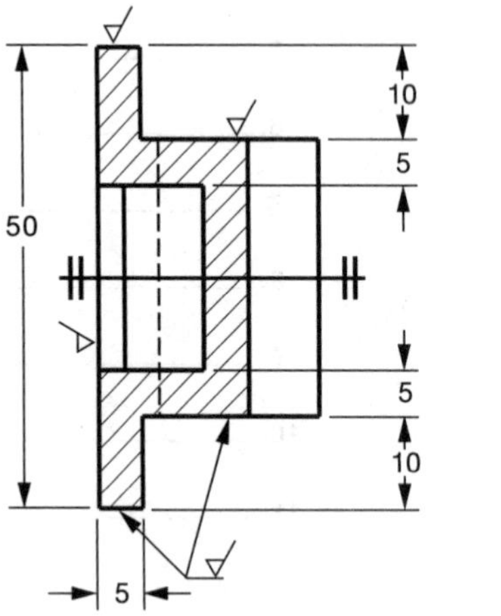

SECTION A-A

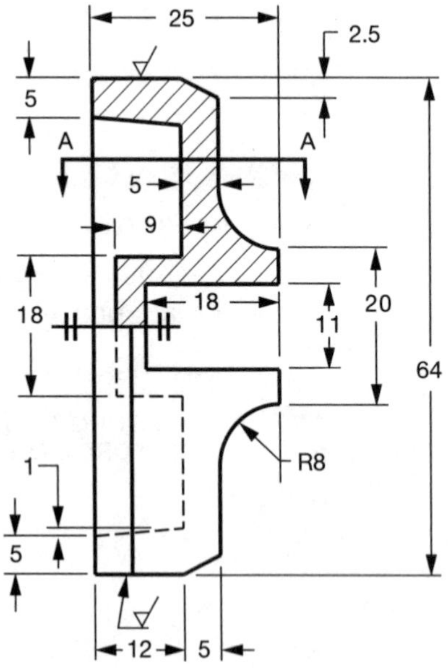

SECTION B-B

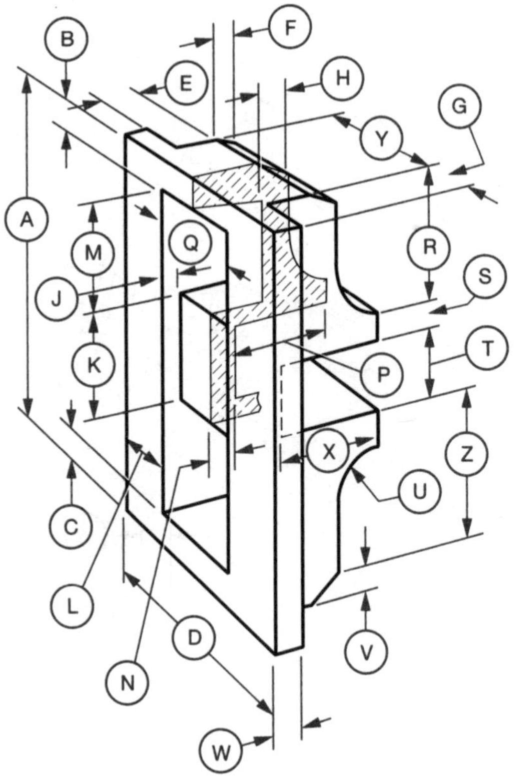

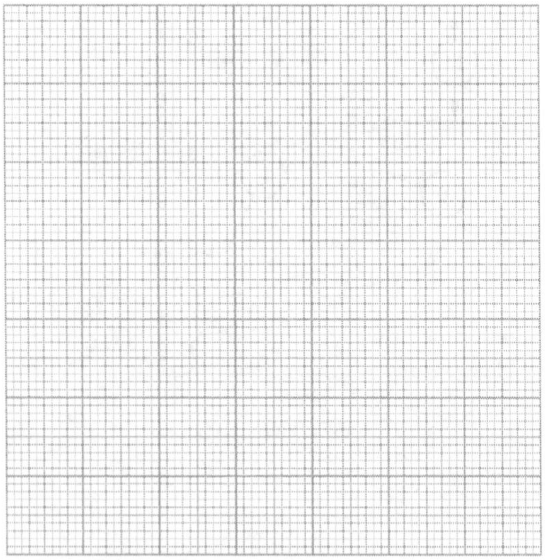

10 mm SQUARES (1 mm GRID)

METRIC
DIMENSIONS ARE IN MILLIMETRES

ASSIGNMENT:

1. MAKE A FREEHAND SKETCH OF THE RIGHT-SIDE VIEW AND SHOW THE POSITION OF THE CUTTING PLANE FOR SECTION B-B.
2. DETERMINE DISTANCES Ⓐ TO Ⓩ.

MATERIAL	GREY IRON		
SCALE	NOT TO SCALE		
DRAWN		DATE	
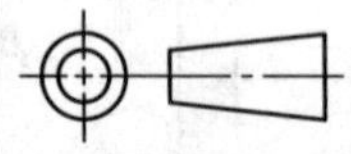	**SLIDE VALVE**		**A-70M**

UNIT 26

CHAIN DIMENSIONING

Most linear dimensions are intended to apply on a point-to-point basis. *Chain* dimensioning is applied directly from one feature to another, as shown in Figure 26–1(A). Such dimensions locate surfaces and features directly between the points indicated, or between corresponding points on the indicated surfaces.

For example, a diameter applies to all diameters of a cylindrical surface (not merely to the diameter at the end where the dimension is shown), a thickness applies to all opposing points on the surfaces, and a hole-locating dimension applies from the hole axis perpendicular to the edge of the part on the same centre line.

BASE LINE DIMENSIONING

When several dimensions extend from a common data point or points on a line or surface, Figure 26–1(B), this is called *base line* or *datum* dimensioning. This form of dimensioning is preferred for parts to be manufactured by numerical control machines.

A *feature* is a physical portion of a part, that is, a surface, hole, tab, or slot.

A *datum* is a theoretically exact point, axis, or plane derived from the true geometric counterpart of a specified datum feature. A datum may be the centre of a circle, the axis of a cylinder, or the axis of symmetry.

The location of a series of holes or step features as shown in Figure 26–1(B) is an example of the use of base line dimensioning. Figure 26–2 illustrates more complex uses of base line dimensioning. Without this type of dimensioning the distances between the first and last steps could vary considerably because of the buildup of tolerances permitted between the adjacent holes. Dimensioning from a datum line controls the tolerances between the holes to the basic general tolerance of ±.02 inch.

In this system, the tolerance from the common point to each of the features must be held to half the tolerance acceptable between individual features. For example, in Figure 26–1(C), if a tolerance between two individual holes of ±.02 inch were desired, each of the dimensions shown would have to be held to ±.01 inch.

REFERENCES

CAN/CSA-B78.2-M91 Dimensioning and Tolerancing of Technical Drawings

ASME Y14.5M-1994 Dimensioning and Tolerancing

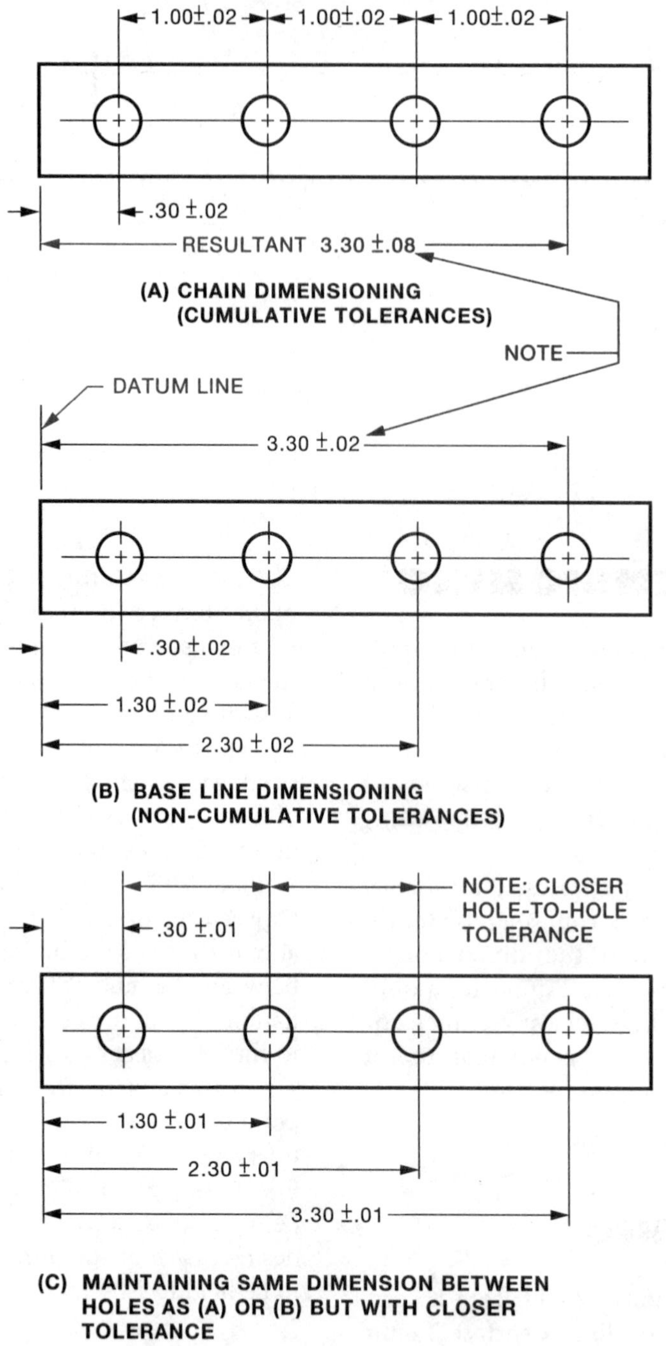
1.00±.02
1.00±.02
1.00±.02
.30 ±.02
RESULTANT 3.30 ±.08
(A) CHAIN DIMENSIONING
(CUMULATIVE TOLERANCES)
NOTE
DATUM LINE
3.30 ±.02
.30 ±.02
1.30 ±.02
2.30 ±.02
(B) BASE LINE DIMENSIONING
(NON-CUMULATIVE TOLERANCES)
NOTE: CLOSER
HOLE-TO-HOLE
TOLERANCE
.30 ±.01
1.30 ±.01
2.30 ±.01
3.30 ±.01
(C) MAINTAINING SAME DIMENSION BETWEEN
HOLES AS (A) OR (B) BUT WITH CLOSER
TOLERANCE

FIGURE 26–1 ■ Comparison between chain dimensioning and base line dimensioning

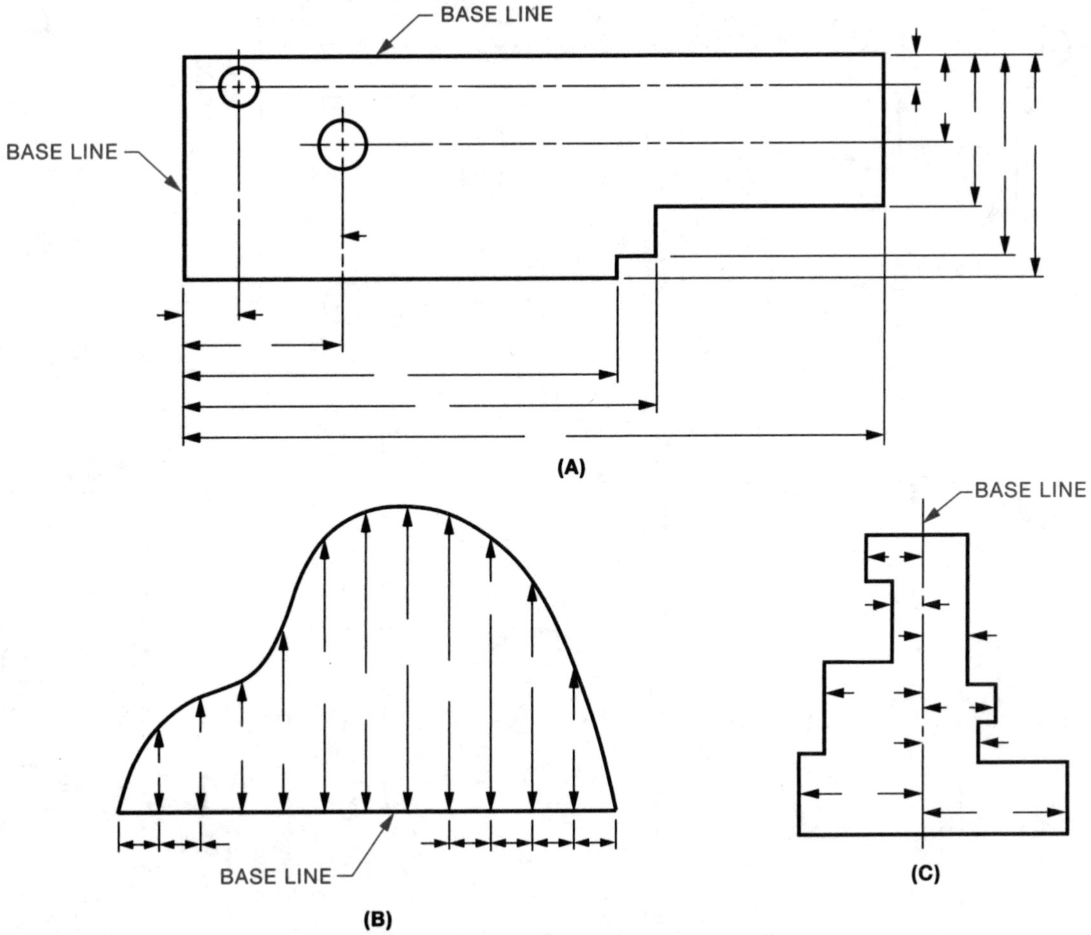

FIGURE 26–2 ■ Applications of base line dimensioning

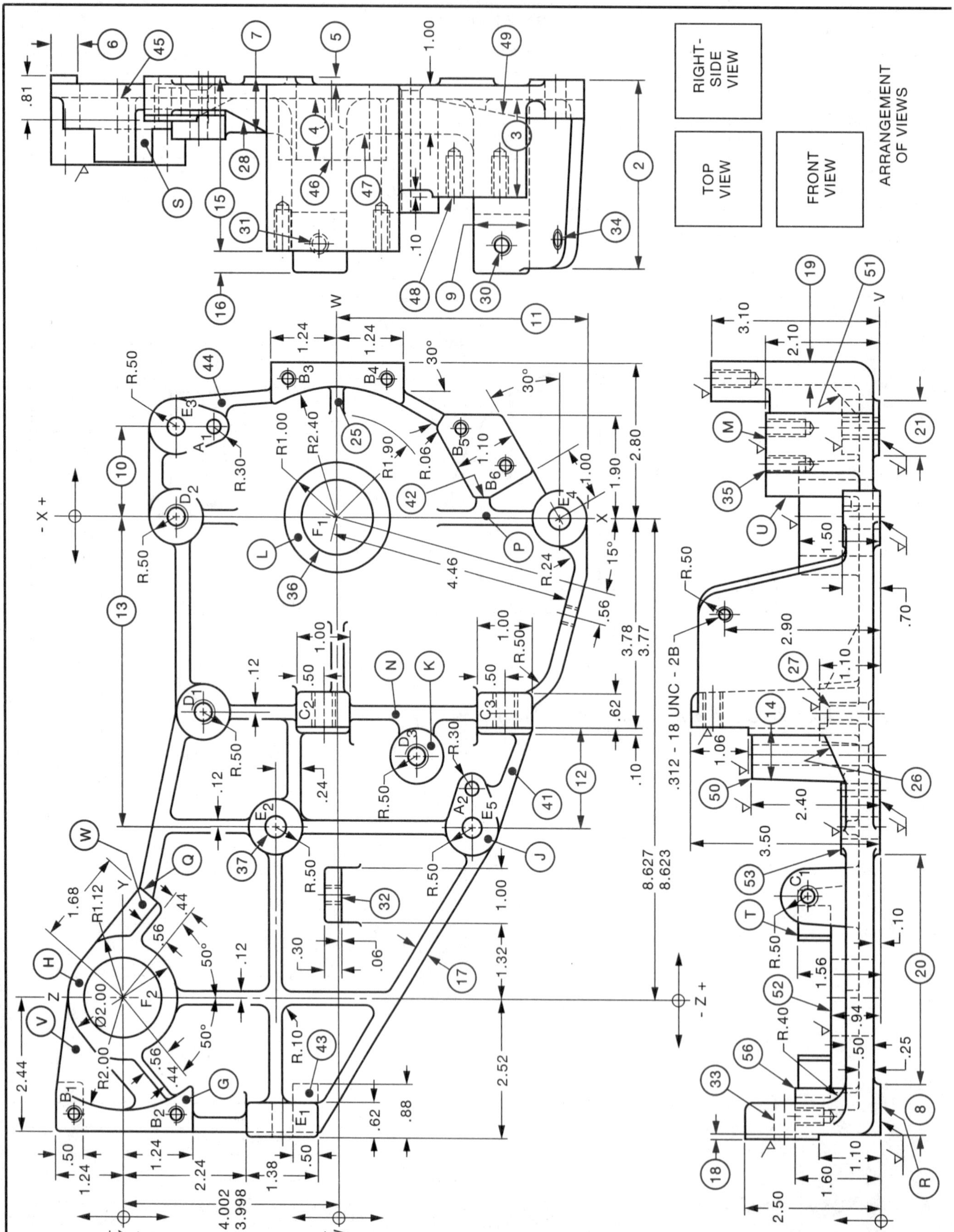
RIGHT-SIDE VIEW
TOP VIEW
FRONT VIEW
ARRANGEMENT OF VIEWS
.312 - 18 UNC - 2B

QUESTIONS

NOTE: Where limit dimensions are given, use larger limit.

1. What are the overall dimensions of the casting?
2. Show a roughness symbol meaning the same as the one given on the drawing.
3. Identify surfaces (G) to (U) on one of the other views.
4. Locate rib (25) on the front view.
5. Locate rib (26) on the top view.
6. Locate rib (27) on the right-side view.
7. Locate rib (28) on the top view.
8. Give the sizes of the following holes: (30), (31), (32), (33), and (34).
9. How deep is hole (35)?
10. What is the tolerance on hole (36)?
11. How deep is hole (37)?
12. Determine distances (2) to (21). (Where limit dimensions are shown, use maximum size.)
13. What is the (A) largest and (B) smallest permissible hole on the part? Do not include tapped holes.
14. What is the smallest tap drill size used?

ANSWERS

1. W ______
   D ______
   H ______
2. ______
3. G ______
   H ______
   J ______
   K ______
   L ______
   M ______
   N ______
   P ______
   Q ______
   R ______
   S ______
   T ______
   U ______
4. ______
5. ______
6. ______
7. ______
8. 30 ______
   31 ______
   32 ______
   33 ______
   34 ______
9. ______
10. ______
11. ______
12. 2 ______ 3 ______
    4 ______ 5 ______
    6 ______ 7 ______
    8 ______ 9 ______
    10 ______ 11 ______
    12 ______ 13 ______
    14 ______ 15 ______
    16 ______ 17 ______
    18 ______ 19 ______
    20 ______ 21 ______
13. A ______
    B ______
14. ______

HOLE SIZE AND LOCATION						
HOLE	DISTANCE FROM					SIZE
	V-V	W-W	X-X	Y-Y	Z-Z	
A_1		2.32	1.62			Ø .252/.250
A_2		-2.50	-4.88			
B_1				.94	-2.12	.312-18 UNC-2B X.75 DEEP
B_2				-.94	-2.12	
B_3		.94	2.50			
B_4		-.94	2.50			
B_5		-2.28	1.62			
B_6		-3.08	.96			
C_1	1.38				-1.82	.375-16 UNC - 2B
C_2	3.00	.28				
C_3	3.00	-3.12				
D_1		2.50	-3.50			Ø .3752/.3750 CSK .06X95°
D_2		3.00	.00			
D_3		-1.48	-4.28			
E_1	1.80			-2.94		Ø.406
E_2		1.18	-5.56			
E_3		3.00	1.62			
E_4		-4.12	.00			
E_5		-2.50	-5.56			
F_1		.00	.00			Ø 1.3765/1.3745
F_2				.00	.00	

NOTE:
—ALL FILLETS R.06 UNLESS OTHERWISE SHOWN
—ALL RIBS AND WEBS .24 THICK
—TOLERANCE ON DIMENSIONS ±.02
—TOLERANCE ON ANGLES ±0.5°
—SURFACES MARKED √ TO BE 250√

MATERIAL	GREY IRON		
SCALE	NOT TO SCALE		
DRAWN		DATE	
INTERLOCK BASE		A-71	

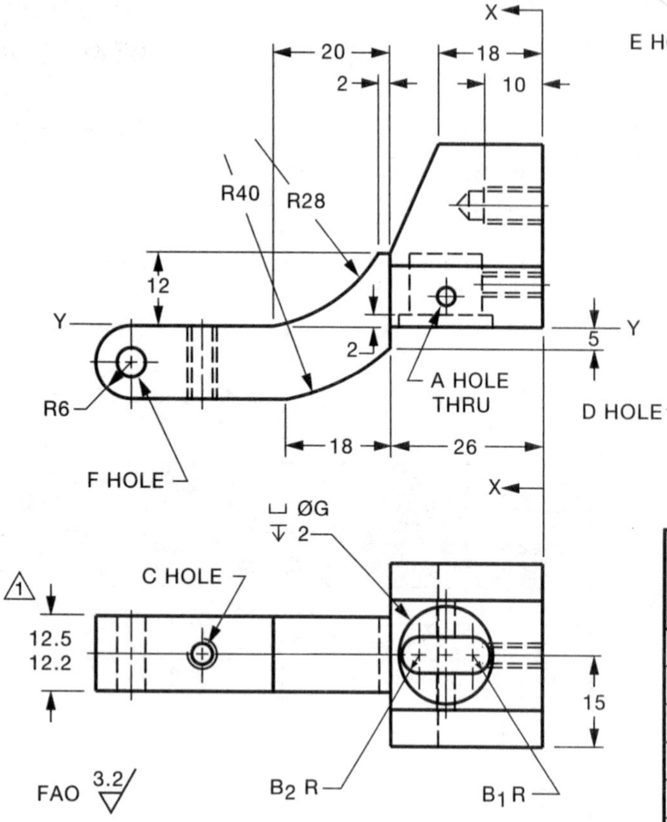

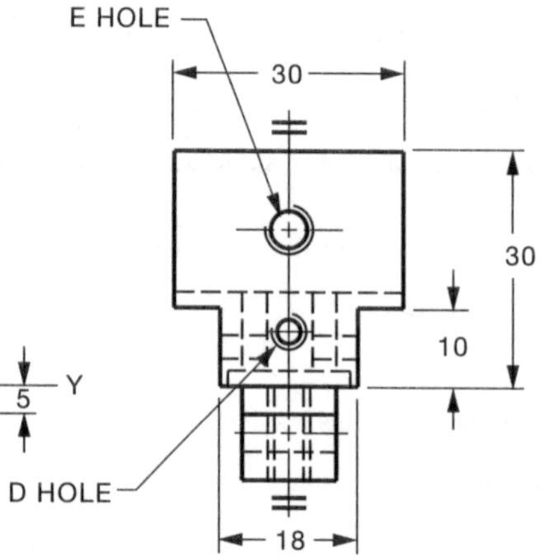

HOLE	HOLE SIZE	DISTANCE FROM	
		X-X	Y-Y
A	Ø3	16.5	5
B_1	R3	12	
B_2	R3	21	
C	M5	58	
D	M4		7
E	M6		20
F	Ø4.78-4.80	70	6
G	Ø16	16.5	

NOTE: UNLESS OTHERWISE SPECIFIED TOLERANCE ON DIMENSIONS ±0.5

ANSWERS

1. ________
2. ________
3. ________
4. ________
5. ________
6. ________
7. ________
8. ________
9. ________
10. ________
11. ________
12. ________
13. ________
14. A ________
    B ________
15. ________
16. A ________
    B ________
    C ________
17. ________

QUESTIONS

1. What is the overall width?
2. What is the overall height?
3. What is the distance from X-X to the centre of hole F?
4. What is the distance from Y-Y to the centre of hole E?
5. What is the horizontal distance between the centre lines of A and F holes?
6. What is the horizontal distance between the centre lines of C hole and B_1 radius?
7. How many full threads does E hole have? (See Table 5 of the Appendix.)
8. How deep is the spotface?
9. What is the tolerance on F hole?
10. What type of projection is used on this drawing?
11. How far apart are the D and E holes?
12. What is the tolerance on the thickness of the material at F hole?
13. What is the length of the C hole?
14. What is the distance from line X-X to the termination of both ends of the 28 radius?
15. What does FAO mean?
16. What is the tap drill size required for the (A) C, (B) D, and (C) E threaded holes?
17. What is the length of the slot?

METRIC
DIMENSIONS ARE IN MILLIMETRES

MATERIAL	ALUMINUM	
SCALE	NOT TO SCALE	
DRAWN		DATE

REVISIONS	1	F. NEWMAN 6/8/02	CH A. HEINEN	CONTACTOR	A-72M
		DIMENSION WAS 12.4-12.7			

UNIT 27

ALIGNMENT OF PARTS AND HOLES

Two important factors that must be considered when drawing an object are the number of views to be drawn and the time required to draw them. If possible, use time-saving devices, such as templates, for drawing standard features.

To simplify the representation of common features, a number of conventional drawing practices are used, Figure 27–1. Many conventions deviate from true projection for the purpose of clarity; others are used to save drafting time. These conventions must be executed carefully; clarity is even more important than speed.

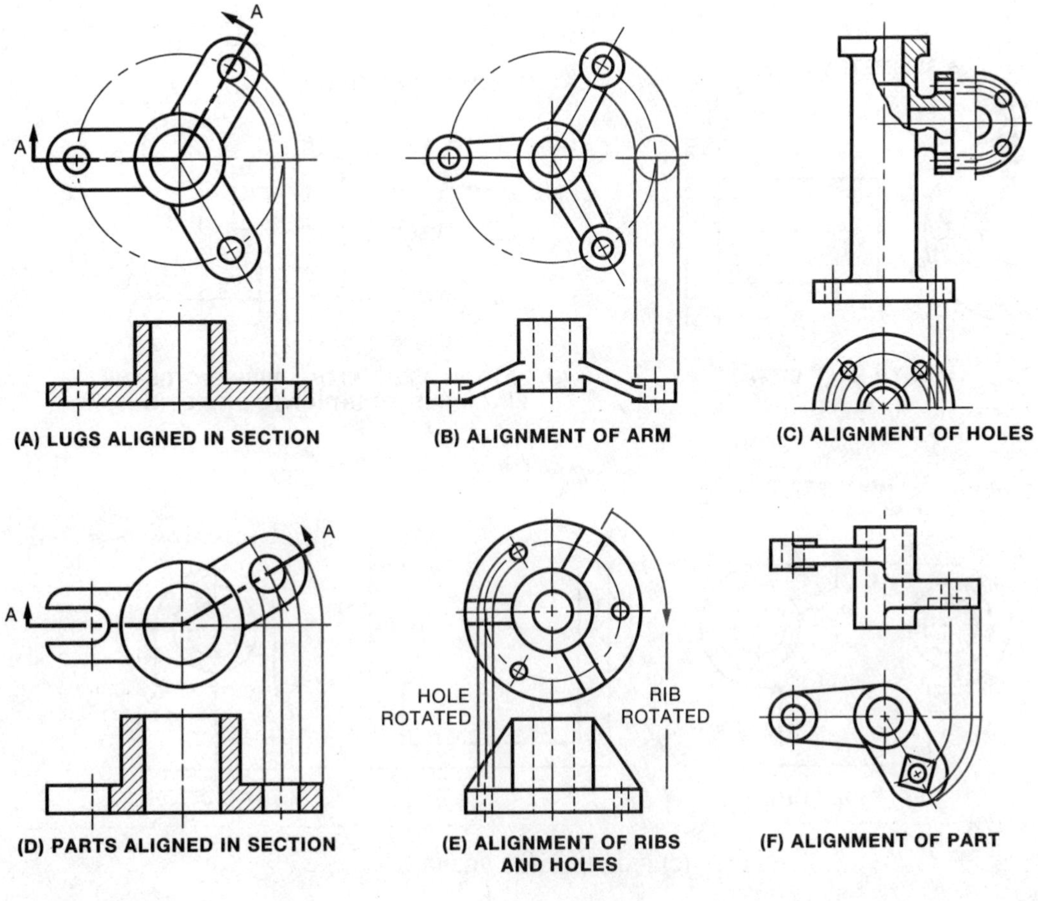

A
A
(A) LUGS ALIGNED IN SECTION
(B) ALIGNMENT OF ARM
(C) ALIGNMENT OF HOLES
A
A
HOLE
ROTATED
RIB
ROTATED
(D) PARTS ALIGNED IN SECTION
(E) ALIGNMENT OF RIBS AND HOLES
(F) ALIGNMENT OF PART

FIGURE 27–1 ■ Alignment of holes and parts to show their true relationship

Foreshortened Projection

When the true projection of ribs or arms results in confusing foreshortening, these parts should be rotated until parallel to the line of the section or projection.

Holes Revolved to Show True Centre Distance

Drilled flanges in elevation or section should show the holes at their true distance from centre, rather than the true projection.

PARTIAL VIEWS

Partial views, which show only a limited portion of the object with remote details omitted, should be used when necessary to clarify the meaning of the drawing, Figure 27–2. Such views are used to avoid the necessity of drawing many hidden features.

On drawings of objects where two side views can be used to better advantage than one, each need not be complete if together they depict the shape. Show only the hidden lines of features immediately behind the view, Figure 27–2(C).

Another type of partial view is shown, Figure 27–3. However, sufficient information is given in the partial view to complete the description of the object. The partial view is limited by a break line. Partial views are used because

- They save time in drawing.
- They conserve space that might otherwise be needed for drawing the object.
- They sometimes permit the drawing to be made to scale large enough to bring out all details clearly, whereas if the whole view were drawn, lack of space might make it necessary to draw a smaller scale, resulting in the loss of detail clarity.
- If the part is symmetrical, a partial view (referred to as a half view) may be drawn on one side of the centre line as shown in Figure 27–4. In the case of the coil frame (drawing A-76) a partial view was used so that the object could be

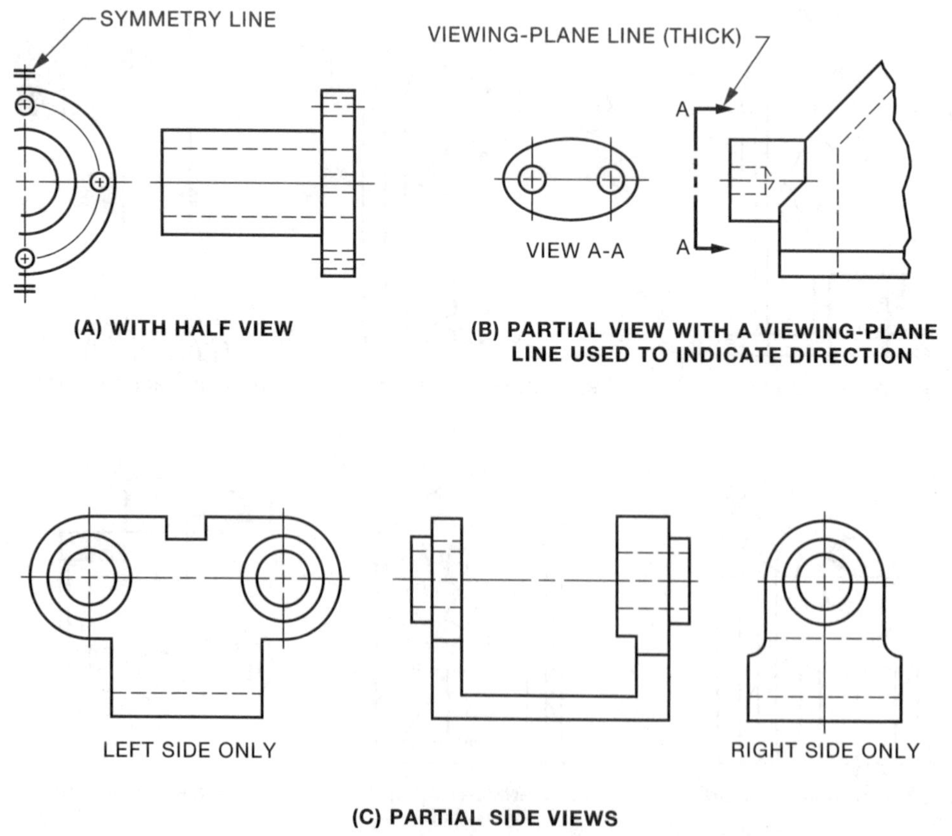
SYMMETRY LINE
(A) WITH HALF VIEW
VIEWING-PLANE LINE (THICK)
A
A
VIEW A-A
(B) PARTIAL VIEW WITH A VIEWING-PLANE LINE USED TO INDICATE DIRECTION
LEFT SIDE ONLY
RIGHT SIDE ONLY
(C) PARTIAL SIDE VIEWS

FIGURE 27–2 ■ Partial views

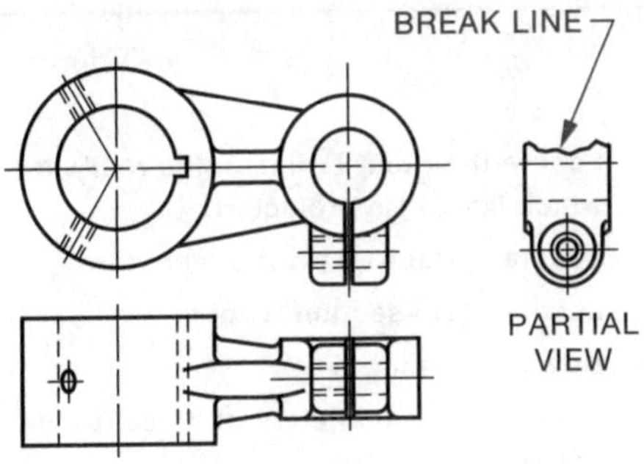
BREAK LINE
PARTIAL VIEW

FIGURE 27–3 ■ Partial view

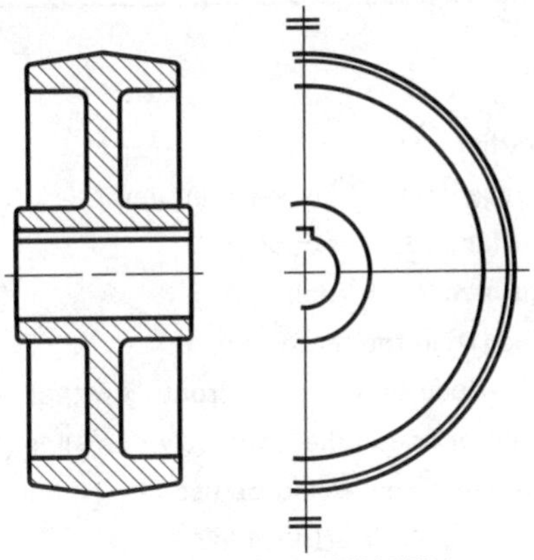
HALF VIEW

FIGURE 27–4 ■ Half views

drawn to a larger scale for clarity, thus saving time and space.

NAMING OF VIEWS FOR SPARK ADJUSTER

The drawing of the spark adjuster, drawing A-73, illustrates several violations of true projection. The names of the views of the spark adjuster could be questionable. The importance lies not in the names, however, but in the relationship of the views to each other. This means that the right view must be on the right side of the front, the left view must be on the left side of the front view, etc. Any combination in Figure 27–5 may be used for naming the views of the spark adjuster.

DRILL SIZES

Twist drills are the most common tools used in drilling. They are made in many sizes. Inch size twist drills are grouped according to decimal inch sizes; by number sizes, from 1 to 80, which correspond to the Stubbs steel wire gauge; by letter sizes A to Z; and by fractional sizes from 1/64th up. Inch twist drill sizes are listed in Table 3 of the Appendix.

Metric twist drill sizes are in millimetres and are classified as *preferred* and *available.* These sizes will eventually replace the fractional-inch, letter, and number size drills that are presently in existence. Metric twist drill sizes are listed in Table 4 of the Appendix.

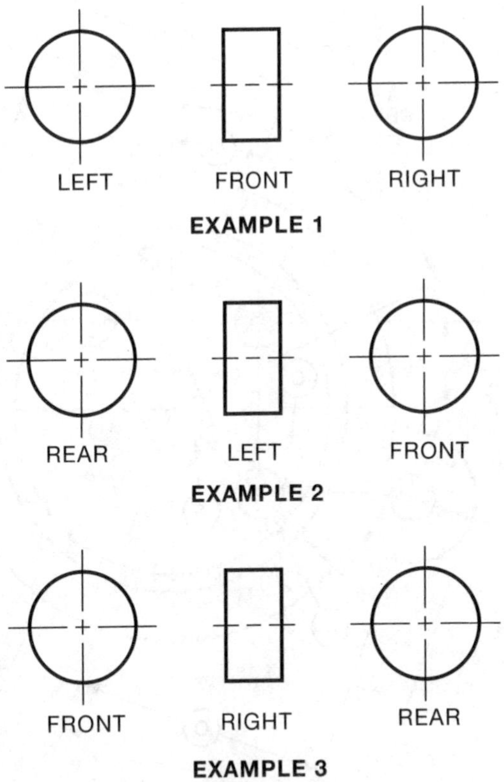
LEFT
FRONT
RIGHT
EXAMPLE 1
REAR
LEFT
FRONT
EXAMPLE 2
FRONT
RIGHT
REAR
EXAMPLE 3

FIGURE 27–5 ■ Naming of views for spark adjuster, drawing A-73

REFERENCES

CAN3B78.1-M83 (R1990) Technical Drawings—General Principles

ASME Y14.3M-1994 Multi and Sectional View Drawings

QUESTIONS

1. What is radius (A)?
2. What surface is line (2) in the rear view?
3. Locate surface (B) in section A-A.
4. Locate surface (C) in section A-A.
5. Locate line (D) in the rear view.
6. Locate a surface or line in the front view that represents line (F).
7. Which point or line in the front view does line (G) represent?
8. What size cap screw would be used in (N) hole?
9. What is the diameter of (K) hole?
10. Locate the point or line in the rear view from which line (1) is projected.
11. Locate surface (H) in the rear view.
12. Locate (Z) in section A-A.
13. How thick is lug (7)?
14. What are the diameters of holes (L), (M), and (N)?
15. Determine angles (O) and (P).
16. Determine distances (Q) through (U).

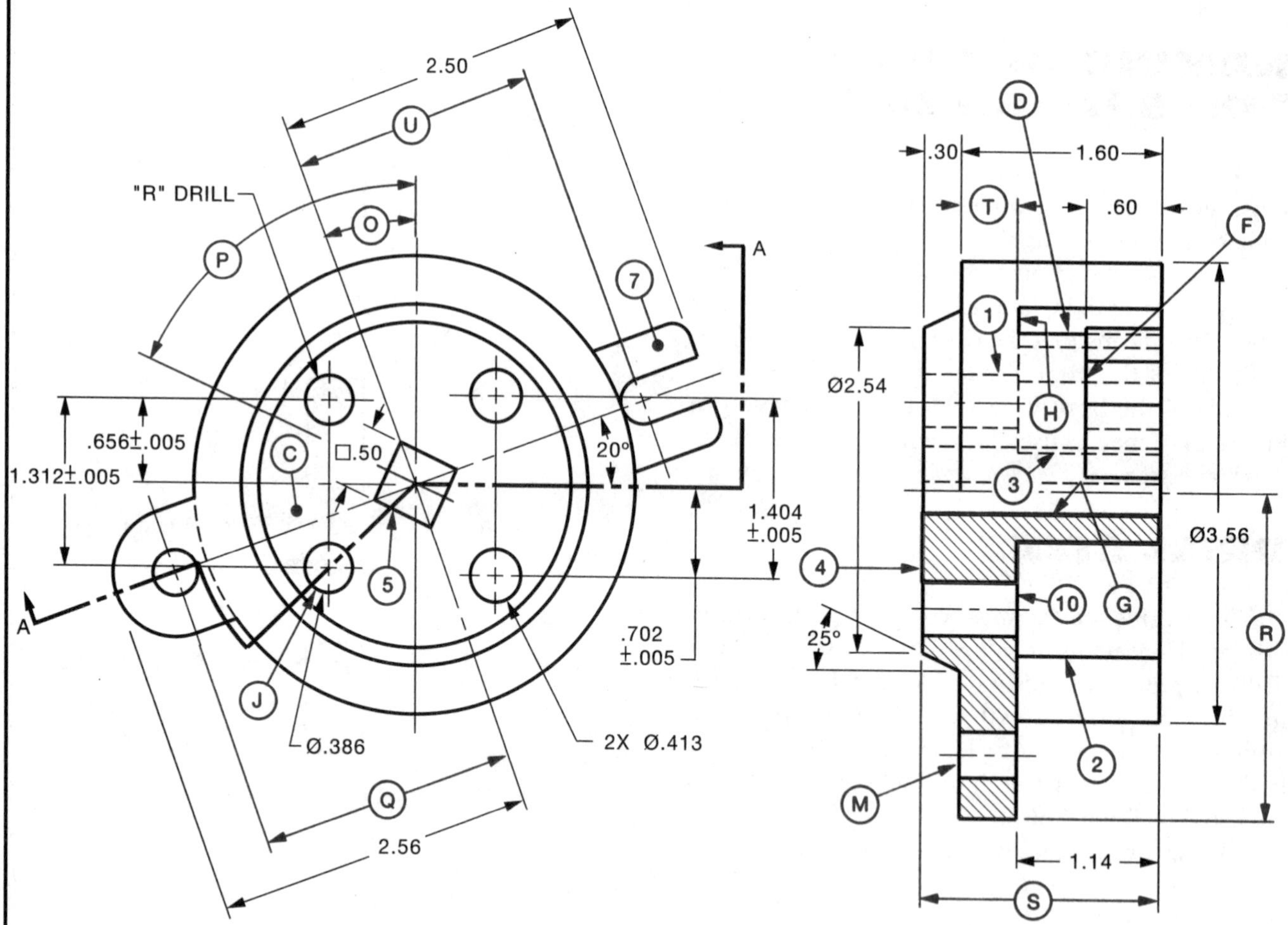

FRONT VIEW

SECTION A-A

RIGHT-SIDE VIEW

NOTE: UNLESS OTHERWISE STATED:
—TOLERANCE ON TWO-PLACE DIMENSIONS ± .02
—TOLERANCE ON THREE-PLACE DIMENSIONS ± .010
—TOLERANCE ON ANGLES ± 0.5°

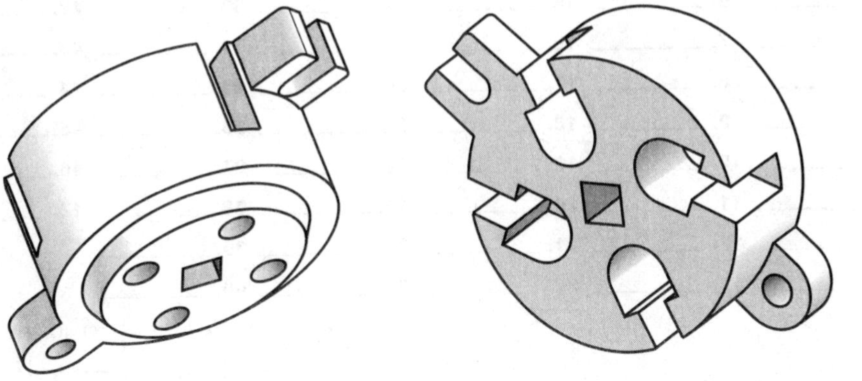

ANSWERS

1. ____________
2. ____________
3. ____________
4. ____________
5. ____________
6. ____________
7. ____________
8. ____________
9. ____________
10. ____________
11. ____________
12. ____________
13. ____________
14. L ____________
    M ____________
    N ____________
15. O ____________
    P ____________
16. Q ____________
    R ____________
    S ____________
    T ____________
    U ____________

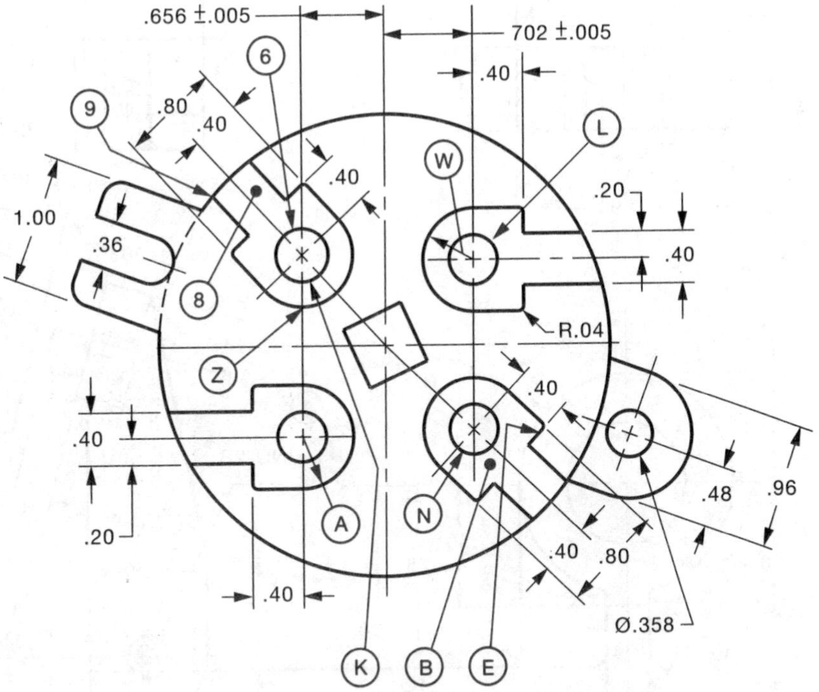
.656 ±.005
702 ±.005
.40
.80
.40
.40
1.00
.36
.20
.40
R.04
.40
.40
.20
.40
.48
.96
.40
.80
Ø.358
.40
6
9
8
W
L
Z
A
N
K
B
E

REAR VIEW

MATERIAL	BAKELITE	
SCALE	1:1	
DRAWN		DATE
	SPARK ADJUSTER	**A-73**

ASSIGNMENT: Determine distances or dimensions of the following:

ANSWERS

A. ______	K. ______	U. ______	5. ______	14. ______	23. ______	32. ______	41. ______
B. ______	L. ______	V. ______	6. ______	15. ______	24. ______	33. ______	42. ______
C. ______	M. ______	W. ______	7. ______	16. ______	25. ______	34. ______	43. ______
D. ______	N. ______	X. ______	8. ______	17. ______	26. ______	35. ______	44. ______
E. ______	P. ______	Y. ______	9. ______	18. ______	27. ______	36. ______	45. ______
F. ______	Q. ______	Z. ______	10. ______	19. ______	28. ______	37. ______	46. ______
G. ______	R. ______	2. ______	11. ______	20. ______	29. ______	38. ______	47. ______
H. ______	S. ______	3. ______	12. ______	21. ______	30. ______	39. ______	
J. ______	T. ______	4. ______	13. ______	22. ______	31. ______	40. ______	

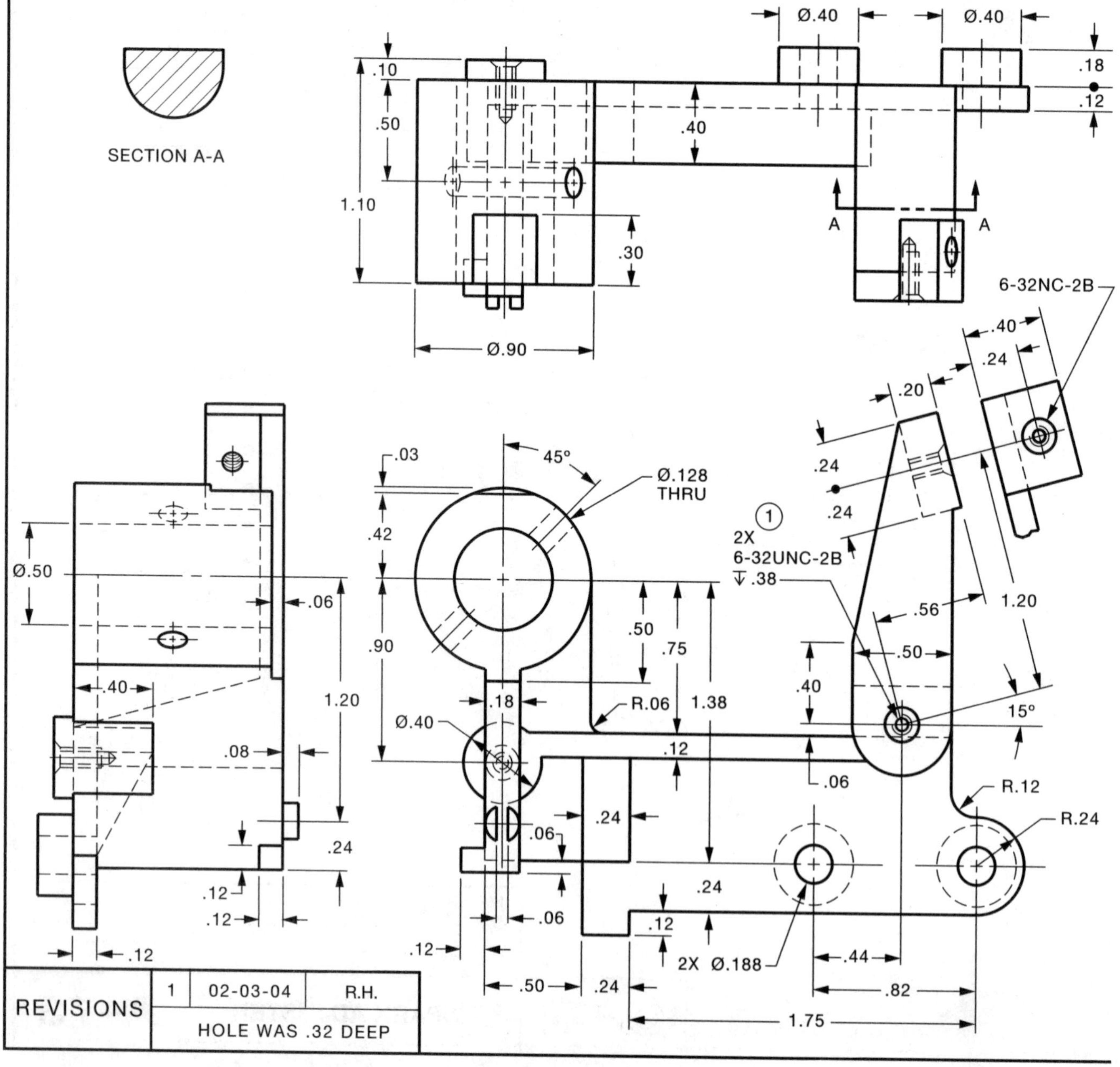

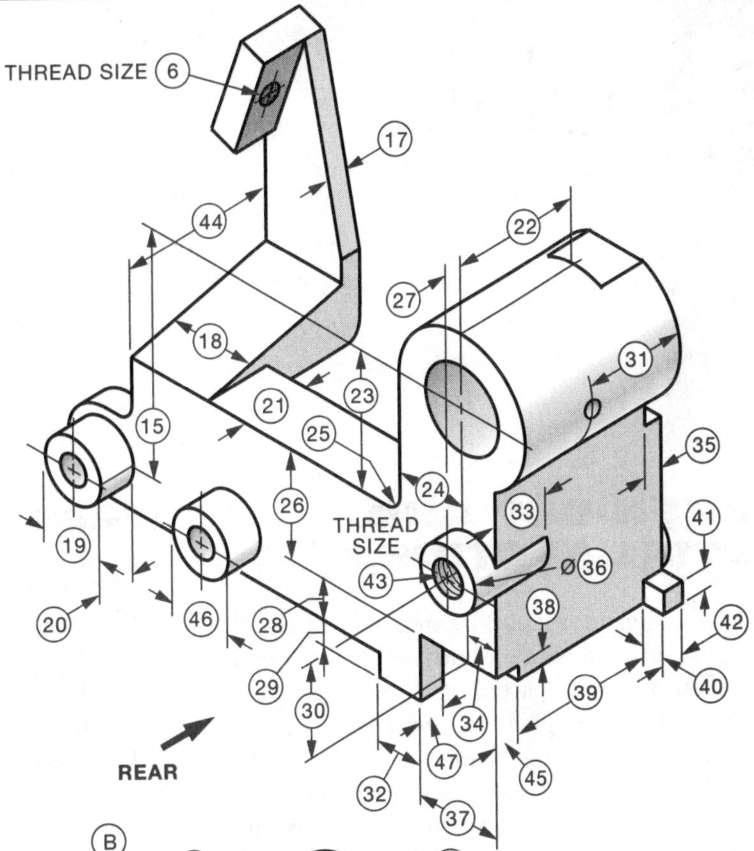
THREAD SIZE 6
THREAD SIZE 43
Ø36
REAR

NOTE: TAPPED HOLES TO BE COUNTERSUNK SLIGHTLY.

UNLESS OTHERWISE SPECIFIED:
—TOLERANCE ON DIMENSIONS ±.02
—TOLERANCE ON ANGLES ±0.5°

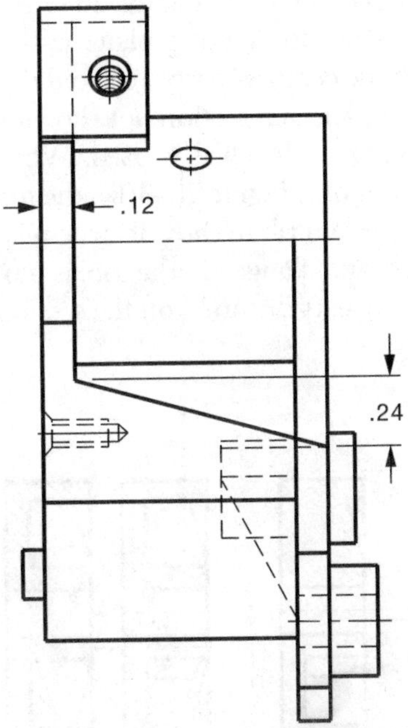
.12
.24

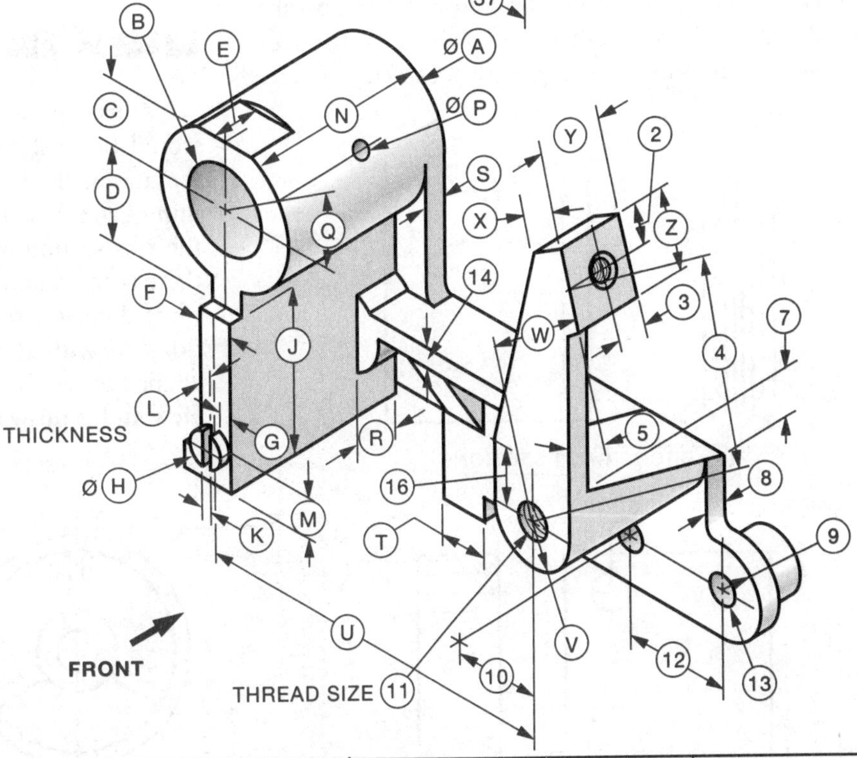
ØA
ØP
THICKNESS L
ØH
THREAD SIZE 11
FRONT

			DRAWN	DATE
	MATERIAL	ALUMINUM	CONTROL BRACKET	A-74
	SCALE	NOT TO SCALE		

28 UNIT

BROKEN-OUT AND PARTIAL SECTIONS

When certain internal and external features of an object should be shown without drawing another view, broken-out and partial sections are used, Figure 28–1. A cutting-plane line or a break line is used to indicate where the section is taken. In the front view of the following assignment, the raise block drawing A-75M, two broken-out sections are used. Although this method of showing a partial section is not commonly used, it is an accepted practice.

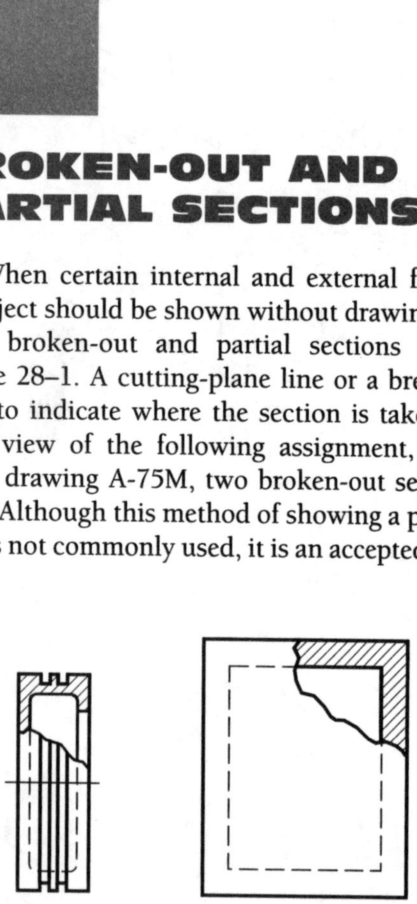

(A) BROKEN-OUT SECTIONS

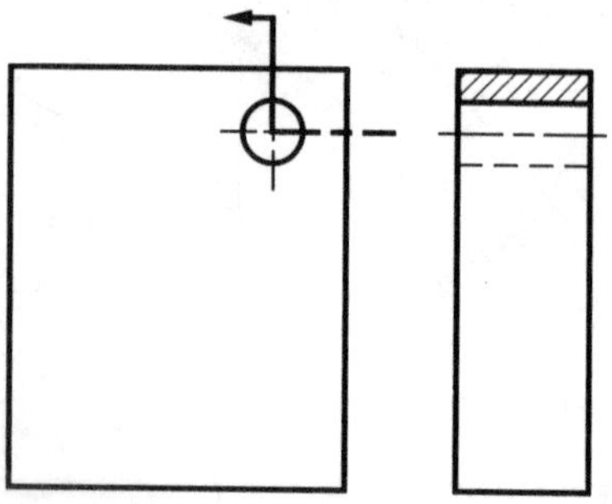

(B) PARTIAL SECTION

FIGURE 28–1 ■ Broken-out and partial sections

WEBS IN SECTION

The conventional (preferred) methods of representing a section of a part having webs or partitions are shown in Figure 28–2. These methods are preferred to drawing the section in true projection. Although the conventional methods are a violation of true projection, they are preferred over true projection because of clarity and ease in drawing.

RIBS IN SECTION

A true projection section view, Figure 28–3(A), would be misleading when the cutting plane passes longitudinally through the centre of a rib. To avoid this impression of solidity, a preferred section not showing the ribs section-lined or crosshatched is used. When there is an odd number of ribs, Figure 28–3(B), the top rib is aligned with the bottom rib to show its true relationship with the hub and flange. If the rib is not aligned or revolved, it appears distorted on the section view and is misleading.

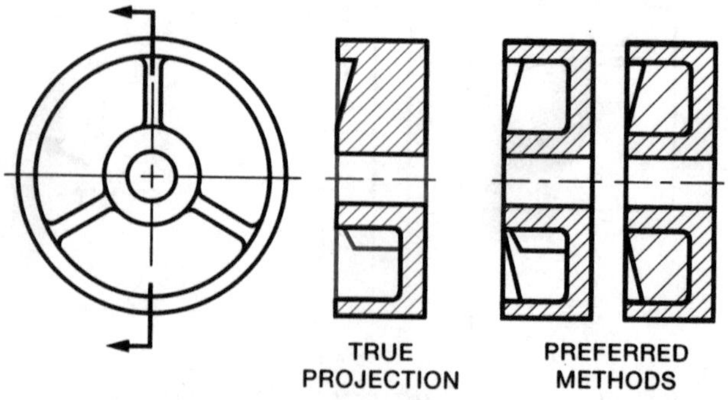

FIGURE 28–2 ■ Conventional methods of sectioning webs

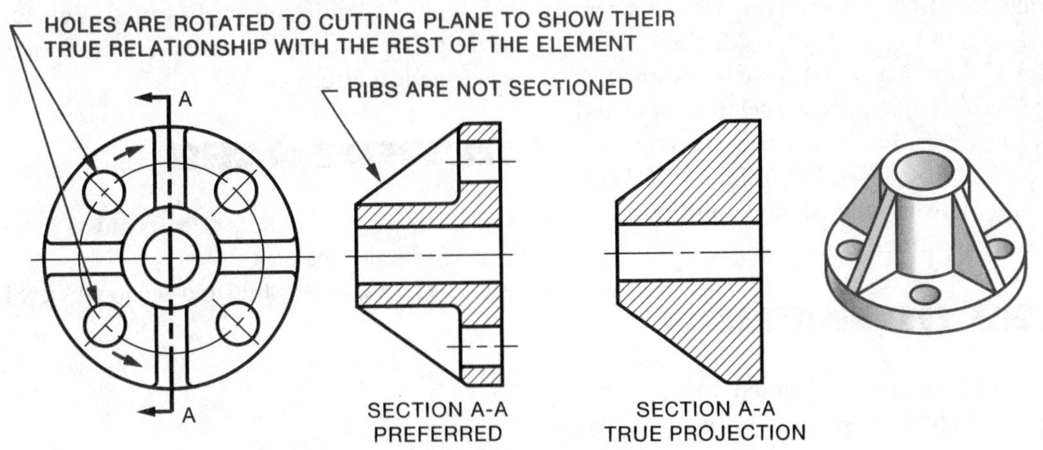
HOLES ARE ROTATED TO CUTTING PLANE TO SHOW THEIR TRUE RELATIONSHIP WITH THE REST OF THE ELEMENT
RIBS ARE NOT SECTIONED
A
A
SECTION A-A PREFERRED
SECTION A-A TRUE PROJECTION

(A) CUTTING PLANE PASSING THROUGH TWO RIBS

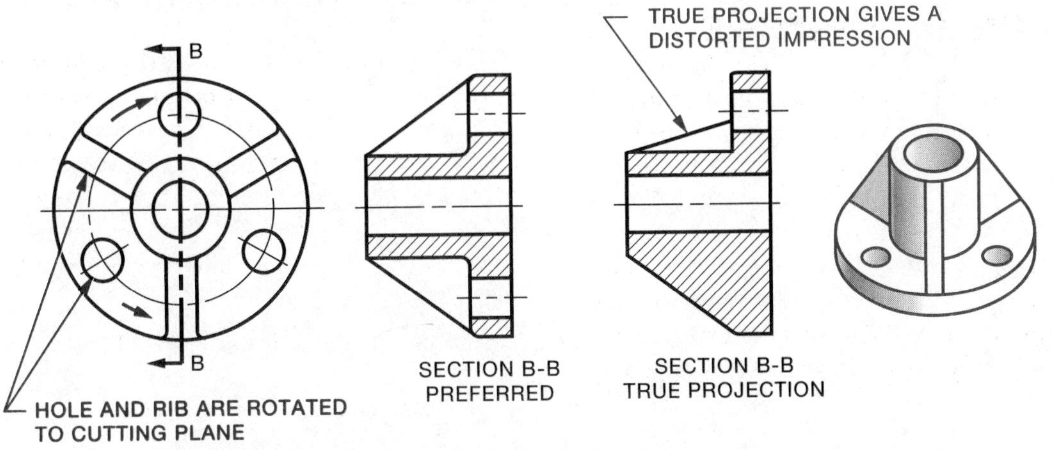
TRUE PROJECTION GIVES A DISTORTED IMPRESSION
B
B
SECTION B-B PREFERRED
SECTION B-B TRUE PROJECTION
HOLE AND RIB ARE ROTATED TO CUTTING PLANE

(B) CUTTING PLANE PASSING THROUGH ONE RIB AND ONE HOLE

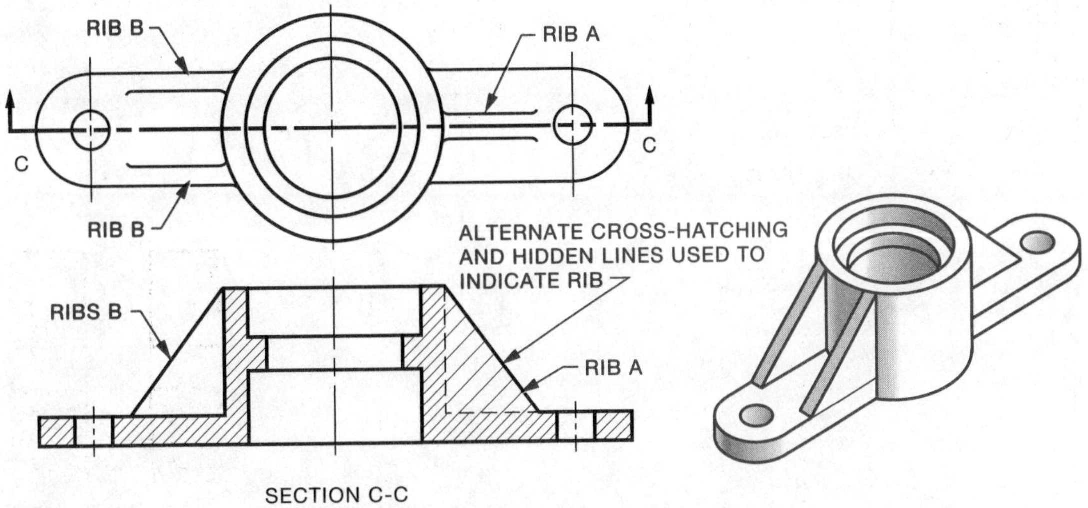
RIB B
RIB A
C
C
RIB B
ALTERNATE CROSS-HATCHING AND HIDDEN LINES USED TO INDICATE RIB
RIBS B
RIB A
SECTION C-C

(C) ALTERNATE METHOD OF SHOWING RIBS IN SECTION

FIGURE 28–3 ■ Ribs in section

An alternate method of identifying ribs in a section view is shown in Figure 28–3(C). If rib A of the base were not sectioned as previously mentioned, it would appear exactly like B in the section view and would be misleading. To distinguish between the ribs on the base, alternate section lining on the ribs is used. The line between the rib and solid portions is shown as a broken line.

SPOKES IN SECTION

Spokes in section are represented in the same manner as ribs. Figure 28–4 shows the preferred method of identifying spokes in section for aligned and unaligned designs. Note that the spokes are not sectioned in either case.

REFERENCES

CAN3-B78.1-M83 (R1990) Technical Drawings—General Principles

ASME Y14.3M-1994 Multi and Sectional View Drawings

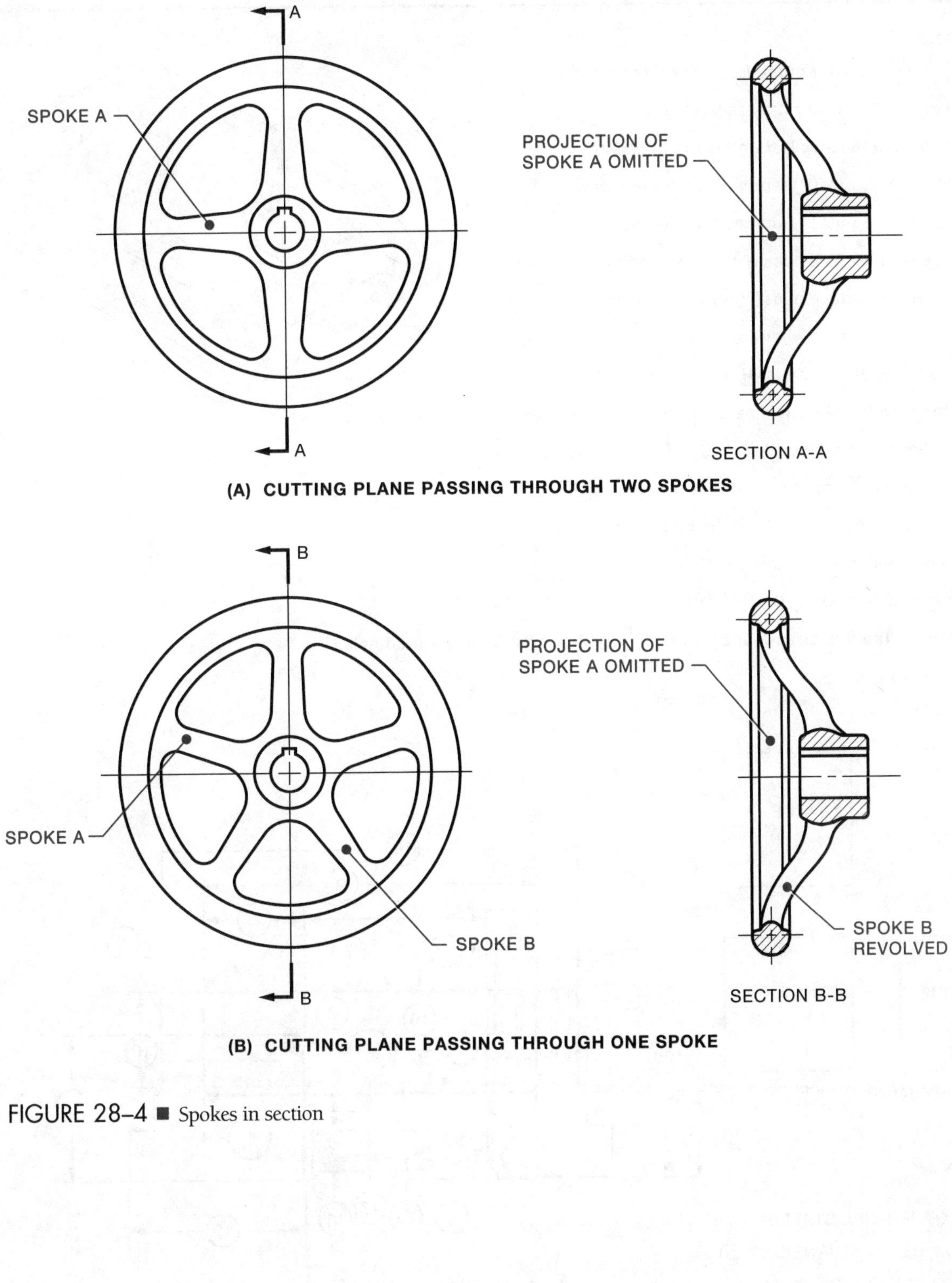
A
SPOKE A
PROJECTION OF
SPOKE A OMITTED
A
SECTION A-A
(A) CUTTING PLANE PASSING THROUGH TWO SPOKES
B
PROJECTION OF
SPOKE A OMITTED
SPOKE A
SPOKE B
SPOKE B
REVOLVED
B
SECTION B-B
(B) CUTTING PLANE PASSING THROUGH ONE SPOKE

FIGURE 28–4 ■ Spokes in section

QUESTIONS

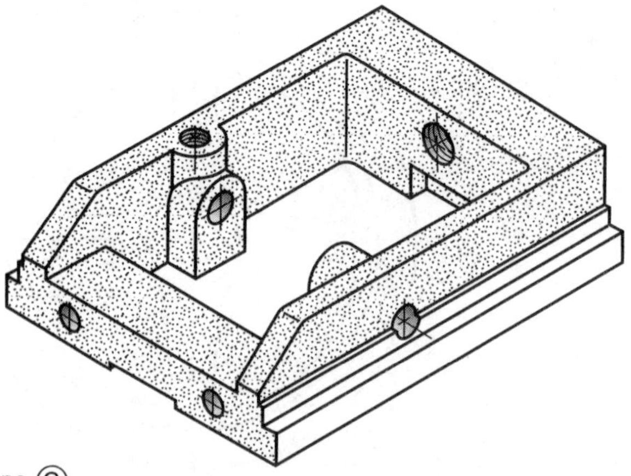

1. What is the diameter of the largest unthreaded hole?
2. What size is the smallest threaded hole?
3. What size are the smallest unthreaded holes?
4. Which surface does ⑦ represent in the top view?
5. Which surface does ① represent in the top view?
6. Which line or surface does ⑥ represent in the left view?
7. Which line or surface does Ⓥ represent in the front view?
8. What was the original width of the part?
9. By which line or surface is Ⓗ represented in the left view?
10. Locate in the left view the line or surface that is represented by line Ⓖ.
11. Which line or surface represents Ⓕ in the top view?
12. Which line represents surface Ⓙ in the left view?
13. Determine the overall depth of the raise block.
14. Determine distances Ⓐ through Ⓔ.
15. Determine distances ⑧ through ⑲.
16. What is the tap drill size required for the (A) M10 and (B) M16 threaded holes?

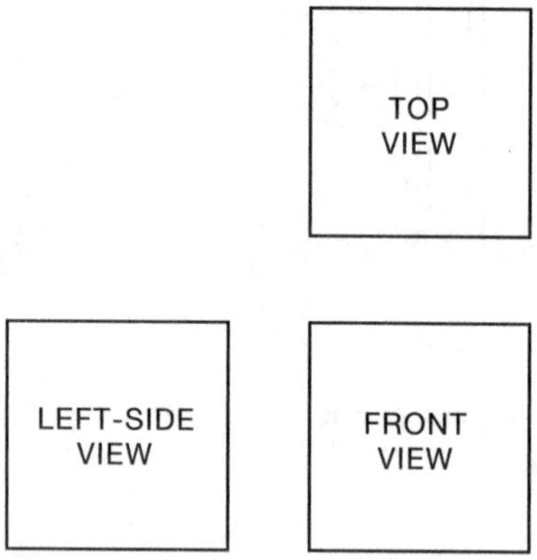

ARRANGEMENT OF VIEWS

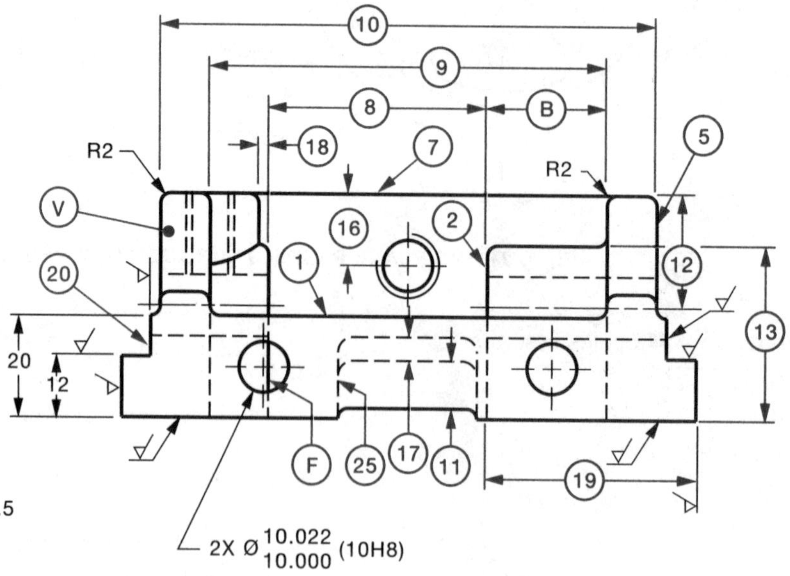

NOTE:
UNLESS OTHERWISE STATED
—TOLERANCE ON DIMENSIONS ±0.5
—TOLERANCE ON ANGLES ±0.5°
—ROUNDS AND FILLETS R3

REVISIONS	1	02-03-04	R. KERR
	166 WAS 170		

ANSWERS

1. ______	6. ______	11. ______	14. C ______	15. 10 ______	15. 15 ______
2. ______	7. ______	12. ______	D ______	11 ______	16 ______
3. ______	8. ______	13. ______	E ______	12 ______	17 ______
4. ______	9. ______	14. A ______	15. 8 ______	13 ______	18 ______
5. ______	10. ______	B ______	9 ______	14 ______	19 ______
					16. A ______
					B ______

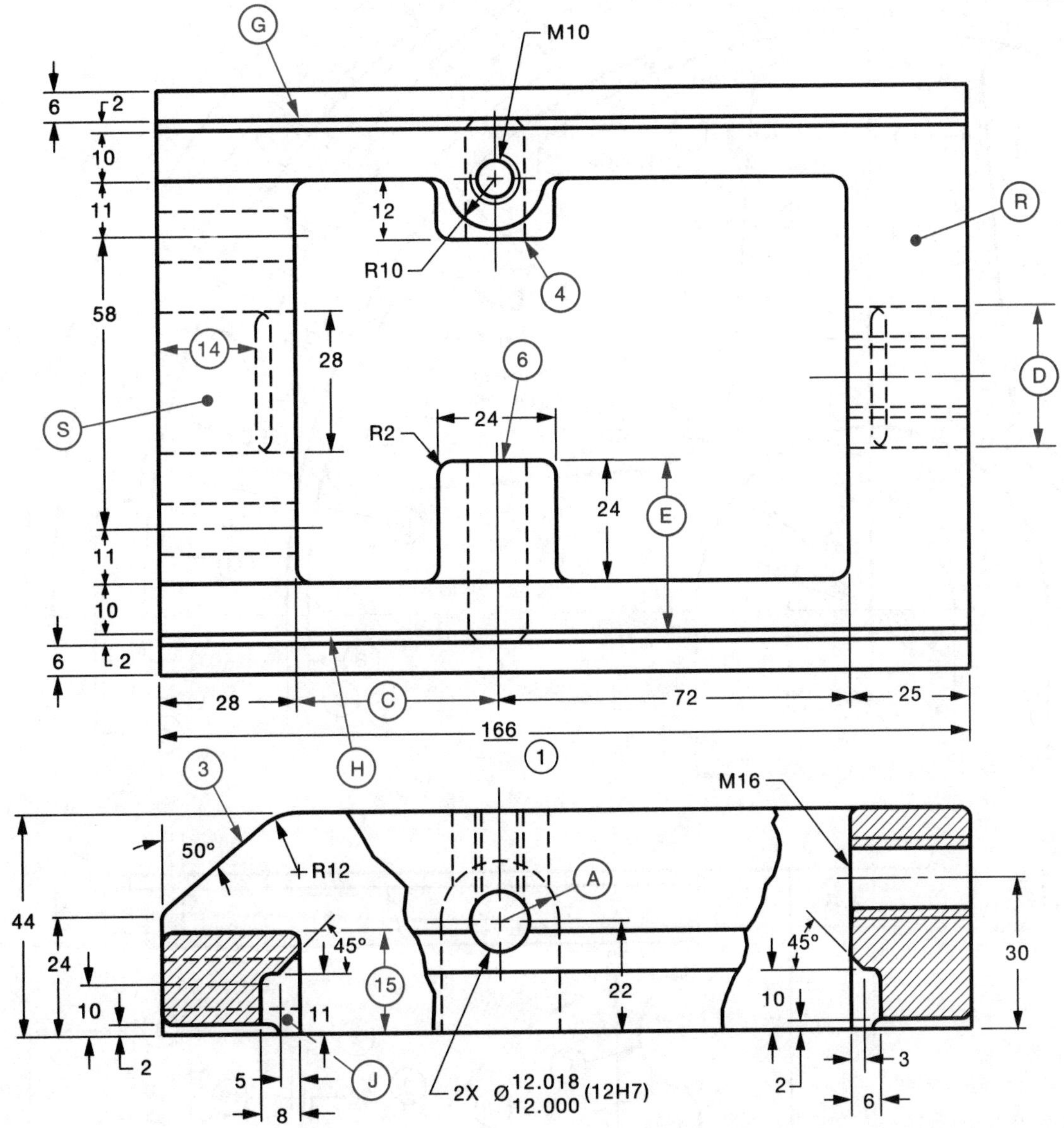

MATERIAL	GREY IRON	
SCALE		
DRAWN		DATE
	RAISE BLOCK	A-75M

METRIC
DIMENSIONS ARE IN MILLIMETRES

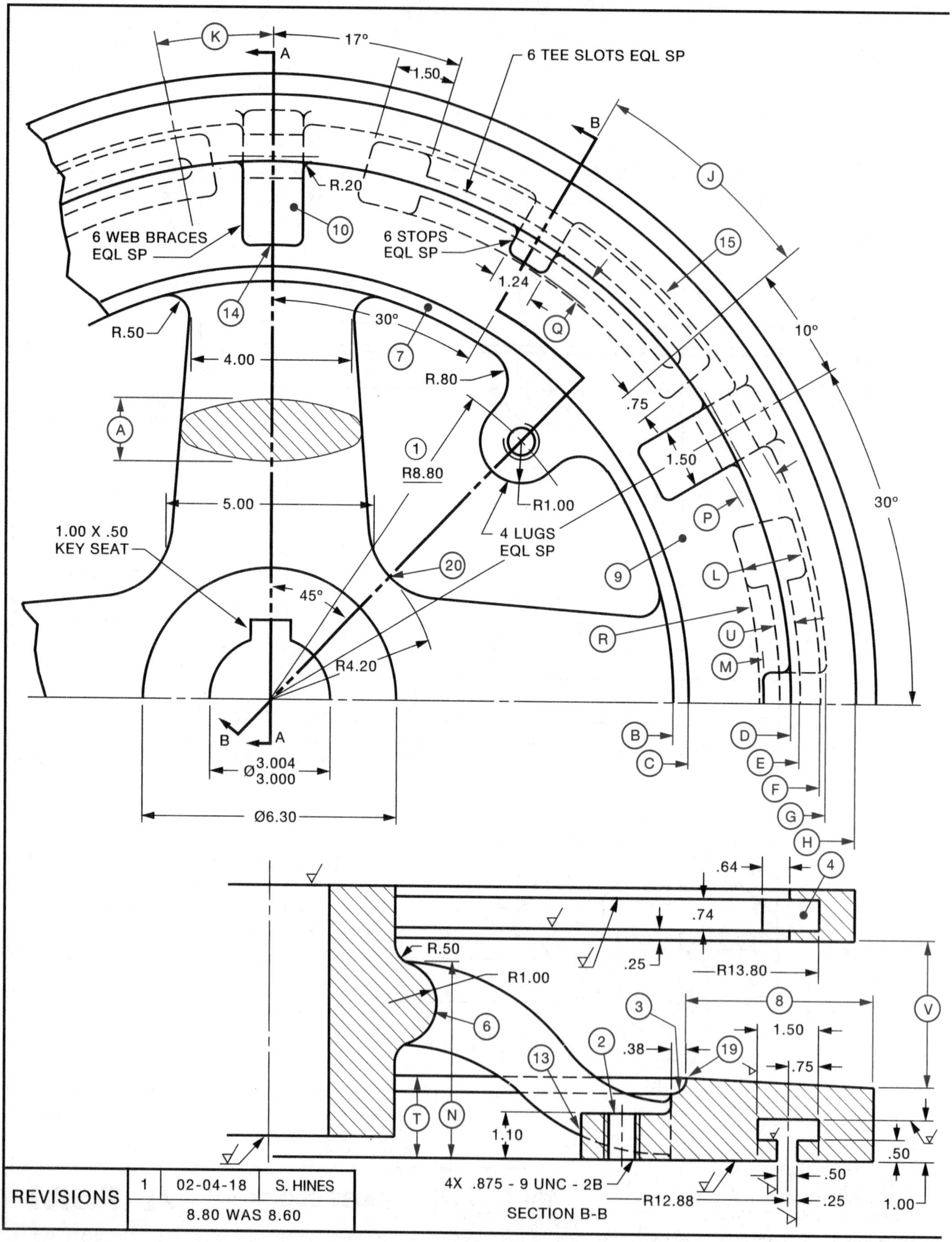

6 TEE SLOTS EQL SP
17°
1.50
R.20
6 WEB BRACES EQL SP
6 STOPS EQL SP
1.24
R.50
30°
4.00
R.80
R8.80
R1.00
4 LUGS EQL SP
5.00
1.00 X .50 KEY SEAT
45°
R4.20
Ø3.004 3.000
Ø6.30
.75
1.50
10°
30°
.64
.74
.25
R13.80
R.50
R1.00
1.50
.38
.75
1.10
4X .875 - 9 UNC - 2B
R12.88
SECTION B-B
.50
.50
.25
1.00

REVISIONS	1	02-04-18	S. HINES
	8.80 WAS 8.60		

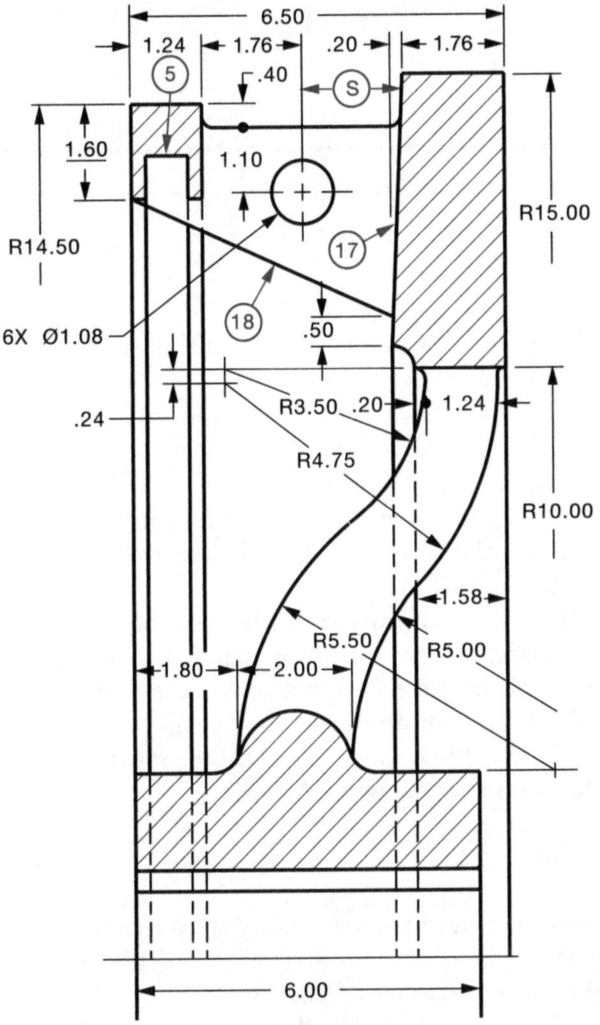

SECTION A-A

NOTE: EXCEPT WHERE OTHERWISE SPECIFIED:
—FEATURES SYMMETRICAL AROUND CENTRE POINT
—TOLERANCE ON DIMENSIONS ±.02
—TOLERANCE ON ANGLES ±0.5°

√ TO BE 125 √

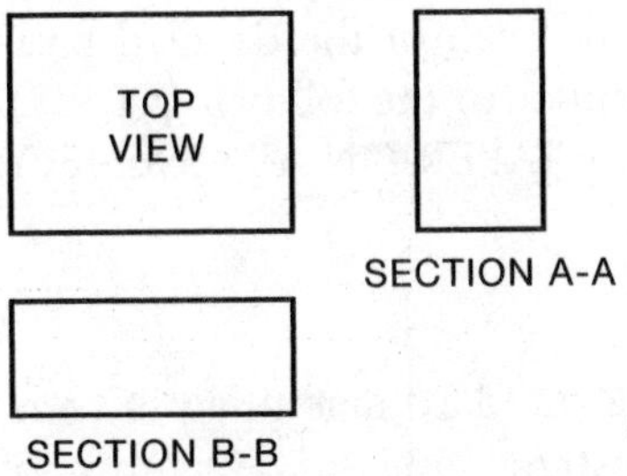

ARRANGEMENT OF VIEWS

ANSWERS

1. ______
2. ______
3. ______
4. ______
5. ______
6. ______
7. ______
8. ______
9. ______
10. ______
11. ______
12. ______
13. ______
14. ______
15. ______
16. ______
17. ______
18. ______
19. ______
20. L ______
N ______
P ______
Q ______
S ______
T ______
U ______
V ______
21. B ______
C ______
D ______
E ______
F ______
G ______
H ______
M ______
R ______
22. ______

QUESTIONS

1. What surface texture is required on the machined surfaces?
2. What is thickness (A), assuming the revolved section was taken at the middle of the arm?
3. What is the total quantity of feature (4)?
4. Locate surface (5) in the top view.
5. Locate point (6) in the top view.
6. How far is line (14) from the centre point?
7. How far is surface (13) from the centre point?
8. Which point on section B-B represents radius (C)?
9. Which line on section B-B represents surface (7)?
10. What is the radius of surface (3)?
11. Determine distance (8).
12. Which line on section A-A represents surface (10)?
13. Which surface in the top view represents line (17)?
14. What is the angle at (J)?
15. What is the angle at (K)?
16. What is the thickness of the web brace?
17. What would be the length of key used between the shaft and coil frame?
18. What is the thickness of the lugs?
19. What is the distance from the Ø1.00 hole to the centre of the coil frame?
20. Determine distances (L), (N), (P), (Q), (S), (T), (U), and (V).
21. Determine radii (B), (C), (D), (E), (F), (G), (H), (M), and (R).
22. What type of sectional view is used to show the shape of the spokes?

MATERIAL GREY IRON	
SCALE	
DRAWN	DATE
COIL FRAME	**A-76**

29 UNIT

PIN FASTENERS

Pin fasteners offer an inexpensive and effective approach to assembly where loading is primarily in shear. They can be divided into two groups: semipermanent and quick release.

Semipermanent pin fasteners require application of pressure or the aid of tools for installation or removal. Representative types include machine pins (dowel, straight, taper, clevis, and cotter pins) and radial locking pins (grooved surface and spring).

Quick release fasteners are more elaborate self-contained pins that are used for rapid manual assembly or disassembly. They use a form of spring-loaded mechanism to provide a locking action in assembly.

Machine Pins

Five types of machine pins are commonly used today: ground dowel pins; commercial straight pins; taper pins; clevis pins; and standard cotter pins, Figure 29–1.

Dowel Pins

Dowel pins or small straight pins have many uses. They are used to hold parts in alignment and to guide parts into desired positions. Dowel pins are most commonly used for the alignment of parts that are fastened with screws or bolts and must be accurately fitted together.

When two pieces are to be fitted together, as in the case of the part in Figure 29–2, one method of alignment is to clamp the two pieces in the desired location, drill and ream the dowel holes, insert the dowel pins, and then drill and tap for the screw holes.

Drill jigs are frequently used when production in the interchangeability of parts is required or when the nature of the piece does not permit the transfer of the dowelled holes from one piece to the other. A drill jig, Figure 29–3, was used in drilling the dowel holes for the spider (drawing A-77M).

Taper Pins

Holes for taper pins are usually sized by reaming. A through hole is formed by step drills and straight fluted reamers. The present trend is toward the use of helically fluted taper reamers, which provide more accurate sizing and require only a pilot hole the size of the small end of the taper pin. The pin is usually driven into the hole until it is fully seated. The taper of the pin aids hole alignment in assembly.

A tapered hole in a hub and a shaft is shown in Figure 29–4. If the hub and shaft are drilled and reamed separately, a misalignment might occur as shown in Figure 29–5. To prevent misalignment, the hub and shaft should be drilled at the same time as the parts are assembled. Each of the detailed parts should carry a note similar to the following: DRILL AND REAM FOR NO. 1 TAPER PIN AT ASSEMBLY.

Cotter Pins

The cotter pin is a standard machine pin commonly used as a fastener in the assembly of machine parts where great accuracy is not

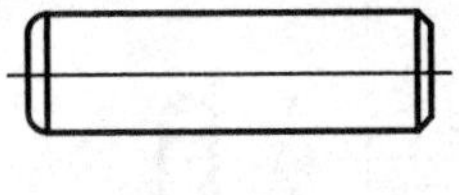	HARDENED AND GROUND DOWEL PIN: Standardized in nominal diameters ranging from .125" to .875". Use for 1. Holding laminated sections together with surfaces either drawn up tightly or separated in some fixed relationship. 2. Fastening machine parts where accuracy of alignment is a primary requirement. 3. Locking components on shafts, in the form of transverse pin key.
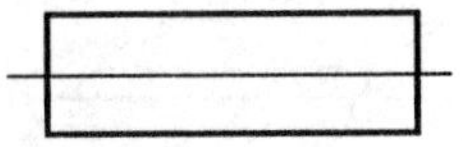	COMMERCIAL STRAIGHT PIN: Standardized in nominal diameters ranging from .188" to .500". Used in a similar manner as a ground dowel pin.
	TAPER PIN: Standard pins have a taper of 1:48 measured on the diameter. Basic dimension is the diameter of the large end. Used for light-duty service in the attachment of wheels, levers, and similar components to shafts. Torque capacity is determined on the basis of double shear, using the average diameter along the tapered section in the shaft for area calculations.
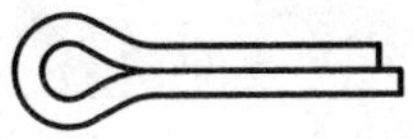	COTTER PIN: Eighteen sizes have been standardized on nominal diameters ranging from .031" to .500". Locking device for other fasteners. Used with a castle or slotted nut on bolt, screw, or studs, it provides a convenient, low-cost locknut assembly. Holds standard clevis pins in place. Can be used with or without a plain washer as an artificial shoulder to lock parts in position on shafts.
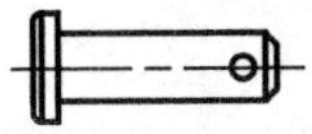	CLEVIS PIN: Standard nominal diameters for clevis pins range from .188" to 1.000". Basic function of the clevis pin is to connect mating yoke, or fork, and eye members in knuckle-joint assemblies. Held in place by a small cotter pin or other fastener means it provides a mobile joint construction that can be readily disconnected for adjustment or maintenance.

FIGURE 29–1 ■ Machine pins

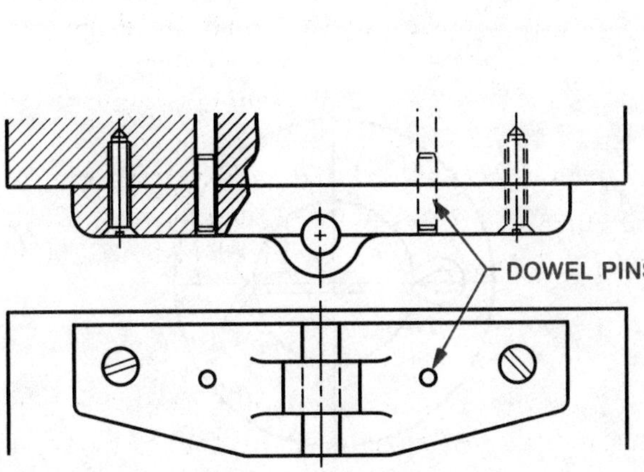

FIGURE 29–2 ■ Aligning parts with dowel pins

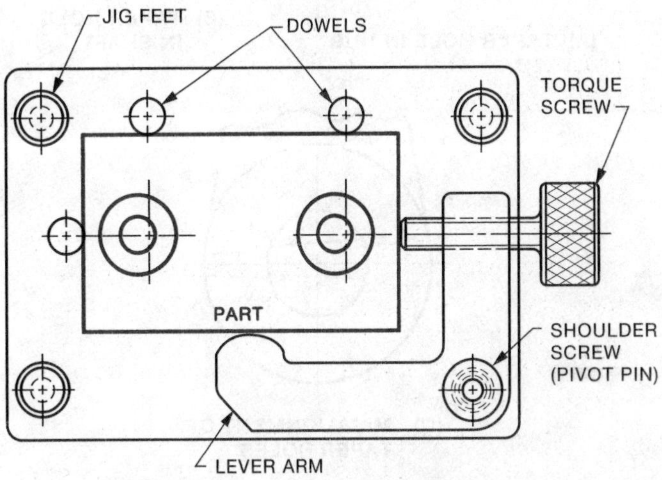

FIGURE 29–3 ■ Dowel pins used to align part during drillings

required, Figure 29–6. There is no standard way to represent cotter pins in assembly drawings. The method of representation shown in Figure 29–7 is, however, commonly used to indicate cotter pins.

Radial-Locking Pins

Low cost, ease of assembly, and high resistance to vibration and impact loads are common attributes of this group of commercial pin devices designed primarily for semipermanent fastening service. Two

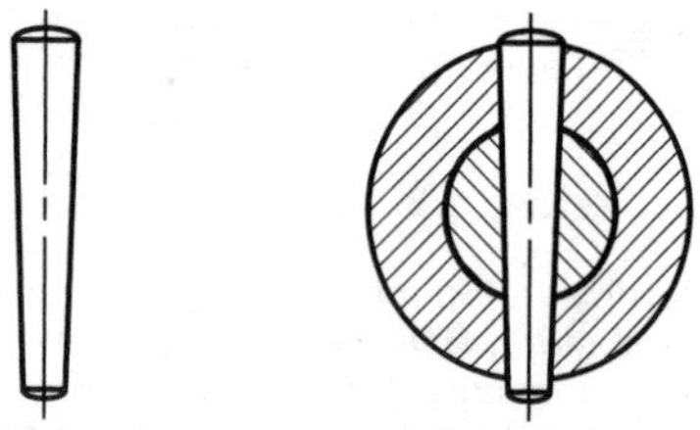

(A) STANDARD TAPER PIN **(B) PARTS HELD WITH TAPER PIN**

FIGURE 29–4 ■ Taper pin application

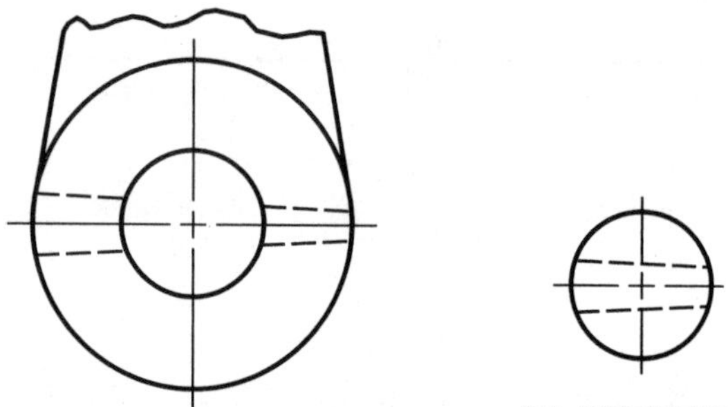

(A) TAPER HOLE IN HUB **(B) TAPER HOLE IN SHAFT**

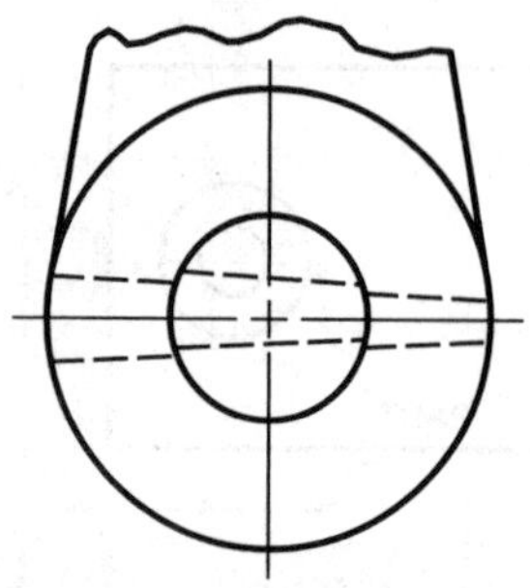

(C) MISALIGNMENT OF TAPER HOLES

FIGURE 29–5 ■ Possibility of hole misalignment if holes are not drilled at assembly

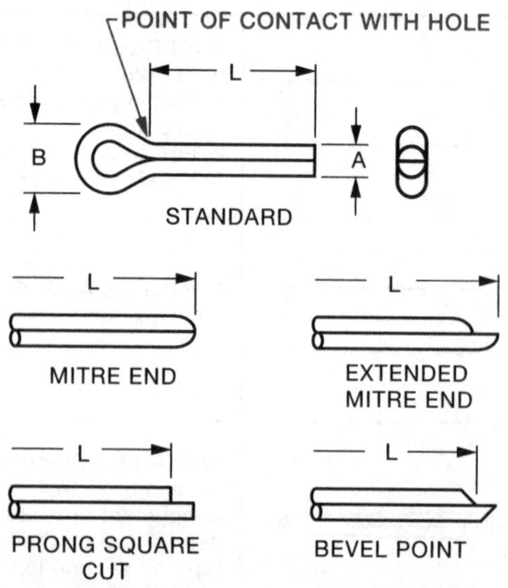
POINT OF CONTACT WITH HOLE
L
B
A
STANDARD
L
MITRE END
L
EXTENDED MITRE END
L
PRONG SQUARE CUT
L
BEVEL POINT

NOMINAL THREAD SIZE in.	(mm)	NOMINAL COTTER PIN SIZE in.	(mm)	COTTER PIN HOLE in.	(mm)	END CLEARANCE* in.	(mm)
.250	(6)	.062	(1.5)	.078	(1.9)	.12	(3)
.312	(8)	.078	(2)	.094	(2.4)	.12	(3)
.375	(10)	.094	(2.5)	.109	(2.8)	.14	(4)
.500	(12)	.125	(3)	.141	(3.4)	.18	(5)
.625	(14)	.156	(3)	.172	(3.4)	.25	(5)
.750	(20)	.156	(4)	.172	(4.5)	.25	(7)
1.000	(24)	.188	(5)	.203	(5.6)	.31	(8)
1.125	(27)	.188	(5)	.203	(5.6)	.39	(8)
1.250	(30)	.219	(6)	.234	(6.3)	.44	(10)
1.375	(36)	.219	(6)	.234	(6.3)	.44	(11)
1.500	(42)	.250	(6)	.266	(6.3)	.50	(12)
1.750	(48)	.312	(8)	.312	(8.5)	.55	(14)

*DISTANCE FROM EXTREME POINT OF BOLT OR SCREW TO CENTRE OF COTTER PIN HOLE.

FIGURE 29–6 ■ Cotter pin data

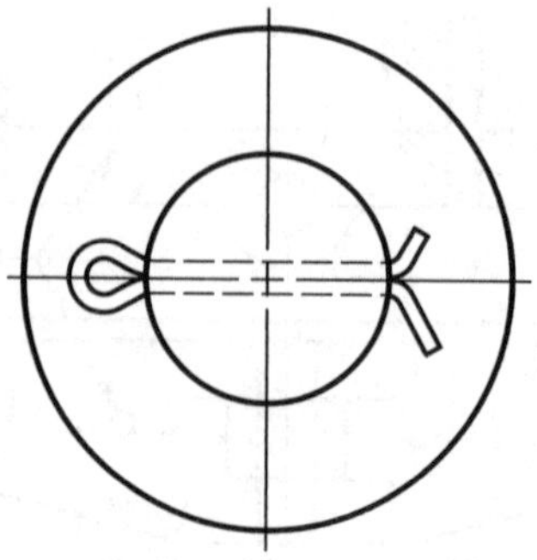

FIGURE 29–7 ■ Cotter pin in an assembly drawing

basic pin forms are used: solid with grooved surfaces, and hollow spring pins, which may be either slotted or spiral wrapped, Figure 29–8. In assembly, radial forces produced by elastic action at the pin surface develop a secure, frictional-locking grip against the hole wall. These pins are reusable and can be removed and reassembled many times without appreciable loss of fastening effectiveness. Live spring action at the pin surface also prevents loosening under shock and vibration loads. The need for accurate sizing of holes is reduced because the pins accommodate variations.

Solid Pins with Grooved Surfaces

The locking action of groove pins is provided by parallel, longitudinal grooves uniformly spaced around the pin surface. Rolled or pressed into solid pin stock, the grooves expand the effective diameter of the pin. When the pin is driven into a drilled hole corresponding in size to the nominal pin diameter, elastic deformation of the raised groove edges produces a secure interference fit with the hole wall. Figure 29–8 shows the six standardized constructions of grooved pins.

(A) SOLID WITH GROOVED SURFACES	
 TYPE A	Full-length grooves. Used for general-purpose fastening.
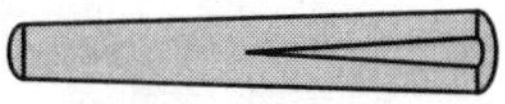 TYPE B	Grooves extend half length of the pin. Used as a hinge or linkage "bolt," but also can be employed for other functions in through-drilled holes where a locking fit over only part of the pin length is required.
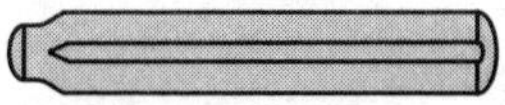 TYPE C	Full-length grooves with pilot section at one end to facilitate assembly. Expanded dimension of this pin is held to a maximum over the full-grooved length to provide uniform locking action. It is recommended for applications subject to severe vibration or shock loads where maximum locking effect is required.
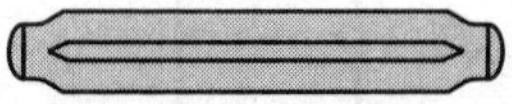 TYPE D	Full-length grooves with pilot section at both ends for hopper feeding, Same as Type C.
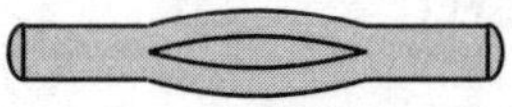 TYPE E	Half-length groove section centred along the pin surface. Used as a cotter pin or in similar functions where an artificial shoulder or a locking fit over the centre portion of the pin is required.
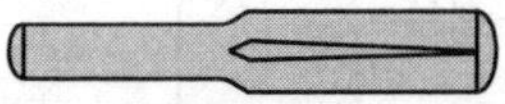 TYPE F	Reverse tapered grooves extend half the pin length. It is the counterpart of the Type B pin for assembly in blind holes.
(B) HOLLOW SPRING PINS	
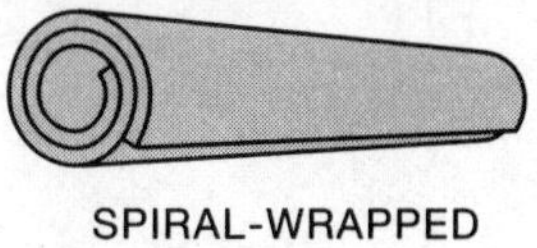 SPIRAL-WRAPPED	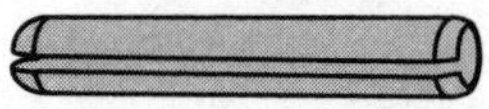 SLOTTED-TUBULAR

FIGURE 29–8 ■ Radial locking pins

Hollow Spring Pins

Spiral-wrapped and slotted-tubular pin forms are made to controlled diameters greater than the holes into which they are pressed. Compressed when driven into the hole, the pins exert spring pressure against the hole wall along their entire engaged length to develop a strong locking action.

SECTION THROUGH SHAFTS, PINS, AND KEYS

Shafts, bolts, nuts, rods, rivets, keys, pins, and similar solid parts, the axes of which lie on the cutting plane, are sectioned only when a broken-out section of the shaft is used to clearly indicate the key, keyseat, and pin, as shown in Figure 29–9.

ARRANGEMENT OF VIEWS OF DRAWING A-77M

Parts that are to be fitted over shafts as a single unit are sometimes made in two or more pieces. This is done for ease in assembly and replacement on the main structure of a machine rather than for ease in manufacture. Drawing A-77M shows two parts that are bolted and dowelled together to form one unit.

The arrangement of views of the spider is illustrated by the diagrams in Figure 29–10. By comparing this figure with the drawing of the spider, note that the two halves together represent the top view. The right view is a full section of each half (**A** and **B**). The front view is a drawing of the front of part **A** only.

Although the front and side views are incomplete, the manner in which they are drawn and the arrangement of the views satisfies the demand for clearness and economy in time and space.

REFERENCES

Machine Design, Fasteners Reference Issue, Nov. 1981
ASME B18.8.2-1995 Taper Pins, Dowel Pins, Straight Pins, Grooved Pins and Spring Pins

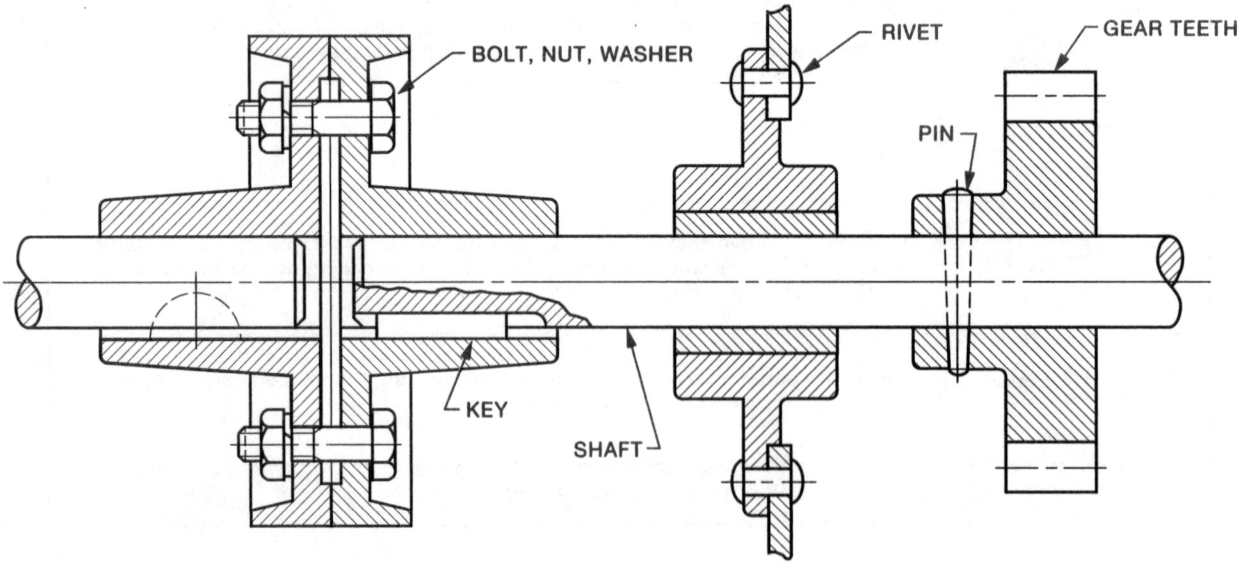

FIGURE 29–9 ■ Parts that are not section lined in section drawings

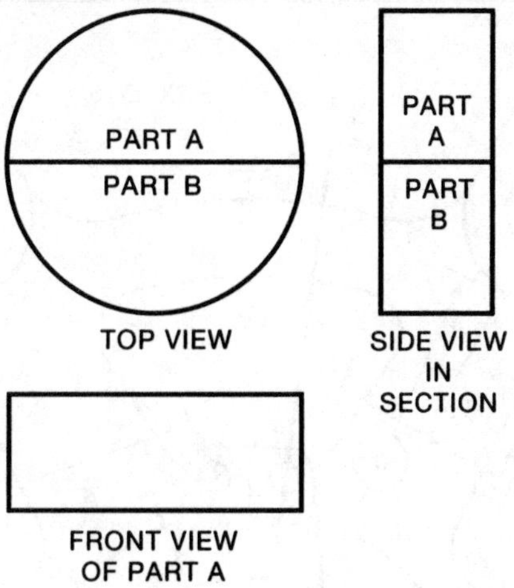
PART A
PART B
TOP VIEW
PART A
PART B
SIDE VIEW IN SECTION
FRONT VIEW OF PART A

FIGURE 29–10 ■ Arrangement of views for spider, drawing A-77M

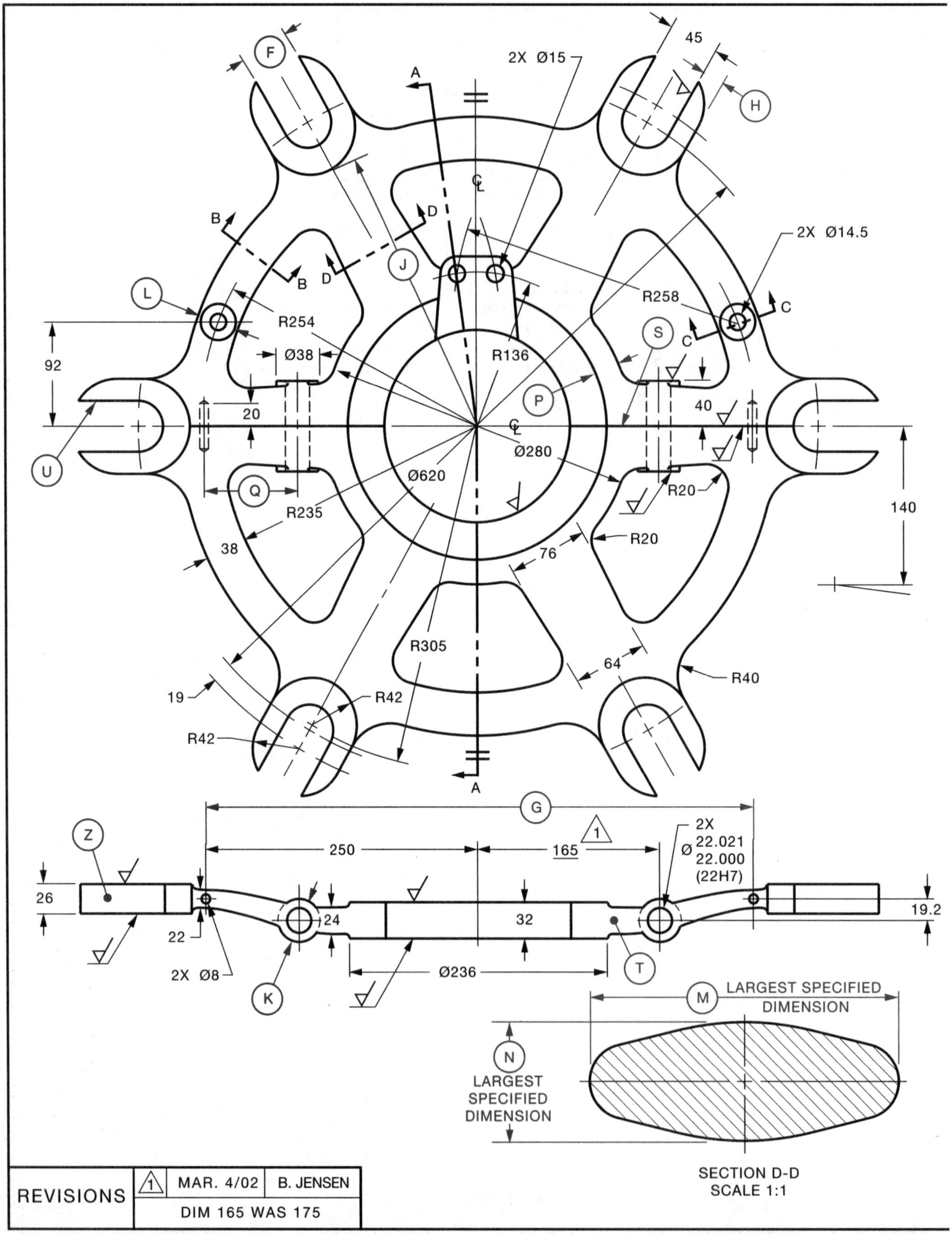
2X Ø15
45
F
H
A
B
D
J
L
2X Ø14.5
R258
C
S
R254
Ø38
R136
92
20
P
40
U
Q
Ø280
R235
Ø620
R20
140
38
76
R20
R305
64
R40
19
R42
R42
A
G
Z
250
165
2X
Ø 22.021
22.000
(22H7)
26
24
32
19.2
22
2X Ø8
Ø236
T
K
M
LARGEST SPECIFIED DIMENSION
N
LARGEST SPECIFIED DIMENSION
SECTION D-D
SCALE 1:1
REVISIONS
1
MAR. 4/02
B. JENSEN
DIM 165 WAS 175

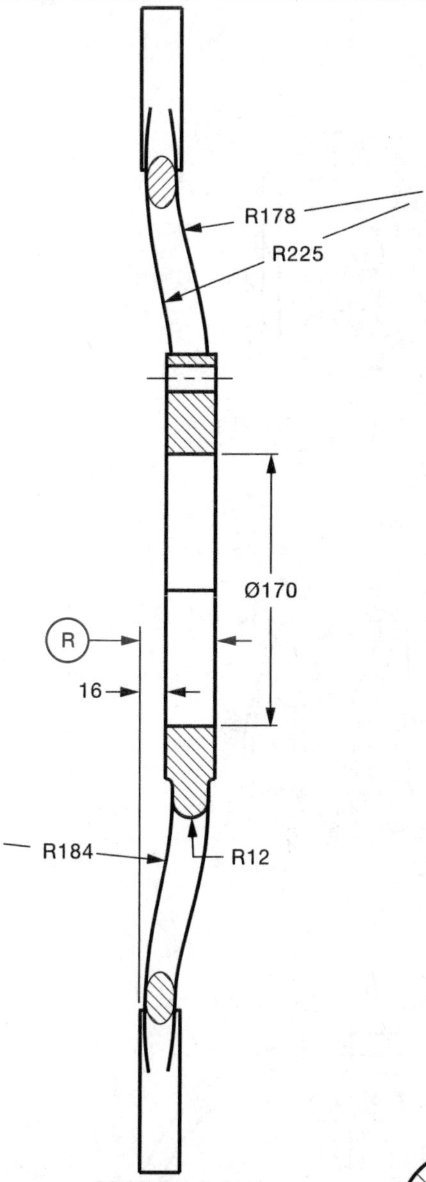
R178
R225
Ø170
R
16
R184
R12

SECTION A-A

QUESTIONS

1. How far were the Ø22 holes moved?
2. What type of projection does the ISO projection symbol (E) indicate?
3. How many different size scales were used to make the drawing?
4. Locate surface (T) in the top view.
5. Locate surface (Z) in the top view.
6. What is the approximate outside diameter of the spider?
7. What will be the rough dimension of casting at (F), assuming that 1.5 mm have been added for each surface to be finished?
8. What would be used to position both halves of the spider together before bolting? What is their size?
9. What size bolts would be used to fasten the spider together?
10. Calculate distances (G), (H), (J), (K), (L), (M), (N), (P), (Q), and (R).
11. With reference to the scales used on the drawings, what percentage larger are the removed sections over the main drawings?

ANSWERS

1. ______
2. ______
3. ______
4. ______
5. ______
6. ______
7. ______
8. ______
9. ______
10. G ______
H ______
J ______
K ______
L ______
M ______
N ______
P ______
Q ______
R ______
11. ______

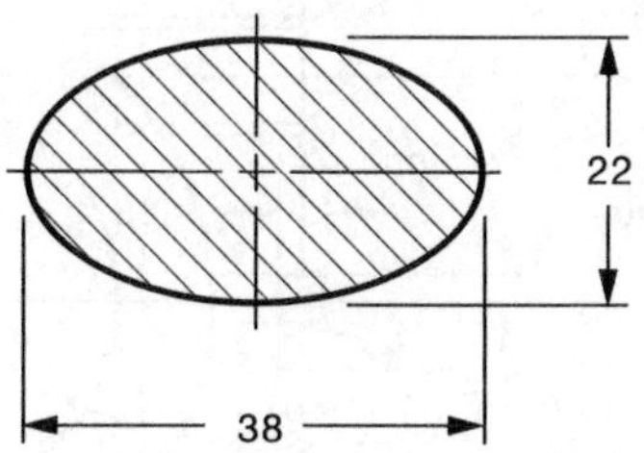
22
38

SECTION B-B
SCALE 1:1

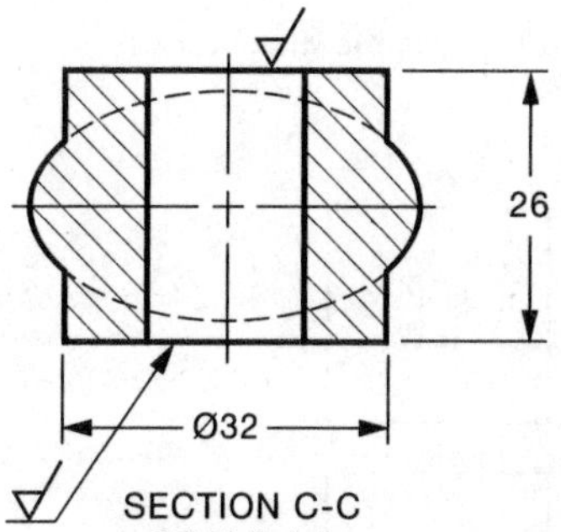
26
Ø32

SECTION C-C
SCALE 1:1

METRIC
DIMENSIONS ARE IN MILLIMETRES

NOTE:
—TOLERANCE ON DIMENSIONS ±0.5
—TOLERANCE ON ANGLES ±0.5°
—√ TO BE 1.6√

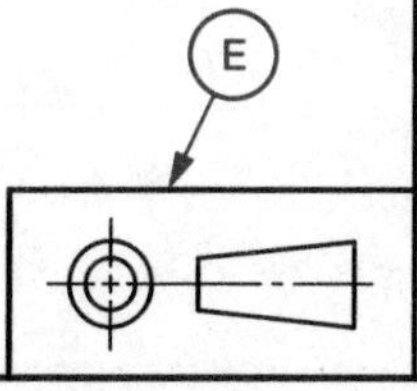
E

MATERIAL	GREY IRON		
SCALE	1:5 EXCEPT WHERE NOTED		
DRAWN		DATE	
SPIDER		**A-77M**	

QUESTIONS

1. Which views are shown?
2. How many surfaces are to be finished?
3. How many scraped surfaces are indicated?
4. How many holes are to be tapped?
5. What is the purpose of tapped hole (R)?
6. Which surface is (3) in the left-side view?
7. Which surface is (2) in the left-side view?
8. Which surface is (4) in the front view?
9. Which surface is (14) in the left-side view?
10. Which surface in the top view and front view is (9)?
11. Which surface in the top view and front view is (8)?
12. Which surface is (12) in the top view?
13. What is the name of part (V)?
14. What is the purpose of part (V)?
15. What do dotted lines at (W) represent?
16. Which surface is line (6) in the front view?
17. Which top view line indicates point (Z)?
18. What is the depth of the tapped hole at (X)?
19. Which edges or surfaces in the left and front views does line (T) represent?
20. What is the diameter of tap drill (Y)? (See Table 6 of the Appendix.)
21. Determine dimensions or operations at (A) to (Q), and (20) to (52).
22. What is the largest permissible diameter of the largest hole?

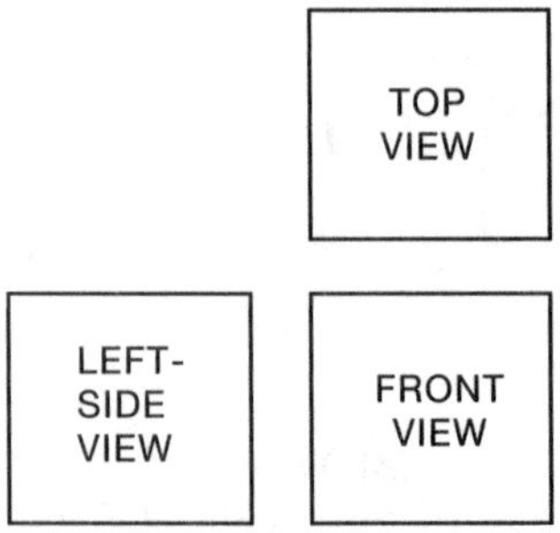

TOP VIEW
LEFT-SIDE VIEW
FRONT VIEW

ARRANGEMENT OF VIEWS

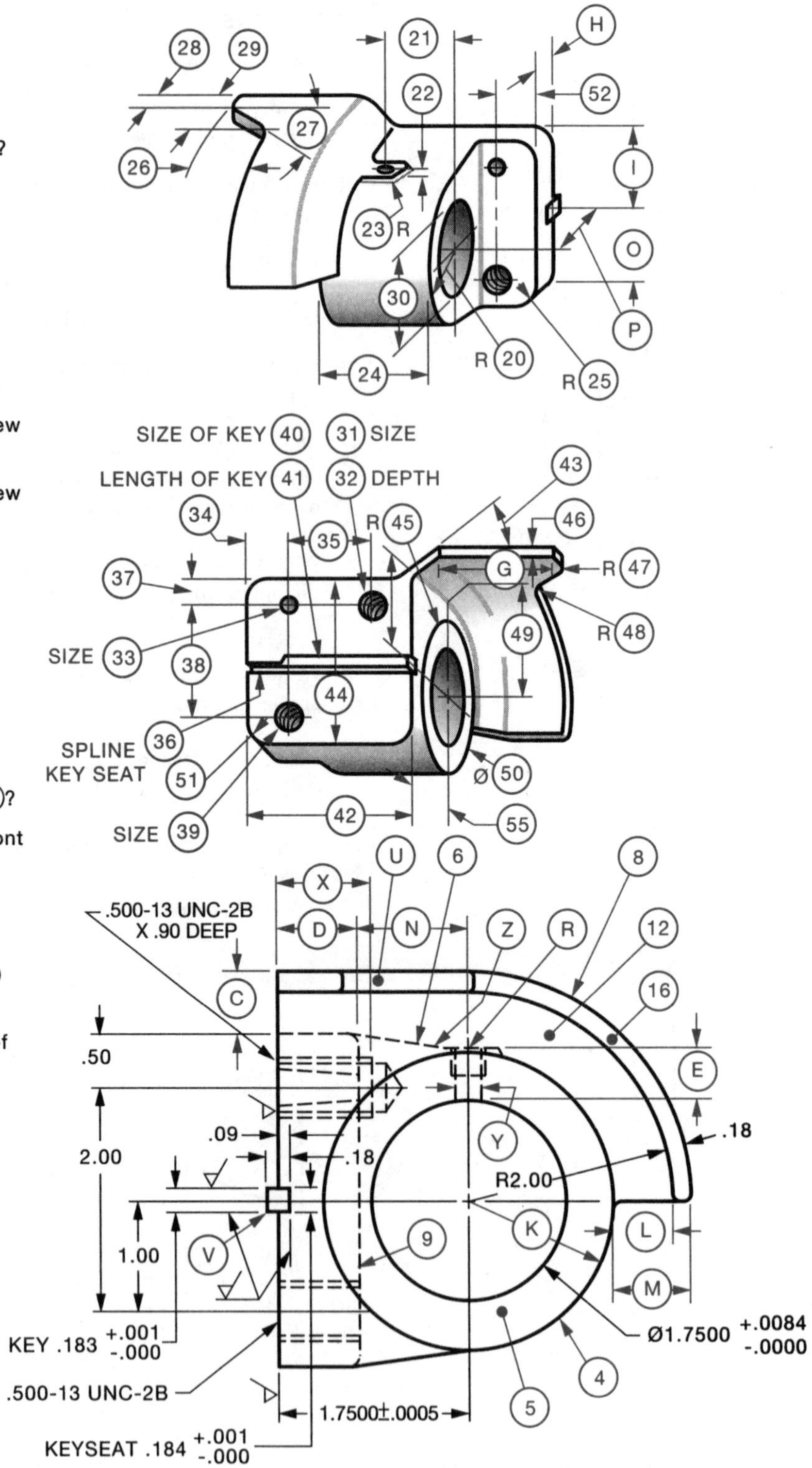

SIZE OF KEY
LENGTH OF KEY
SIZE
DEPTH
SIZE
SPLINE KEY SEAT
SIZE
.500-13 UNC-2B X .90 DEEP
.50
2.00
.09
.18
.18
R2.00
1.00
KEY .183 +.001 -.000
.500-13 UNC-2B
1.7500±.0005
KEYSEAT .184 +.001 -.000
Ø1.7500 +.0084 -.0000

NOTE: UNLESS OTHERWISE SPECIFIED:
—TOLERANCE ON DIMENSIONS ±.02
—TOLERANCE ON ANGLES ±0.5°

REVISIONS	1		

ANSWERS

1. ______	4. ______	9. ______	12. ______	17. ______	21. A ______	21. 30 ______
______	5. ______	10. T.V. ______	13. ______	18. ______	B ______	31 ______
______	6. ______	F.V. ______	14. ______	19. F.V. ______	C ______	32 ______
2. ______	7. ______	11. T.V. ______	15. ______	L.V. ______	D ______	33 ______
3. ______	8. ______	F.V. ______	16. ______	20. ______	E ______	34 ______
					F ______	35 ______
					G ______	36 ______
					H ______	37 ______
					I ______	38 ______
					J ______	39 ______
					K ______	40 ______
					L ______	41 ______
					M ______	42 ______
					N ______	43 ______
					O ______	44 ______
					P ______	45 ______
					Q ______	46 ______
					20 ______	47 ______
					21 ______	48 ______
					22 ______	49 ______
					23 ______	50 ______
					24 ______	51 ______
					25 ______	52 ______
					26 ______	22. ______
					27 ______	
					28 ______	
					29 ______	

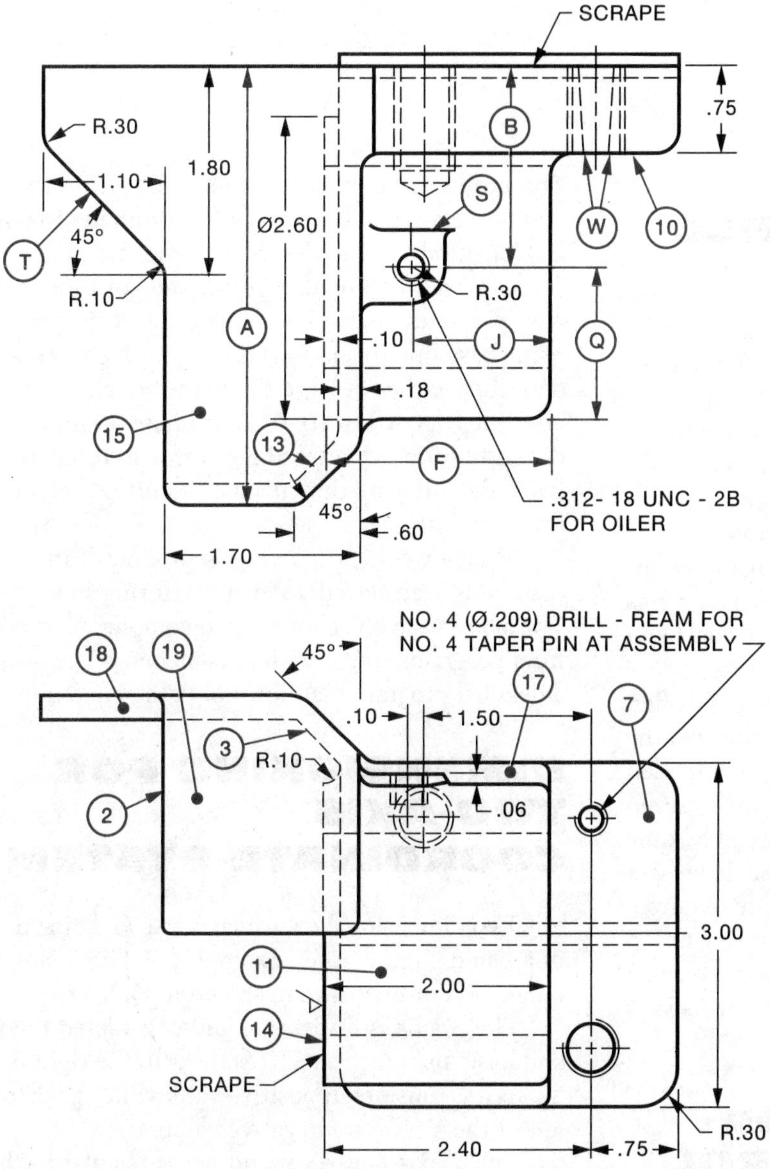
SCRAPE
R.30
1.10
1.80
.75
B
T
45°
Ø2.60
S
W
10
R.10
R.30
A
.10
J
Q
.18
15
13
F
45°
.312- 18 UNC - 2B
FOR OILER
.60
1.70
NO. 4 (Ø.209) DRILL - REAM FOR
NO. 4 TAPER PIN AT ASSEMBLY
18
19
45°
17
7
.10
1.50
3
R.10
2
.06
3.00
11
2.00
14
SCRAPE
R.30
2.40
.75

NOTE: FINISH AND SCRAPE SURFACE BEFORE CUTTING SPLINE KEY SEAT.

MATERIAL	GREY IRON	
SCALE	NOT TO SCALE	
DRAWN		DATE
	HOOD	**A-78**

30 UNIT

DRAWINGS FOR NUMERICAL CONTROL

Numerical control (NC) is a means of automatically directing some or all of the functions of a machine from instructions. The instructions are normally stored on tape and are fed to the controller through a tape reader. The controller interprets the coded instructions and directs the machine through the required operations.

It has been established that because of the consistent high accuracy of numerically controlled machines, and because human error has been almost entirely eliminated, scrap has been considerably reduced.

Another area where numerically controlled machines are better is in the quality or accuracy of the work. In most cases, a numerically controlled machine can produce parts more accurately at no additional cost, resulting in reduced assembly time and better interchangeability of parts. This latter fact is especially important when spare parts are required.

Computer-aided design and computer-aided manufacturing techniques are now widely used in conjunction with numerical control processes in industry.

DIMENSIONING FOR NUMERICAL CONTROL

Common guidelines have been established for dimensioning for numerical control that enable dimensioning and tolerancing practices to be used effectively for both NC and conventional fabrication. The numerical control concept is based on the system of rectangular or Cartesian coordinates in which any position can be described in terms of distance from an origin point along either two or three mutually perpendicular axes. Each object is prepared using base line (or datum) dimensioning methods as described earlier in Unit 26. First, the selection of an absolute (0, 0, 0) or (0, 0) coordinate origin is made depending on whether the control is three-axis or two-axis. All part dimensions would be referenced from that origin.

After a working drawing is produced, the information is transferred to manufacturing equipment. This allows the NC computer to compile instructions from programs stored within its memory. The result is a detailed program plan for tool-path generation.

DIMENSIONING FOR TWO-AXIS COORDINATE SYSTEM

Two dimensional coordinates (X, Y) define points in a plane, Figure 30–1. Examples of parts using rectangular coordinates were shown in Unit 17.

The **X** axis is horizontal and considered the first and basic reference axis. Distances to the right of the **Y** axis are considered positive values and those to the left of the **Y** axis are negative values.

The **Y** axis is vertical and perpendicular to the **X** axis in the plane of a drawing showing **XY** relationships. Distances above the **X** axis are considered positive **Y** values, and below the **X** axis negative values. The position where the **X** and **Y** axes cross is called the origin, or zero point.

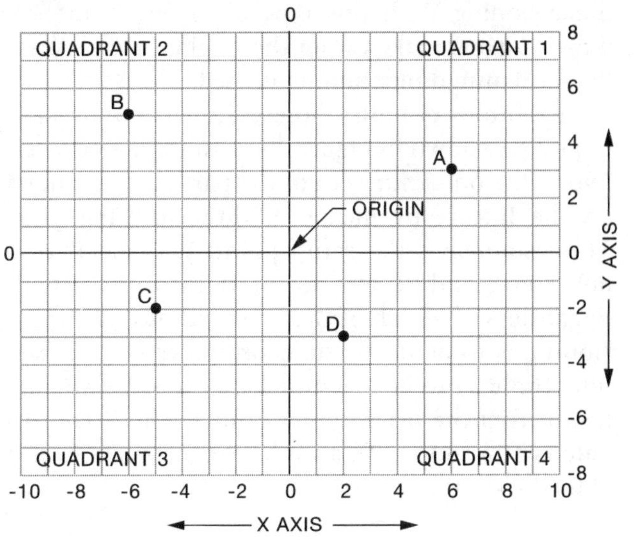

FIGURE 30–1 ■ Two-dimensional coordinates

For example, four points lie in a plane, as shown in Figure 30–1. The plane is divided into four quadrants, the origin being in the centre. Point **A** lies in quadrant 1 and is located at position (6, 3) with the X coordinate first, followed by the Y coordinate. Point **B** lies in quadrant 2 and is located at position (-6, 5). Point **C** lies in quadrant 3 and is located at position (-5, -2). Point **D** lies in quadrant 4 and is located at position (2, -3).

Designing for NC would be greatly simplified if all work were done in the first quadrant because all of the values would be positive, and the plus and minus signs would not be required. For that reason many NC systems place the origin (0, 0) to the lower left of the part. This way only the positive values apply. However, any of the four quadrants may be used.

Some NC machines, called two-axis machines, are designed for locating points in only the X and Y directions. The function of these machines is to move the machine table or tool to a specified position in order to perform work, as shown in Figure 30–2.

With the fixed spindle and movable table, as shown in Figure 30–2(B), hole **A** is drilled, then the table moves to the left, positioning point **B** below the drill. This is the most frequently used method. With the fixed table and movable spindle, as shown in Figure 30–2(C), hole **A** is drilled, then the spindle moves to the right, positioning the drill above point **B**. This changes the direction of the motion, but the movement of the cutter as delivered to the work remains the same.

Origin (Zero Point)

This is the position where all coordinate dimensions are measured. A setup point is located on the part or the fixture holding the part. It may be the intersection of two finished surfaces, the centre of a previously machined hole in the part, or a feature of the fixture.

Setup Point

The part must be accurately positioned on the fixture before any work is performed. This establishes a setup point, which is accurately located in relationship to the origin. It may be located on the

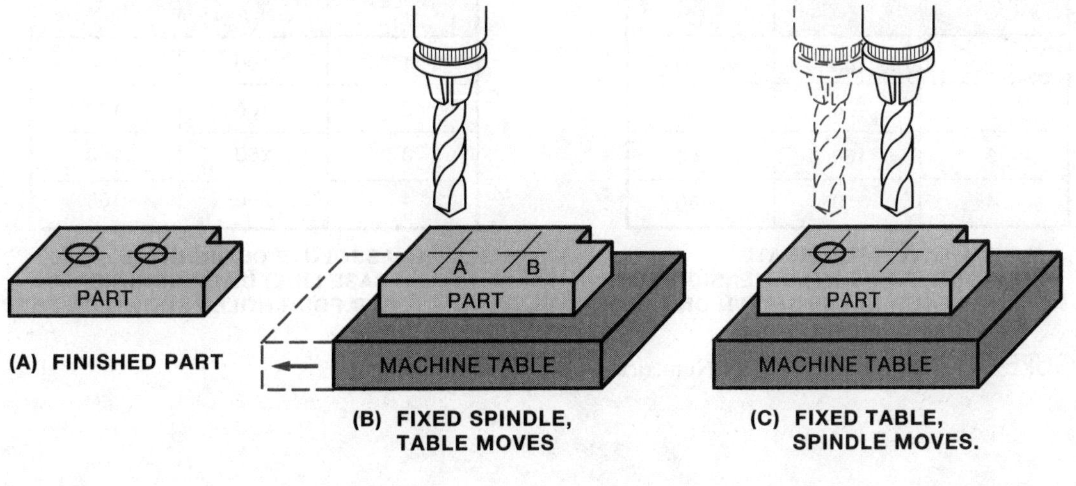

FIGURE 30–2 ■ Positioning the work

part or on the fixture holding the part. It may be the intersection of two finished surfaces, the centre of a previously machined hole, or a feature of the fixture.

Relative Coordinate (Point-to-Point) Programming

With point-to-point programming, each new position is given from the last position. To compute the next position wanted, it is necessary to establish the sequence in which the work is to be done.

Absolute Coordinate Programming

Many systems use absolute coordinate programming instead of the point-to-point method of dimensioning. With this type of dimensioning, all dimensions are taken from the origin; as such, base line or datum dimensioning is used.

Examples of both of these dimensioning techniques are shown in Figure 30–3. In these examples, two of the outer surfaces of the part are positioned on the fixture by means of three locating pins. This establishes the setup point. It is located 80 mm above and 80 mm to the right of the origin. Regardless of which of the two methods of dimensioning is to be used, the coordinates for the first hole (hole 1) to be machined are the same and are taken from the origin (zero point). The X coordinate is 100 (80 + 20), and the Y coordinate is also 100 (80 + 20).

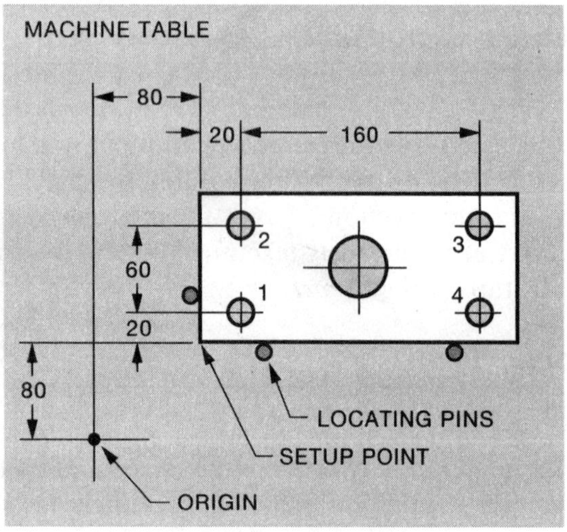

POINT-TO-POINT DIMENSIONING

HOLE	X	Y
1	100	100
2	0	60
3	160	0
4	0	-60

(A) RELATIVE COORDINATE (POINT-TO-POINT) DIMENSIONING FOR FOUR HOLES SHOWN ON PART

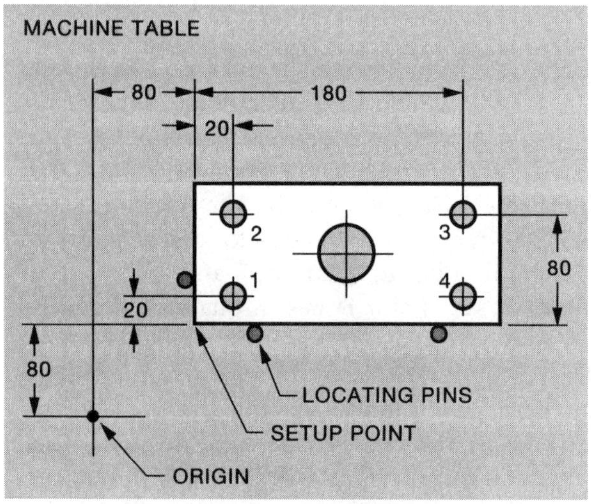

BASE LINE DIMENSIONING

HOLE	X	Y
1	100	100
2	100	160
3	260	160
4	260	100

(B) ABSOLUTE COORDINATE (BASE LINE) DIMENSIONING FOR FOUR HOLES SHOWN ON PART

FIGURE 30–3 ■ Dimensioning for Numerical Control

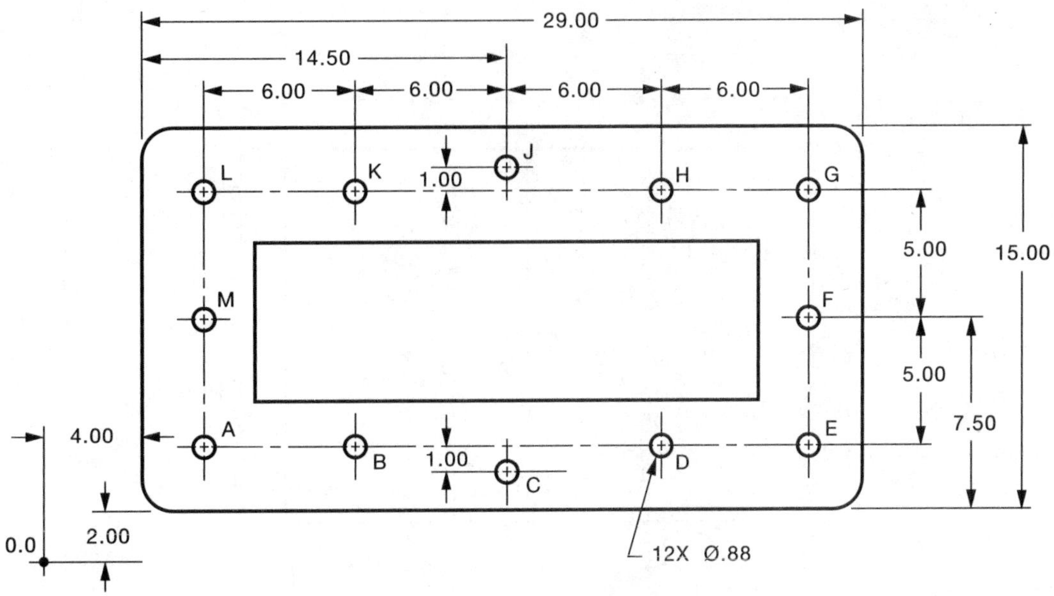

ABSOLUTE COORDINATES		HOLE	RELATIVE COORDINATES	
X	Y		X	Y
		A		
		B		
		C		
		D		
		E		
		F		
		G		
		H		
		J		
		K		
		L		
		M		

ASSIGNMENT:
Place the X and Y coordinates for each of the circular holes in the chart. The letters at the holes indicates the sequence in which they are to be drilled. Note the location of the origin.
Note: The letter I is not used to identify a hole.

COVER PLATE | **A-79**

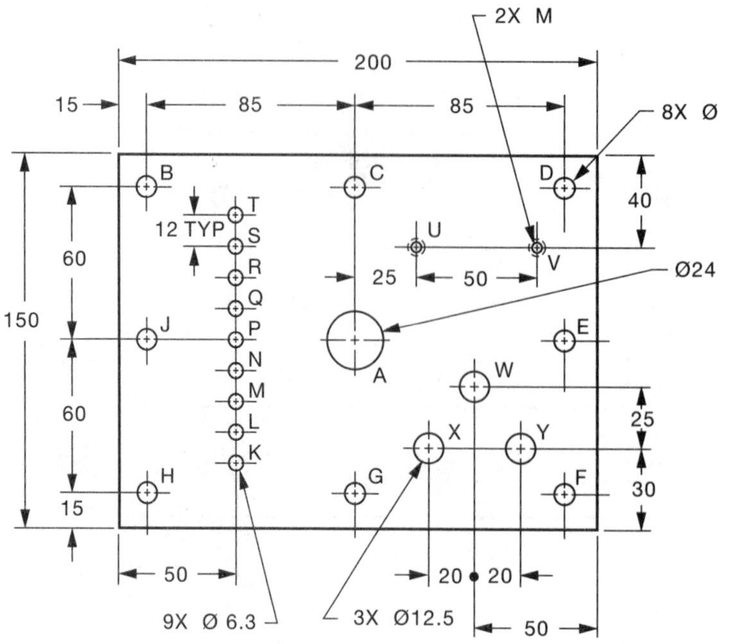

POINT-TO-POINT PROGRAMMING		
HOLE	X AXIS	Y AXIS
A		
B		
C		
D		
E		
F		
G		
H		
J		
K		
L		
M		

POINT-TO-POINT PROGRAMMING		
HOLE	X AXIS	Y AXIS
N		
P		
Q		
R		
S		
T		
U		
V		
W		
X		
Y		

ASSIGNMENT:
Place the X and Y coordinates for each of the holes in the chart. Point-to-point programming is to be used to locate each hole. The letters at the holes indicates the sequence in which they are to be drilled. Origin for the X and Y coordinates is the bottom left-hand corner of the part.
Note: Letters I and O are not used to identify holes.

METRIC
DIMENSIONS ARE IN MILLIMETRES

TERMINAL BOARD	A-80M

UNIT 31

ASSEMBLY DRAWINGS

The term *assembly drawing* refers to the type of drawing in which the various parts of a machine or structure are drawn in their relative positions in the completed unit.

In addition to showing how the parts fit together, the assembly drawing is used mainly

- To represent the proper working relationships of the mating parts of a machine or structure and the function of each.
- To give a general idea of how the finished product should look.
- To aid in securing overall dimensions and centre distances in assembly.
- To give the detailer data needed to design the smaller units of a larger assembly.
- To supply illustrations that may be used for catalogues, maintenance manuals, or other illustrative purposes.

In order to show the working relationship of interior parts, the principles of projection may be violated and details omitted for clarity. Assembly drawings should not be overly detailed because precise information describing part shapes is provided on detail drawings.

Detail dimensions that would confuse the assembly drawing should be omitted. Only such dimensions as centre distances, overall dimensions, and dimensions showing the relationship of the parts as they apply to the mechanism as a whole should be included. There are times when a simple assembly drawing may be dimensioned so that no other detail drawings are needed. In such a case, the assembly drawing becomes a working assembly drawing.

Sectioning is used more extensively on assembly drawings than on detail drawings. The conventional method of section lining is used on assembly drawings to show the relationship of the various parts, Figure 31–1.

Subassembly Drawings

Subassembly drawings are often made of smaller mechanical units. When combined in final assembly, they make a single machine. For a lathe, subassembly drawings would be furnished for the headstock, the apron, and other units of the carriage. These units might be machined and assembled in different departments by following the subassembly drawings. The individual units would later be combined in final assembly according to the assembly drawing.

Identifying Parts of an Assembly Drawing

When a machine is designed, an assembly drawing or design layout is first drawn to visualize clearly the method of operation, shape, and clearances of the various parts. From this assembly drawing, the detail drawings are made and each part is given a part number.

To assist in the assembly of the machine, item numbers corresponding with the part numbers of various details are placed on the assembly drawing attached to the corresponding part with a leader. The part number is often enclosed in a small circle, called a balloon, which helps distinguish part numbers from dimensions.

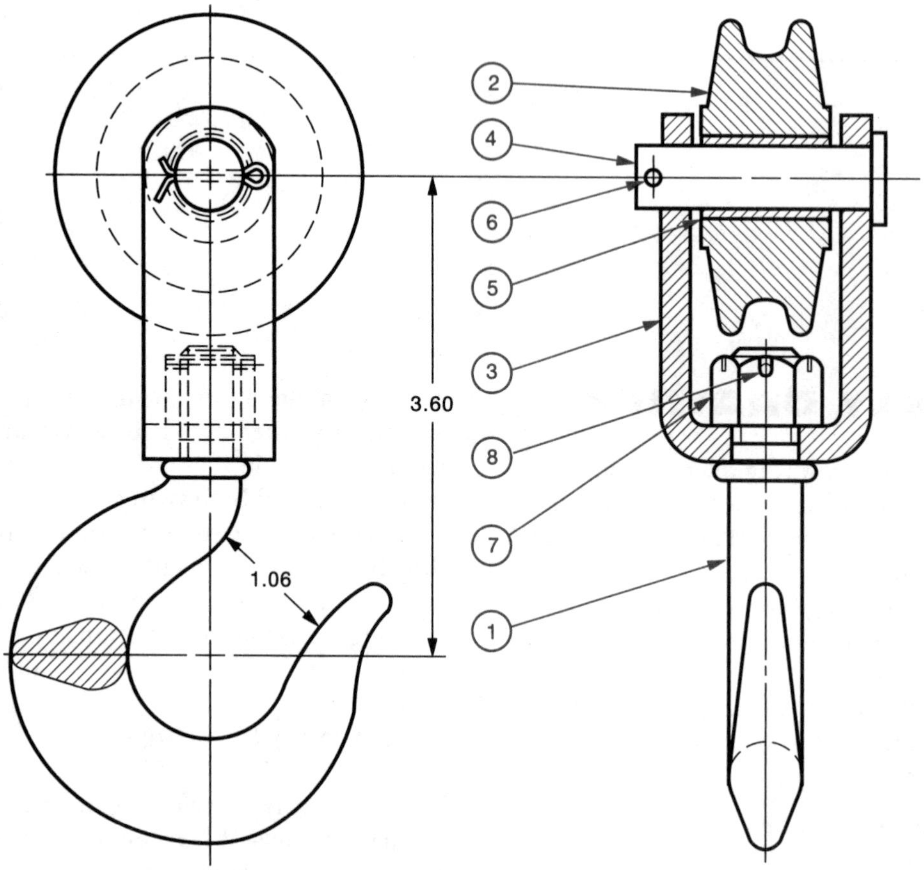

QTY	ITEM	MATL	DESCRIPTION	PT NO
1	LOCKING PIN	STL	SPRING Ø.126X.75	8
1	NUT - HEX SLOTTED	STL	.500 - 13 UNC - 2B	7
1	COTTER PIN	STL	BEVEL Ø.125 X .75	6
1	BUSHING		BOSTON 6054	5
1	CLEVIS PIN	STL	Ø.50 X 2.00	4
1	SUPPORT	SAE 1020	.25 X 1.00 X 6.00	3
1	PULLEY	GI	B14351	2
1	HOOK	WI	B14352	1

NORDALE MACHINES COMPANY
ALBANY, NEW YORK

CRANE HOOK
SCALE

FIGURE 31–1 ■ A typical assembly drawing

BILL OF MATERIAL (ITEMS LIST)

A *bill of material* or *items list* is an itemized list of all the components shown on an assembly drawing or a detail drawing, Figure 31–2. Often, a bill of material is placed on a separate sheet of paper for handling and duplicating. For castings, a pattern number would appear in the size column instead of the physical size of the part.

Standard components, which are purchased rather than fabricated, including bolts, nuts, and bearings, should have a part number and appear on the bill of material. There should be sufficient information in the descriptive column to enable the purchasing agent to order these parts.

Standard components are incorporated in the design of machine parts for economical production. These parts are specified on the drawing according to the manufacturer's specification. The use of manufacturers' catalogues is essential for determining detailing standards, characteristics of a special part, methods of representation, etc. However, it should be pointed out that manufacturers' catalogues are very unreliable for specifying parts; they should be used as a guide only. To protect the integrity of a design, a purchase part drawing must be made. This overcomes the frequent problem whereby the component supplier makes changes, unknown to the user, which frequently affect the design.

The four-wheel trolley (drawing A-83) includes many standard parts—Grease cups, lockwashers, Hyatt roller bearings, rivets, and nuts—all of which are standard purchased items. These parts are not detailed but are described in the bill of material. However, the special countersunk head bolts and the taper washers, commonly called Dutchmen, are not standard parts and must therefore be made especially for this particular assembly.

4	NUT-HEX REG	STL	.375 - 16 UNC	7
4	BOLT-HEX REG	STL	.375 - 16 UNC X 1.50	6
1	KEY	MS	WOODRUFF 608	5
2	BEARINGS	SKF	RADIAL BALL 620	4
1	SHAFT	CRS	Ø1.00 X 6.50 LG	3
1	SUPPORT	MST	.375 X 2.00 X 5.50	2
1	BASE	GI	PATTERN - A3154	1
QTY	ITEM	MATL	DESCRIPTION	PT NO

FIGURE 31–2 ■ Bill of material for assembly drawing

SWIVELS AND UNIVERSAL JOINTS

A *swivel* is composed of two or more pieces constructed so that each part rotates in relation to the other around a common axis, Figure 31–3(A).

A *universal joint* is composed of three or more pieces designed to permit the free rotation of two shafts whose axes deviate from a straight line, Figure 31–3(B).

In practice, universal joints are constructed in many different forms. The design of the universal joint is influenced by the requirements of the working mechanism and the cost of the parts.

Universal joints are used by the designer where a rotating or swinging motion is wanted or where power must be delivered along shafts that are not in a straight line.

REFERENCE

ASME Y14.24-1999 Types and Applications of Engineering Drawings

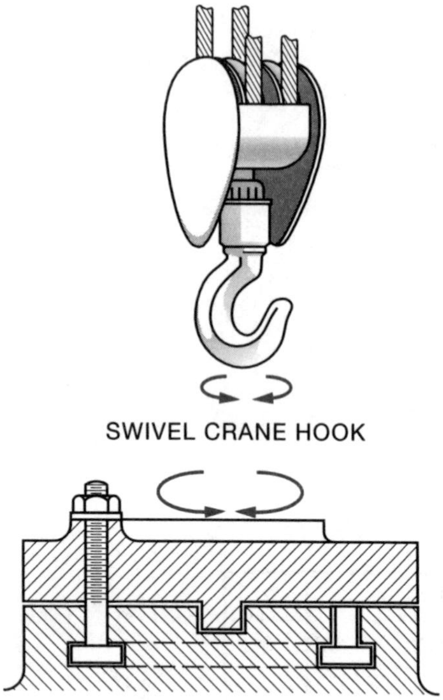

(A) SWIVELS

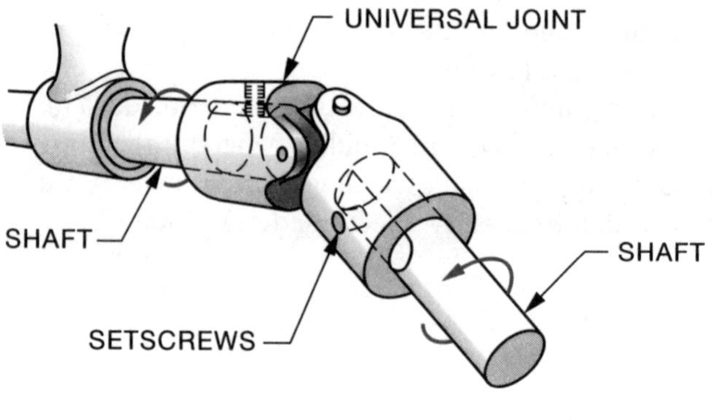

(B) UNIVERSAL JOINT

FIGURE 31–3 ■ Swivels and universal joints

ASSIGNMENT

A-81 Universal Trolley

ANSWERS

1. ________ 6. ________ 11. ________
2. ________ 7. ________ 12. ________
3. ________ 8. ________ 13. ________
4. ________ 9. ________
5. ________ 10. ________

LEFT-SIDE VIEW	FRONT VIEW
	BOTTOM VIEW

ARRANGEMENT OF VIEWS

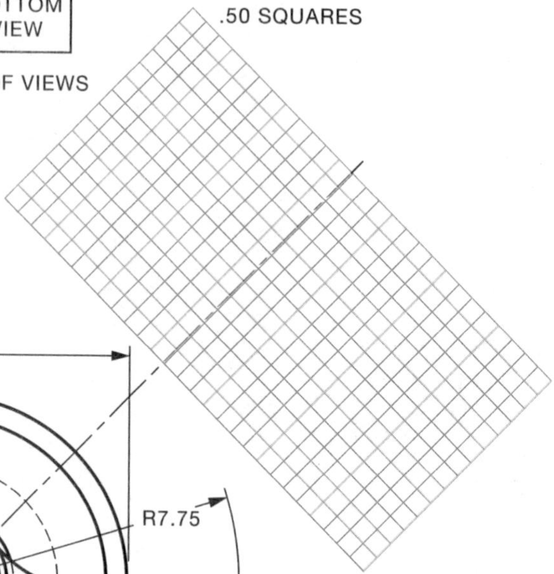

DRAW SECTIONED AUXILIARY VIEW ASSEMBLY HERE

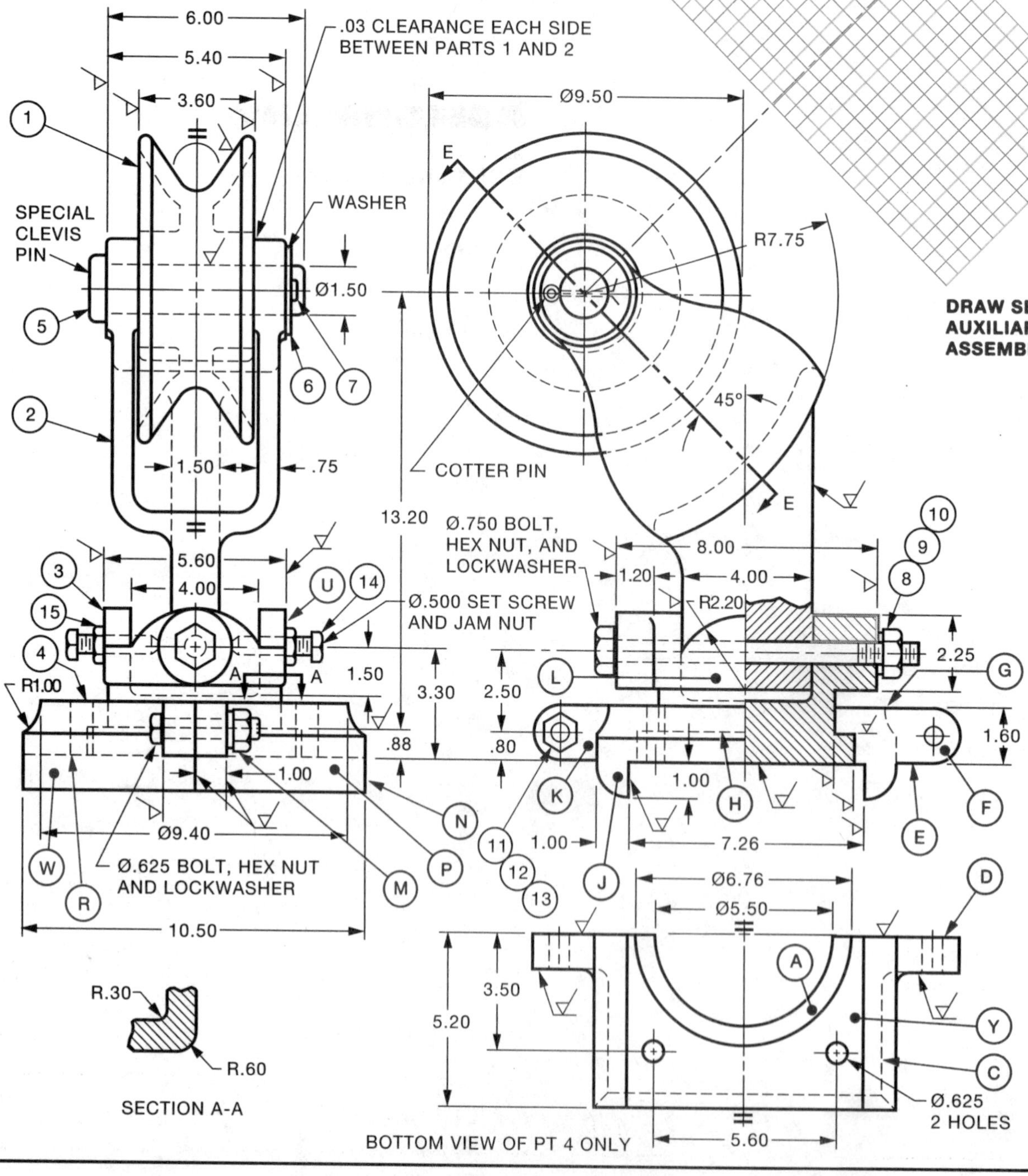

ASSIGNMENT:

1. Make a sectioned auxiliary view assembly taken on cutting-plane line E-E.
2. Make a three-view sketch of part 3 in the space provided. Do not include dimensions.

BILL OF MATERIAL

Complete the bill of material for the universal trolley assembly and place the part numbers on the assembly drawing. Refer to manufacturer's catalogues and drafting manuals for standard components. Two lines in the bill of material may be used for one part if required. Sizes for cast iron parts need not be shown.

QUESTIONS

1. Locate surface (F) on the bottom view.
2. Is surface (J) shown in the bottom view?
3. Which line or surface in the left-side view represents surface (J)?
4. How many different parts are used to make the trolley?
5. What is the total number of parts used to make the trolley?
6. How many tapped holes (excluding the nuts) are there?
7. What is the total number of holes in parts (1) to (4)? Note: Count through holes as two holes.
8. Which line or surface in the bottom view represents the intersection of lines at point (G)?
9. Locate surface (A) in the front view.
10. Locate surface (Y) in the left-side view.
11. What is the overall height of the assembly?
12. Locate surface (L) in the left-side view.
13. What is the total number of surfaces that are to be finished for parts (1) to (4)? Note: One or more surfaces can be on the same plane. Where one finish mark is shown on matched surfaces of castings, this implies that both surfaces are to be finished.

NOTE: UNLESS OTHERWISE SPECIFIED:

—TOLERANCE ON DIMENSIONS ±.02

—TOLERANCE ON ANGLES ±0.5°

—SURFACES ✓ TO BE 125✓

1.00 IN. SQUARES

SKETCH PT 3 HERE

QTY	ITEM	MATL	DESCRIPTION	PT NO
	STAND	GI		4
	SWIVEL	GI		3
	SUPPORT	MI		2
	TROLLEY WHEEL	MI		1

SCALE	
DRAWN	DATE

UNIVERSAL TROLLEY — **A-81**

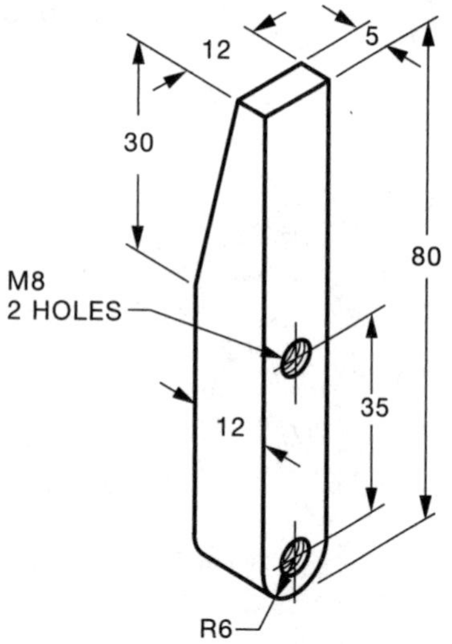

PT 1 MOVABLE JAW
1 REQD MATL - SAE 1020

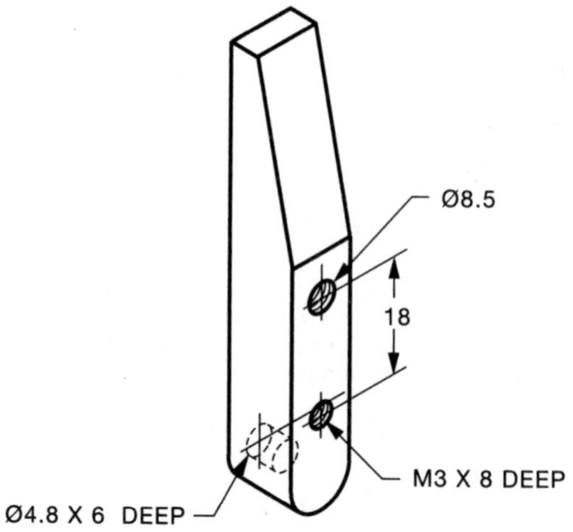

PT 2 STATIONARY JAW
1 REQD MATL - SAE 1020
AS SHOWN, OTHERWISE SAME
AS PART 1.

10 mm SQUARES (1 mm GRID)

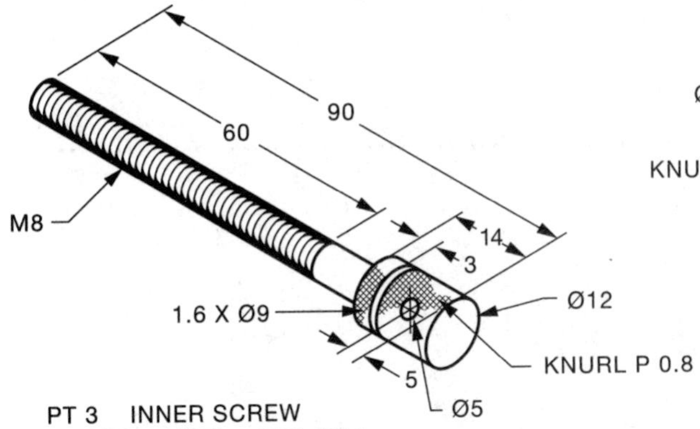
90
60
M8
14
3
1.6 X Ø9
Ø12
5
KNURL P 0.8
Ø5

PT 3 INNER SCREW
1 REQD MATL - SAE 1112

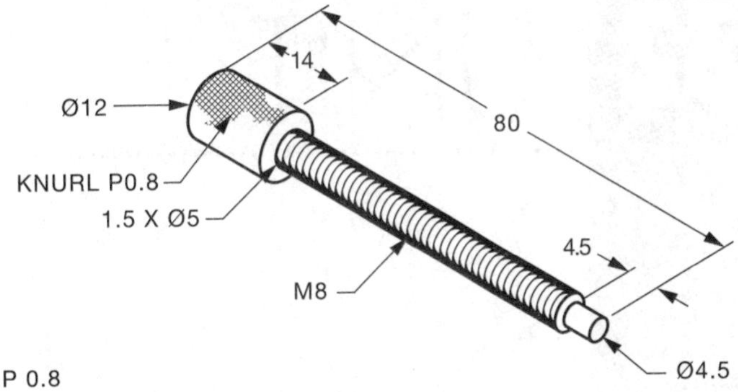
Ø12
14
80
KNURL P0.8
1.5 X Ø5
4.5
M8
Ø4.5

PT 4 OUTER SCREW
1 REQD MATL - SAE 1112

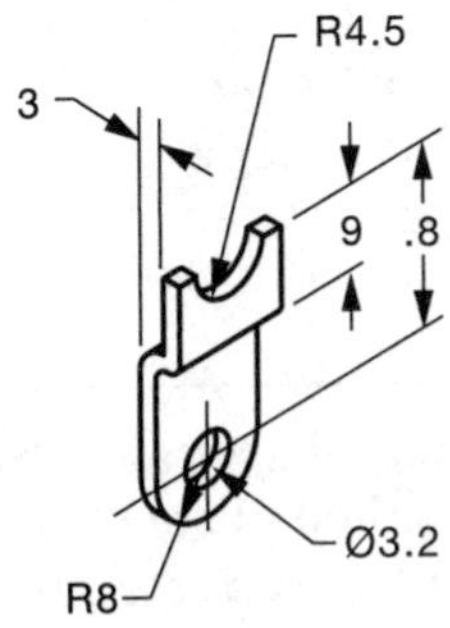
R4.5
3
9
.8
Ø3.2
R8

PT 5 CLIP 1 REQD
MATL - 1.60 (16 USS) STL

PT 6 CAP SCREW
1 REQD M3 X 8 LG RD HD

ASSIGNMENT:
In the graph area provided make a one-view assembly drawing of the parallel clamps. Use simplified thread conventions (Unit 15) and complete the items list calling for all parts. Identify the parts on the assembly. The only dimension required is the maximum opening of the jaws. Show the parts on the items list. Scale 1:1.

QTY	ITEM	MATL	DESCRIPTION	PT NO
				8
				7
				6
				5
				4
				3
				2
				1

METRIC
DIMENSIONS ARE IN MILLIMETRES

	PARALLEL CLAMP ASSEMBLY	**A-82M**

32 UNIT

STRUCTURAL STEEL SHAPES

Structural steel is widely used in the metal trades for the fabrication of machine parts because the many standard shapes lend themselves to many different types of construction. Drawings A-86 and A-88 show two assemblies where components made from structural steel shapes are used.

Remember that the steel produced at the rolling mills and shipped to the fabricating shop comes in a wide variety of shapes and forms (approximately 600). At this stage it is called *plain material.*

The great bulk of this material can be designated as shown in Figure 32–1.

Abbreviations

When structural steel shapes are designated on drawings, a standard method of abbreviating should be followed that will identify the group of shapes without reference to the manufacturer and without the use of inches and pounds per foot.

SYMBOL	WWF	W	M	S	C	MC
SHAPE	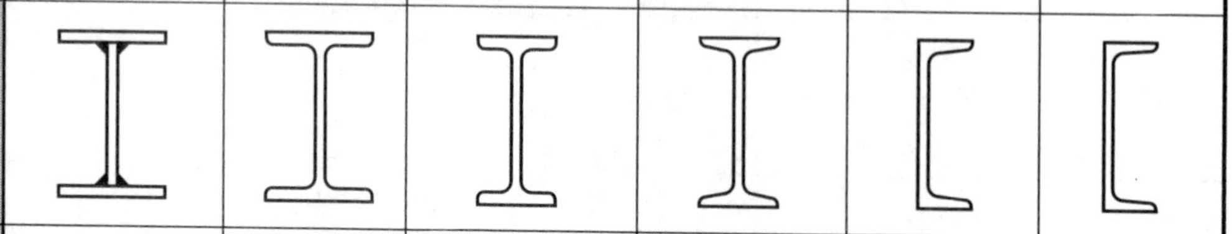					
NAME	WELDED WIDE FLANGE SHAPES	WIDE FLANGE SHAPES	MISCELLANEOUS SHAPES	STANDARD BEAMS	STANDARD CHANNELS	MISC. CHANNELS

SYMBOL	WWT	WT OR MT	L	
SHAPE	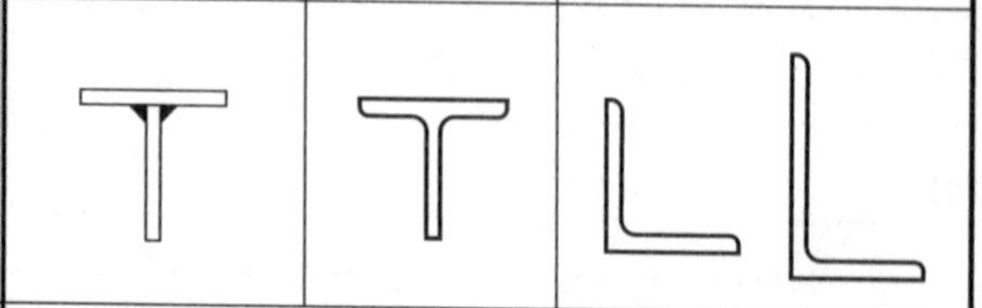			
NAME	STRUCTURAL TEES		EQUAL LEG ANGLES	UNEQUAL LEG ANGLES

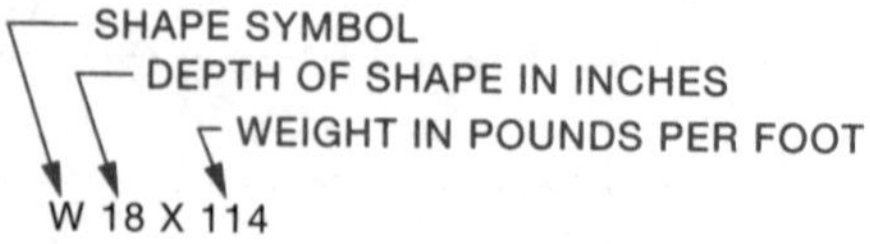
SHAPE SYMBOL
DEPTH OF SHAPE IN INCHES
WEIGHT IN POUNDS PER FOOT
W 18 X 114

(A) INCH DESIGNATION

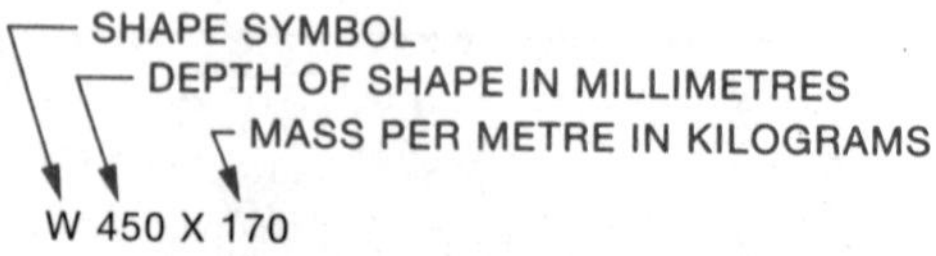
SHAPE SYMBOL
DEPTH OF SHAPE IN MILLIMETRES
MASS PER METRE IN KILOGRAMS
W 450 X 170

(B) METRIC DESIGNATION

FIGURE 32–1 ■ Common structural steel shapes and drawing callout

Therefore, it is recommended that structural steel be abbreviated as listed in Figure 32–2.

The abbreviations shown are intended only for use on design drawings. When lists of materials are being prepared for ordering from the mills, the requirements of the respective mills from which the material is to be ordered should be observed.

S-shaped beams and all standard and miscellaneous channel have a slope on the inside flange of 16.67 percent (16.67 percent slope is equivalent to 9 degrees 28′ or a bevel of 1:6). All other beams have parallel face flanges.

PHANTOM OUTLINES

At times, a part or mechanism not included in the actual detail or assembly drawing is shown to clarify how the mechanism will connect with or operate from an adjacent part. This part is shown by drawing light dash lines (one long line and two short dashes) in the operating position. Such a drawing of the extra part is known as a *phantom drawing* or view drawn in *phantom*, Figure 32–3.

On the drawing of the four-wheel trolley (drawing A-83), the track the wheels run on is an S beam.

SHAPE	U.S. CUSTOMARY EXAMPLES SEE NOTE 1		METRIC SIZE EXAMPLES SEE NOTE 2
	NEW DESIGNATION	OLD DESIGATION	
Welded Wide Flange Shapes (WWF Shapes)			
- Beam	WWF48 X 230	48WWF320	WWF1000 X 244
- Columns			WWF350 X 315
Wide Flange Shapes (W Shapes)	W24 X 76	24WF76	W600 X 114
	W14 X 26	14B26	W160 X 18
Miscellaneous Shapes (M Shapes)	M8 X 18.5	8M18.5	M200 X 56
	M10 X 9	10JR9.0	M160 X 30
Standard Beams (S Shapes)	S24 X 100	24I100	S380 X 64
Standard Channels (C Shapes)	C12 X 20.7	12C20.7	C250 X 23
Structural Tees			
- cut from WWF Shapes	WWT24 X 160	ST24WWF160	WWT280 X 210
- cut from W Shapes	WT12 X 38	ST122F38	WT130 X 16
- cut from M Shapes	MT4 X 9.25	ST4M9.25	MT100 X 14
Bearing Piles (HP Shapes)	HP14 X 73	14BP73	HP350 X 109
Angles (L Shapes)	L6 X 6 X .75	L6 X 6 X 3/4	L75 X 75 X 6
(leg dimensions X thickness)	L6 X 4 X .62	L6 X 4 X 5/8	L150 X 100 X 13
Plates (width X thickness)	20 X .50	20 X 1/2	500 X 12
Square Bar (side)	⧄1.00	BAR 1 ⧄	⧄25
Round Bar (diameter)	Ø1.25	BAR 1-1/4 Ø	Ø30
Flat Bar (width X thickness)	250 X .25	BAR 2-1/2 X 1/4	60 X 6
Round Pipe (type of pipe X OD X wall thickness)	12.75 OD X .375	12-3/4 X 3/8	XS 102 OD X 8
Square and Rectangular Hollow Structural Sections (outside dimensions X wall thickness)	HSS4 X 4 X .375	4X 4RT X 3/8	HSS102 X 102 X 8
	HSS8 X 4 X .375	8 X 4RT X 3/8	
Steel Pipe Piles (OD X wall thickness)			320 OD X 6

NOTE 1 - VALUES SHOWN ARE NOMINAL DEPTH (INCHES) X WEIGHT PER FOOT LENGTH (POUNDS).

NOTE 2 - VALUES SHOWN ARE NOMINAL DEPTH (MILLIMETRES) X MASS PER METRE LENGTH (KILOGRAMS).

NOTE 3 - METRIC SIZE EXAMPLES SHOWN ARE NOT NECESSARILY THE EQUIVALENTS OF THE INCH SIZE EXAMPLES SHOWN.

FIGURE 32–2 ■ Abbreviations for shapes, plates, bars, and tubes

The wheels are set at an angle to the vertical plane in order to ride upon the sloping bottom flange of the S beam. The outline of the beam is shown by dash lines and, while not an integral part of the trolley, the outline or phantom view of the S beam shows clearly how the trolley operates.

CONICAL WASHERS

Conical washers, Figure 32–4, are available in a variety of sizes to accommodate the slopes found on structural steel shapes. A typical application can be found on the four-wheel trolley, parts **D** and **W** (drawing A-83).

REFERENCES

Canadian Institute of Steel Construction
American Institute of Steel Construction

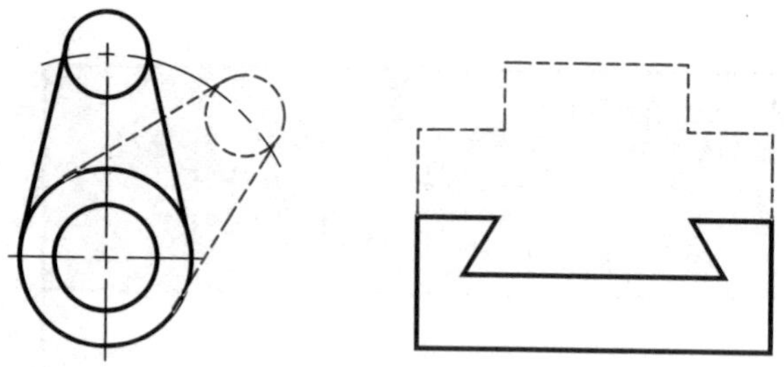

FIGURE 32–3 ■ Phantom lines

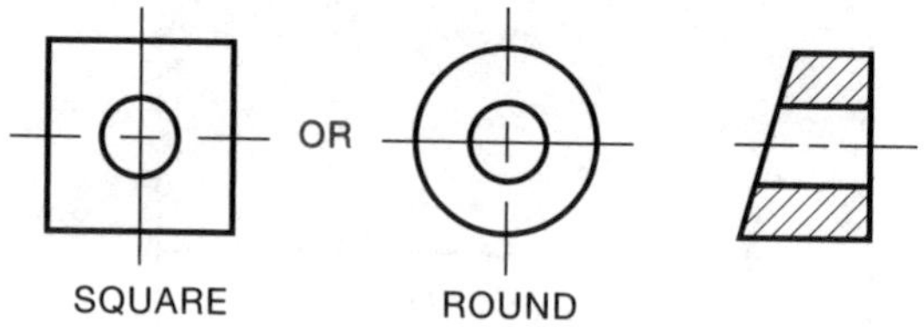

FIGURE 32–4 ■ Conical washers

ASSIGNMENT

A-83 Four-Wheel Trolley

ASSIGNMENT:

1. Sketch the secondary auxiliary view of part (A) in the space provided. (Project from primary auxiliary view.)
2. In the space provided, make a detail drawing with dimensions of parts (C) and (D).

QUESTIONS

1. What does hidden line (E) indicate?
2. Which cutting plane in the primary auxiliary view indicates (A) where the section to the left of line N-N is taken and (B) where the section to the right of line N-N is taken?
3. What is the slope of angle (J)?
4. Locate part (K) in the section view.
5. What is the wheel diameter of the trolley?
6. Locate parts (2), (3), (5), (A), (C), (V), and (Z) in the primary auxiliary view.
7. What are the names of parts (T), (U), (V), (W), (X), and (Y) ?
8. What is the diameter of the bearing rollers?
9. Determine distance (L).

ANSWERS

1. ________ 3 ________ U ________
2. A ________ 5 ________ V ________
B ________ A ________ W ________
3. ________ C ________ X ________
4. ________ V ________ Y ________
5. ________ Z ________ 8. ________
6. 2 ________ 7. T ________ 9. ________

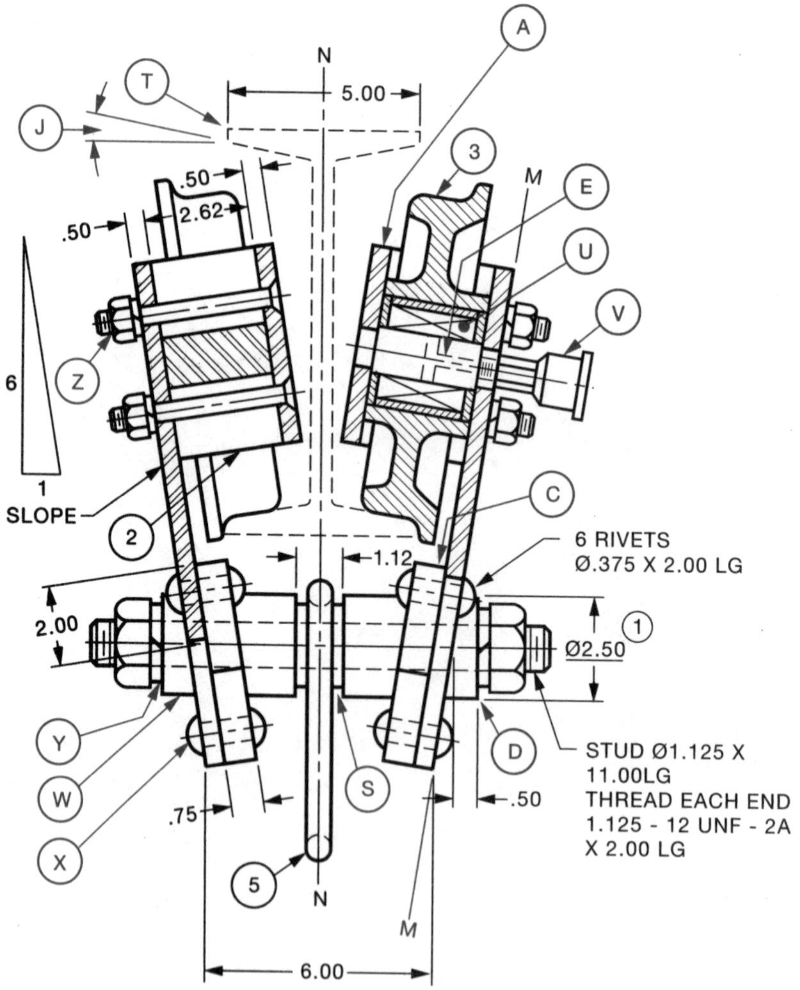
A
N
T
5.00
J
3
M
E
.50
2.62
.50
U
V
6
Z
1
SLOPE
2
C
6 RIVETS
Ø.375 X 2.00 LG
1.12
2.00
1
Ø2.50
Y
W
X
S
D
.50
.75
5
N
M
6.00
STUD Ø1.125 X
11.00LG
THREAD EACH END
1.125 - 12 UNF - 2A
X 2.00 LG

S BEAM - S10 X 35
WHEEL - Ø8,00
SHAFT - Ø1.374
BEARING - 2.835 OD
-ROLLERS - Ø.562

REVISIONS	1	02-04-21	F. NEWMAN
	2.50 WAS 2.60		

SKETCH PART D HERE

SKETCH PART C HERE

.50 INCH SQUARES (.25 IN. GRID)

SKETCH SECONDARY AUXILIARY VIEW OF PART A HERE

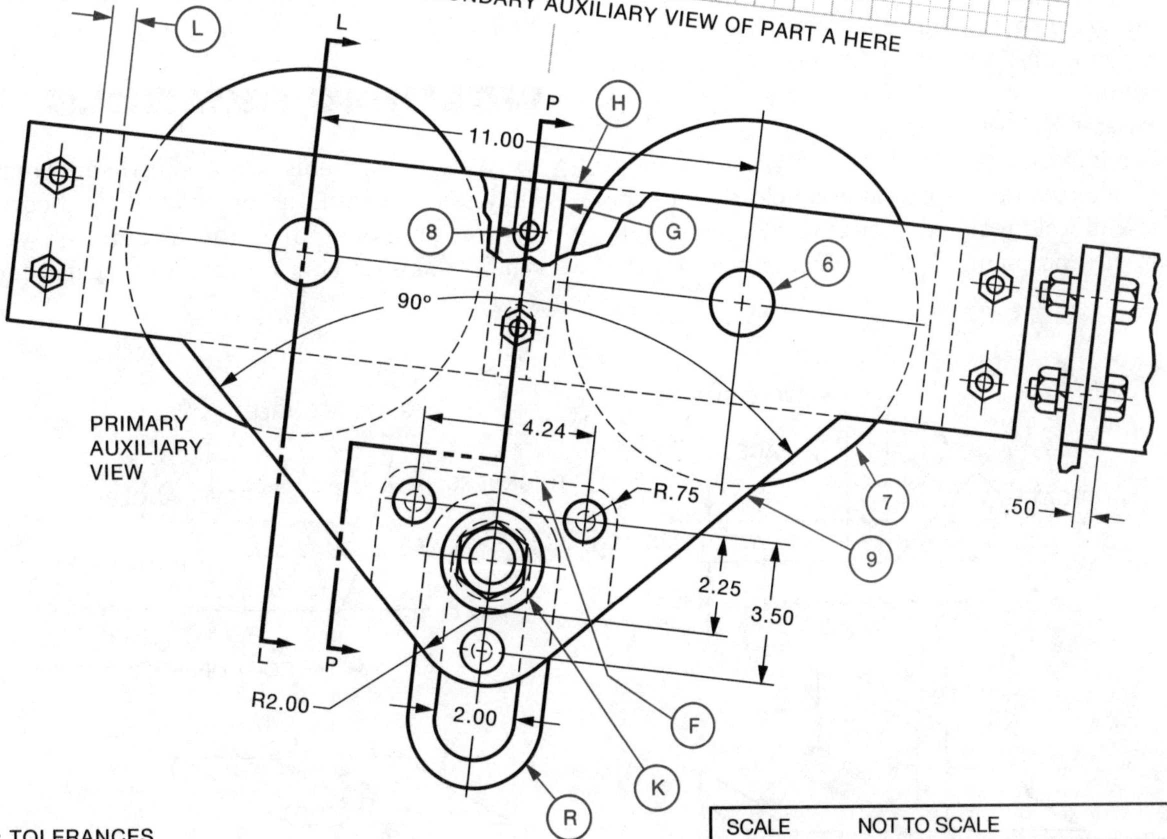
L
L
P
H
11.00
G
8
6
90°
PRIMARY
AUXILIARY
VIEW
4.24
R.75
7
9
.50
2.25
3.50
L
P
R2.00
2.00
F
K
R

NOTE: TOLERANCES
—ON DIMENSIONS ±.02
—ON ANGLES ±0.5°

SCALE	NOT TO SCALE	
DRAWN		DATE
FOUR-WHEEL TROLLEY		A-83

33 UNIT

WELDING DRAWINGS

The primary importance of welding is the uniting of pieces of metal so they will operate properly as a unit to support the loads to be carried. In order to design and build such a structure, to be economical and efficient, a basic knowledge of welding is essential. Figure 33–1 illustrates many basic welding terms.

The introduction of welding symbols on a drawing enables the designer to indicate clearly the type and size of weld required to meet the design requirements. It is becoming increasingly important for the designer to indicate the required type of weld correctly. Basic welding joints are shown in Figure 33–2. Points that must be made clear are the type of weld, the joint penetration, the weld size, and the root opening (if any). These points can be clearly indicated on the drawing by the welding symbol.

WELDING SYMBOLS

Welding symbols are a shorthand language. They save time and money and, if used correctly, ensure understanding and accuracy. Welding symbols should be a universal language; for this

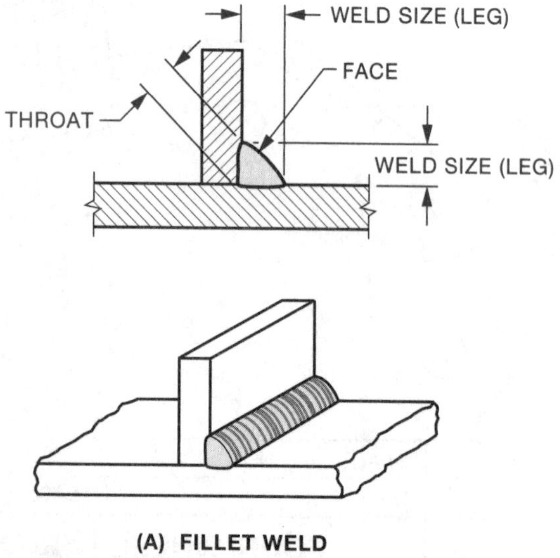

FIGURE 33–1 ■ Basic welding nomenclature

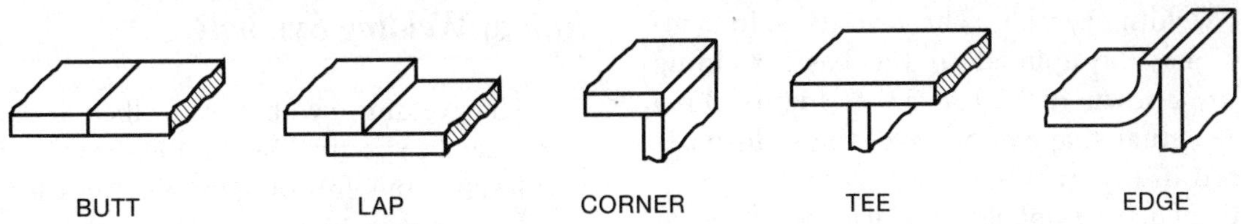
BUTT
LAP
CORNER
TEE
EDGE

FIGURE 33–2 ■ Basic welding joins

reason the symbols of the American Welding Society have been adopted.

A distinction between the terms *weld symbol* and *welding symbol* should be understood. The weld symbol indicates the type of weld. The welding symbol is a method of representing the weld on drawings. It includes supplementary information and consists of the following eight elements. Not all elements need be used unless required for clarity.

1. reference line
2. arrow
3. basic weld symbol
4. dimensions and other data
5. supplementary symbols
6. finish symbols
7. tail
8. specification, process, or other reference

The size and spacing of welds shown on the welding symbol are given in inches or millimetres (metric).

Figure 33–3 illustrates the position of the weld symbols and other information in relation to

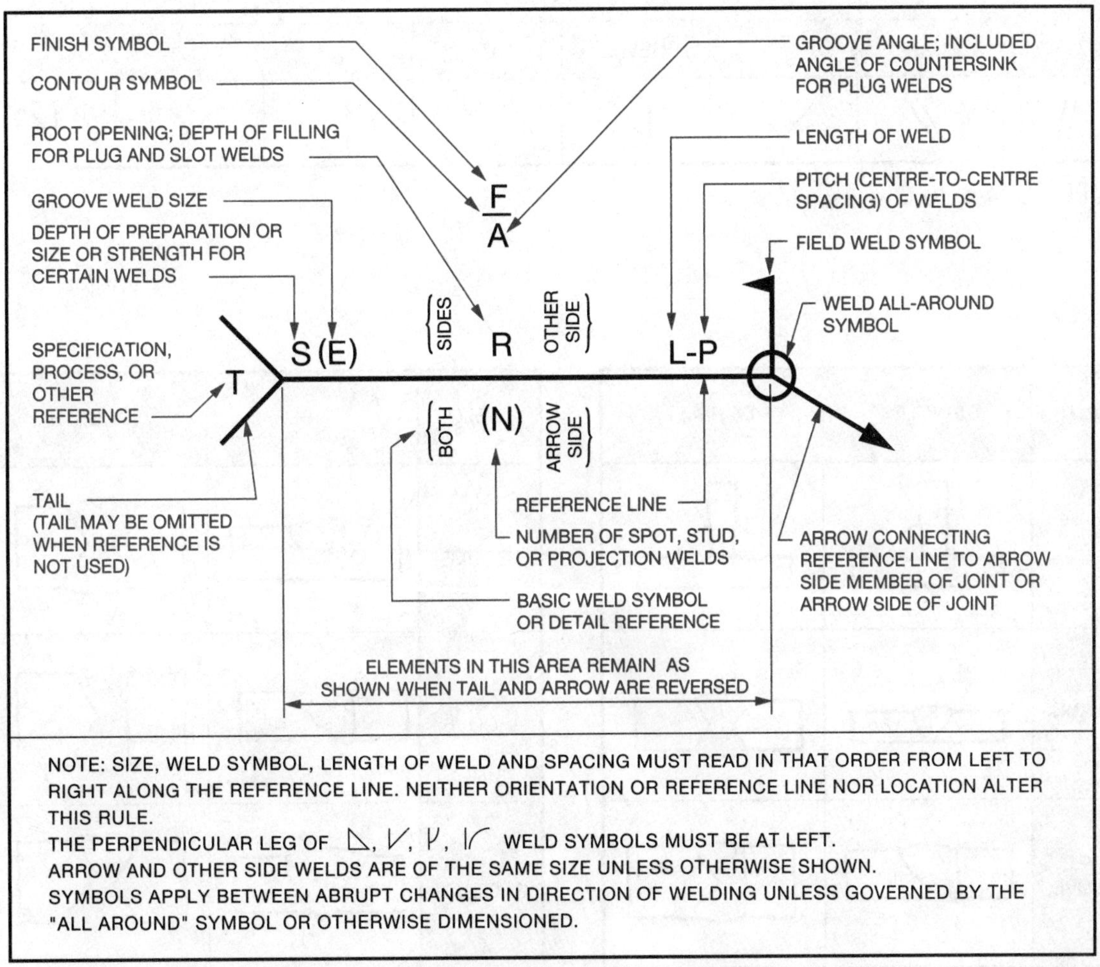
FINISH SYMBOL
CONTOUR SYMBOL
ROOT OPENING; DEPTH OF FILLING FOR PLUG AND SLOT WELDS
GROOVE WELD SIZE
DEPTH OF PREPARATION OR SIZE OR STRENGTH FOR CERTAIN WELDS
SPECIFICATION, PROCESS, OR OTHER REFERENCE
TAIL (TAIL MAY BE OMITTED WHEN REFERENCE IS NOT USED)
GROOVE ANGLE; INCLUDED ANGLE OF COUNTERSINK FOR PLUG WELDS
LENGTH OF WELD
PITCH (CENTRE-TO-CENTRE SPACING) OF WELDS
FIELD WELD SYMBOL
WELD ALL-AROUND SYMBOL
F
A
S (E)
R
(N)
L-P
T
SIDES
BOTH
OTHER SIDE
ARROW SIDE
REFERENCE LINE
NUMBER OF SPOT, STUD, OR PROJECTION WELDS
BASIC WELD SYMBOL OR DETAIL REFERENCE
ARROW CONNECTING REFERENCE LINE TO ARROW SIDE MEMBER OF JOINT OR ARROW SIDE OF JOINT
ELEMENTS IN THIS AREA REMAIN AS SHOWN WHEN TAIL AND ARROW ARE REVERSED
NOTE: SIZE, WELD SYMBOL, LENGTH OF WELD AND SPACING MUST READ IN THAT ORDER FROM LEFT TO RIGHT ALONG THE REFERENCE LINE. NEITHER ORIENTATION OR REFERENCE LINE NOR LOCATION ALTER THIS RULE.
THE PERPENDICULAR LEG OF , , , WELD SYMBOLS MUST BE AT LEFT.
ARROW AND OTHER SIDE WELDS ARE OF THE SAME SIZE UNLESS OTHERWISE SHOWN.
SYMBOLS APPLY BETWEEN ABRUPT CHANGES IN DIRECTION OF WELDING UNLESS GOVERNED BY THE "ALL AROUND" SYMBOL OR OTHERWISE DIMENSIONED.

FIGURE 33–3 ■ Standard location of elements of a welding symbol the basic welding symbol. The various weld symbols that may be applied to the basic welding symbol are shown in Figure 33–4. Figure 33–5 shows the actual shape of many of the weld types symbolized in Figure 33–4.

Supplementary symbols may also be added to the basic welding symbol. The supplementary symbols are illustrated in Figure 33–6.

Any welding joint indicated by a symbol will always have an arrow side and an other side. The words arrow side, other side, and both sides are used accordingly to locate the weld with respect to the joint.

Tail of Welding Symbol

The welding symbol and allied process to be used may be specified by placing the appropriate letter designations from Figure 33–7 in the tail of the welding symbol, Figure 33–8.

Codes, specifications, or any other applicable documents may be specified by placing the reference in the tail of the welding symbol. Information contained in the referenced document need not be repeated in the welding symbol.

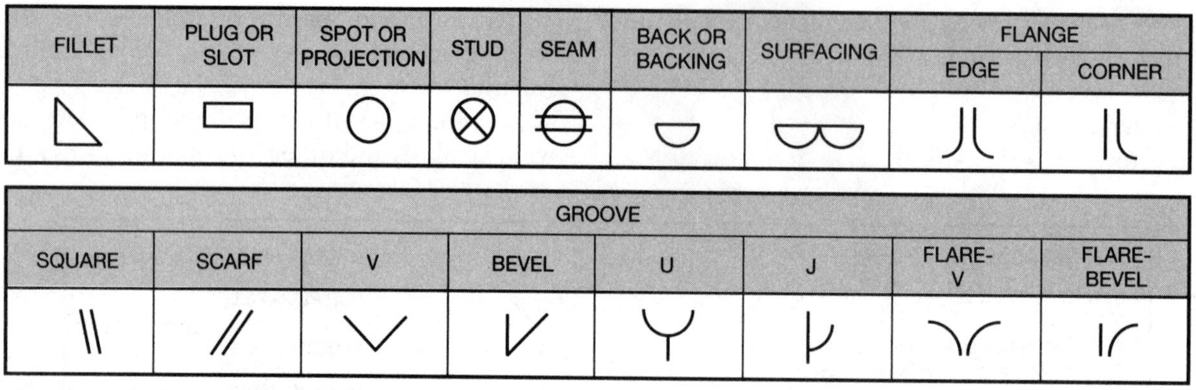
FILLET
PLUG OR SLOT
SPOT OR PROJECTION
STUD
SEAM
BACK OR BACKING
SURFACING
FLANGE
EDGE
CORNER
GROOVE
SQUARE
SCARF
V
BEVEL
U
J
FLARE-V
FLARE-BEVEL

FIGURE 33–4 ■ Basic weld symbols

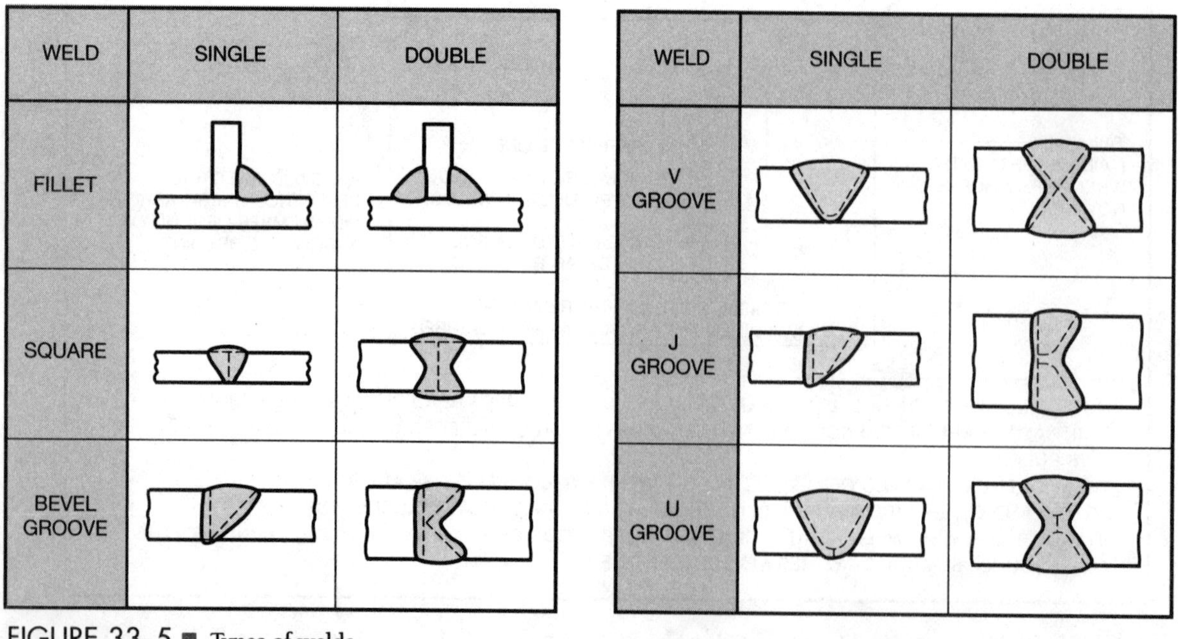
WELD
SINGLE
DOUBLE
FILLET
SQUARE
BEVEL GROOVE
WELD
SINGLE
DOUBLE
V GROOVE
J GROOVE
U GROOVE

FIGURE 33–5 ■ Types of welds

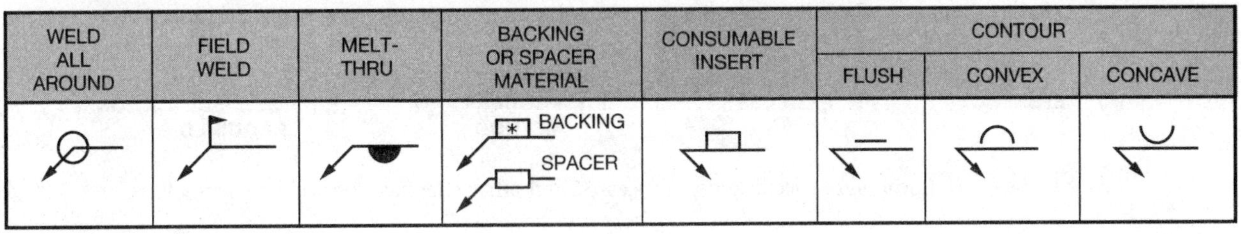
WELD ALL AROUND
FIELD WELD
MELT-THRU
BACKING OR SPACER MATERIAL
CONSUMABLE INSERT
CONTOUR
FLUSH
CONVEX
CONCAVE
BACKING
SPACER

FIGURE 33–6 ■ Supplementary symbols

Welding Process	Welding Process (Specific)	Letter Designation
Brazing (B)	Infrared Brazing Torch Brazing Furnace Brazing Induction Brazing Resistance Brazing Dip Brazing	IRB TB FB IB RB DB
Oxyfuel Gas Welding (OFW)	Oxyacetylene Welding Oxyhydrogen Welding Pressure Gas Welding	OAW OHW PGW
Resistance Welding (RW)	Resistance-Spot Welding Resistance-Seam Welding Projection Welding Flash Welding Upset Welding Percussion Welding	RSW RSEW PW FW UW PEW
Arc Welding (AW)	Stud Arc Welding Plasma-Arc Welding Submerged Arc Welding Gas Tungsten-Arc Welding Gas Metal-Arc Welding Flux Cored Arc Welding Shielded Metal-Arc Welding Carbon-Arc Welding	SW PAW SAW GTAW GMAW FCAW SMAW CAW
Other Processes	Thermit Welding Laser Beam Welding Induction Welding Electroslag Welding Electron Beam Welding	TW LBW IW ESW EBW
Solid State Welding (SSW)	Ultrasonic Welding Friction Welding Forge Welding Explosion Welding Diffusion Welding Cold Welding	USW FRW FOW EXW DFW CW

Cutting Method	Letter Designation
Arc Cutting	AC
Air Carbon-Arc Cutting	AAC
Carbon-Arc Cutting	CAC
Metal-Arc Cutting	MAC
Plasma-Arc Cutting	PAC
Oxygen Cutting	OC
Chemical Flux Cutting	FOC
Metal Powder Cutting	POC
Oxygen-Arc Cutting	AOC

FIGURE 33–7 ■ Designation of welding process by letters

Multiple Reference Lines

Two or more reference lines may be used to indicate a sequence of operations. The first operation is specified on the reference line nearest the arrow. Subsequent operations are specified sequentially on other reference lines, Figure 33–9.

Weld Locations on Symbol

Welds on the arrow side of the joint are shown by placing the weld symbol on the bottom side of the reference line. Welds on the other side of the joint are shown by placing the weld symbol on the top side of the reference line. Welds on both sides of the joint are shown by placing the weld symbol on both sides of the reference line. A weld extending completely around a joint is indicated by means of a weld-all-around symbol placed at the intersection of the reference line and the arrow.

Field welds (welds not made in the shop or at the initial place of construction) are indicated by means of the field weld symbol placed at the intersection of the reference line and the arrow.

All weld dimensions on a drawing may be subject to a general note. Such a note might state: ALL FILLET WELDS .25 UNLESS OTHERWISE NOTED.

Only the basic fillet welds will be discussed in this unit. Figure 33–10 illustrates several typical fillet welding symbols and the resulting welds.

FILLET WELDS

1. Fillet weld symbols are drawn with the perpendicular leg always to the left.

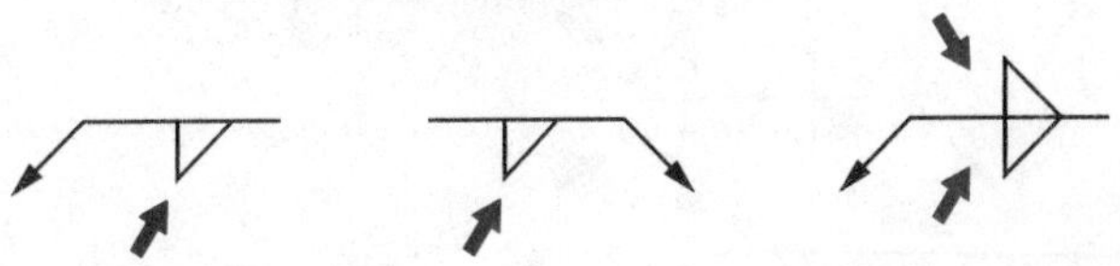

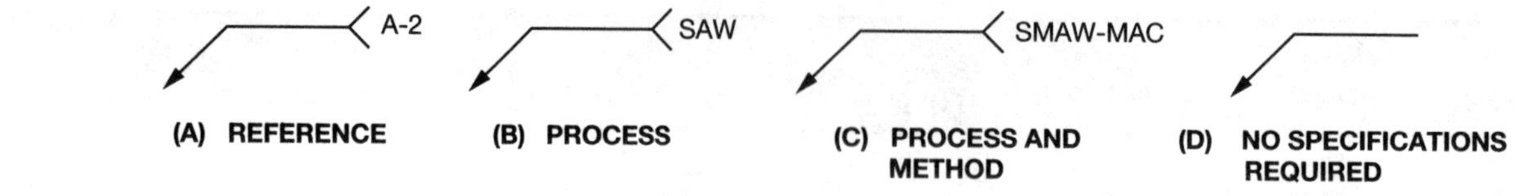
A-2
SAW
SMAW-MAC
(A) REFERENCE
(B) PROCESS
(C) PROCESS AND METHOD
(D) NO SPECIFICATIONS REQUIRED

FIGURE 33–8 ■ Location of specifications, processes, and other references on welding symbols

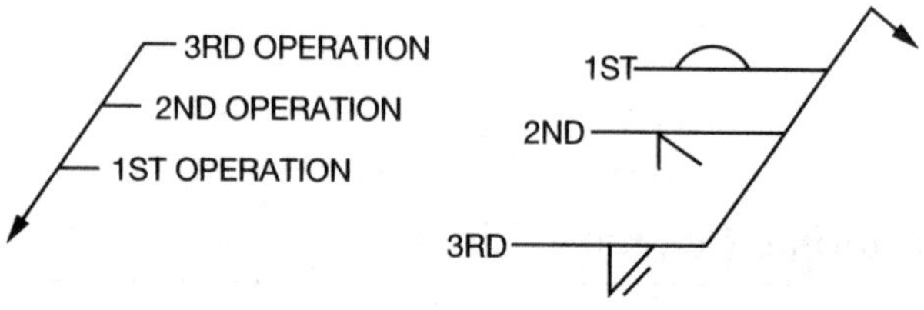
3RD OPERATION
2ND OPERATION
1ST OPERATION
1ST
2ND
3RD

FIGURE 33–9 ■ Multiple reference lines

2. Dimensions of fillet welds are shown on the same side of the reference line and to the left of the weld symbol.

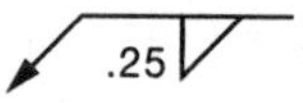
.25

3. The dimensions of fillet welds on both sides of a joint are shown whether the dimensions are identical or different.

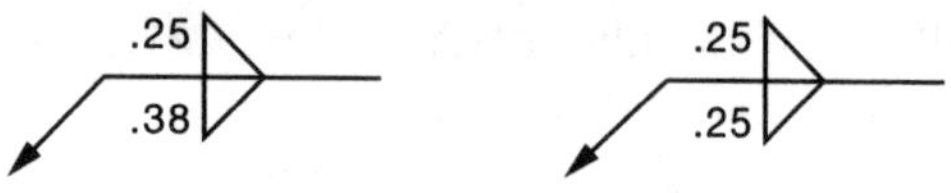
.25
.38
.25
.25

4. The dimension does not need to be shown when a general note is placed on the drawing to specify the dimension of fillet welds.

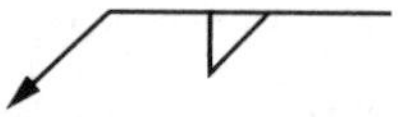

NOTE: SIZE OF FILLET WELDS .25 UNLESS OTHERWISE SPECIFIED.

5. The *length* of a fillet weld, when indicated on the welding symbol, is shown to the right of the weld symbol.

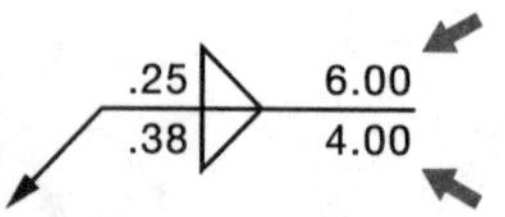
.25
.38
6.00
4.00

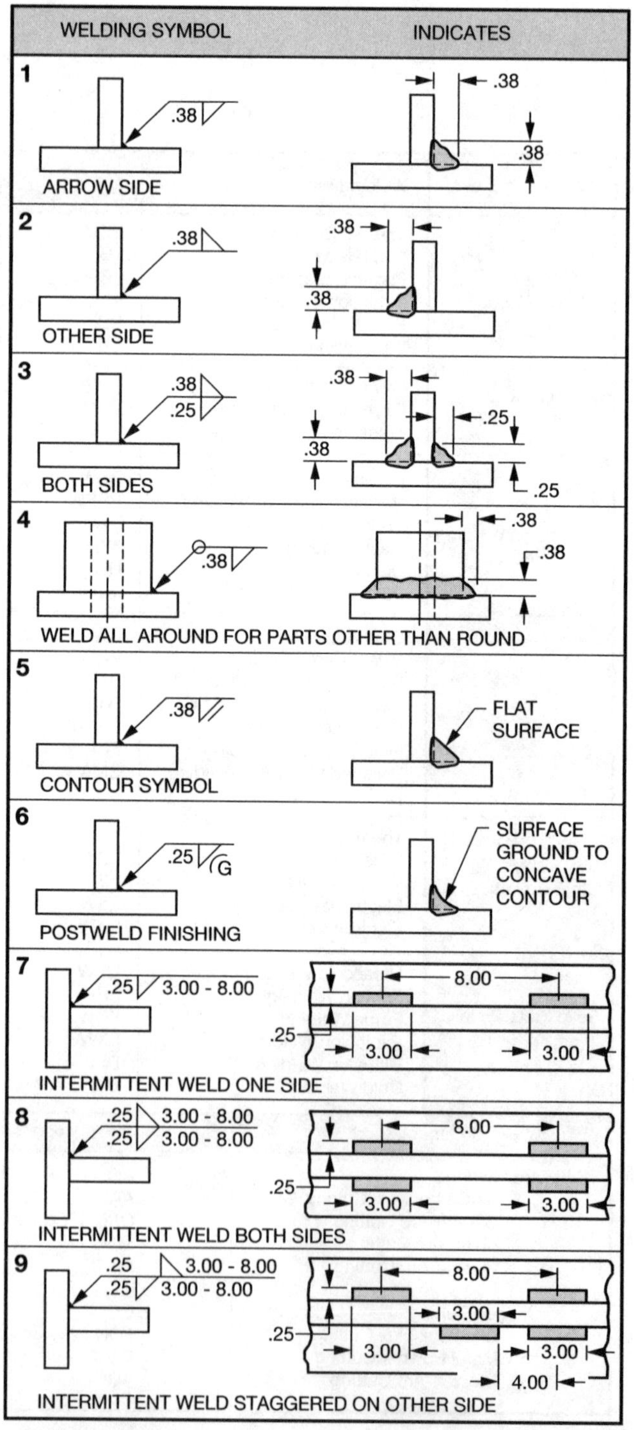
WELDING SYMBOL
INDICATES
1
.38
ARROW SIDE
2
OTHER SIDE
3
.38
.25
BOTH SIDES
4
WELD ALL AROUND FOR PARTS OTHER THAN ROUND
5
FLAT SURFACE
CONTOUR SYMBOL
6
.25
G
SURFACE GROUND TO CONCAVE CONTOUR
POSTWELD FINISHING
7
.25 3.00 - 8.00
8.00
3.00
INTERMITTENT WELD ONE SIDE
8
.25 3.00 - 8.00
.25 3.00 - 8.00
INTERMITTENT WELD BOTH SIDES
9
4.00
INTERMITTENT WELD STAGGERED ON OTHER SIDE

FIGURE 33–10 ■ Typical fillet welds

6. The *pitch* (centre-to-centre spacing) of an intermittent fillet weld is shown as the distance between centres of increments on one side of the joint. It is shown to the right of the length dimension following a hyphen.

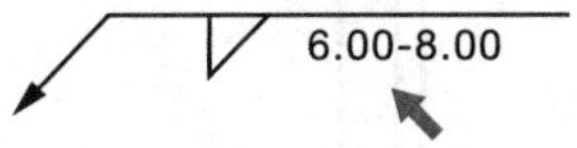

7. Staggered intermittent fillet welds are illustrated by staggering the weld symbols.

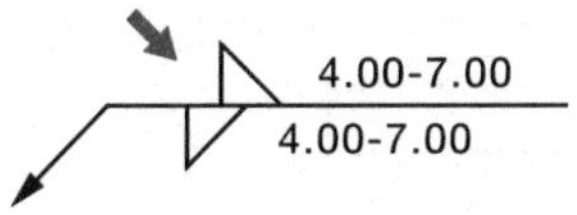

8. Fillet welds that are to be welded with approximately flat, convex, or concave faces without postweld finishing are specified by adding the flat, convex, or concave contour symbol to the weld symbol.

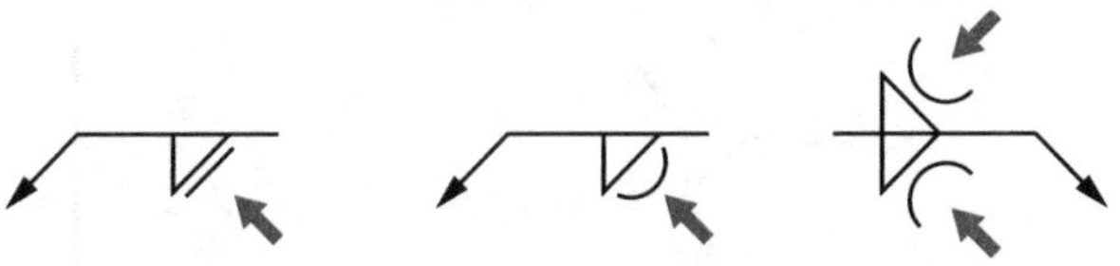

9. Fillet welds whose faces are to be finished approximately flat, convex, or concave by postweld finishing are specified by adding both the appropriate contour and finishing symbol to the weld symbol.

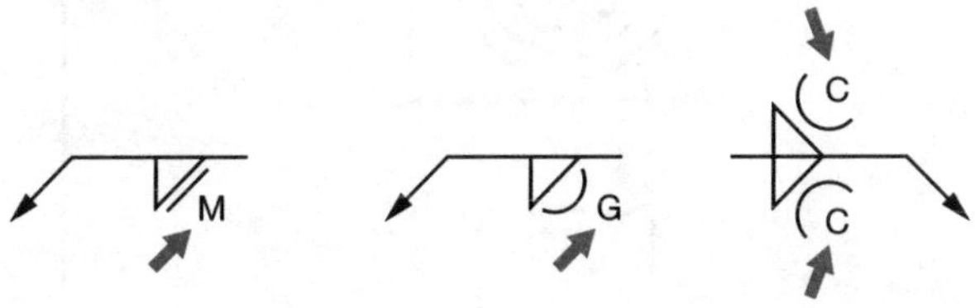

The following finishing symbols may be used to specify the method of finishing, but not the degree of finish:

C — Chipping
G — Grinding
H — Hammering
M — Machining
R — Rolling

10. A weld, with a length less than the available joint length whose location is significant, is specified on the drawing in a manner similar to that shown in Figure 33–11.
11. Weld-all-around symbol. A continuous weld extending around a series of connected joints may be specified by the addition of the weld-all-around symbol at the junction of the arrow and reference line. The series of joints may involve different directions and may lie on more than one plane, Figure 33–12(A).

    Welds extending around a pipe or circular or oval holes do not require the weld-all-around symbol, Figure 33–12(B).

REFERENCES

Canadian Welding Bureau
American Welding Society

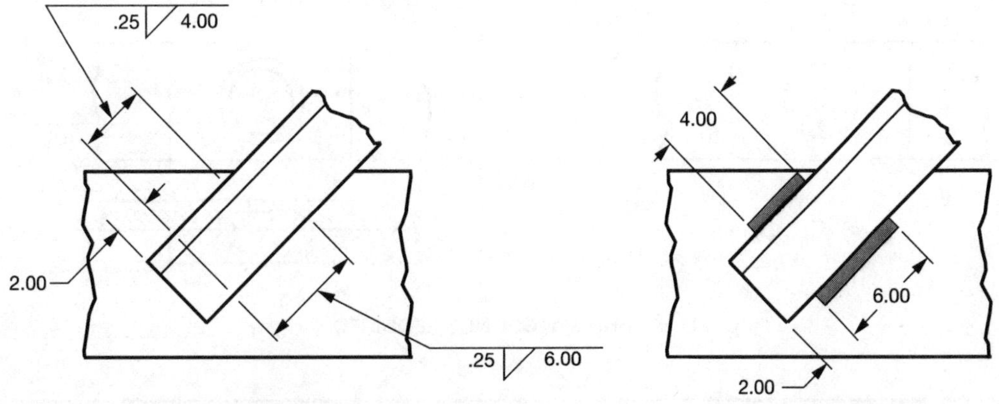

(A) DRAWING CALLOUT (B) INTERPRETATION

FIGURE 33–11 ■ Welds definitely located

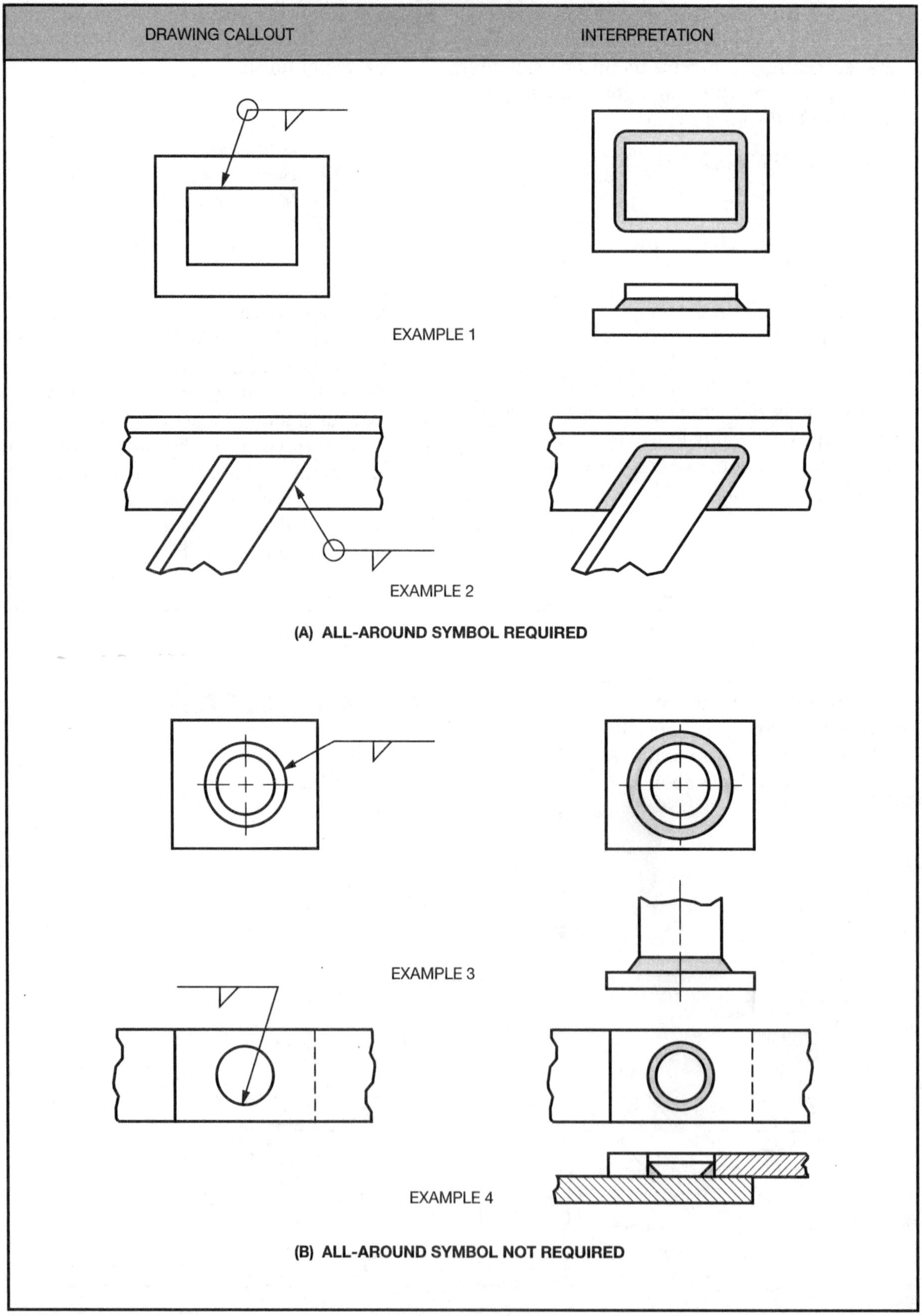
DRAWING CALLOUT
INTERPRETATION
EXAMPLE 1
EXAMPLE 2
(A) ALL-AROUND SYMBOL REQUIRED
EXAMPLE 3
EXAMPLE 4
(B) ALL-AROUND SYMBOL NOT REQUIRED

FIGURE 33–12 ■ The use of all-around symbols

DESIRED WELD	DRAWING CALLOUT

A

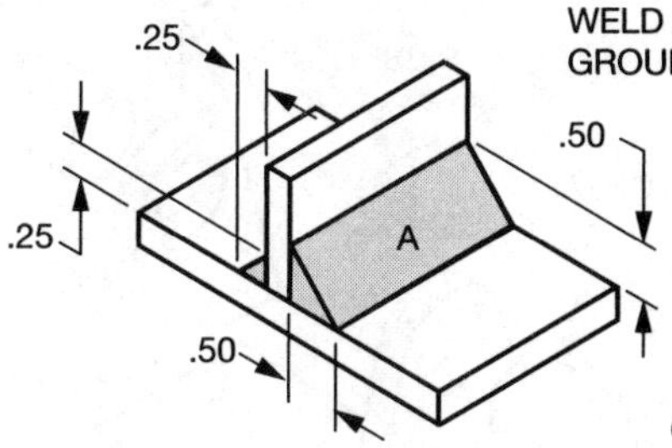
.25
.25
.50
.50
A

WELD A TO BE GROUND FLAT

GAS METAL ARC WELDING PROCESS TO BE USED

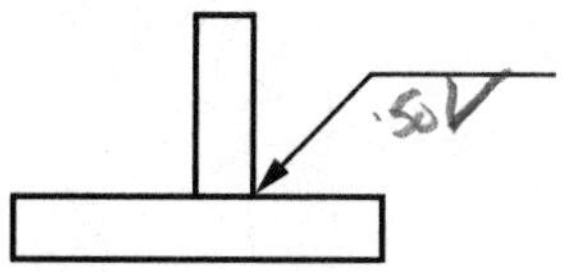
.50

B

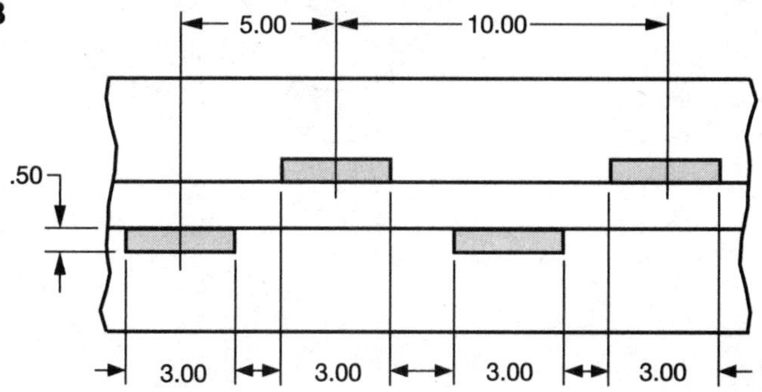
5.00
10.00
.50
3.00
3.00
3.00
3.00

WELDS APPROX. CONCAVE WITHOUT POSTWELD FINISHING

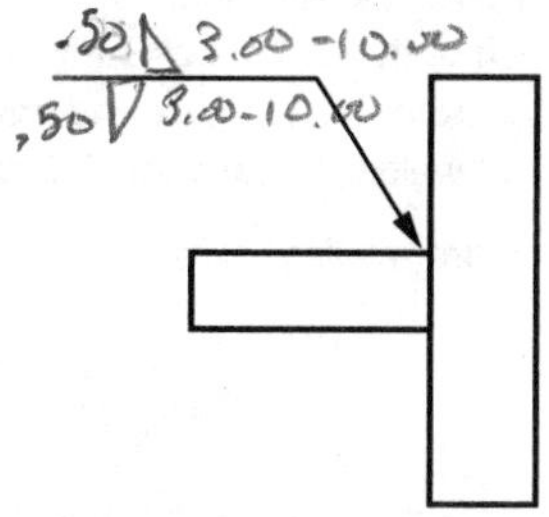
.50 3.00-10.00
.50 3.00-10.00

C

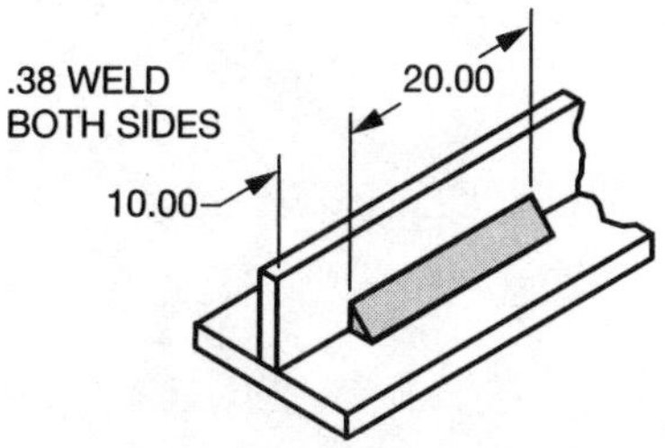
.38 WELD
BOTH SIDES
20.00
10.00

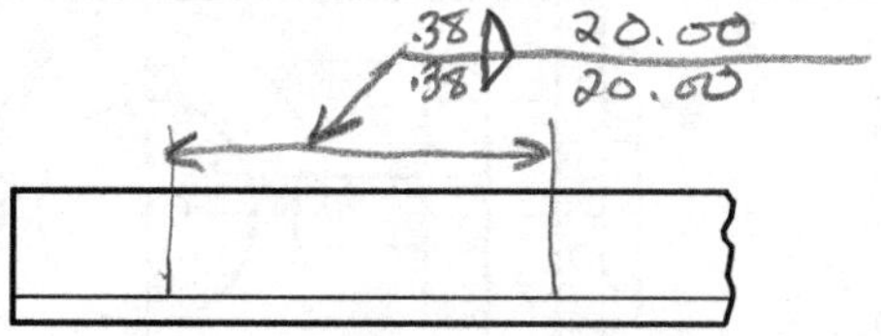
.38 20.00
.38 20.00

D

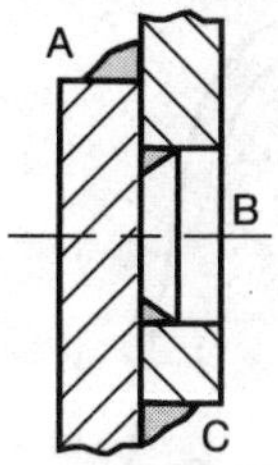
A
B
C

A - .38 CARBON ARC WELD

B - .31 WELD GROUND FLAT

C - .38 CARBON ARC WELD

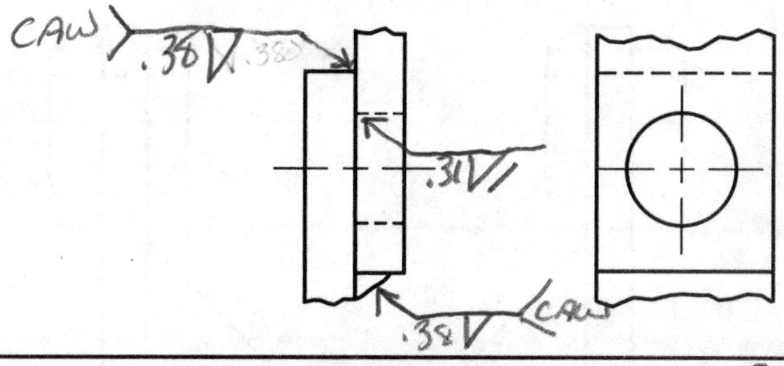
CAW
.38
.31
.38
CAW

E

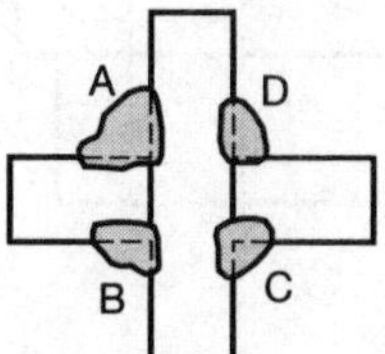
A
B
C
D

A - .50 WELD

B - .38 WELD

C - .31 WELD

D - .25 WELD

WELDS C AND D NOT MADE IN THE SHOP

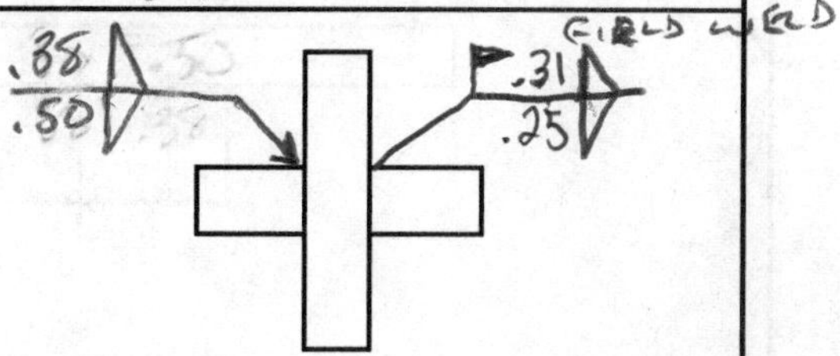
.38
.50
FIELD WELD
.31
.25

ASSIGNMENT:
COMPLETE THE WELDING SYMBOLS SHOWN TO THE RIGHT OF THE DESIRED WELD

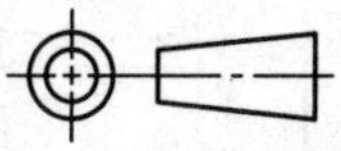

FILLET WELDS **A-84**

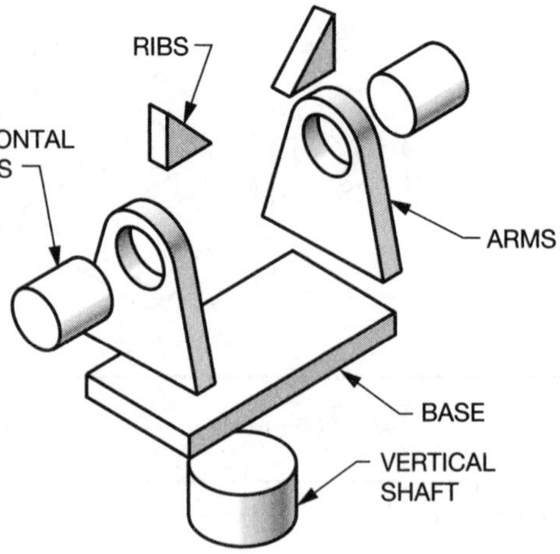
RIBS
HORIZONTAL SHAFTS
ARMS
BASE
VERTICAL SHAFT

ASSIGNMENT:
Add the following welds to the assembly drawing:

- Horizontal shafts welded both sides to arms with .25 fillet welds on outside and .19 fillet welds inside. Weld to be flat without postweld finishing.
- Arms welded both sides to base with .19 fillet welds.
- Ribs welded both sides to base and arms with .12 fillet welds.
- Vertical shaft welded to base with .25 fillet weld ground concave.

Process - Carbon arc welding.

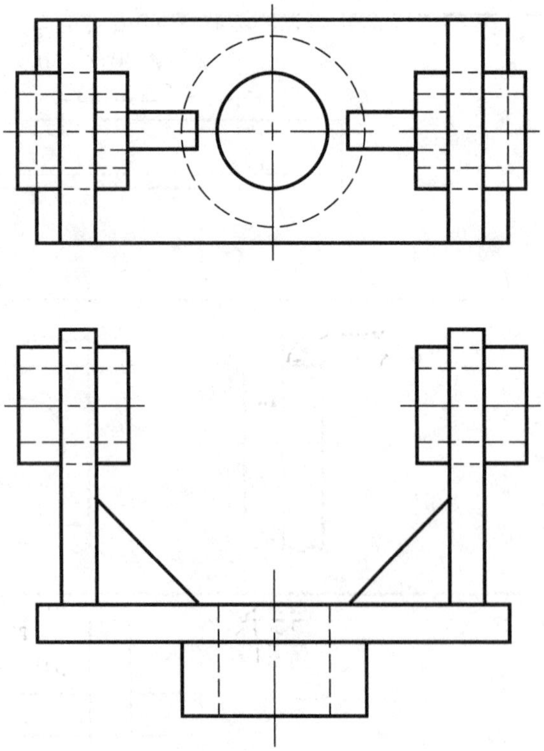

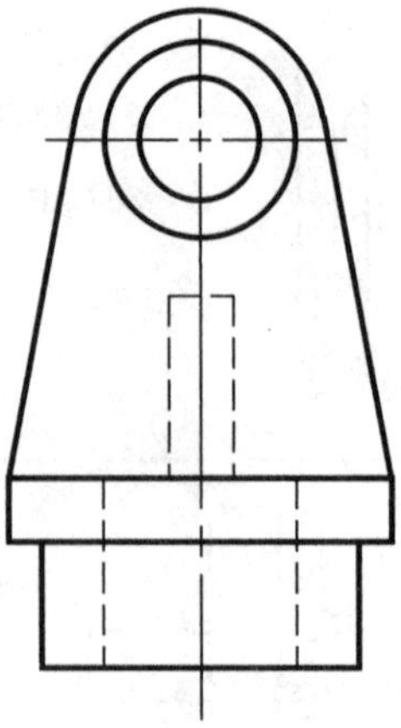

	SHAFT SUPPORT	A-85

UNIT 34

GROOVE WELDS

1. Bevel-groove, J-groove, and flare bevel-groove weld symbols are always drawn with the perpendicular leg to the left.
2. Dimensions of single-groove welds are shown on the same side of the reference line as the weld symbol.
3. Each groove of a double-groove joint is dimensioned; however, the root opening need appear only once.
4. For bevel-groove and J-groove welds, a broken arrow is used, when necessary, to identify the member to be prepared, Figure 34–1.
5. The depth of groove preparation "S" and size (E) of a groove weld, when specified, are placed to the left of the weld symbol. Either or both may be shown. Except for square-groove welds, the groove weld size (E) in relation to the depth of the groove preparation "S" is shown as "S(E)," Figure 34–2.
6. Only the groove weld size is shown for square-groove welds.
7. When no depth of groove preparation and no groove weld size are specified on the welding symbol for single-groove and symmetrical double-groove welds, complete joint penetration is required, Figure 34–3.
8. When the groove welds extend only partly through the member being joined, the size of

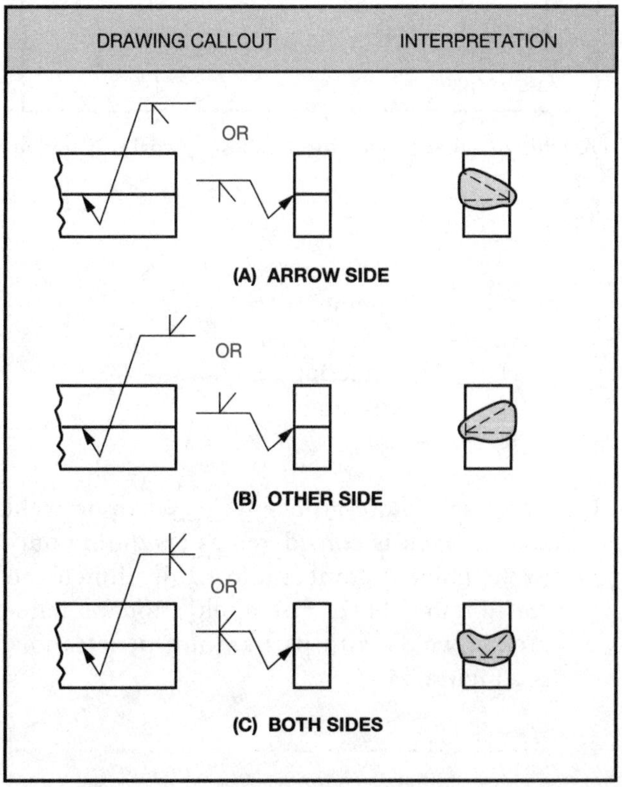

DRAWING CALLOUT
INTERPRETATION
OR
(A) ARROW SIDE
OR
(B) OTHER SIDE
OR
(C) BOTH SIDES

FIGURE 34–1 ■ Application of break in arrow on welding symbol

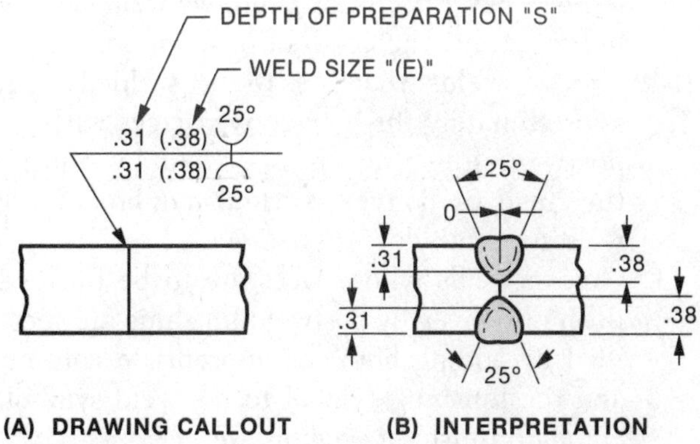

DEPTH OF PREPARATION "S"
WELD SIZE "(E)"
25°
.31 (.38)
.31 (.38)
25°
25°
0
.31
.38
.31
.38
25°
(A) DRAWING CALLOUT
(B) INTERPRETATION

FIGURE 34–2 ■ Groove weld symbol showing use of combined dimensions

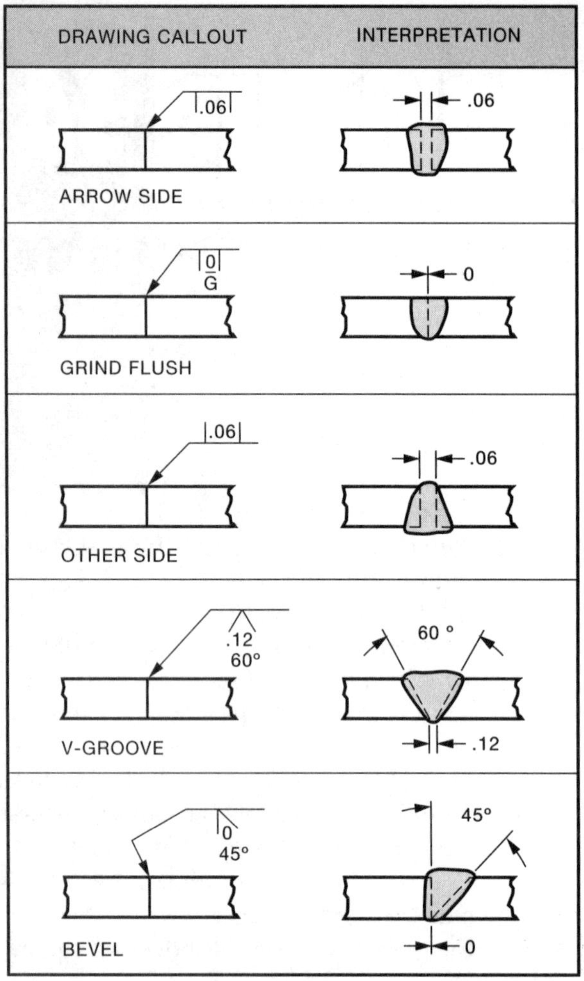

FIGURE 34–3 ■ Single-groove welds—complete joint penetration

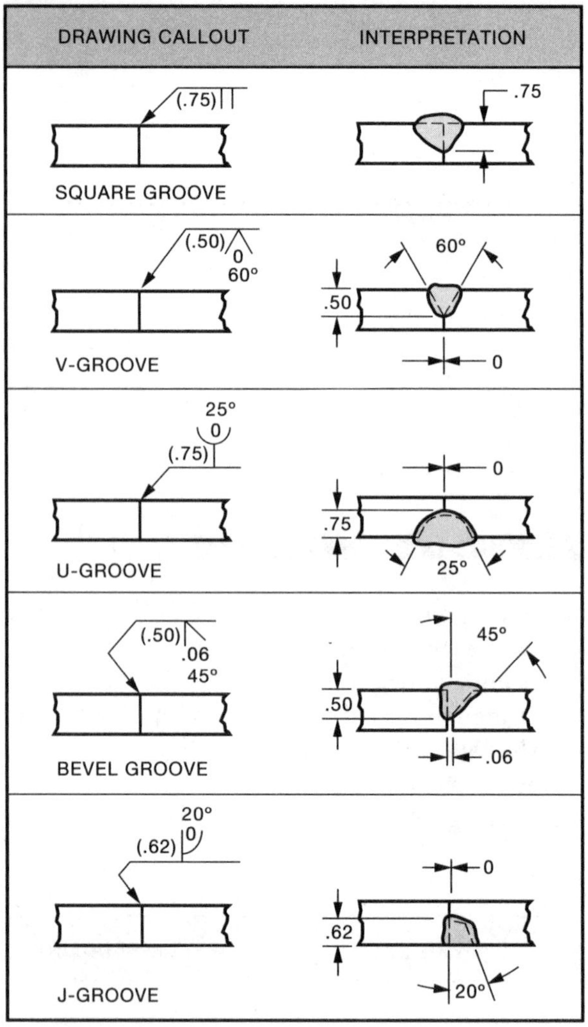

FIGURE 34–4 ■ Single-groove welds—partial penetration

the weld is shown on the weld symbol, Figures 34–4, 34–5, and 34–6.

9. A dimension not in parentheses placed to the left of a bevel, V-, J-, or U-groove weld symbol indicates only the depth of penetration.
10. Groove welds that are to be welded with approximately flush or convex faces without postweld finishing are specified by adding the flush or convex contour symbol to the welding symbol.
11. Groove welds whose faces are to be finished flush or convex by postweld finishing are specified by adding both the appropriate contour and the finishing symbol to the weld symbol. Standard finishing symbols are

    C — Chipping
    G — Grinding
    H — Hammering
    M — Machining
    R — Rolling

12. The size of flare-groove welds when no weld size is given is considered as extending only to the tangent points indicated by dimension "S," Figure 34–7. For application of flare-groove welds with partial joint penetration, see Figure 34–7.

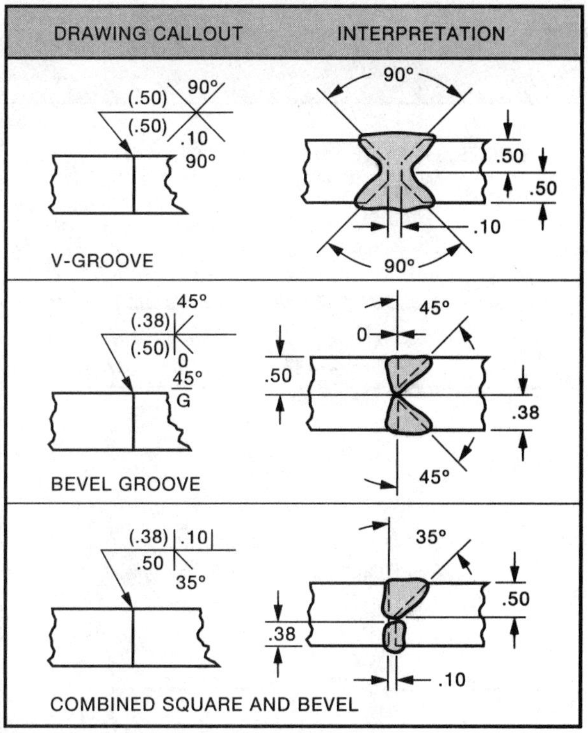

FIGURE 34–5 ■ Double-groove welds

SUPPLEMENTARY SYMBOLS

Back and Backing Welds

The back or backing weld symbol is used to indicate bead-type back or backing welds of single-groove welds.

The back and backing weld symbols are identical. The sequence of welding determines which designation applies. The back weld is made after the groove weld and the backing weld is made before the groove weld.

1. The back weld symbol is placed on the side of the reference line opposite a groove weld symbol. When a single reference line is used, "BACK WELD" is specified in the tail of the symbol. Alternatively, if a multiple reference line is used, the back weld symbol is placed on a reference line subsequent to the reference line specifying the groove weld, Figure 34–8(A).
2. The backing weld symbol is placed on the side of the reference line opposite the groove weld

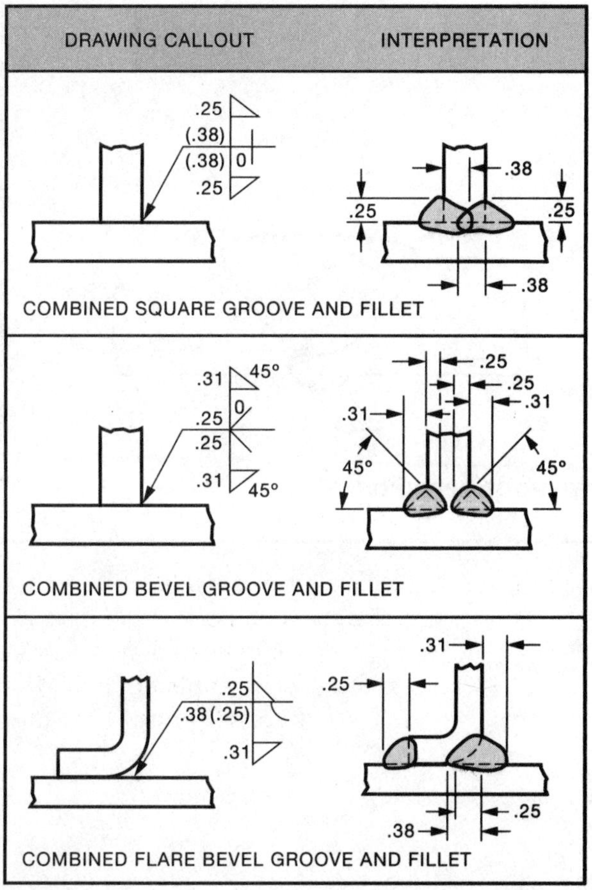

FIGURE 34–6 ■ Combined groove and fillet welds

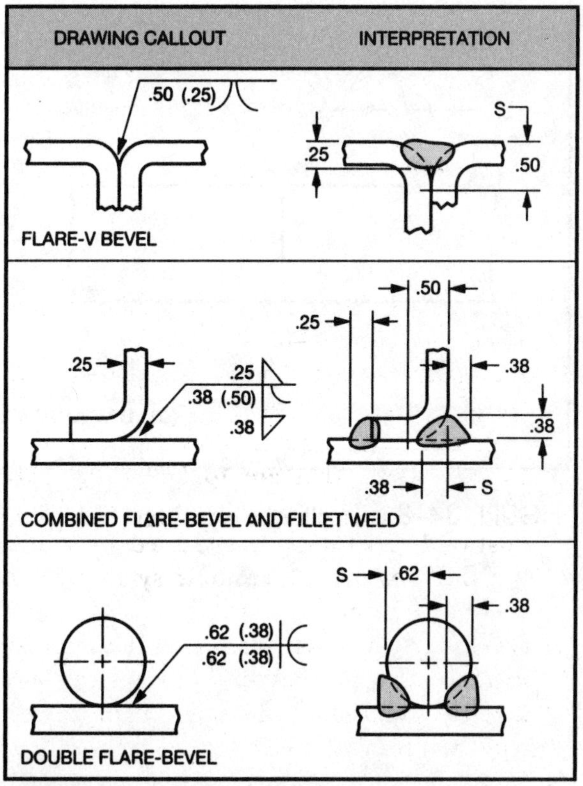

FIGURE 34–7 ■ Flare-V and flare bevel groove welds with partial joint penetration

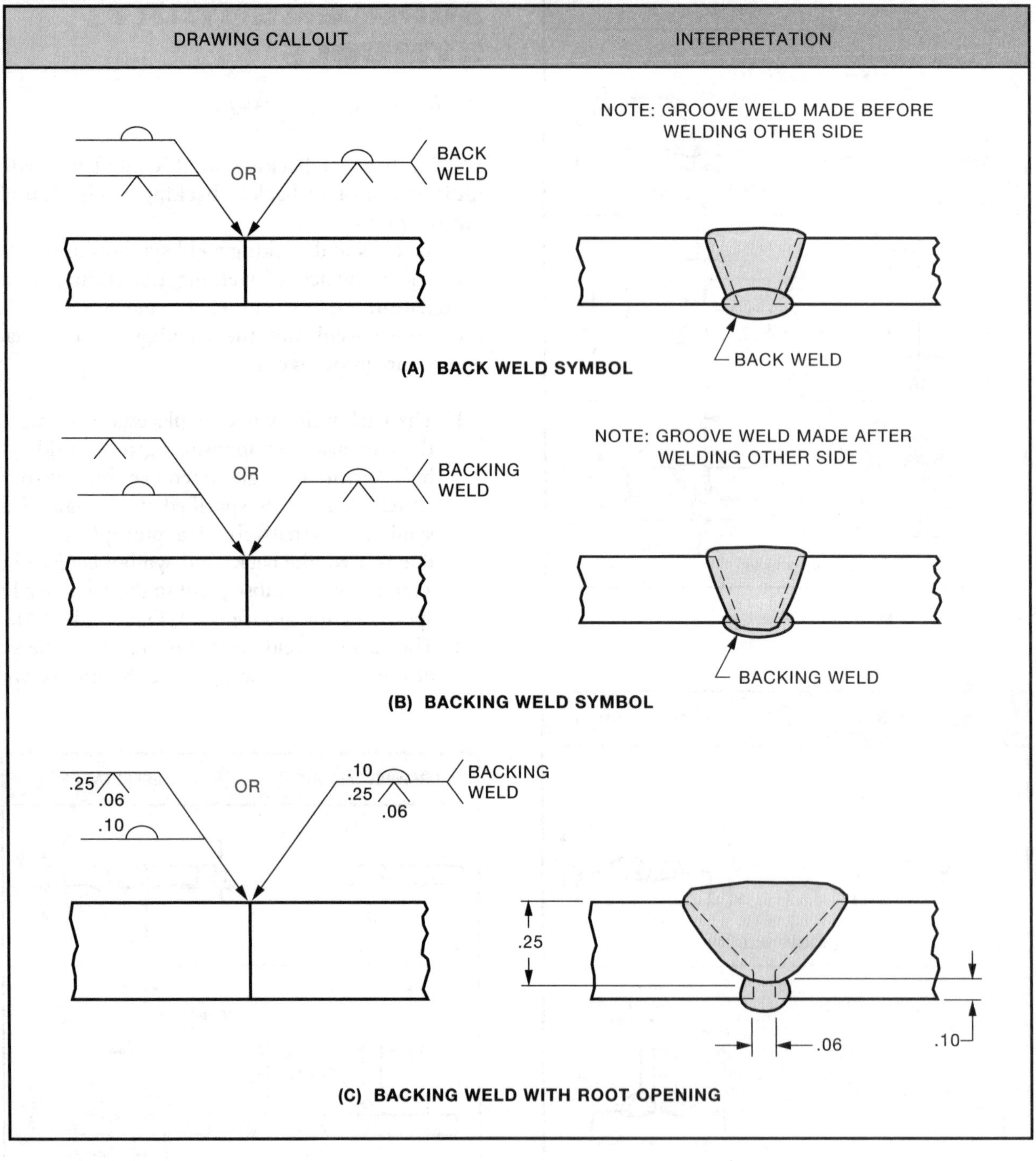
DRAWING CALLOUT
INTERPRETATION
NOTE: GROOVE WELD MADE BEFORE WELDING OTHER SIDE
OR
BACK WELD
BACK WELD
(A) BACK WELD SYMBOL
NOTE: GROOVE WELD MADE AFTER WELDING OTHER SIDE
OR
BACKING WELD
BACKING WELD
(B) BACKING WELD SYMBOL
.25
.06
.10
OR
.10
.25
.06
BACKING WELD
.25
.06
.10
(C) BACKING WELD WITH ROOT OPENING

FIGURE 34–8 ■ Application of back and backing weld symbol

symbol. When a single reference line is used, "BACKING WELD" is specified in the tail of the arrow. If a multiple reference line is used, the backing weld symbol is placed on a reference line before that specifying the groove weld, Figures 34–8(B) and (C).

Melt-Through Symbol

The melt-through symbol is used only when complete root penetration plus visible root reinforcement is required in welds made from one side.

The melt-through symbol is placed on the side of the reference line opposite the weld symbol, Figure 34–9.

The height of root reinforcement may be specified by placing the required dimension to the left of the melt-through symbol. The height of root reinforcement may be unspecified.

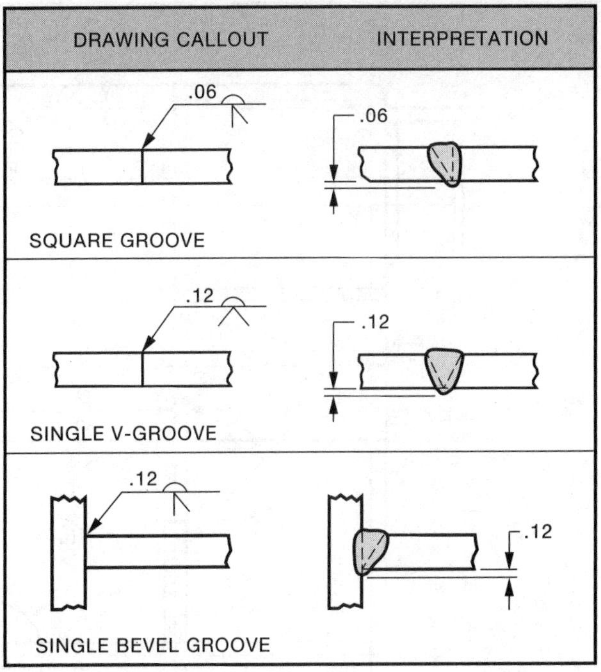

FIGURE 34–9 ■ Application of melt-through groove weld symbols

REFERENCES

Canadian Welding Bureau
ANSI/AWS A2.4-86 Standard Symbols for Welding, Brazing, and NDE

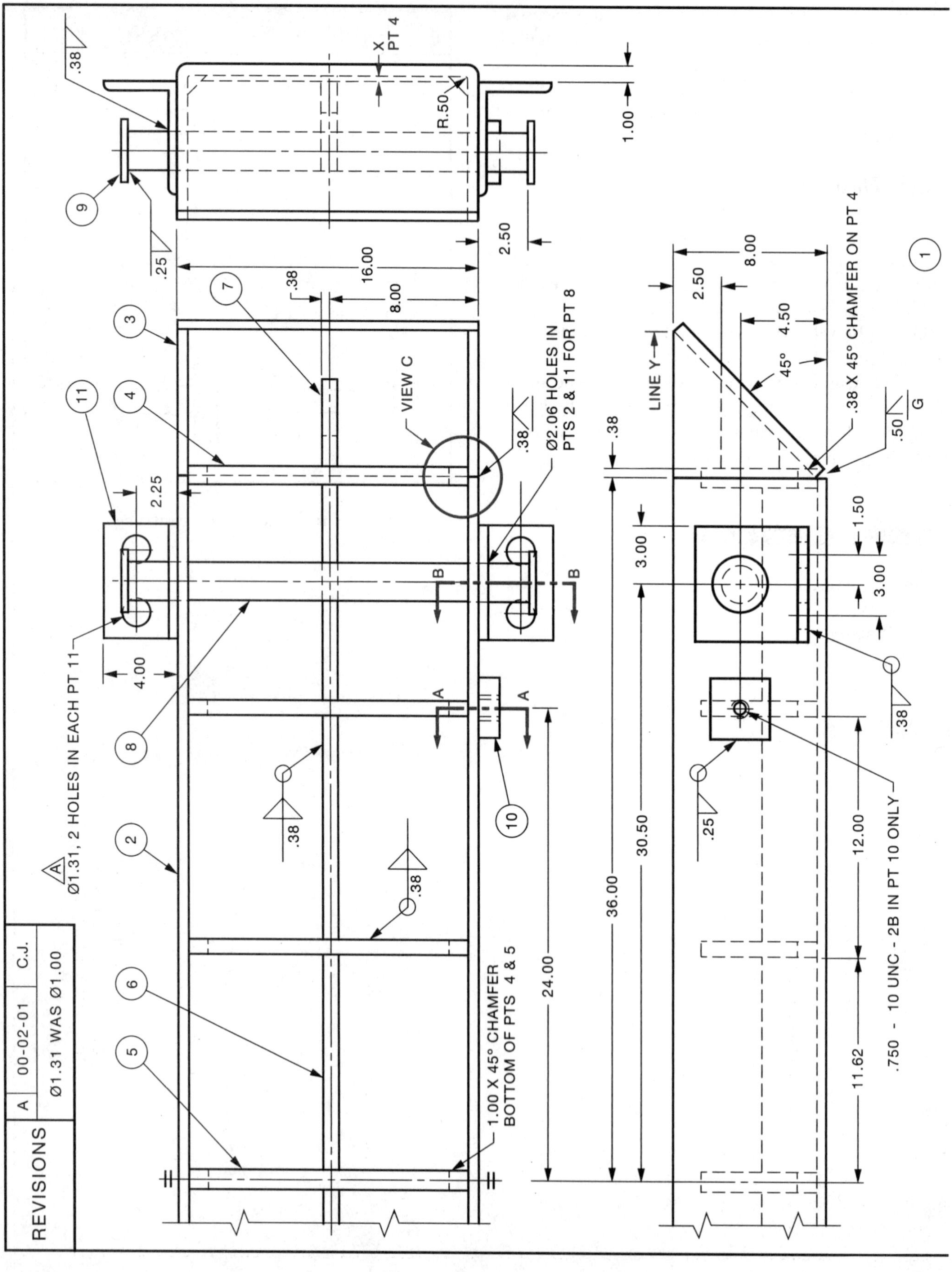
REVISIONS
A
00-02-01
C.J.
Ø1.31 WAS Ø1.00
Ø1.31, 2 HOLES IN EACH PT 11
1.00 X 45° CHAMFER BOTTOM OF PTS 4 & 5
VIEW C
Ø2.06 HOLES IN PTS 2 & 11 FOR PT 8
X PT 4
R.50
LINE Y
.38 X 45° CHAMFER ON PT 4
.750 - 10 UNC - 2B IN PT 10 ONLY
A
A
B
B
G
16.00
8.00
2.50
1.00
2.25
4.00
24.00
36.00
30.50
12.00
11.62
3.00
1.50
4.50
45°

ASSIGNMENT:
On the graph sections, complete the sketches and darken in the welds.

QUESTIONS

1. How many Ø1.31 holes are there in the complete assembly?
2. How deep is the .750 tapped hole?
3. What was the original size of the Ø1.31 hole?
4. What is the overall height of the assembly?
5. Determine the distance from line Y to the centre line of the assembly.
6. Determine distance X.
7. What is the developed width of part 2? Use inside dimensions of the channel.
8. What is the clearance for fitting on the length of part 5?
9. What is the length of (A) part 2; (B) part 4, allowing .25 for clearance; (C) part 7; and (D) part 8?
10. What is the difference between part 4 and part 5?
11. How many 1.00 chamfers are needed?
12. What does G mean on .50 bevel weld symbols?
13. What type of weld is used to fasten part 11 to part 2?
14. What type of weld is used to join part 3 to part 2 at the sides?
15. How many parts make up the assembly?
16. Complete the missing sizes in the Bill of Material. Use inside travel for calculating part 2.

NOTE: UNLESS OTHERWISE SPECIFIED:
—TOLERANCE ON LINEAR DIMENSIONS ±.04
—TOLERANCE ON ANGLES ±0.5°
—TOLERANCE ON HOLES ±.004

1.00 SQUARES

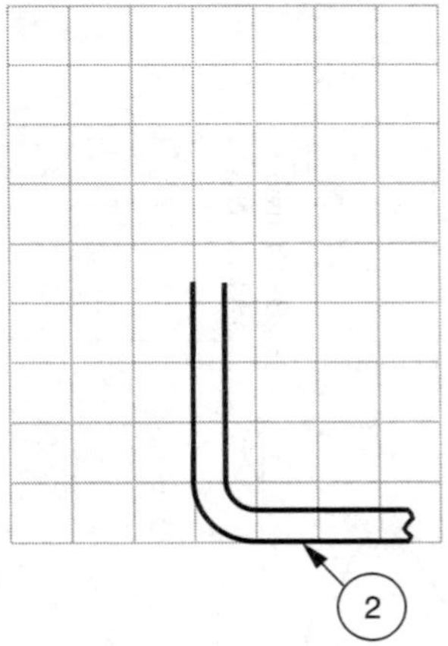
2

SECTION A-A

1.00 SQUARES

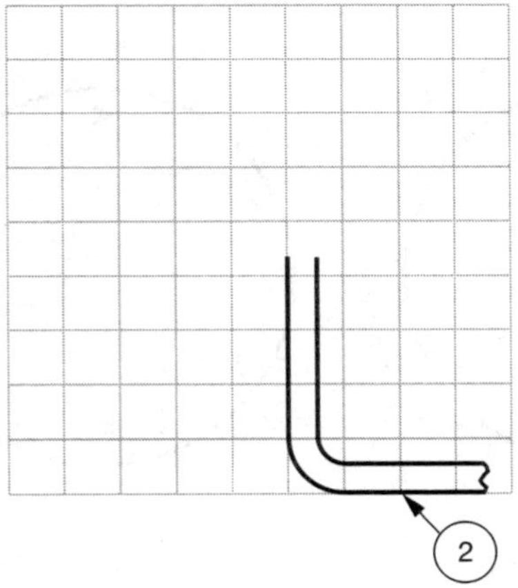
2

SECTION B-B

.50 SQUARES

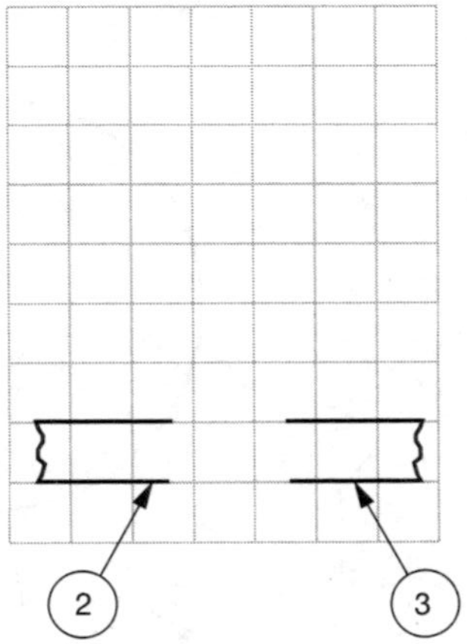
2
3

ENLARGED VIEW C

ANSWERS

1. ______ **2.** ______ **3.** ______
4. ______ **5.** ______ **6.** ______ **7.** ______ **8.** ______
9. A ______ **B** ______ **C** ______ **D** ______ **10.** ______
11. ______ **12.** ______ **13.** ______ **14.** ______ **15.** ______

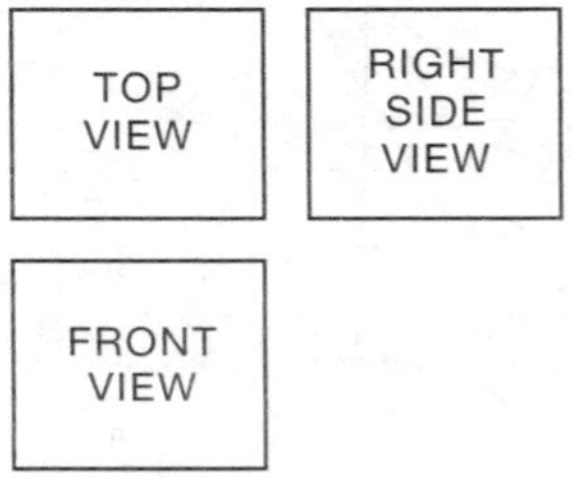
TOP VIEW
RIGHT SIDE VIEW
FRONT VIEW

ARRANGEMENT OF VIEWS

QTY	ITEM	MATL	DESCRIPTION	PT NO
4	LOCATING ANGLE	STL	6.00 X 4.00 X .50 X 6.00 LG	11
2	GROUND BAR	STL BAR	1.00 X 3.00 X 3.00	10
4	RETAINER	STL PL	.50 X Ø3.00	9
2	DRAW BAR	STL RD	Ø2.00 X	8
2	GUSSET	STL BAR	.75 X 3.00 X	7
6	GUSSET	STL BAR	.75 X 3.00 X 11.25	6
5	GUSSET	STL BAR	.75 X 6.00 X 14.75	5
2	GUSSET	STL BAR	.75 X 6.00 X	4
2	END PLATE	STL PL	.50 X 10.62 X 25.90	3
1	BASE	STL PL	.50 X X	2
1	SKID ASS'Y			1

BASE SKID **A-86**

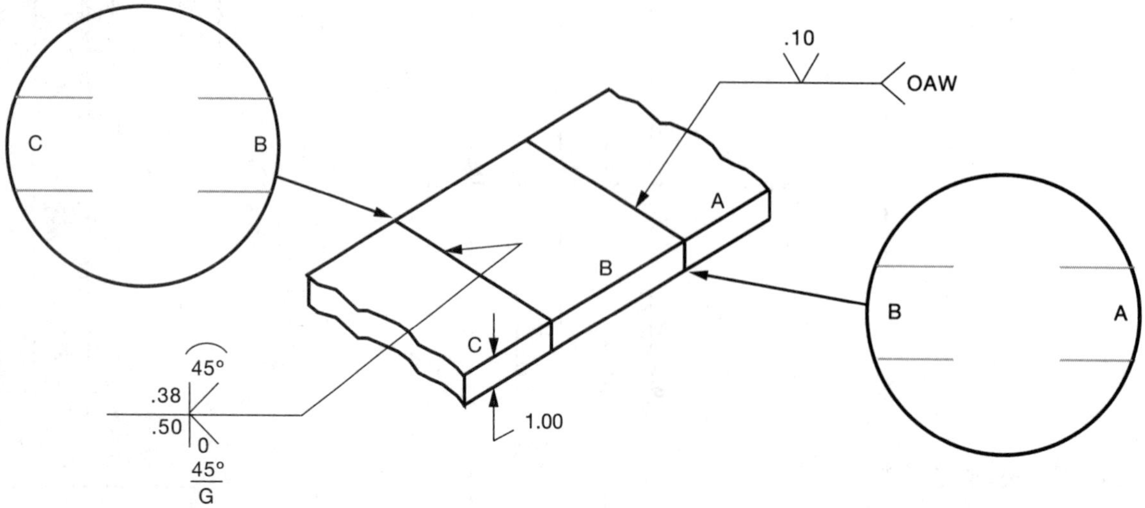
.10
OAW
C
B
A
B
C
B
A
45°
.38
.50
0
45°
G
1.00

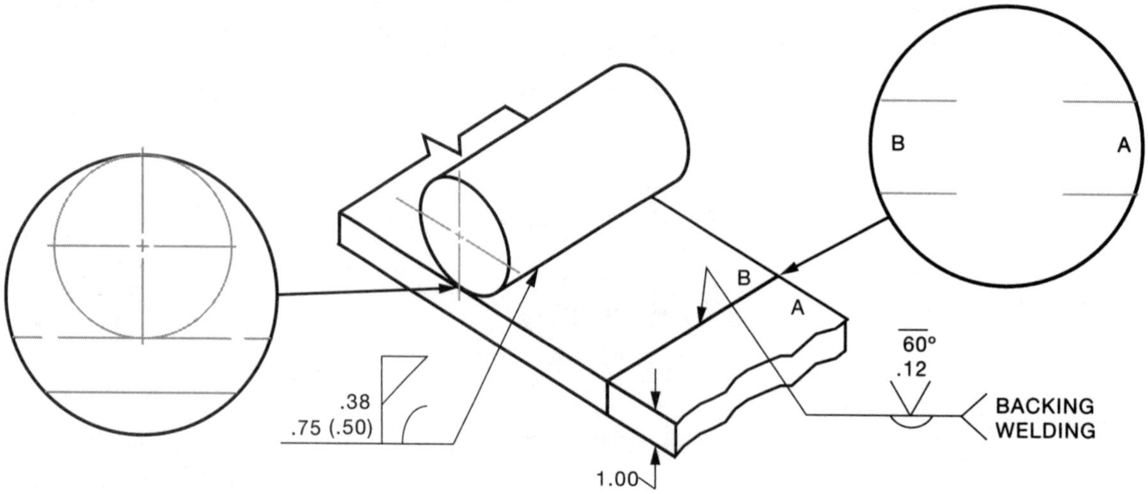
B
A
B
A
60°
.12
BACKING
WELDING
.38
.75 (.50)
1.00

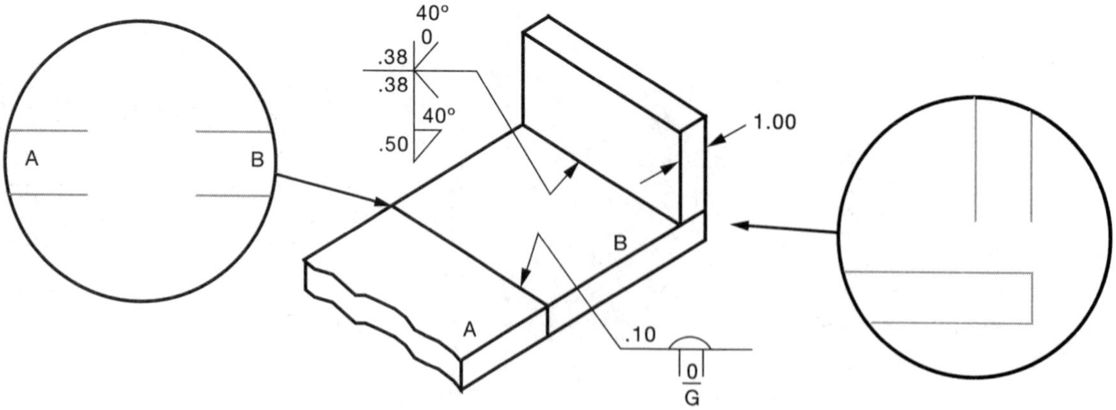
40°
0
.38
.38
40°
.50
1.00
A
B
B
A
.10
0
G

ASSIGNMENT: IN THE CIRCLED AREAS PROVIDED, MAKE DETAIL SKETCHES OF THE WELDS SHOWN.

GROOVE WELDS	**A-87**

UNIT 35

OTHER BASIC WELDS

Plug Welds (Figure 35–1)

1. Holes in the arrow-side member of a joint for plug welding are specified by placing the weld symbol below the reference line.

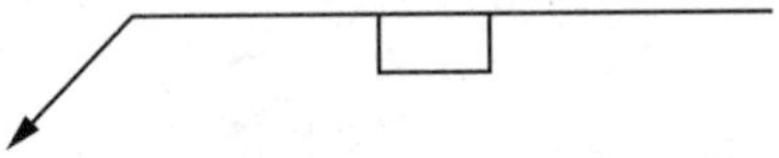

2. Holes in the other-side member of a joint for plug welding are indicated by placing the weld symbol above the reference line.

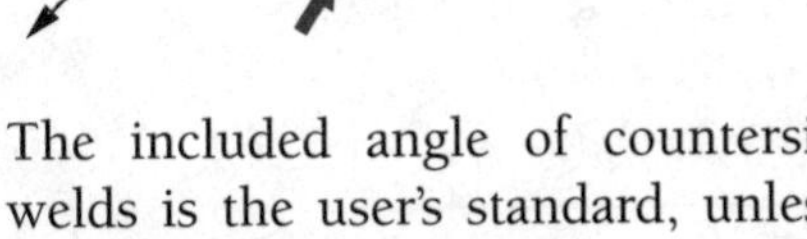

3. The size of a plug weld is shown on the same side and to the left of the weld symbol.

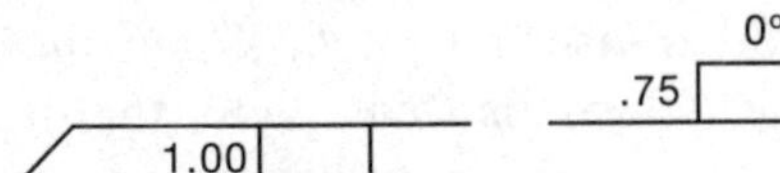

4. The included angle of countersink of plug welds is the user's standard, unless otherwise indicated. Included angle, when not the user's standard, is shown.

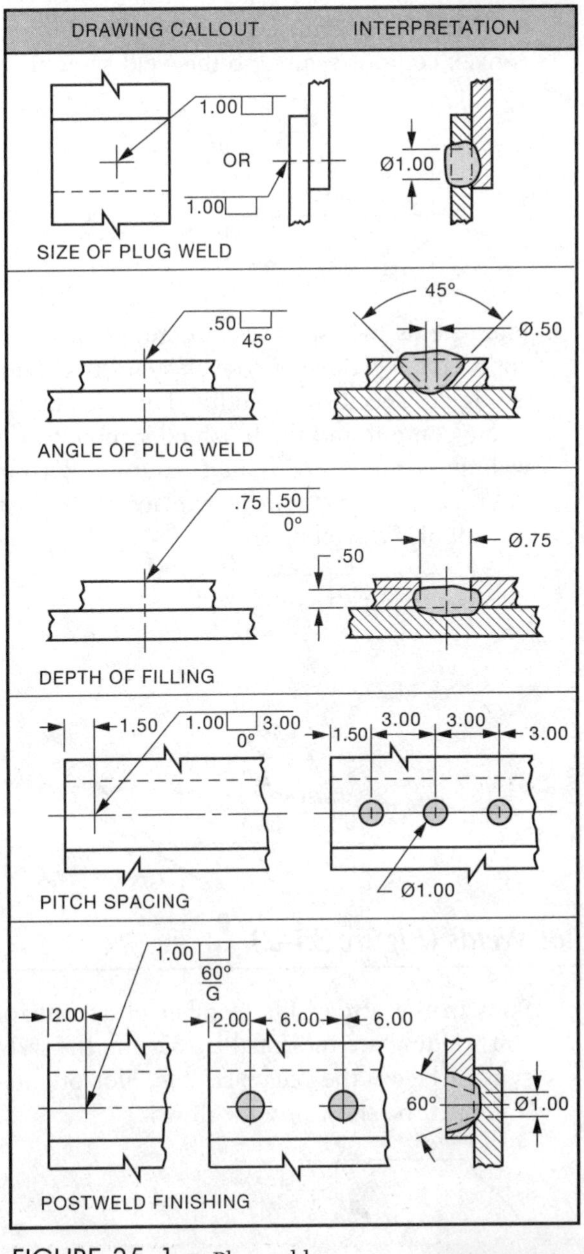

FIGURE 35–1 ■ Plug welds

5. The depth of filling of plug welds is complete unless otherwise indicated. When the depth of filling is less than complete, the depth of filling, in inches or millimetres, is shown inside the weld symbol.

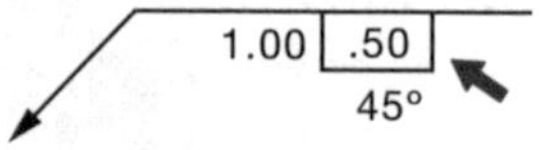

6. Pitch (centre-to-centre spacing) of plug welds is shown to the right of the weld symbol.

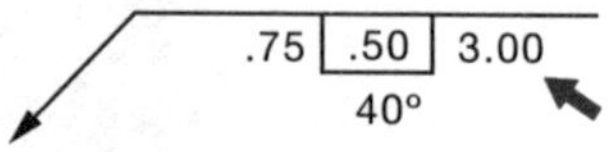

7. Plug welds that are to be welded with approximately flush or convex faces without postweld finishing are specified by adding the flush or convex contour symbol to the weld symbol.

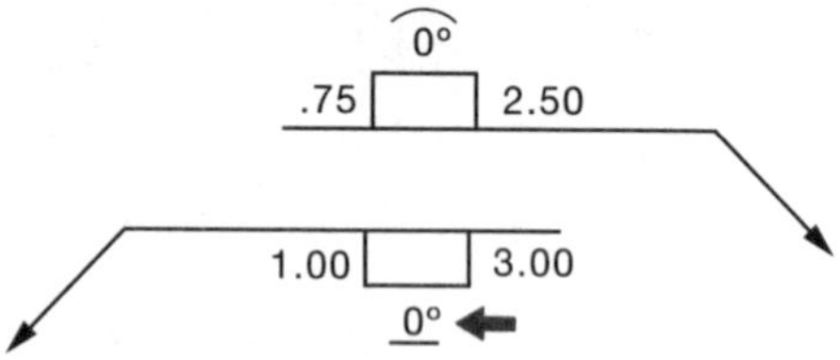

8. Plug welds whose faces are to be finished approximately flush or convex by postweld finishing are specified by adding both the appropriate contour and the finishing symbol to the welding symbol. Welds that require a flat but not flush surface require an explanatory note in the tail of the symbol.

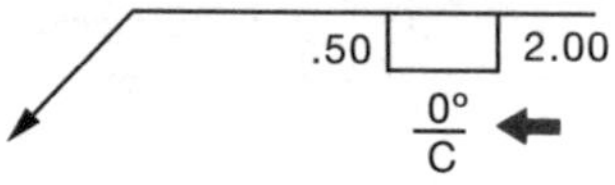

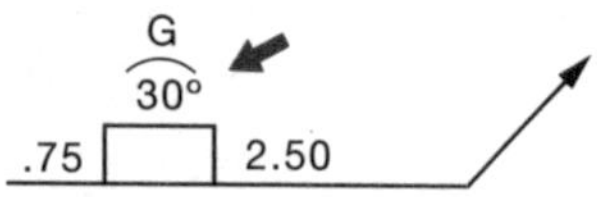

Slot Welds (Figure 35–2)

1. Slots in the arrow-side member of a joint for slot welding are indicated by placing the weld symbol below the reference line. Slot orientation must be shown on the drawing.

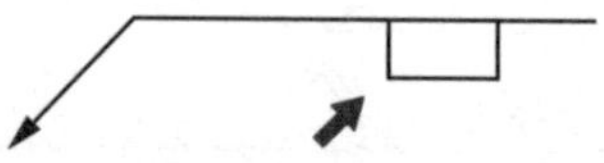

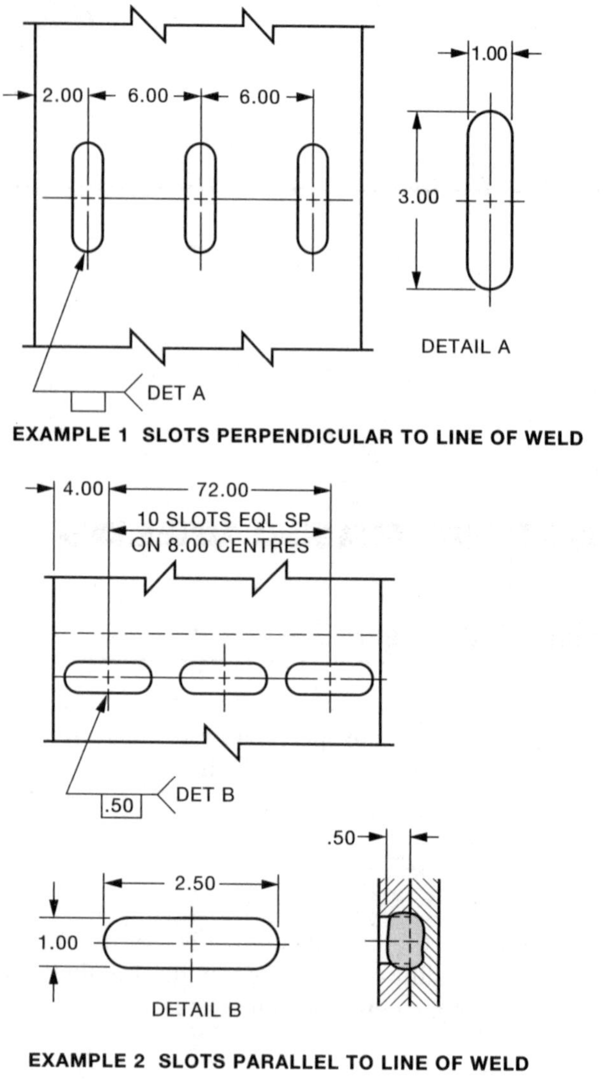

FIGURE 35–2 ■ Slot welds

2. Slots in the other-side member of a joint for slot welding are indicated by placing the weld symbol above the reference line.

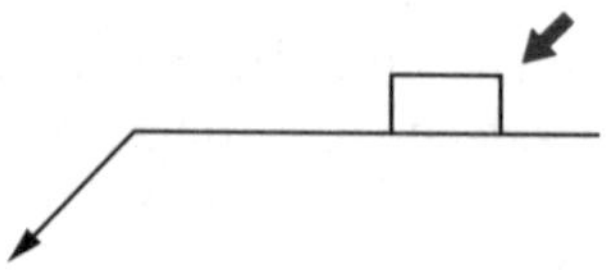

3. Depth of filling of slot welds is complete unless otherwise indicated. When the depth of filling is less than complete, the depth of filling, in inches or millimetres, is shown inside the welding symbol.

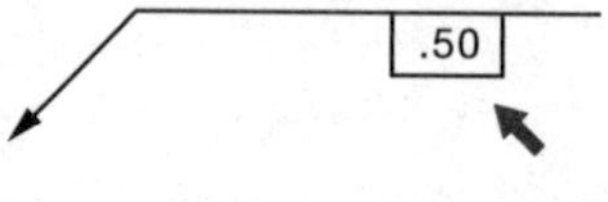

4. Length, width, spacing, included angle of countersink, orientation, and location of slot welds cannot be specified on the welding symbol. These data are to be specified on the drawing or by a detail with reference to it on the welding symbol.

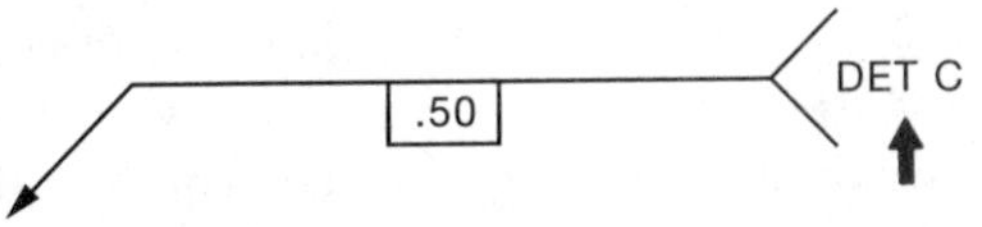

5. Slot welds that are to be welded with approximately flush or convex faces without postweld finishing are specified by adding the flush or convex contour symbol to the weld symbol.

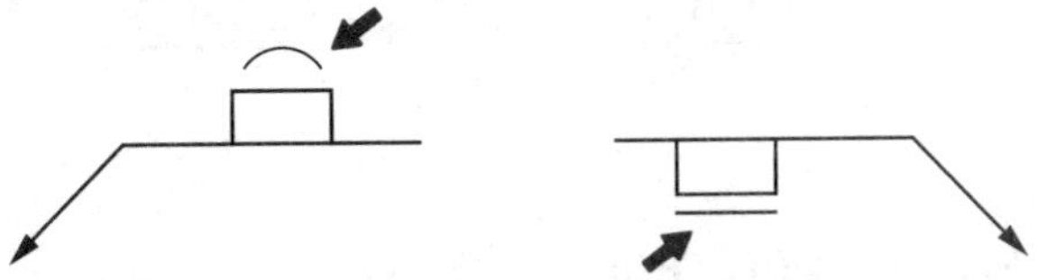

6. Slot welds whose faces are to be finished approximately flush or convex by postweld finishing are specified by adding both the appropriate contour and finishing symbol to the welding symbol. Welds that require a flat but not flush surface require an explanation note in the tail of the symbol.

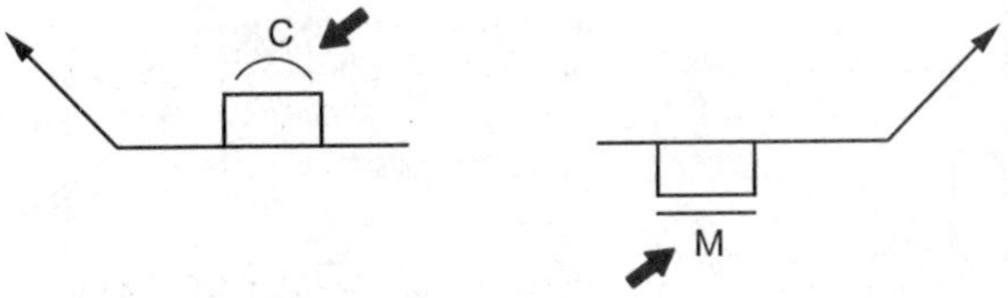

Spot Welds (Figure 35–3)

1. The symbol for all spot or projection welds is a circle, regardless of the welding process used. There is no attempt to provide symbols for different ways of making a spot weld, such as resistance, arc, and electron beam welding. The symbol for a spot weld is a circle placed

- below the reference line, indicating arrow side
- above the reference line, indicating other side
- on the reference line, indicating that there is no arrow or other side

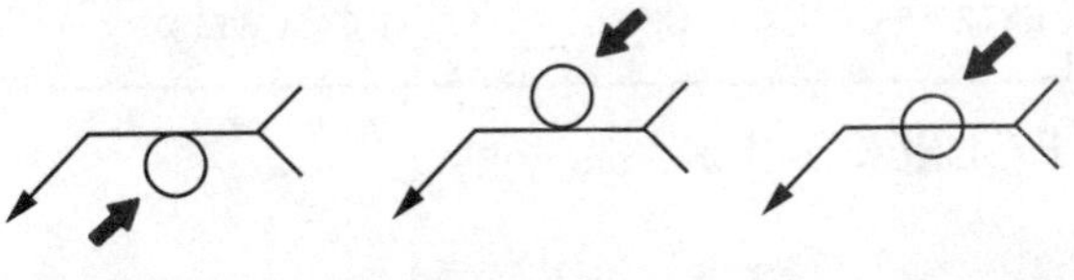

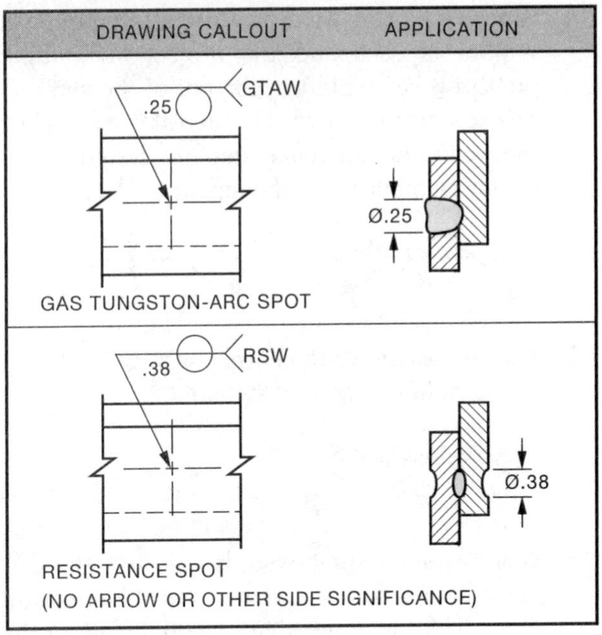

FIGURE 35–3 ■ Spot welds

2. Dimensions of spot welds are shown on the same side of the reference line as the weld symbol, or on either side when the symbol is located astride the reference line and has no arrow-side or other-side significance. They are dimensioned by either the size or the strength. The size is designated as the diameter of the weld and is shown to the left of the weld symbol. The strength of the spot weld is designated in pounds (or newtons) per spot and is shown to the left of the weld symbol.

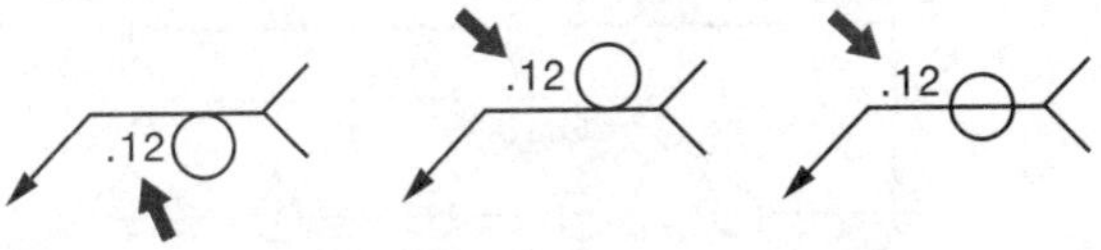

SPECIFYING DIAMETER OF SPOT

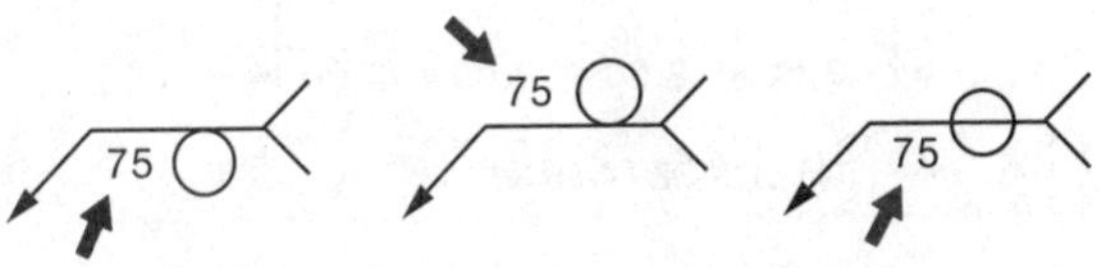

SPECIFYING STRENGTH OF SPOT

3. The process reference is to be indicated in the tail of the welding symbol.

4. When projection welding is used, the spot weld symbol is used and the projection welding process is referenced in the tail of the symbol. The spot weld symbol is located above or below (not on) the reference line to designate on which member the embossment is placed.

5. The pitch (centre-to-centre spacing) is shown to the right of the weld symbol.

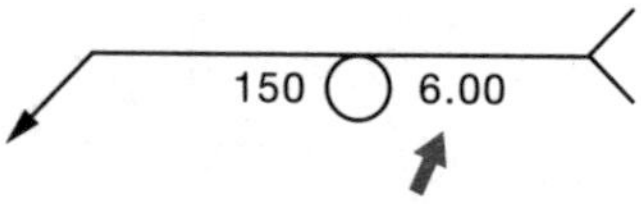

6. When spot welding extends less than the distance between abrupt changes in the direction of the welding or less than the full length of the joint, the extent is dimensioned.

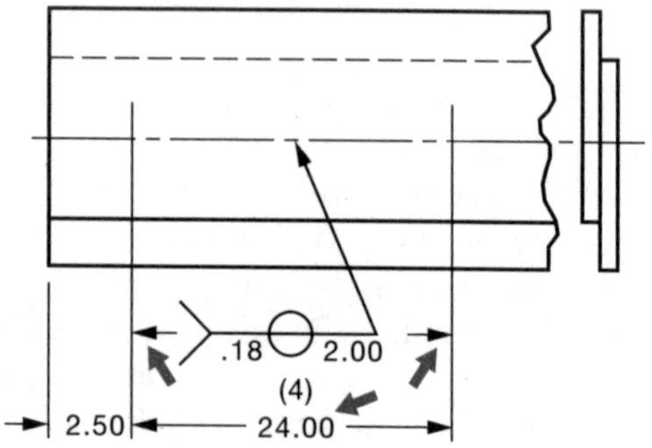

(A) DRAWING CALLOUT

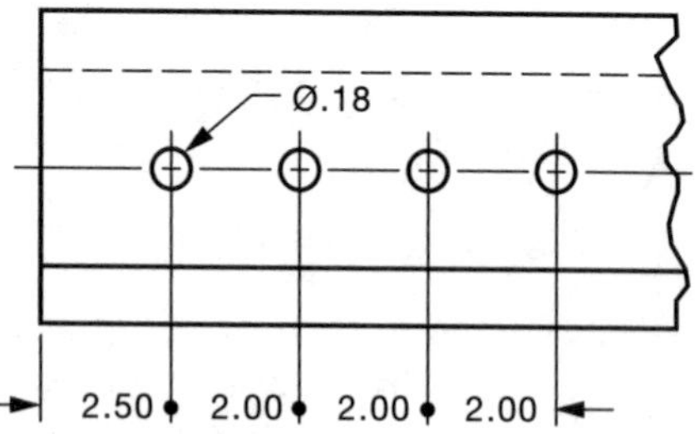

INTERPRETATION

7. Where the exposed surface of either member of a spot welded joint is to be welded with approximately flush or convex faces without postweld finishing, the surface is specified by adding the flush or convex contour symbol to the weld symbol.

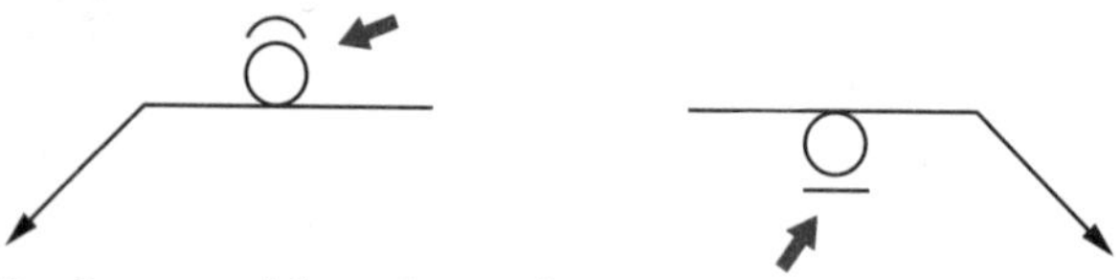

8. Spot welds whose faces are to be finished approximately flush or convex by postweld finishing are specified by adding both the appropriate contour and finishing symbol to the welding symbol. Welds that require a flat but not flush surface require an explanatory note in the tail of the symbol.

Seam Welds (Figure 35–4)

1. The symbol for all seam welds is a circle traversed by two horizontal parallel lines. This

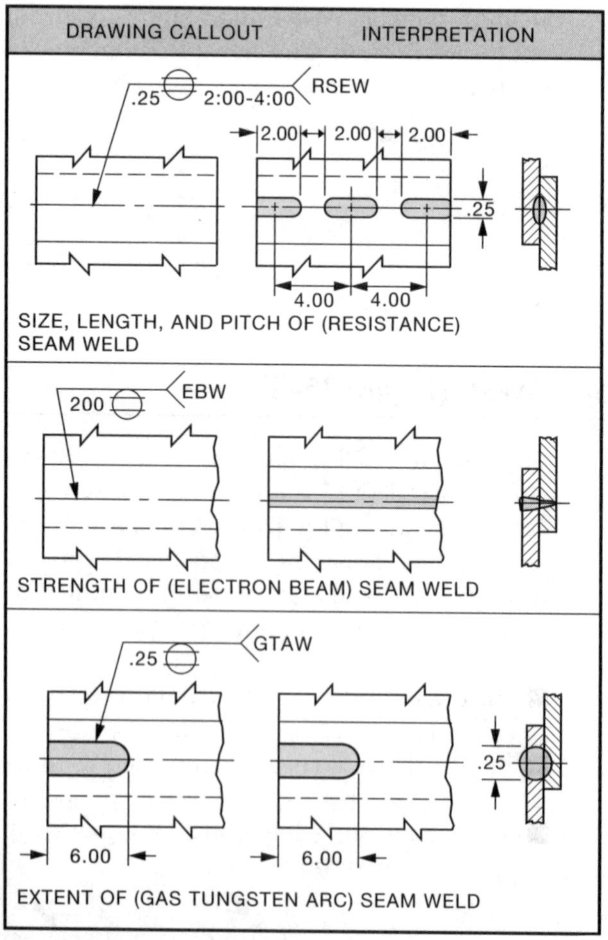

FIGURE 35–4 ■ Seam welds

symbol is used for all seam welds regardless of the way they are made. The seam weld symbol is placed (1) below the reference line to indicate arrow side, (2) above the reference line to indicate other side, and (3) on the reference line to indicate that there is no arrow or other side significance.

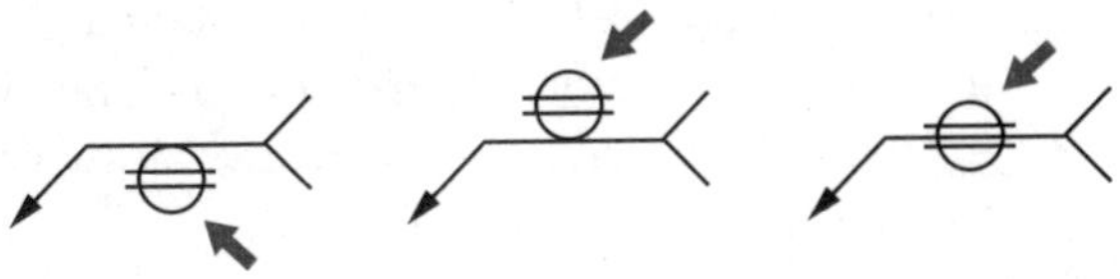

2. Dimensions of seam welds are shown on the same side of the reference line as the weld symbol or all on either side when the symbol is centred on the reference line. They are dimensioned by either size or strength. The size of the seam welds is designated as the width of the weld at the faying surfaces and is shown to the left of the weld symbol. The strength of seam welds is designated in pounds per linear inch (lb/in.) or newtons per millimetre (N/mm) and is shown to the left of the weld symbols.

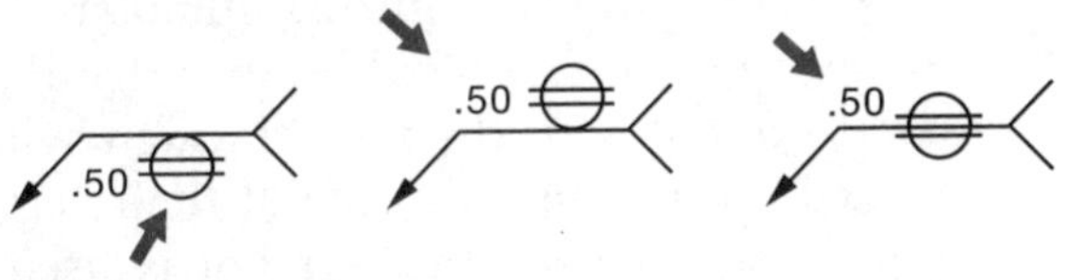
.50
.50
.50

SPECIFYING WIDTH OF WELD

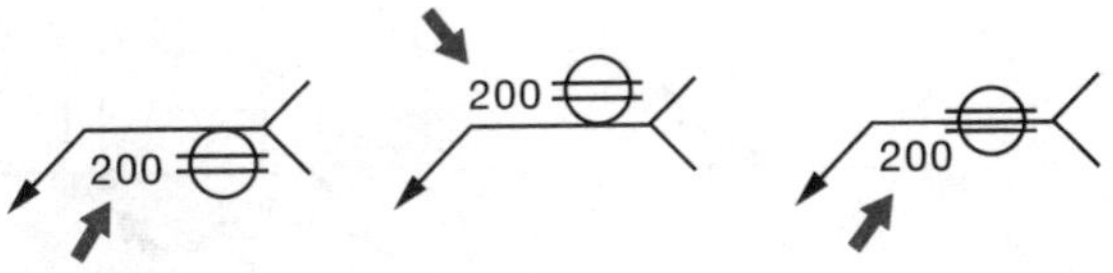
200
200
200

SPECIFYING STRENGTH OF WELD

3. The process reference is indicated in the tail of the welding symbol.

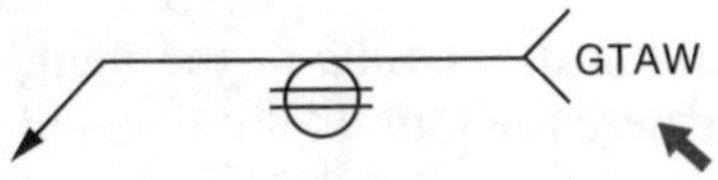
GTAW

4. The length of a seam weld, when indicated on the welding symbol, is shown to the right of the weld symbol. When seam welding extends for the full distance between abrupt changes in the direction of the welding, no length dimension needs to be shown on the welding symbol. When a seam weld extends less than the full length of the joint, the extent of the weld should be shown.

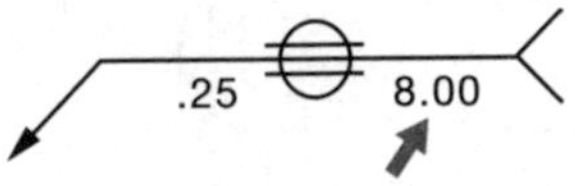
.25
8.00

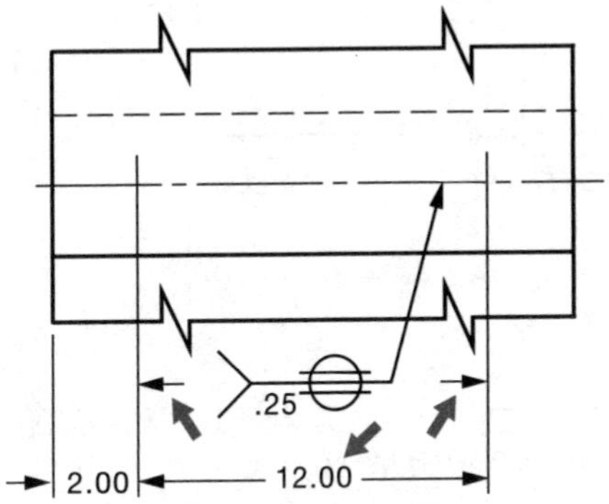
.25
2.00
12.00

5. The pitch of an intermittent seam weld is shown as the distance between centres of the weld increments. The pitch is shown to the right of the length dimension.

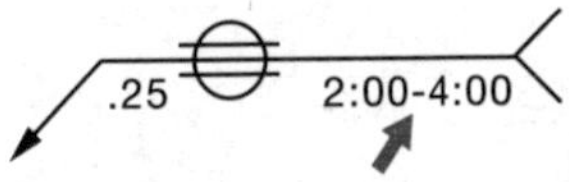
.25
2:00-4:00

6. When the exposed surface of either member of a seam-welded joint is to be welded with approximately flush or convex faces without postweld finishing, that surface is specified by adding the flush or convex contour symbol to the weld symbol.

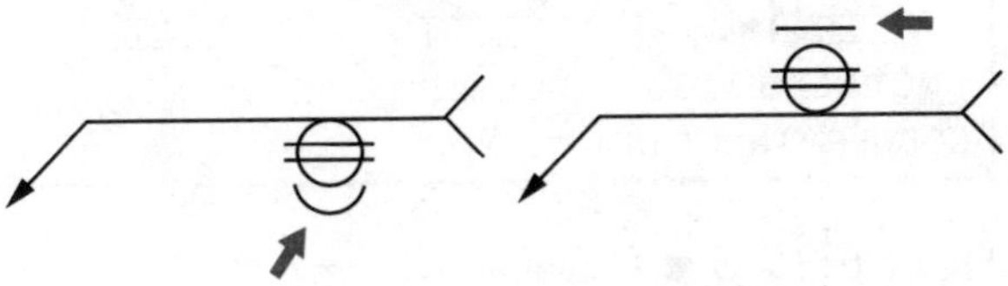

7. Seam welds with faces to be finished approximately flush or convex are specified by adding both the appropriate contour and finish symbol to the welding symbol.

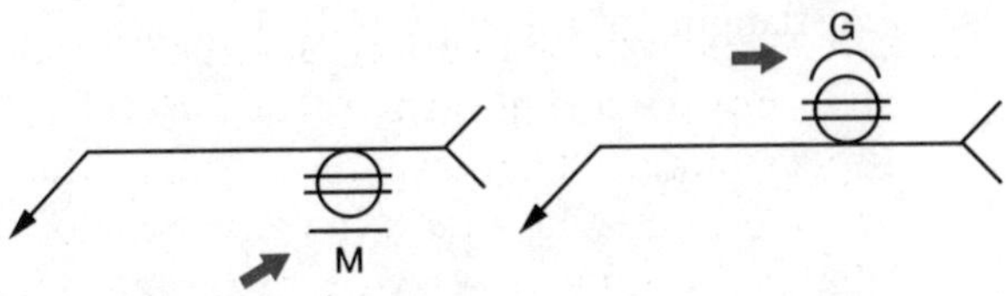
G
M

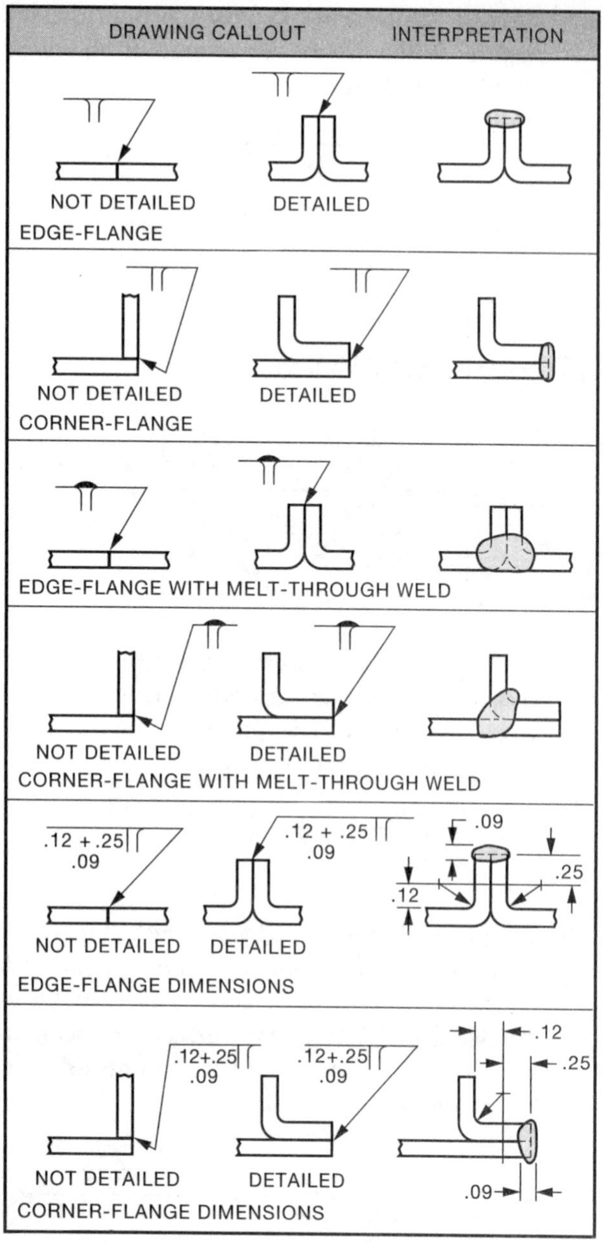

FIGURE 35–5 ■ Flange welds

Flange Welds (Figure 35–5)

The following welding symbols are intended to be used for light-gauge metal joints involving the flaring or flanging of the edges to be joined:

1. Edge-flange welds are shown by the edge-flange-weld symbol.

2. Corner-flange welds on joints detailed on the drawing are specified by the corner-flange weld symbol. Weld symbols are always drawn with the perpendicular leg to the left.

3. Corner-flange welds on joints not detailed on the drawing are specified by the corner-flange weld symbol. A broken arrow points to the member being flanged.

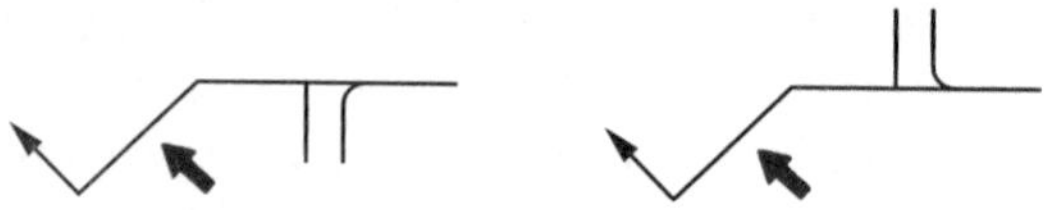

4. Edge-flange welds requiring complete joint penetration are specified by the edge-flange weld symbol with the melt-through symbol placed on the opposite side of the reference line. The same welding symbol is used for joints either detailed or not detailed on the drawing.

5. Corner-flange welds requiring complete joint penetration are specified by the corner-flange weld symbol with the melt-through symbol placed on the opposite side of the reference line. A broken arrow points to the member to be flanged where the joint is not detailed.

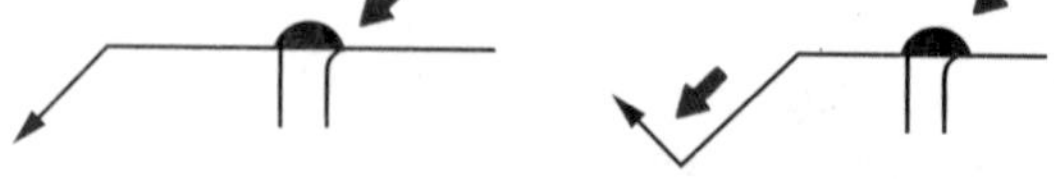

6. Dimensions of flange welds are shown on the same side of the reference line as the weld symbol. The radius and the height, separated by a plus (+), are placed to the left of the weld symbol. The radius and the height read in that order from left to right along the reference line.

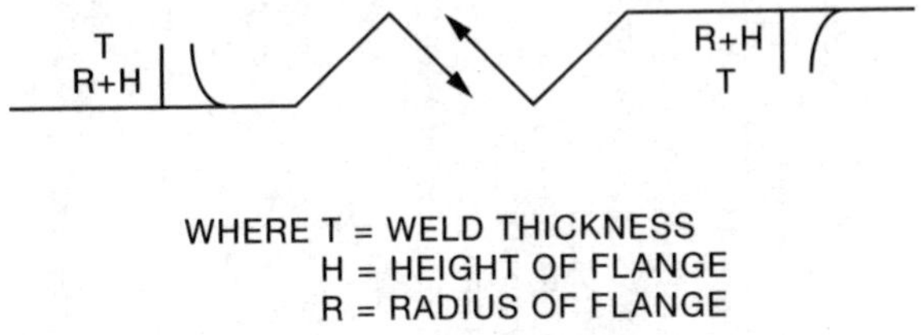
T
R+H
R+H
T
WHERE T = WELD THICKNESS
H = HEIGHT OF FLANGE
R = RADIUS OF FLANGE

7. The size (thickness) of flange welds is specified by a dimension placed above or below the flange dimensions.

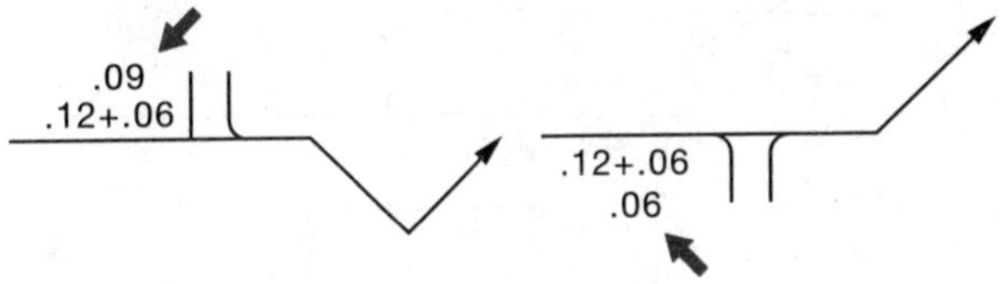
.09
.12+.06
.12+.06
.06

REFERENCES

Canadian Welding Bureau
ANSI/AWS A2.4-86 Standard Symbols for Welding, Brazing, and NDE

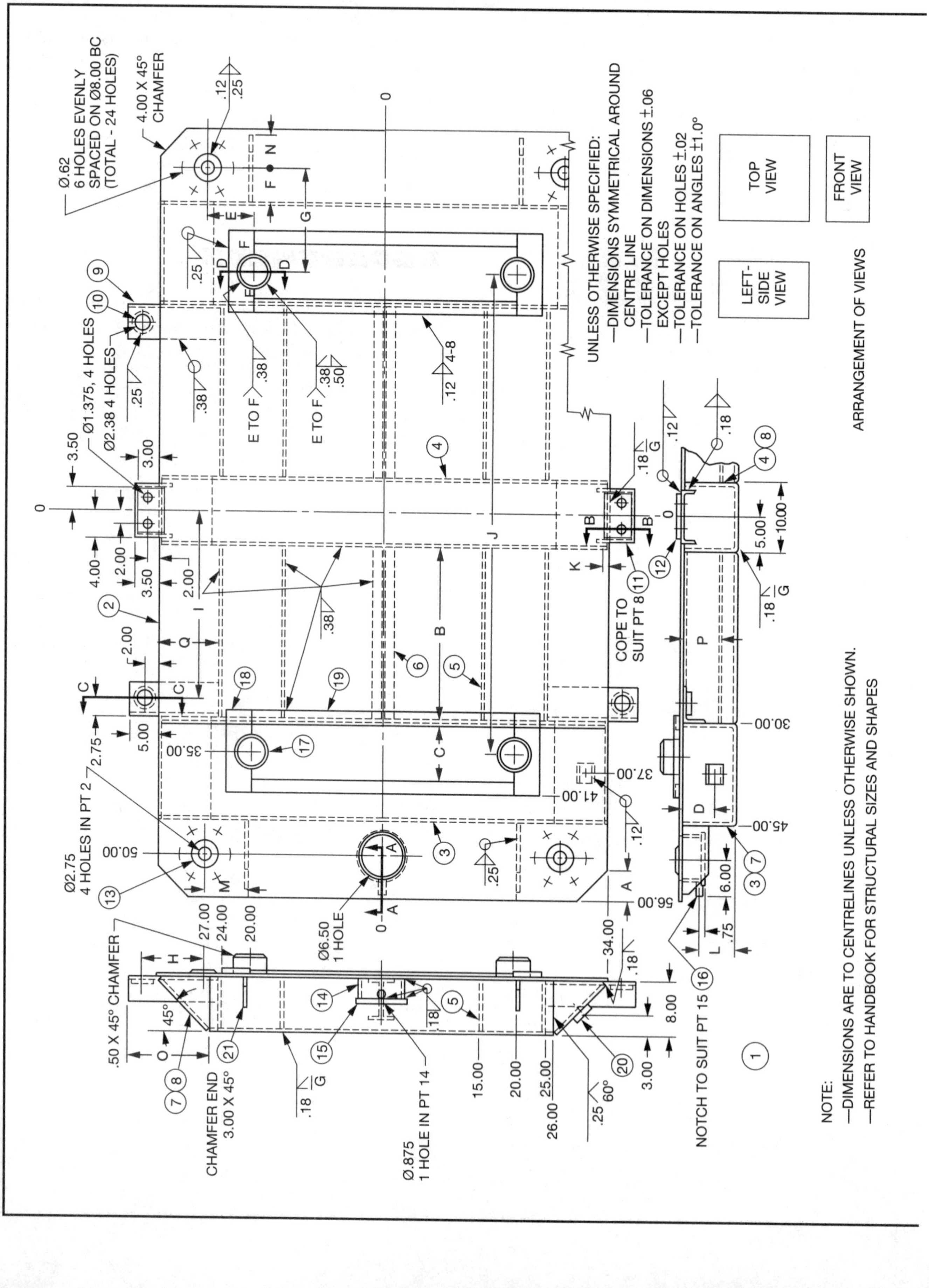
Ø.62
6 HOLES EVENLY SPACED ON Ø8.00 BC (TOTAL - 24 HOLES)
4.00 X 45° CHAMFER
Ø1.375, 4 HOLES
Ø2.38 4 HOLES
Ø2.75
4 HOLES IN PT 2
Ø6.50
1 HOLE
Ø.875
1 HOLE IN PT 14
.50 X 45° CHAMFER
CHAMFER END
3.00 X 45°
NOTCH TO SUIT PT 15
COPE TO SUIT PT 8
E TO F
E TO F
UNLESS OTHERWISE SPECIFIED:
—DIMENSIONS SYMMETRICAL AROUND CENTRE LINE
—TOLERANCE ON DIMENSIONS ±.06 EXCEPT HOLES
—TOLERANCE ON HOLES ±.02
—TOLERANCE ON ANGLES ±1.0°
TOP VIEW
LEFT-SIDE VIEW
FRONT VIEW
ARRANGEMENT OF VIEWS
NOTE:
—DIMENSIONS ARE TO CENTRELINES UNLESS OTHERWISE SHOWN.
—REFER TO HANDBOOK FOR STRUCTURAL SIZES AND SHAPES

.50 SQUARES

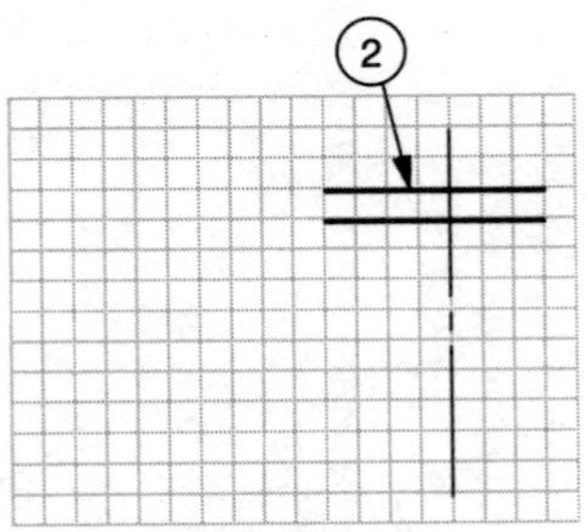

SECTION A-A

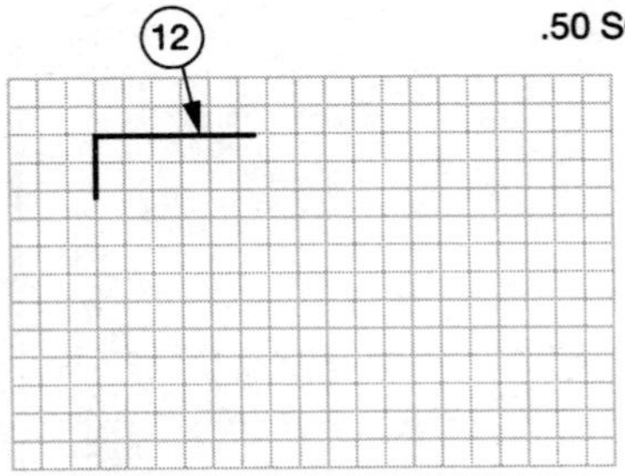

SECTION B-B

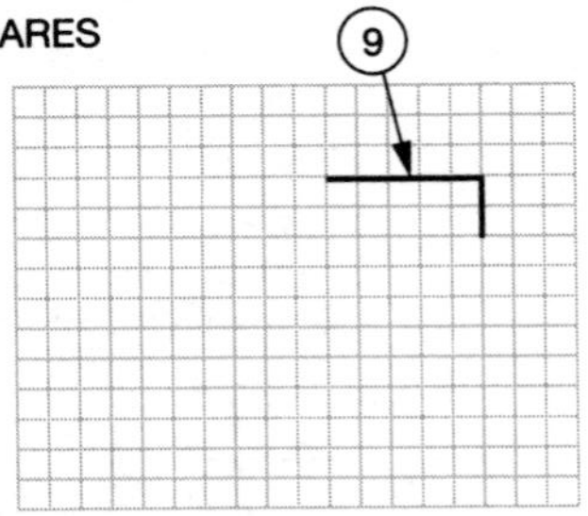

SECTION C-C

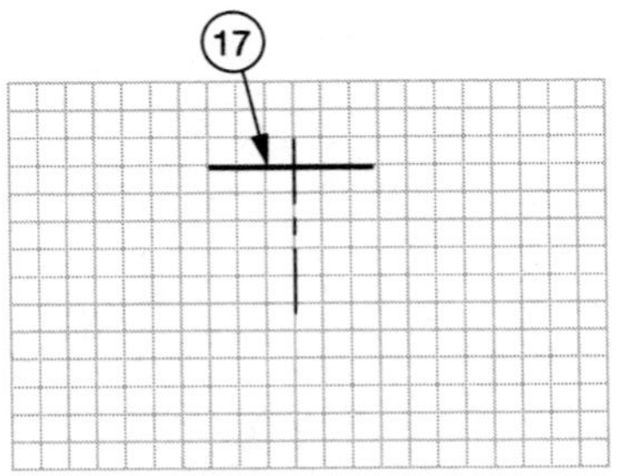

SECTION D-D

ASSIGNMENT:

1. In the areas provided, sketch sections A-A, B-B, C-C, and D-D, and darken in the welds.
2. Sketch one-half the development of part 8, showing dimensions and indicating bend lines. (Use inside travel.)

ANSWERS

1. A ______ B ______ C ______ D ______ E ______ F ______ G ______ H ______ I ______ J ______ K ______ L ______ M ______ N ______ O ______ P ______

2. A ______ B ______ C ______

3. ______

4. A ______ B ______

5. ______

6. ______

7. ______

8. ______

9. ______

10. ______

QUESTIONS

1. Determine dimensions A to P.
2. What is the overall (A) width, (B) depth, and (C) height of the complete assembly?
3. Assuming the formed channels to have square inside corners, what is the width of the material used to make part 3? (Use inside travel.)
4. What is the (A) width and (B) depth of the base plate, part 2?
5. If steel weighs .281 pound per cu. in., what is the weight of the base plate, part 2? (Disregard holes and chamfers.)
6. Determine the distance from the bottom of the S-beam part 6) to the bottom of the base assembly.
7. What is the angle between the Ø.62 holes?
8. If 6-in. pipe has an OD of 6.62 in., what distance does part 15 project beyond part 14?
9. Determine the distance part 16 projects into part 14.
10. What is the area enclosed by parts 17, 18, and 19?
11. Complete the Bill of Material.

4	RIB	STL	.50 X 4.00 X 10.00	21
1	GROUND PAD		DWG A - 4158	20
4	RETAINER	STL	.50 X 2.00 X LG	19
4	RETAINER	STL	.75 X 4.00 X LG	18
4	BUMPER PIN	STL	Ø5.00 X 3.00	17
1	NIPPLE	STL	.50 IPS X 3.00 LG	16
1	END PLATE	STL	Ø7.20 X .50 THK	15
1	SUMP	STL	6.00 IPS X 3.00 LG	14
4	FLANGE	STL	WELD -IN FLANGE 3.00 IPS	13
2	SUPPORT	STL	.75 X 4.50 X 7.00	12
2	SUPPORT	STL	C8 X 11.5 X LG	11
4	SUPPORT	STL	Ø3.50 X 1.00 THK	10
4	DRAW BAR	STL	L5.00 X 3.50 X .50 X LG	9
2	RIB END	STL	.50 X 10.50 X 20.00 LG	8
4	RIB END	STL	.50 X 10.50 X 25.00	7
2	RIB	STL	S6 X 12.5 X 25.00 LG	6
4	RIB	STL - PL	.50 X X LG	5
1	RIB	STL - PL	.50 X X LG	4
2	RIB	STL - PL	.50 X X LG	3
1	BASE PLATE	STL - PL	.50 X X LG	2
1	BASE ASSEMBLY			1
QTY	ITEM BASE ASSEMBLY	MATL	DESCRIPTION	PT NO

DRAWN SCALE NONE	BASE ASSEMBLY	A-88

DRAWING CALLOUT	INTERPRETATION

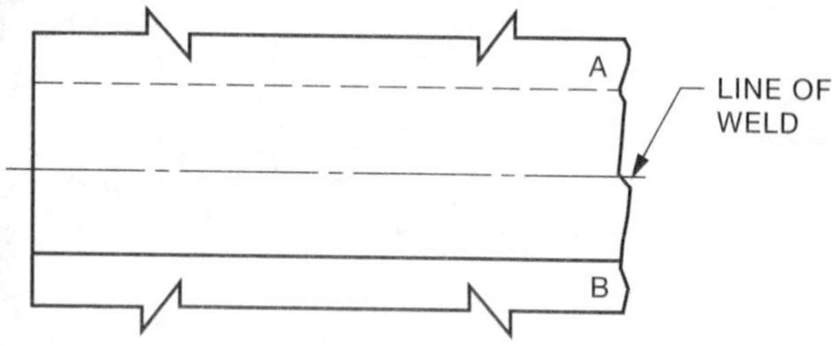

SECTION THROUGH WELD

ASSEMBLY 1 - PLUG WELDS

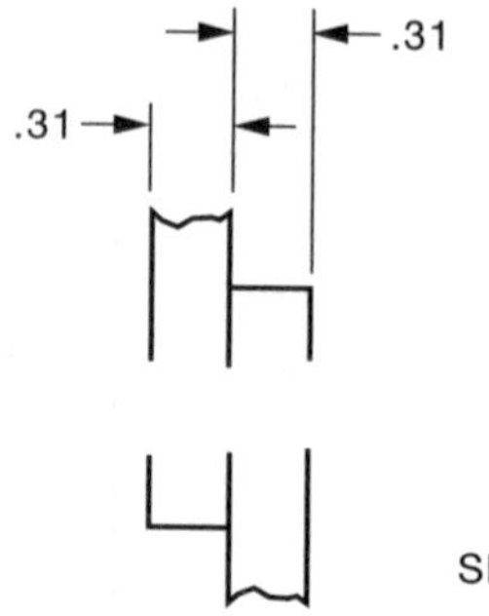

SLOT DETAIL

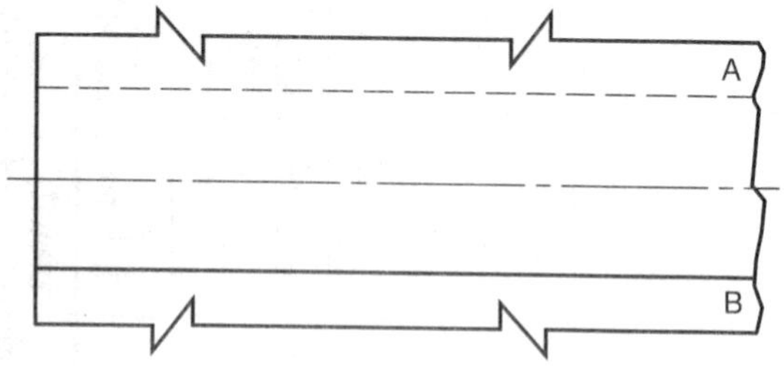

SECTION THROUGH WELD

ASSEMBLY 2 - SLOT WELDS

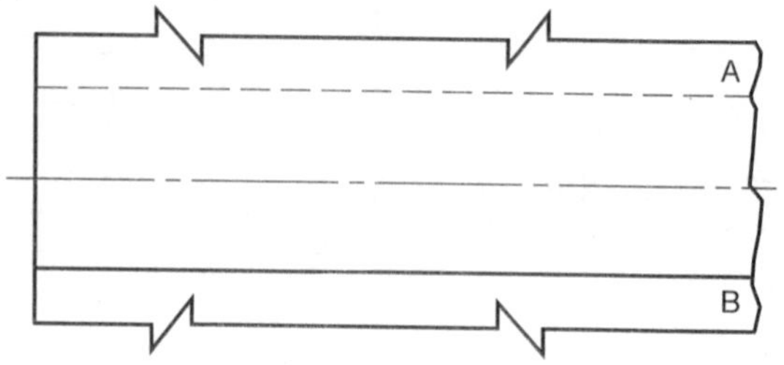

ASSEMBLY 3 - SPOT WELDS

SECTION THROUGH WELD

ASSEMBLY 1 - PLUG WELDS	ASSEMBLY 2 - SLOT WELDS	ASSEMBLY 3 - SPOT WELDS
- HOLES IN PART B - HOLES - Ø.62 X 0° CSK - CENTRE OF FIRST HOLE 2.50 FROM LEFT SIDE - CENTRE SPACING OF WELDS - 4.00 - HOLES COMPLETELY FILLED - POSTWELD FINISH - CONVEX BY CHIPPING	- HOLES IN PART A, PERPENDICULAR TO LINE OF WELD - SLOT SIZE .75 X 2.00 X 30° CSK - CENTRE OF FIRST HOLE 3.00 FROM LEFT SIDE - CENTRE SPACING OF WELDS - 6.00 - DEPTH OF FILLING .19	- GAS TUNGSTEN ARC WELD - CENTRE SPACING OF WELDS - 3.00 - CENTRE OF FIRST SPOT 2.00 FROM LEFT SIDE - WELD ARROW SIDE - STRENGTH OF SPOT WELDS - 300 LB. - TOTAL STRENGTH OF JOINT = 2400 LB.

ASSIGNMENT: SHOW THE DRAWING CALLOUT AND INTERPRETATION FOR THE THREE ASSEMBLIES SHOWN.	**PLUG, SLOT, AND SPOT WELDS**	**A-89**

DRAWING CALLOUT	INTERPRETATION

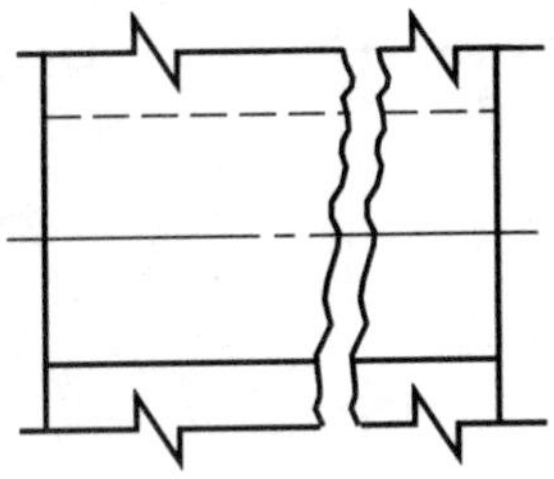

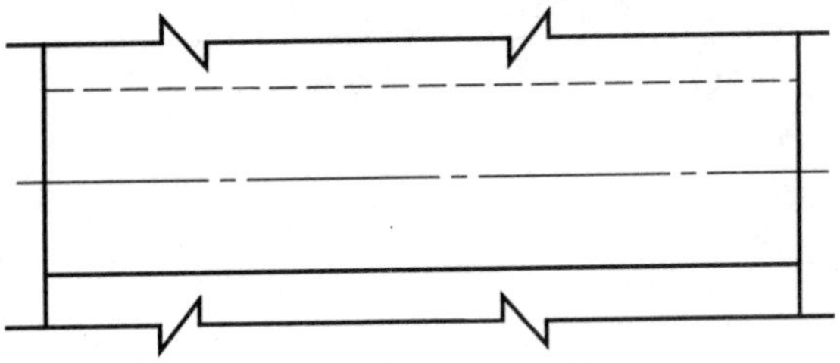

ASSEMBLY 1 - SEAM WELD

SECTION THROUGH WELD

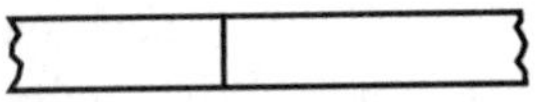

EDGE FLANGE WELD ONLY

COMPLETE JOINT PREPARATION

EDGE FLANGE WELD ONLY

COMPLETE JOINT PREPARATION

ASSEMBLY 2 - EDGE FLANGE WELD

CORNER FLANGE WELD ONLY

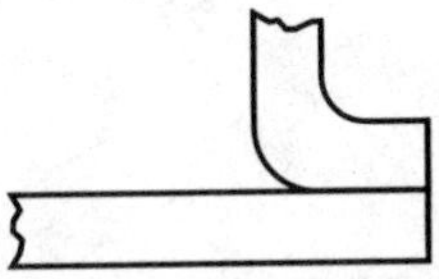

COMPLETE JOINT PREPARATION

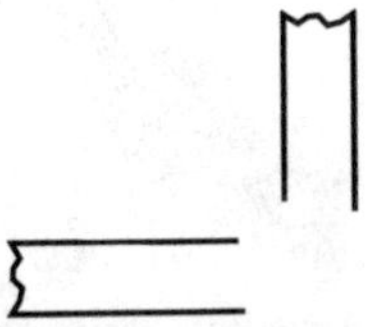

CORNER FLANGE WELD ONLY

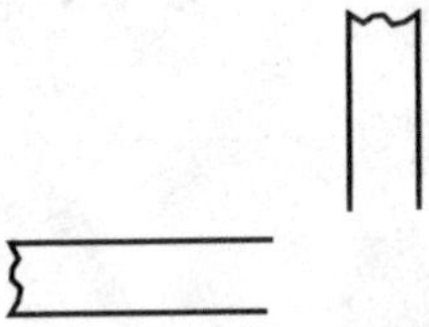

COMPLETE JOINT PREPARATION

ASSEMBLY 3 - CORNET FLANGE WELD

ASSEMBLY 1 - RESISTANCE SEAM WELD	ASSEMBLY 2 - EDGE FLANGE WELD	ASSEMBLY 3 - CORNER FLANGE WELD
- SIZE .25	- WELD THICKNESS .10	- WELD THICKNESS .20
- LENGTH 1.50	- HEIGHT OF FLANGE .20	- HEIGHT OF FLANGE .16
- PITCH 3.00	- RADIUS OF FLANGE .30	- RADIUS OF FLANGE .24

ASSIGNMENT: SHOW THE DRAWING CALLOUT AND INTERPRETATION FOR THE THREE ASSEMBLIES SHOWN.	**SEAM AND FLANGE WELDS**	**A-90**

36 UNIT

GEARS

The function of a gear is to transmit rotary or reciprocating motion from one machine part to another. Gears are often used to reduce or increase the r/min of a shaft. *Gears* are rolling cylinders or cones. They have teeth on their contact surfaces to ensure the transfer of motion, Figure 36–1.

There are many kinds of gears; they may be grouped according to the position of the shafts they connect. *Spur gears* connect parallel shafts, *bevel gears* connect shafts having intersecting axes, and *worm gears* connect shafts having axes that do not intersect. A spur gear with a rack converts rotary motion to reciprocating or linear motion. The smaller of two gears is the *pinion*.

FIGURE 36–1 ■ Gears

A simple gear drive consists of a toothed driving wheel meshing with a similar driving wheel. Tooth forms are designed to ensure uniform angular rotation of the driven wheel during tooth engagement.

SPUR GEARS

Spur gears, which are used for drives between parallel shafts, have teeth on the rim of the wheel, Figure 36–2. A pair of spur gears operates as though it consists of two cylindrical surfaces with formed teeth that maintain constant speed ratio between the driving and the driven wheel.

Gear design is complex, dealing with such problems as strength, wear, noise, and material selection. Usually, a designer selects a gear from a catalogue. Most gears are made of cast iron or steel. However, brass, bronze, and fibre are used when factors such as wear or noise must be considered.

Theoretically, the teeth of a spur gear are built around the original frictional cylindrical surface called the *pitch circle,* Figure 36–3.

The angle between the direction of pressure between contacting teeth and a line tangent to the pitch circle is the *pressure angle.*

The 14.5-degree pressure angle has been used for many years and remains useful for duplicate or replacement gearing.

The 20- and 25-degree pressure angles have become the standard for new gearing because of their smoother and quieter operation and greater load-carrying ability.

Gear Terms

The following terms, shown in Figures 36–4 and 36–5, are used in spur gear train calculations

Pitch Diameter (PD)

The diameter of an imaginary circle on which the gear tooth is designed.

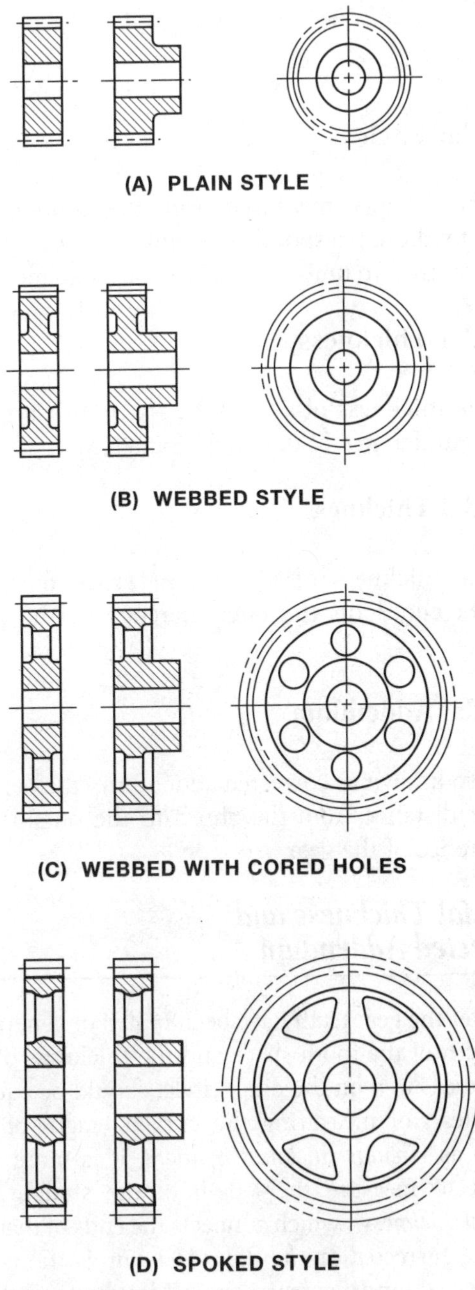
(A) PLAIN STYLE
(B) WEBBED STYLE
(C) WEBBED WITH CORED HOLES
(D) SPOKED STYLE
FIGURE 36–2 ■ Stock spur gear styles

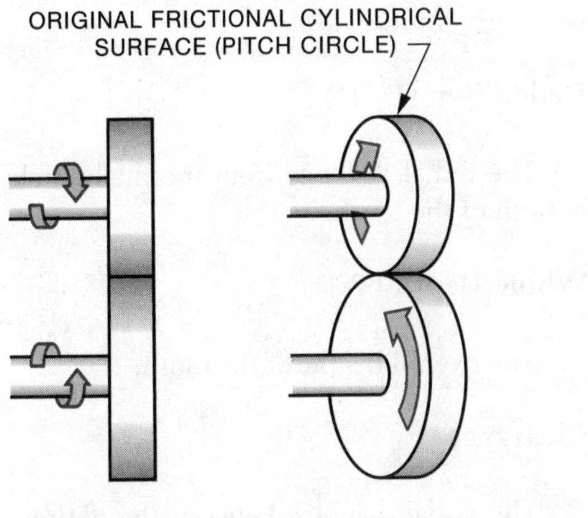
ORIGINAL FRICTIONAL CYLINDRICAL SURFACE (PITCH CIRCLE)
FIGURE 36–3 ■ The pitch circle of spur gears

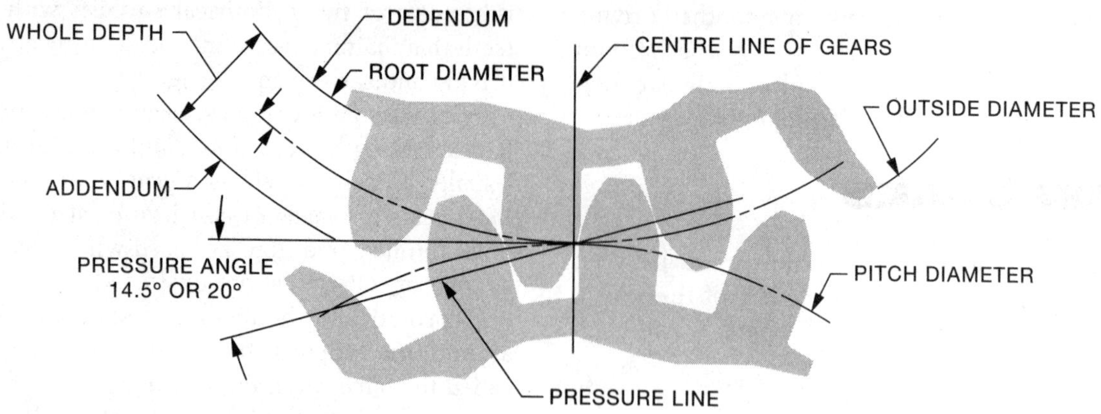

FIGURE 36–4 ■ Meshing of gear teeth showing symbols

Number of Teeth (N)

The number of teeth on the gear.

Diametral Pitch (DP)

The diametral pitch is a ratio of the number of teeth (N) to a unit length of pitch diameter, DP = N/PD.

Outside Diameter (OD)

The overall gear diameter.

Root Diameter (RD)

The diameter at the bottom of the tooth.

Addendum (ADD)

The radial distance from the pitch circle to the top of the tooth.

Dedendum (DED)

The radial distance from the pitch circle to the bottom of the tooth.

Whole Depth (WD)

The overall height of the tooth.

Clearance

The radial distance between the bottom of one tooth and the top of the mating tooth.

Circular Pitch

The distance measured from the point of one tooth to the corresponding point on the adjacent tooth on the circumference of the pitch diameter.

Circular Thickness

The thickness of a tooth or space measured on the circumference of the pitch diameter.

Chordal Thickness

The thickness of a tooth or space measured along a chord on the circumference of the pitch diameter.

Chordal Addendum

Also known as corrected addendum, the perpendicular distance from the chord to the outside circumference of the gear.

Chordal Thickness and Corrected Addendum

After the gear teeth have been milled or generated, the width of the tooth space and the thickness of the tooth, measured on the pitch circle, should be equal.

Instead of measuring the curved length of line known as *circular thickness of tooth,* it is more convenient to measure the length of the straight line *(chordal thickness)*, which connects the ends of that arc.

The *corrected* or *chordal addendum* is the radial distance extending from the addendum circle to the chord.

TERM AND SYMBOL	FORMULA	
	INCH GEARS	METRIC GEARS
Pitch Diameter - PD	PD = N ÷ DP	PD = MDL X N
Number of Teeth - N	N = PD X DP	N = PD ÷ MDL
Module - MDL		MDL = PD ÷ N
Diametral Pitch - DP	DP = N ÷ PD	
Addendum - ADD	14.5° or 20° ADD = 1 ÷ DP 20° stub ADD = 0.8 ÷ DP	14.5° or 20° ADD = MDL 20° stub ADD = 0.8 X MDL
Dedendum - DED	14.5° or 20° DED = 1.157 ÷ DP 20° stub DED = 1 ÷ DP	14.5° or 20° DED = 1.157 X MDL 20° stub DED = MDL
Whole Depth - WD	14.5° or 20° WD = 2.157 ÷ DP 20 stub WD = 1.8 ÷ DP	14.5° or 20° WD = 2.157 X MDL 20° stub WD = 1.8 X MDL
Clearance - CL	14.5° or 20° CL = 0.157 ÷ DP 20° stub CL = 0.2 ÷ DP	14.5° or 20° CL = 0.157 X MDL 20° stub CL = 0.2 X MDL
Outside Diameter - OD	14.5° or 20° OD = PD + 2 ADD = (N + 2) ÷ DP	14.5° or 20° OD = PD + 2 ADD = PD + 2 MDL
	20° stub OD = PD + 2 ADD = (N + 1.6) ÷ DP	20° stub OD = PD + 2 ADD = PD + 1.6 MDL
Root Diameter - RD	14.5° or 20° RD = PD - 2 DED = (N - 2.314) ÷ DP	14.5° or 20° RD = PD - 2 DED = PD - 2.314 MDL
	20° stub RD = PD - 2 DED = (N - 2) ÷ DP	20° stub RD = PD - 2 DED = PD - 2 MDL
Base Circle - BC	BC = PD Cos PA	BC = PD Cos PA
Pressure Angle - PA	14.5° or 20°	14.5° or 20°
Circular Pitch - CP	CP = 3.1416 PD ÷ N = 3.1416 ÷ DP	CP = 3.1416 PD ÷ N = 3.1416 MDL
Circular Thickness - T	T = 3.1416 PD ÷ 2 N = 1.5708 ÷ DP	T = 3.1416 PD ÷ 2N = 1.5708 PD ÷ N = 1.5708 MDL
Chordal Thickness - Tc	TC = PD sin (90° ÷ N)	Tc = PD sin (90° ÷ N)
Chordal Addendum - ADDc	ADDc = ADD + (T^2 ÷ 4 PD)	ADDc = ADD + (T^2 ÷ 4PD)
Working Depth - WKG DP	WKG DP = 2 ADD	WKG DP = 2 ADD

FIGURE 36–5 ■ Spur gear abbreviations and formulas

A gear tooth vernier caliper may be used to measure accurately the thickness of a gear tooth at the pitch line. To use the gear tooth vernier, which measures only a straight line or chordal distance, it is necessary to set the tongue to the computed chordal addendum and then measure the chordal thickness.

Working Drawings of Spur Gears

The working drawings of gears, which are normally cut from blanks, are not complicated. A sectional view is sufficient unless a front view is required to show web or arm details. Because the teeth are cut to shape by cutters, they need not be shown in the front view, drawing 91.

ANSI recommends the use of phantom lines for the outside and root circles. In the section view, the root and outside circles are shown as solid lines.

The dimensioning for the gear is divided into two groups because the finishing of the gear blank and the cutting of the teeth are separate operations in the shop. The gear blank dimensions are shown on the drawing, whereas the gear tooth information is given in a table.

The only differences in terminology between inch-size and metric-size gear drawings are the terms *diametral pitch* and *module.*

For inch-size gears, the term *diametral pitch* is used instead of the term *module.* The diametral pitch is a ratio of the number of teeth to unit length of pitch diameter.

$$\text{Diametral pitch} = DP = \frac{N}{PD}$$

Module is the term used on metric gears. It is the length of pitch diameter per tooth measure in millimetres.

$$\text{Module} = MDL = \frac{PD}{N}$$

From these definitions it can be seen that the module is equal to the reciprocal of the diametral pitch and thus is not its metric dimensional equivalent. If the diametral pitch is known, the module can be obtained.

$$\text{Module} = 25.4 \div \text{diametral pitch}$$

Gears presently being used in North America are designed in the inch system and have a standard diametral pitch instead of a preferred standard module. Therefore, it is recommended that the diametral pitch be referenced beneath the module when gears designed with standard inch pitches are used. For gears designed with standard modules, the diametral pitch need not be referenced on the gear drawing. The standard modules for metric gears are 0.8, 1, 1.25, 2.25, 3, 4, 6, 7, 8, 9, 10, 12, and 16. See Figure 36–6 for gear teeth sizes.

Examples of Spur Gear Calculations

The pitch diameter of a gear can easily be found if the number of teeth and diametral pitch are known. The outside diameter is equal to the pitch diameter plus two addendums. The addendum for a 14.5- or 20-degree spur gear tooth is equal to 1 ÷ DP.

Examples

1. A 14.5-degree spur gear has a DP of 4 and 34 teeth.

$$\text{Pitch diameter} = \frac{N}{DP} = 34 \div 4 = 8.500 \text{ in.}$$

$$OD = PD + 2\ ADD = 8.500 + 2(1/4) = 9.000 \text{ in.}$$

2. The outside diameter of a 14.5-degree spur gear is 6.500 in. The gear has 24 teeth.

$$OD = \frac{N+2}{DP} = \frac{24+2}{DP}$$

$$DP = \frac{26}{6.500} = 4$$

$$\text{Addendum} = \frac{1}{DP} = 1/4 = .250 \text{ in.}$$

$$\begin{aligned}\text{Pitch diameter} &= OD - 2\ ADD\\ &= 6.500 - 2(.250)\\ &= 6.000 \text{ in.}\end{aligned}$$

3. A 14.5-degree spur gear has a module of 6.35 and 38 teeth.

$$\begin{aligned}\text{Pitch diameter} &= N \times MDL\\ &= 38 \times 6.35\\ &= 241.3 \text{ mm}\end{aligned}$$

$$\begin{aligned}OD &=\\ PD + 2\ ADD &= 241.3 + 2(6.35)\\ &= 254 \text{ mm}\end{aligned}$$

REFERENCE

ASME Y14.7.1-1971 (R1998) Gear Drawing Standards—
Part 1

MODULE	DIAMETRAL PITCH	PRESSURE ANGLE	
FOR METRIC-SIZE GEARS	FOR INCH-SIZE GEARS	14.5°	20°
6.35	4		
5.08	5		
4.23	6		
3.18	8		
2.54	10		
2.17	12		
1.59	16		
1.27	20		
1.06	24		

NOTE: MODULE SIZES SHOWN ARE CONVERTED INCH SIZES.

FIGURE 36–6 ■ Gear teeth sizes

QUESTIONS

1. What is the hub diameter?
2. What is the maximum thickness of the spokes?
3. What is the average width of the spokes?
4. How many surfaces indicate that allowance must be added to pattern for finishing?
5. Determine distance (J) for the pattern. Assume .10 is allowed on pattern for each surface to be finished.
6. Determine distance (K) for the pattern.
7. What is the outside diameter of the pattern?
8. Determine distance (L) for the pattern.
9. What is the width of the pattern ?
10. What is the diametral pitch of the gear?
11. Calculate the centre-to-centre distance if this gear were to mesh with a pinion having (A) 24 teeth, (B) 36 teeth, and (C) 32 teeth. } SEE UNIT 38
12. Calculate distances (E) through (H).
13. Calculate the following: addendum, dedendum, circular pitch, and root diameter.
14. Complete the missing information in the cutting data table.

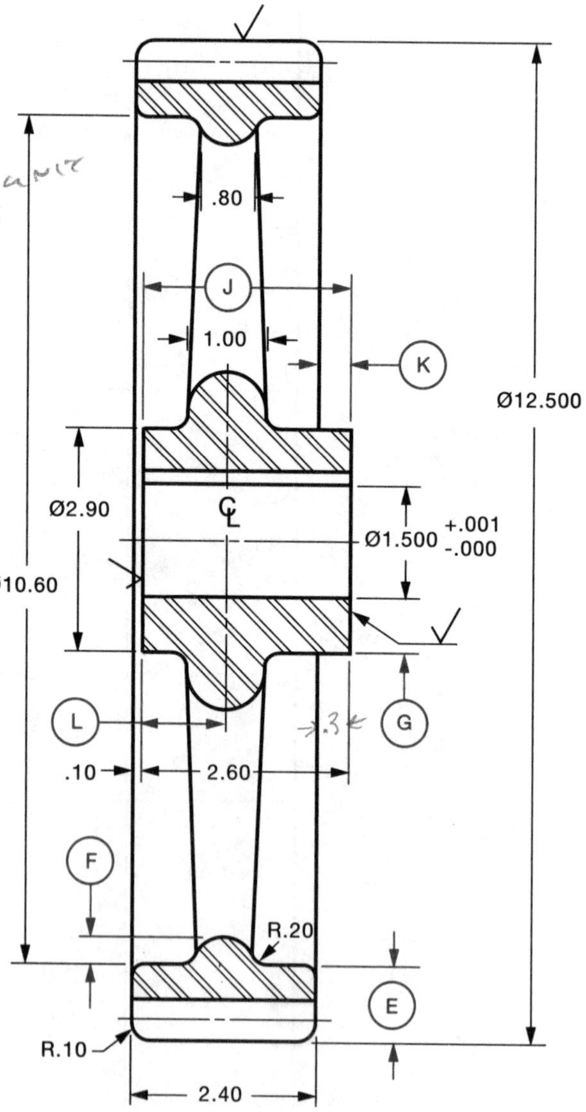

ANSWERS

1. 2.90
2. 1.00
3. 1.70
4. 3
5. 2.8
6. .4
7. 12.70
8. 1.15
9. 2.8
10. 4
11. A 12+6=18÷2=9
B 12+9=21÷2=10.500
C 12+8=20÷2=10

12. E .95
F .4
G .700
H .95

13. ADD .250
DED ______
CP ______
RD ______

14. PD ______
WD ______
ADDc ______
Tc ______

CUTTING DATA	
NUMBER OF TEETH	48
PITCH DIAMETER	
DIAMETRAL PITCH	4
PRESSURE ANGLE	20°
WHOLE DEPTH	
CHORDAL ADDENDUM	
CHORDAL THICKNESS	

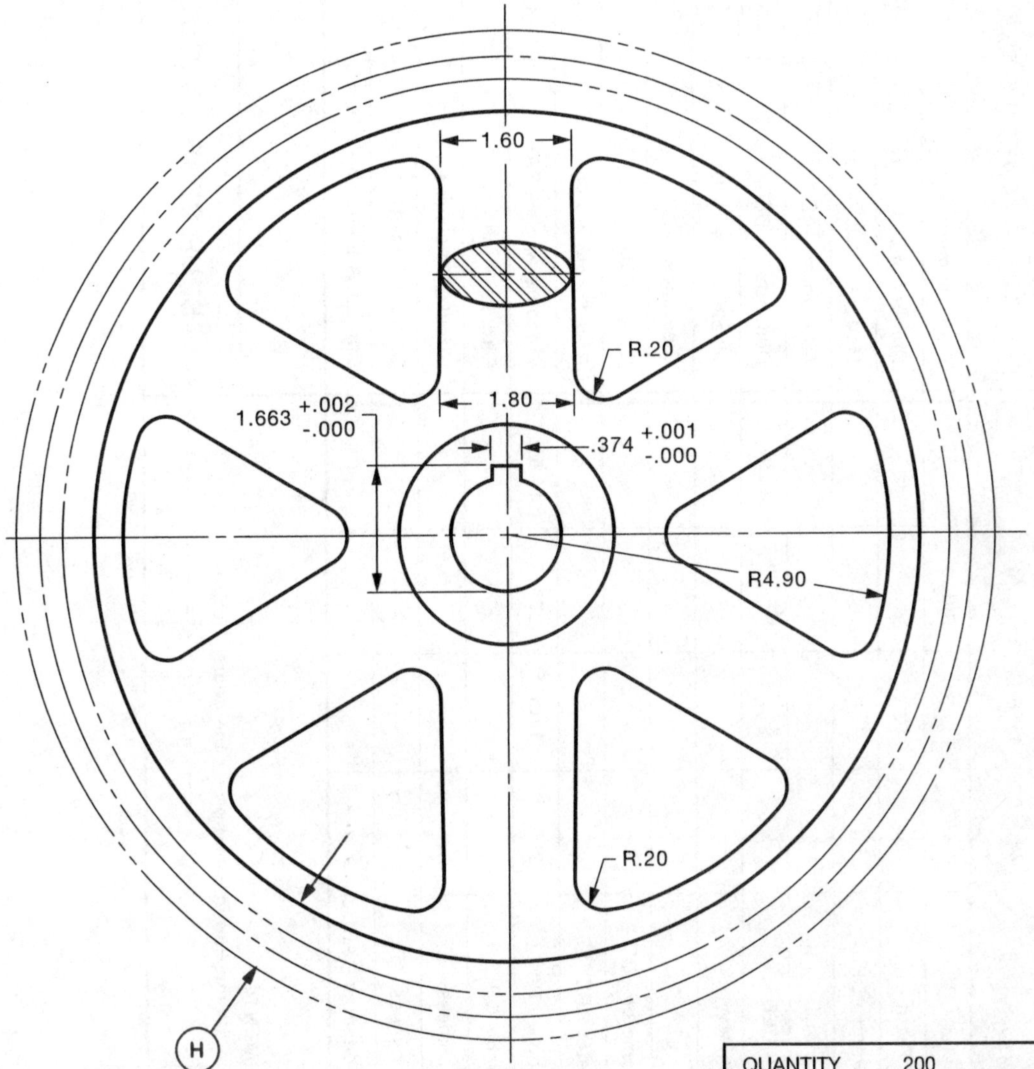

QUANTITY	200	
MATERIAL	CAST STEEL	
SCALE	1:2	
DRAWN		DATE
	SPUR GEAR	**A-91**

N ÷ DP
24 ÷ 6 = 4
1.157 ÷ DP

INCH GEARS					METRIC GEARS				
TERM AND SYMBOL	GEAR 1	GEAR 2	GEAR 3	GEAR 4	TERM AND SYMBOL	GEAR 5	GEAR 6	GEAR 7	GEAR 8
Pitch Diameter - PD	4	5.000	3.000	2.250	Pitch Diameter - PD		89.04		
Number of Teeth - N	24	40		36	Number of Teeth - N	40			30
Diametral Pitch - DP	6		10		Module - MDL	5.08	3.18	6	4
Addendum - ADD	.167				Addendum - ADD				
Dedendum - DED	.193				Dedendum - DED				
Whole Depth - WD					Whole Depth - WD				
Clearance - CL					Clearance - CL				
Outside Diameter - OD					Outside Diameter - OD			228	
Root Diameter - RD					Root Diameter - RD				
Pressure Angle - PA	20°	14.5°	20°	14.5°	Pressure Angle - PA	14.5°	20°	20°	14.5°
Circular Pitch - CP					Circular Pitch - CP				
Circular Thickness - T	.262				Circular Thickness - T				
Chordal Thickness - Tc	.2616				Chordal Thickness - Tc				
Chordal Addendum - ADDc	.1713				Chordal Addendum - ADDc				

ASSIGNMENT:
Complete the missing information for the gears shown.

SPUR GEAR CALCULATIONS — **A-92**

UNIT 37

BEVEL GEARS

Drawings of bevel gears may be more easily interpreted and understood as a result of having a working knowledge of the parts, principles, and formulas underlying spur gears.

Spur gears transmit motion by or through shafts that are parallel and in the same plane, whereas bevel gears transmit motion between shafts that are in the same plane but whose axes would meet if extended. Theoretically, the teeth of a spur gear may be said to be built about the original frictional cylindrical surface known as *pitch circle,* whereas the teeth of a bevel gear are formed about the frustum of the original conical surface called *pitch cone,* Figure 37–1.

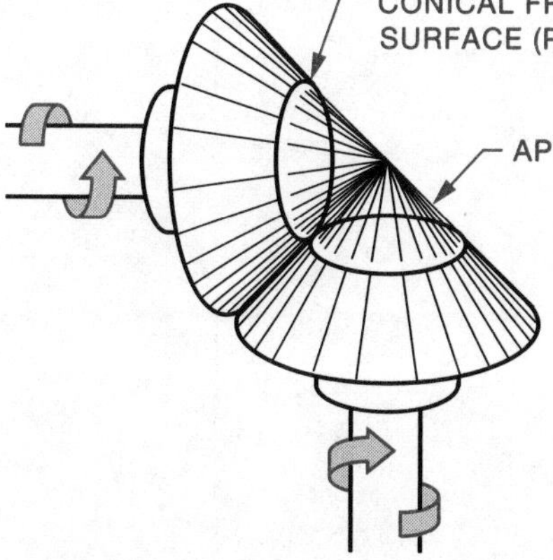

FIGURE 37–1 ■ Principle as applied to bevel gears

One type of bevel gear that is commonly used is the mitre gear. The term mitre gear refers to a pair of bevel gears of the same size that transmit motion at right angles.

Whereas any two spur gears of the same diametral pitch will mesh, this is not true of bevel gears except for mitre gears. On each pair of mating bevel gears, the diameters of the gears determine the angles at which the teeth are cut.

Working drawings of bevel gears, like spur gears, give only the dimensions of the bevel gear blank. Cutting data for the teeth are given in a note or table. A single section view is used unless a second view is required to show such details as spokes. Sometimes both the bevel gear and pinion are drawn together. Dimensions and cutting data depend on the method used in cutting the teeth, but the information in Figures 37–2 and 37–3 is commonly used.

REFERENCE

ASME Y14.7.2-1978 (R1999) Gear and Spline Drawing Standards—Part 2

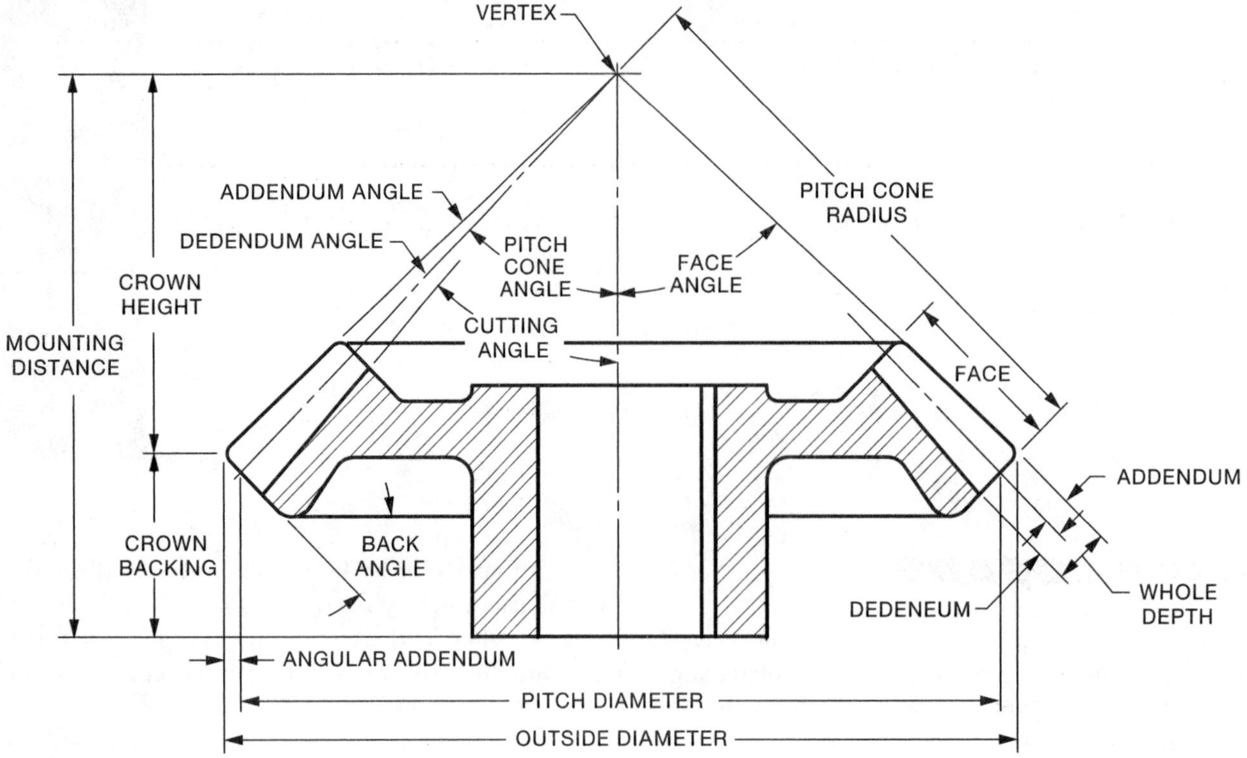

FIGURE 37–2 ■ Bevel gear nomenclature

TERM	FORMULA
Addendum, dedendum, whole depth, pitch diameter, diametral pitch, number of teeth, circular pitch, chordal thickness, circular thickness	Same as for spur gears. Refer to Figure 36-5.
Pitch Cone Angle (Pitch Angle)	$\text{Tan pitch angle} = \dfrac{\text{PD of gear}}{\text{PD of pinion}} = \dfrac{\text{N of gear}}{\text{N of pinion}}$
Pitch Cone Radius	$\dfrac{\text{PD}}{2 \times \text{sin of pitch angle}}$
Addendum Angle	$\text{Tan addendum angle} = \dfrac{\text{Addendum}}{\text{Pitch cone radius}}$
Dedendum Angle	$\text{Tan dedendum angle} = \dfrac{\text{Dedendum}}{\text{Pitch cone radius}}$
Face Angle	Pitch cone angle plus addendum angle
Cutting Angle	Pitch cone angle minus dedendum angle
Back Angle	Same as pitch cone angle
Angular Addendum	Cosine of pitch cone angle x addendum
Outside Diameter	Pitch diameter plus two angular addendums
Crown Height	Divide $\frac{1}{2}$ the outside diameter by the tangent of the face angle
Face Width	$1\frac{1}{2}$ to $2\frac{1}{2}$ times the circular pitch
Chordal Addendum	$\text{Addendum} + \dfrac{\text{Circular thickness}^2 \times \text{Cos pitch cone angle}}{4\ \text{PD}}$

FIGURE 37–3 ■ Bevel gear formulas

CUTTING DATA	
NO. OF TEETH	28
DIAMETRAL PITCH	4
PRESSURE ANGLE	20°
CUTTING ANGLE	?
WHOLE DEPTH	?
CHORDAL ADDENDUM	.2539
CHORDAL THICKNESS	.3918

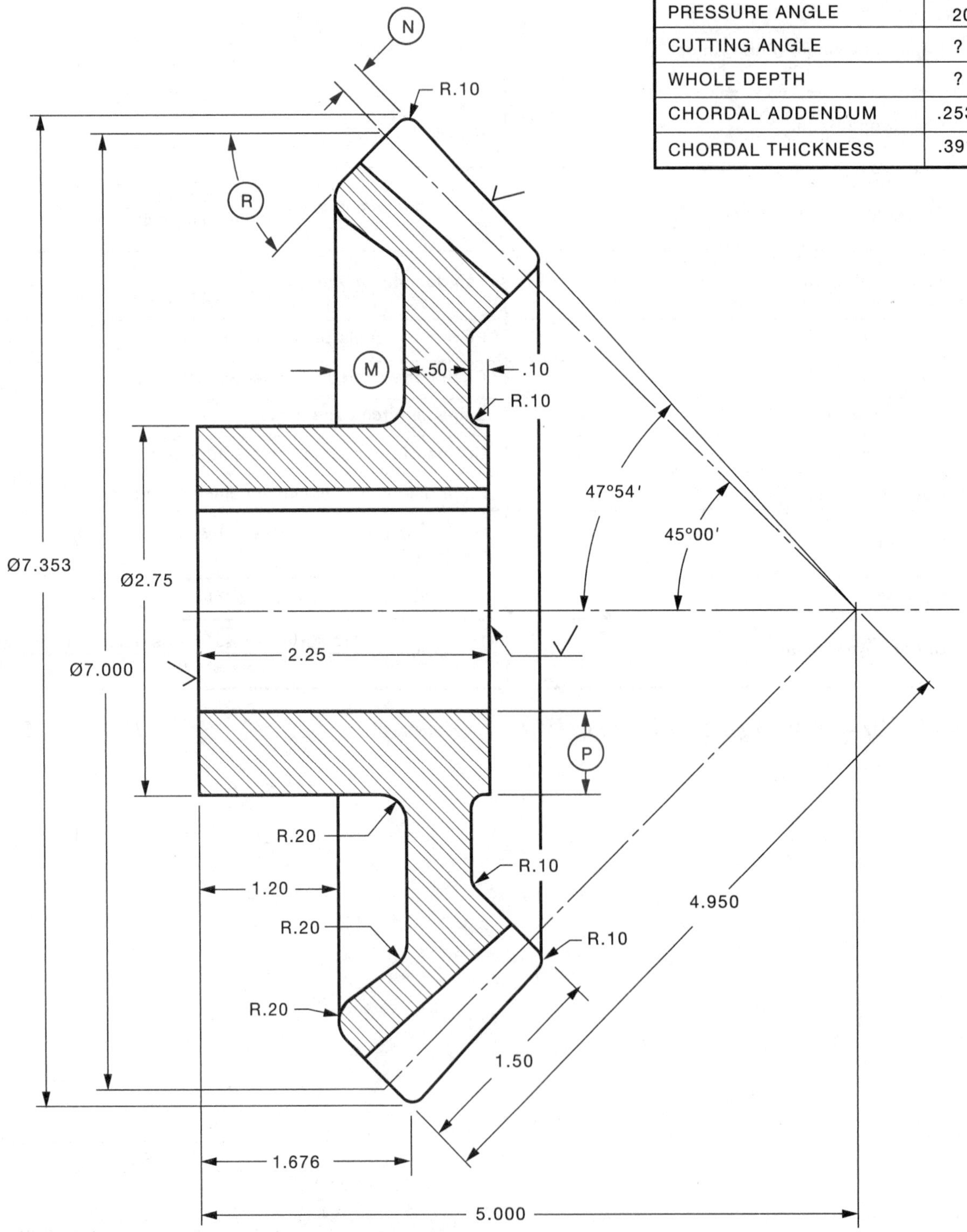

QUESTIONS

1. The drafter neglected to put on angle dimension (R). What should it be?
2. How many finished surfaces are indicated?
3. List those dimensions shown on the drawing that are not used by the patternmaker, Assume that the hole will not be cored.
4. What is the pitch cone angle?
5. What is the pitch diameter?
6. Indicate those dimensions on the drawing that the machinist would use to machine the blank before the teeth are cut.
7. What is the depth of teeth at the large end?
8. What is the pitch cone radius?
9. What is the face angle?
10. What is the addendum angle?
11. What is the cutting angle?
12. What is the mounting distance?
13. What is the crown height?
14. What is the angular addendum?
15. What is the face width?
16. Determine dimensions (M), (N), and (P).

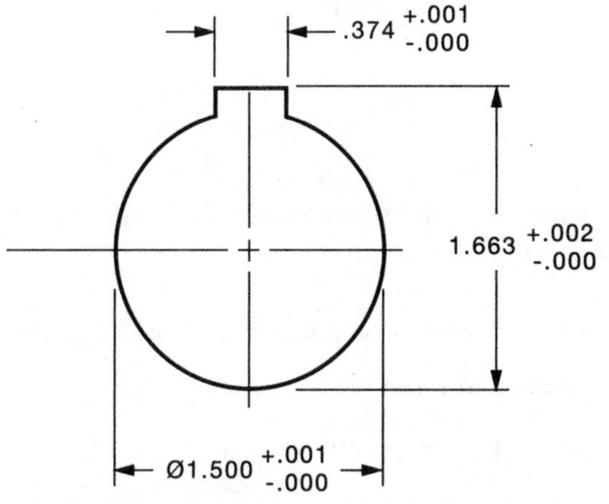

ANSWERS

1. ______
2. ______
3. ______
______
______
______
______
4. ______
5. ______
6. ______
______
______
______
______
______
7. ______
8. ______
9. ______
10. ______
11. ______
12. ______
13. ______
14. ______
15. ______
16. M ______
N ______
P ______

QUANTITY	50		
MATERIAL	CAST STEEL		
SCALE	1:1		
DRAWN		DATE	
MITRE GEAR		A-93	

38 UNIT

GEAR TRAINS

Centre Distance

The centre distance between the two shaft centres is determined by adding the pitch diameter of the two gears together and dividing the sum by 2.

Examples

1. An 8DP, 24-tooth pinion mates with a 96-tooth gear. Find the centre distance.

   Pitch diameter of pinion =
   N ÷ DP = 24 ÷ 8 = 3.000 in.

   Pitch diameter of gear =
   N ÷ DP = 96 ÷ 8 = 12.000 in.

   Sum of the two pitch diameters =
   3.000 + 12.000 = 15.000 in.

   Centre distance =
   1/2 sum of the two pitch diameters =

   $$\frac{15.000}{2} = 7.500 \text{ in.}$$

2. A 2.54 module, 28-tooth pinion mates with an 84-tooth gear. Find the centre distance.

Pitch diameter (PD) =
number of teeth × module =
28 × 2.54 = 71.12 (pinion) =
84 × 2.54 = 213.36 (gear)

Sum of the two pitch diameters =
71.12 + 213.36 = 284.48 mm

Centre distance =
1/2 sum of the two pitch diameters =
284.48 ÷ 2 = 142.24 mm

Ratio

The ratio of gears is a relationship between any of the following:

- the r/min (revolutions per minute) of the gears
- the number of teeth on the gears
- the pitch diameter of the gears

The ratio is obtained by dividing the larger value of any of the three by the corresponding smaller value.

3. A gear rotates at 90 r/min and the pinion at 360 r/min.

$$\text{Ratio} = \frac{360}{90} = 4 \text{ or ratio} = 4:1$$

4. A gear has 72 teeth; the pinion, 18 teeth.

$$\text{Ratio} = \frac{72}{18} = 4 \text{ or ratio} = 4:1$$

5. A gear with a pitch diameter of 8.500 in. meshes with a pinion having a pitch diameter of 2.125 in.

$$\text{Ratio} = \frac{\text{PD of gear}}{\text{PD of pinion}} = \frac{8.500}{2.125} = 4$$

$$\text{or ratio} = 4{:}1$$

Figure 38–1 illustrates how this type of information would be shown on an engineering sketch.

Motor Drive

Drawing A-94 shows a motor drive similar to the type used to operate a load-ratio control switch on a power transformer.

The load-ratio control switch is operated by a small motor with a speed of 1080 r/min. The shaft speed at the switch is reduced to 9 r/min by a series of spur and mitre gears.

When the operator pushes a button, the motor is activated until the circuit breaker pointer rotates 90 degrees and one of the arms depresses the roller and breaks the circuit. During this time the load-ratio control switch shaft will rotate 360 degrees, moving the contractor in the load-ratio control switch one position. This will be shown on the dial by the position indicator.

To simplify the assembly, only the pitch diameters of the gears are shown and much of the hardware has been omitted.

When referring to the direction in which the gears rotate, the terms clockwise (CWISE) or (CW) and anticlockwise (AWISE) or counterclockwise (CCW) are used.

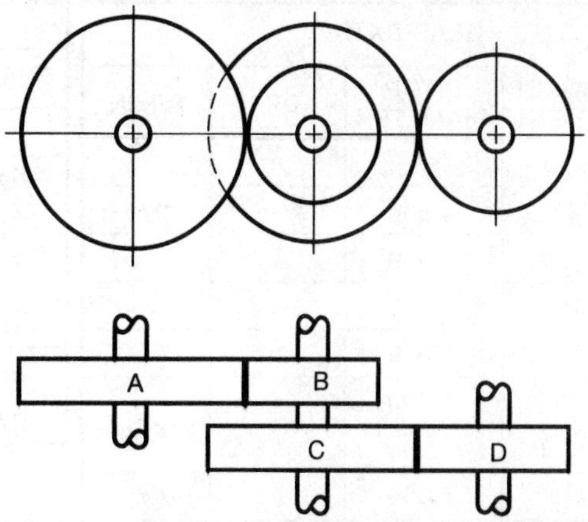

GEAR	PD	N	DP	R/MIN	CENTRE DISTANCE
A	6.000	24	4	300	4.500
B	3.000	12	4	600	
C	6.000	48	8	600	4.000
D	2.000	16	8	1800	

FIGURE 38–1 ■ Gear train data

GEAR DATA				
GEAR	NO. OF TEETH	PITCH DIAMETER	DP	R/MIN
G_1	24		20	
G_2		4.800		270
G_3	20	1.000		
G_4	100			
G_5		1.000	20	
G_6		6.000		
G_7	18			
G_8		7.200		
G_9	72		20	
G_{10}		2.500	10	
G_{11}	25			

SHAFT DATA			
SHAFT	GEARS ON SHAFT	R/MIN	SHAFT* ROTATION
S_1			
S_2			
S_3			
S_4			
S_5			
S_6			
S_7			C-C WISE

*AS VIEWED FROM FRONT OR BOTTOM OF MOTOR DRIVE ASSEMBLY

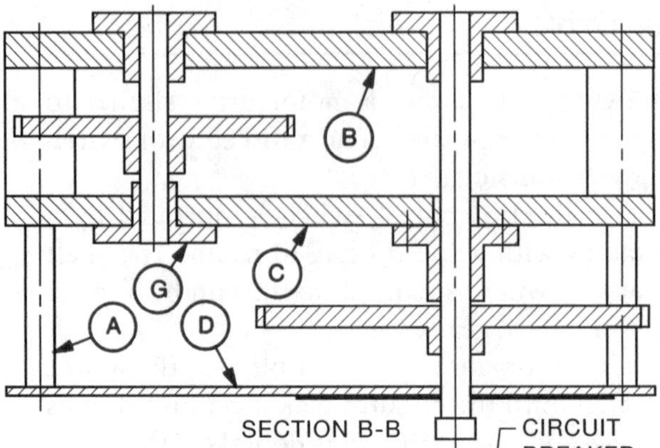

SECTION B-B

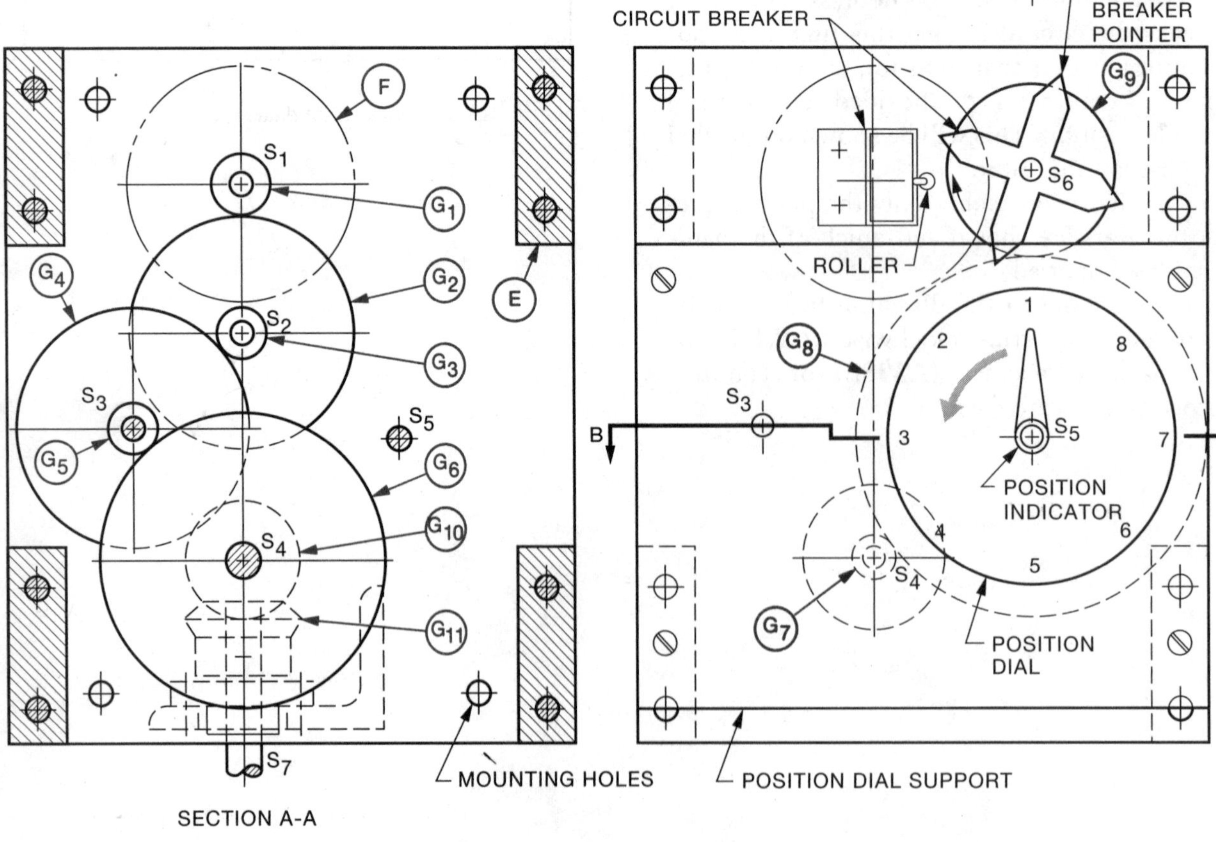

SECTION A-A

ASSIGNMENT:
Complete the information shown in the gear and shaft tables.

QUESTIONS

1. What are the names of parts (A) to (G)?
2. How many spur gears are shown?
3. How many mitre gears are shown?
4. How many gear shafts are there?
5. What is the ratio between the following gears: (A) G_1 and G_2, (B) G_3 and G_4 (C) G_5 and G_6, (D) G_7 and G_8, (E) G_8 and G_9, (F) G_{10} and G_{11}.
6. What is the centre-to-centre distance between the following shafts: (A) S_1: and S_2, (B) S_2 and S_3, (C) S_3 and S_4, (D) S_4 and S_5, (E) S_5 and S_6?
7. How many seconds does it take to turn the load-ratio control switch one position?
8. How many seconds does it take the position indicator to move continuously from position 4 to position 7?
9. What is the r/min ratio between the motor and the switch?
10. If the shaft S_7 rotates 1800 degrees, how many degrees does the position indicator rotate?

ANSWERS

1. A ______
 B ______
 C ______
 D ______
 E ______
 F ______
 G ______
2. ______
3. ______
4. ______
5. A ______
 B ______
 C ______
 D ______
 E ______
 F ______
6. A ______
 B ______
 C ______
 D ______
 E ______
7. ______
8. ______
9. ______
10. ______

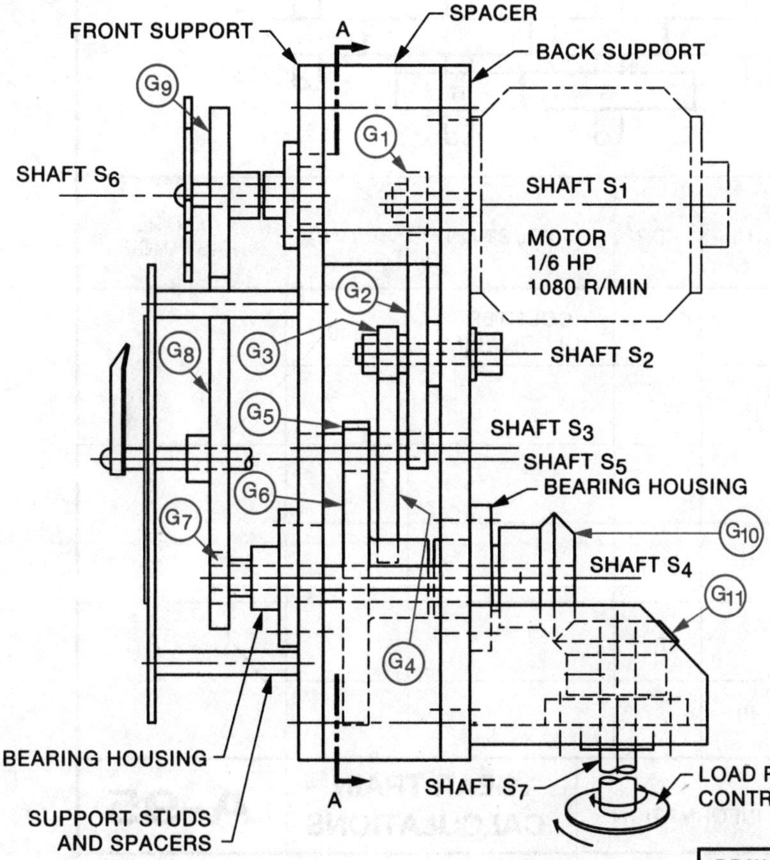

FRONT SUPPORT
A
SPACER
BACK SUPPORT
G9
G1
SHAFT S6
SHAFT S1
MOTOR
1/6 HP
1080 R/MIN
G2
G8
G3
SHAFT S2
G5
SHAFT S3
SHAFT S5
G6
BEARING HOUSING
G7
G10
SHAFT S4
G11
G4
BEARING HOUSING
SHAFT S7
LOAD RATIO
CONTROL SWITCH
SUPPORT STUDS
AND SPACERS

ONE COMPLETE REVOLUTION OF THE SHAFT S_7 MOVES THE POSITION INDICATOR ONE POSITION.

DRAWN	DATE
MOTOR DRIVE ASSEMBLY	A-94

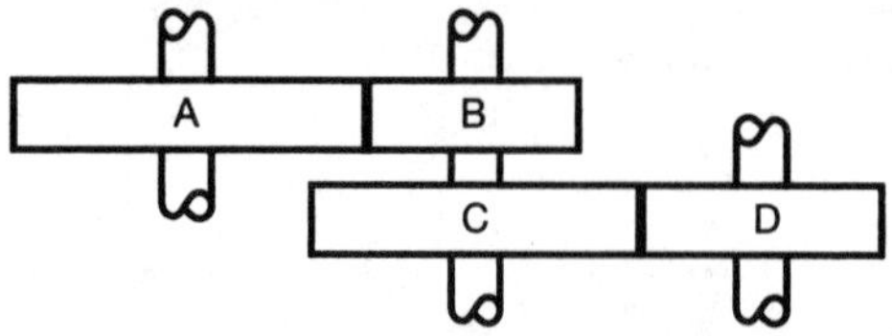

GEAR	PD	N	DP	DIRECTION	R/MIN	CENTRE DISTANCE
A	7.000		4	CLOCKWISE	300	
B		12				
C	6.000					
D		12	3			

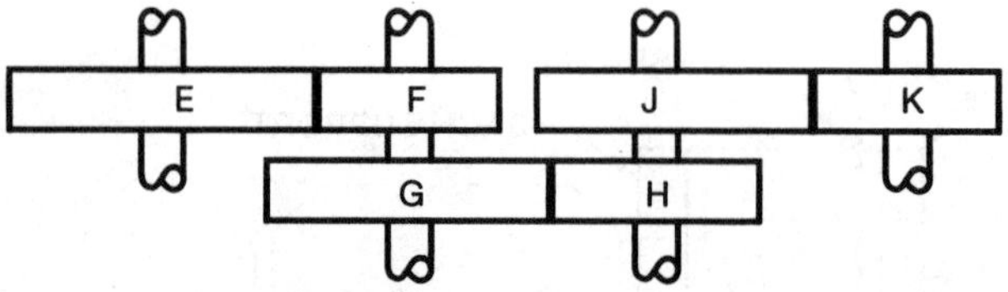

GEAR	PD	N	DP	DIRECTION	R/MIN	CENTRE DISTANCE
E	7.500		4	COUNTER-CLOCKWISE	240	
F		18				
G	10.000					
H	3.200	16				
J	8.000		6			
K		40				

ASSIGNMENT:
FILL IN THE MISSING INFORMATION.

GEAR TRAIN CALCULATIONS

A-95

UNIT 39

CAMS

The cam is invaluable in the design of automatic machinery. Cams make it possible to impart any desired motion to another mechanism.

A *cam* is a rotating, oscillating, or reciprocating machine element that has a surface or groove formed to impart special or irregular motion to a second part called a *follower.* The follower rides against the curved surface of the cam. The distance that the follower rises and falls in a definite period of time is determined by the shape of the cam profile.

Types of Cams

The type and shape of cam used is dictated by the required relationship of the parts and the motions of both, Figure 39–1. The cams that are generally used are either radial or cylindrical. The follower of a radial or face cam moves in a plane perpendicular to the axis of the cam, while in the cylindrical type of cam the movement of the follower is parallel to the cam axis.

A simple OD (outside diameter) or plate cam is shown in Figure 39–2. The hole in the plate is bored off-centre, causing the follower to move up and down as it revolves. The follower can be any type that will roll or slide on the surface of the cam. The follower used with this cam is called a flat face follower.

The cam shown in Figure 39–3 is a drum or barrel-type cam that transmits motion transversely to a lever connected to a conical follower, which rides in the groove as the cam revolves.

Cam Displacement Diagrams

In preparing cam drawings, a cam displacement diagram is drawn first to plot the motion of the follower. The curve on the drawing represents the path of the follower, not the face of the cam. The diagram may be any convenient length, but often it is drawn equal to the circumference of the base circle of the cam and the height is drawn equal to the follower displacement. The lines drawn on the motion diagram are shown as radial lines on the cam drawing; the sizes are transferred from the motion diagram to the cam drawing.

Figure 39–4 shows a cam displacement diagram having a modified uniform type of motion plus two dwell periods. Most cam displacement diagrams have 360-degree cam displacement angles. For drum or cylindrical grooved cams, the displacement diagram is often replaced by the developed surface of the cam.

The cylindrical feeder cam (drawing A-96) is a drum or barrel cam. In addition to the working views of the cam, a development of the contour of the grooves is shown. This development aids the machinist in scribing and laying out the contour of the cam action lobes on the surface of the cam blank preparatory to machining grooves.

Regardless of the type of cam or follower, the purpose of all cams is to impart motion to other mechanisms in various directions in order to actuate machines to do specific jobs.

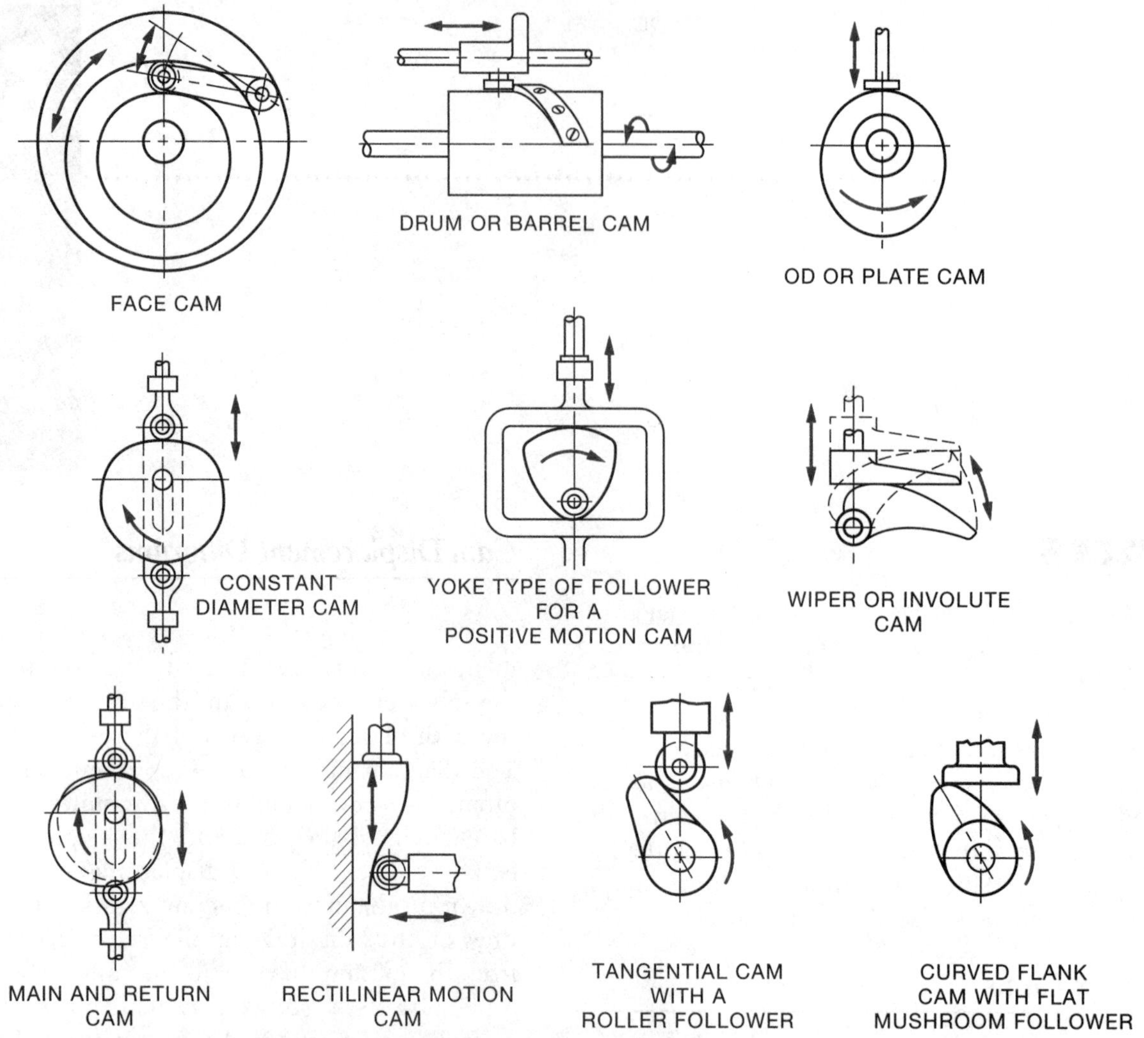
FACE CAM
DRUM OR BARREL CAM
OD OR PLATE CAM
CONSTANT DIAMETER CAM
YOKE TYPE OF FOLLOWER FOR A POSITIVE MOTION CAM
WIPER OR INVOLUTE CAM
MAIN AND RETURN CAM
RECTILINEAR MOTION CAM
TANGENTIAL CAM WITH A ROLLER FOLLOWER
CURVED FLANK CAM WITH FLAT MUSHROOM FOLLOWER

FIGURE 39–1 ■ Common types of cams

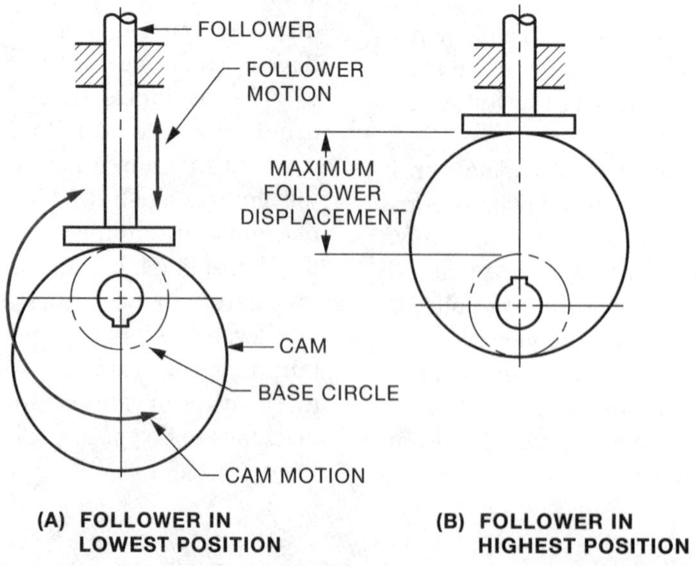
FOLLOWER
FOLLOWER MOTION
MAXIMUM FOLLOWER DISPLACEMENT
CAM
BASE CIRCLE
CAM MOTION
(A) FOLLOWER IN LOWEST POSITION
(B) FOLLOWER IN HIGHEST POSITION

FIGURE 39–2 ■ Eccentric plate cam

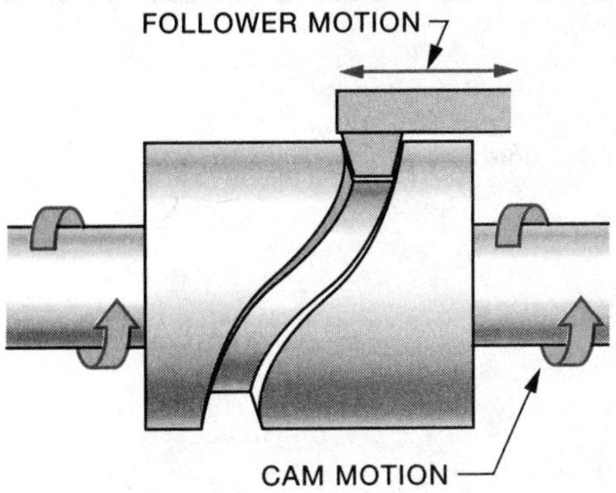

FIGURE 39–3 ■ Drum or barrel-type cam

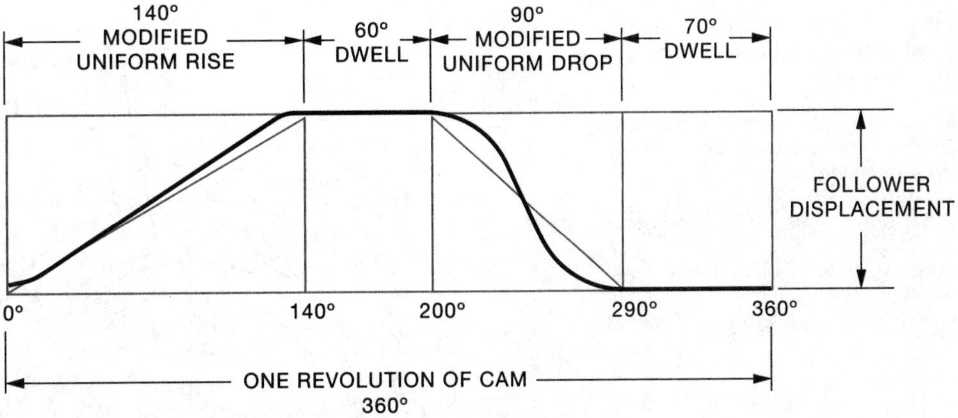

FIGURE 39–4 ■ Cam displacement diagram

QUESTIONS

1. Through what thickness of metal is hole (2) drilled?
2. Locate line (4) in the right-side view.
3. Locate line (11) in the cam displacement diagram.
4. Locate line (6) in another view.
5. Locate line (9) in the right-side view.
6. What is the maximum permissible diameter of hole (2)?
7. Locate line (8) in the front view.
8. Locate line (43) in the right-side view.
9. What is the total follower displacement of the cam follower for (A) the finishing cut and (B) the roughing cut?
10. Assuming a .06 in. allowance for machining, what would be the outside diameter of the cam before finishing? /PER SIDE.
11. What is the total number of through holes?
12. Locate lines (30) to (41) on other view.
13. Determine distances (A) to (M).

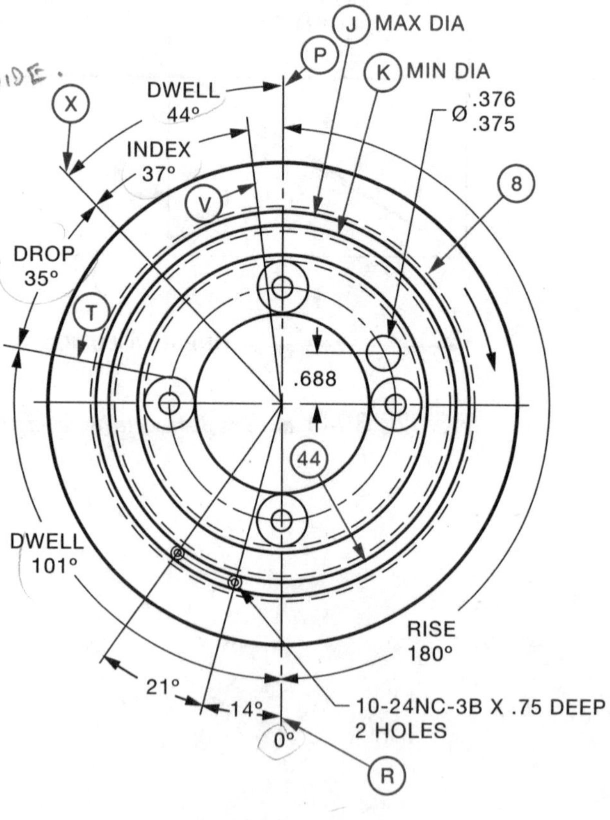

ROUGHING CAM DATA
LEFT-SIDE VIEW

ANSWERS

1.	.50	12. 30	Y	13. A	.937
2.	7	31	Q	B	1.502
3.	3	32	S	C	.625
4.	7	33	W	D	2.100
5.	13	34	U	E	.936
6.	.376	35	N	F	.836
7.	15	36	V	G	ø3.00
8.	12	37	X	H	.688
9. A	.562	38	T	J	5.065
B	.688	39	P	K	4.56
10.	6.432	40	R	L	1.625
11.	6	41	Z	M	.940

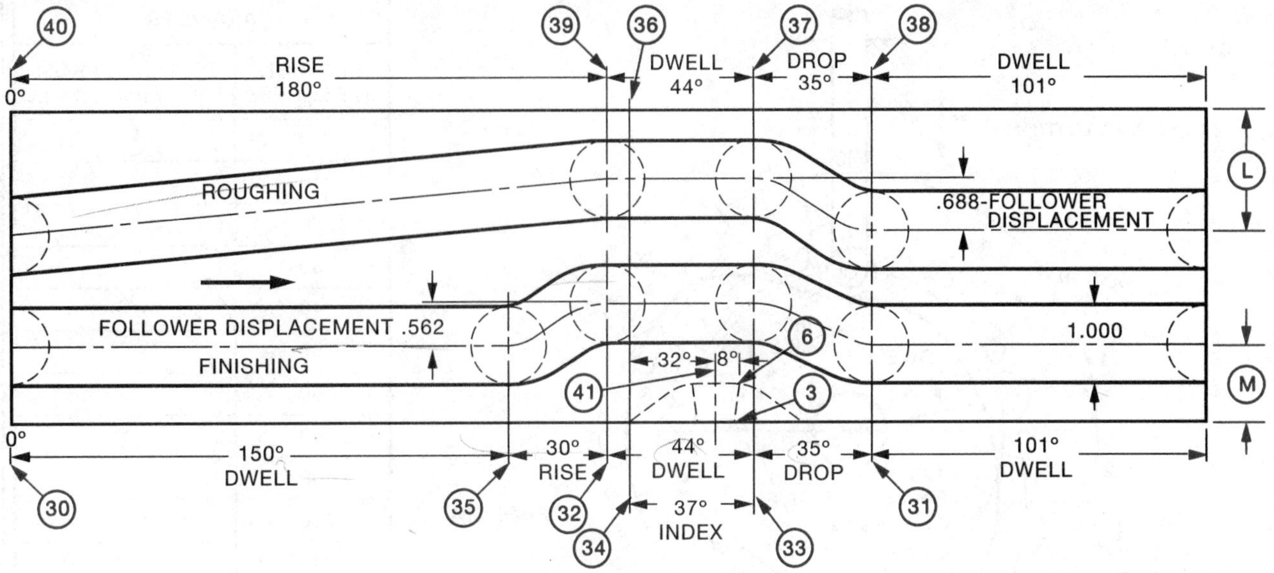
RISE
180°
0°
DWELL
44°
DROP
35°
DWELL
101°
ROUGHING
.688-FOLLOWER
DISPLACEMENT
FOLLOWER DISPLACEMENT .562
FINISHING
1.000
32°
8°
150°
DWELL
30°
RISE
44°
DWELL
35°
DROP
101°
DWELL
37°
INDEX
40
39
36
37
38
L
M
6
41
3
30
35
32
34
33
31

CAM DISPLACEMENT DIAGRAM

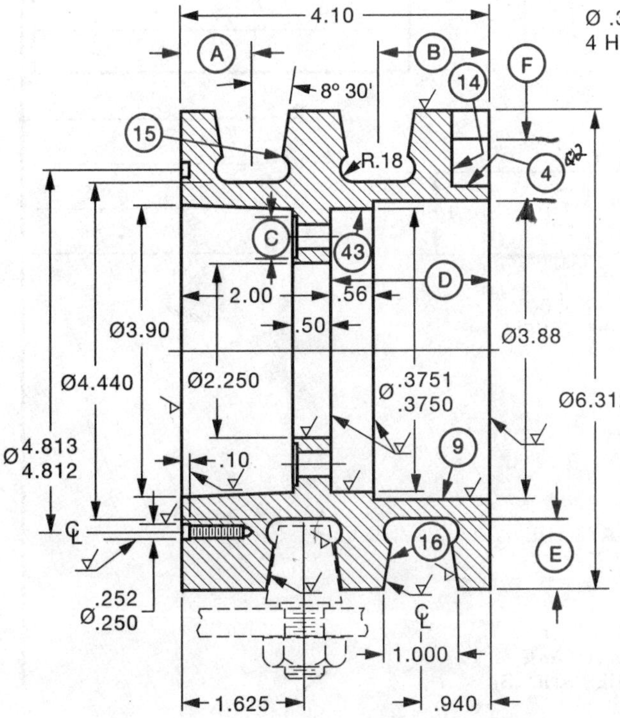
4.10
A
B
F
8° 30'
14
15
R.18
4
C
43
2.00
.56
D
.50
Ø3.88
Ø3.90
Ø4.440
Ø2.250
Ø .3751
.3750
Ø6.312
Ø 4.813
4.812
.10
9
E
16
.252
Ø.250
1.000
1.625
.940

SECTION A-A

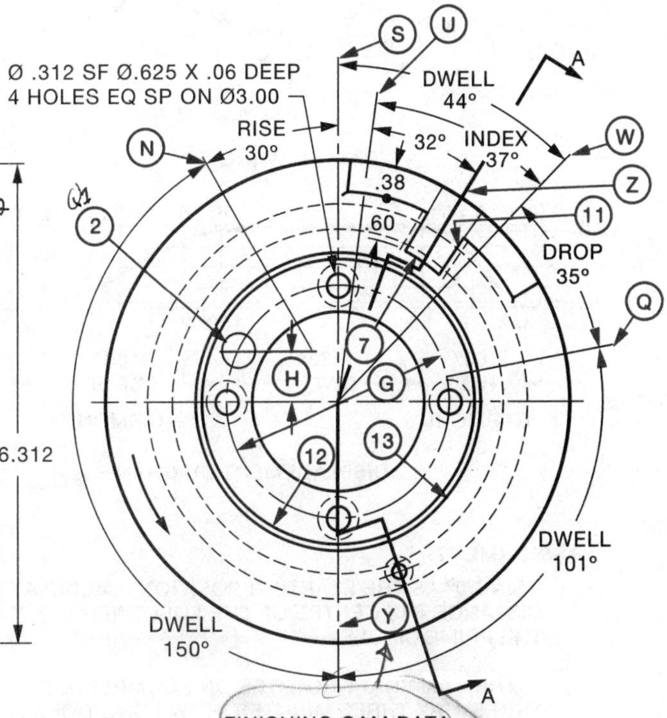
Ø .312 SF Ø.625 X .06 DEEP
4 HOLES EQ SP ON Ø3.00
S
U
A
DWELL
44°
RISE
30°
32°
INDEX
37°
N
W
Z
.38
.60
11
2
DROP
35°
Q
7
H
G
12
13
DWELL
101°
Y
DWELL
150°
A

FINISHING CAM DATA
RIGHT-SIDE VIEW

NOTE: UNLESS OTHERWISE SHOWN:
—TOLERANCE ON TWO-PLACE DECIMAL DIMENSIONS ±.02
—TOLERANCE ON THREE-PLACE DECIMAL DIMENSIONS ±.005
—TOLERANCE ON ANGLES ±30'
—SURFACES ✓ TO BE 63✓

MATERIAL		
SCALE	NOT TO SCALE	
DRAWN		DATE
	CYLINDRICAL FEEDER CAM	A-96

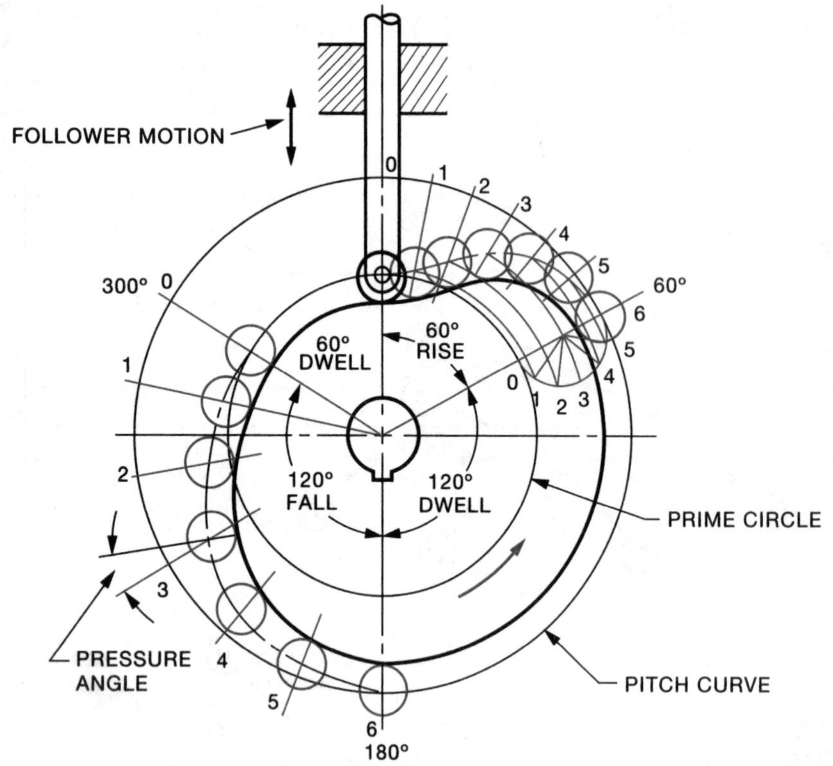
FOLLOWER MOTION
300° 0
1
2
3
4
5
6
180°
60° DWELL
60° RISE
120° FALL
120° DWELL
60°
PRIME CIRCLE
PITCH CURVE
PRESSURE ANGLE

CAM DRAWING

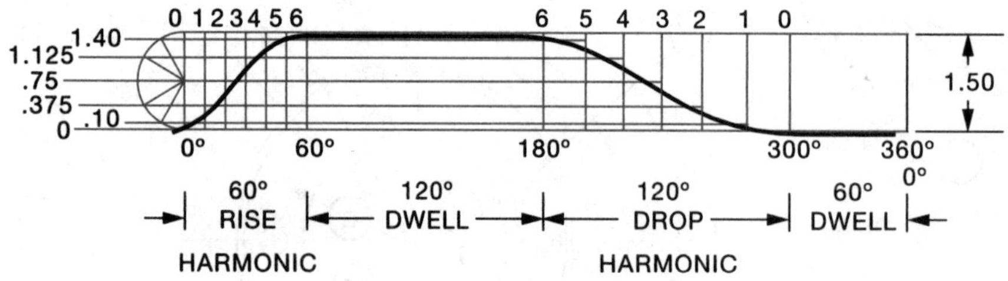
0 1 2 3 4 5 6
6 5 4 3 2 1 0
1.40
1.125
.75
.375
.10
0
1.50
0°
60°
180°
300°
360° 0°
60° RISE HARMONIC
120° DWELL
120° DROP HARMONIC
60° DWELL

DISPLACEMENT DIAGRAM

ANSWERS	
POSITION IN DEGREES	DISTANCE FROM THE PRIME CIRCLE
0	0
10	.100
20	.375
30	.750
40	1.250
50	1.450
60	1.500
180	1.500
200	1.400
220	1.250
240	.750
260	.375
280	.100
300	0
360	0

2. A 30 SEC.
B 1 MIN
3. A 1 MIN
B 30 SEC.

ASSIGNMENT:

1. USING 0° AS THE STARTING POSITION, CALCULATE THE DISTANCE THE CENTRE OF THE FOLLOWER IS FROM THE PRIME CIRCLE.

2. IF THE CAM SHAFT ROTATES ONE COMPLETE REVOLUTION EVERY THREE MINUTES, HOW LONG DOES IT TAKE FOR THE CAM FOLLOWER TO (A) RISE 1.50 INCHES AND (B) DROP 1.50 INCHES?

3. HOW LONG DOES THE CAM FOLLOWER REMAIN AT DWELL WHEN (A) IN THE UPPER POSITION AND (B) IN THE LOWER POSITION?

PLATE CAM	A-97

UNIT 40

ANTIFRICTION BEARINGS

Antifriction bearings, also known as *roller-element* bearings, use a type of rolling element between the loaded members. Relative motion is accommodated by rotation of the elements. Roller-element bearings are usually housed in bearing races conforming to the element shapes. In addition, a cage or separator is often used to locate the elements within the bearings. These bearings are usually categorized by the form of the rolling element and in some instances by the load type they carry, Figures 40–1 and 40–2. Roller-element bearings are generally classified as either ball or roller.

Ball Bearings

Ball bearings may be roughly divided into three categories: radial, angular contact, and thrust. Radial-contact ball bearings are designed for applications in which the load is primarily radial with only low-magnitude thrust loads. Angular-contact bearings are used where loads are combined radial and high thrust, and where precise shaft location is required. Thrust bearings handle loads that are primarily thrust.

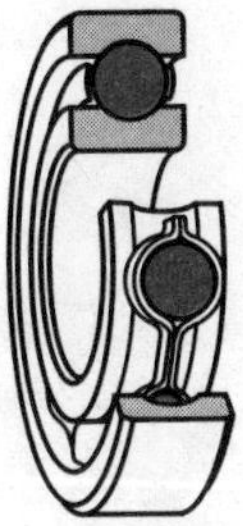

SINGLE ROW, DEEP GROOVE BALL BEARINGS

The *single row, deep groove ball bearing* will sustain, in addition to radial load, a substantial thrust load in either direction, even at very high speeds. This advantage results from the intimate contact existing between the balls and the deep, continuous groove in each ring. When using this type of bearing, careful alignment between the shaft and housing is essential. This bearing is also available with seals, which serve to exclude dirt and retain lubricant.

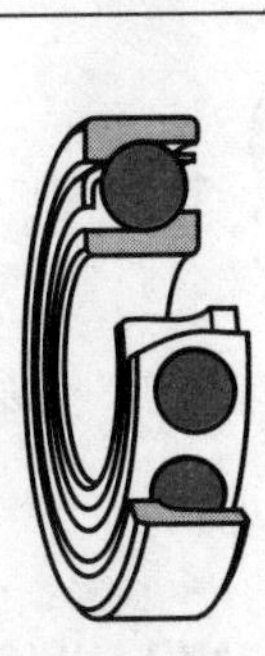

ANGULAR CONTACT BALL BEARINGS

The *angular contact ball bearing* supports a heavy thrust load in one direction, sometimes combined with a moderate radial load. A steep contact angle, assuring the highest thrust capacity and axial rigidity, is obtained by a high thrust supporting shoulder on the inner ring and a similar high shoulder on the opposite side of the outer ring. These bearings can be mounted singly or, when the sides are flush ground, in tandem for constant thrust in one direction; mounted in pairs, also when sides are flush ground, for a combined load, either face-to-face or back-to-back.

FIGURE 40–1A ■ Roller-element bearings

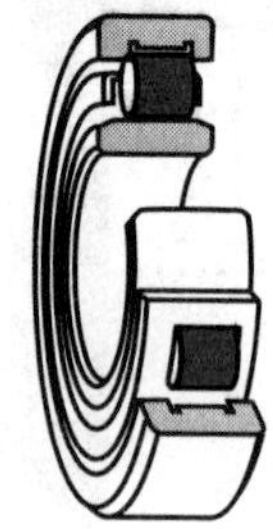

CYLINDRICAL ROLLER BEARINGS

The *cylindrical roller bearing* has high radial capacity and provides acccurate guiding of the rollers, resulting in a close approach to true rolling. Consequent low friction permits operation at high speed. Those types that have flanges on one ring only allow a limited free axial movement of the shaft in relation to the housing. They are easy to dismount even when both rings are mounted with a tight fit. The double row type assures maximum radial rigidity and is particularly suitable for machine tool spindles.

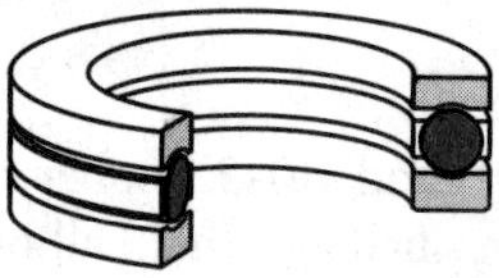

BALL THRUST BEARINGS

The *ball thrust bearing* is designed for thrust load in one direction only. The load line through the balls is parallel to the axis of the shaft, resulting in high thrust capacity and minimum axial deflection. Flat seats are preferred, particularly where the load is heavy or where close axial positioning of the shaft is essential; for example, in machine tool spindles.

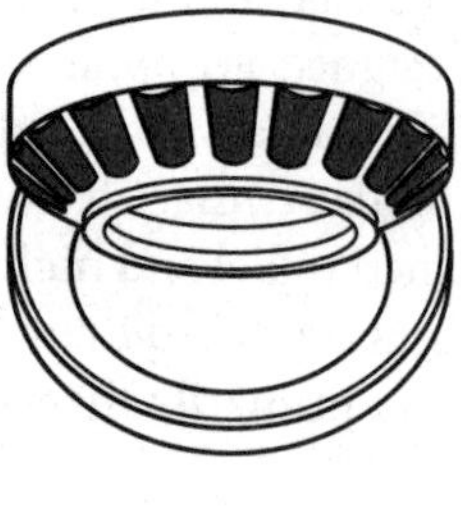

SPHERICAL ROLLER THRUST BEARINGS

The *spherical roller thrust bearing* is designed to carry heavy thrust loads, or combined loads that are predominantly thrust. This bearing has a single row of rollers that roll on a spherical outer race with full self-alignment. The cage, centred by an inner ring sleeve, is constructed so that lubricant is pumped directly against the inner ring's unusually high guide flange. This ensures good lubrication between the roller ends and the guide flange. The spherical roller thrust bearing operates best with relatively heavy oil lubrication.

FIGURE 40–1B ■ Roller-element bearings, continued

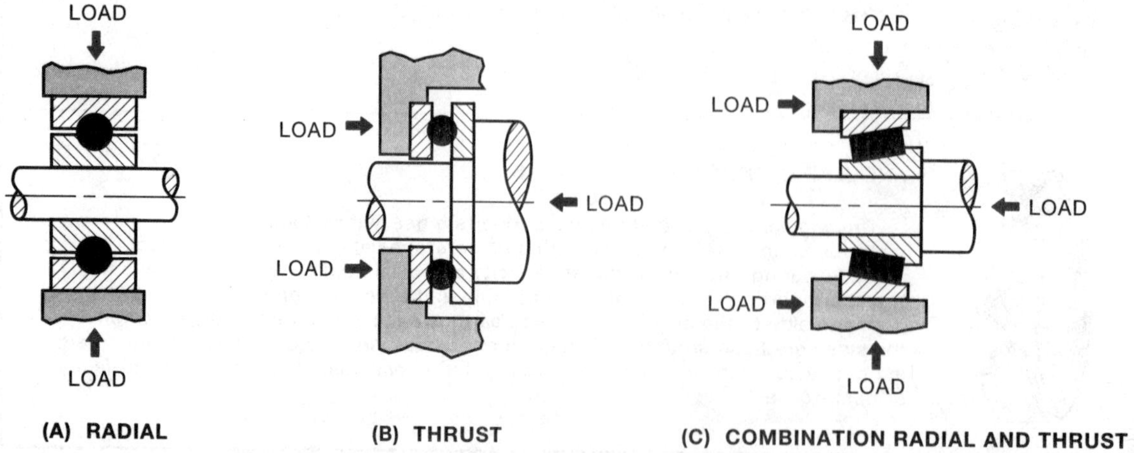

FIGURE 40–2 ■ Types of bearing loads

Roller Bearings

Roller bearings have higher load capacities than ball bearings for a given envelope size. They are widely used in moderate-speed, heavy-duty applications. The four principal types of roller bearings are cylindrical, needle, tapered, and spherical. Cylindrical roller bearings use cylinders with approximate length-diameter ratios ranging from 1:1 to 1:3 as rolling elements. Needle roller bearings use cylinders or needles of greater length-diameter ratios. Tapered and spherical roller bearings are capable of supporting combined radial and thrust loads.

The rolling elements of tapered roller bearings are truncated cones. Spherical roller bearings are available with both barrel and hourglass roller shapes. The primary advantage of spherical roller bearings is their self-aligning capability. Plain bearings are covered in Unit 23.

RETAINING RINGS

Retaining rings, or snap rings, are designed to provide a removable shoulder to locate, retain, or lock components accurately on shafts and in bored and housings, Figures 40–3 and 40–4. They are easily installed and removed. Because they are usually made of spring steel, retaining rings have a high shear strength and impact capacity. In addition to fastening and positioning, a number of rings are designed for taking up end play caused by accumulated tolerances or wear in the parts being retained.

O-RING SEALS

O-rings are used as an axial mechanical seal (a seal that forms a running seal between a moving shaft and a housing) or a static seal (no moving parts). The advantage of using an O-ring as a gasket-type seal, Figure 40–5, over conventional gaskets is that the nuts need not be tightened uniformly and sealing compounds are not required. A rectangular groove is the most common type of groove used for O-rings.

CLUTCHES

Clutches are used to start and stop machines or rotating elements without starting or stopping the prime mover. They are also used for automatic disconnection and quick starts and stops, and to permit shaft rotation in one direction only, such as the *overrunning* clutch shown in Figure 40–6. A full complement of sprags between concentric inner and outer races transmits power from one race to the other by wedging action of the sprags when either race is rotated in the driving direction. Rotation in the opposite direction frees the sprags and the clutch is disengaged or overruns, Figure 40–6. This type of clutch is used in the power drive, drawing A-98.

BELT DRIVES

A *belt drive* consists of an endless flexible belt connecting two wheels or pulleys. Belt drives depend on friction between belt and pulley surfaces for transmission of power.

In a V-belt drive, the belt has a trapezoidal cross section, and runs in V-shaped grooves on the pulleys. These belts are made of cords or cables, impregnated and covered with rubber or other organic compound. The covering is formed to produce the required cross section. V-belts are usually manufactured as endless belts, although open-end and link types are available.

In the case of V-belts, the friction for the transmission of the driving force is increased by the wedging of the belt into the grooves on the pulley.

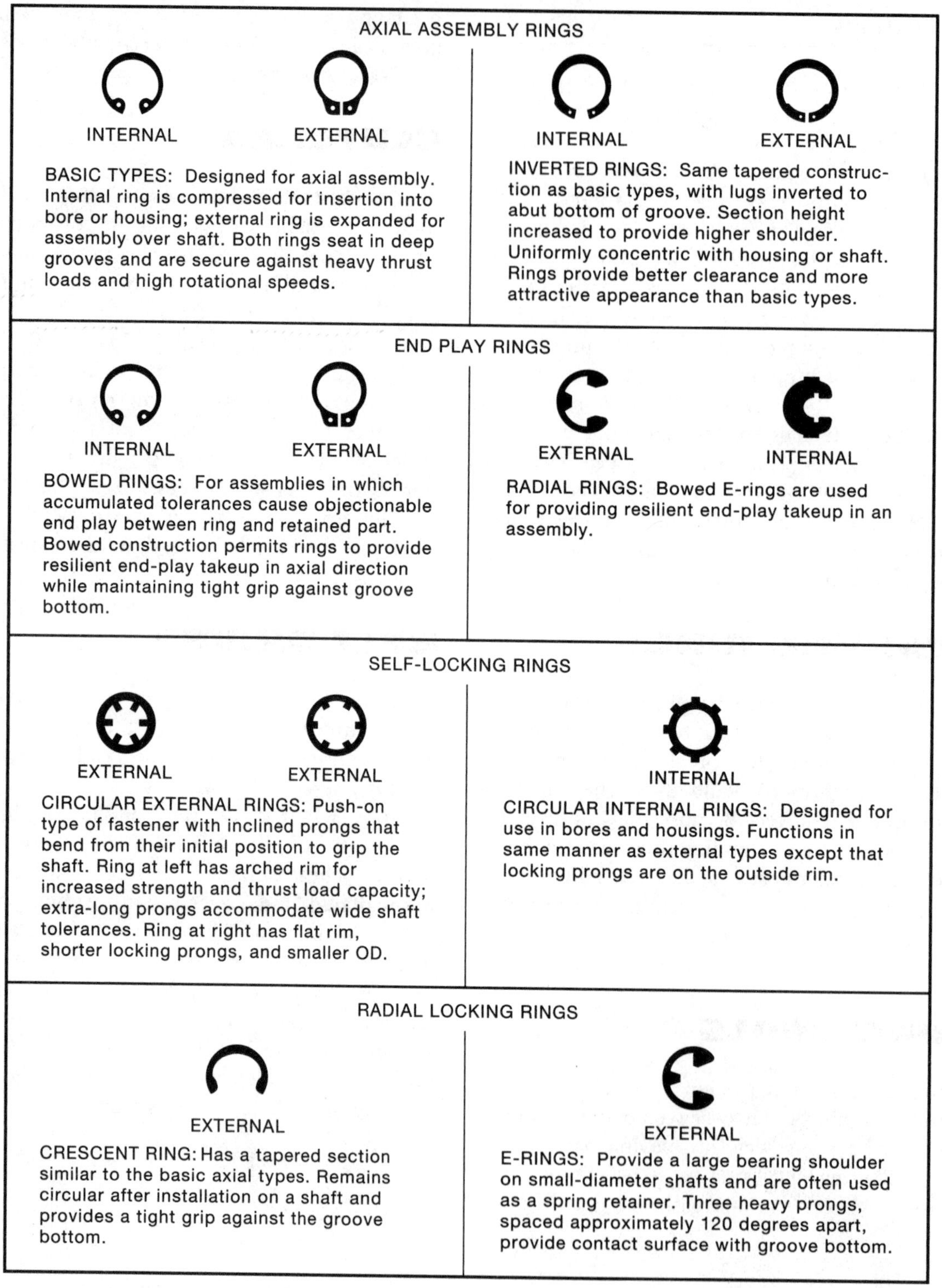
AXIAL ASSEMBLY RINGS
INTERNAL
EXTERNAL
BASIC TYPES: Designed for axial assembly. Internal ring is compressed for insertion into bore or housing; external ring is expanded for assembly over shaft. Both rings seat in deep grooves and are secure against heavy thrust loads and high rotational speeds.
INTERNAL
EXTERNAL
INVERTED RINGS: Same tapered construction as basic types, with lugs inverted to abut bottom of groove. Section height increased to provide higher shoulder. Uniformly concentric with housing or shaft. Rings provide better clearance and more attractive appearance than basic types.
END PLAY RINGS
INTERNAL
EXTERNAL
BOWED RINGS: For assemblies in which accumulated tolerances cause objectionable end play between ring and retained part. Bowed construction permits rings to provide resilient end-play takeup in axial direction while maintaining tight grip against groove bottom.
EXTERNAL
INTERNAL
RADIAL RINGS: Bowed E-rings are used for providing resilient end-play takeup in an assembly.
SELF-LOCKING RINGS
EXTERNAL
EXTERNAL
CIRCULAR EXTERNAL RINGS: Push-on type of fastener with inclined prongs that bend from their initial position to grip the shaft. Ring at left has arched rim for increased strength and thrust load capacity; extra-long prongs accommodate wide shaft tolerances. Ring at right has flat rim, shorter locking prongs, and smaller OD.
INTERNAL
CIRCULAR INTERNAL RINGS: Designed for use in bores and housings. Functions in same manner as external types except that locking prongs are on the outside rim.
RADIAL LOCKING RINGS
EXTERNAL
CRESCENT RING: Has a tapered section similar to the basic axial types. Remains circular after installation on a shaft and provides a tight grip against the groove bottom.
EXTERNAL
E-RINGS: Provide a large bearing shoulder on small-diameter shafts and are often used as a spring retainer. Three heavy prongs, spaced approximately 120 degrees apart, provide contact surface with groove bottom.

FIGURE 40–3 ■ Stamped retaining rings

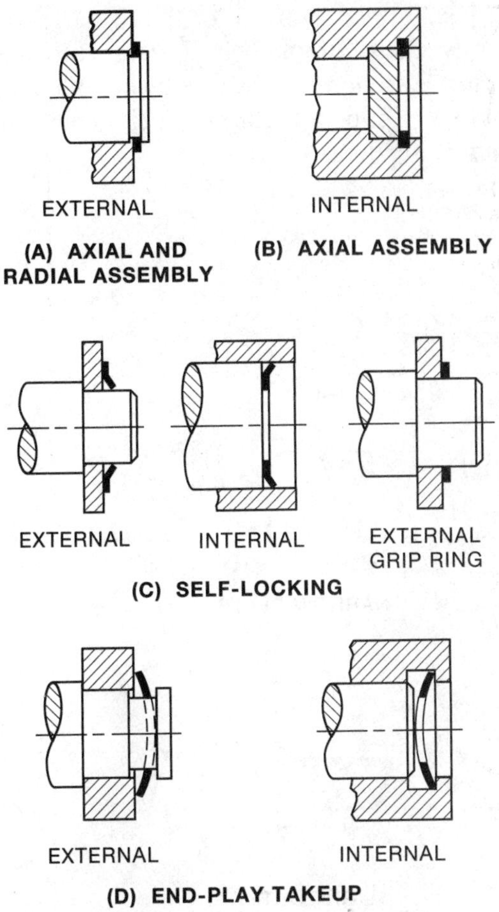
EXTERNAL
INTERNAL
(A) AXIAL AND RADIAL ASSEMBLY
(B) AXIAL ASSEMBLY
EXTERNAL
INTERNAL
EXTERNAL GRIP RING
(C) SELF-LOCKING
EXTERNAL
INTERNAL
(D) END-PLAY TAKEUP

FIGURE 40–4 ■ Retaining ring application

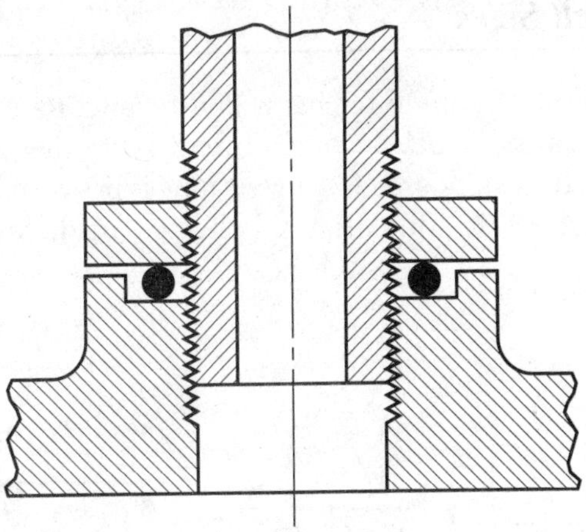

FIGURE 40–5 ■ O-ring seal

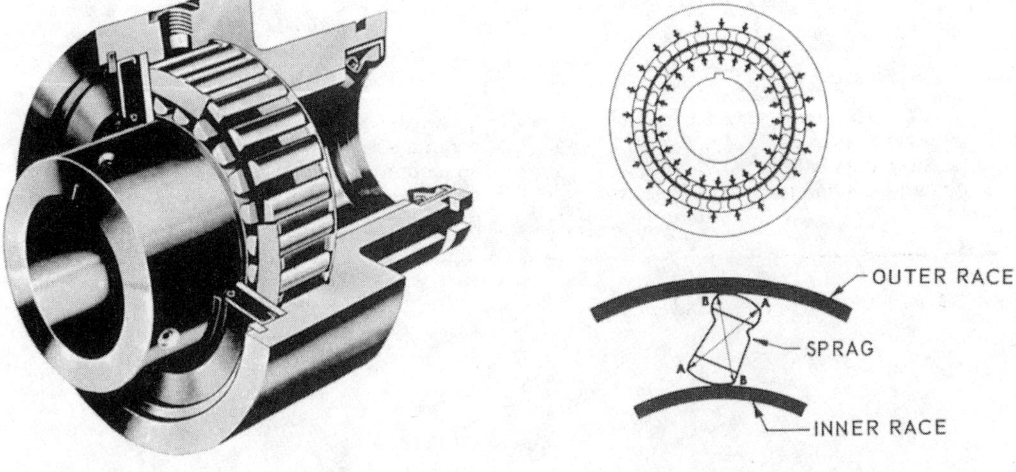
OUTER RACE
SPRAG
INNER RACE
A
B
A
B

FIGURE 40–6 ■ Overrunning clutch

V-Belt Sizes

To facilitate interchangeability and to ensure uniformity, V-belt manufacturers have developed industrial standards for the various types of V-belts, Figure 40–7. Industrial V-belts are made in two types: heavy duty (conventional and narrow) and light duty. Conventional belts are available in A, B, C, D, and E sections. Narrow belts are made in 3V, 5V, and 8V sections. Light-duty belts come in 3L, 4L, and 5L sections.

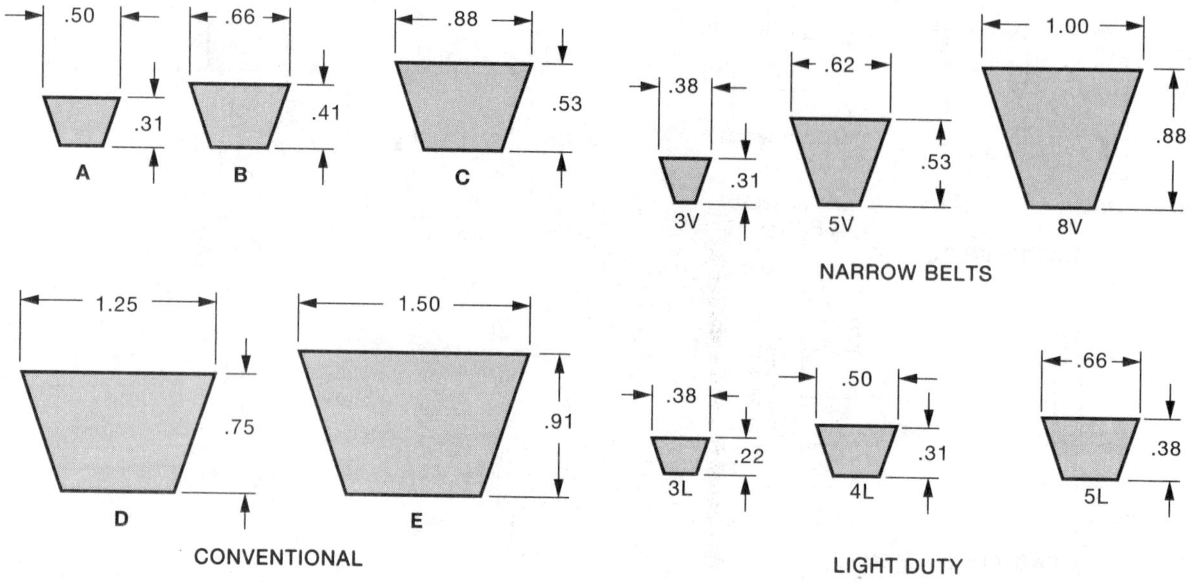

FIGURE 40–7 ■ V-belt sizes

Sheaves and Bushings

Sheaves, the grooved wheels of pulleys, are sometimes equipped with tapered bushings for ease of installation and removal. Figure 40–8. They have extreme holding power, providing the equivalent of a shrink fit. The sheave and bushing used in the power drive, drawing A-98, have a six-hole drilling arrangement in both the sheave and bushing, making it possible to insert the cap screw from either side. This is especially advantageous for applications where space is at a premium.

REFERENCES

A.O. Dehayt, "Basic Bearing Types," *Machine Design* 40, No. 14

ASME B27.7-1977 (R1999) General Purpose Tapered and Reduced Cross Section Retaining Rings, Metric

SKF Co. Ltd.

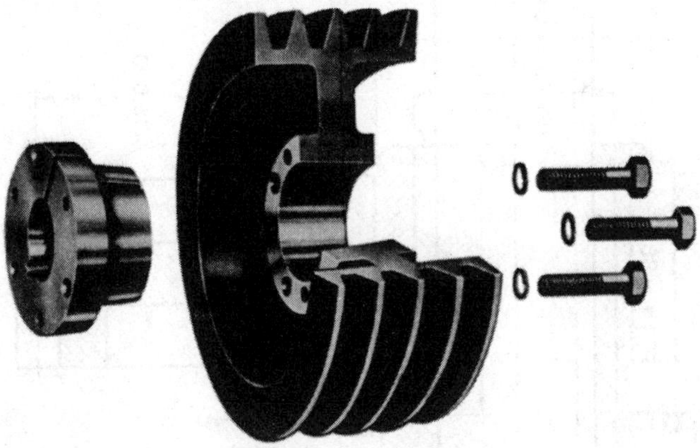

FIGURE 40–8 ■ V-belt sheave and bushing

NOTE: ALL DIMENSIONS SHOWN ARE NOMINAL SIZE.

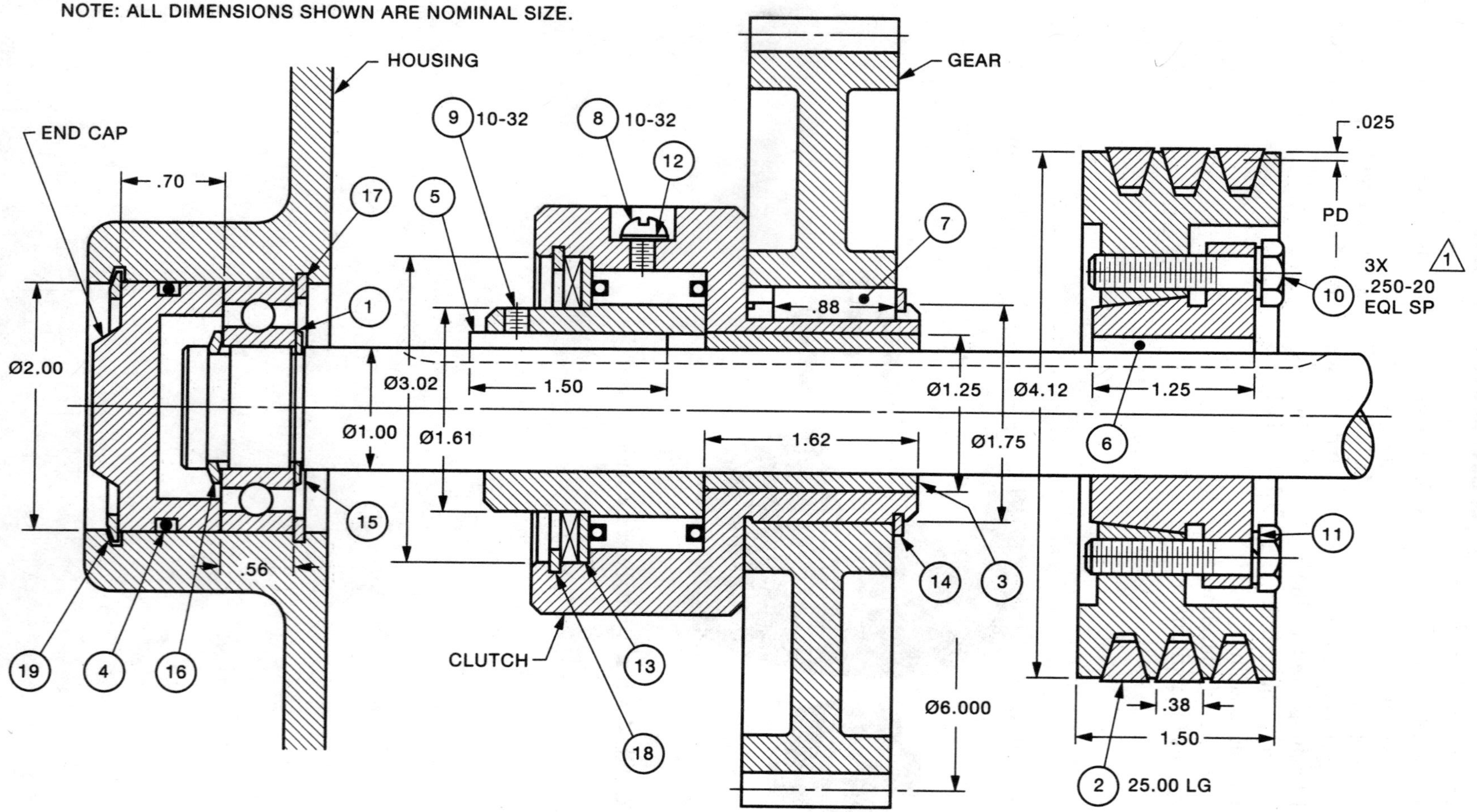

ASSIGNMENT:
In the sketching area provided, make a one-view detail drawing of the end cap, using dimensions taken from O-ring catalogues for the groove. Use your judgment for dimensions not shown.

BILL OF MATERIAL
Complete the Bill of Material for parts 1 to 19. Refer to manufacturers' catalogues and tables found in drafting manuals.

1.00 INCH SQUARES (.10 IN. GRID)

QTY	ITEM	MAIL	DESCRIPTION	PT NO
				19
				18
				17
				16
				15
				14
				13
				12
				11
				10
				9
				8
				7
				6
				5
				4
				3
				2
				1

ANSWERS

1. 3
2. RETAINING RING
   CAP SCREWS
   SET SCREW
   KEY
   PRESS FIT
3. 3
4. 3
5. 6
6. SLEEVE
7. BALL BEARING
8. O-RING
9. NO
10. OMIT
11. 4.07
12. 3V

QUESTIONS

1. How many cap screws fasten the sheave to the bushing?
2. List five parts or methods that are used to lock or join parts together on this assembly.
3. How many V-belts are used?
4. How many keys are there?
5. How many retaining rings are used?
6. What type of bearing is part (3)?
7. What type of bearing is part (1)?
8. What prevents the oil from leaking out between the housing and the end cap?
9. Can the gear be driven in both directions?
10. If the pitch on the gear is 8, what is the number of teeth?
11. What is the pitch diameter of the sheave?
12. What size V-belt is required?

REVISIONS	1	00-03-01	CAMPBELL
	PT 10 WAS 12-24 UNC		

SCALE NOT TO SCALE
DRAWN
DATE

POWER DRIVE

A-98

41 UNIT

RATCHET WHEELS

Ratchet wheels are used to transform reciprocating or oscillatory motion into intermittent motion, to transmit motion in one direction only, or to serve as an indexing device.

Common forms of ratchets and pawls are shown in Figure 41–1. The teeth in the ratchet engage with the teeth in the pawl, permitting rotation in one direction only.

When a ratchet wheel and pawl are designed, points A, B, and C, as shown in Figure 41–1(A), are positioned on the same circle to ensure that the smallest forces are acting on the system.

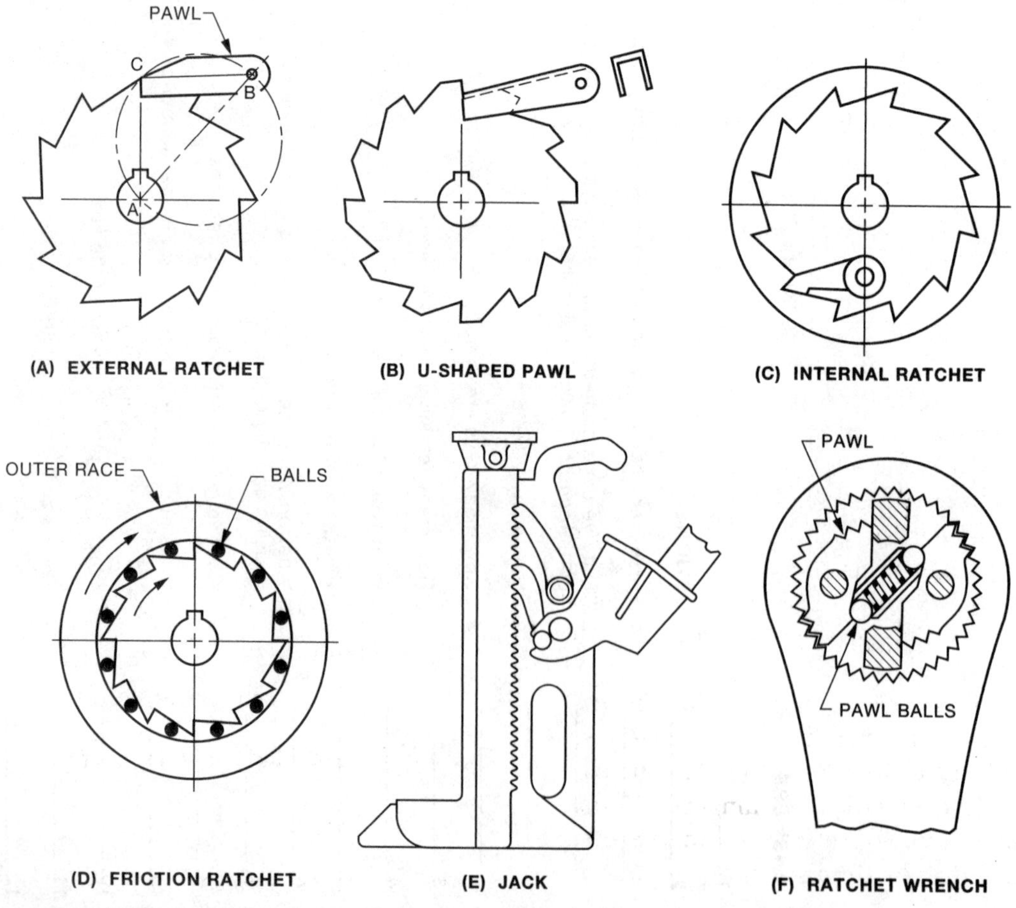
PAWL
C
B
A
(A) EXTERNAL RATCHET
(B) U-SHAPED PAWL
(C) INTERNAL RATCHET
OUTER RACE
BALLS
PAWL
PAWL BALLS
(D) FRICTION RATCHET
(E) JACK
(F) RATCHET WRENCH

FIGURE 41–1 ■ Ratchets and pawls

Mechanical Advantage

Mechanical advantage occurs when a weight in one place lifts a heavier weight in another place, or a force applied at one point on a lever produces a greater force at another point. Examples of mechanical advantage are the teeter-totter, the winch, and the gears shown in Figure 41–2.

The teeter-totter shows how mechanical advantage can be applied. If a 10-pound (lb.) weight is placed on one end of a teeter-totter and a 20 lb. weight is placed on the other end, the 10 lb. weight goes up and the 20 lb. weight goes down when placed equidistant from the fulcrum. If the fulcrum is moved to make the distance from the 10 lb. weight to the fulcrum twice that of the distance between the fulcrum and the 20 lb. weight, the weights become balanced. If the fulcrum is moved still closer to the 20 lb. weight, the 10 lb. weight goes down and the 20 lb. weight goes up.

As the distance between the fulcrum and the 10 lb. weight increases, the distance that the 10 lb. weight moves must increase proportionately to maintain the same movement of the 20 lb. weight. Thus, a light mass can move a heavier weight, but in doing so, the smaller weight must travel farther than the larger one.

Mechanical advantage also occurs when a winch or different-size gears are used. With the winch design shown in Figure 41–2(B), a mechanical advantage of 10 is obtained because the handle is 10 times the distance from the fulcrum as compared with the centre of the rope.

The mechanical advantage of gears can easily be determined by obtaining the ratio between the number of teeth on the gears or the ratio between the pitch diameters.

In the winch, drawing A-99, the centre of the handle bar is 10 in. from the centre of the shaft to which the pinion gear is attached. Half the pitch diameter of the pinion is .625 in. This produces a mechanical advantage of 10:.625 or 16:1. Further mechanical advantage is gained through the gear attached to the Ø1.00 shaft on which the rope revolves.

The hand will move a distance of approximately 63 in. when turning the handle one complete revolution. This will turn the rope drum one-fifth of a revolution (50:10 teeth ratio), winding a Ø.25 rope up approximately 4 in. A greater force can be exerted using the winch than by simply pulling the rope.

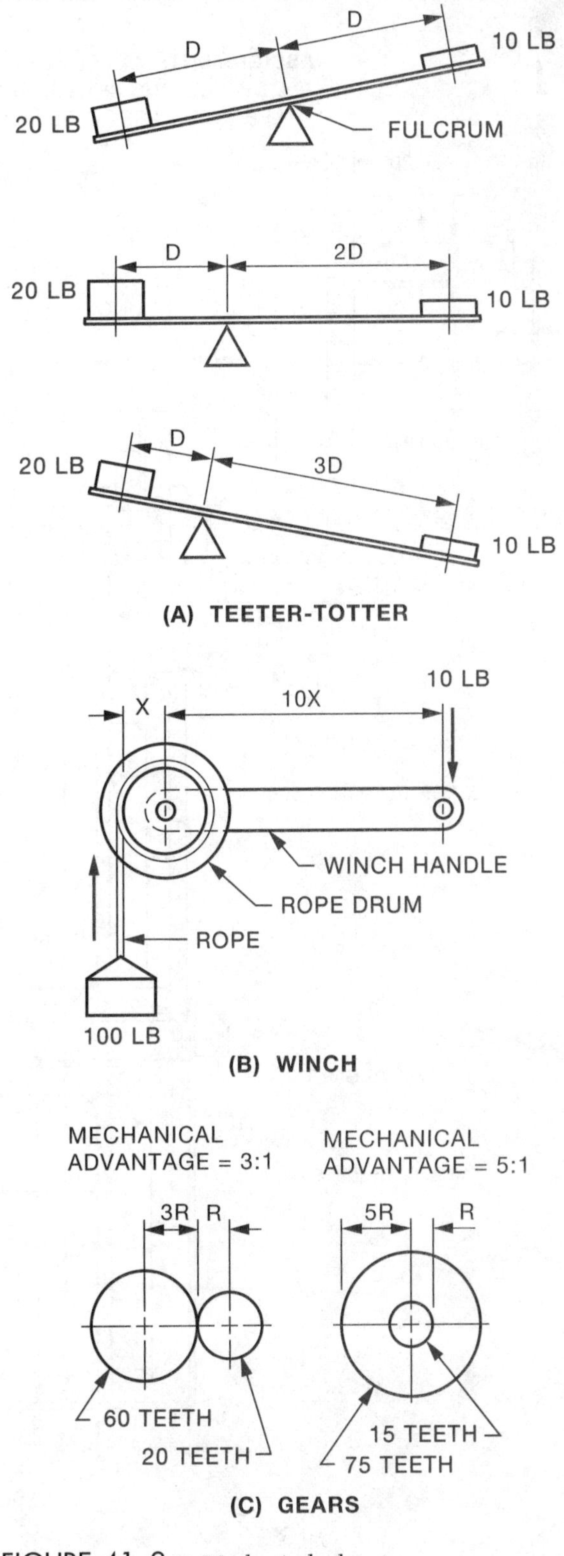

FIGURE 41–2 ■ Mechanical advantage

ASSIGNMENT: MAKE DETAIL DRAWINGS OF THE PARTS. NOTE THAT ALL DIMENSIONS SHOWN ARE NOMINAL SIZES. ALLOWANCES AND TOLERANCES ARE TO BE DETERMINED.

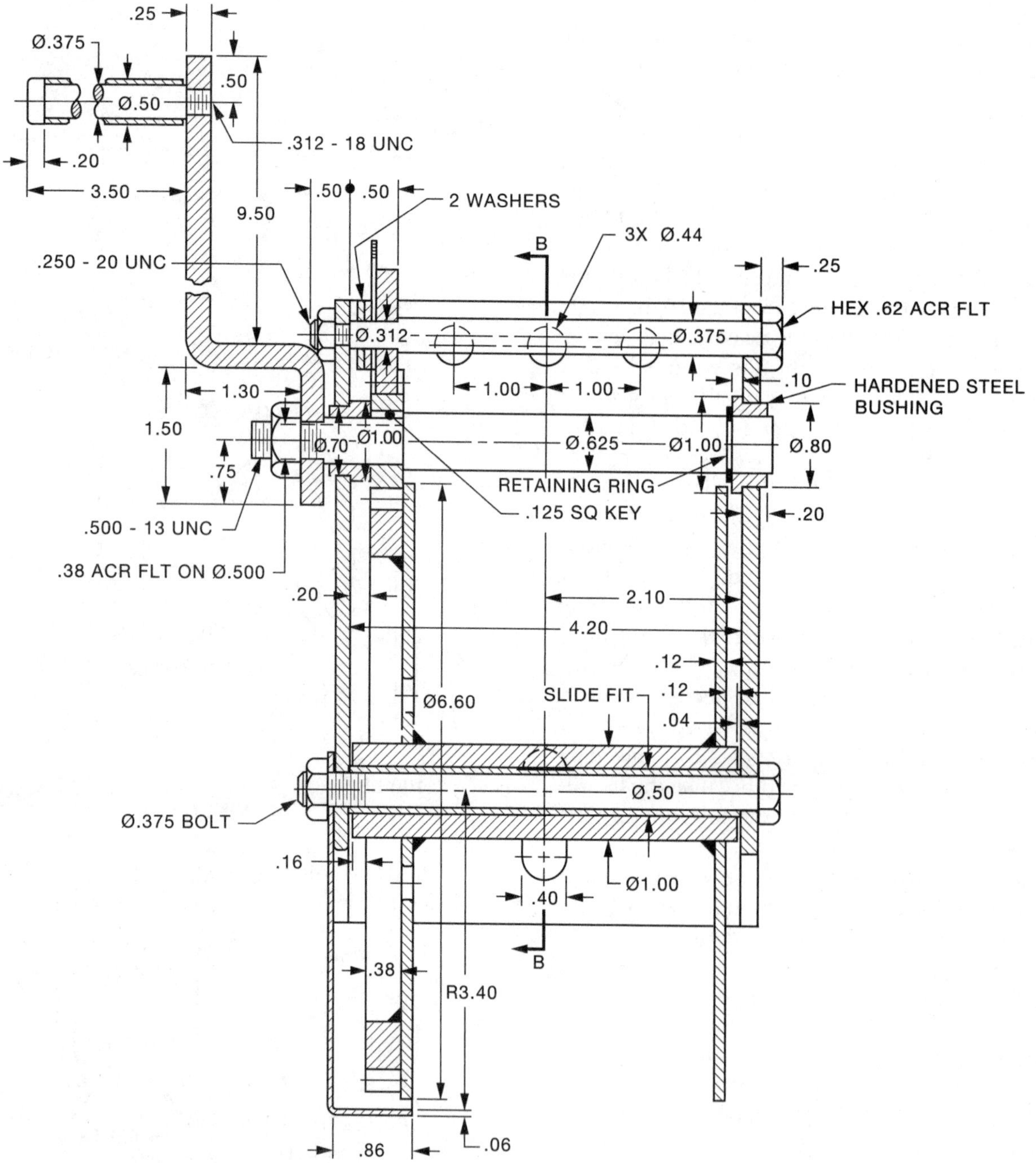

SECTION A-A

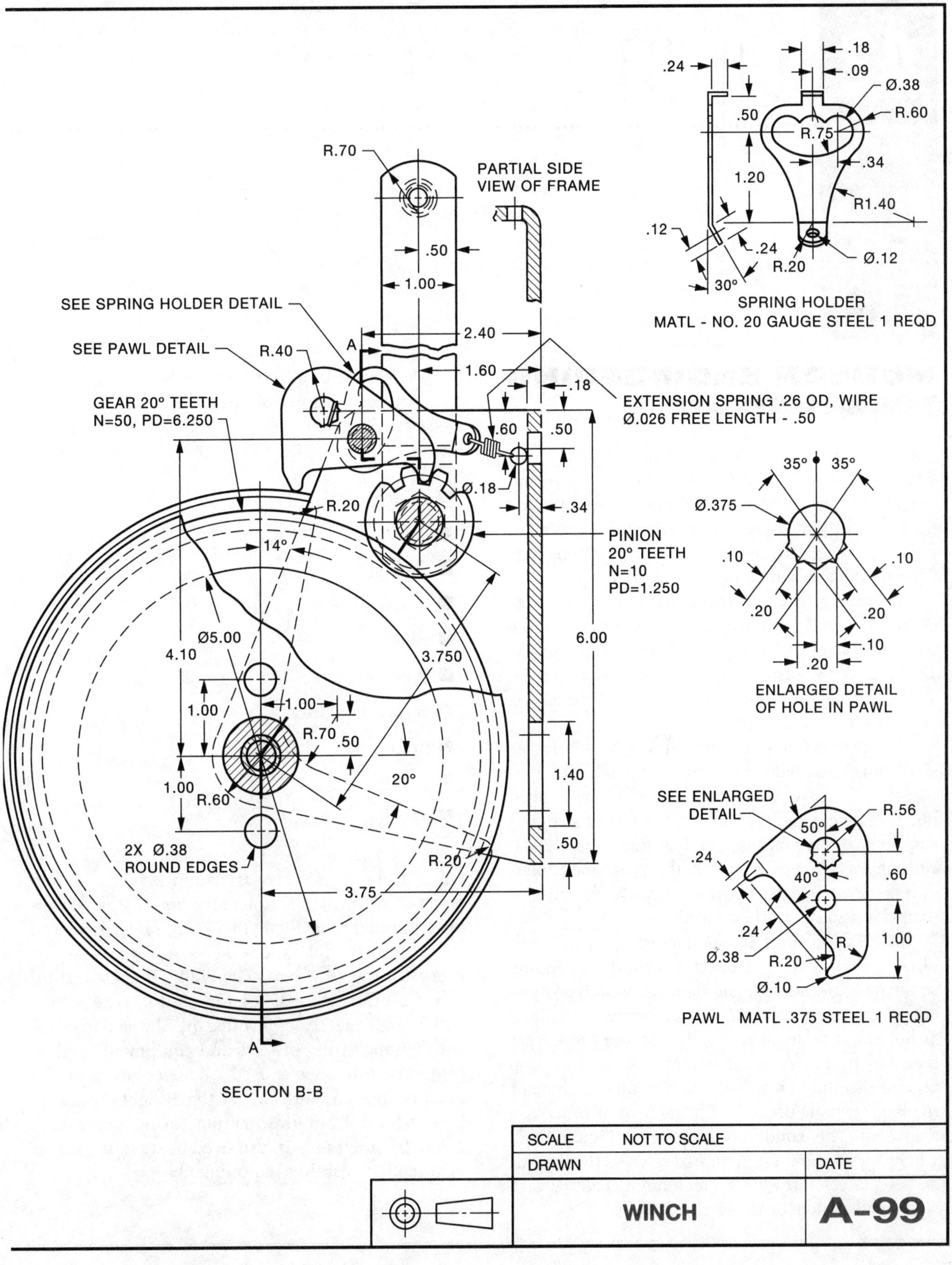
R.70
PARTIAL SIDE VIEW OF FRAME
.50
1.00
SEE SPRING HOLDER DETAIL
SEE PAWL DETAIL
R.40
A
2.40
1.60
.18
GEAR 20° TEETH N=50, PD=6.250
EXTENSION SPRING .26 OD, WIRE Ø.026 FREE LENGTH - .50
.60
.50
Ø.18
R.20
.34
14°
PINION 20° TEETH N=10 PD=1.250
Ø5.00
4.10
3.750
6.00
1.00
1.00
R.70
.50
20°
1.40
1.00
R.60
2X Ø.38 ROUND EDGES
R.20
.50
3.75
A
SECTION B-B
.24
.18
.09
Ø.38
.50
R.60
R.75
.34
1.20
R1.40
.12
.24
Ø.12
R.20
30°
SPRING HOLDER
MATL - NO. 20 GAUGE STEEL 1 REQD
35°
35°
Ø.375
.10
.10
.20
.20
.10
.20
ENLARGED DETAIL OF HOLE IN PAWL
SEE ENLARGED DETAIL
R.56
50°
.24
40°
.60
.24
1.00
R
Ø.38
R.20
Ø.10
PAWL MATL .375 STEEL 1 REQD
SCALE NOT TO SCALE
DRAWN
DATE
WINCH
A-99

42 UNIT

MODERN ENGINEERING TOLERANCING

An engineering drawing of a manufactured part conveys information from the designer to the manufacturer and inspector. It must contain all information necessary for the part to be correctly manufactured. It must also enable the inspector to determine precisely whether the finished parts are acceptable.

Therefore, each drawing must convey three essential items of information: the material to be used, the size or dimensions of the part, and the shape or geometric characteristics of the part. The drawing must also indicate the permissible variation of size and form.

The actual size of a feature must be within the size limits specified on the drawing. Each measurement made at any cross section of the feature must not be greater than the maximum limit of size, nor smaller than the minimum limit of size, Figure 42–1. Although each part is within the prescribed tolerance zones, the parts may not be usable because of their deviation from their form.

In order to meet functional requirements, it is often necessary to control errors of form, including squareness, roundness, and flatness, as well as deviation from true size. In the case of mating parts, such as holes and shafts, it is usually necessary to ensure that they do not cross the boundary of perfect form at their maximum material size (the smallest hole or the largest shaft) because of being bent or otherwise deformed. This condition is shown in Figure 42–2, where features are not permitted to cross the boundary of perfect form at the maximum material size (the smallest hole or the largest shaft).

The system of *geometric tolerancing* offers a precise interpretation of drawing requirements. Geometric tolerancing controls geometric characteristics of parts. These characteristics include

- straightness
- flatness
- circularity
- cylindricity
- angularity
- parallelism
- perpendicularity
- runout
- profile
- position

Other techniques, such as datum systems, datum targets, and projected tolerance zones were developed in order to facilitate this precise interpretation.

Geometric tolerances need not be used for every feature of a part. Generally, if each feature meets all dimensional tolerances, form variations will be adequately controlled by the accuracy of the manufacturing process and equipment used. A geometric tolerance is used when geometric errors must be limited more closely than might ordinarily be expected from the manufacturing process. A geometric tolerance is also used to state functional or interchangeability requirements.

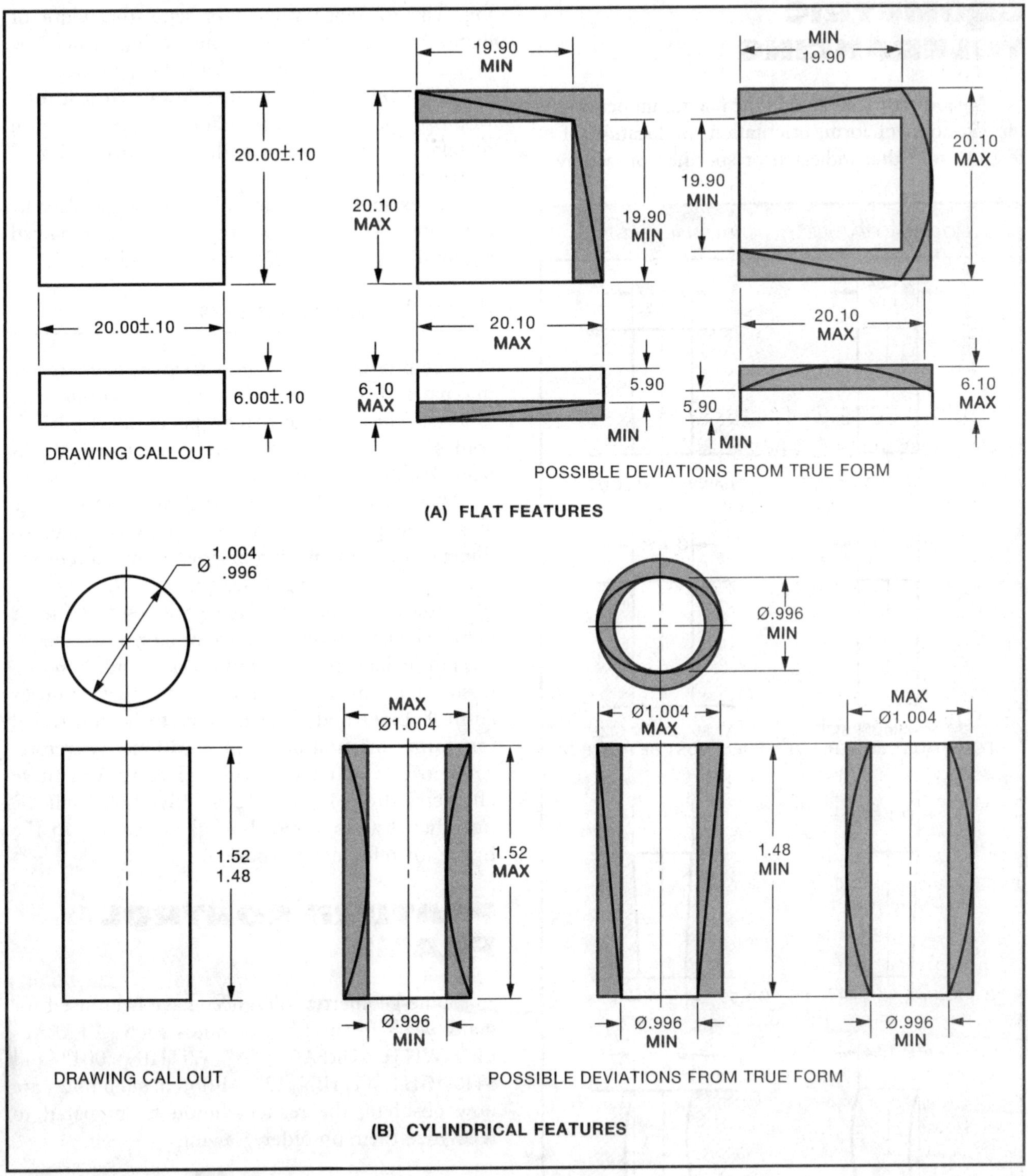

FIGURE 42–1 ■ Deviations of shape permitted by toleranced dimensions

GEOMETRIC TOLERANCING

A geometric tolerance is the maximum permissible variation of form, orientation, or location of a feature from that indicated or specified on a drawing. The tolerance value represents the width or diameter of the tolerance zone within which the point, line, or surface of the feature should lie.

From this definition, it follows that a feature would be permitted to have any variation of form or take up any position within the specified geometric tolerance zone.

For example, a line controlled in a single plane by a straightness tolerance of .008 in. must be contained within tolerance zone .008 in. wide, Figure 42–3.

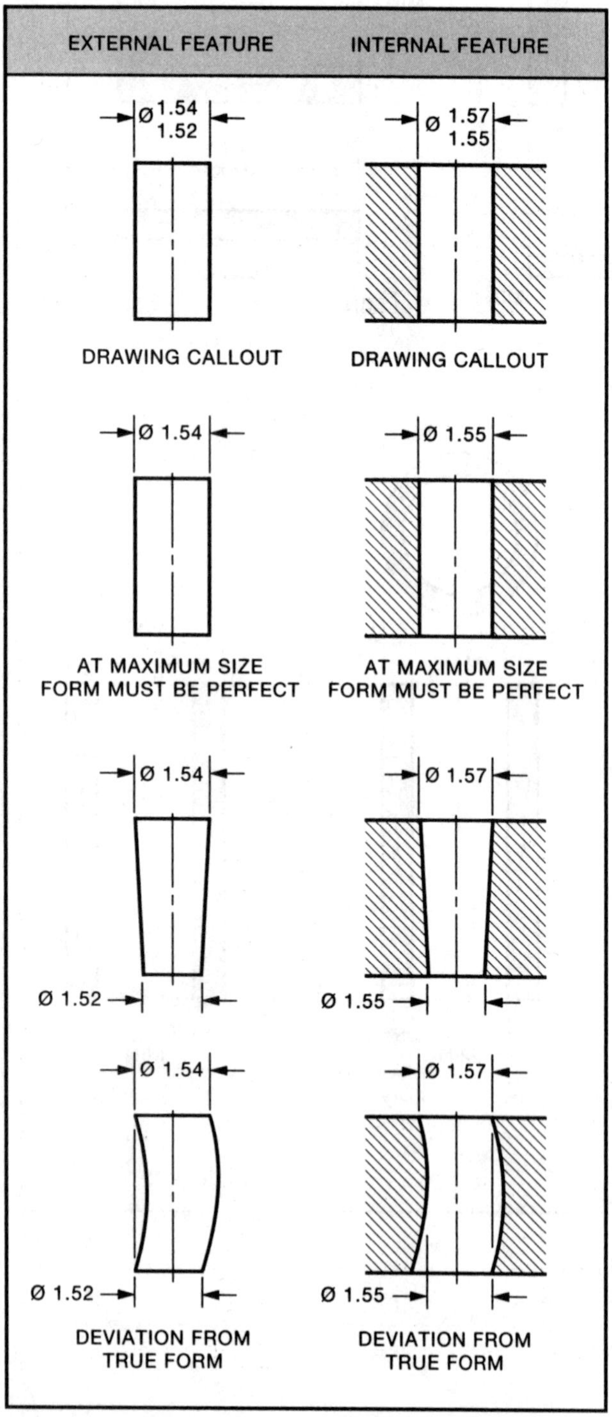

FIGURE 42–2 ■ Examples of deviation of form when perfect form at the maximum material size is required

Points, Lines, and Surfaces

The production and measurement of engineering parts deal, in most cases, with surfaces of objects. These surfaces may be flat, cylindrical, conical, or spherical, or have some more or less irregular shape or contour.

Measurement, however, usually has to take place at specific points. A line or surface is evaluated dimensionally by making a series of measurements at various points along its length.

Surfaces are considered to be composed of a series of line elements running in two or more directions.

Points have position but no size, and therefore position is the only characteristic that requires control. Lines and surfaces have to be controlled for form, orientation, and location. Therefore, geometric tolerances provide for control of these characteristics, Figure 42–4. (Symbols will be introduced as required, but all are shown in the figure for reference purposes.)

FEATURE CONTROL FRAME

Some geometric tolerances have been used for many years in the form of notes such as PARALLEL WITH SURFACE "A" WITHIN .001" and STRAIGHT WITHIN .12". Although such notes are now obsolete, the reader should be prepared to recognize them on older drawings.

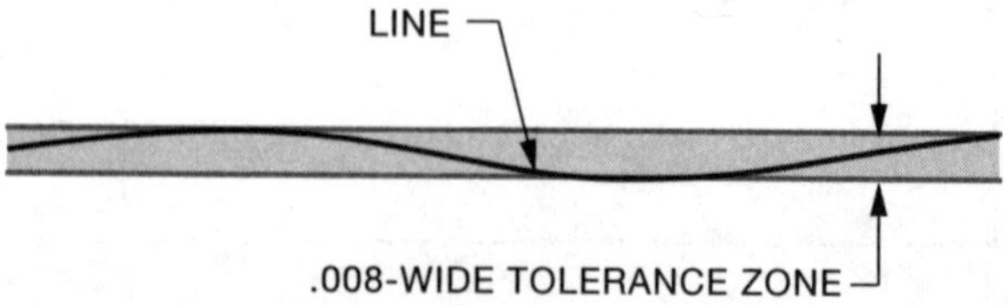

FIGURE 42–3 ■ Tolerance zone for straightness of a line

The current method is to specify geometric tolerances by means of the feature control frame, Figure 42–5.

A feature control frame consists of a rectangular frame divided into two or more compartments. The first compartment (starting from the left) contains the geometric characteristic. The second compartment contains the allowable tolerance. Where applicable, the tolerance is preceded by the diameter symbol and followed by a modifying symbol. Other compartments are added when datums must be specified.

The feature control frame is related to the feature by one of the following methods.

Application to Surfaces (Figure 42–6A)

The arrowhead of the leader from the feature control frame should touch the surface of the feature

FEATURE	TYPE OF TOLERANCE	CHARACTERISTIC	SYMBOL	SEE UNIT
INDIVIDUAL FEATURES	FORM	STRAIGHTNESS	—	42 & 43
		FLATNESS	▱	44
		CIRCULARITY (ROUNDNESS)	○	44
		CYLINDRICITY	⌭	44
INDIVIDUAL OR RELATED FEATURES	PROFILE	PROFILE OF A LINE	⌒	51
		PROFILE OF A SURFACE	⌓	51
RELATED FEATURES	ORIENTATION	ANGULARITY	∠	46 & 47
		PERPENDICULARITY	⊥	
		PARALLELISM	//	
	LOCATION	POSITION	⌖	49
		CONCENTRICITY	◎	
		SYMMETRY	⌯	
	RUNOUT	CIRCULAR RUNOUT	*↗	52
		TOTAL RUNOUT	*⌰	
SUPPLEMENTARY SYMBOLS		AT MAXIMUM MATERIAL CONDITION	Ⓜ	43 & 49
		AT LEAST MATERIAL CONDITION	Ⓛ	
		PROJECTED TOLERANCE ZONE	Ⓟ	
		BASIC DIMENSION	[XX]	45
		DATUM FEATURE	▷–[A]	45
		DATUM TARGET	Ø.50 / A2	48

* MAY BE FILLED IN

FIGURE 42–4 ■ Geometric characteristic symbols

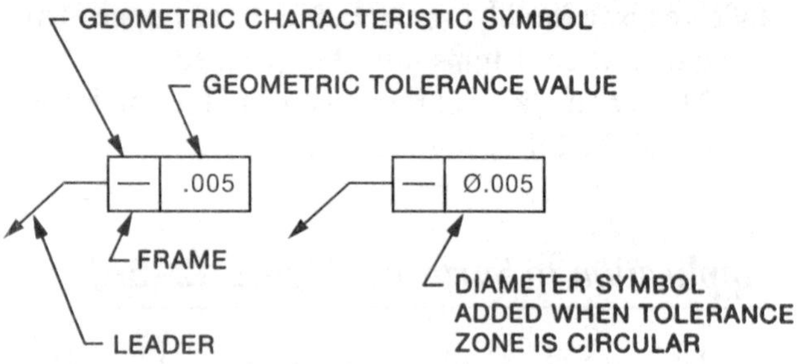

FIGURE 42–5 ■ Feature control frame

or the extension line of the surface, but not in line with the dimension.

- Attaching a side or end of the frame to an extension line extending from a place surface feature.

  The leader from the feature control frame should be directed at the feature in its characteristic profile. Thus, in Figure 42–7, the straightness tolerance is directed to the side view, and the circularity tolerance to the end view. This may not always be possible; a tolerance connected to an alternative view, such as circularity tolerance connected to a side view, is acceptable. When it is more convenient, or when space is limited, the arrowhead may be directed to an extension line, but not in line with the dimension line.

Applications to Features of Size (Figure 42–6B)

- Locating the frame below or attached to the leader directed callout or dimension pertaining to the feature. (See Unit 43.)
- Locating the frame below the size dimension to control the centre line, axis, or centre plane of the feature. (See Unit 43.)

When two or more feature control frames apply to the same feature, they are drawn together with a single leader and arrowhead, Figure 42–8.

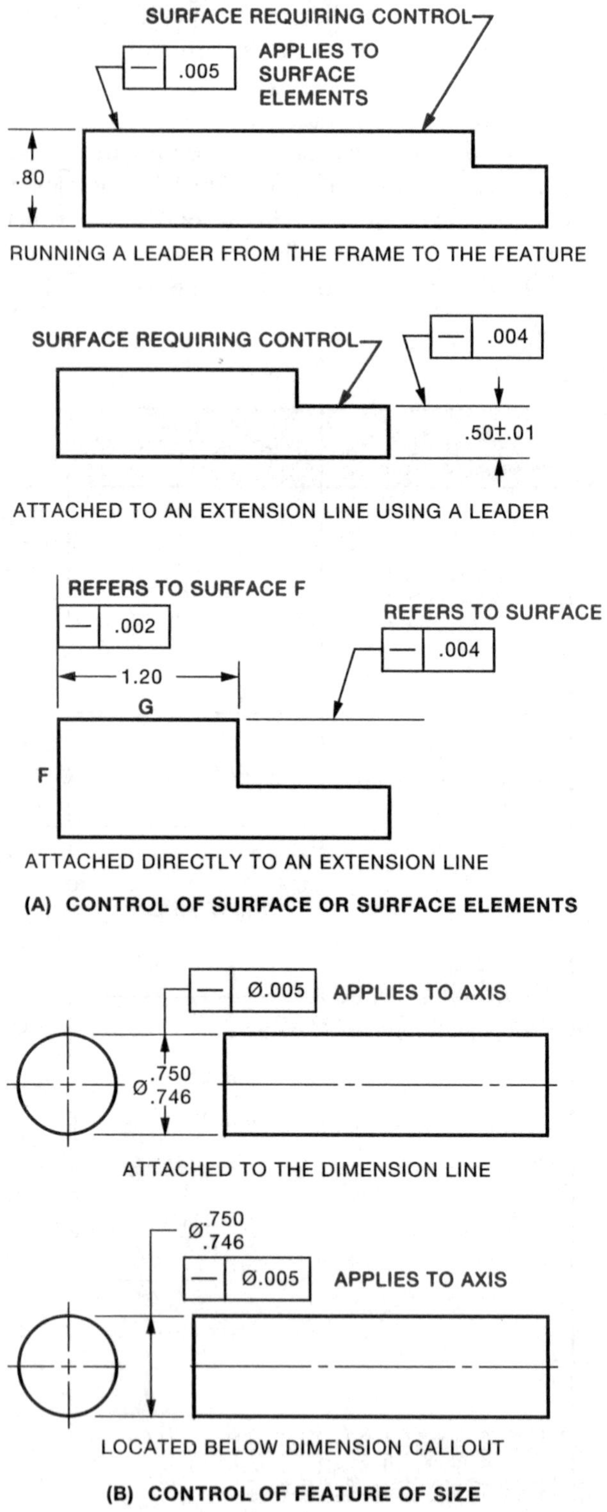

FIGURE 42–6 ■ Application of feature control frame

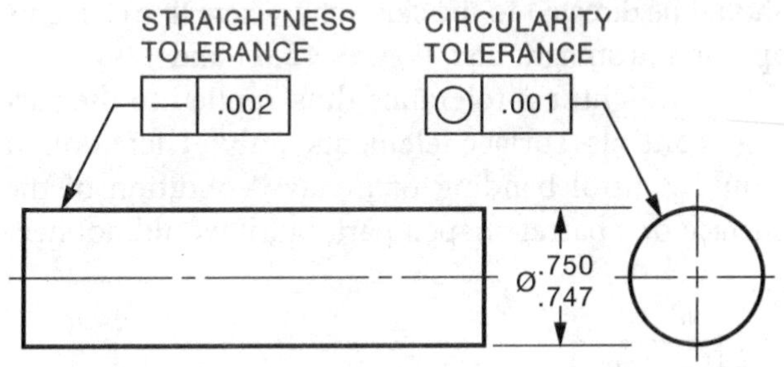

FIGURE 42–7 ■ Preferred location of feature control symbol when referring to a surface

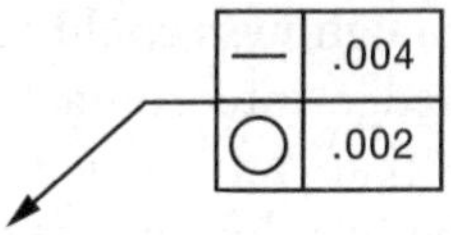

FIGURE 42–8 ■ Combined feature control frames directed to one surface

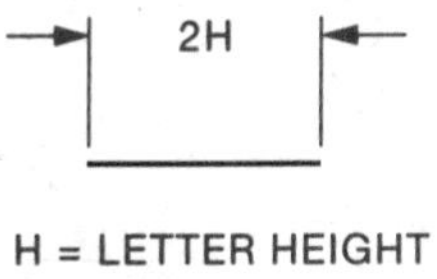

FIGURE 42–9 ■ Straightness symbol

FORM TOLERANCES

Form tolerances control straightness, flatness, circularity, and cylindricity. Orientation tolerances control angularity, parallelism, and perpendicularity.

Form tolerances are applicable to single (individual) features or elements of single features and, as such, do not require locating dimensions. The form tolerance must be less than the size tolerance.

Form and orientation tolerances critical to function and interchangeability are specified where the tolerances of size and location do not provide sufficient control. A tolerance of form or orientation may be specified where no tolerance of size is given, for example, the control of flatness.

STRAIGHTNESS

Straightness is a condition in which the elements of a surface or its axes are in a straight line. The geometric characteristic symbol for straightness is a horizontal line, Figure 42–9. A straightness tolerance specifies a tolerance zone within which the considered element of the surface or axis must lie. A straightness tolerance is applied to the view where the elements to be controlled are represented by a straight line.

STRAIGHTNESS CONTROLLING SURFACE ELEMENTS

Straightness is fundamentally a characteristic of a line, such as the edge of a part or a line scribed on a surface. A straightness tolerance is specified on a drawing by means of a feature control frame, which is directed by a leader to the line requiring control, Figure 42–10. It states in symbolic form that the line shall be straight within .006 in. This means that the line shall be contained within a tolerance zone consisting of the area between two parallel straight lines in the same plane separated by the specified tolerance.

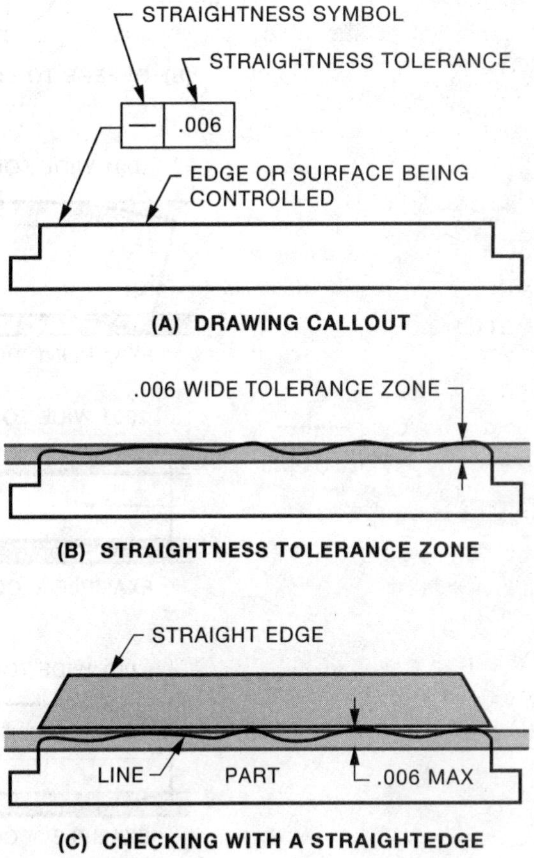

FIGURE 42–10 ■ Straightness tolerance applied to a flat surface

Theoretically, straightness could be measured by bringing a straightedge into contact with the line and determining that any space between the straightedge and the line does not exceed the specified tolerance.

For cylindrical parts or curved surfaces that are straight in one direction, the feature control frame should be directed to the side view, where line elements appear as a straight line, Figures 42–11 and 42–12.

A straightness tolerance thus applied to the surface controls surface elements only. Therefore, it would control bending or a wavy condition of the surface or a barrel-shaped part, but it would not nec-

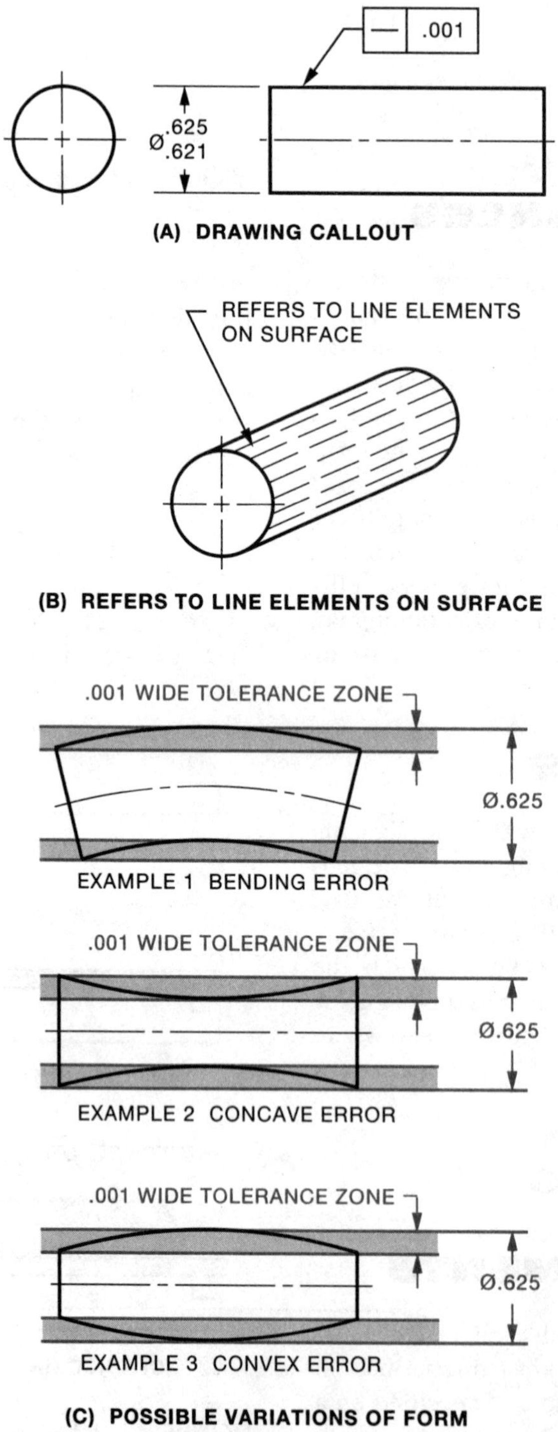

— .001
Ø .625 .621
(A) DRAWING CALLOUT
REFERS TO LINE ELEMENTS ON SURFACE
(B) REFERS TO LINE ELEMENTS ON SURFACE
.001 WIDE TOLERANCE ZONE
Ø.625
EXAMPLE 1 BENDING ERROR
.001 WIDE TOLERANCE ZONE
Ø.625
EXAMPLE 2 CONCAVE ERROR
.001 WIDE TOLERANCE ZONE
Ø.625
EXAMPLE 3 CONVEX ERROR
(C) POSSIBLE VARIATIONS OF FORM

FIGURE 42–11 ■ Specifying the straightness of line elements of a cylindrical surface essarily control the straightness of the axes or the conicity of the cylinder.

Straightness of a cylindrical surface is interpreted to mean that each line element of the surface shall be contained within a tolerance zone consisting of the space between two parallel lines, separated by the width of the specified tolerance, when the part is rolled along one of the planes. Theoretically, this could be measured by rolling the part on a flat surface and measuring the space between the part and the plate to ensure that it does not exceed the specified tolerance, Figure 42–13.

A straightness tolerance can be applied to a conical surface in the same manner as for a cylindrical surface, Figure 42–14, and will ensure that the rate of taper is uniform. The actual rate of taper, or the taper angle, must be separately toleranced.

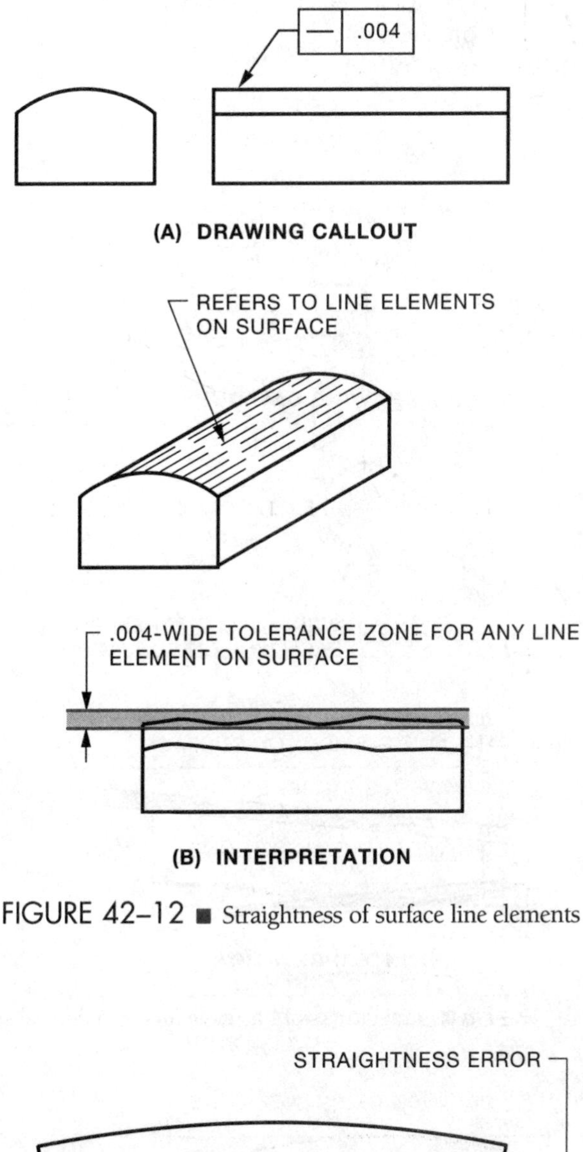
.004
(A) DRAWING CALLOUT
REFERS TO LINE ELEMENTS ON SURFACE
.004-WIDE TOLERANCE ZONE FOR ANY LINE ELEMENT ON SURFACE
(B) INTERPRETATION

FIGURE 42–12 ■ Straightness of surface line elements

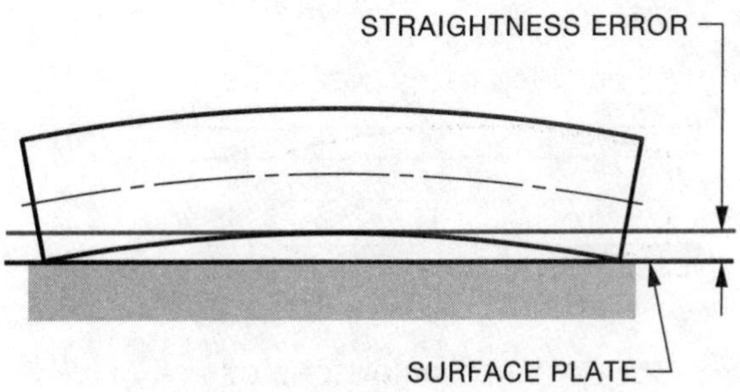
STRAIGHTNESS ERROR
SURFACE PLATE

FIGURE 42–13 ■ Measuring the straightness of a cylindrical surface

A straightness tolerance applied to a flat surface indicates straightness control in one direction only and must be directed to the line on the drawing representing the surface to be controlled and the direction in which control is required, Figure 42–15. It is then interpreted to mean that each line element on the surface in the indicated direction shall lie within a tolerance zone.

Different straightness tolerances may be specified in two or more directions when required. However, if the same straightness tolerance is required in two coordinate directions on the same surface, a flatness tolerance rather than a straightness tolerance is used.

If it is not otherwise necessary to draw all three views, the straightness tolerances may all be shown on a single view by indicating the direction with short lines terminated by arrowheads, Figure 42–15C.

REFERENCES

CAN/CSA-B78.2-M91 Dimensioning and Tolerancing of Technical Drawings

ASME Y14.5M-1994 Dimensioning and Tolerancing

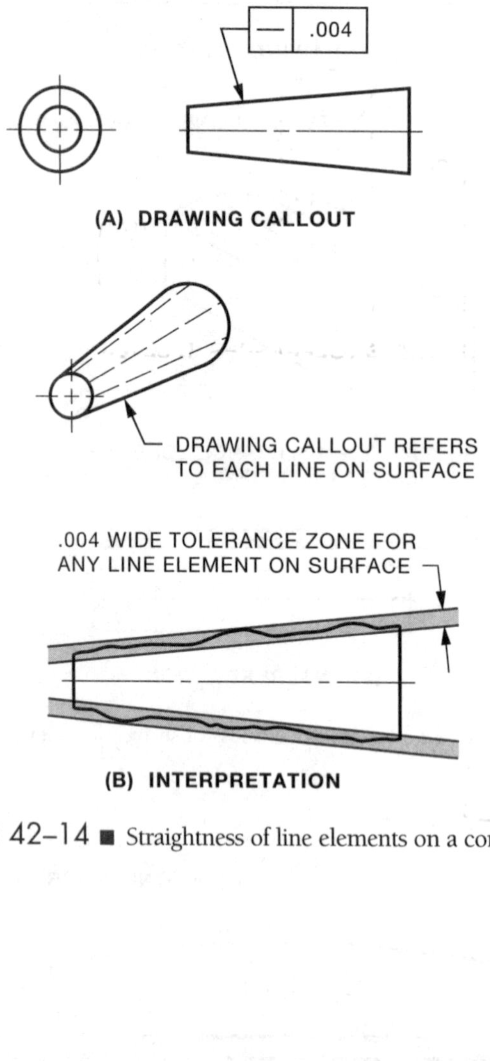
.004
(A) DRAWING CALLOUT
DRAWING CALLOUT REFERS
TO EACH LINE ON SURFACE
.004 WIDE TOLERANCE ZONE FOR
ANY LINE ELEMENT ON SURFACE
(B) INTERPRETATION

FIGURE 42–14 ■ Straightness of line elements on a conical surface

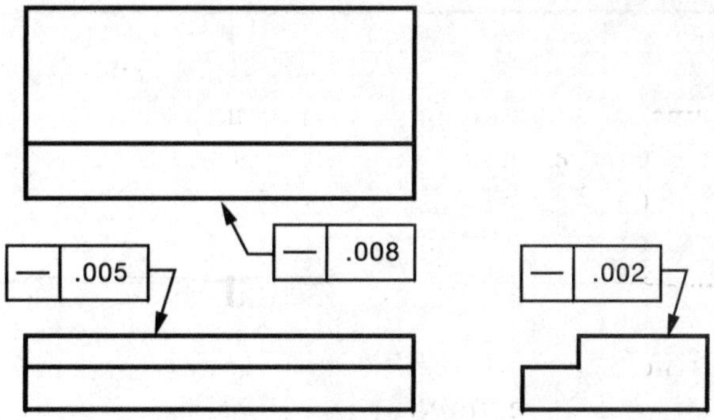
— .008
— .005
— .002

(A) DRAWING CALLOUT

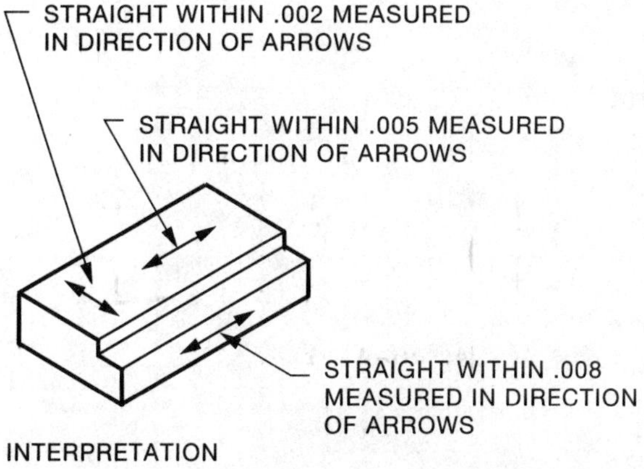
STRAIGHT WITHIN .002 MEASURED IN DIRECTION OF ARROWS
STRAIGHT WITHIN .005 MEASURED IN DIRECTION OF ARROWS
STRAIGHT WITHIN .008 MEASURED IN DIRECTION OF ARROWS
INTERPRETATION

(B) STRAIGHTNESS TOLERANCES IN SEVERAL DIRECTIONS

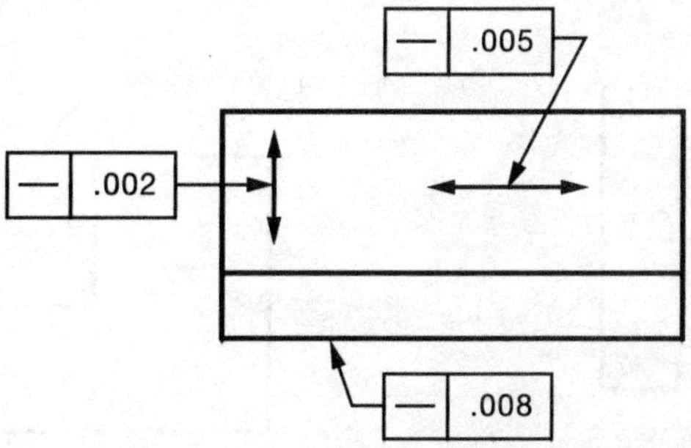
— .005
— .002
— .008

(C) THREE STRAIGHTNESS TOLERANCES ON ONE VIEW

FIGURE 42–15 ■ Straightness tolerances in several directions

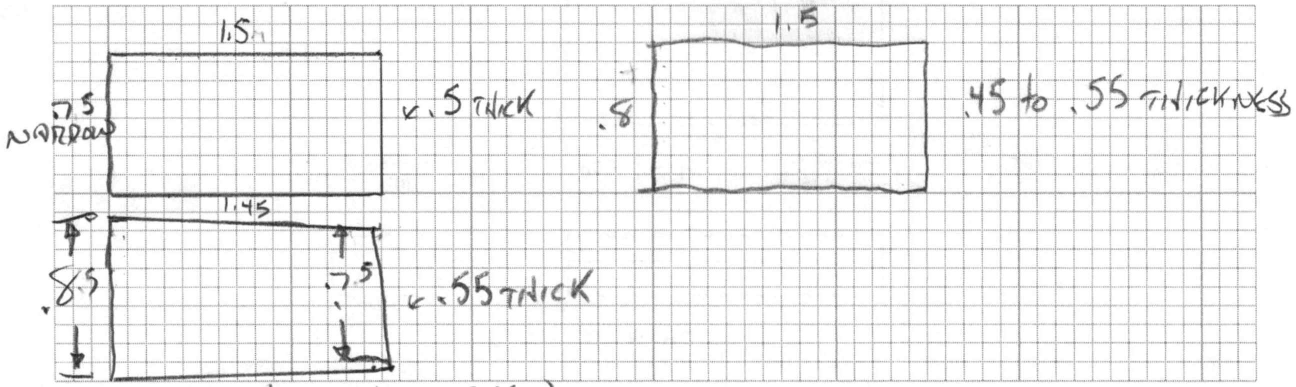
1.5
.75
NARROW
←.5 THICK
1.45
.85
.75
←.55 THICK
1.5
.8
.45 to .55 THICKNESS

CONE WITH UNEVEN LENGTH

FIGURE 1

1.00 INCH SQUARES (.10 IN. GRID)

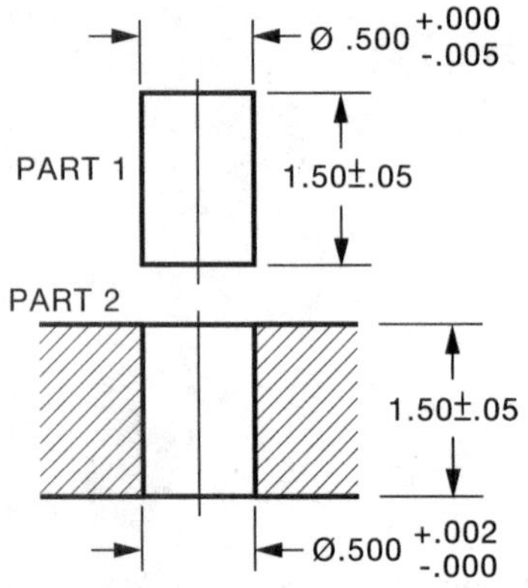
Ø .500 +.000 -.005
PART 1
1.50±.05
PART 2
1.50±.05
Ø.500 +.002 -.000

FIGURE 2

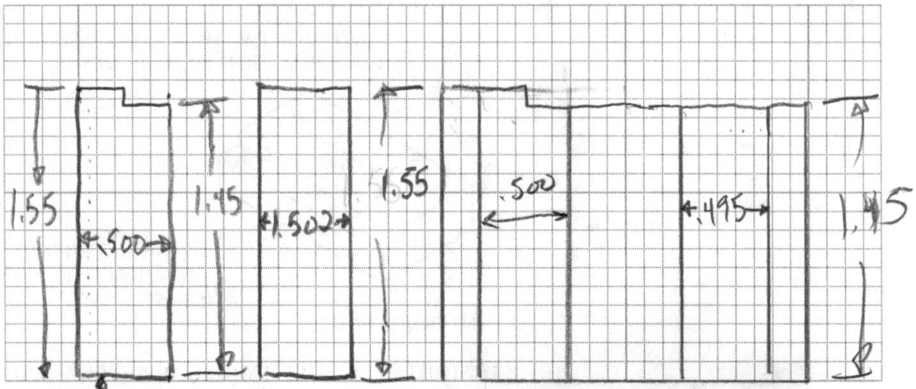
1.55
.500
1.45
1.502
1.55
.500
.495
1.45

GO
NO-GO

RING AND PLUG GAUGE FOR FIGURE 2

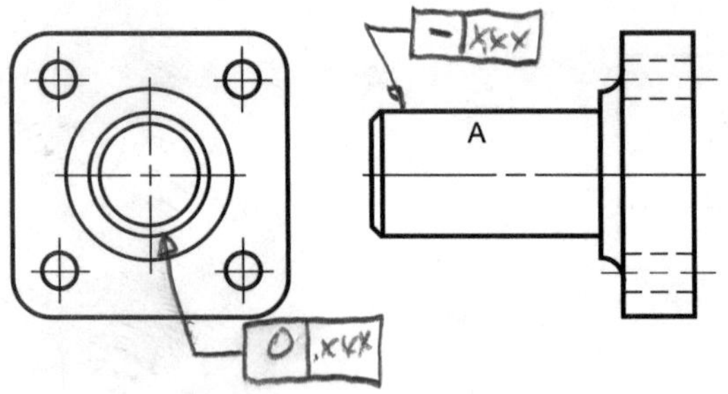
A

FIGURE 3

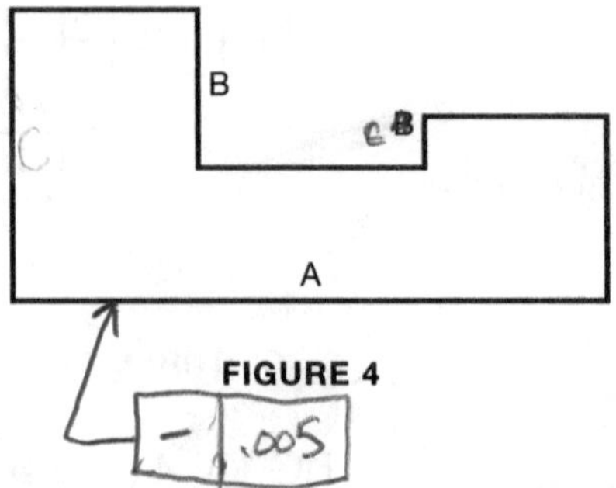
B
A
.005

FIGURE 4

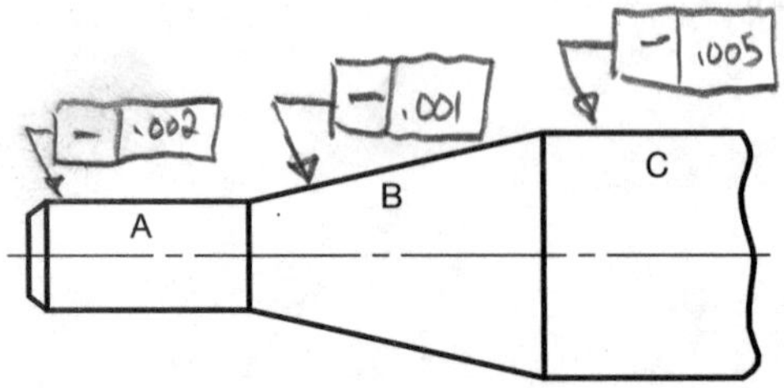
.002
.001
.005
A
B
C

FIGURE 5

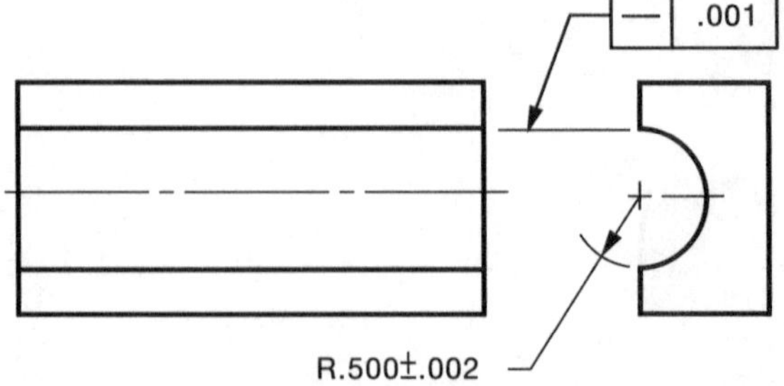
.001
R.500±.002

FIGURE 6

ANSWERS

1. SEE FIGURE 1
2. SEE FIGURE 2
3. SEE FIGURE 3
4. SEE FIGURE 4
5. SEE FIGURE 5
6. A .001
   B .001
   C .001
7. SEE FIGURE 7B
8. YES → ACCEPTABLE MEETS STRAIGHTNESS + ½ OF 1.00 TOLERANCE

ASSIGNMENT:

1. A rectangular part .80 X 1.50 X .50 in. thick has a tolerance of ±.05 in. on the dimensions. Similar to Figure 42-1, show three different permissible deviations for the part on the graph, Figure 1. Add dimensions.

2. Make a sketch, complete with dimensions, of a ring and plug gauge to check the hole and shaft shown in Figure 2.

3. Apply two feature control frames, one to denote circularity (roundness) and the other to control straightness of the surface of the cylindrical feature "A" shown in Figure 3.

4. With reference to Figure 4, add the geometric tolerances:
   (A) Surface A is to be straight within .005 in.
   OMIT (B) Surfaces B and C are to be straight within .008 in.
   Use a minimum of two different methods of connecting the feature control frames to the surfaces requiring straightness control.

5. Add the following straightness tolerances to the surfaces shown in Figure 5:
   (A) Surface A -.002 in.
   (B) Surface B -.001 in.
   (C) Surface C -.005 in.

6. Figure 6. What is the maximum permissible deviation from straightness if the radius is (A) .498 in., (B) .500, in., and (C) .502 in.?

7. Place the feature control frames shown in Figure 7(A) on either the front or side views of Figure 7(B).

8. Is the part shown in Figure 8 acceptable? State your reason.

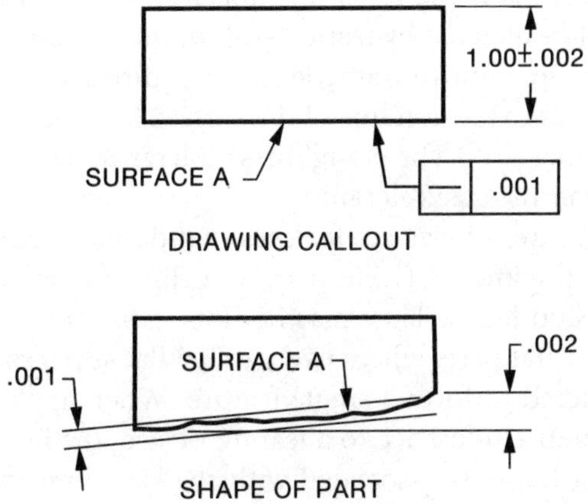
1.00±.002
SURFACE A
— .001
DRAWING CALLOUT
SURFACE A
.001
.002
SHAPE OF PART

FIGURE 8

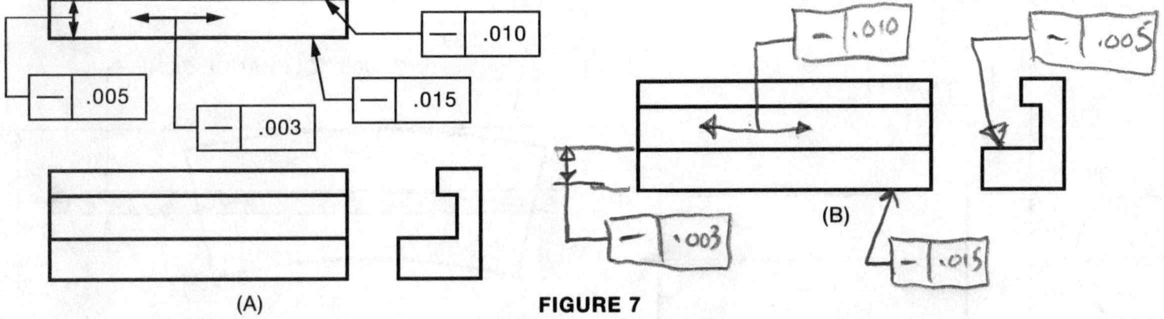
— .010
— .005
— .015
— .003
(A)
(B)
— .010
— .005
— .003
— .015

FIGURE 7

43 UNIT

STRAIGHTNESS OF A FEATURE OF SIZE

Features of Size

Geometric tolerances that have so far been considered concern only lines, line elements, and single surfaces. These are features having no diameter or thickness, and the form tolerances applied to them cannot be affected by feature size. In these examples, the feature control frame leader was directed to the surface or extension line of the surface but not to the size dimension. The straightness tolerance had to be less than the size tolerance.

Features of size are features that do have diameter or thickness. These may be cylinders, such as shafts and holes. They may be slots, tabs, or rectangular or flat parts where two parallel flat surfaces are considered to form a single feature. When applying a geometric tolerance to a feature of size, the feature control frame is associated with the size dimension or attached to an extension of the dimension line.

Circular Tolerance Zones

When the resulting tolerance zone is cylindrical, such as when straightness of the axis of a cylindrical feature is specified, a diameter symbol precedes the tolerance value in the feature control frame. The feature control frame is located below the dimension pertaining to the feature, Figure 43–1.

FEATURE OF SIZE DEFINITIONS

Before proceeding with examples of features of size, it is essential to understand certain terms.

Maximum Material Condition (MMC)

When a feature or part is at the limit of size that results in it containing the maximum amount of material, it is said to be at MMC. Thus, it is the maximum limit of size for an external feature, such as a

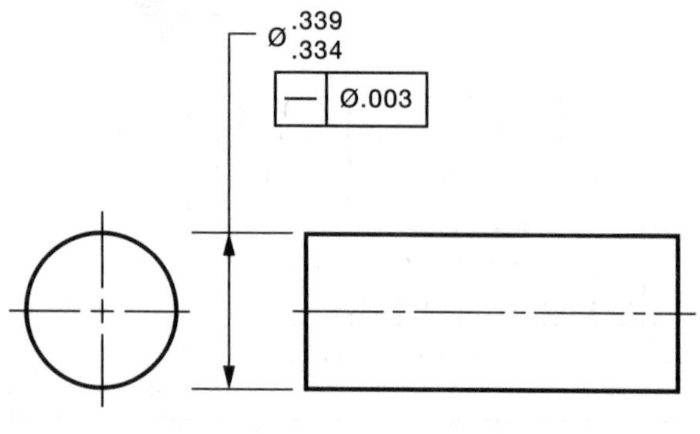

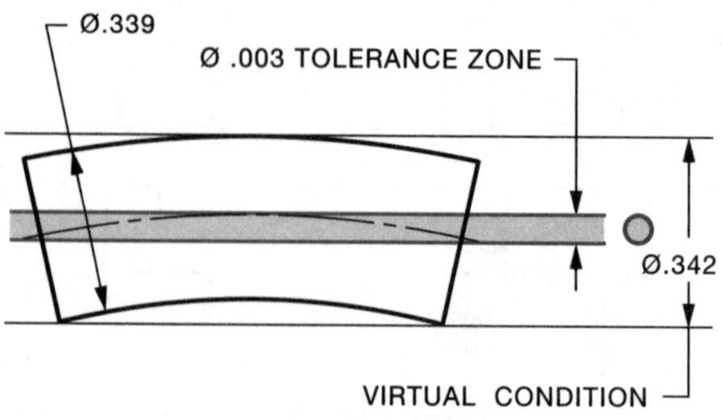

FIGURE 43–1 ■ Circular tolerance zone

shaft, or the minimum limit of size for an internal feature, such as a hole, Figure 43–2.

Virtual Condition

Virtual condition refers to the overall envelope of perfect form within which the feature would just fit. It is the boundary formed by the MMC limit of size of a feature plus or minus the applied geometric tolerances. For an external feature such as a shaft, it is the maximum material size plus the effect of permissible form variations, such as straightness, flatness, roundness, cylindricity, and orientation tolerances. For an internal feature such as a hole, it is the maximum material size minus the effect of such form variations, Figure 43–2 and 43–3.

Parts are generally toleranced so they will assemble when mating features are at MMC. Additional tolerance on form or location is permitted when features depart from their MMC size.

Least Material Condition (LMC)

This term refers to that size of a feature that results in the part containing the minimum amount of material. Thus it is the minimum limit of size for an external feature, such as a shaft, and the maximum limit of size for an internal feature, such as a hole, Figure 43–3.

Regardless of Feature Size (RFS)

This term means that the size of the geometric tolerance remains the same for any feature lying within its limits of size.

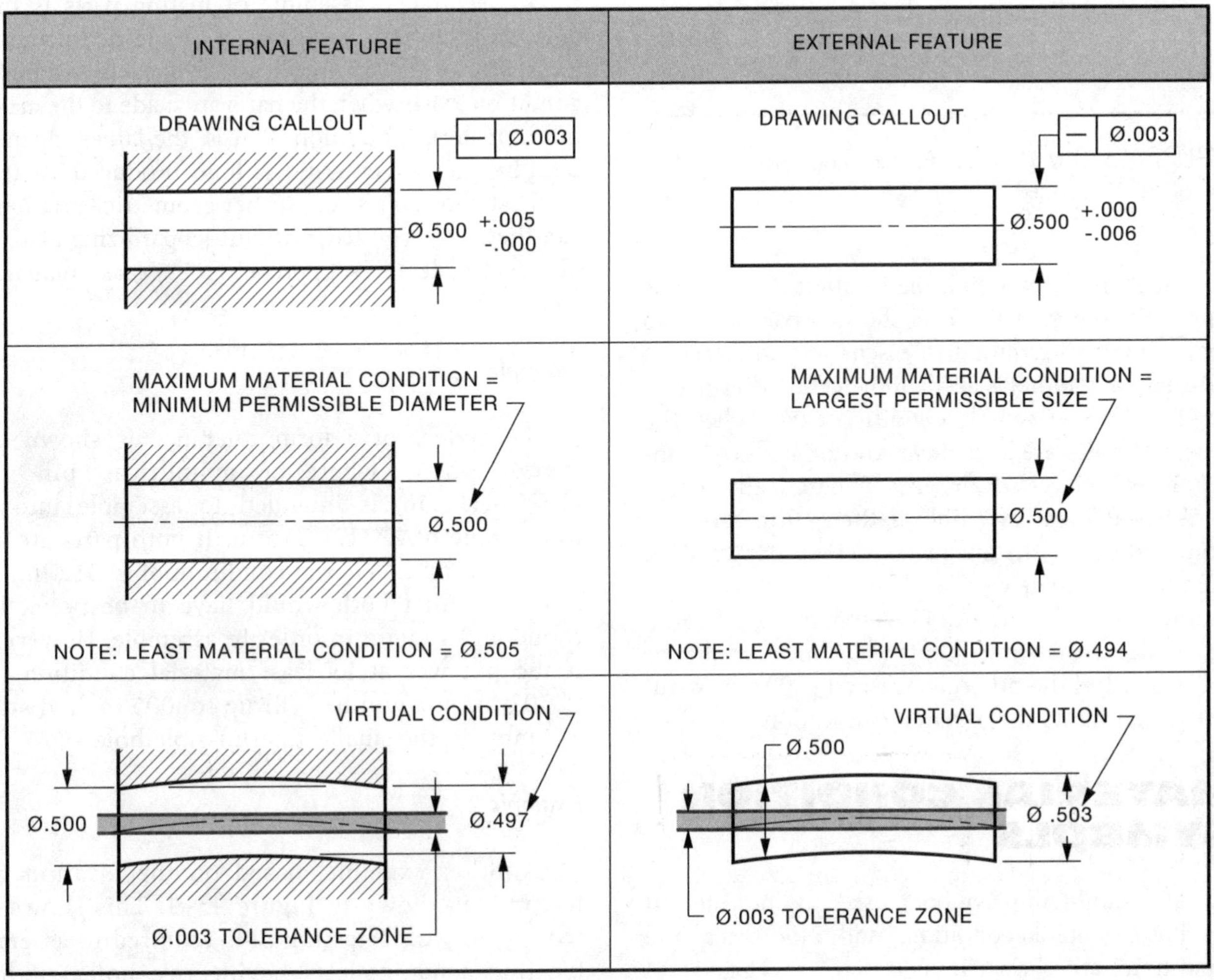

FIGURE 43–2 ■ Maximum material condition and virtual condition

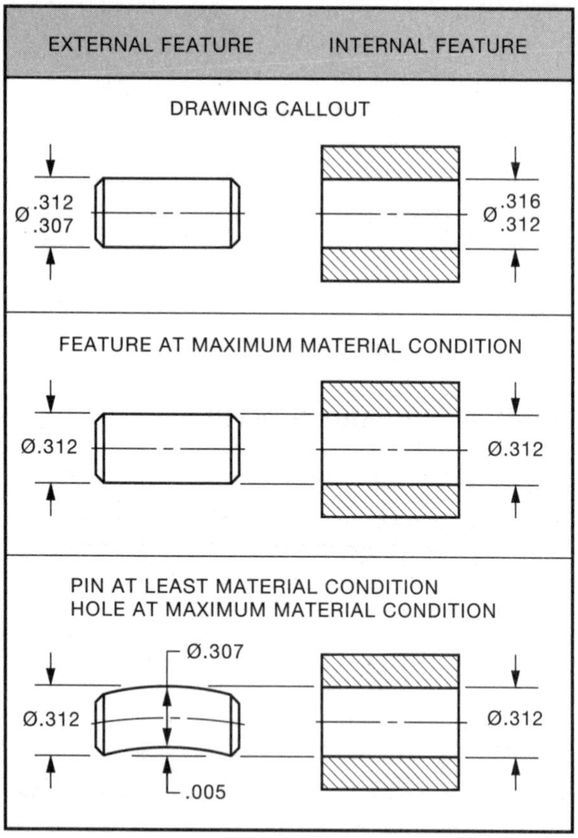

FIGURE 43–3 ■ Effect of form variation when only feature of size is specified

An example based on the location of features is shown in Figure 43–4. This shows a part with two projecting pins required to assemble into a mating part having two holes at the same centre distance.

The worst assembly condition exists when the pins and holes are at their maximum material condition, which is Ø.250 in. Theoretically, these parts would just assemble if their form, orientation, and centre distance were perfect. However, if the pins and holes were at their least material condition of Ø.247 and Ø.253, respectively, it would be evident that one centre distance could be increased and the other decreased be .003 in. without jeopardizing the assembly condition.

MATERIAL CONDITION SYMBOLS

The modifying symbols used to indicate "at maximum material condition," and "at least material condition" are shown in Figure 43–5. The use of these symbols in local or general notes is prohibited.

Prior to 1994, the ANSI Y14.5 Dimensioning and Tolerancing Standard used a material condition symbol for "regardless of feature size," but this practice is now discontinued.

Applicability of RFS, MMC, and LMC

Applicability of RFS, MMC, and LMC is limited to features subject to variations in size. They may be datum features or other features whose axes or centre planes are controlled by geometric tolerances. In such cases, the following practices apply: RFS applies, with respect to the individual tolerance, datum reference, or both, where no modifying symbol is shown. (See Figures 43–2 and 43–11.) MMC or LMC must be specified on the drawing where it is required. (See Figure 43–12.)

EXAMPLES

If freedom of assembly of mating parts is the chief criterion for establishing a geometric tolerance for a feature of size, the least favourable assembly condition exists when the parts are made to the maximum material condition, that is, the largest diameter pin allowed entering a hole produced to the smallest allowable size. Further geometric variations can then be permitted, without jeopardizing assembly, as the features approach their least material condition.

Example 1

The effect of a form tolerance is shown in Figure 43–3, where a cylindrical pin of Ø.307–.312 in. is intended to assemble into a round hole of Ø.312–.316 in. If both parts are at their maximum material condition of Ø.312 in., it is evident that both would have to be perfectly round and straight in order to assemble. However, if the pin was at its least material condition of Ø.307 in., it could be bent up to .005 in. and still assemble in the smallest permissible hole.

Example 2

Another example, based on the location of features, is shown in Figure 43–4. This shows a part with two projecting pins required to assemble into a mating part having two holes at the same centre distance.

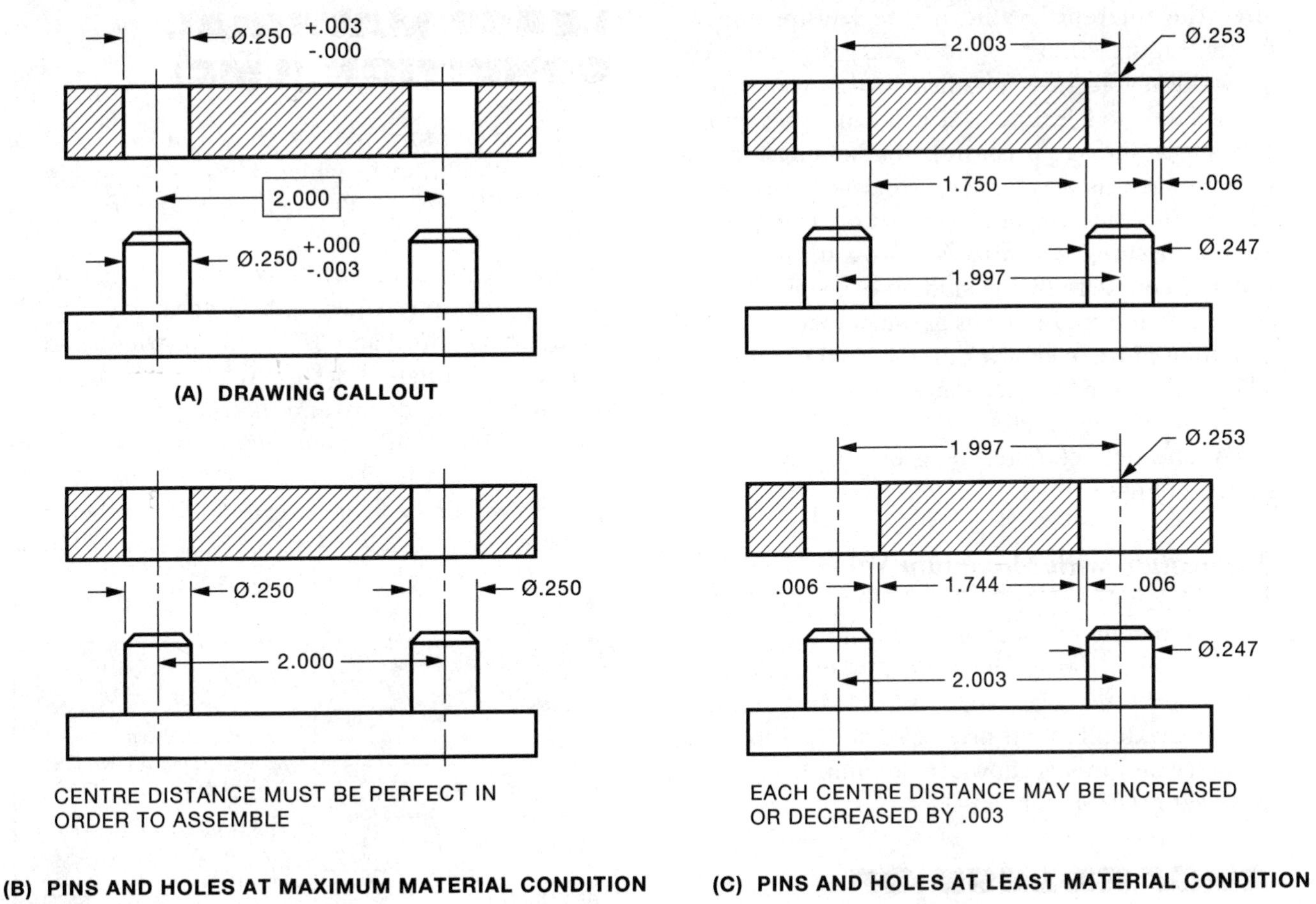

FIGURE 43–4 ■ Effect of location

The worst assembly condition exists when the pins and holes are at their maximum material condition, which is Ø.250 in. Theoretically, these parts would just assemble if their form, orientation (squareness to the surface), and centre distances were perfect. However, if the pins and holes were at their least material condition of Ø.247 in. and Ø253 in., respectively, it would be evident that one centre distance could be increased and the other decreased by .003 in. without jeopardizing the assembly condition.

MAXIMUM MATERIAL CONDITION (MMC)

The symbol for maximum material condition is shown in Figure 43–6. The symbol dimensions are based on percentages of the recommended letter height of dimensions.

If a geometric tolerance is required to be modified on an MMC basis, it is specified on the drawing by including the symbol Ⓜ immediately

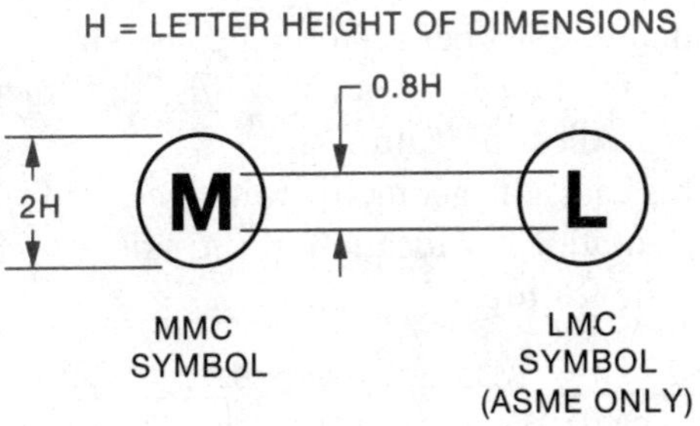

FIGURE 43–5 ■ Modifying symbols

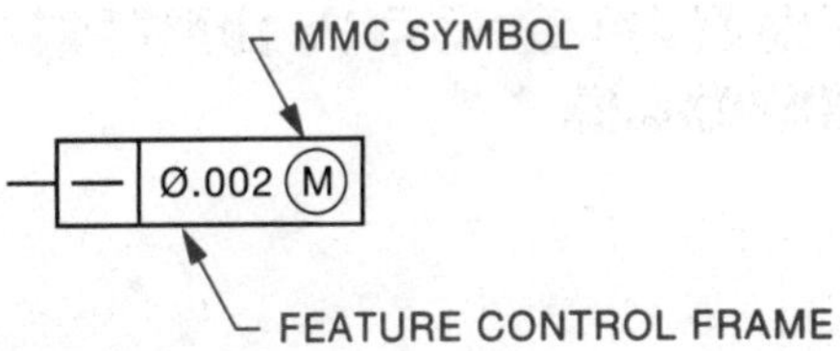

FIGURE 43–6 ■ Application of MMC symbol

after the tolerance value in the feature control frame, Figure 43–6.

A form tolerance modified in this way can be applied only to a feature of size; it cannot be applied to a single surface. It controls the boundary of the feature, such as a complete cylindrical surface, or two parallel surfaces of a flat feature. This permits the feature surface or surfaces to cross the maximum material boundary by the amount of the form tolerance. If design requirements are such that the virtual condition must be kept within the maximum material boundary, the form tolerance must be specified as zero at MMC, Figure 43–7.

Application of MMC to geometric symbols is shown in Figure 43–8.

Application with Maximum Value

It is sometimes necessary to ensure that the geometric tolerance does not vary over the full range permitted by the size variations. For such applications, a maximum limit may be set to the geometric tolerance and this is shown in addition to that permitted at MMC, Figure 43–9.

REGARDLESS OF FEATURE SIZE (RFS)

When MMC or LMC is not specified with a geometric tolerance for a feature of size, no relationship is intended to exist between the feature size and the geometric tolerance. In other words, the tolerance applies regardless of feature size.

In this case, the geometric tolerance controls the form, orientation, or location of the axis, or median plane of the feature.

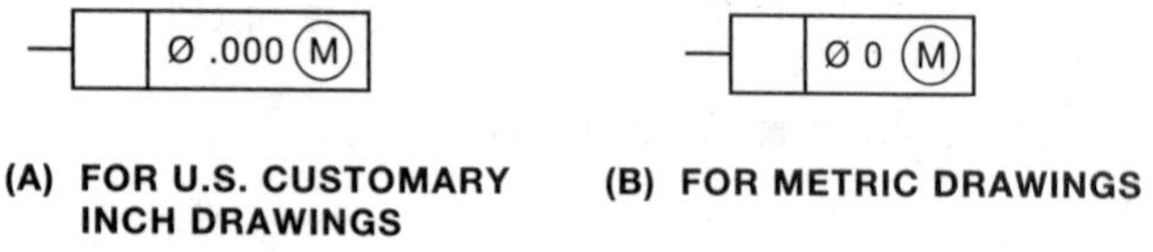
Ø .000 (M)
Ø 0 (M)
(A) FOR U.S. CUSTOMARY INCH DRAWINGS
(B) FOR METRIC DRAWINGS

FIGURE 43–7 ■ MMC symbol with zero tolerances

LEAST MATERIAL CONDITION (LMC)

The symbol for LMC is shown in Figure 43–5. It is the condition in which a feature of size contains the least amount of material within the stated limits of size.

Specifying LMC is limited to positional tolerance applications where MMC does not provide the desired control and RFS is too restrictive. LMC is used to maintain a desired relationship between the surface of a feature and its true position at tolerance extremes. It is used only with a tolerance of position. See Unit 49.

CSA will probably include the LMC symbol in its next revision of CAN/CSA-B78.2-M91 Dimensioning and Tolerancing of Technical Drawings.

CHARACTERISTIC TOLERANCE		FEATURE BEING CONTROLLED
STRAIGHTNESS	—	NO FOR A PLANE SURFACE OR A LINE ON A SURFACE YES FOR A FEATURE OF SIZE OF WHICH IS SPECIFIED BY A TOLERANCED DIMENSION, SUCH AS A HOLE, SHAFT, OR SLOT
PARALLELISM	//	
PERPENDICULARITY	⊥	
ANGULARITY	∠	
POSITION	⌖	
FLATNESS	▱	NO FOR ALL FEATURES
CIRCULARITY (ROUNDNESS)	○	
CYLINDRICITY	⌭	
CONCENTRICITY	◎	
PROFILE OF A LINE	⌒	
PROFILE OF A SURFACE	⌓	
CIRCULAR RUNOUT	↗	
TOTAL RUNOUT	⌰	
SYMMETRY	⌯	

FIGURE 43–8 ■ Application of MMC to geometric symbols

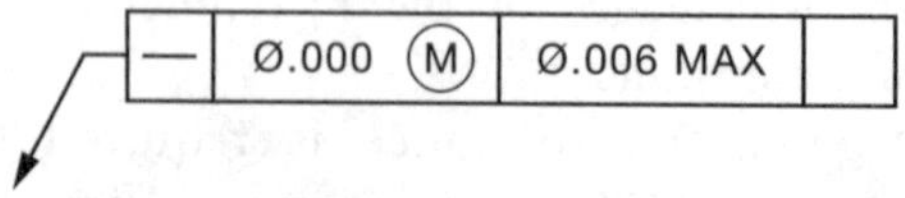
—
Ø.000 (M)
Ø.006 MAX

FIGURE 43–9 ■ Tolerance with a maximum value

STRAIGHTNESS OF A FEATURE OF SIZE

Figures 43–10 and 43–11 show examples of cylindrical parts where all circular elements of the surface are to be within the specified size tolerance; however, the boundary of perfect form at MMC may be violated. This violation is permissible when the feature control frame is associated with the size dimensions or attached to an extension of the dimension line. In these two figures, a diameter symbol precedes the tolerance value and the tolerance is applied on an RFS and an MMC basis, respectively. Normally, the straightness tolerance is smaller than the size tolerance, but a specific design may allow the situation depicted in the figures. The collective effect of size and form variations can produce a virtual condition equal to the MMC size plus the straightness tolerance. (See Figure 43–11.) The derived median plane of the feature must lie within a cylindrical tolerance zone as specified.

Straightness—RFS

When applied on an RFS basis (as in Figure 43–10), the maximum permissible deviation from straightness is .015 in., regardless of the feature size. Note that the absence of a modifying symbol indicates that RFS applies.

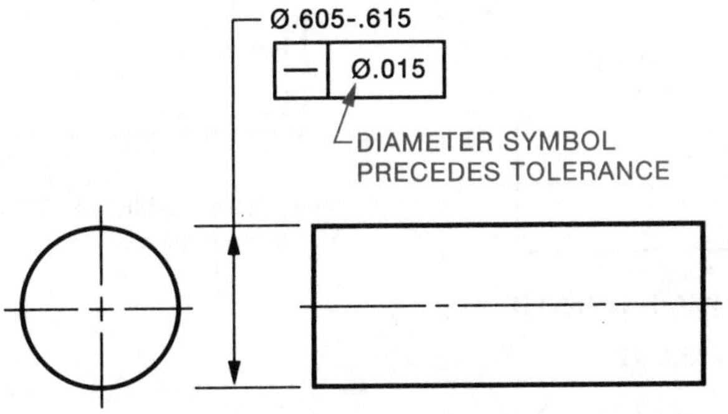

(A) DRAWING CALLOUT

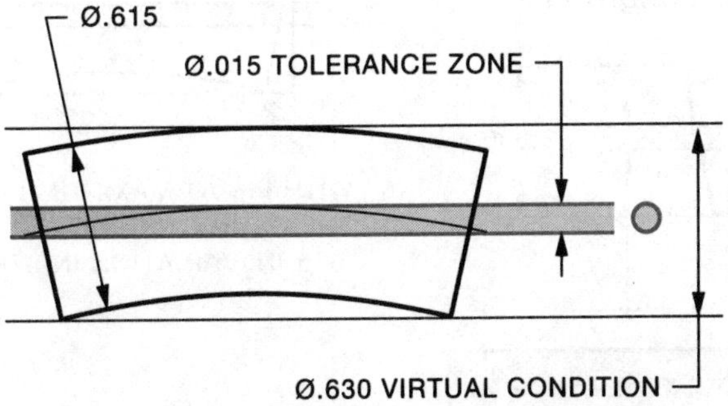

FEATURE SIZE	DIAMETER TOLERANCE ZONE ALLOWED
.615	.015
.614	.015
.613	.015
↓	↓
.606	.015
.605	.015

(B) INTERPRETATION

FIGURE 43–10 ■ Specifying straightness—RFS

Straightness—MMC

If the straightness tolerance of .015 in. is required only at MMC, further straightness error can be permitted without jeopardizing assembly, as the feature approaches its least material size (Figure 43–11). The maximum straightness tolerance is the specified tolerance plus the amount the feature departs from its MMC size. The median line of the actual feature must lie within the derived cylindrical tolerance zone such as given in the table of Figure 43–11.

Straightness—Zero MMC

It is quite permissible to specify a geometric tolerance of zero MMC, which means that the virtual condition coincides with the maximum material

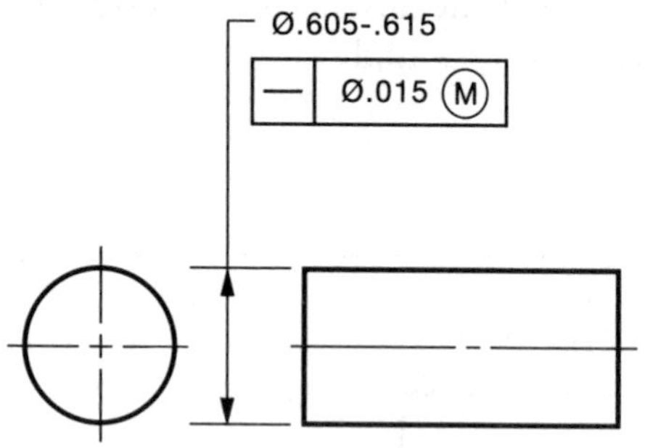
Ø.605-.615
Ø.015 (M)

NOTE: PERFECT FORM AT MMC NOT REQ'D

(A) DRAWING CALLOUT

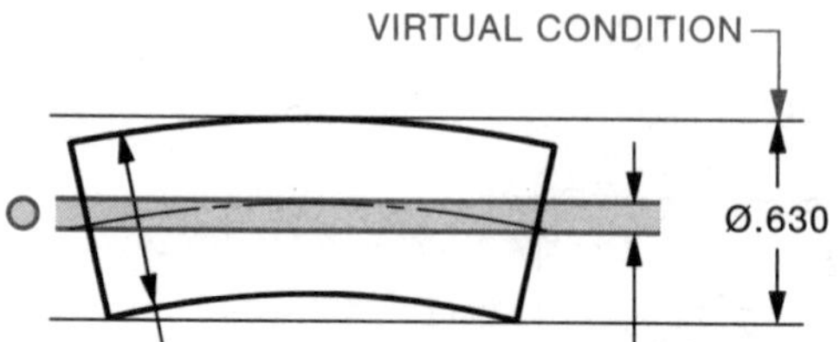
VIRTUAL CONDITION
Ø.630

FEATURE SIZE	DIAMETER TOLERANCE ZONE ALLOWED
.615	.015
.614	.016
.613	.017
↓	↓
.606	.025
.605	.024

(B) INTERPRETATION

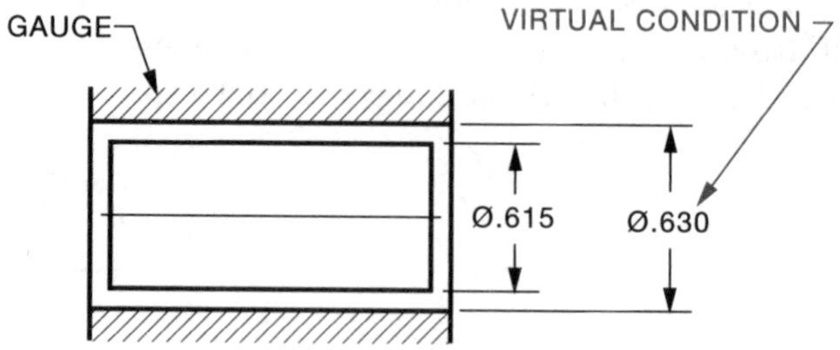
GAUGE
VIRTUAL CONDITION
Ø.615
Ø.630

MAXIMUM DIAMETER OF THE PIN WITH PERFECT FORM IN A GAUGE

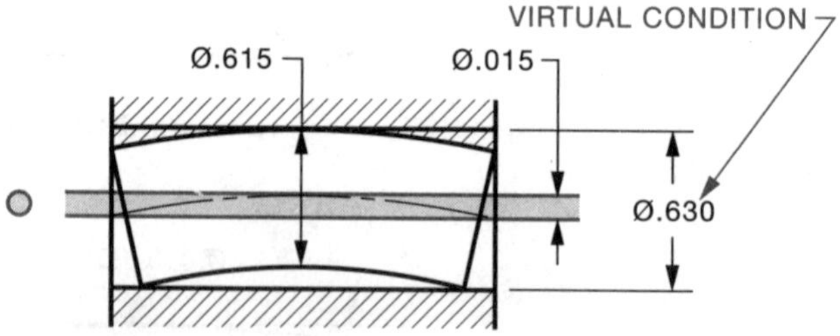
VIRTUAL CONDITION
Ø.615
Ø.015
Ø.630

WITH PIN AT MAXIMUM DIAMETER (.615 IN) THE GAUGE WILL ACCEPT THE PIN WITH UP TO .015-IN. VARIATION IN STRAIGHTNESS

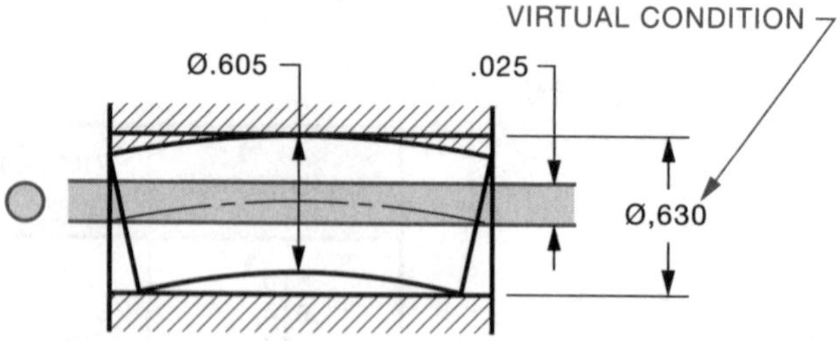
VIRTUAL CONDITION
Ø.605
.025
Ø,630

WITH PIN AT MINIMUM DIAMETER (.605 IN) THE GAUGE WILL ACCEPT THE PIN WITH UP TO .025-IN VARIATION IN STRAIGHTNESS

(C) ACCEPTANCE BOUNDARY

FIGURE 43–11 ■ Specifying straightness—MMC

size, Figure 43–12. Therefore, if a feature is at its maximum material limit everywhere, no errors of straightness are permitted.

Straightness on the MMC basis can be applied to any part or feature having straight-line elements in a plane that includes the diameter or thickness. This also includes parts toleranced on an RFS basis. However, it should not be used for features that do not have a uniform cross section.

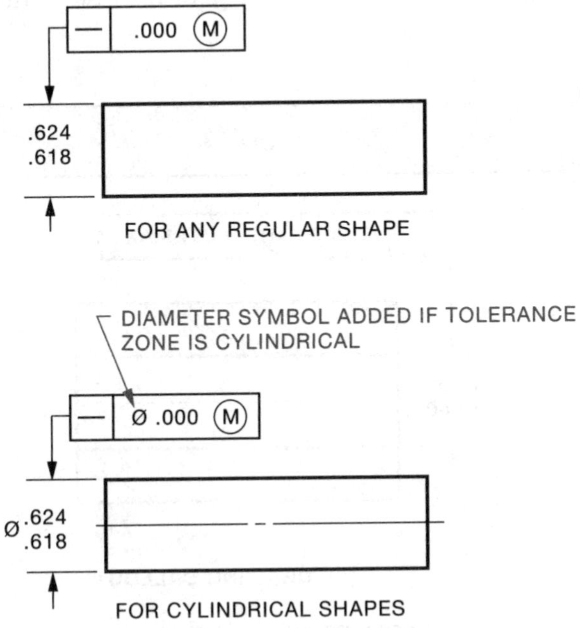
.000 (M)
.624
.618
FOR ANY REGULAR SHAPE
DIAMETER SYMBOL ADDED IF TOLERANCE ZONE IS CYLINDRICAL
Ø .000 (M)
Ø .624
.618
FOR CYLINDRICAL SHAPES

(A) DRAWING CALLOUT

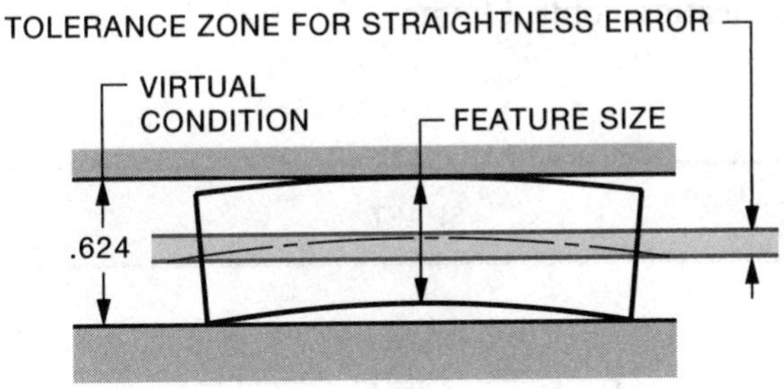
TOLERANCE ZONE FOR STRAIGHTNESS ERROR
VIRTUAL CONDITION
FEATURE SIZE
.624

FEATURE SIZE	PERMISSIBLE STRAIGHTNESS ERROR
.624	.000
.623	.001
.622	.002
.621	.003
.620	.004
.619	.005
.618	.006

(B) PERMISSIBLE VARIATIONS

FIGURE 43–12 ■ Straightness—zero MMC

Straightness with a Maximum Value

If it is desired to ensure that the straightness error does not become too great when the part approaches the least material condition, a maximum value may be added, Figure 43–13. The maximum overall tolerance follows in a separate compartment in the feature control frame.

Straightness per Unit Length

Straightness may be applied on a unit-length basis as a means of preventing an abrupt surface variation within a relatively short length of the feature, Figure 43–14. Caution should be exercised when using unit control without specifying a maximum limit for the total length because of the rela-

SHAFT

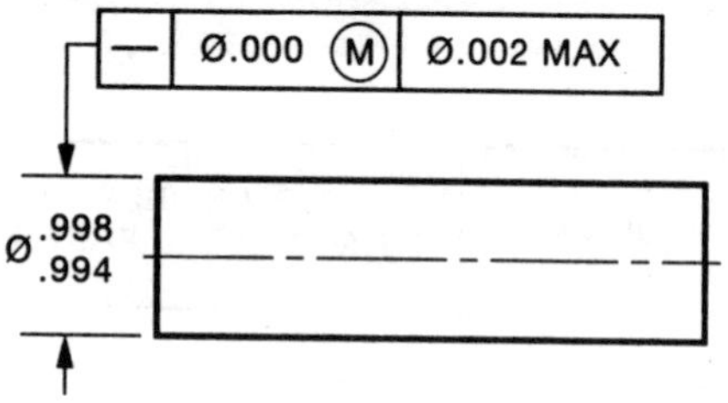

— | Ø.000 (M) | Ø.002 MAX
Ø .998 .994

(A) DRAWING CALLOUT

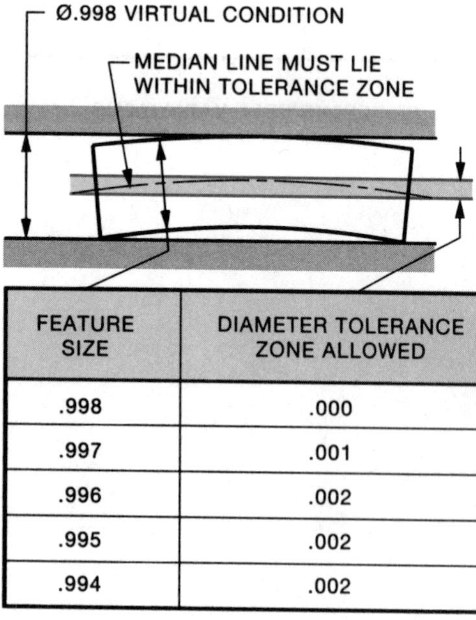

Ø.998 VIRTUAL CONDITION
MEDIAN LINE MUST LIE WITHIN TOLERANCE ZONE

FEATURE SIZE	DIAMETER TOLERANCE ZONE ALLOWED
.998	.000
.997	.001
.996	.002
.995	.002
.994	.002

(B) PERMISSIBLE VARIATIONS

HOLE

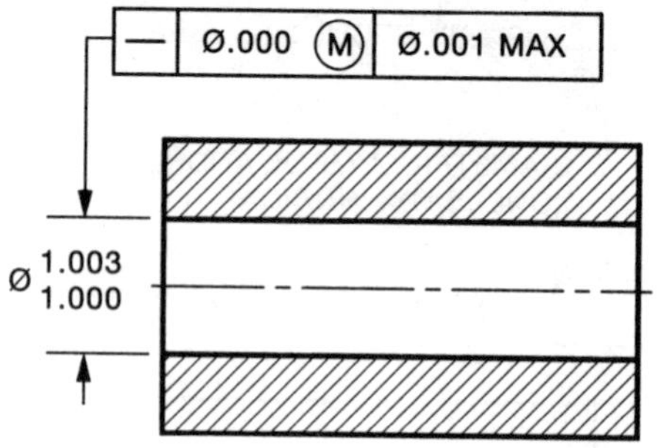

— | Ø.000 (M) | Ø.001 MAX
Ø 1.003 1.000

(A) DRAWING CALLOUT

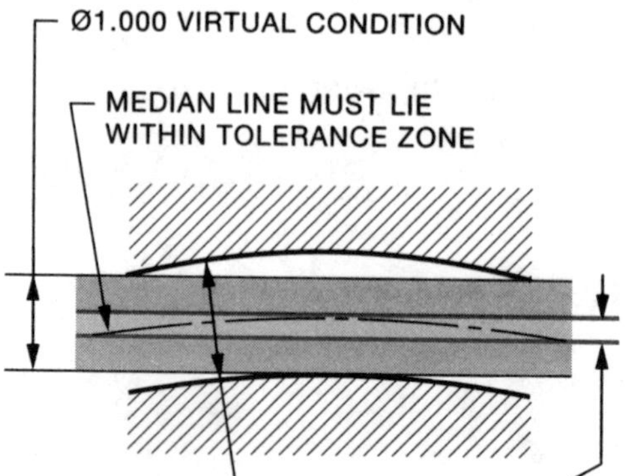

Ø1.000 VIRTUAL CONDITION
MEDIAN LINE MUST LIE WITHIN TOLERANCE ZONE

FEATURE SIZE	DIAMETER TOLERANCE ZONE ALLOWED
1.000	.000
1.001	.001
1.002	.001
1.003	.001

(B) PERMISSIBLE VARIATIONS

FIGURE 43–13 ■ Straightness of a shaft and hole with a maximum value—MMC tively large variations that may result if no such restriction is applied. If the feature has a uniformly continuous bow throughout its length that just conforms to the tolerance applicable to the unit length, then the overall tolerance may result in an unsatisfactory part. Figure 43–15 illustrates the possible condition if the straightness per unit length given in Figure 43–14 is used alone, that is, if straightness for the total length is not specified.

REFERENCES

CAN/CSA B78.2-M91 Dimensioning of Tolerancing of Technical Drawings
ASME Y14.5M-1994 Dimensioning and Tolerancing

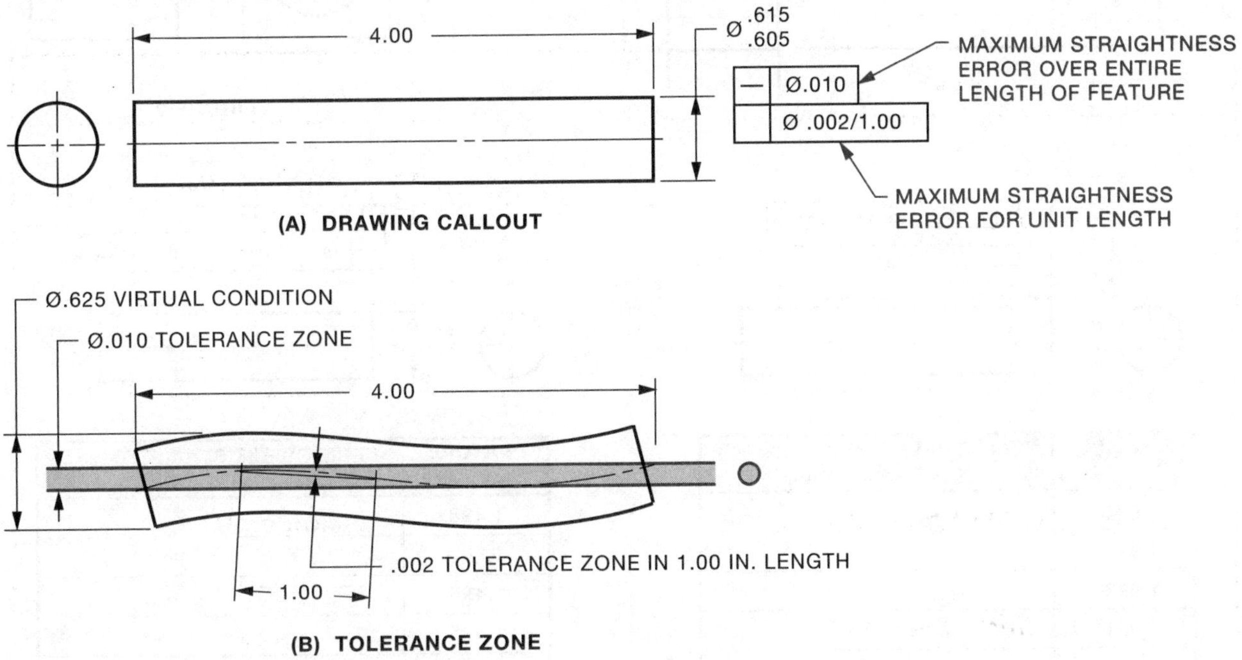

FIGURE 43–14 ■ Specifying straightness per unit length with specified total straightness, both RFS

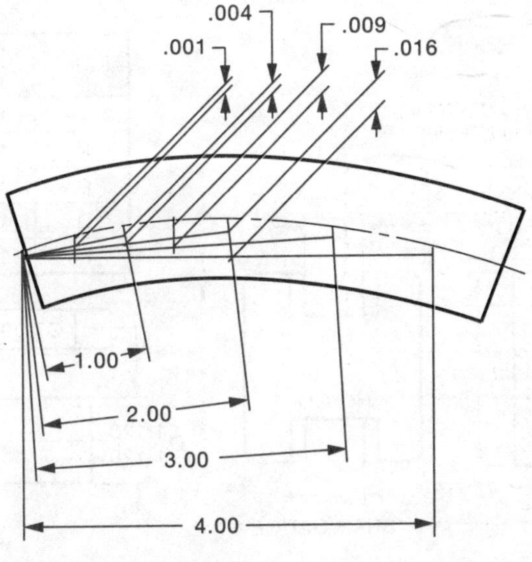

FIGURE 43–15 ■ Possible results of specifying straightness per unit length RFS with no maximum value

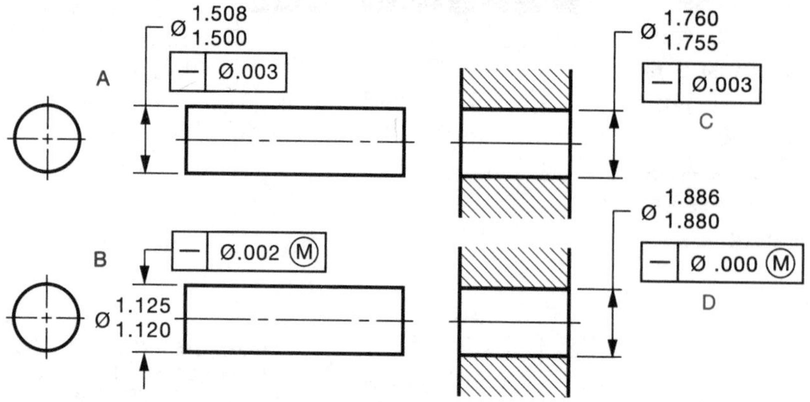
Ø 1.508
1.500
— Ø.003
A
B
— Ø.002 Ⓜ
Ø 1.125
1.120
Ø 1.760
1.755
— Ø.003
C
Ø 1.886
1.880
— Ø .000 Ⓜ
D

FIGURE 1

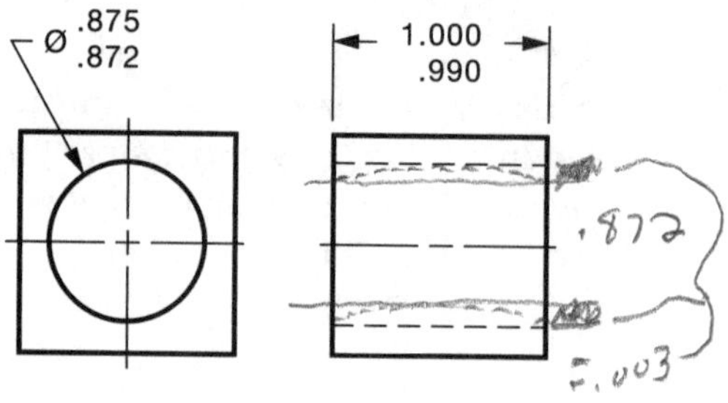
Ø .875
.872
1.000
.990
.872
=.003

FIGURE 2

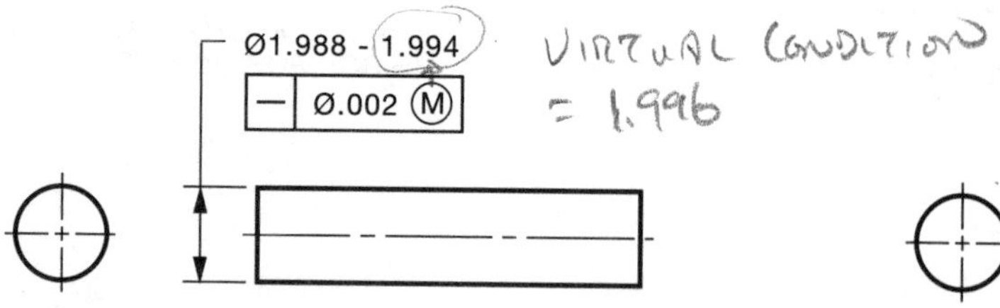
Ø1.988 - 1.994
— Ø.002 Ⓜ
VIRTUAL CONDITION
= 1.996

FEATURE SIZE (DIA)	PERMISSIBLE STRAIGHTNESS TOLERANCE (DIA)
1.994	.002
1.993	.003
1.992	.004
1.991	.005
1.990	.006
1.989	.007
1.988	.008

FIGURE 3

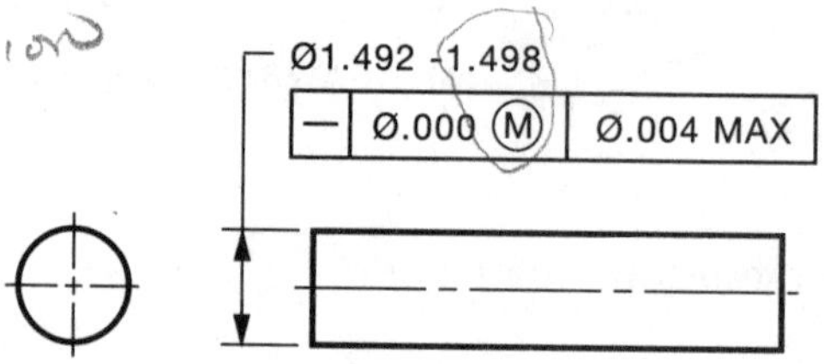
Ø1.492 - 1.498
— Ø.000 Ⓜ Ø.004 MAX

FEATURE SIZE (DIA)	PERMISSIBLE STRAIGHTNESS TOLERANCE(DIA)
1.498	.000
1.497	.001
1.496	.002
1.495	.003
1.494	.004
1.493	.004
1.492	.004

FIGURE 4

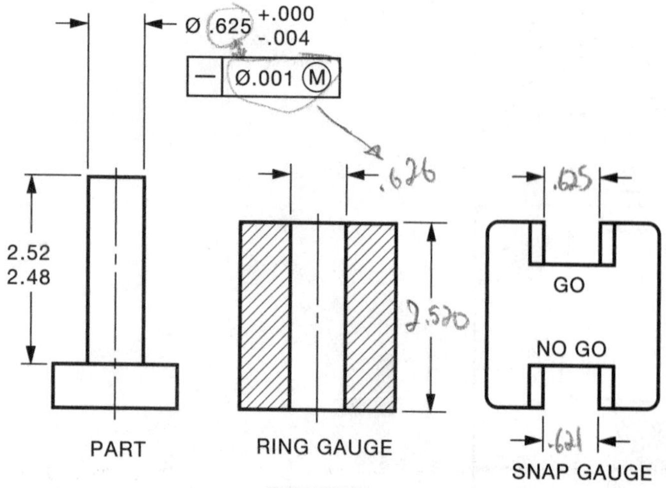
Ø .625 +.000
-.004
— Ø.001 Ⓜ
.626
2.52
2.48
2.520
.625
GO
NO GO
.621
PART
RING GAUGE
SNAP GAUGE

FIGURE 5

PART	FEATURE SIZE (DIA)	STRAIGHTNESS DEVIATION
A	1.126	.002
B	1.123	.005
C	1.122	.003
D	1.121	.004
E	1.120	.005

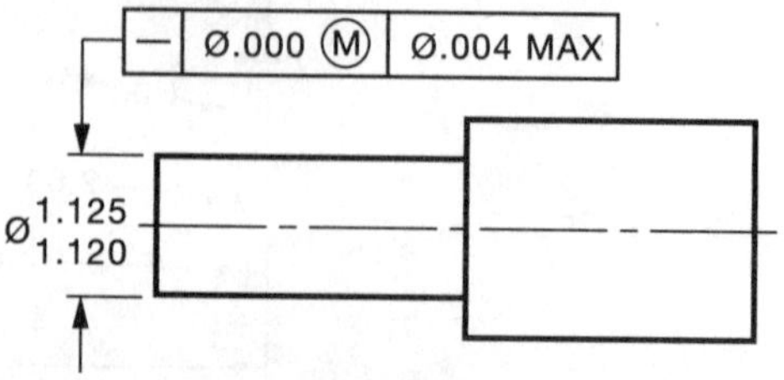
— Ø.000 Ⓜ Ø.004 MAX
Ø 1.125
1.120

FIGURE 6

ASSIGNMENT:

1. What is the virtual condition for each of the parts shown in Figure 1?

2. The hole shown in Figure 2 does not have a straightness tolerance. What is the maximum permissible deviation from straightness if perfect form at the maximum material size is required?

3. Complete the charts shown in Figures 3 and 4, showing the largest permissible straightness error for the feature sizes shown.

4. Dimension the ring and snap gauges shown in Figure 5 to check the pin shown. The ring gauge should be such a size as to check the entire length of the pin. The two open ends of the snap gauge should measure the minimum and maximum acceptable pin diameters.

5. With reference to Figure 6, are parts A to E acceptable? State your reasons if a part is not acceptable.

6. A straightness tolerance of .004 in., regardless of feature size, is to be applied to the shaft shown in Figure 7. Apply the appropriate straightness tolerance to the drawing.

7. With reference to Figure 8, what is the maximum deviation permitted from straightness for the cylindrical surface if it was (A) at MMC, (B) at LMC, and (C) Ø.623?

8. The shaft, Figure 9, is to have a maximum straightness tolerance of .002 in. for any 1.00 in. of its length, but may have a maximum straightness tolerance of .005 in. over the entire length. Apply the appropriate straightness tolerances to the drawing.

ANSWERS

1. A 1.511
   B 1.127
   C 1.752
   D 1.880
2. .003
3. SEE FIGURES 3 & 4
4. SEE FIGURE 5
5. A NO
   OVERSIZE
   B NO
   OVERSIZE
   C YES
   D YES
   E NO
   STANDARD DEVIATION EXCEEDED
6. SEE FIGURE 7
7. A .001
   B .001
   C .001
8. SEE FIGURE 9

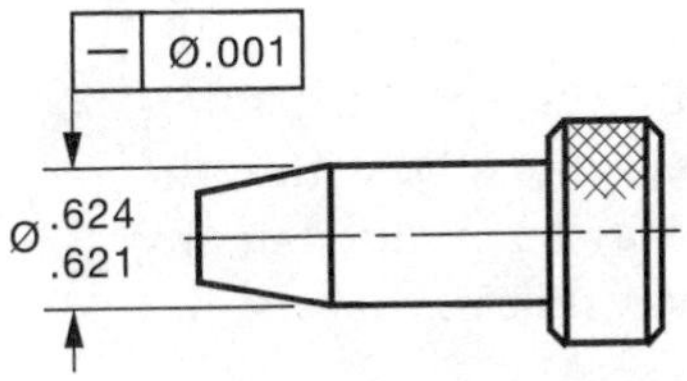

Ø.001
Ø .624
.621

FIGURE 8

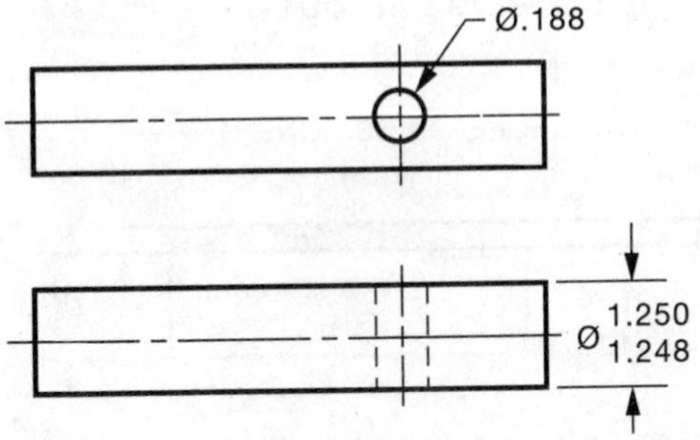

Ø.188
Ø 1.250
1.248

FIGURE 7

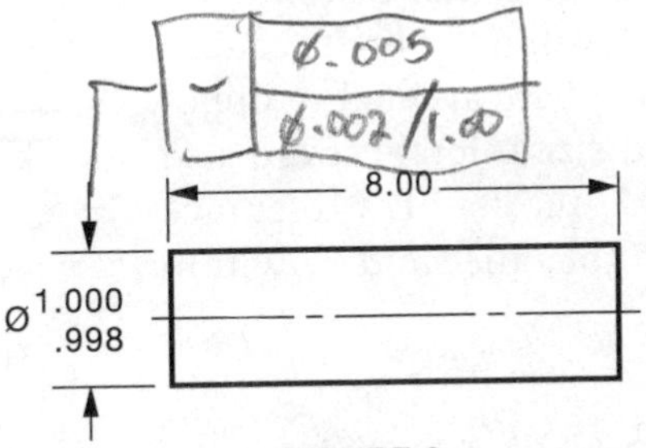

Ø.005
Ø.002/1.00
8.00
Ø 1.000
.998

FIGURE 9

STRAIGHTNESS OF A FEATURE OF SIZE

A-101

44 UNIT

FORM TOLERANCES

Form tolerances are used to control straightness, flatness, circularity, and cylindricity.

FLATNESS

Flatness of a surface is a condition in which all surface elements are in one plane. The symbol for flatness is a parallelogram with angles of 60°.

A flatness tolerance is applied to a line representing the surface of a part by means of a feature control frame, Figure 44–1.

A flatness tolerance means that all points on the surface shall be contained within a tolerance zone consisting of the space between two parallel planes that are separated by the specified tolerance. These two parallel planes must lie within the limits of size. These planes may be oriented in any manner to contain the surface; that is, they are not necessarily parallel to the base.

The flatness tolerance must be less than the size tolerance and be contained within the limits of size.

When flatness tolerances are applied to opposite surfaces of a part and size tolerances are also shown, as in Figure 44–2, the flatness tolerance must be less than the size tolerance and lie within the limits of size.

Flatness per Unit Area

Flatness may be applied, as in the case of straightness, on a unit basis as a means of preventing an abrupt surface variation within a relatively small area of the feature. The unit variation is used either in combination with a specified total variation or alone. Caution should be exercised when using unit control alone for the same reason as was given for straightness.

Because flatness involves surface area, the size of the unit area—for example, 1.00 × 1.00 in.—is specified to the right of the flatness tolerance, separated by a slash line, Figure 44–3.

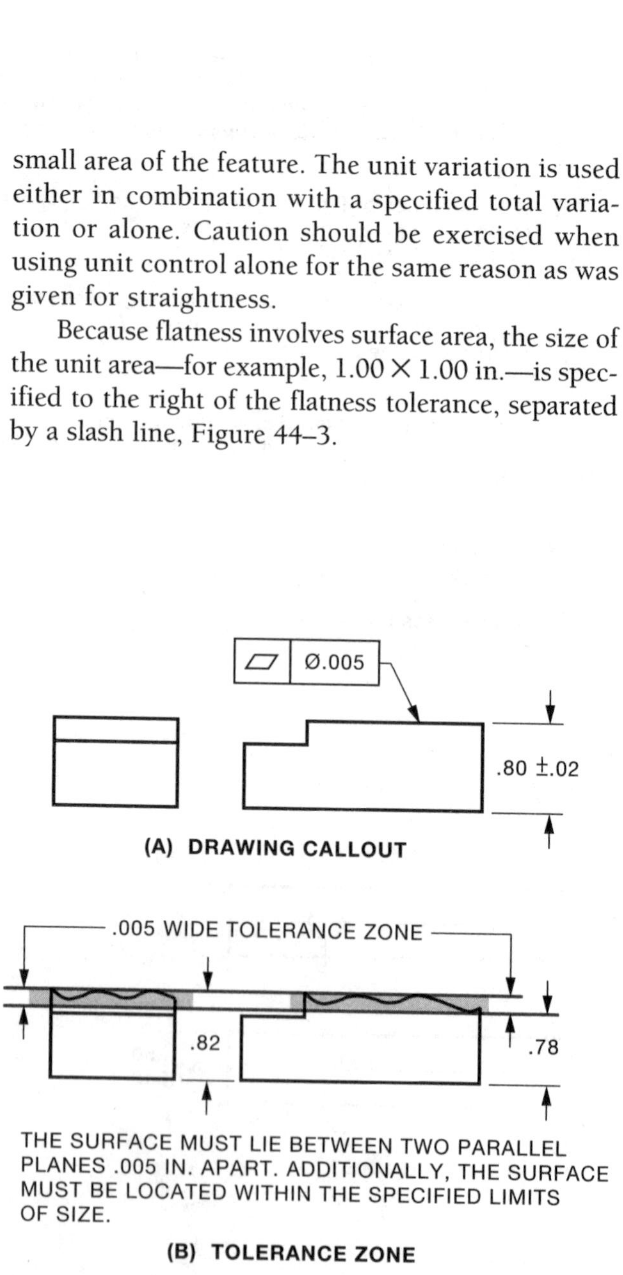

Ø.005
.80 ±.02
(A) DRAWING CALLOUT
.005 WIDE TOLERANCE ZONE
.82
.78
THE SURFACE MUST LIE BETWEEN TWO PARALLEL PLANES .005 IN. APART. ADDITIONALLY, THE SURFACE MUST BE LOCATED WITHIN THE SPECIFIED LIMITS OF SIZE.
(B) TOLERANCE ZONE

FIGURE 44–1 ■ Specifying flatness for a surface

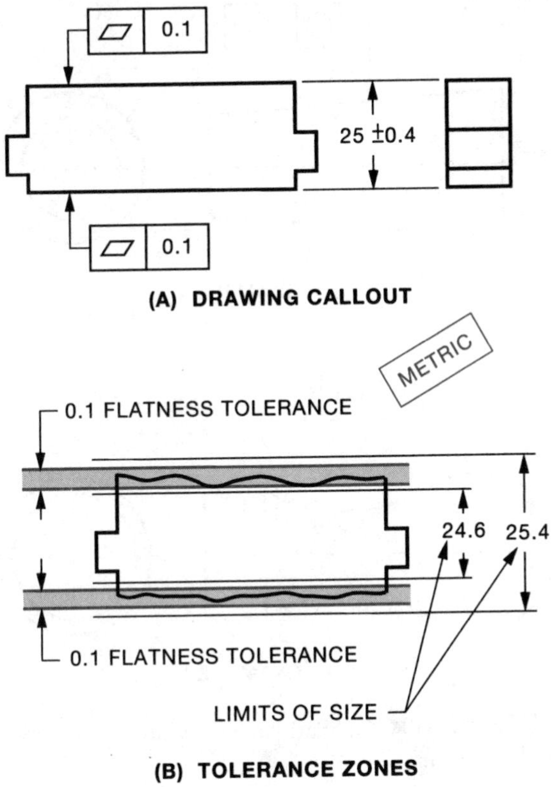
0.1
25 ±0.4
0.1
(A) DRAWING CALLOUT
METRIC
0.1 FLATNESS TOLERANCE
24.6
25.4
0.1 FLATNESS TOLERANCE
LIMITS OF SIZE
(B) TOLERANCE ZONES

FIGURE 44–2 ■ Location of flatness tolerance within limits of size

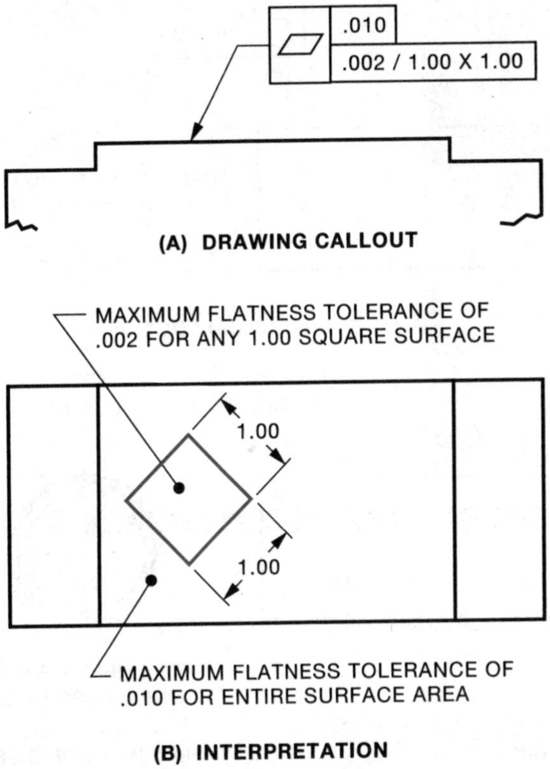
.010
.002 / 1.00 X 1.00
(A) DRAWING CALLOUT
MAXIMUM FLATNESS TOLERANCE OF .002 FOR ANY 1.00 SQUARE SURFACE
1.00
1.00
MAXIMUM FLATNESS TOLERANCE OF .010 FOR ENTIRE SURFACE AREA
(B) INTERPRETATION

FIGURE 44–3 ■ Overall flatness tolerance combined with a flatness for a unit area

CIRCULARITY

Circularity refers to a condition of a circular line or the surface of a circular feature where all points on the line or on the circumference of a plane cross section of the feature are the same distance from a common axis or centre point. It is similar to straightness except that it is wrapped around a circular cross section.

Examples of circular features would include disks, spheres, cylinders, and cones.

Errors of circularity (out-of-roundness) of a circular line on the periphery of a cross section of a circular feature may occur (1) as ovality, where differences appear between the major and minor axes; (2) as lobing, where in some instances the diametral values may be constant or nearly so; or (3) as random irregularities from a true circle. All these errors are illustrated in Figure 44–4.

The geometric characteristic symbol for circularity is a circle. A circularity tolerance may be specified by using this symbol in the feature control frame, Figure 44–5.

A circularity tolerance is measured radially and specifies the width between two concentric circular rings for a particular cross section within which the circular line or the circumference of the feature in that plane shall lie, Figure 44–6. Additionally,

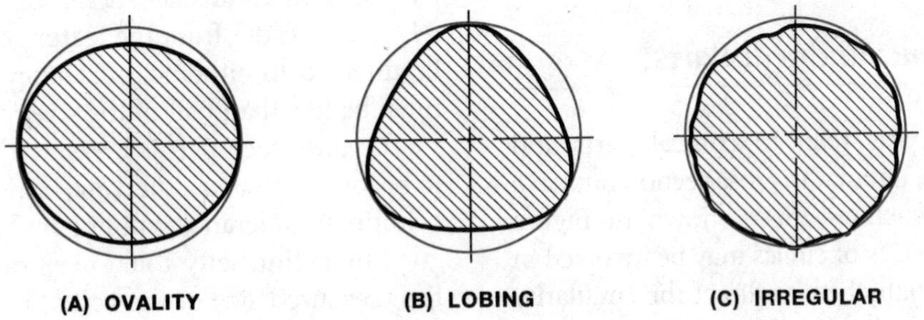
(A) OVALITY
(B) LOBING
(C) IRREGULAR

FIGURE 44–4 ■ Common types of circularity errors

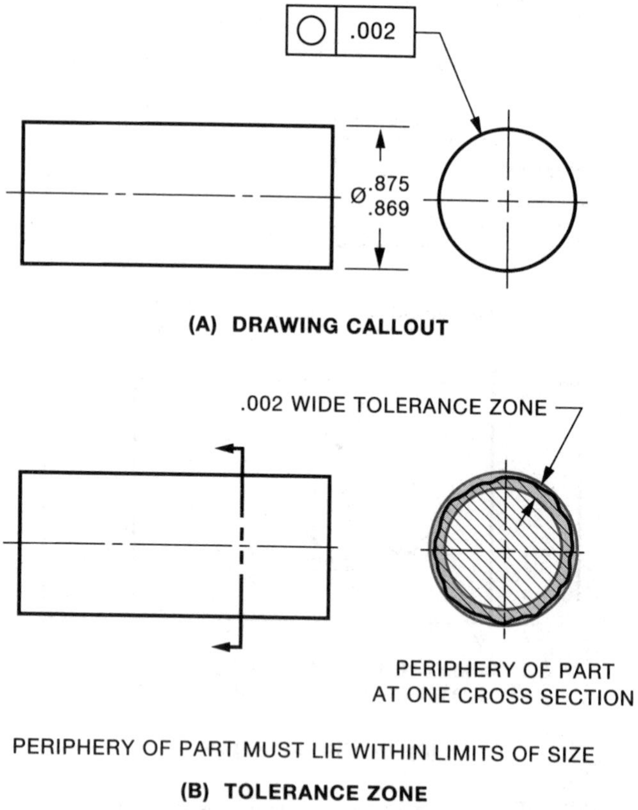
.002
Ø .875
.869
(A) DRAWING CALLOUT
.002 WIDE TOLERANCE ZONE
PERIPHERY OF PART
AT ONE CROSS SECTION
PERIPHERY OF PART MUST LIE WITHIN LIMITS OF SIZE
(B) TOLERANCE ZONE

FIGURE 44–5 ■ Circularity tolerance applied to a cylindrical feature

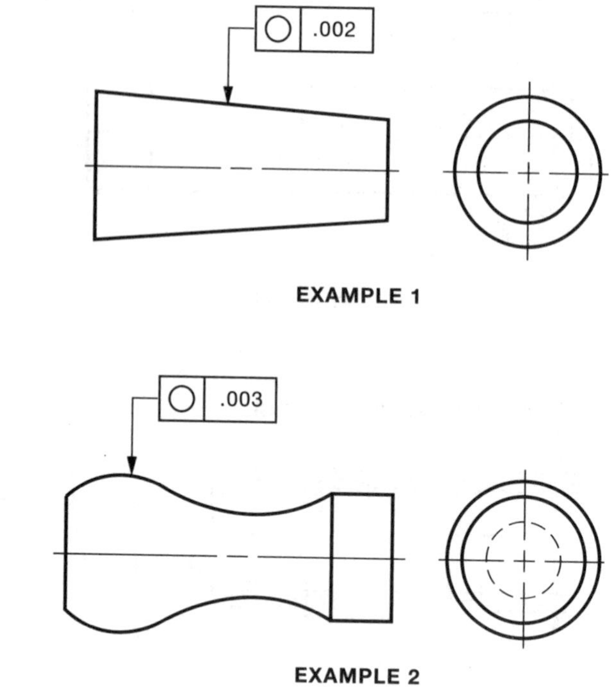
.002
EXAMPLE 1
.003
EXAMPLE 2

FIGURE 44–6 ■ Circularity tolerance applied to noncylindrical features

each circular element of the surface must be within the specified limits of size.

Because circularity is a form of tolerance, it is not related to datums.

A circularity tolerance may be specified by using the circularity symbol in the feature control frame. It is expressed on an RFS basis. The absence of a modifying symbol in the feature control frame means that RFS applies to the circularity tolerance.

A circularity tolerance cannot be modified on an MMC basis because it controls surface elements only. The circularity tolerance must be less than half the size tolerance because it must lie in a space equal to half the size tolerance.

Circularity of Noncylindrical Parts

Noncylindrical parts refer to conical parts and other features that are circular in cross section but have variable diameters, such as those shown in Figure 44–6. Because many sizes of circles may be involved in the end view, it is usually best to direct the circularity tolerance to the longitudinal surfaces as shown.

CYLINDRICITY

Cylindricity is a condition of a surface in which all points of the surface are the same distance from a common axis. The cylindricity tolerance is a composite control of form that includes circularity, straightness, and parallelism of the surface element of a cylindrical feature. It is like a flatness tolerance wrapped around a cylinder.

The geometric characteristic symbol for cylindricity consists of a circle with two tangent lines at 60°.

A cylindricity tolerance that is measured radially specifies a tolerance zone bounded by two concentric cylinders within which the surface must lie. The cylindricity tolerance must be within the specified limits of size. In the case of cylindricity, unlike that of circularity, the tolerance applies simultaneously to both circular and longitudinal elements of the surface, Figure 44–7. The leader from the feature control symbol may be directed to either view. The cylindricity tolerance must be less than half of the size tolerance.

Because each part is measured for form deviation, it becomes obvious the total range of the specified cylindricity tolerance will not always be available.

The cylindricity tolerance zone is controlled by the measured size of the actual part. The part size is first determined; then the cylindricity tolerance is

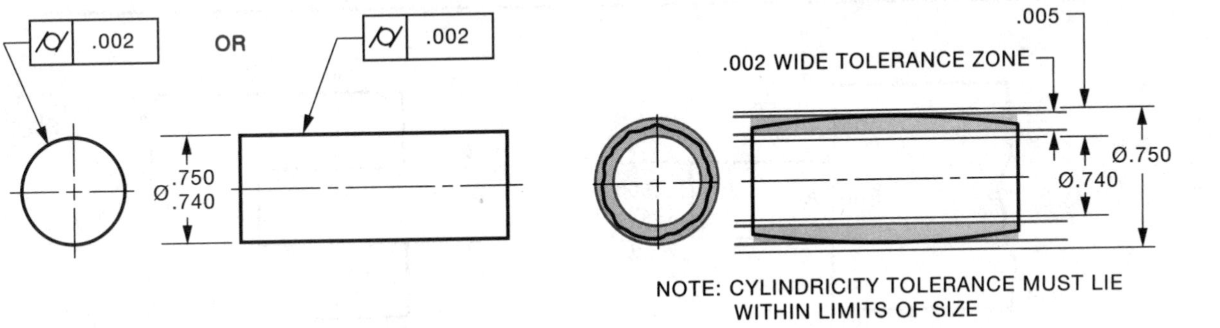
.002
OR
.002
Ø .750
.740
.005
.002 WIDE TOLERANCE ZONE
Ø.750
Ø.740
NOTE: CYLINDRICITY TOLERANCE MUST LIE WITHIN LIMITS OF SIZE
(A) DRAWING CALLOUT
(B) TOLERANCE ZONE

FIGURE 44–7 ■ Cylindrical tolerance directed to either view

added as a refinement to the actual size of the part. If, in the example shown in Figure 44–7, the largest measurement of the produced part is Ø.748 in., which is near the high limit of size (.750 in.), the largest diameter of the two concentric cylinders for the cylindricity tolerance would be Ø.748 in. The smaller of the concentric cylinders would be .748 minus twice the cylindricity tolerance (2 × .002) = Ø.744 in. The cylindricity tolerance zone must also lie between the limits of size, and the entire cylindrical surface of the part must lie between these two concentric circles to be acceptable.

If, on the other hand, the largest diameter measured for a part was Ø.743 in., which is near the lower limit of size (.740 in.), the cylindricity deviation of that part cannot be greater than .0015 in. because it would exceed the lower limit of size.

Likewise, if the smallest measured diameter of a part was .748 in., which is near the high limit of size, the largest diameter of the two concentric cylinders for the cylindricity tolerance would be Ø.750 in., which is the maximum permissible diameter of the part. In this case, the cylindricity tolerance could not be greater than (.750–.748)/2 or .001 in.

Figure 44–8 shows some permissible form errors for the part shown in Figure 44–7.

Cylindricity tolerances can be applied only to cylindrical surfaces, such as round holes and shafts. No specific geometric tolerances have been devised for other circular forms, which require the use of several geometric tolerances. A conical surface, for example, must be controlled by a combination of tolerances for circularity, straightness, and angularity.

Because cylindricity is a form tolerance much like that of a flatness tolerance in that it controls surface elements only, it cannot be modified on an MMC basis. The absence of a modifying symbol in the feature control frame indicates that RFS applies.

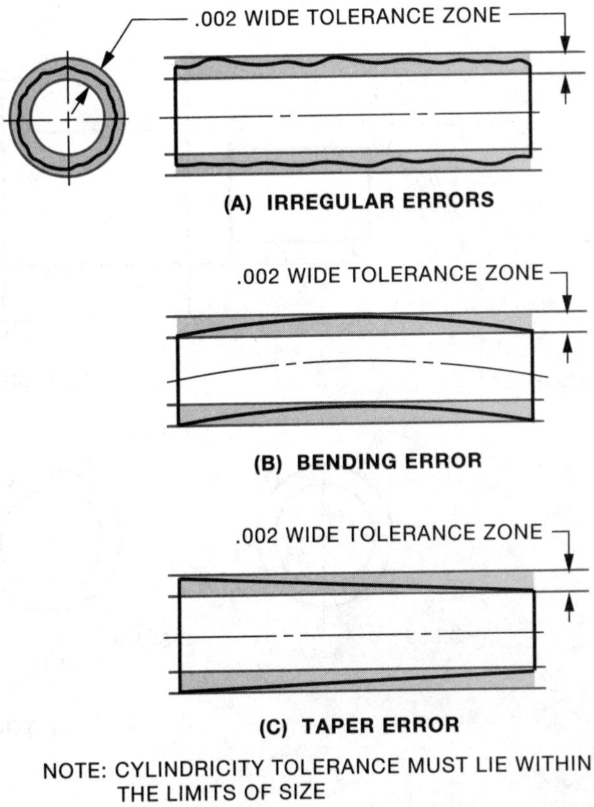
.002 WIDE TOLERANCE ZONE
(A) IRREGULAR ERRORS
.002 WIDE TOLERANCE ZONE
(B) BENDING ERROR
.002 WIDE TOLERANCE ZONE
(C) TAPER ERROR
NOTE: CYLINDRICITY TOLERANCE MUST LIE WITHIN THE LIMITS OF SIZE

FIGURE 44–8 ■ Permissible form errors for part shown in Figure 44–7

REFERENCES

CAN/CSA-B78.2-M91 Dimensioning and Tolerancing of Technical Drawings
ASME Y14.5M-1994 Dimensioning and Tolerancing

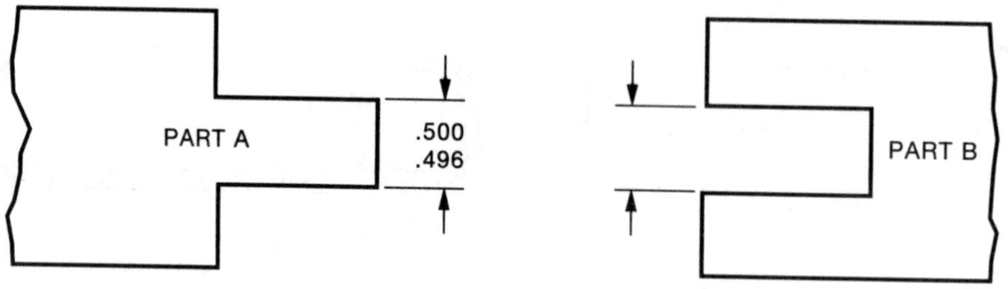
PART A
.500
.496
PART B

FIGURE 1

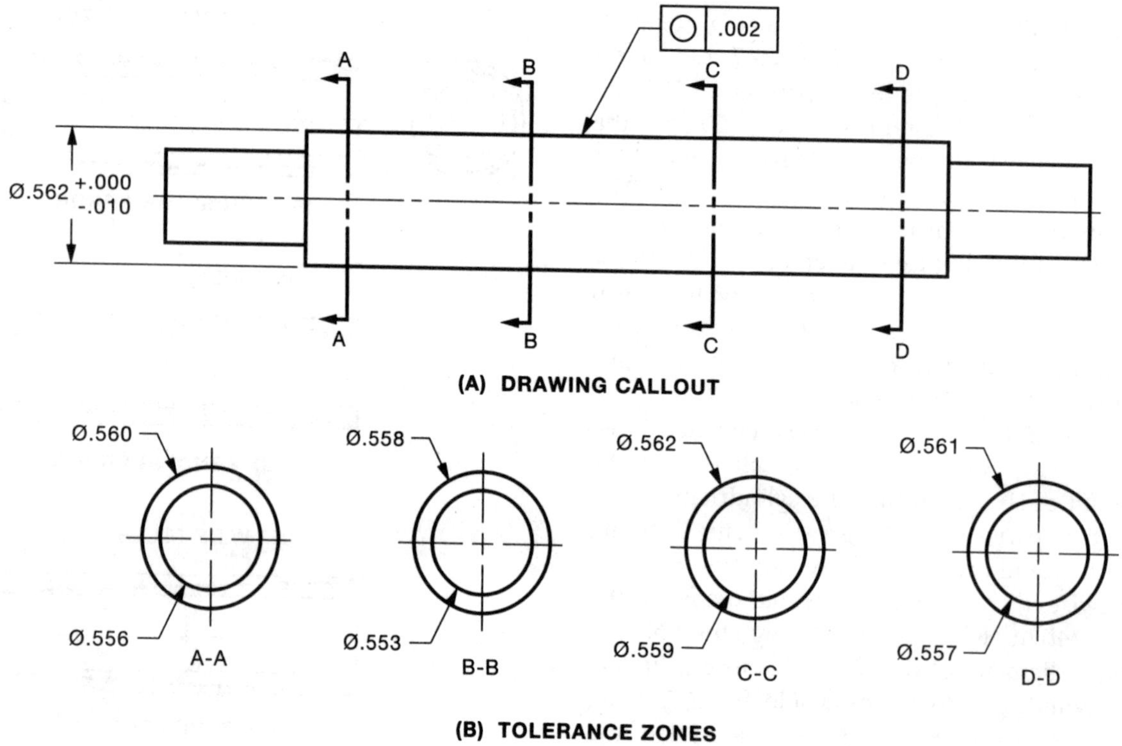
.002
A
B
C
D
Ø.562 +.000 -.010
A
B
C
D
(A) DRAWING CALLOUT
Ø.560
Ø.556
A-A
Ø.558
Ø.553
B-B
Ø.562
Ø.559
C-C
Ø.561
Ø.557
D-D
(B) TOLERANCE ZONES

FIGURE 2

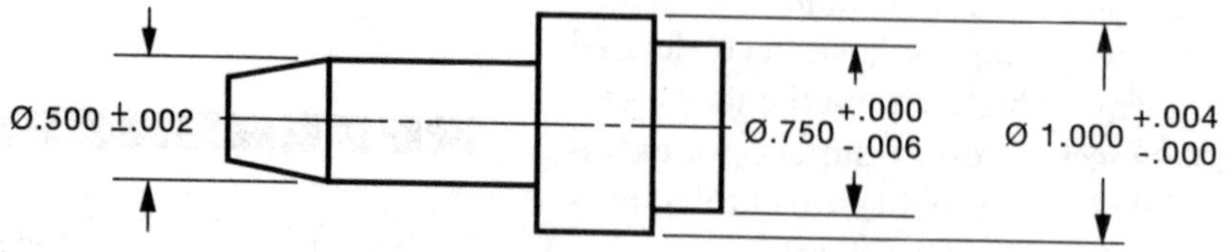
Ø.500 ±.002
Ø.750 +.000 -.006
Ø 1.000 +.004 -.000

FIGURE 3

ASSIGNMENT:

1. With reference to Figure 1, part A is required to fit into part B so that there will be no interference and the maximum clearance will never exceed .006 in. Add the maximum limits of size to part B. Flatness tolerances of .001 in. are to be added to the two surfaces of each part.

2. Measurements for circularity for the parts shown in Figure 2 were made at the cross sections A-A to D-D. All points on the periphery fell within the two rings. The outer ring was the smallest that could be circumscribed about the profile, and the inner ring was the largest that could be inscribed within the profile. State which sections meet drawing requirements.

3. Add the largest permissible circularity tolerances to the three diameters shown in Figure 3.

4. (A) It is required that the parts shown in Figure 4 will assemble with a minimum radial clearance of .0010 in. (per side). Dimension the shaft accordingly.
   (B) Would adding a cylindricity tolerance to Figure 4 alter the size of the shaft?
   (C) What is the largest cylindricity tolerance that could be realized for the hole and shaft in Figure 4 if the following measurements were recorded: 0.7510-in. hole, 0.7476-in. shaft?

5. Apply cylindricity tolerances to the three features dimensioned in Figure 5. The cylindricity tolerances are to be 25 percent of the size of the tolerances.

ANSWERS

1. SEE FIGURE 1
2. A-A ______
   B-B ______
   C-C ______
   D-D ______
3. SEE FIGURE 3
4. A. SEE FIGURE 4
   B. ______
   C. H ______
      S ______
5. SEE FIGURE 5

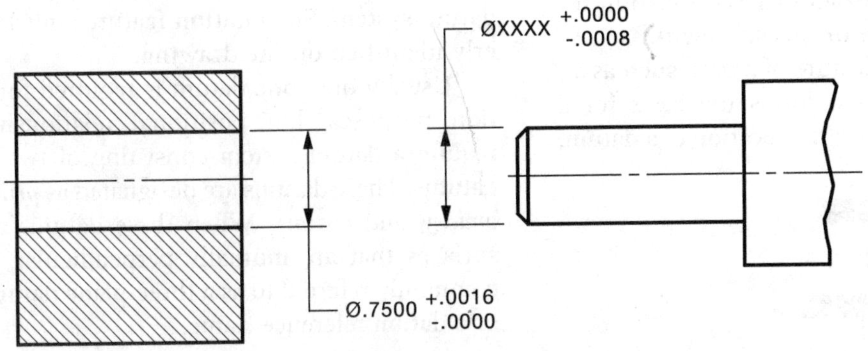
ØXXXX +.0000 -.0008
Ø.7500 +.0016 -.0000

FIGURE 4

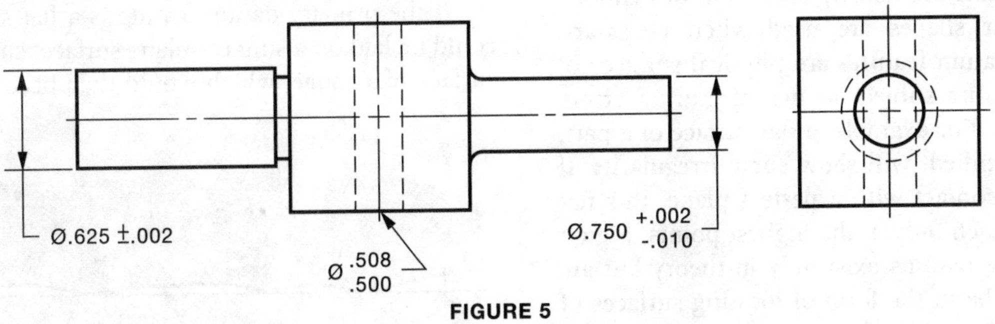
Ø.625 ±.002
Ø .508 .500
Ø.750 +.002 -.010

FIGURE 5

FORM TOLERANCES A-102

45 UNIT

DATUMS AND THE THREE-PLANE CONCEPT

A datum is a point, axis, or plane from which dimensions are measured or to which geometric tolerances are referenced. (A datum has an exact form and represents an exact or fixed location for purposes of manufacture or measurement.)

A datum feature is a feature of a part, such as an edge, surface, or hole, that forms the basis for a datum or is used to establish the location of a datum.

DATUMS FOR GEOMETRIC TOLERANCING

Datums are exact geometric points, axes, or surfaces, each based on one or more datum features of the part. Surfaces are usually either flat or cylindrical, but other shapes are used when necessary. Because the datum features are physical surfaces of the part, they are subject to manufacturing errors and variations. For example, a flat surface of a part, if greatly magnified, will show some irregularity. If brought into contact with a perfect plane, this flat surface will touch only at the highest points, Figure 45–1. The true datums exist only in theory but are considered to be in the form of locating surfaces of machines, fixtures, and gauging equipment on which the part rests or with which it makes contact during manufacture and measurement.

THREE-PLANE SYSTEM

Geometric tolerances, such as straightness and flatness, refer to unrelated lines and surfaces and do not require the use of datums.

Orientation and locational tolerances refer to related features; that is, they control the relationship of features to one another or to a datum or datum system. Such datum features must be properly identified on the drawing.

Usually only one datum is required for orientation purposes, but positional relationships may require a datum system consisting of two or three datums. These datums are designated as *primary, secondary,* and *tertiary.* When these datums are plane surfaces that are mutually perpendicular, they are commonly referred to as a three-plane datum system or a datum reference frame.

Primary Datum

If the primary datum feature is a flat surface, it could be laid on a suitable plane surface, such as the surface of a gauge, which would then become a pri-

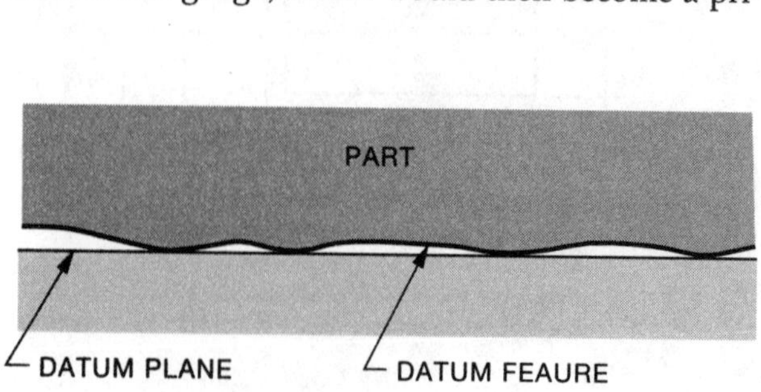

FIGURE 45–1 ■ Magnified section of a flat surface

mary datum, Figure 45–2. Theoretically, there will be a minimum of three high spots on the flat surface coming in contact with the gauge surface.

Secondary Datum

If the part is brought into contact with a secondary plane while lying on the primary plane, it will theoretically touch at a minimum of two points, Figure 45–3.

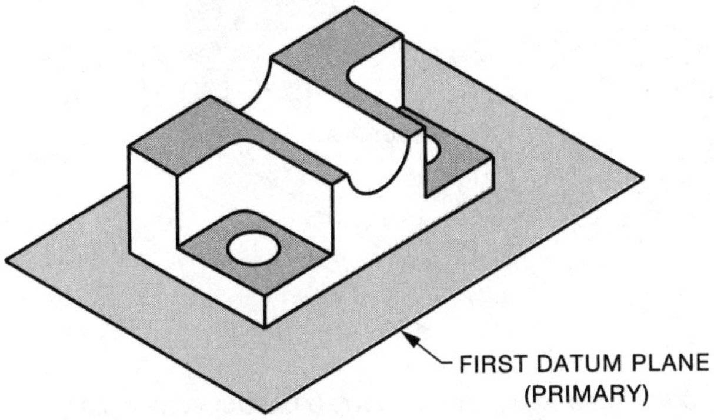
FIRST DATUM PLANE
(PRIMARY)
PRIMARY DATUM FEATURE MUST TOUCH PRIMARY DATUM PLANE AT A MINIMUM OF THREE PLACES

FIGURE 45–2 ■ Primary datum

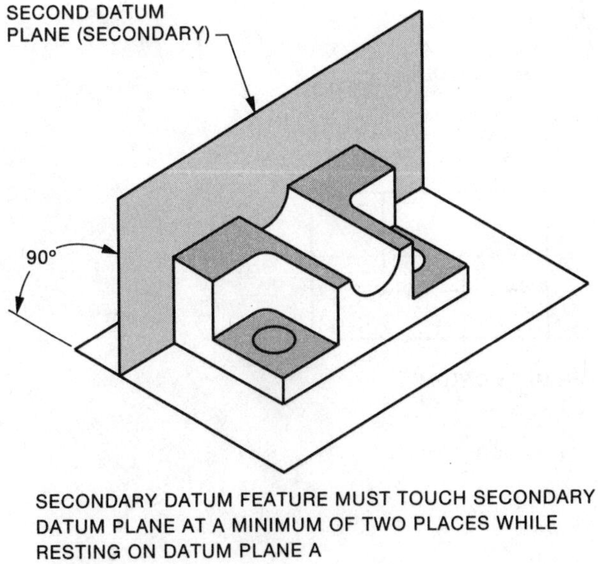
SECOND DATUM PLANE (SECONDARY)
90°
SECONDARY DATUM FEATURE MUST TOUCH SECONDARY DATUM PLANE AT A MINIMUM OF TWO PLACES WHILE RESTING ON DATUM PLANE A

FIGURE 45–3 ■ Secondary datum

Tertiary Datum

The part can be slid along while maintaining contact with both the primary and secondary planes until it contacts a third plane, Figure 45–4. This plane then becomes the tertiary datum and the part will, in theory, touch it at only one point.

These three planes constitute a datum system from which measurements can be taken. They will appear on the drawing as shown in Figure 45–5, except that the datum features should be identified in their correct sequence by the methods described later in the unit.

UNEVEN SURFACES

When establishing a datum plane from a datum-feature surface, it is assumed that the surface will be reasonably flat and that the part would normally rest on three high spots on the surface. If the surface has a tendency toward concavity, Figure 45–6, no particular problems will arise.

However, if the surface is somewhat convex, it will have a tendency to rock on one or two high spots. In such cases it is intended that the datum plane should lie in the direction where the rock is equalized as far as possible. This usually results in the least possible deviation of the actual surface from the datum plane.

For example, in Figure 45–7, the datum plane is plane B and not plane A, because this results in deviation Z, which is less than deviation X.

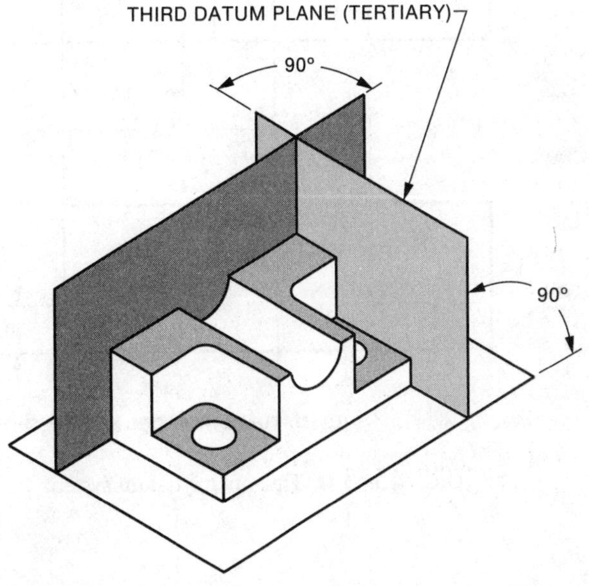
THIRD DATUM PLANE (TERTIARY)
90°
90°

FIGURE 45–4 ■ Tertiary datum

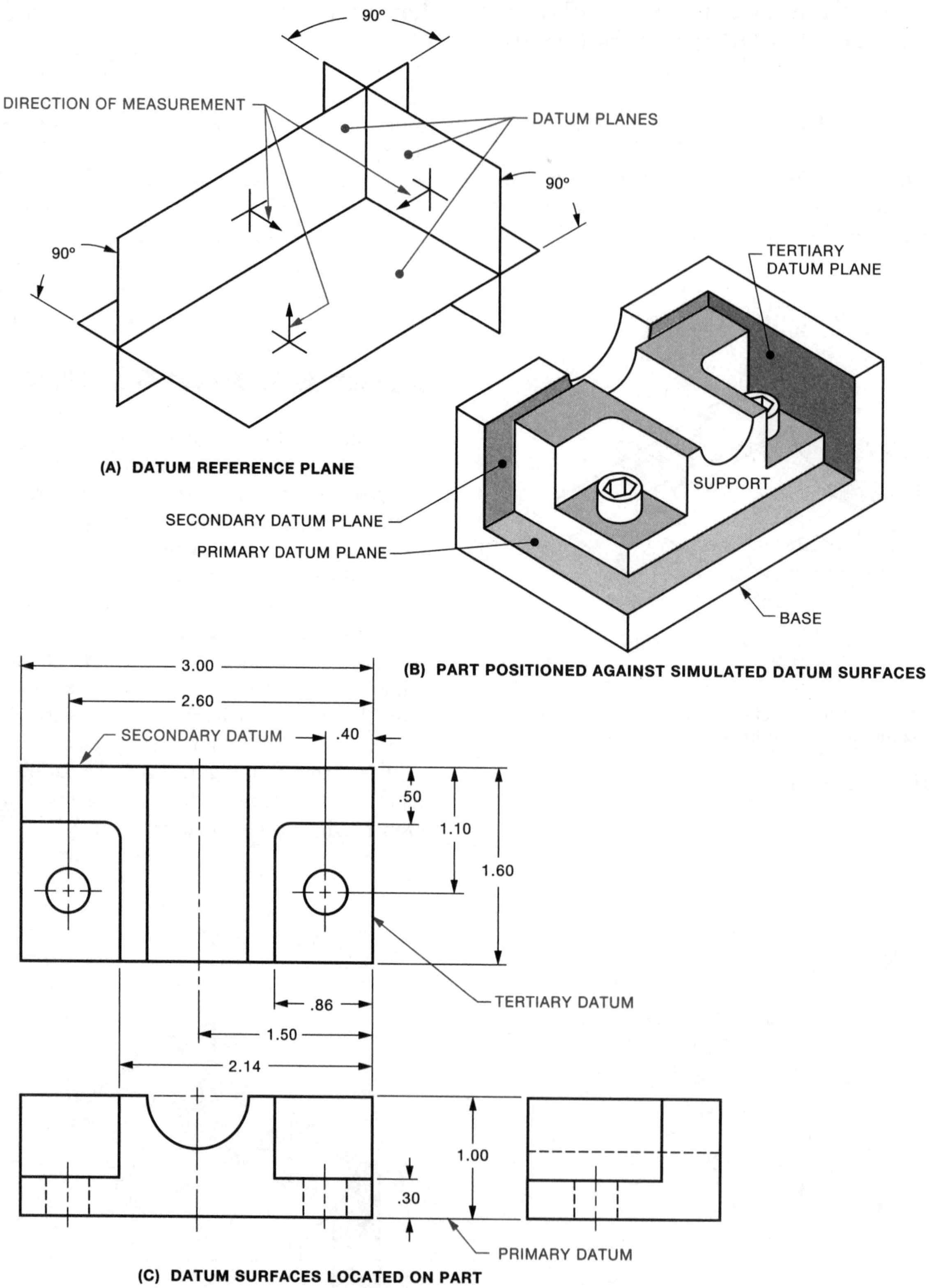
90°
DIRECTION OF MEASUREMENT
DATUM PLANES
90°
90°
(A) DATUM REFERENCE PLANE
TERTIARY DATUM PLANE
SUPPORT
SECONDARY DATUM PLANE
PRIMARY DATUM PLANE
BASE
(B) PART POSITIONED AGAINST SIMULATED DATUM SURFACES
3.00
2.60
SECONDARY DATUM
.40
.50
1.10
1.60
TERTIARY DATUM
.86
1.50
2.14
1.00
.30
PRIMARY DATUM
(C) DATUM SURFACES LOCATED ON PART

FIGURE 45–5 ■ Three-plane datum system

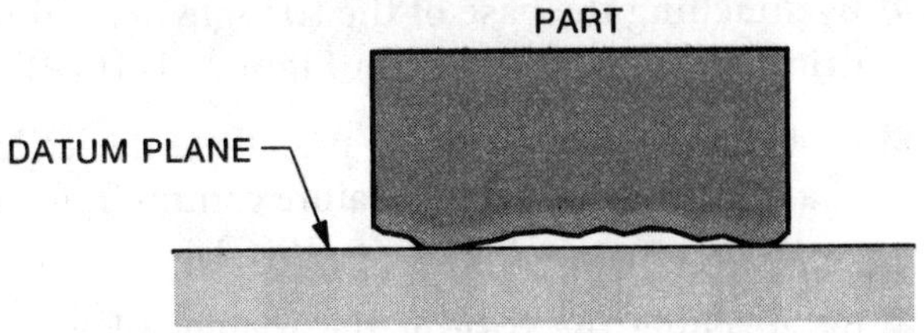

FIGURE 45–6 ■ Concave surface as a datum feature

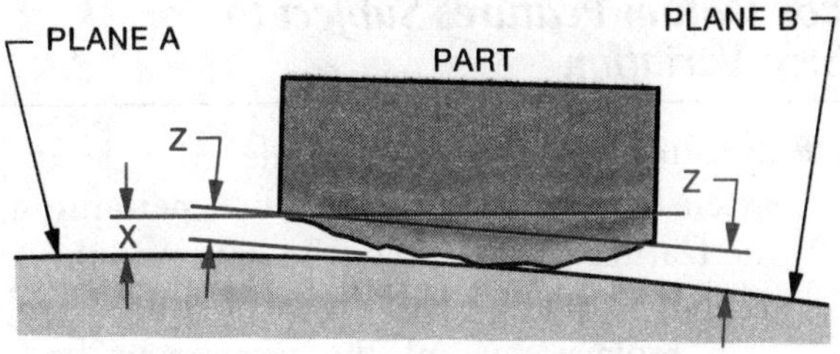

FIGURE 45–7 ■ Datum plane for convex feature

If such conditions are likely to exist, the surface should be controlled by a flatness tolerance (and may have to be machined) or the datum-target method should be used as explained in Unit 48.

DATUM FEATURE SYMBOL

Datum symbols have two functions. They indicate the datum surface or feature on the drawing and identify the datum feature so it can be easily referred to in other requirements.

The datum feature symbol is shown in Figure 45–8. The datum is identified by a capital letter placed horizontally in a square frame attached by a leader to a triangular base, which terminates at the datum feature. The only difference between the ASME and ISO datum feature symbols is the shape of the triangular base.

This identifying symbol may be directed to the datum feature in any one of the following ways.

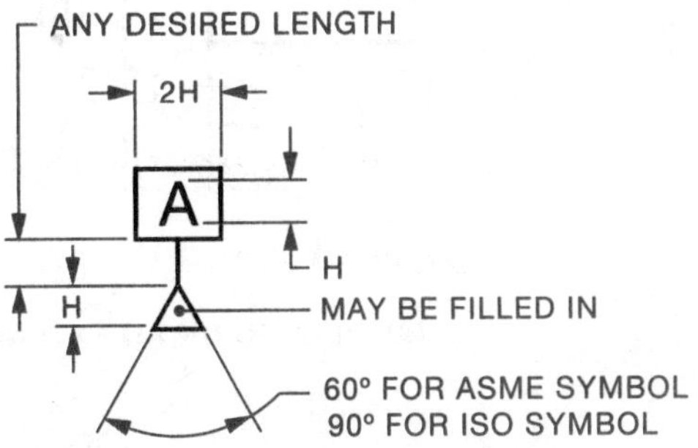

FIGURE 45–8 ■ Datum feature symbol

For Datum Features Not Subject to Size Variation

- By attaching the base of the triangle to an extension line from the feature, providing it is a plane surface, but clearly separated from the dimension line, or to the surface itself. See Figures 45–9(A) and (B).
- When only a part of a surface is to be designated as a datum, such as shown in Figure 45–9(C), a chain line drawn parallel to the surface is used to indicate the portion of the surface acting as the datum.

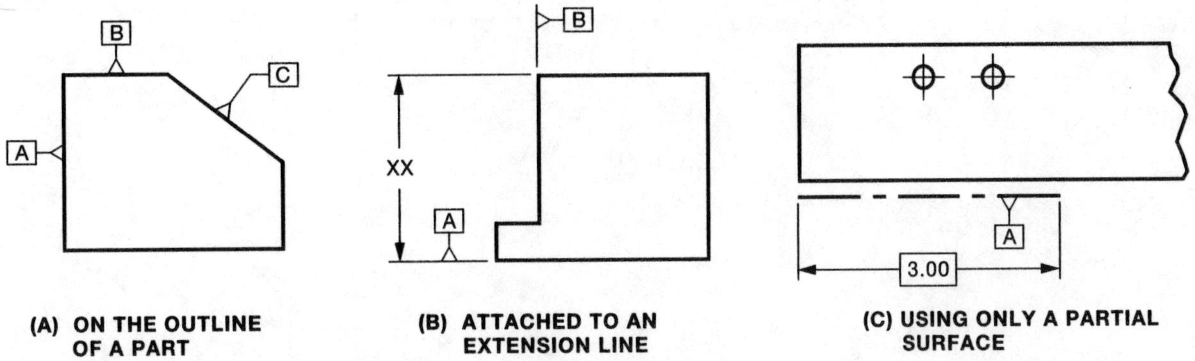

FIGURE 45–9 ■ Placement of datum feature symbols for features not subject to size variation

For Datum Features Subject to Size Variation

- By attaching the base of the triangle to an extension of the dimension line pertaining to the feature of size when the datum is the axis or centre plane. The datum feature symbol may replace part of the dimension line as shown in Figure 45–10(A).
- By attaching the base of the triangle to a cylindrical feature, as shown in Figure 45–10(B).
- By attaching the base of the triangle to the leader of a dimension where no feature control frame is used, as shown in Figure 45–10(C).
- By attaching the base of the triangle above or below the feature control frame, as shown in Figure 45–10(D).

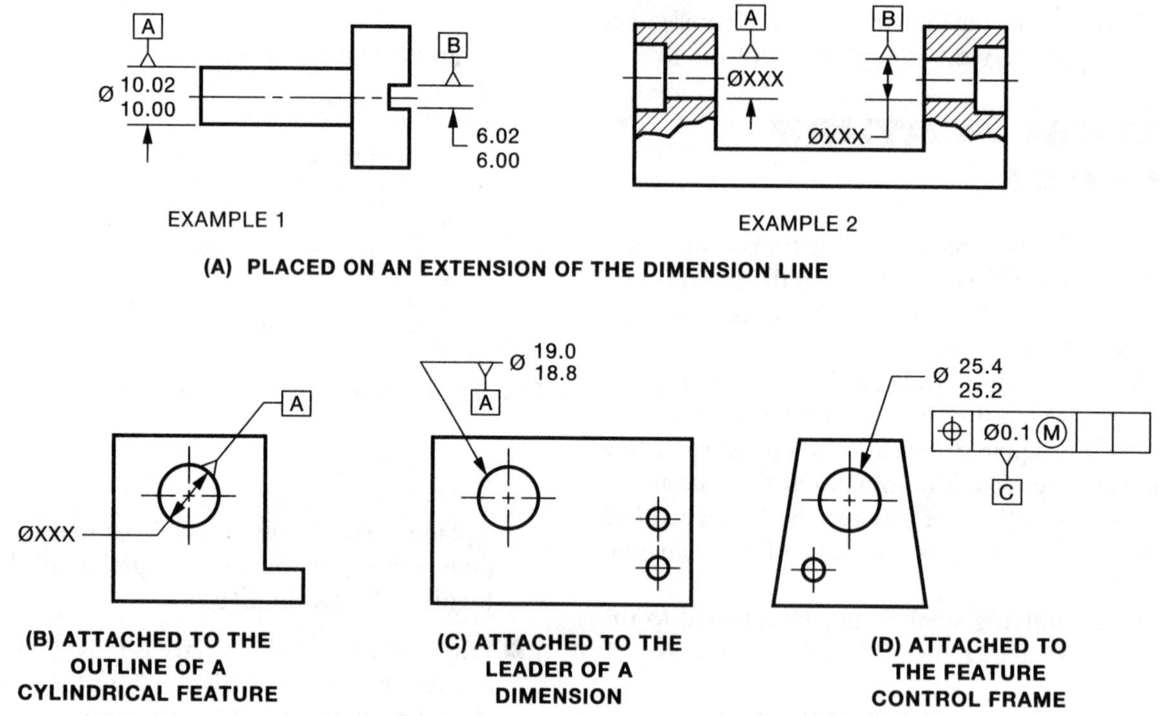

FIGURE 45–10 ■ Placement of datum feature symbols for features subject to size variations

Former ANSI Datum Feature Symbol

Prior to 1994, the United States (ANSI) used the symbol shown in Figures 45–11 and 45–12 to identify the datum feature. It is shown here because many drawings presently in existence show this symbol.

Association with Geometric Tolerances

The datum letter is placed in the feature control frame by adding an extra compartment for the datum reference, Figure 45–13.

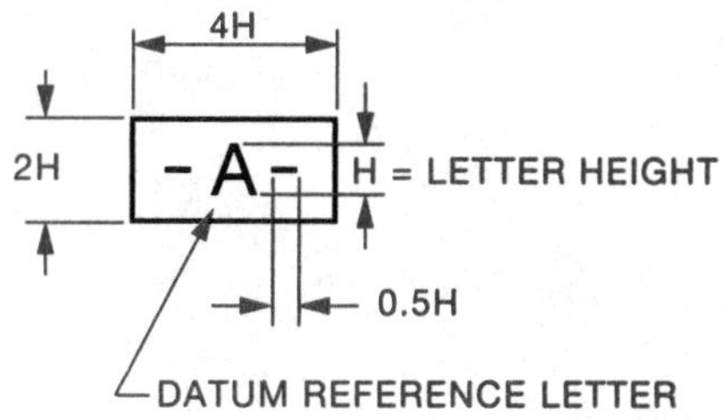

FIGURE 45–11 ■ Former ANSI datum feature symbol

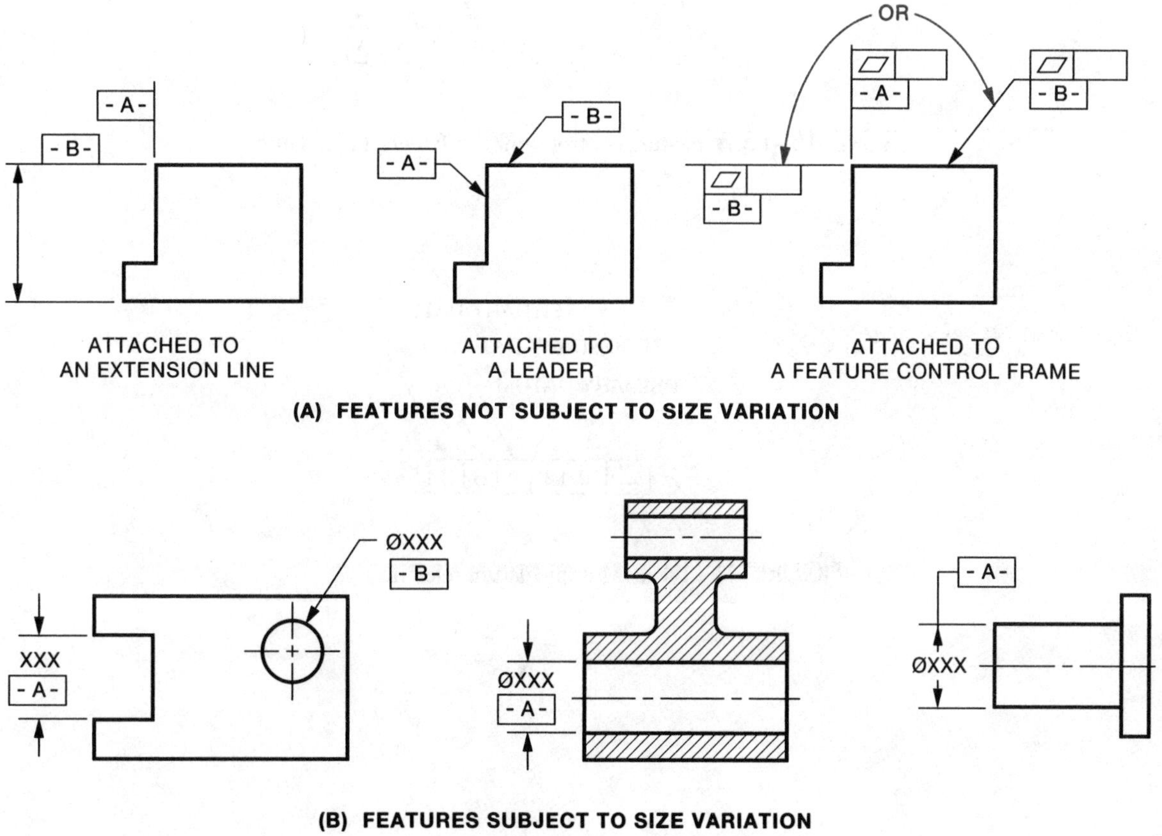

FIGURE 45–12 ■ Placement of former ANSI datum feature symbol

If two or more datum references are involved, additional frames are added and the datum references are placed in these frames in the correct order; that is, primary, secondary, and tertiary datums, Figure 45–14.

Multiple Datum Features

If a single datum is established by two datum features, such as two flat or cylindrical surfaces, Figure 45–15, the features are identified by separate letters. Both letters are then placed in the same compartment of the feature control frame, separated by a dash. The datum in this case is the common axis or plane between the two datum features.

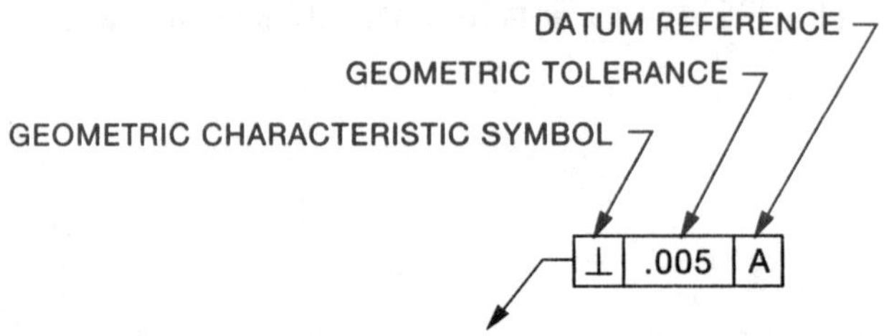

FIGURE 45–13 ■ Feature control symbol referenced to a datum

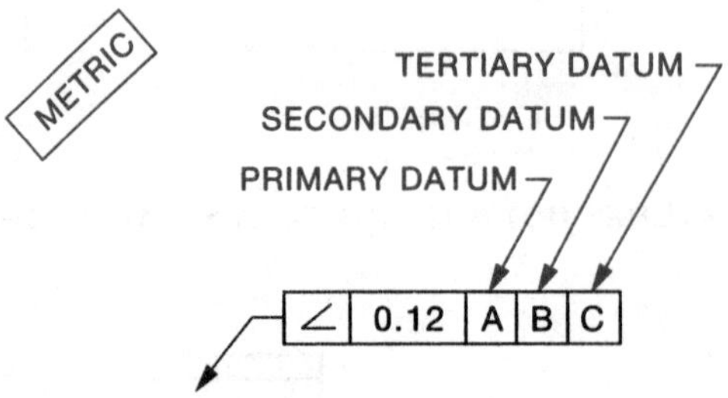

FIGURE 45–14 ■ Multiple datum references

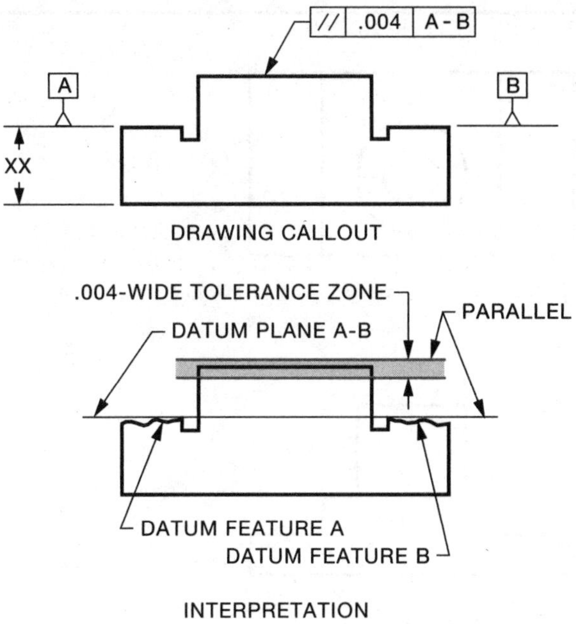

(A) COPLANAR DATUM FEATURES

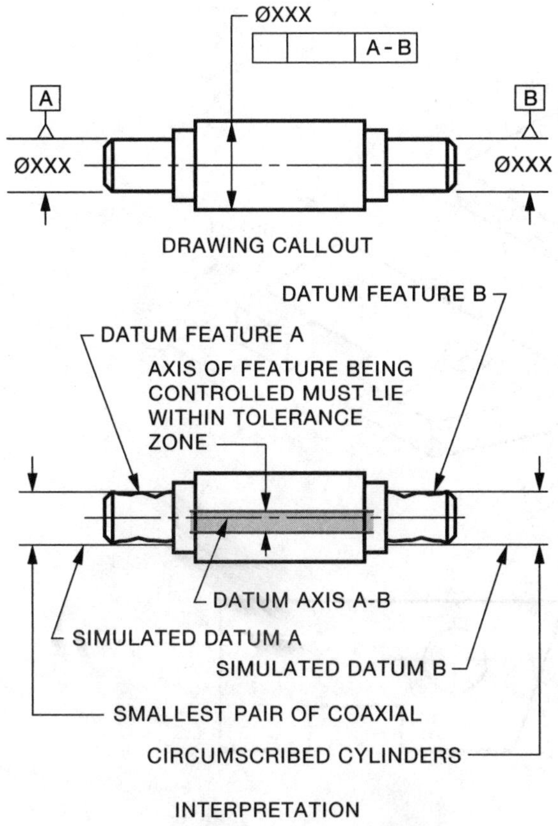

(B) COAXIAL DATUM FEATURES

FIGURE 45–15 ■ Two datum features for one datum

Partial Surfaces as Datums

It is often desirable to specify only part of a surface, instead of the entire surface, to serve as a datum feature. This may be indicated by means of a thick chain line drawn parallel to the surface profile (dimension for length and location), Figure 45–16, or by a datum-target area as described in Unit 48. Figure 45–16 illustrates a long part where holes are located only at one end.

REFERENCES

CAN/CSA-B78.2-M91 Dimensioning and Tolerancing of Technical Drawings
ASME Y14.5M-1994 Dimensioning and Tolerancing

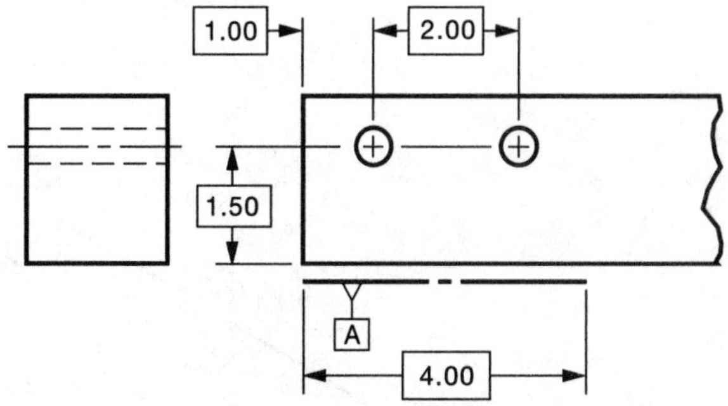

(A) DRAWING CALLOUT

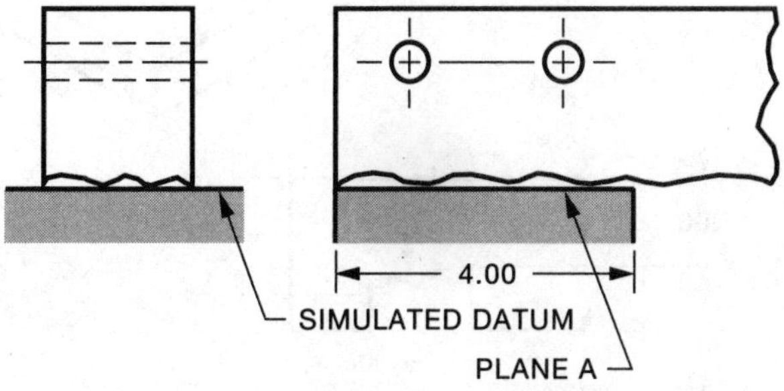

(B) INTERPRETATION

FIGURE 45–16 ■ Partial datum

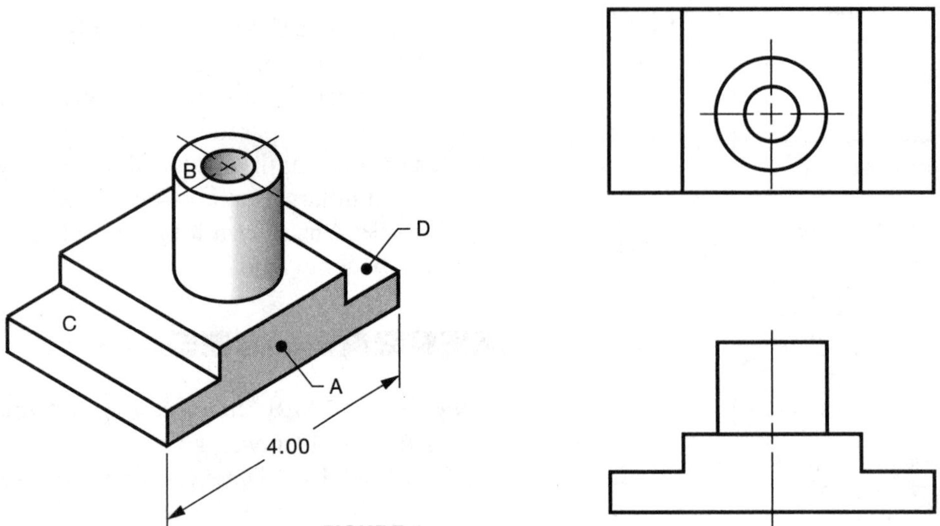
B
D
C
A
4.00

(A) **FIGURE 1** (B)

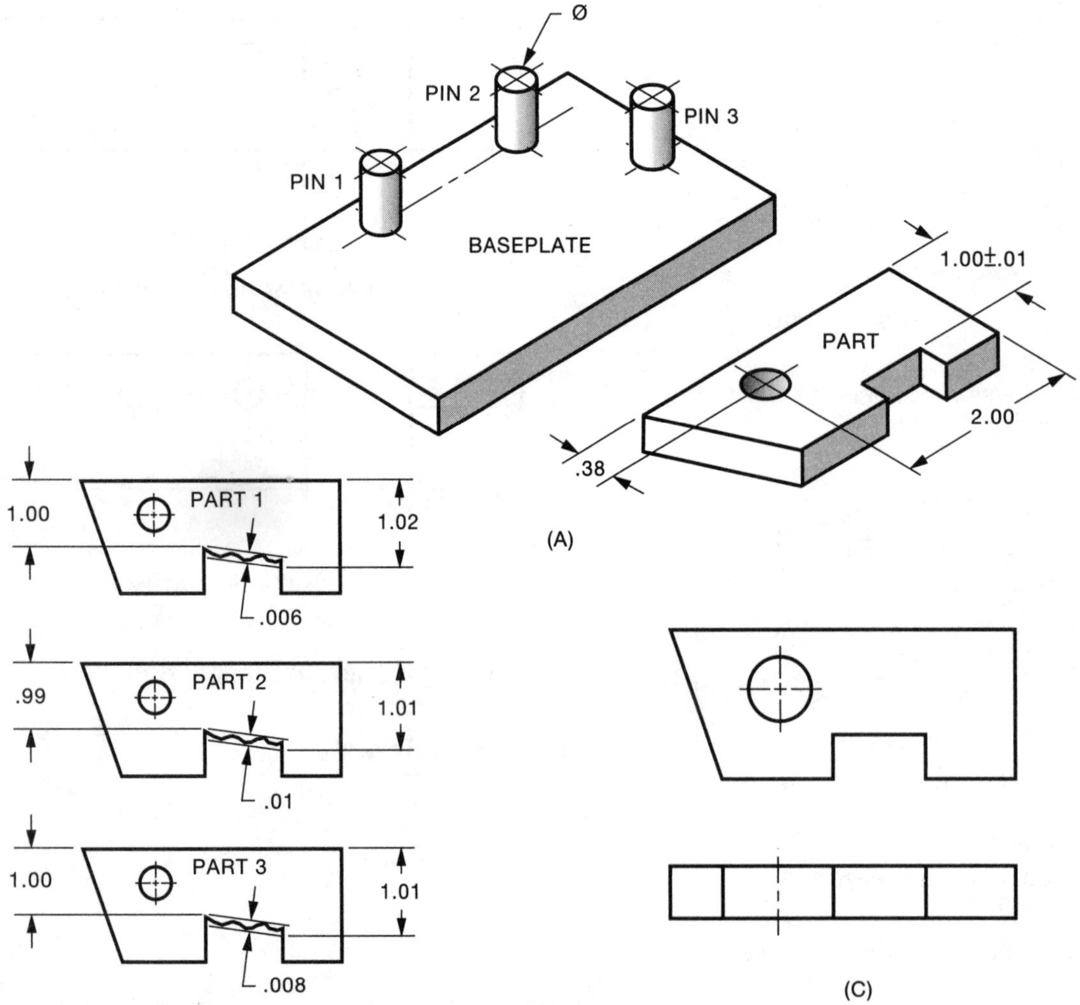
Ø
PIN 2
PIN 3
PIN 1
BASEPLATE
1.00±.01
PART
2.00
.38
(A)
1.00
PART 1
1.02
.006
.99
PART 2
1.01
.01
1.00
PART 3
1.01
.008
(C)

(B) **FIGURE 2**

ASSIGNMENT:

1. Show the following information on the two-view drawing in Figure 1:

   (A) Surface A is datum A and is to be straight within .008 in. for the 4.00 in. length, but the straightness error should not exceed .002 in. for any 1.00 in. length.
   (B) Surface B is datum B and is to be flat within .004 in.
   (C) The base is to be flat within .005 in.
   (D) Surfaces C and D are datum features C and D, respectively, which form a single datum. } OMIT.
   (E) The surface of the cylinder is to be straight within .003 in.

2. (A) Pins 1, 2, and 3 are used to establish the secondary and tertiary datums for the part shown in Figure 2. What is used for the primary datum?
   (B) On the two-view drawing shown in Figure 2C, identify the primary, secondary, and tertiary datum planes as A, B, and C, respectively.
   (C) How far is the centre of the hole from the (1) tertiary datum and (2) secondary datum?
   (D) The back of the slot is to be flat within .008 in. and the secondary datum is to be flat within .004 in. Place these form tolerances on Figure 2(C).
   (E) Are the parts shown in Figure 2(B) acceptable? If not, state your reasons.

3. (A) The bottom surface of the part shown in Figure 3 is to be flat within .004 in. and is to be identified as datum B. Specify both the datum and the tolerance on the drawing.
   (B) What is the maximum height of the part shown in Figure 3?

4. What is the minimum number of contact points in a three-plane datum system for the (A) primary datum, (B) secondary datum, and (C) tertiary datum?

ANSWERS

1. SEE FIGURE 1

2. A ____________

   B SEE FIGURE 2C

   C-1 ____________

   C-2 ____________

   D SEE FIGURE 2C

   E PT 1 ____________

   PT 2 ____________

   PT 3 ____________

3. A SEE FIGURE 3

   B ____________

4. A ____________

   B ____________

   C ____________

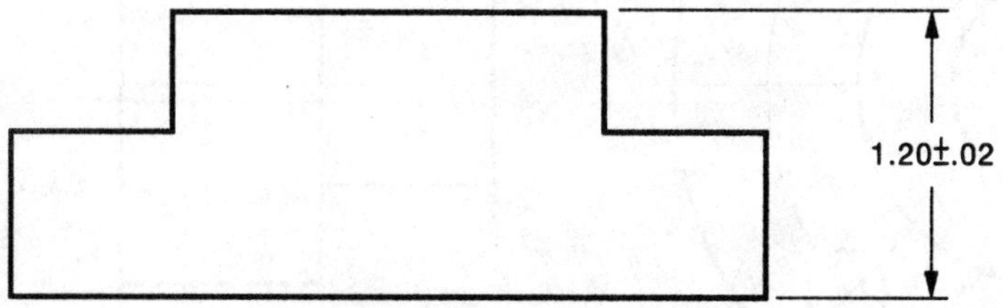

FIGURE 3

	DATUMS	A-103

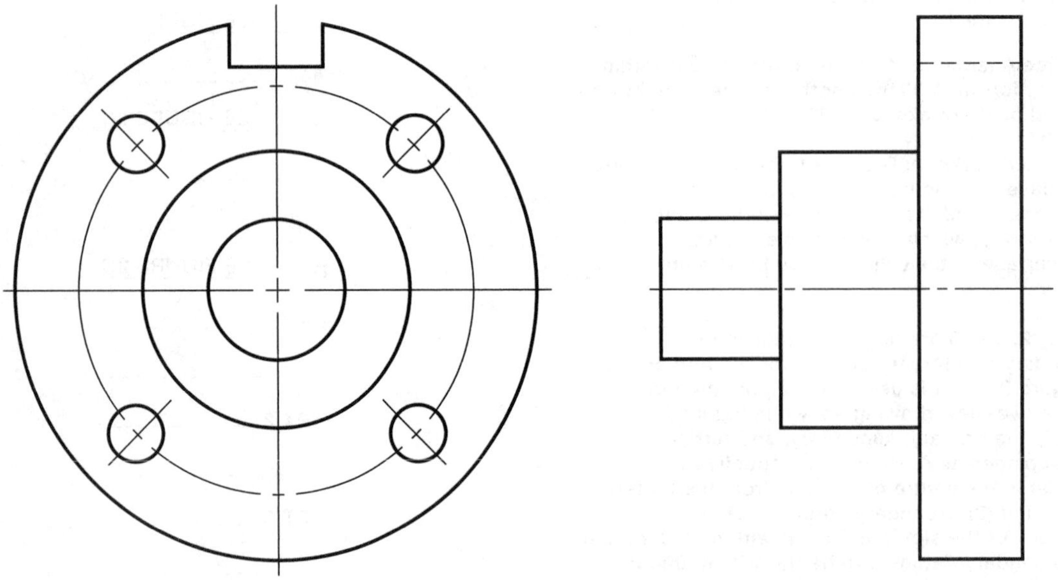

FORMER ANSI DRAWING CALLOUT

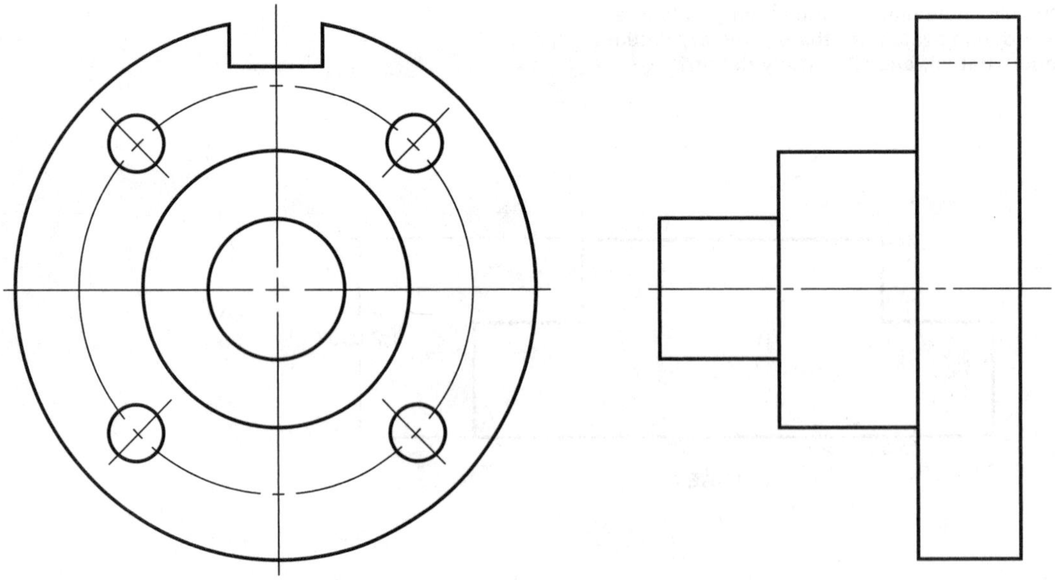

PRESENT CSA AND ASME DRAWING CALLOUT

ASSIGNMENT:

Anyone involved with the use of technical drawings must be capable of interpreting drawings using current and formerly used symbols on drawings. From the following information, add the geometric tolerances and datums to the two drawings, one using former ANSI drawing standards, the other using the current ASME, ISO, and CSA drawing standards.

1. Diameter M to be datum A.
2. The end face of diameter N to be used as datum B.
3. The width of the slot to be datum C.
4. The end face to be flat within 0.25 mm.
5. The axes of diameter M must be straight within 0.1 mm regardless of feature size.
6. The surface of diameter L to be straight within 0.2 mm.

ANSWERS

1. A ____________
   B ____________
   C ____________
2. ____________
   ____
3. ____________

QUESTIONS

1. What are the names given to the planes of a three-plane datum system?
2. What is the name of the symbol that identifies a datum on a drawing?
3. What is the minimum number of contact points between the secondary datum feature and the datum plane?

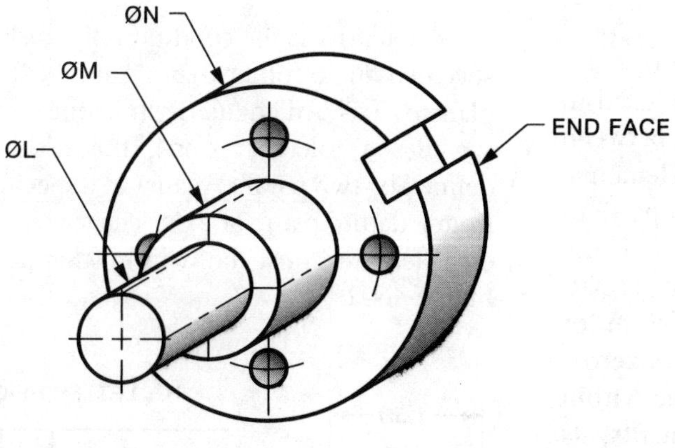

METRIC
DIMENSIONS ARE IN MILLIMETRES

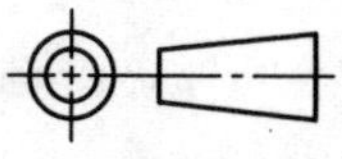

	AXLE	A-104M

46 UNIT

ORIENTATION TOLERANCING FOR FLAT SURFACES

Orientation refers to the angular relationship that exists between two or more lines, surfaces, or other features. Orientation tolerances control angularity, parallelism, and perpendicularity. Because, to a certain degree, the limits of size control form and parallelism, and tolerances of location (see Unit 49) control orientation, the extent of this control should be considered before specifying form or orientation tolerances.

A tolerance of form or orientation may be specified where the tolerances of size and location do not provide sufficient control.

Orientation tolerances, when applied to plane surfaces, control flatness if a flatness tolerance is not specified.

The general geometric characteristic for orientation is termed *angularity.* This term may be used to describe angular relationships, of any angle, between straight lines or surfaces with straight line elements, such as flat or cylindrical surfaces. For two particular types of angularity, special terms are used. These are *perpendicularity,* or squareness, for features related to each other by a 90° angle, and *parallelism* for features related to one another by an angle of zero.

An orientation tolerance specifies a zone within which the considered feature, its line elements, its axis, or its centre plane must be contained.

Reference to a Datum

An orientation tolerance indicates a relationship between two or more features. Whenever possible, the feature to which the controlled feature is related should be designated as a datum. Sometimes this does not seem possible, for example, where two surfaces are equal and cannot be distinguished from one another. The geometric tolerance could theoretically be applied to both surfaces without a datum, but it is generally preferable to specify two similar requirements, using each surface in turn as the datum.

Angularity, parallelism, and perpendicularity are orientation tolerances applicable to related features. Relation to more than one datum feature should be considered if required to stabilize the tolerance zone in more than one direction.

There are three geometric symbols for orientation tolerances, Figure 46–1. The proportions are based on the height of the lettering used on the drawing.

Angularity Tolerance

Angularity is the condition of a surface or axis at a specified angle (other than 0° and 90°) from a datum plane or axis. An angularity tolerance for a flat surface specifies a tolerance zone, the width of which is defined by two parallel planes at a specified basic angle from a datum plane or axis. The surface of the considered feature must lie within this tolerance zone, Figure 46–2.

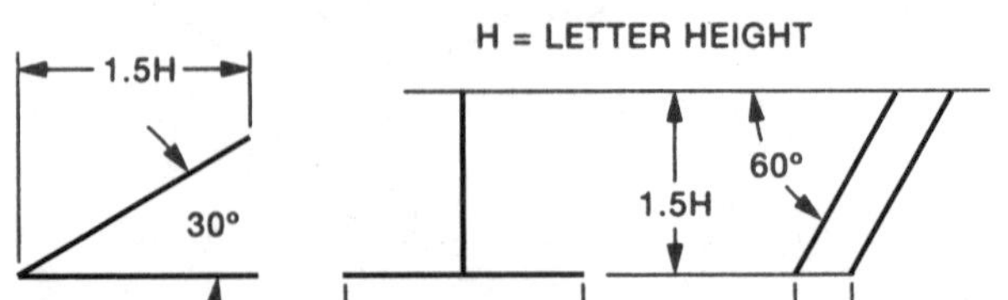

FIGURE 46–1 ■ Orientation symbols

For geometric tolerancing of angularity, the angle between the datum and the controlled feature should be stated as a basic angle. Therefore, it should be enclosed in a rectangular frame (basic dimension symbol) as shown in Figure 46–2 to indicate that the general tolerance note does not apply. However, the angle need not be stated for either perpendicularity (90°) or parallelism (0°).

Perpendicularity Tolerance

Perpendicularity is the condition of a surface at 90° to a datum plane or axis. A perpendicularity tolerance for a flat surface specifies a tolerance zone defined by two parallel planes perpendicular to a datum plane or axis. The surface of the considered feature must lie within this, Figure 46–2.

Parallelism Tolerance

Parallelism is the condition of a surface equidistant at all points from a datum plane. A parallelism tolerance for a flat surface specifies a tolerance zone defined by two planes or lines parallel to a datum plane or axis. The line elements of the surface must be within this tolerance zone, Figure 46–2.

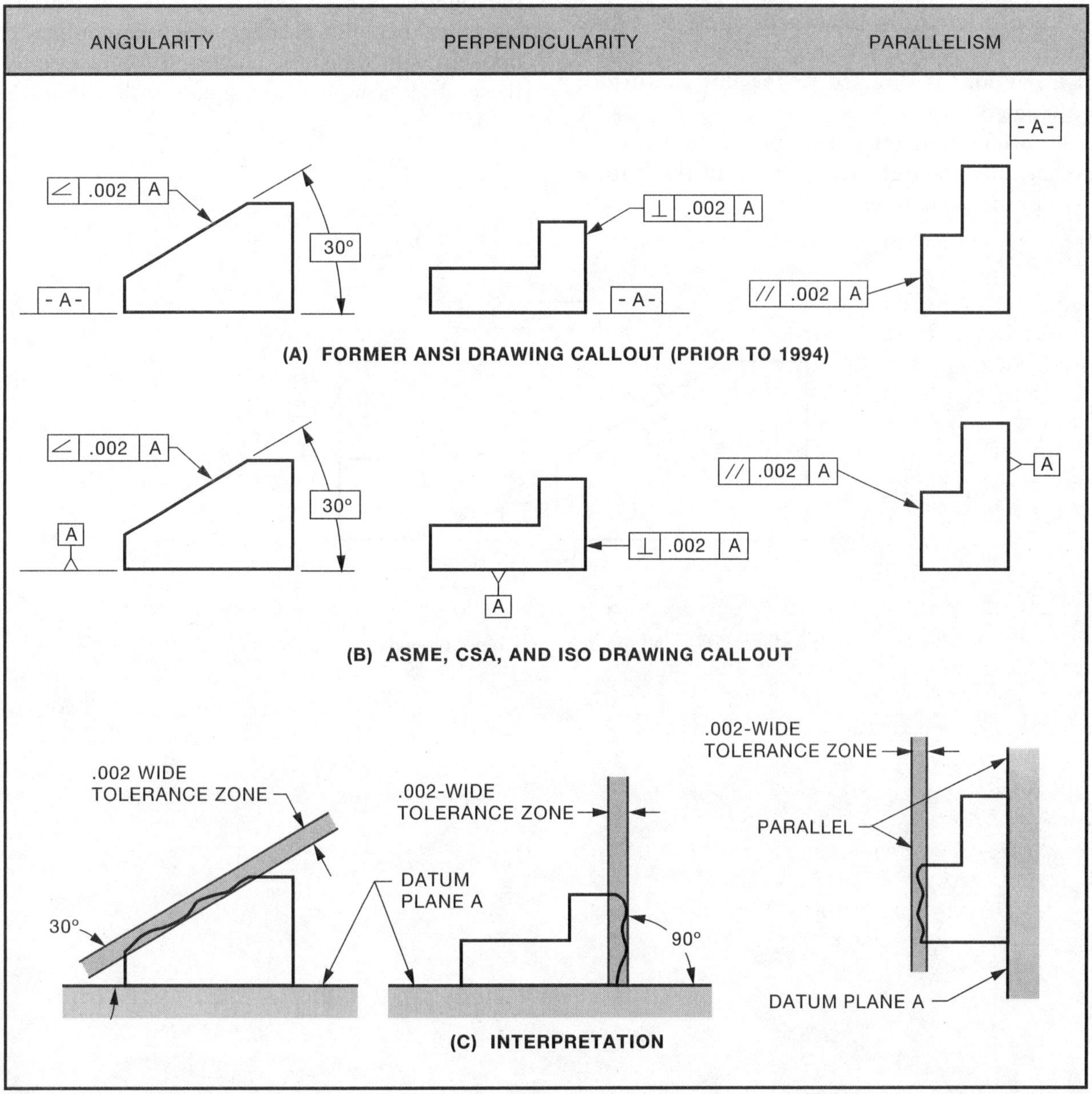

FIGURE 46–2 ■ Orientation tolerancing of flat surfaces

ORIENTATION TOLERANCING FOR FLAT SURFACES

Figure 46–2 shows three simple parts in which one flat surface is designated as a datum feature and another flat surface is related to it by one of the orientation tolerances.

Each of these tolerances is interpreted to mean that the designated surface shall be contained within a tolerance zone consisting of the space between two parallel planes, separated by the specified tolerance (.002 in.) and related to the datum by the basic angle specified (30°, 90°, or 0°).

When orientation tolerances apply to a line or surface, a leader is attached to the feature control frame and is directed to the line or surface requiring control.

An orientation tolerance applied to a feature automatically ensures that the form of the feature is within the same tolerance.

Therefore, when an orientation tolerance is specified, there is no need to also specify a form tolerance for the same feature unless a smaller tolerance is necessary.

Control in Two Directions

The measuring principles for angularity indicate the method of aligning the part prior to making angularity measurements. Proper alignment ensures that line elements of the surface perpendicular to the angular line elements are parallel to the datum.

For example, the part in Figure 46–3 will be aligned so that line elements running horizontally in the right-hand view will be parallel to datum A. However, these line elements will bear a proper relationship with the sides, ends, and top faces only if these surfaces are true and square with datum B.

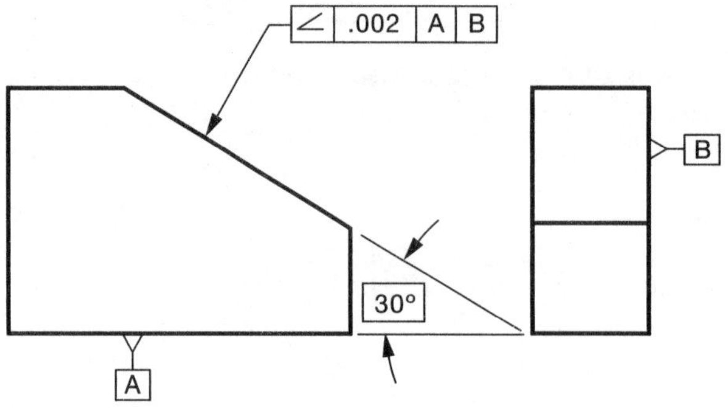

FIGURE 46–3 ■ Angularity referenced to a datum system

Applying Form and Orientation Tolerances to a Single Feature

When both form and orientation tolerances are applied to a feature, the form tolerance must be less than the orientation tolerance. An example is shown in Figure 46–4, where the flatness of the surface must be controlled to a greater degree than its orientation. The flatness tolerance must lie within the angularity tolerance zone.

REFERENCES

CAN/CSA-B78.2-M91 Dimensioning and Tolerancing of Technical Drawings
ASME Y14.5M-1994 Dimensioning and Tolerancing

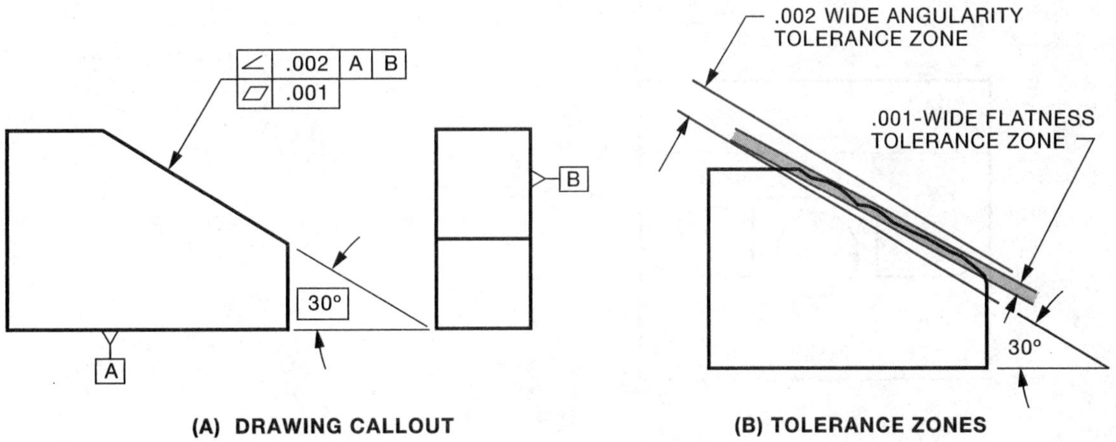

FIGURE 46–4 ■ Applying both an angularity and a flatness tolerance to a feature

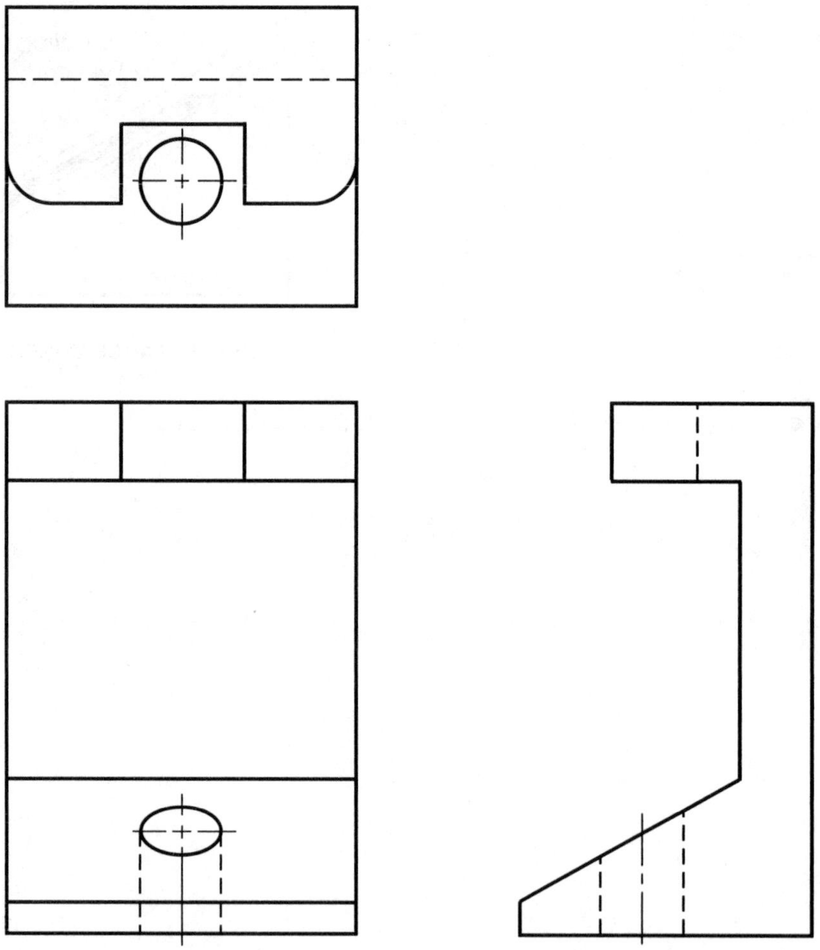

FIGURE 1

ASSIGNMENT:

From the information shown in Figure 2 and the following, add the geometric tolerances and basic dimensions to Figure 1.

1. Surfaces A, B, and D are to be datums A, B, and D, respectively.
2. The back is to be perpendicular to the bottom within .01 in. and flat within .006 in.
3. The top is to be parallel with the bottom within .005 in.
4. Surface C is to have an angularity tolerance of .008 in. with the bottom. Surface D is to be the secondary datum for this requirement.
5. The bottom is to be flat within .002 in.
6. The sides of the slot are to be parallel to each other within .002 in. and perpendicular to the back (datum B) within .004 in. One side of the slot is to be datum E.

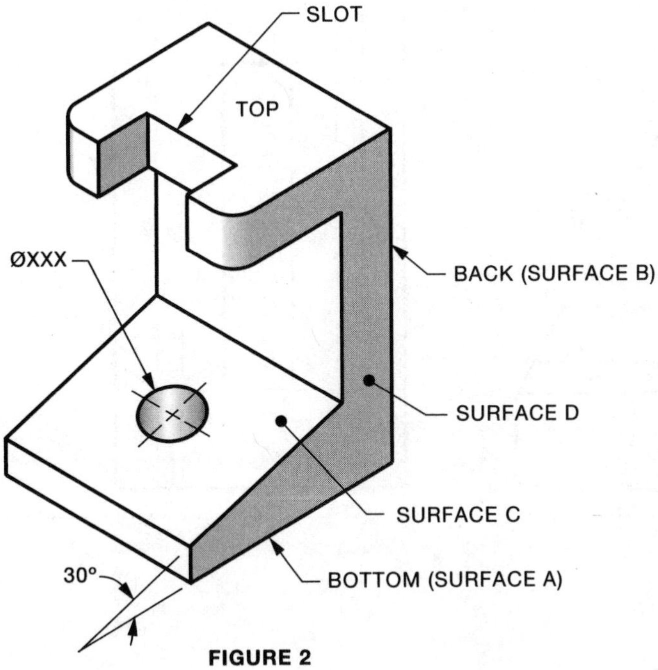
SLOT
TOP
ØXXX
BACK (SURFACE B)
SURFACE D
SURFACE C
BOTTOM (SURFACE A)
30°

FIGURE 2

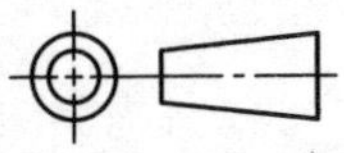

STAND

A-105

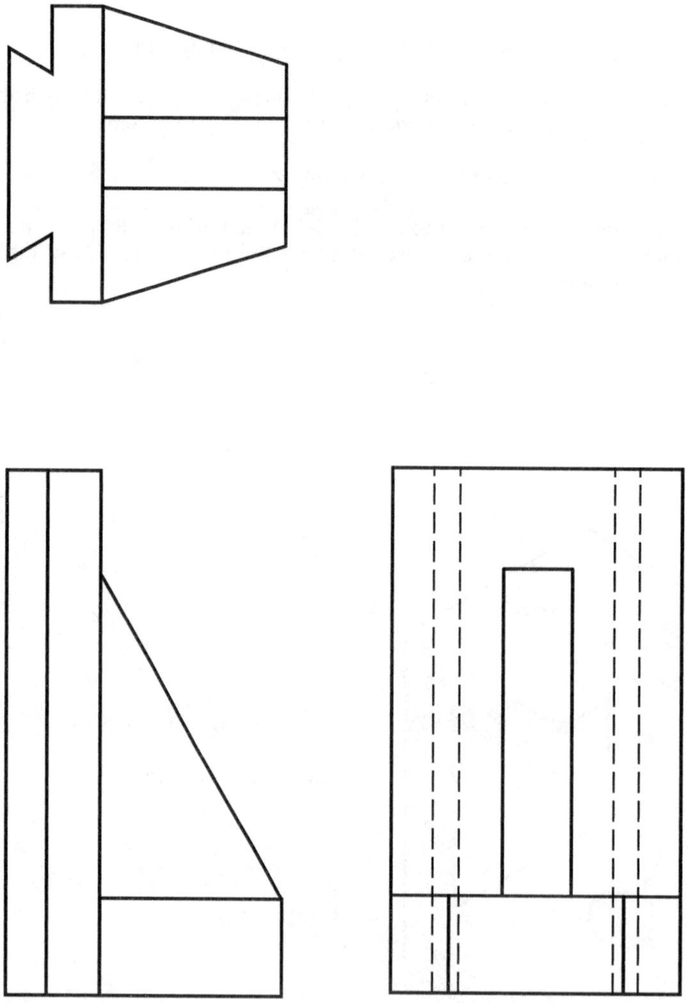

FIGURE 1

ASSIGNMENT:

From the information shown in Figure 2 and the following, add the geometric tolerances and basic dimensions to Figure 1.

1. Surfaces A, B, C, D, and E are to be datums A, B, C, D, and E, respectively.
2. Surface C is to have a flatness tolerance of 0.2 mm.
3. Surfaces F and G of the dovetail are to have an angularity tolerance of 0.05 mm, with a single datum established by the two datum features D and E. These surfaces are to be flat within 0.02 mm.
4. Surface H is to be parallel to surface B within 0.05 mm.
5. Surface C is to be perpendicular to surfaces D and E within 0.04 mm.

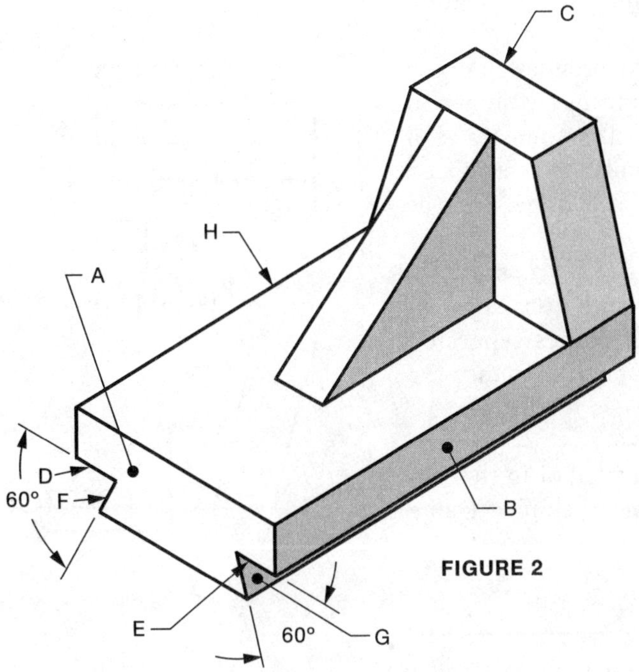

FIGURE 2

METRIC
DIMENSIONS ARE IN MILLIMETRES

	CUT-OFF STAND	**A-106M**

47 UNIT

ORIENTATION TOLERANCING FOR FEATURES OF SIZE

When orientation tolerances apply to the axis of cylindrical features or to the datum planes of two flat surfaces, the feature control frame is associated with the size dimension of the feature requiring control, Figure 47–1.

Tolerances intended to control orientation of the axis of a feature are applied to drawings as shown in Figure 47–2. Although this unit deals mostly with cylindrical features, methods similar to those given here can be applied to noncircular features, such as square and hexagonal shapes.

The axis of the cylindrical feature must be contained within a tolerance zone consisting of the space between two parallel planes separated by the specified tolerance. The parallel planes are related to the datum by the basic angles of 45°, 90°, or 0° in Figure 47–2.

The absence of a modifying symbol in the tolerance compartment of the feature control frame indicates that RFS applies.

Angularity Tolerance

The tolerance zone is defined by two parallel planes at the specified basic angle from a datum plane or axis, within which the axis of the considered feature must lie. Figure 47–3 illustrates the tolerance zone for angularity.

Perpendicularity Tolerance

A perpendicularity tolerance specifies one of the following:

1. A cylindrical tolerance zone perpendicular to a datum plane or axis within which the centre

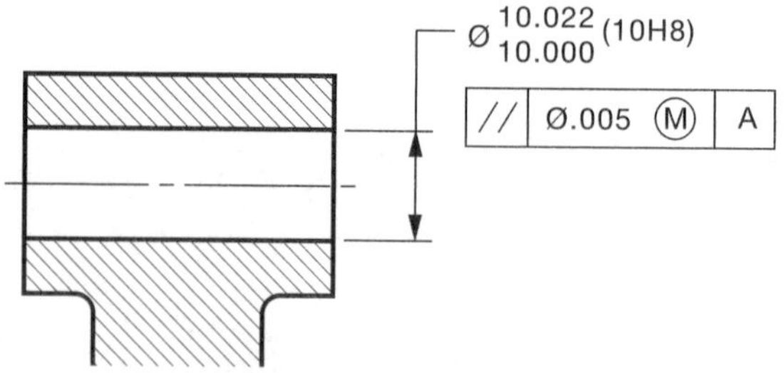

(A) ATTACHED TO A DIMENSION

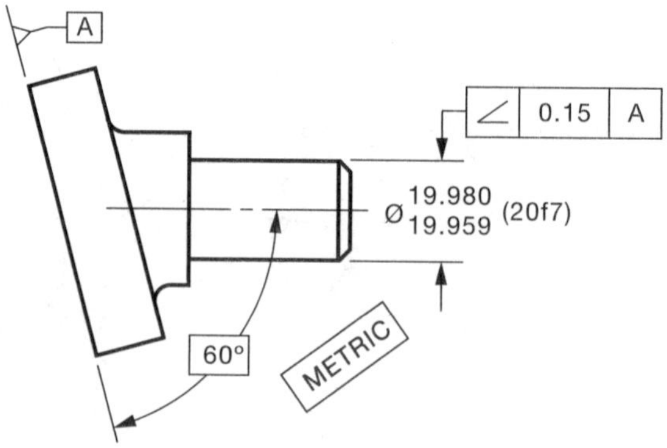

(B) ATTACHED TO THE EXTENSION OF THE DIMENSION LINE

FIGURE 47–1 ■ Feature control frame associated with size dimension line of the considered feature must lie. (See Figure 47–2.)

2. A tolerance zone defined by two parallel planes perpendicular to a datum axis within which the axis of the considered feature must lie. (See Figure 47–3.)

When the tolerance is one of perpendicularity, the tolerance zone planes can be revolved around the feature axis without affecting the angle. The tolerance zone therefore becomes a cylinder. This cylindrical zone is perpendicular to the datum and has a diameter equal to the specified tolerance, Figure 47–4. A diameter symbol precedes the perpendicularity tolerance.

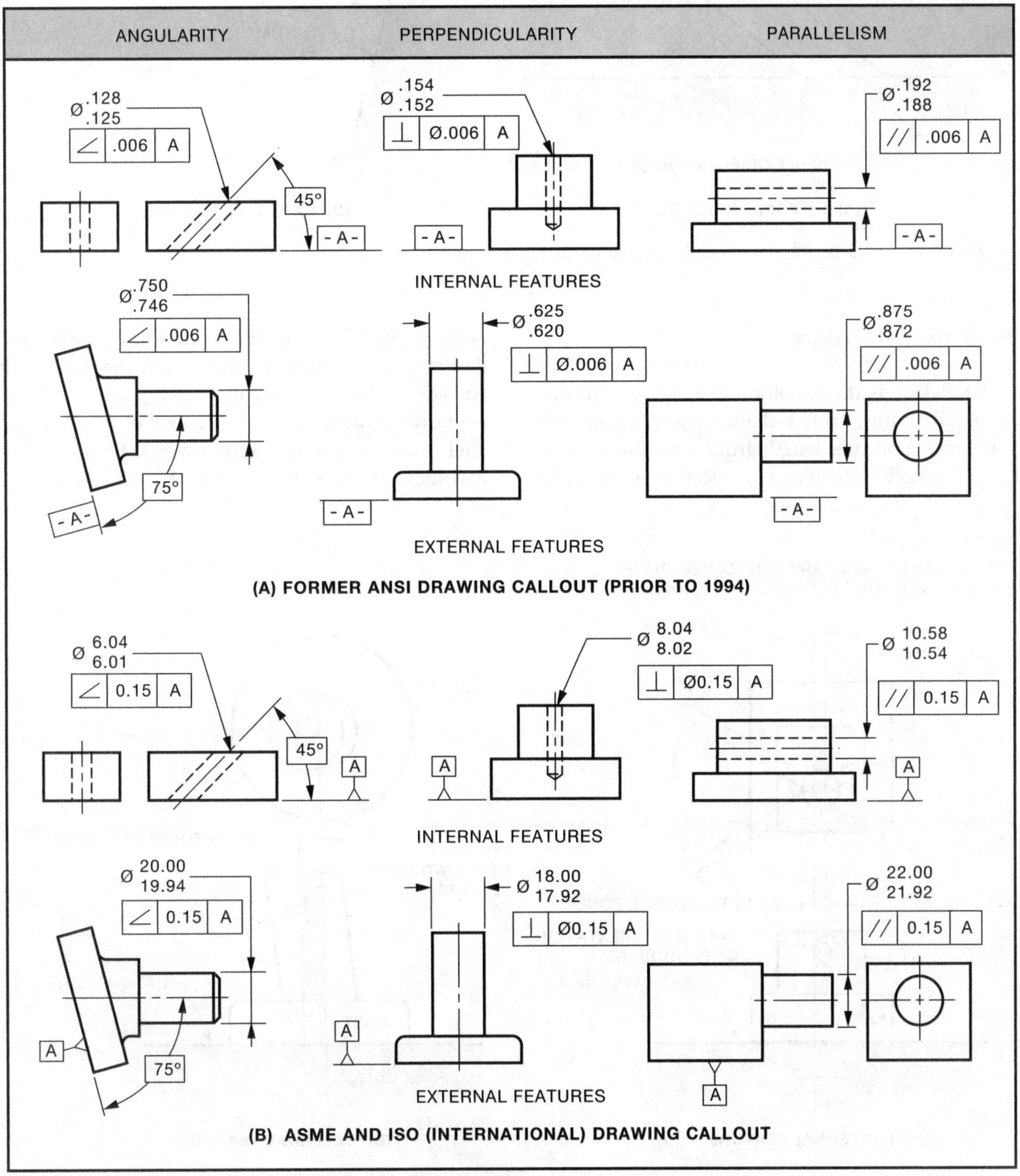

FIGURE 47–2 ■ Orientation tolerances for cylindrical features—RFS

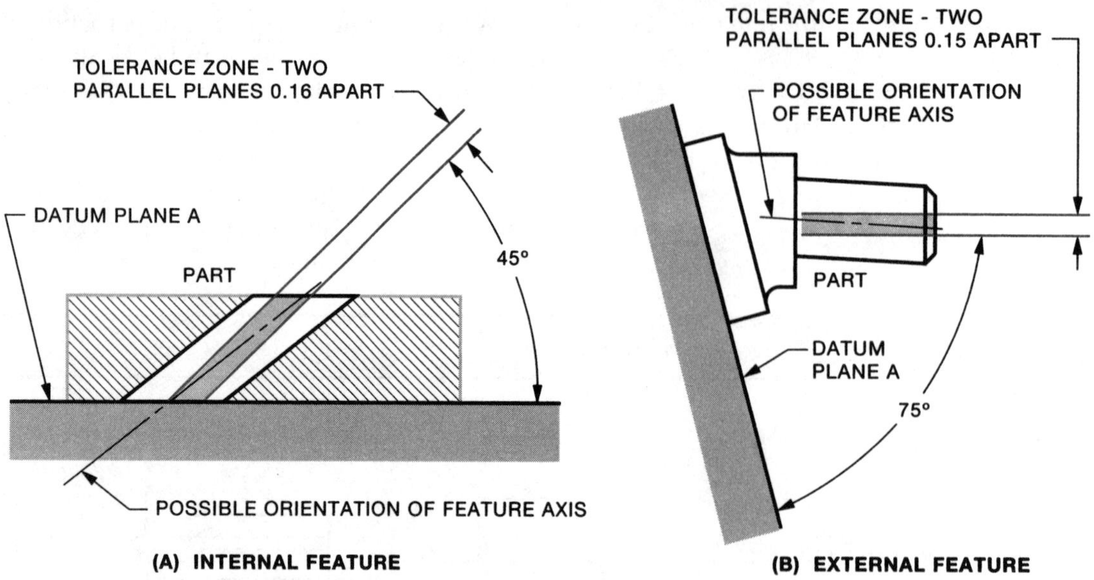

FIGURE 47–3 ■ Tolerance zone for angularity shown in Figure 47–2

Parallelism Tolerance

Parallelism is the condition of a surface equidistant at all points from a datum plane or an axis equidistant along its length from a datum axis or plane. A parallelism tolerance specifies a tolerance zone defined by two planes or lines parallel to a datum plane or axis, within which the axis of the considered feature must lie (see Figure 47–5); or a cylindrical tolerance zone, the axis of which is parallel to the datum axis within which the axis of the considered feature must lie (see Figure 47–10.)

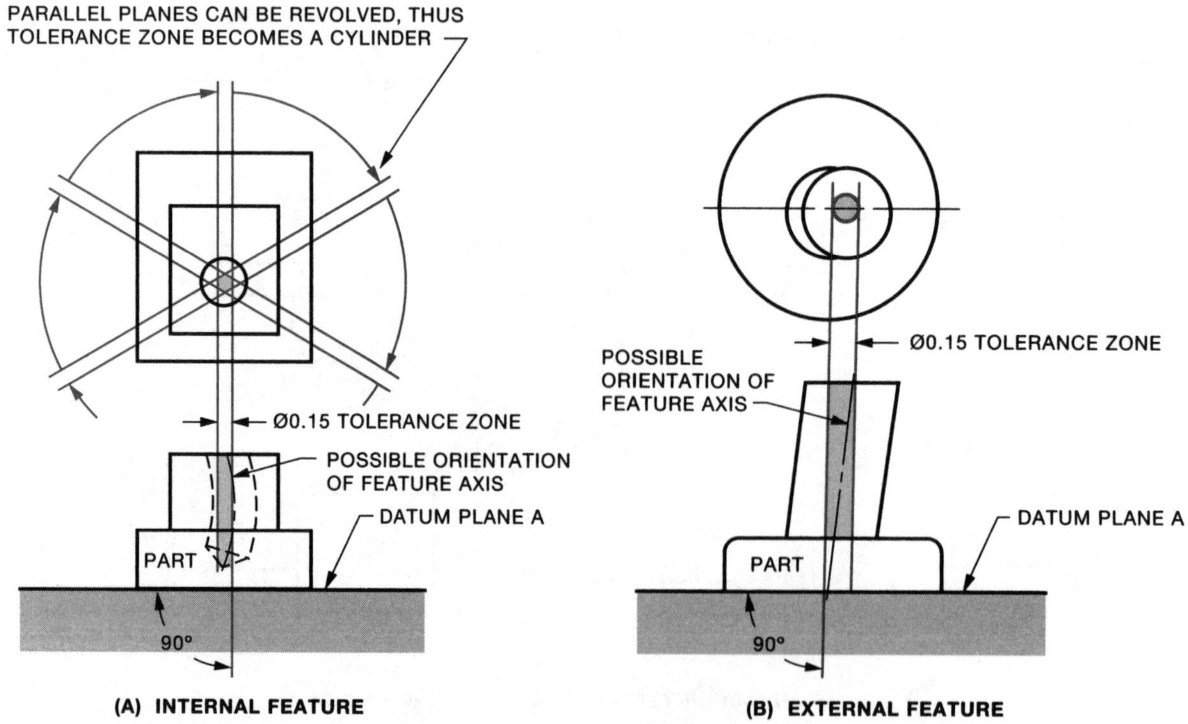

FIGURE 47–4 ■ Tolerance zone for perpendicularity shown in Figure 47–2

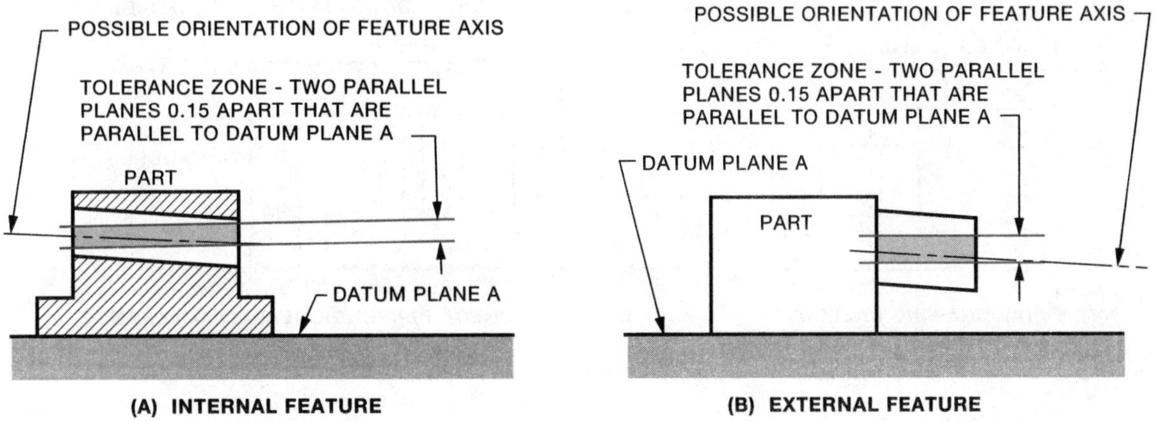

FIGURE 47–5 ■ Tolerance zones for parallelism shown in Figure 47–2

Control In Two Directions

The feature control frame for angularity shown in Figure 47–2 controls angularity with the base (datum A) only. If control with a side is also required, the side should be designated as the secondary datum, Figure 47–6. The centre line of the hole must lie within the two parallel planes.

Control on an MMC Basis

Example 1

As a hole is a feature of size, any of the tolerances shown in Figure 47–2 can be modified on an MMC basis. This is specified by adding the symbol Ⓜ after the tolerance; Figure 47–7 shows an example.

Examples 2 and 3

Because the cylindrical features represent features of size, orientation tolerances may be applied on an MMC basis. This is indicated by adding the modifying symbol after the tolerance as shown in Figures 47–8 and 47–9.

INTERNAL CYLINDRICAL FEATURES

Figure 47–2 shows some simple parts in which the axis or centre line of a hole is related by an orientation tolerance to a flat surface. The flat surface is designated as the datum feature.

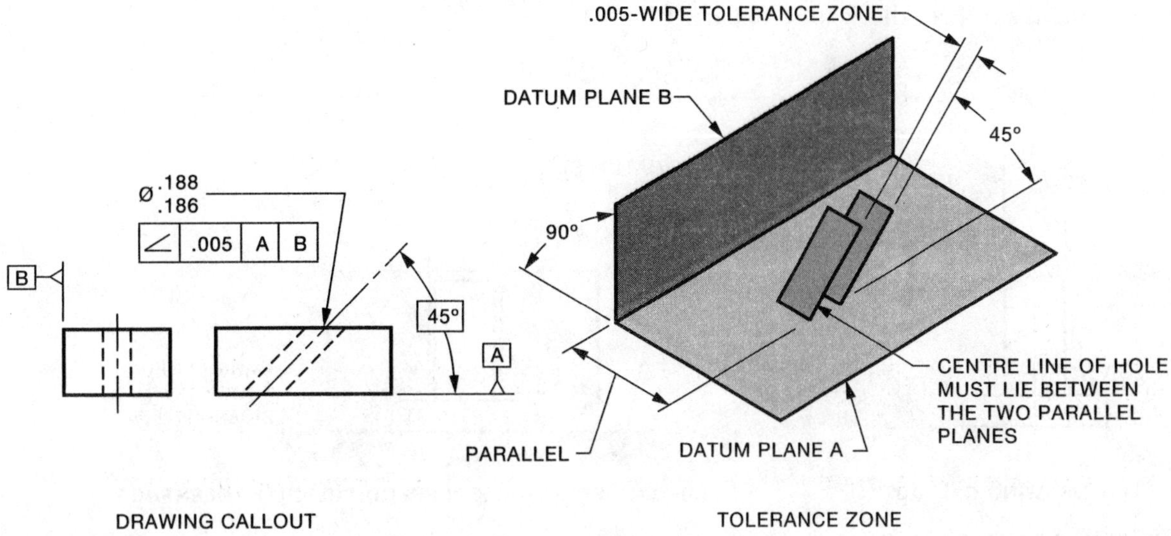

FIGURE 47–6 ■ Angularity tolerances referenced to two datums

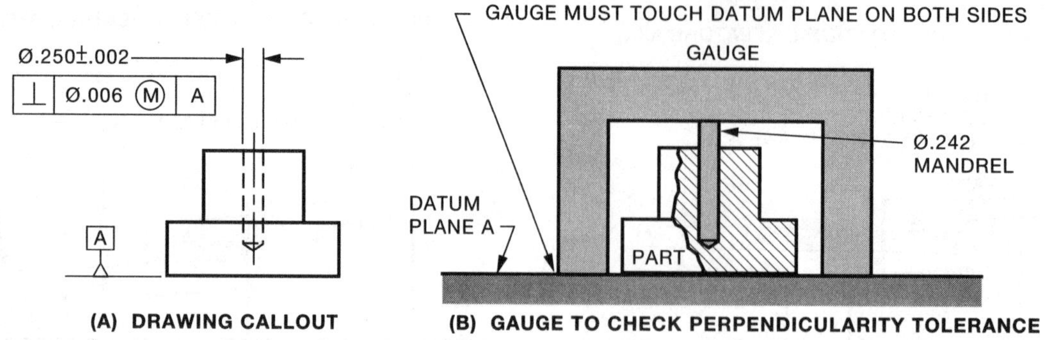

FIGURE 47–7 ■ Perpendicularity tolerance for a hole on an MMC basis

The axis of each hole must be contained within a tolerance zone consisting of the space between two parallel planes. These planes are separated by a specified tolerance of .006 in. for the parts shown in Figure 47–2(A), and by a specified tolerance of 0.15 mm for the parts shown in Figure 47–2(B).

Specifying Parallelism for an Axis

Figure 47–10 specifies parallelism for an axis when both the feature and the datum feature are shown on an RFS basis. Regardless of feature size, the feature axis must lie within a cylindrical tolerance zone of .002-in. diameter whose axis is parallel to datum axis A. Additionally, the feature axis must be within any specified tolerance of location.

Figure 47–11 specifies parallelism for an axis when the feature is shown on an MMC basis and the datum feature is shown on an RFS basis. Where the feature is at the maximum material condition (.392 in.), the maximum parallelism tolerance is .002 in. diameter. Where the feature departs from its MMC size, an increase in the parallelism tolerance is allowed equal to the amount of such departure. Additionally, the feature axis must be within any specified tolerance of location.

Perpendicularity for a Median Plane

Regardless of feature size, the centre plane of the feature shown in Figure 47–12 must lie between two parallel planes, .005 in. apart, that are perpendicular to datum plane A. Additionally, the feature centre plane must be within any specified tolerance of location.

Perpendicularity for an Axis (Both Feature and Datum RFS)

Regardless of feature size, the feature axis shown in Figure 47–13 must lie between two parallel planes, .005 in. apart, that are perpendicular to datum axis A. Additionally, the feature axis must be within any specified tolerance of location.

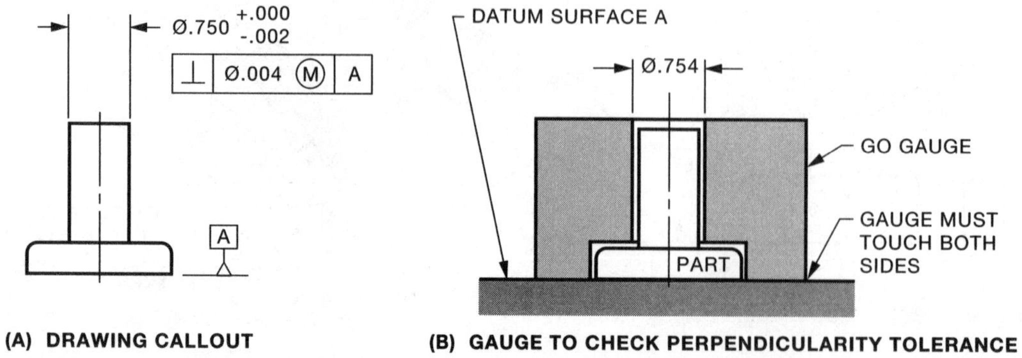

FIGURE 47–8 ■ Perpendicularity tolerance for a shaft on an MMC basis

Perpendicularity for an Axis (Tolerance at MMC)

Where the feature shown in Figure 47–14 is at the MMC (Ø2.000), its axis must be perpendicular within .002 in. to the datum plane A. Where the feature departs from MMC, an increase in the perpendicularity tolerance is allowed equal to the amount of such departure. Additionally, the feature axis must be within the specified tolerance of location.

Perpendicularity for an Axis (Zero Tolerance at MMC)

Where the feature shown in Figure 47–15 is at the MMC (Ø2.000), its axis must be perpendicular to datum plane A. Where the feature departs from MMC, an increase in the perpendicularity tolerance is allowed equal to the amount of such departure. Additionally, the feature axis must be within any specified tolerance of location.

Perpendicularity with a Maximum Tolerance Specified

Where the feature shown in Figure 47–16 is at MMC (50.00 mm), its axis must be perpendicular to datum plane A. Where the feature departs from MMC, an increase in the perpendicularity tolerance is allowed equal to the amount of such departure, up to the 0.1 mm maximum. Additionally, the feature axis must be within any specified tolerance of location.

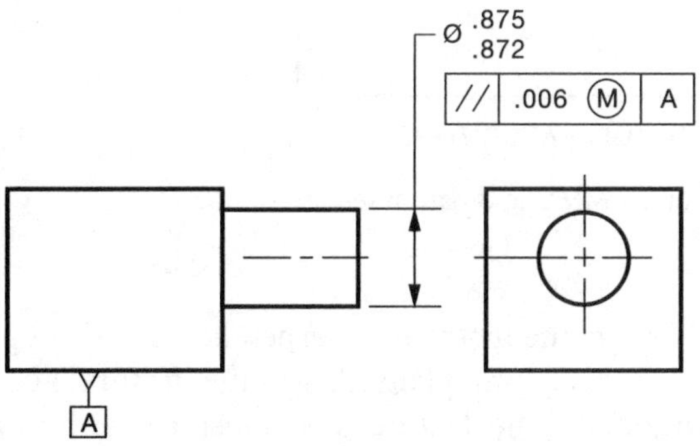

(A) DRAWING CALLOUT

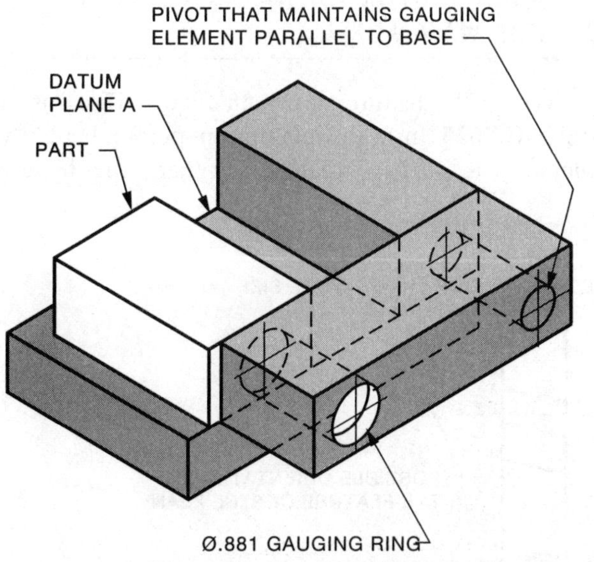

(B) GAUGE TO CHECK PARALLELISM TOLERANCE

FIGURE 47–9 ■ Parallelism tolerance for a shaft on an MMC basis

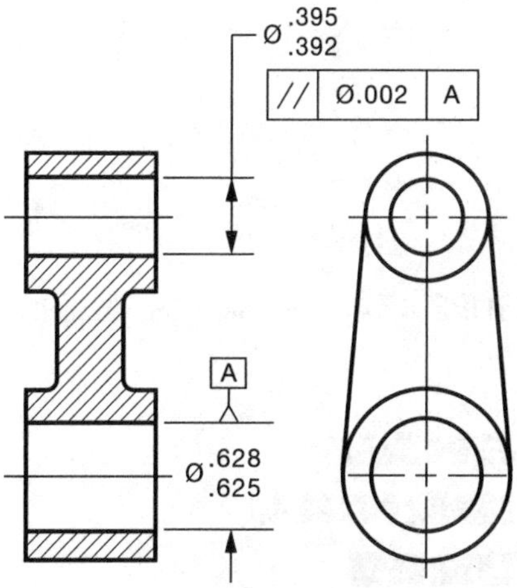

(A) DRAWING CALLOUT

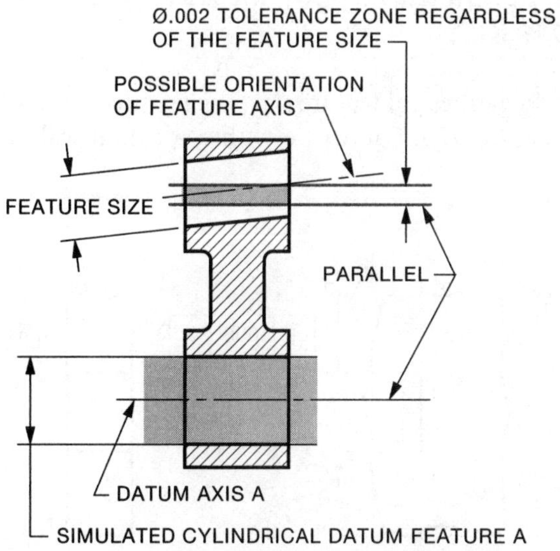

(B) TOLERANCE ZONE

FIGURE 47–10 ■ Specifying parallelism for an axis (both feature and datum feature RFS)

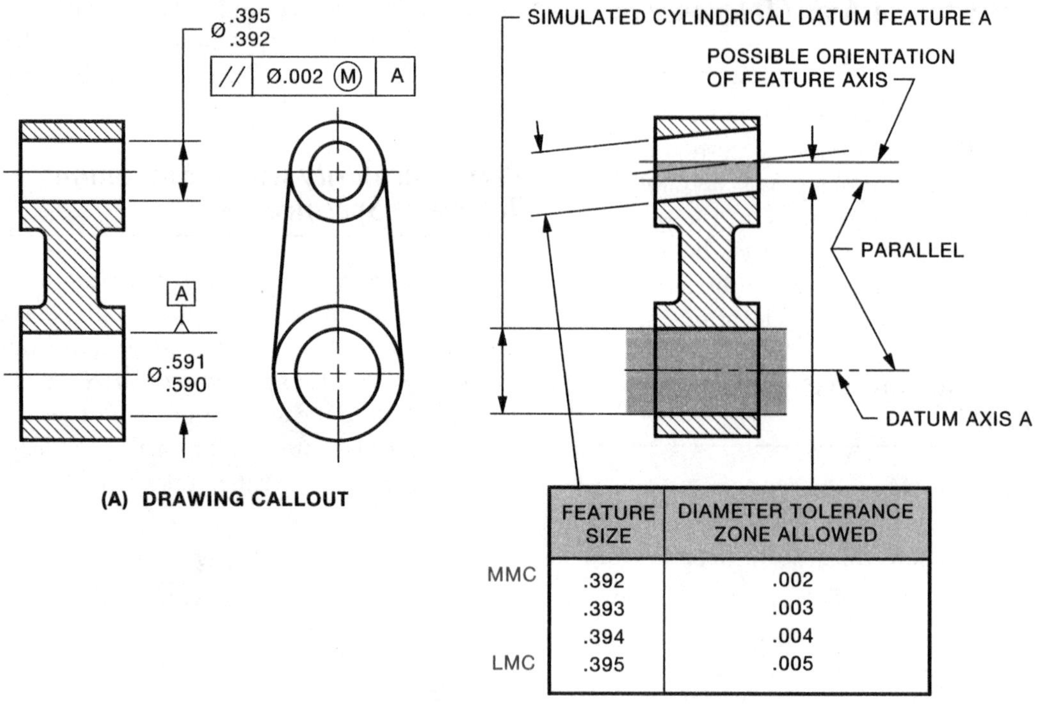
Ø .395
.392
// Ø.002 (M) A
A
Ø .591
.590
(A) DRAWING CALLOUT
SIMULATED CYLINDRICAL DATUM FEATURE A
POSSIBLE ORIENTATION
OF FEATURE AXIS
PARALLEL
DATUM AXIS A
MMC
LMC

	FEATURE SIZE	DIAMETER TOLERANCE ZONE ALLOWED
MMC	.392	.002
	.393	.003
	.394	.004
LMC	.395	.005

(B) TOLERANCE ZONE

FIGURE 47–11 ■ Specifying parallelism for an axis (feature at MMC and datum feature RFS)

EXTERNAL CYLINDRICAL FEATURES

Perpendicularity for an Axis (Pin or Boss RFS)

Regardless of feature size, the feature axis shown in Figure 47–17 must lie within a cylindrical zone (.001-in. diameter) that is perpendicular to and projects from datum plane A for the feature height. Additionally, the feature axis must be within any specified tolerance of location.

Perpendicularity for an Axis (Pin or Boss at MMC)

Where the feature shown in Figure 47–18 is at MMC (∅.625 in.), the maximum perpendicularity tolerance is .001-in. diameter. Where the feature

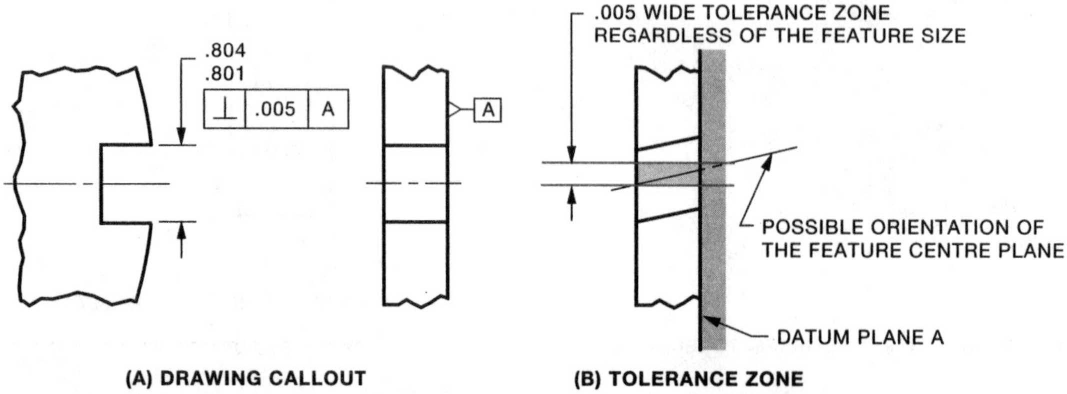
.804
.801
⊥ .005 A
A
.005 WIDE TOLERANCE ZONE
REGARDLESS OF THE FEATURE SIZE
POSSIBLE ORIENTATION OF
THE FEATURE CENTRE PLANE
DATUM PLANE A
(A) DRAWING CALLOUT
(B) TOLERANCE ZONE

FIGURE 47–12 ■ Specifying perpendicularity for a median plane (feature RFS)

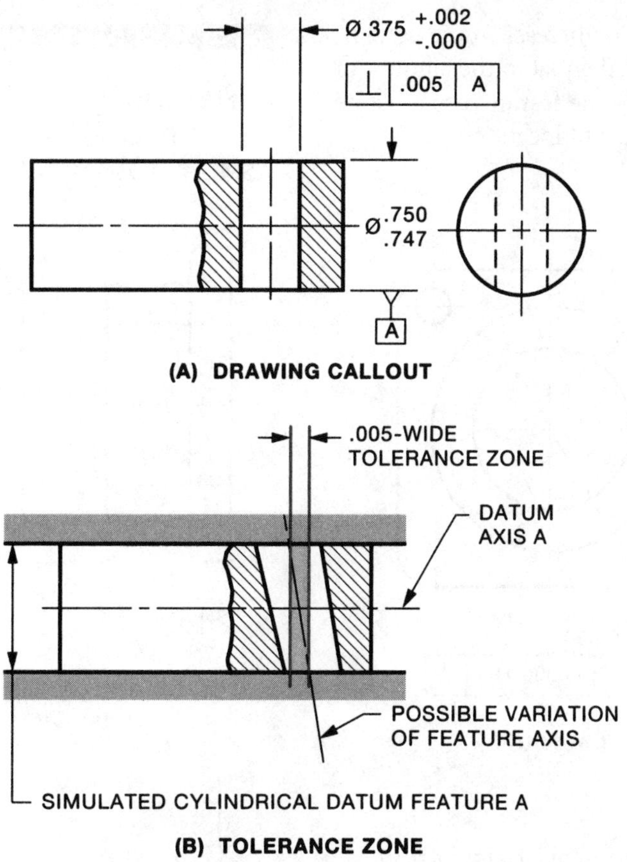
Ø.375 +.002 -.000
⊥ .005 A
Ø.750 .747
A
(A) DRAWING CALLOUT
.005-WIDE TOLERANCE ZONE
DATUM AXIS A
POSSIBLE VARIATION OF FEATURE AXIS
SIMULATED CYLINDRICAL DATUM FEATURE A
(B) TOLERANCE ZONE

FIGURE 47–13 ■ Specifying perpendicularity for an axis (both feature and datum feature SRFS)

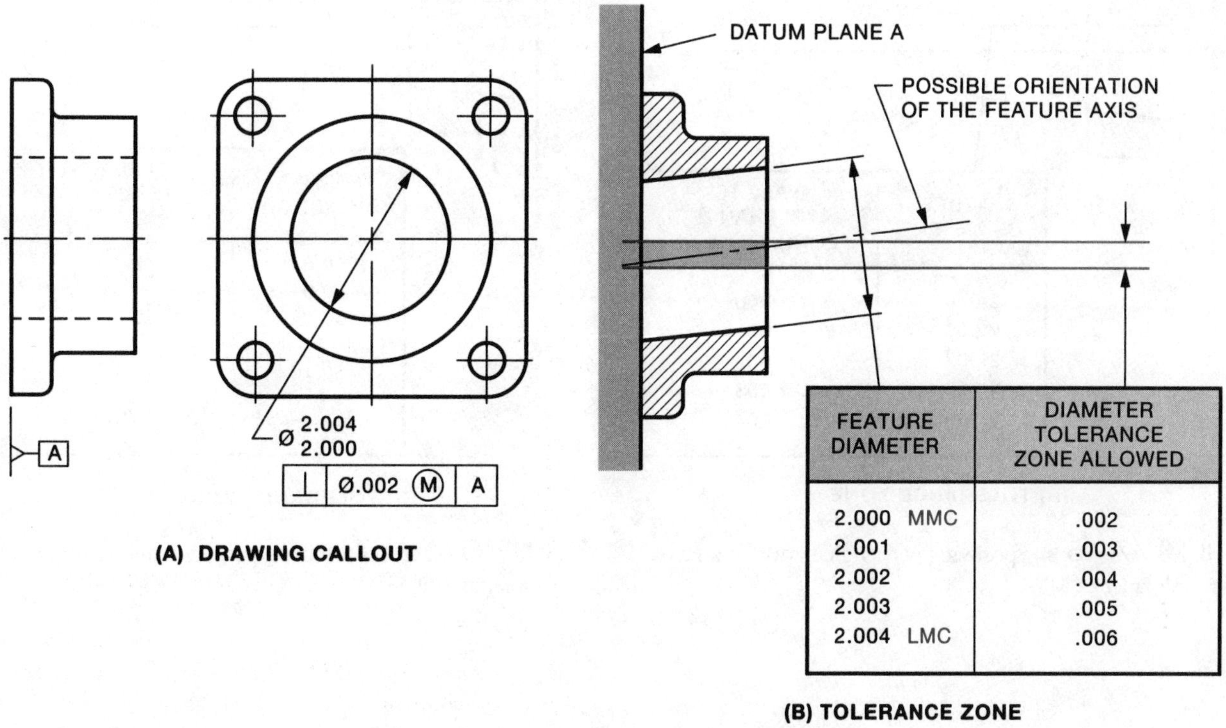
A
Ø 2.004 2.000
⊥ Ø.002 Ⓜ A
(A) DRAWING CALLOUT
DATUM PLANE A
POSSIBLE ORIENTATION OF THE FEATURE AXIS
(B) TOLERANCE ZONE

FEATURE DIAMETER	DIAMETER TOLERANCE ZONE ALLOWED
2.000 MMC	.002
2.001	.003
2.002	.004
2.003	.005
2.004 LMC	.006

FIGURE 47–14 ■ Specifying perpendicularity for an axis (tolerance at MMC)

departs from its MMC size, an increase in the perpendicularity tolerance is allowed equal to the amount of such departure. Additionally, the feature axis must be within any specified tolerance of location.

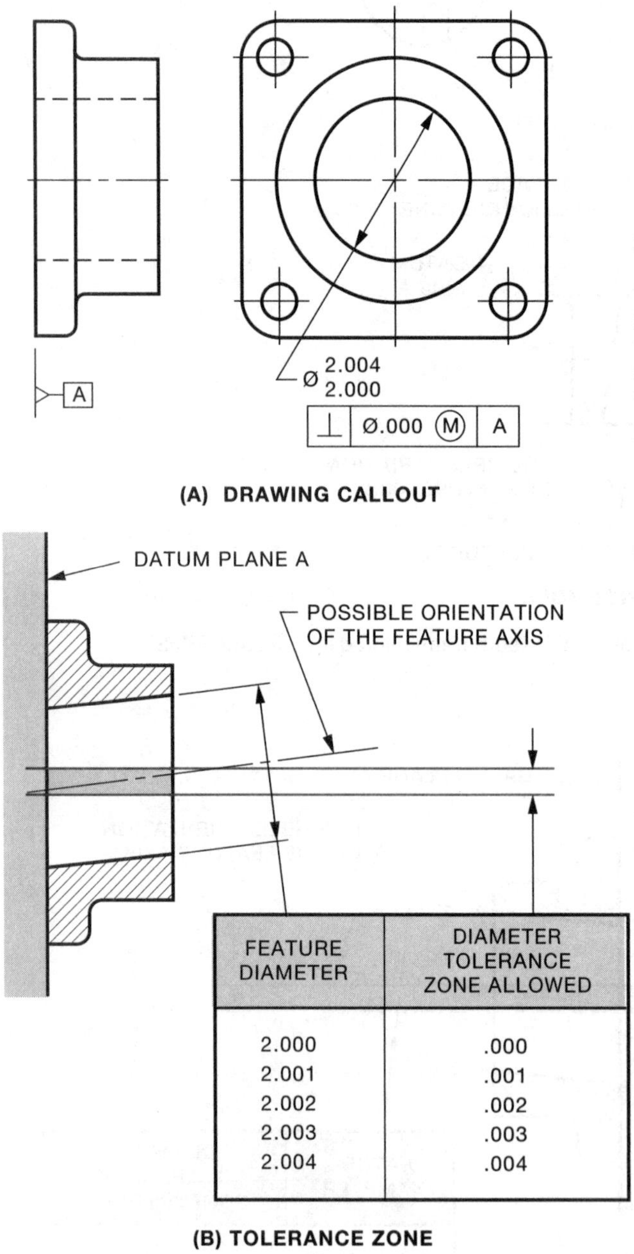
A
Ø 2.004
2.000
⊥ | Ø.000 Ⓜ | A
(A) DRAWING CALLOUT
DATUM PLANE A
POSSIBLE ORIENTATION
OF THE FEATURE AXIS
(B) TOLERANCE ZONE

FEATURE DIAMETER	DIAMETER TOLERANCE ZONE ALLOWED
2.000	.000
2.001	.001
2.002	.002
2.003	.003
2.004	.004

FIGURE 47–15 ■ Specifying perpendicularity for an axis (zero tolerance at MMC)

REFERENCES

CAN/CSA B78.2-M91 Dimensioning and Tolerancing of Technical Drawings

ASME Y14.5M-1994 Dimensioning and Tolerancing

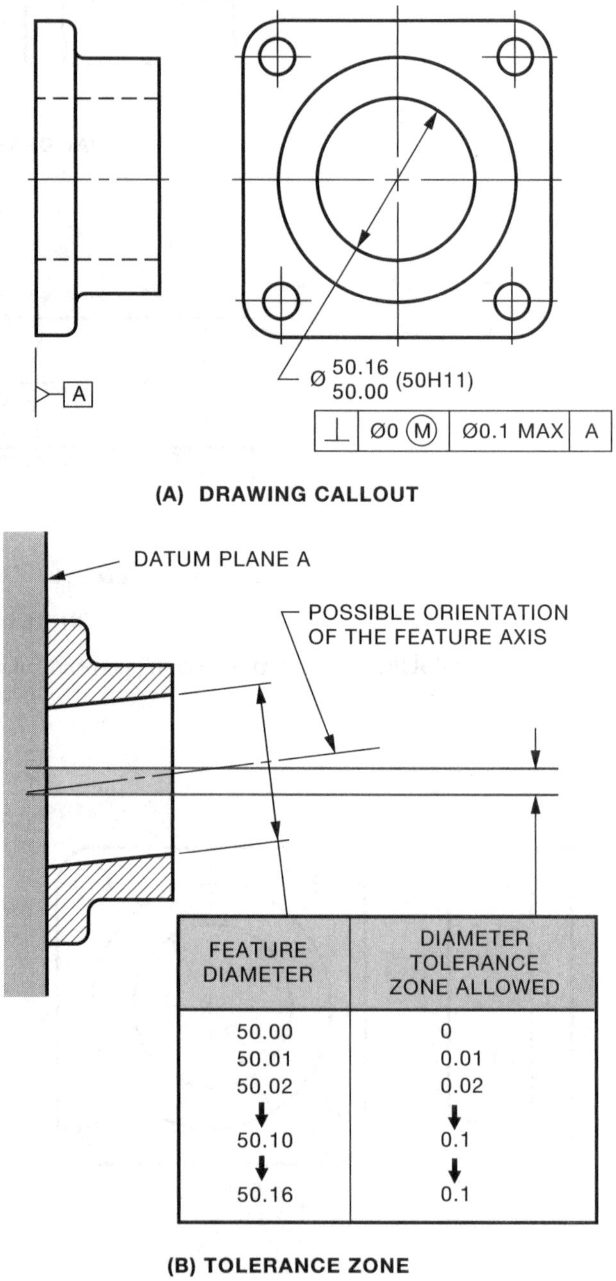
A
Ø 50.16
50.00 (50H11)
⊥ | Ø0 Ⓜ | Ø0.1 MAX | A
(A) DRAWING CALLOUT
DATUM PLANE A
POSSIBLE ORIENTATION
OF THE FEATURE AXIS
(B) TOLERANCE ZONE

FEATURE DIAMETER	DIAMETER TOLERANCE ZONE ALLOWED
50.00	0
50.01	0.01
50.02	0.02
↓	↓
50.10	0.1
↓	↓
50.16	0.1

FIGURE 47–16 ■ Specifying perpendicularity for an axis (zero tolerance at MMC with a maximum specified)

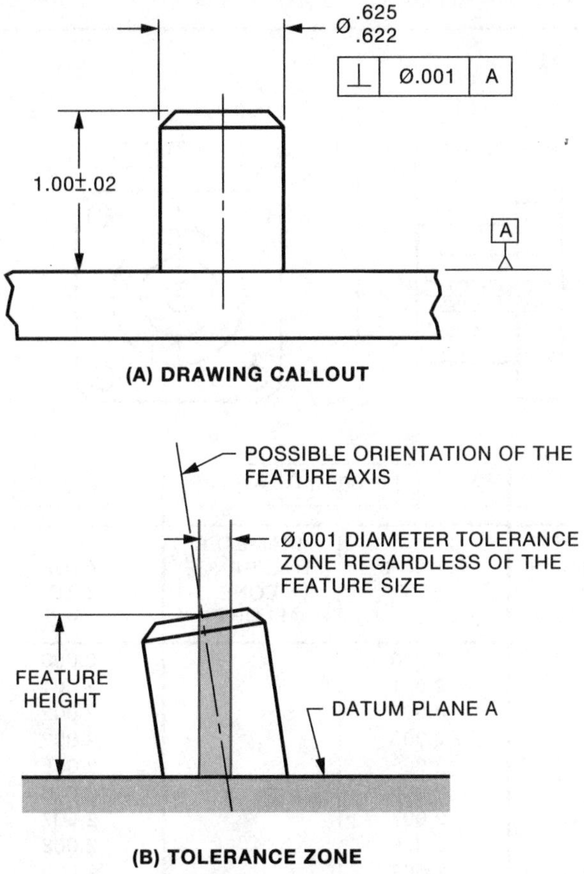

FIGURE 47–17 ■ Specifying perpendicularity for an axis (pin or boss RFS)

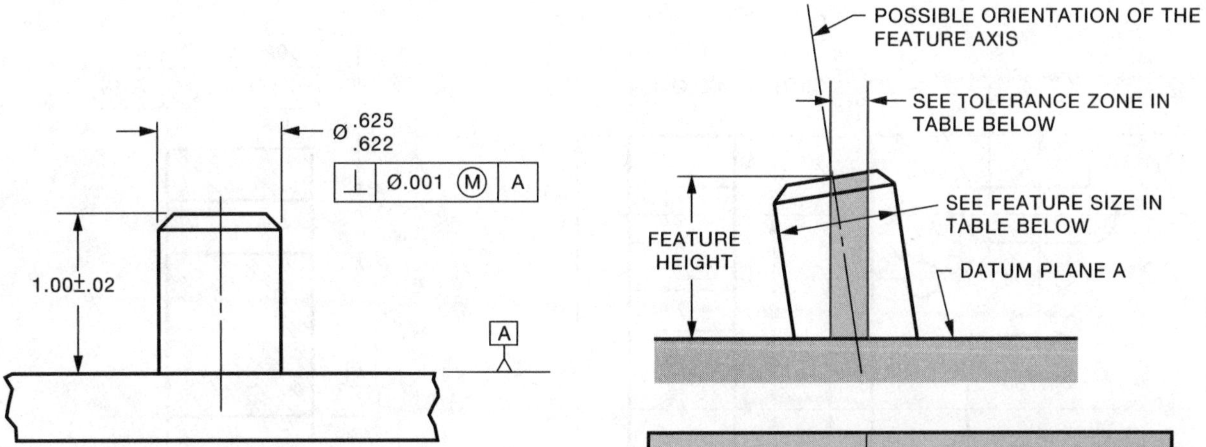

(A) DRAWING CALLOUT

FEATURE SIZE	DIAMETER TOLERANCE ZONE ALLOWED
MMC .625	.001
.624	.002
.623	.003
LMC .622	.004

(B) TOLERANCE ZONE

FIGURE 47–18 ■ Specifying perpendicularity for an axis (pin or boss at MMC)

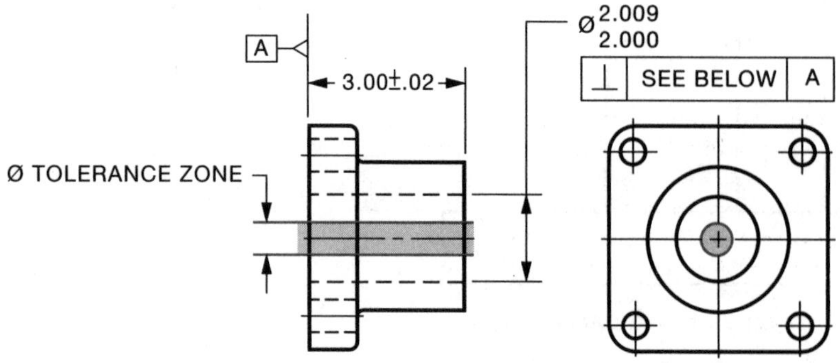

⊥ Ø.004 A		⊥ Ø.000 Ⓜ A		⊥ Ø.000 Ⓜ Ø.005 MAX A	
FEATURE SIZE Ø	DIAMETER TOLERANCE ZONE ALLOWED	FEATURE SIZE Ø	DIAMETER TOLERANCE ZONE ALLOWED	FEATURE SIZE Ø	DIAMETER TOLERANCE ZONE ALLOWED
2.000		2.000		2.000	
2.001		2.001		2.001	
2.002		2.002		2.002	
2.003		2.003		2.003	
2.005		2.005		2.005	
2.006		2.006		2.006	
2.007		2.007		2.007	
2.008		2.008		2.008	
2.009		2.009		2.009	

FIGURE 1

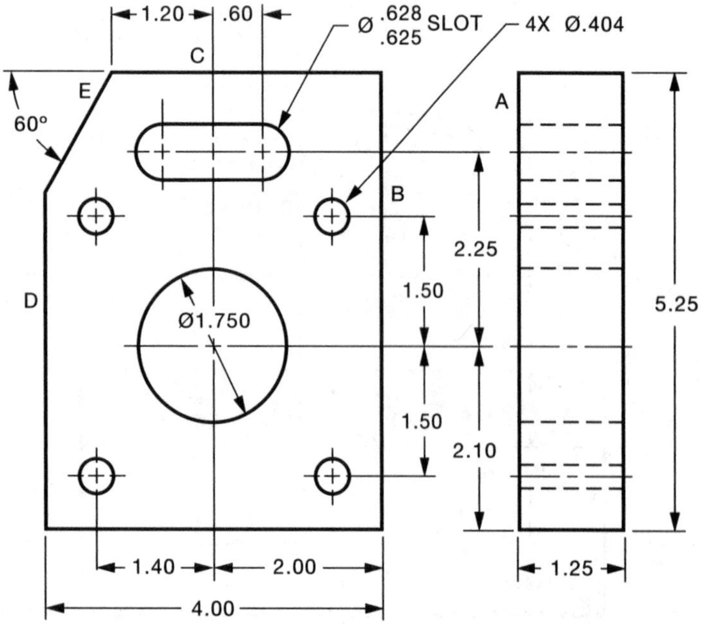

FIGURE 2

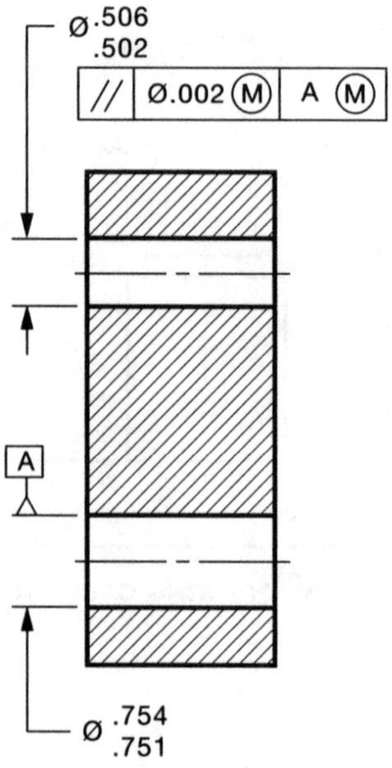

FIGURE 3

ASSIGNMENT:

1. Complete the tables shown in Figure 1 showing the maximum permissible tolerance zones for the three perpendicularity tolerances.

2. Add the following information to Figure 4: (refer to Figure 2)
   (A) Surfaces marked A, B, and C are datums A, B, and C, respectively.
   (B) Surface A is perpendicular to surfaces B and C within .01 in.
   (C) Surface D is parallel to surface B within .004 in.
   (D) The slot is parallel to surface C within .002 in. and perpendicular to surface A within .001 in. at MMC.
   (E) The Ø1.750 hole has an RC7 fit (show the size of the hole as limits) and is perpendicular to surface A within .002 in. at MMC.
   (F) Surface E has an angularity tolerance of .010 in. with surface C.
   (G) Surface A is to be flat within .002 in. for any one-inch-square surface with a maximum flatness tolerance of .005 in.
   (H) Indicate which dimensions are basic.

3. With reference to Figure 3, what is the maximum diameter of the tolerance zone allowed when the Ø.506 in. hole is at (A) MMC, (B) LMC, and (C) Ø.504 in?

4. If the symbol Ⓜ was removed from the tolerance shown in Figure 3, what maximum diameter of the tolerance zone is allowed when the hole is at (A) MMC, (B) LMC, and (C) Ø.504 in.?

ANSWERS

1. SEE FIGURE 1

2. SEE FIGURE 4

3. A ______
   B ______
   C ______

4. A ______
   B ______
   C ______

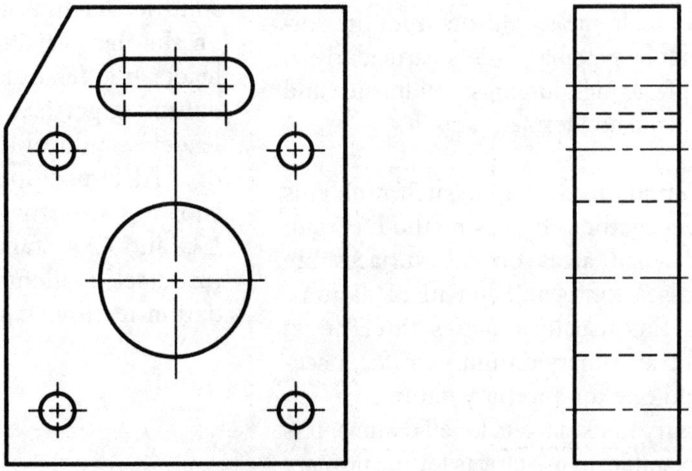

FIGURE 4

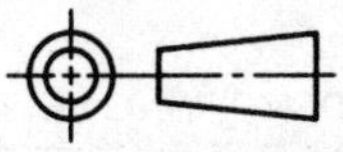

ORIENTATION TOLERANCING FOR FEATURES OF SIZE

A-107

48 UNIT

DATUM TARGETS

The full feature surface was used to establish a datum for the features so far designated as datum features. This may not always be practical for the following reasons:

1. The surface of a feature may be so large that a gauge designed to make contact with the full surface may be too expensive or too cumbersome to use.
2. Functional requirements of the part may necessitate the use of only a portion of a surface as a datum feature, for example, the portion that contacts a mating part in assembly.
3. A surface selected as a datum feature may not be sufficiently true and a flat datum feature may rock when placed on a datum plane, so that accurate and repeatable measurements from the surface would not be possible. This is particularly so for surfaces of castings, forgings, weldments, and some sheet-metal and formed parts.

A useful technique to overcome such problems is the datum-target method. In this method, certain points, lines, or small areas on the surfaces are selected as the bases for establishment of datums. For flat surfaces, this usually requires three target points or areas for a primary datum, two for a secondary datum, and one for a tertiary datum.

It is not necessary to use targets for all datums. It is quite logical, for example, to use targets for the primary datum and other surfaces or features for secondary and tertiary datums if required; or to use a flat surface of a part as the primary datum and to locate fixed points or lines on the edges as secondary and tertiary datums.

Datum targets should be spaced as far apart from each other as possible to provide maximum stability for making measurements. Dimensions locating target areas are basic and are shown enclosed in a rectangular frame.

DATUM-TARGET SYMBOL

Points, lines, and areas on datum features are designated on the drawing by means of a datum-target symbol, Figure 48–1. The symbol is placed outside the part outline with a leader directed to the target point (indicated by an "X"), target line, or target area, as applicable. ISO and CSA standards use an arrow at the end of this leader. ASME does not show this arrow. See Figure 48–2. The use of a solid leader line indicates that the datum target is on the near (visible) surface. The use of a dashed leader line (as in Figure 48–10B) indicates that the datum target is on the far (hidden) surface. The leader should not be shown in either a horizontal or vertical position. ASME drawing standards omit showing an arrow at the end of this leader, while ISO and CSA standards show one. The datum feature itself is identified in the usual manner with a datum-feature symbol.

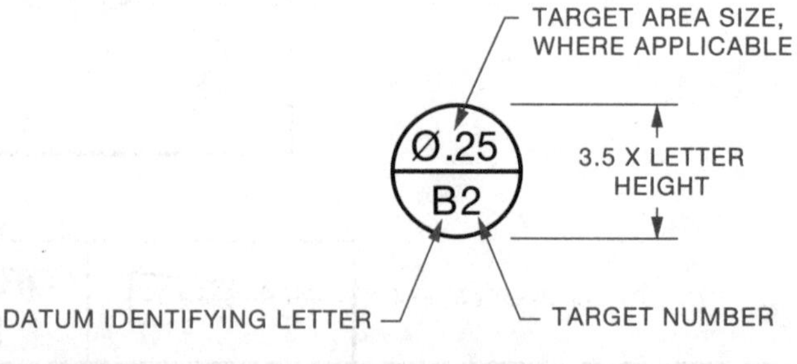

FIGURE 48–1 ■ Datum-target symbol

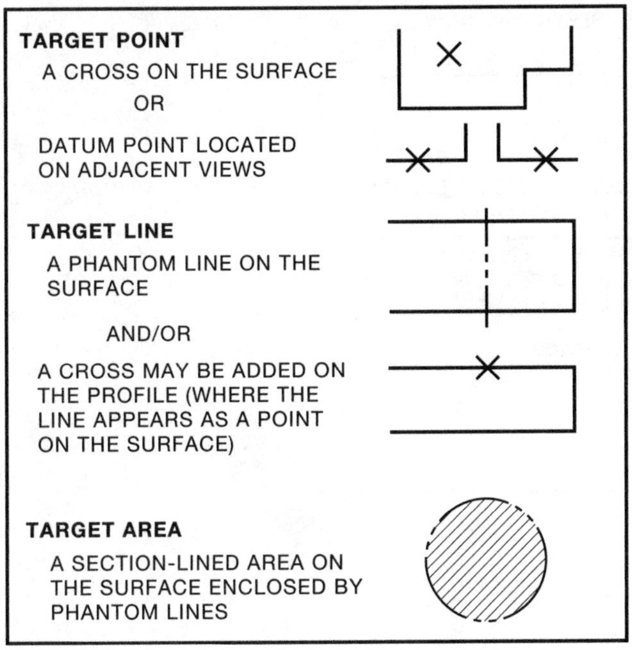

FIGURE 48–2 ■ Identification of datum targets

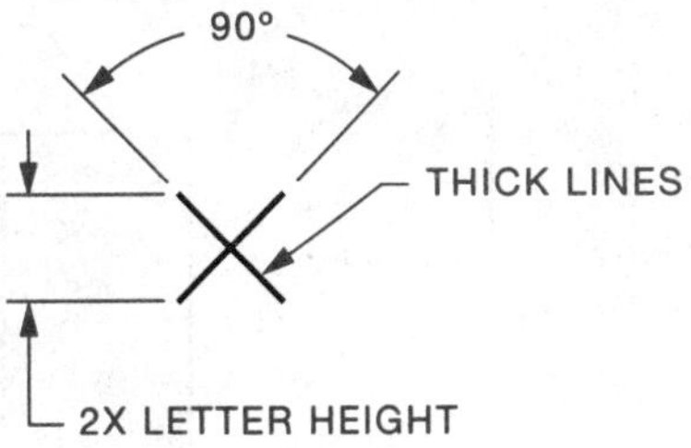

FIGURE 48–3 ■ Symbol for a datum-target point

The datum-target symbol is a circle having a diameter approximately 3.5 times the height of the lettering used on the drawing. The circle is divided horizontally into two halves. The lower half contains a letter identifying the associated datum, followed by the target number assigned sequentially starting with 1 for each datum. For example, in a three-plane, six-point datum system, if the datums are A, B, and C, the datums would be A1, A2, A3, B1, B2, and C1 (see Figure 48–14). Where the datum target is an area, the area size may be entered in the upper half of the symbol; otherwise, the upper half is left blank.

Identification of Targets

Datum-Target Points

Each target point is shown on the surface, in its desired location, by means of a cross drawn at approximately 45° to the coordinate dimensions. The cross is twice the height of the lettering used, Figures 48–3 and 48–4(A). When the view that would show the location of the datum-target point is not drawn, its point location is dimensioned on the two adjacent views, Figure 48–4(B).

Target points may be represented on tools, fixtures, and gauges by spherically ended pins, Figure 48–5.

Datum-Target Lines

A datum-target line is indicated by the symbol X on an edge view of a surface, a phantom line on the direct view, or both, Figure 48–6. When the length of the datum-target line must be controlled, its length and location are dimensioned.

Datum-target lines can be represented in tooling and gauging by the side of a round pin, Figure 48–7.

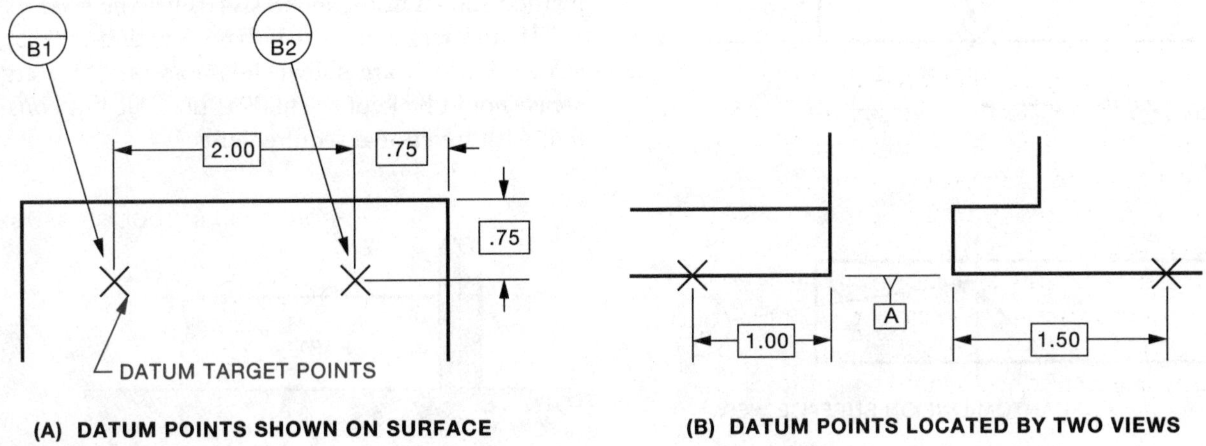

FIGURE 48–4 ■ Datum target points

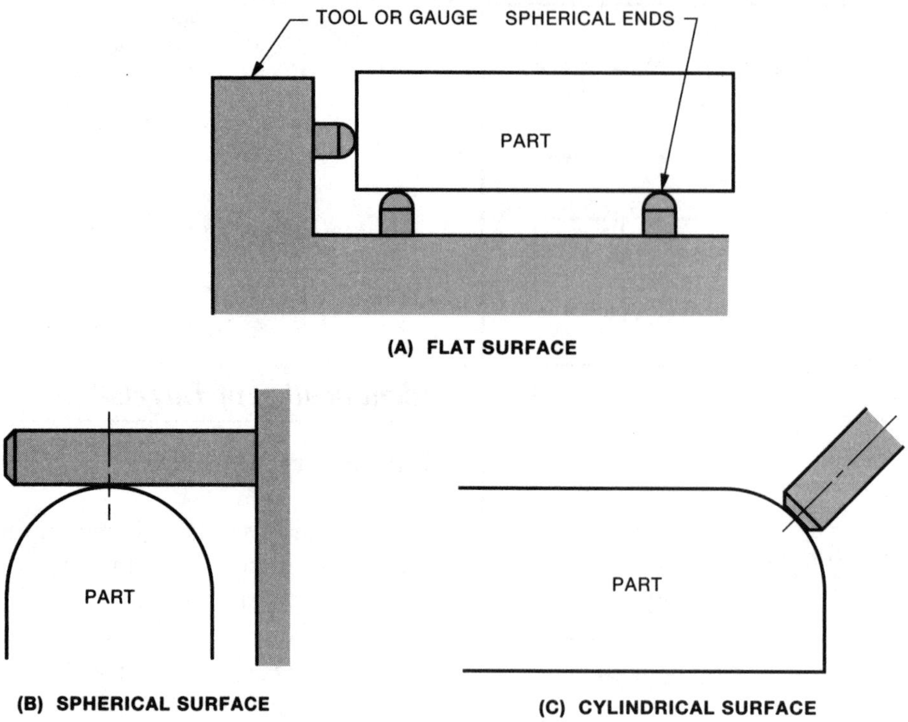

FIGURE 48–5 ■ Location of part on datum-target points

It should be noted that if a line is designated as a tertiary datum feature, it will touch the gauge pin theoretically at only one point. If it is a secondary datum feature, it will touch at two points.

The application and use of a surface and three lines as datum features are shown in Figures 48–8 and 48–9.

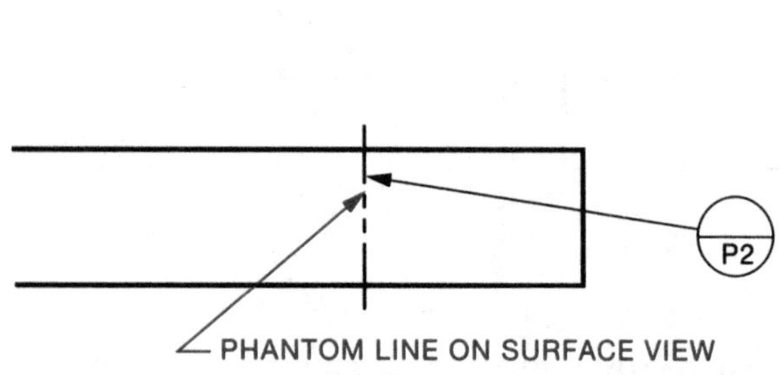

FIGURE 48–6 ■ Datum-target line

Datum-Target Areas

Where it is determined that an area or areas of flat contact are necessary to ensure establishment of the datum (that is, where spherical or pointed pins would be inadequate), a target area of the desired shape is specified. The datum-target area is indicated by section lines inside a phantom outline of the desired shape, with controlling dimensions added. The diameter of circular areas is given in the upper half of the datum-target symbol, Figure 48–10(A). Where a circular target area is too small to be drawn to scale, the method shown in Figure 48–10(B) may be used.

Datum-target areas may have any desired shape, a few of which are shown in Figure 48–11. Target areas should be kept as small as possible but consistent with functional requirements.

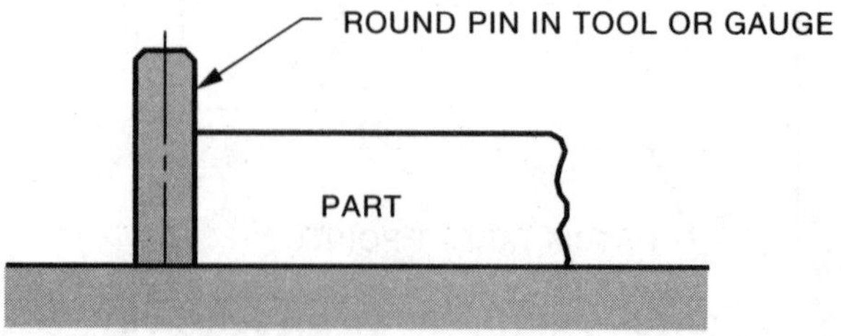

FIGURE 48–7 ■ Locating a datum line

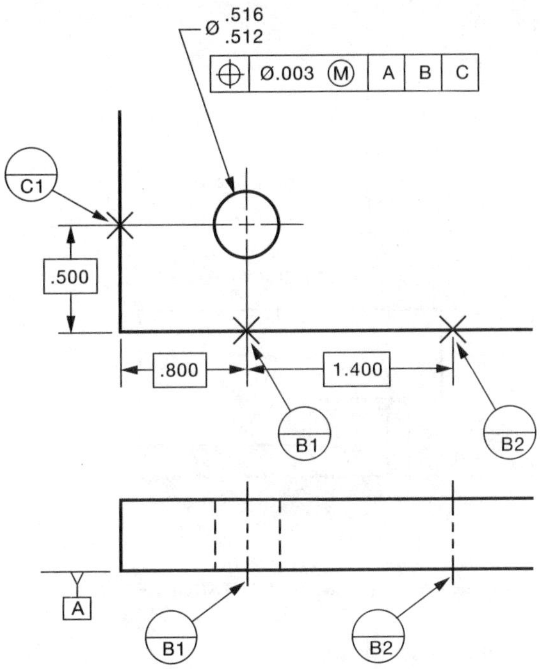

FIGURE 48–8 ■ Part with a surface and three target lines used as datum features

Targets Not in the Same Plane

In most applications, datum target points that form a single datum are all located on the same surface (as shown in Figure 48–4(A). However, this is not essential. They may be located on different surfaces to meet functional requirements, Figure 48–12.

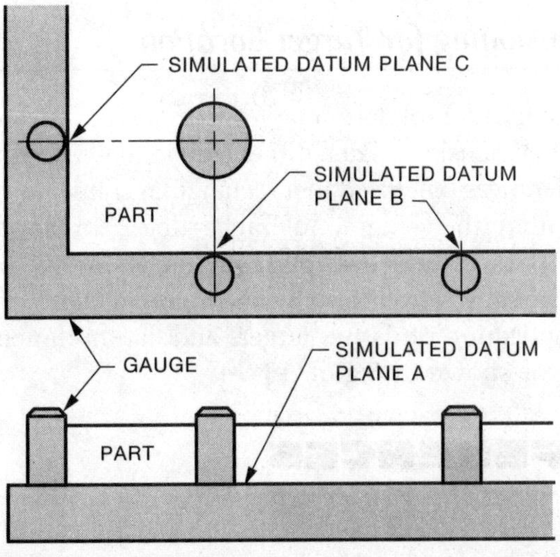

FIGURE 48–9 ■ Location of part in Figure 48–8 in a gauge

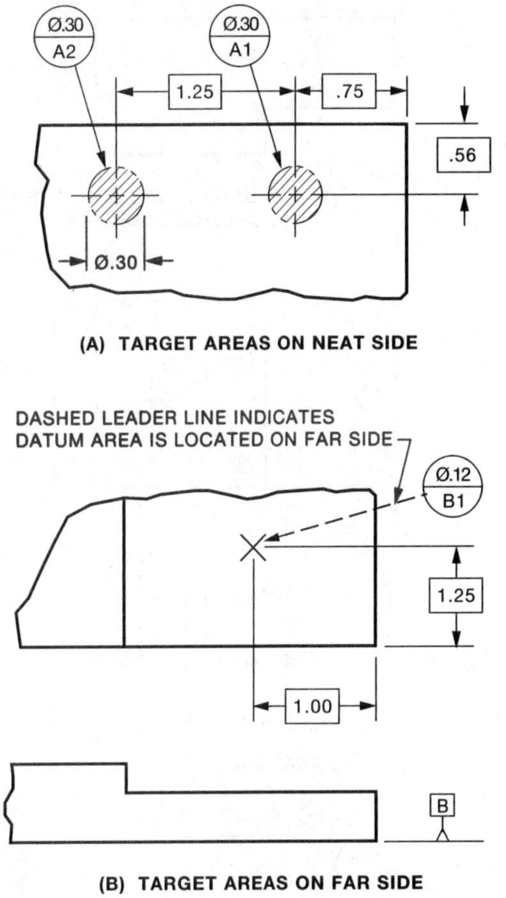

FIGURE 48–10 ■ Datum-target areas

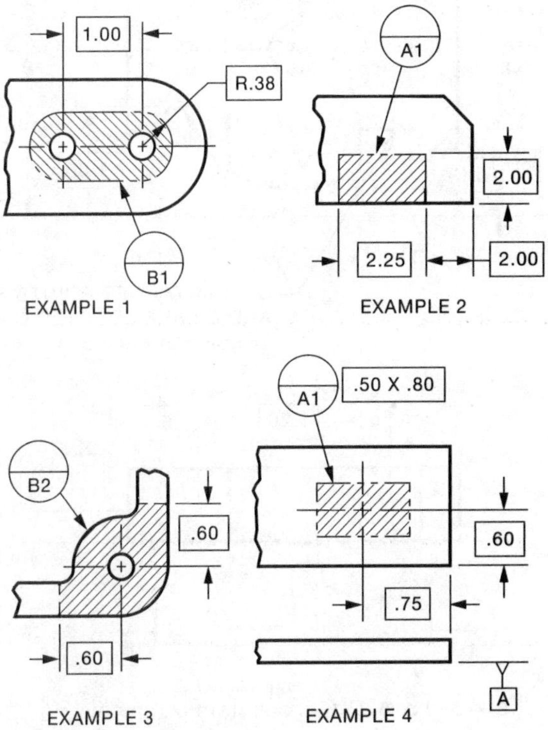

FIGURE 48–11 ■ Typical target areas

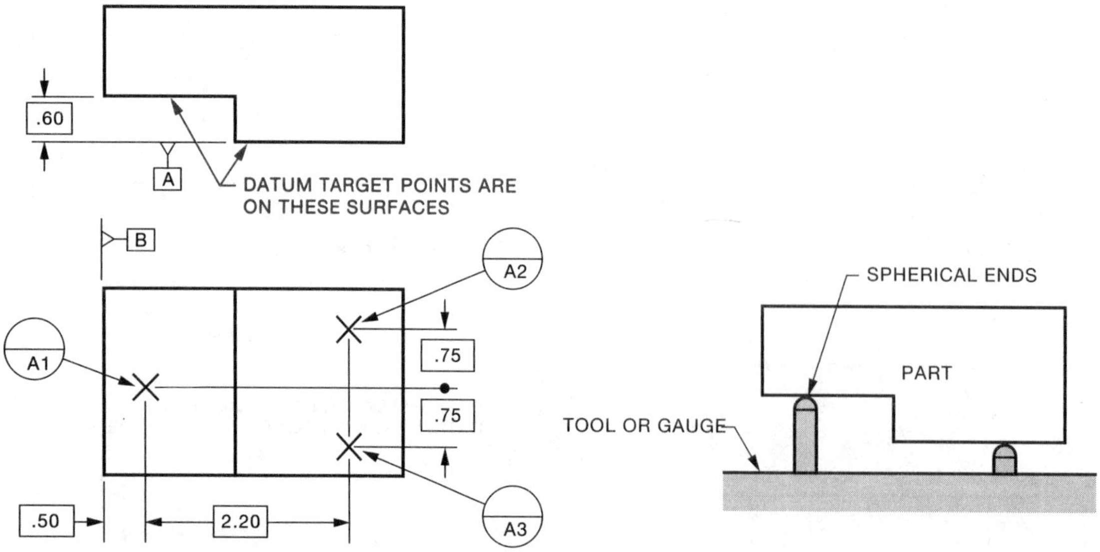

(A) DRAWING CALLOUT

(B) LOCATION OF PART ON DATUM-TARGET POINTS

FIGURE 48–12 ■ Datum-target points on different planes used as the primary datum

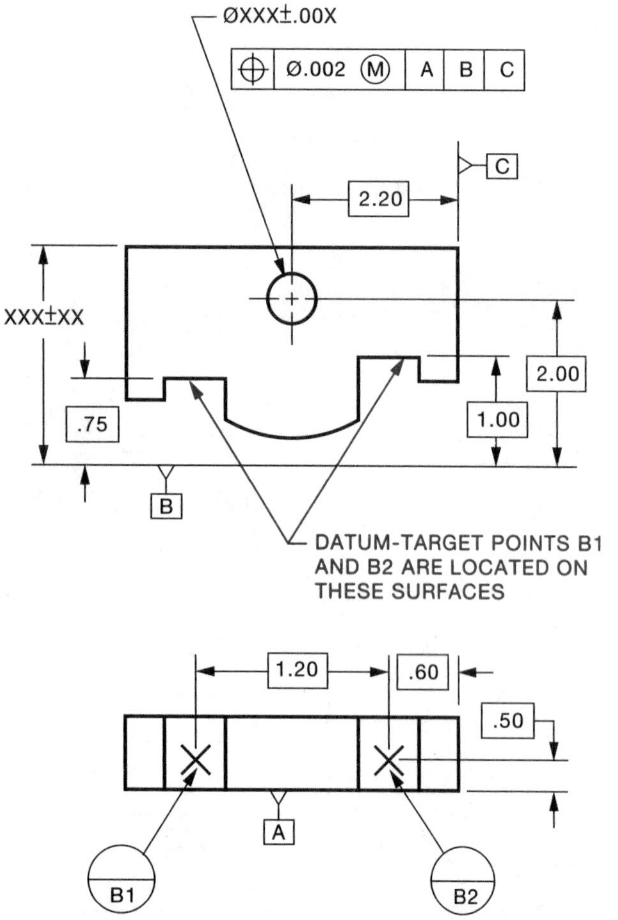

FIGURE 48–13 ■ Datum outside of part profile

In some cases, the datum plane may be located in space, not actually touching the part, Figure 48–13. In such applications, the controlled features must be dimensioned from the specified datum, and the position of the datum from the datum targets must be shown by means of exact datum dimensions. For example, in Figure 48–13, datum B is positioned by means of datum dimensions .75 in., 1.00 in., and 2.00 in. The top surface is controlled from this datum by means of a toleranced dimension. The hole is positioned by means of the basic dimension 2.00 in. and a positional tolerance.

Dimensioning for Target Location

The location of datum targets is shown by means of basic dimensions. Each dimension is shown, without tolerances, enclosed in a rectangular frame, indicating that the general tolerance does not apply. Dimensions locating a set of datum targets should be dimensionally related or have a common origin.

Application of datum targets and datum dimensioning is shown in Figure 48–14.

REFERENCES

CAN/CSA-B78.2-M91 Dimensioning and Tolerancing of Technical Drawings
ASME Y14.5M-1994 Dimensioning and Tolerancing

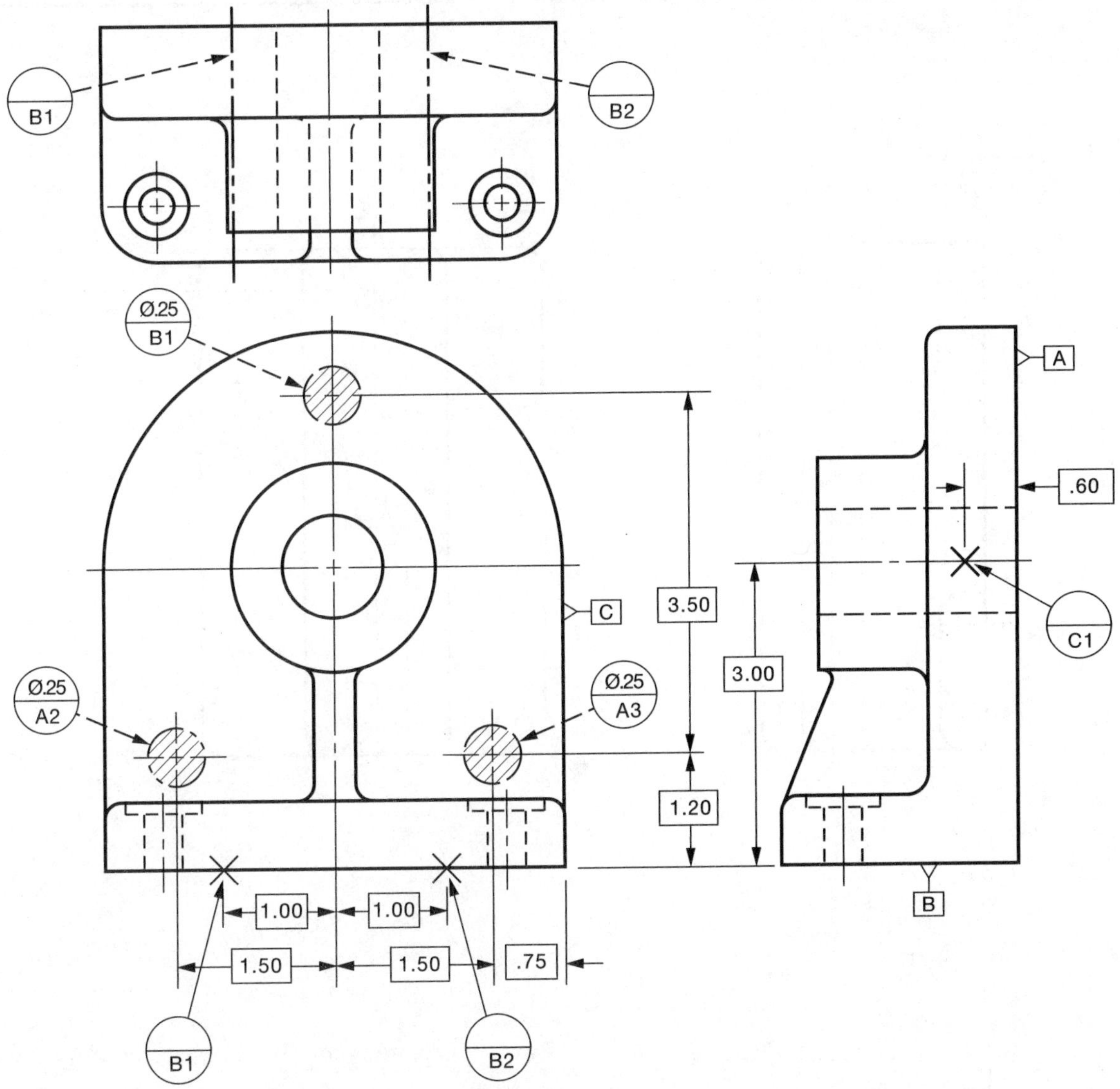

FIGURE 48–14 ■ Application of datum targets and dimensioning

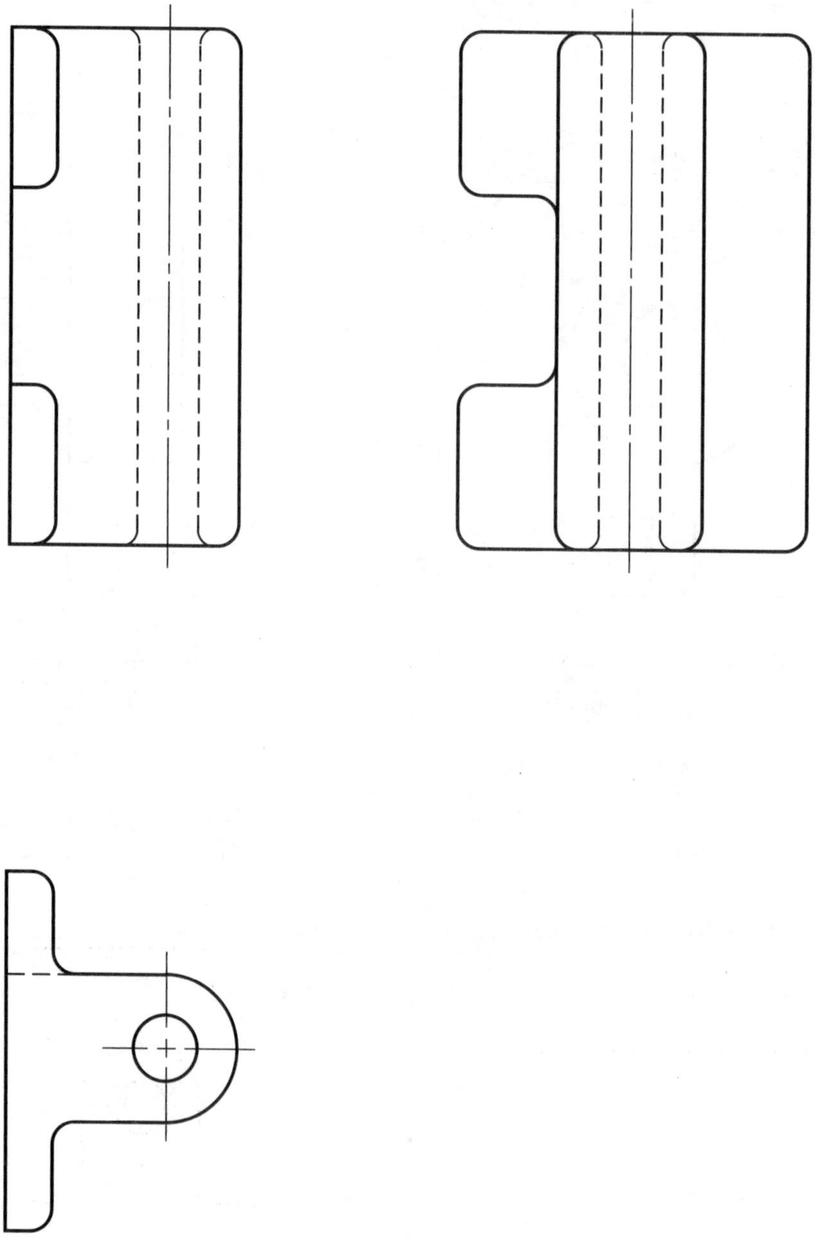

FIGURE 1

ANSWERS

1. A ____________
   B ____________
   C ____________
2. ____________
3. ____________
4. ____________
5. ____________
6. ____________
   ____
   ____
   ____
7. ____________
8. ____________

ASSIGNMENT:

From the information shown in Figure 2, show on Figure 1 the datum features and only the dimensions related to the datums.

QUESTIONS

1. What are the three types of datum targets?
2. What type of dimensions are used to locate datum targets?
3. What is the minimum number of contact points for a primary datum?
4. What is the minimum number of contact points for a tertiary datum?
5. What type of leader line is used to indicate that the datum target is on the far (hidden) surface?
6. What information is contained in the lower half of the datum-target symbol?
7. How is a target point identified on a drawing?
8. How is a datum-target line identified on the edge view of a surface?

DATUM AND LOCATION				
DATUM DESCRIPTION		LOCATION FROM		
		PRIMARY DATUM PLANE	SECONDARY DATUM PLANE	TERTIARY DATUM PLANE
DATUM A TARGET AREAS Ø.30	A1		.40	.50
	A2		.40	5.90
	A3		4.00	3.20
DATUM B TARGET LINES	B1			1.00
	B2			5.40
DATUM C TARGET POINT	C1	1.00	1.80	

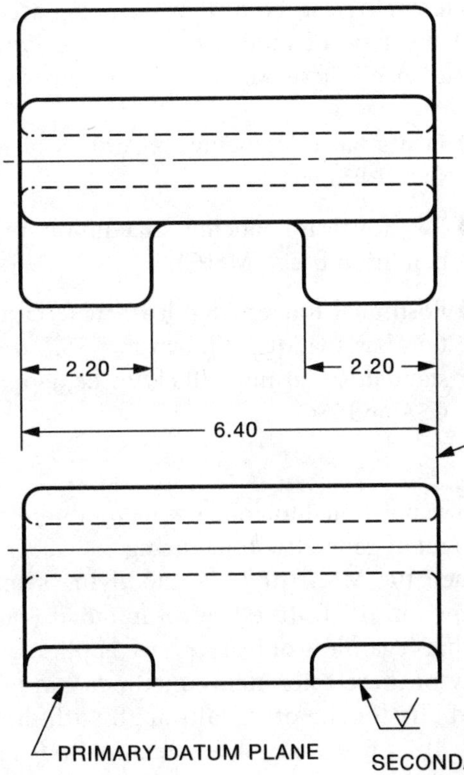
2.20
2.20
6.40
TERTIARY DATUM PLANE
PRIMARY DATUM PLANE
SECONDARY DATUM PLANE

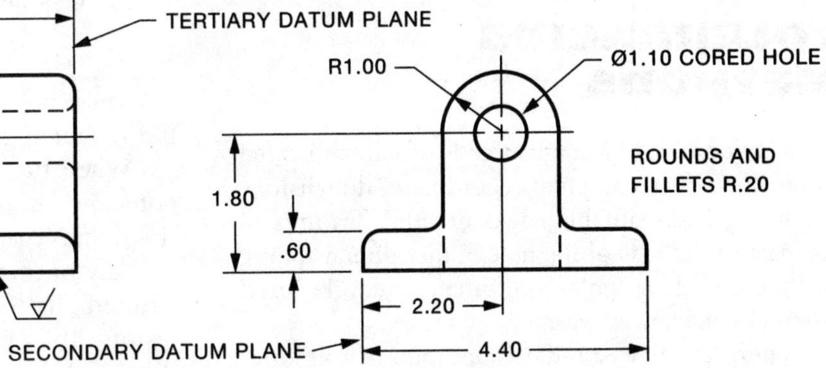
R1.00
Ø1.10 CORED HOLE
ROUNDS AND FILLETS R.20
1.80
.60
2.20
4.40

FIGURE 2

	BEARING HOUSING	**A-108**

49 UNIT

TOLERANCING OF FEATURES BY POSITION

The location of features is one of the most frequently used applications of dimensions on technical drawings. Tolerancing may be accomplished either by coordinate tolerances applied to the dimensions or by geometric (positional) tolerancing.

Positional tolerancing is especially useful when applied on an MMC basis to groups or patterns of holes or other small features in the mass production of parts. This method meets functional requirements in most cases and permits assessment with simple gauging procedures.

Most units in this section are devoted to the principles involved in the location of small round holes, because they represent the most commonly used applications.

TOLERANCING METHODS

The location of a single hole is usually indicated by means of rectangular coordinate dimensions extending from suitable edges or other features of the part to the axis of the hole. Other dimensioning methods, such as polar coordinates, may be used when circumstances warrant.

There are two standard methods of tolerancing the location of holes: coordinate and positional tolerancing.

1. Coordinate tolerancing, Figure 49–1(A), refers to tolerances applied directly to the coordinate dimensions or to applicable tolerances specified in a general tolerance note.
2. Positional tolerancing, Figures 49–1(B) to 49–1(D), refers to a tolerance zone within which the centre line of the hole or shaft is permitted to vary from its true position. Positional tolerancing can be further classified according to the type of modifying associated with the tolerance. These are

- Positional tolerancing, regardless of feature size (RFS).
- Positional tolerancing, maximum material condition basis (MMC).
- Positional tolerancing, least material condition basis (LMC). Shown in ASME drawing standards and most likely to be adopted by CSA and ISO.

These positional tolerancing methods are part of the system of geometric tolerancing.

When the MMC or LMC modifying symbol is not shown in the feature control frame, it is understood that regardless of feature, size applies.

Any of these tolerancing methods can be substituted one for the other, although with differing results. It is necessary, however, to first analyze the widely used method of coordinate tolerancing in order to then explain and understand the advantages and disadvantages of the positional tolerancing methods.

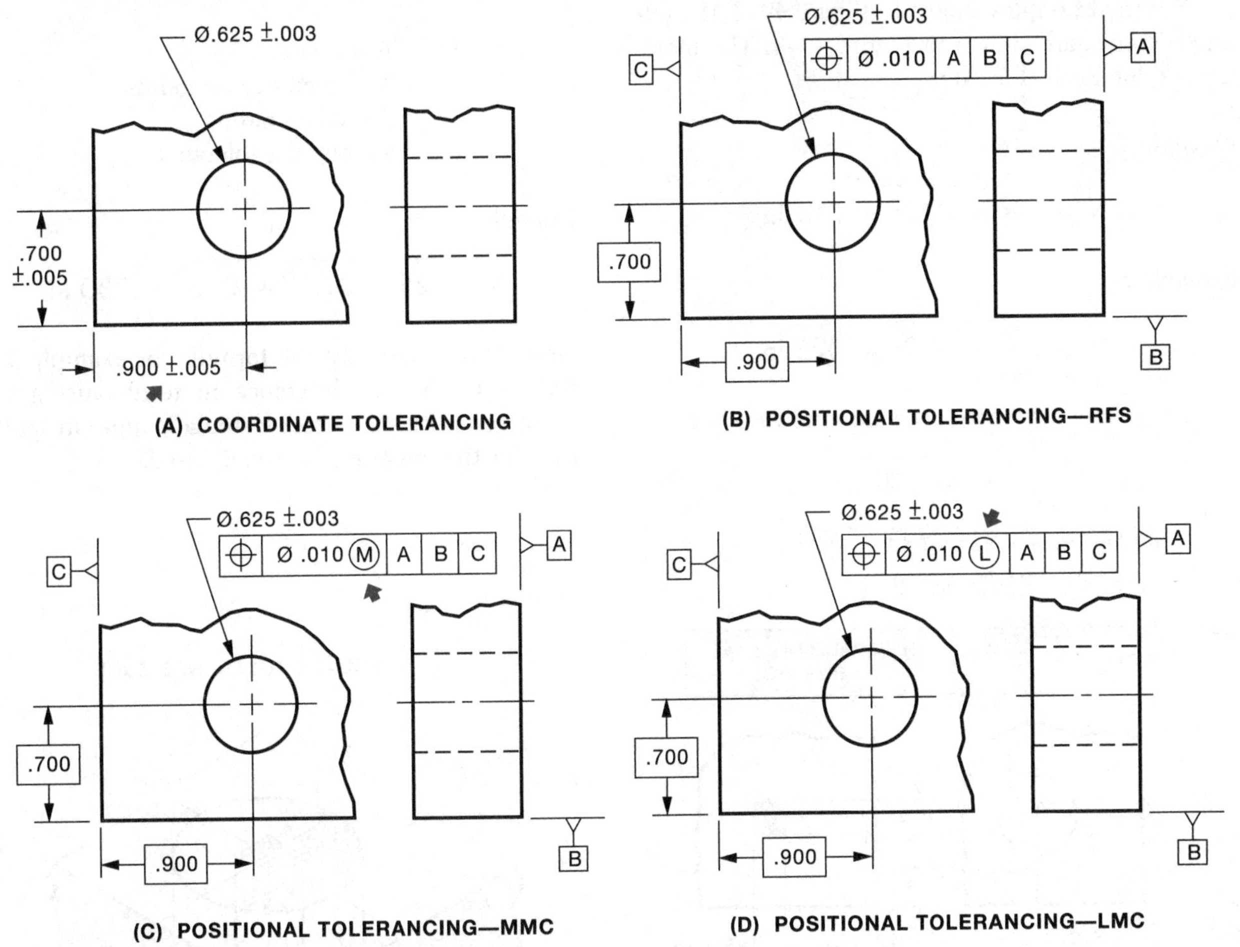

FIGURE 49–1 ■ Comparison of tolerancing methods

COORDINATE TOLERANCING

Coordinate dimensions and tolerances may be applied to the location of a single hole, Figure 49–2. They indicate the location of the hole axis and result in a rectangular or wedge-shaped tolerance zone within which the axis of the hole must lie.

If the two coordinate tolerances are equal, the tolerance zone formed will be a square. Unequal tolerances result in a rectangular tolerance zone. Polar dimensioning, in which one of the locating dimensions is a radius, gives an annual segment tolerance zone. For simplicity, square tolerance zones are used in the analysis of most of the examples in this section.

It should be noted that the tolerance zone extends for the full depth of the hole; that is, the whole length of the axis. This is illustrated in Figure 49–3. In most of the illustrations, tolerances will be analyzed as they apply at the surface of the part, where the axis is represented by a point.

Maximum Permissible Error

The actual position of the feature axis may be anywhere within the rectangular tolerance zone. For square tolerance zones, the maximum allowable variation from the desired position occurs in a direction of 45° from the direction of the coordinate dimensions, Figure 49–4.

For rectangular tolerance zones, this maximum tolerance is the square root of the sum of the squares of the individual tolerances. This is expressed mathematically as

$$\sqrt{X^2 + Y^2}$$

For the examples shown in Figure 49–2, the tolerance zones are shown in Figure 49–5. The maximum tolerance values are

Example 1

$$\sqrt{.010^2 + .010^2} = .014 \text{ in.}$$

Example 2

$$\sqrt{.010^2 + .020^2} = .022 \text{ in.}$$

For polar coordinates, the extreme variation is

$$\sqrt{A^2 + T^2}$$

Where: $A = R \tan a$
T = tolerance on radius
R = mean radius
a = angular tolerance

Example 3

$$\sqrt{(1.25 \times .017)^2 + .020^2} = .030 \text{ in.}$$

Note: Mathematically, the formula for example 3 is incorrect, but the difference in results using the more complicated correct formula is quite insignificant for the tolerances normally used.

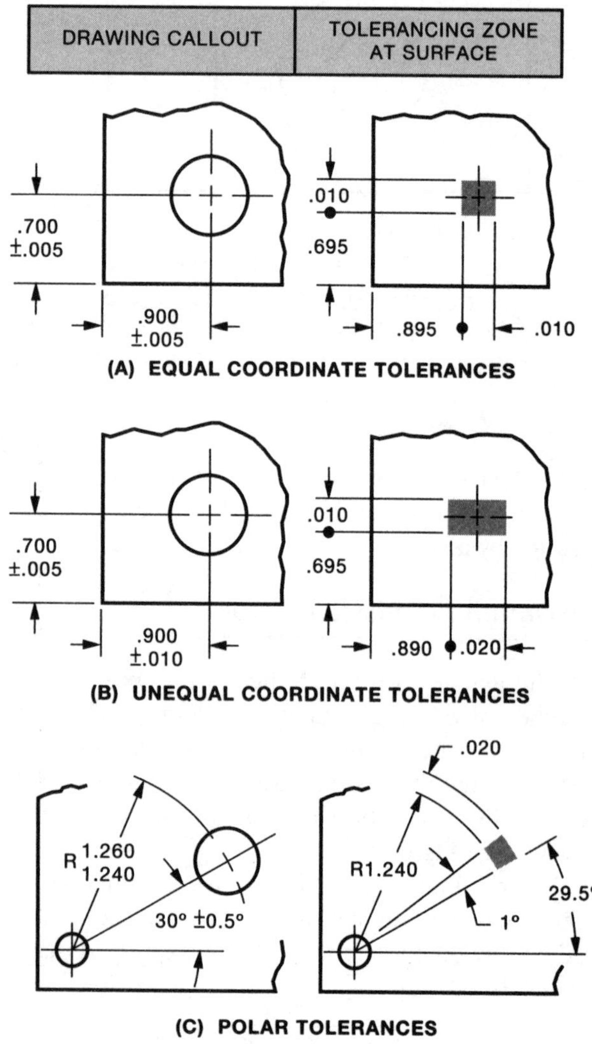

FIGURE 49–2 ■ Tolerance zones for coordinate tolerances

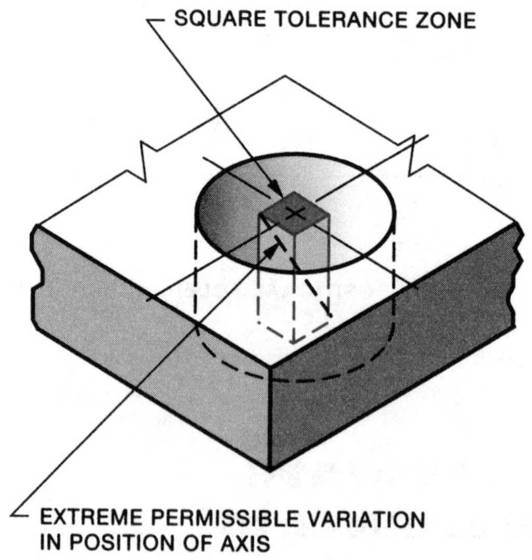

FIGURE 49–3 ■ Tolerance zone extending a part

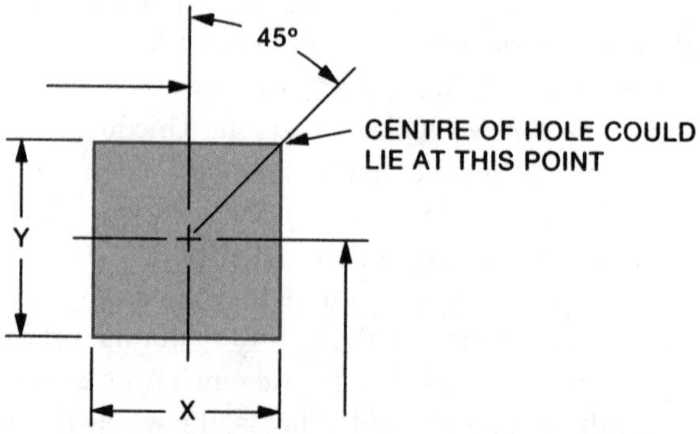

FIGURE 49–4 ■ Maximum permissible error for square tolerance zone

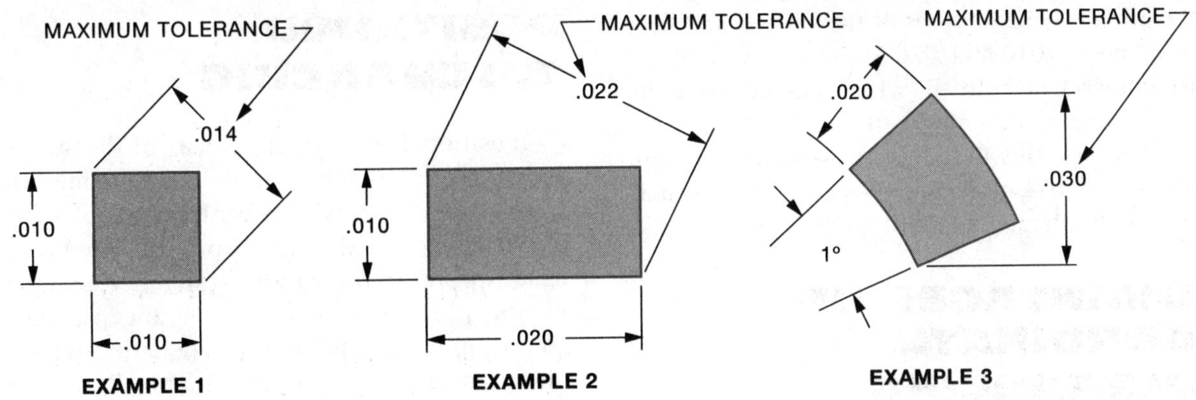

FIGURE 49–5 ■ Tolerance zones for examples shown in Figure 49–2

Some values of tan A for commonly used angular tolerances are as follows.

A	Tan a	A	Tan a	A	Tan a
0° 5′	.00145	0° 25′	.00727	0° 45′	.01309
0° 10′	.00291	0° 30′	.00873	0° 50′	.01454
0° 15′	.00436	0° 35′	.01018	0° 55′	.01600
0° 20′	.00582	0° 40′	.01164	1° 0′	.01745

Use of Chart

A quick and easy method of finding the maximum positional error permitted with coordinate tolerancing without having to calculate squares and square roots is to use a chart like that shown in Figure 49–6.

In the first example shown in Figure 49–2, the tolerance in both directions is .010 in. The extensions of the horizontal and vertical lines of .010 in the chart intersect at point A, which lies between the radii of .014 and .015 in. When rounded to three decimal places, this indicates a maximum permissible variation from true position of .014 in.

In the second example shown in Figure 49–2, the tolerances are .010 in. in one direction and .020 in.

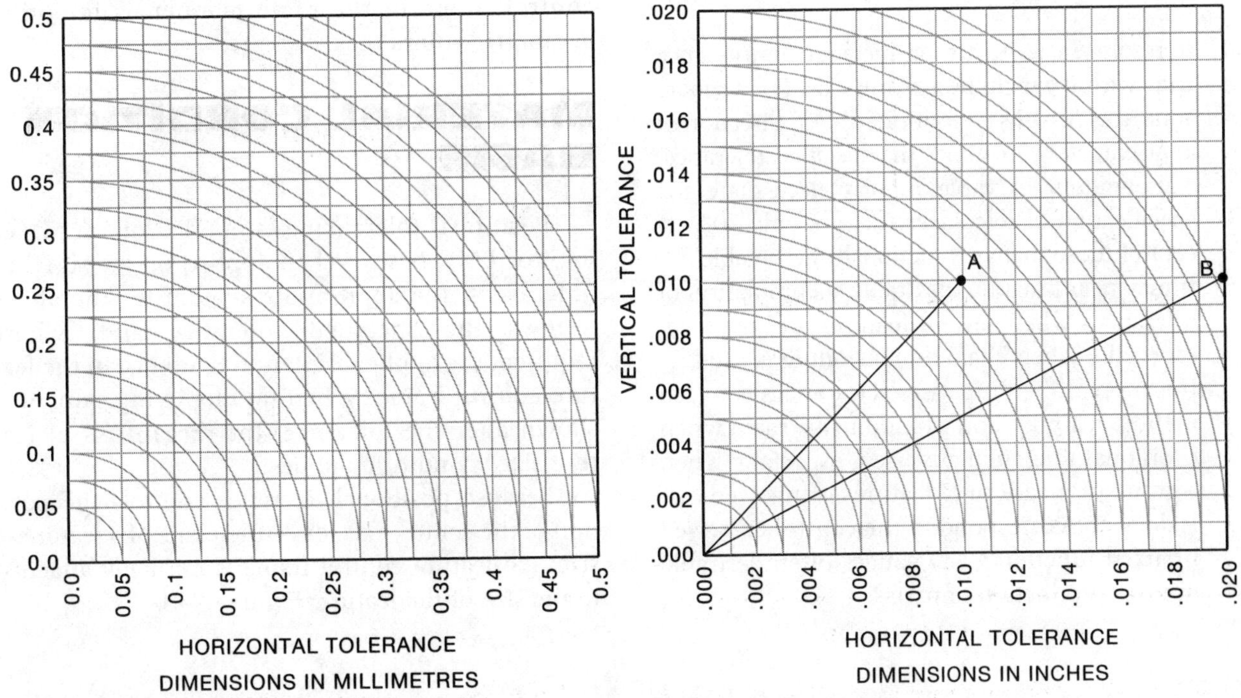

FIGURE 49–6 ■ Charts for calculating maximum tolerance using coordinate tolerancing

in the other. The extensions of the vertical and horizontal lines at .010 and .020 in., respectively, in the chart intersect at point B, which lies between the radii of .022 and .023 in. When rounded off to three decimal places, this indicates a maximum variation of position of .022 in. Figure 49–6 also shows a chart for use with tolerances in millimetres.

ADVANTAGES OF COORDINATE TOLERANCING

The advantages claimed for direct coordinate tolerancing are as follows:

1. It is simple and easily understood and, therefore, is a method commonly used.
2. It permits direct measurements to be made with standard instruments and does not require the use of special purpose functional gauges or other calculations.

DISADVANTAGES OF COORDINATE TOLERANCING

There are a number of disadvantages to the direct tolerancing method. Among these are

1. It results in a square or rectangular tolerance zone within which the axis must lie. For a square zone, this permits a variation in a 45° direction of approximately 1.4 times the specified tolerance. This amount of variation may necessitate the specification of tolerances that are only 70 percent of those that are functionally acceptable.
2. It may result in an undesirable accumulation of tolerances when several features are involved, especially when chain dimensioning is used.
3. It is more difficult to assess clearances between mating features and components than when positional tolerancing is used, especially when a group or a pattern of features is involved.
4. It does not correspond to the control exercised by fixed functional GO gauges often desirable in mass production of parts.

POSITIONAL TOLERANCING

Positional tolerancing is part of the system of geometric tolerancing. It defines a zone within which the centre, axis, or centre plane of a feature of size is permitted to vary from true (theoretically exact) position. A positional tolerance is indicated by the position symbol, a tolerance, a material condition basis, and appropriate datum references placed in a feature control frame. Basic dimensions represent the exact values to which geometric positional tolerances are applied elsewhere, by symbols or notes on the drawing. They are enclosed in a rectangular frame (basic dimension symbol), Figure 49–7. Where the dimension represents a diameter, the symbol ∅ is included in the rectangular frame. General tolerance notes do not apply to basic dimensions. The frame size need not be any larger than that necessary to enclose the dimension. It is necessary to identify features on the part to establish datums for dimensions locating true positions. The datum features are identified with datum-feature symbols and the applicable datum references are included in the feature control frame.

The geometric characteristic symbol for position is a circle with two solid centre lines, Figure 49–7. This symbol is used in the feature control frame in the same manner as for other geometric tolerances.

MATERIAL CONDITION BASIS

Positional tolerancing is applied on an MMC, RFS, or LMC basis. When applied on an MMC or LMC basis, the appropriate symbol for the above follows the specified tolerance and, where required, the applicable datum reference in the feature control frame. When no modifying symbol is shown after the tolerance, the "regardless of feature size" condition applies.

Because positional tolerance controls the position of the centre, axis, or centre plane of a feature of size, the feature control frame is normally attached to the size of the feature, Figure 49–8.

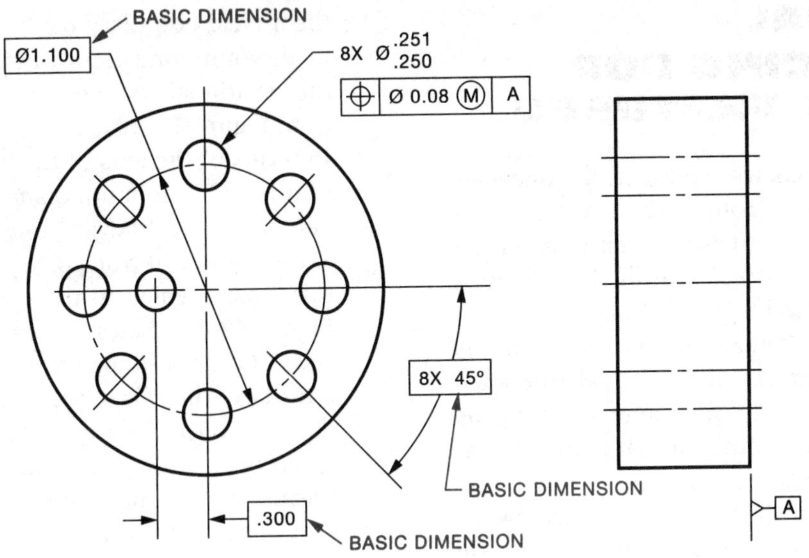

FIGURE 49–7 ■ Identifying basic dimensions

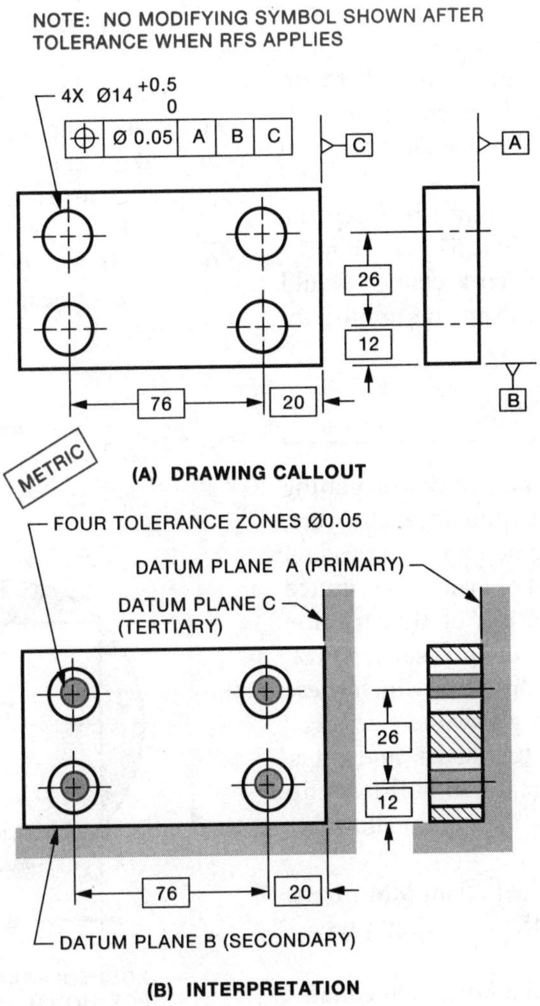

FIGURE 49–8 ■ Positional tolerancing—RFS

POSITIONAL TOLERANCING FOR CIRCULAR FEATURES

The positional tolerance represents the diameter of a cylindrical tolerance zone, located at true position as determined by the basic dimensions on the drawing. The axis or centre line of the feature must lie within this cylindrical tolerance zone.

Except for the fact that the tolerance zone is circular instead of square, a positional tolerance on this basis has exactly the same meaning as direct coordinate tolerancing but with equal tolerances in all directions.

It has already been shown that with rectangular coordinate tolerancing, the maximum permissible error in location is not the value indicated by the horizontal and vertical tolerances, but rather is equivalent to the length of the diagonal between the two tolerances. For square tolerance zones, this is 1.4 times the specified tolerance values. The specified tolerance can therefore be increased to an amount equal to the diagonal of the coordinate tolerance zone without affecting the clearance between the hole and its mating part.

This does not affect the clearance between the hole and its mating part, yet it offers 57 percent more tolerance area, Figure 49–9. Such a change would most likely result in a reduction in the number of parts rejected for positional errors.

Positional Tolerancing—MMC

The positional tolerance and MMC of mating features are considered in relation to each other. MMC by itself means a feature of a finished product contains the maximum amount of material permitted by the toleranced size dimension of that feature. Thus for holes, slots, and other internal features, maximum material is the condition in which these factors are at their minimum allowable sizes. For shafts, as well as for bosses, lugs, tabs, and other external features, maximum material is the condition in which these are at their maximum allowable sizes.

A positional tolerance applied on an MMC basis may be explained in either of the following ways:

1. **In terms of the surface of a hole.** While maintaining the specified size limits of the hole, no element of the hole surface shall be inside a theoretical boundary having a diameter equal to the minimum limit of size (MMC) minus the positional tolerance located at true position, Figure 49–10.
2. **In terms of the axis of the hole.** Where a hole is at MMC (minimum diameter), its axis must fall within a cylindrical tolerance zone whose axis is located at true position. The diameter of this zone is equal to the positional tolerance, Figure 49–11, holes A and B. This tolerance zone also defines the limits of variation in the attitude of the axis of the hole in relation to the datum surface, Figure 49–11, hole C. It is only when the feature is at MMC that the specified positional tolerance applies. Where the actual size of the feature is larger than MMC, additional or bonus positional tolerance results. This increase of positional tolerance is equal to the difference between the specified maximum material limit of size (MMC) and the actual size of the feature.

The problems of tolerancing for the position of holes are simplified when positional tolerancing is applied on an MMC basis. Positional tolerancing simplifies measuring procedures of functional GO gauges. It also permits an increase in positional variations as the size departs from the maximum material size without jeopardizing free assembly of mating features.

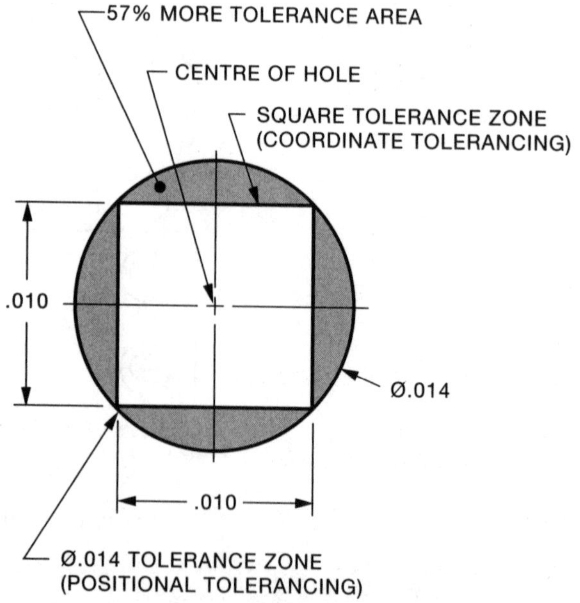

FIGURE 49–9 ■ Relationship of tolerance zones

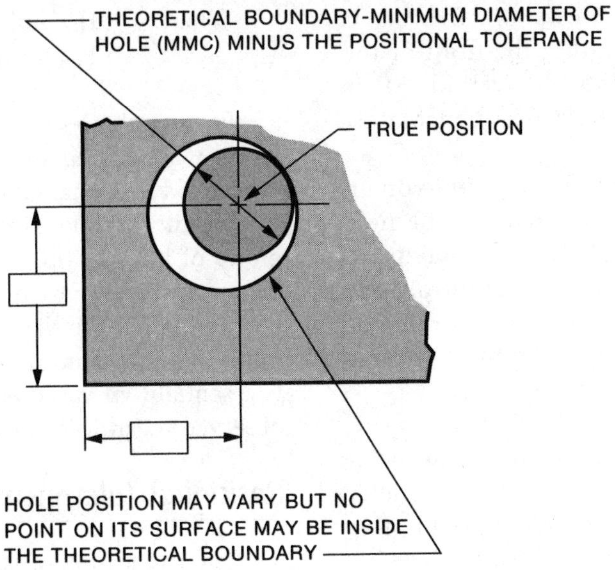
THEORETICAL BOUNDARY-MINIMUM DIAMETER OF HOLE (MMC) MINUS THE POSITIONAL TOLERANCE
TRUE POSITION
HOLE POSITION MAY VARY BUT NO POINT ON ITS SURFACE MAY BE INSIDE THE THEORETICAL BOUNDARY

FIGURE 49–10 ■ Boundary for surface of a hole—MMC

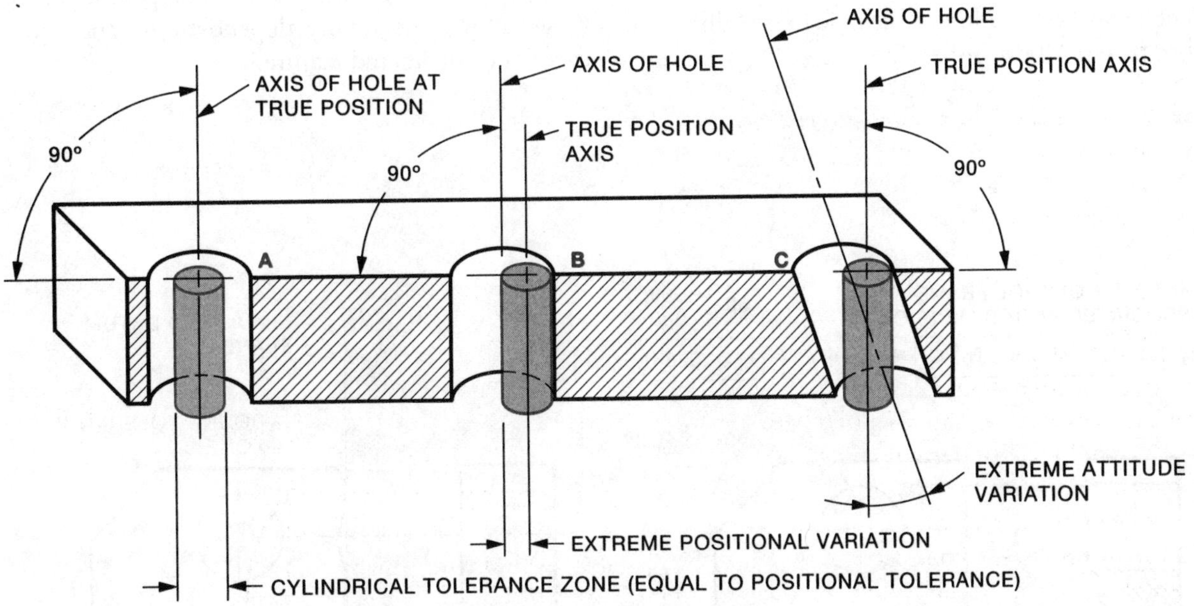
AXIS OF HOLE
AXIS OF HOLE AT TRUE POSITION
AXIS OF HOLE
TRUE POSITION AXIS
TRUE POSITION AXIS
90°
90°
90°
A
B
C
EXTREME ATTITUDE VARIATION
EXTREME POSITIONAL VARIATION
CYLINDRICAL TOLERANCE ZONE (EQUAL TO POSITIONAL TOLERANCE)

HOLE A—AXIS OF HOLE IS COINCIDENT WITH TRUE POSITION AXIS

HOLE B—AXIS OF HOLE IS LOCATED AT EXTREME POSITION TO THE LEFT OF TRUE POSITION AXIS (BUT WITHIN TOLERANCE ZONE)

HOLE C—AXIS OF HOLE IS INCLINED TO EXTREME ATTITUDE WITHIN TOLERANCE ZONE

NOTE: THE LENGTH OF THE TOLERANCE ZONE IS EQUAL TO THE LENGTH OF THE FEATURE UNLESS OTHERWISE SPECIFIED ON THE DRAWING.

FIGURE 49–11 ■ Hole axes in relationship to positional tolerance zones

A positional tolerance on an MMC basis is specified on a drawing, on either the front or the side view, Figure 49–12. The MMC symbol Ⓜ is added in the feature control frame immediately after the tolerance.

A positional tolerance applied to a hole on an MMC basis means that the boundary of the hole must fall outside a perfect cylinder having a diameter equal to the minimum limit of size minus the positional tolerance. This cylinder is located with its axis at true position. The hole must, of course, meet its diameter limits.

The effect is illustrated in Figure 49–13, where the gauge cylinder is shown at true position and the minimum and maximum diameter holes are drawn to show the extreme permissible variations in position in one direction.

Therefore, if a hole is at its maximum material condition (minimum diameter), the position of its axis must lie within a circular tolerance zone having a diameter equal to the specified tolerance. If the hole is at its maximum diameter (least material condition), the diameter of the tolerance zone for the axis is increased by the amount of the feature tolerance. The greatest deviation of the axis in one direction from true position is therefore

$$\frac{H + P}{2} = \frac{.006 + .028}{2} = .017 \text{ in.}$$

Where: H = hole diameter tolerance
P = positional tolerance

Positional tolerancing on an MMC basis is preferred when production quantities warrant the provision of functional GO gauges, because gauging is then limited to one simple operation, even when a group of holes is involved. This method also facilitates manufacture by permitting larger variations in position when the diameter departs from the maximum material condition. It cannot be used when it is essential that variations in location of the axis be observed regardless of feature size.

Positional Tolerancing at Zero MMC

The application of MMC permits the tolerance to exceed the value specified, provided features are within size limits and parts are acceptable. This is accomplished by adjusting the minimum size limit of a hole to the absolute minimum required for the insertion of an applicable fastener located precisely at true position, and specifying a zero tolerance at MMC, Figure 49–14. In this case, the positional tolerance allowed is totally dependent on the actual size of the considered feature.

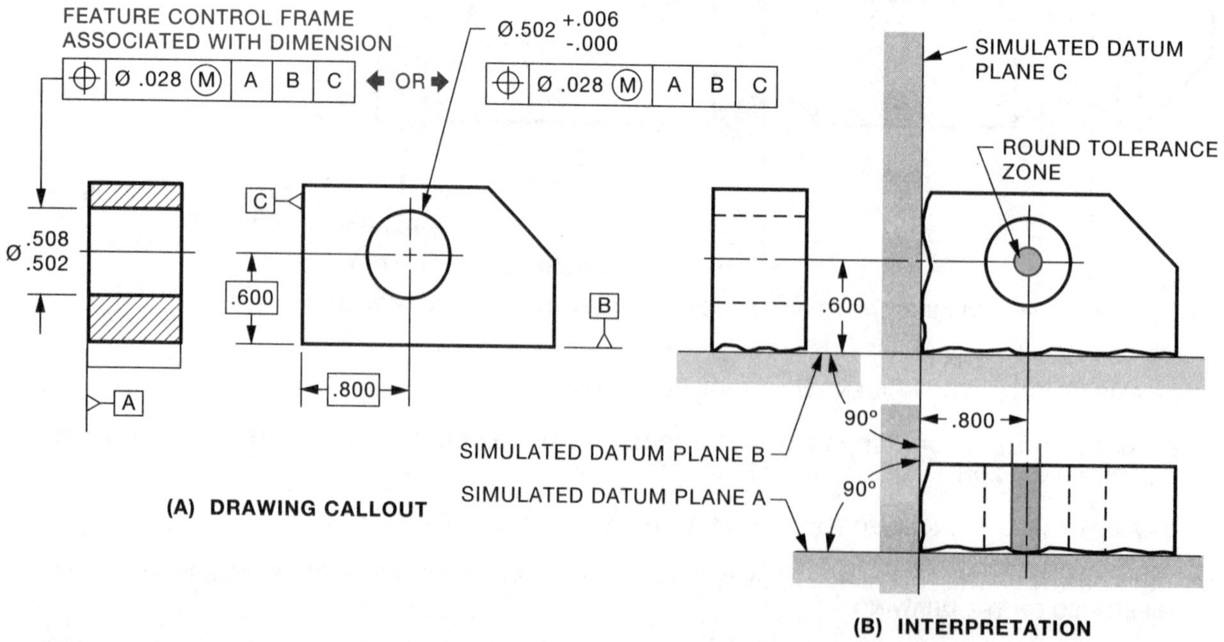

FIGURE 49–12 ■ Positional tolerancing—MMC

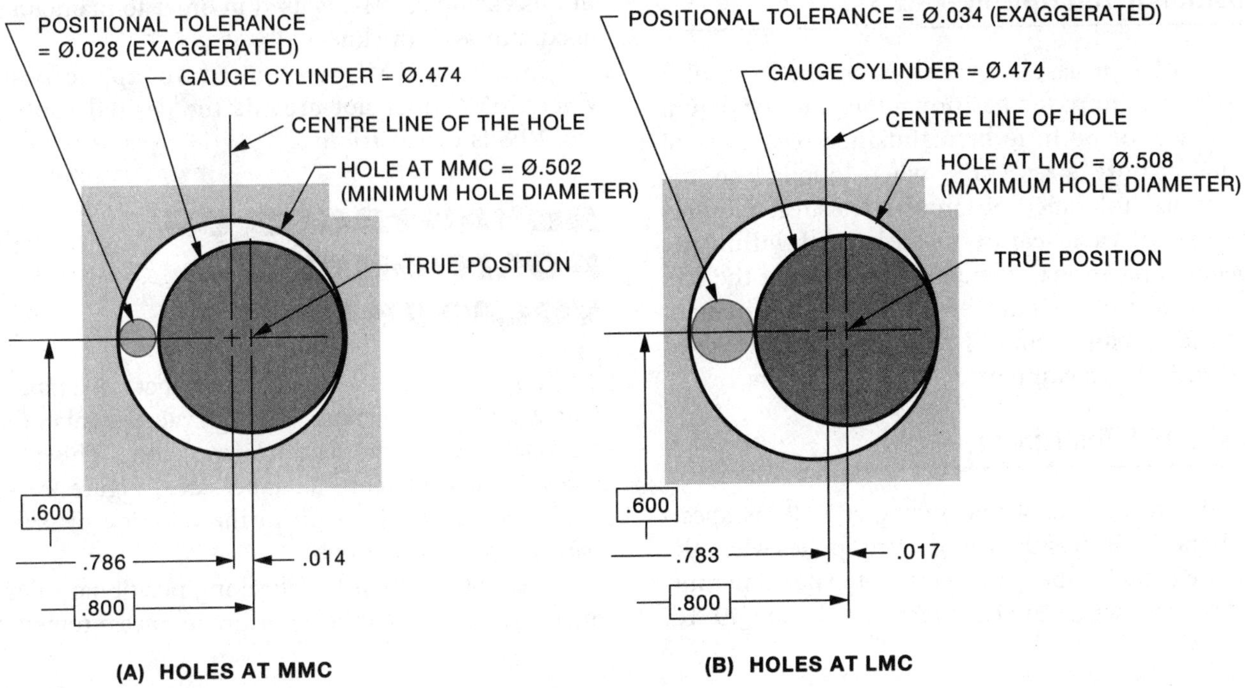
POSITIONAL TOLERANCE
= Ø.028 (EXAGGERATED)
GAUGE CYLINDER = Ø.474
CENTRE LINE OF THE HOLE
HOLE AT MMC = Ø.502
(MINIMUM HOLE DIAMETER)
TRUE POSITION
.600
.786
.014
.800
(A) HOLES AT MMC
POSITIONAL TOLERANCE = Ø.034 (EXAGGERATED)
GAUGE CYLINDER = Ø.474
CENTRE LINE OF HOLE
HOLE AT LMC = Ø.508
(MAXIMUM HOLE DIAMETER)
TRUE POSITION
.600
.783
.017
.800
(B) HOLES AT LMC

FIGURE 49–13 ■ Positional variations for tolerancing for Figure 49–12

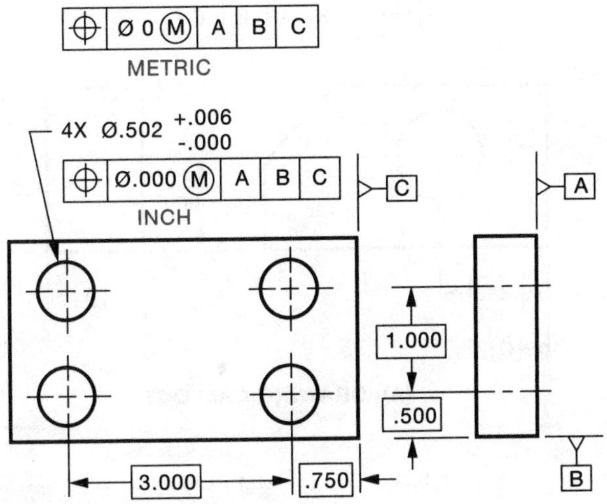
Ø 0 (M) A B C
METRIC
4X Ø.502 +.006 -.000
Ø.000 (M) A B C
INCH
C
A
1.000
.500
3.000
.750
B

FIGURE 49–14 ■ Positional tolerancing—zero (MMC)

Positional Tolerancing—RFS

In certain cases, the design or function of a part may require the positional tolerance or datum reference, or both, to be maintained regardless of actual feature sizes. RFS, where applied to the positional tolerance of circular features, requires the axis of each feature to be located within the specified positional tolerance regardless of the size of the feature, Figure 49–15. This requirement imposes a closer control of the features involved and introduces complexities in verification.

Positional Tolerancing—LMC

Where positional tolerancing at LMC is specified, the stated positional tolerance applies when the feature contains the least amount of material permitted by its toleranced size dimension, Figure 49–16. In this example, LMC is used in order to maintain a maximum wall thickness.

Specifying LMC is limited to applications where MMC does not provide the desired control and RFS is too restrictive.

ADVANTAGES OF POSITIONAL TOLERANCING

It is practical to replace coordinate tolerances with a positional tolerance having a value equal to the diagonal of the coordinate tolerance zone. This provides 57 percent more tolerance area, Figure 49–9, and would probably result in the rejection of fewer parts for positional errors.

A simple method for checking positional tolerance errors is to take coordinate measurements

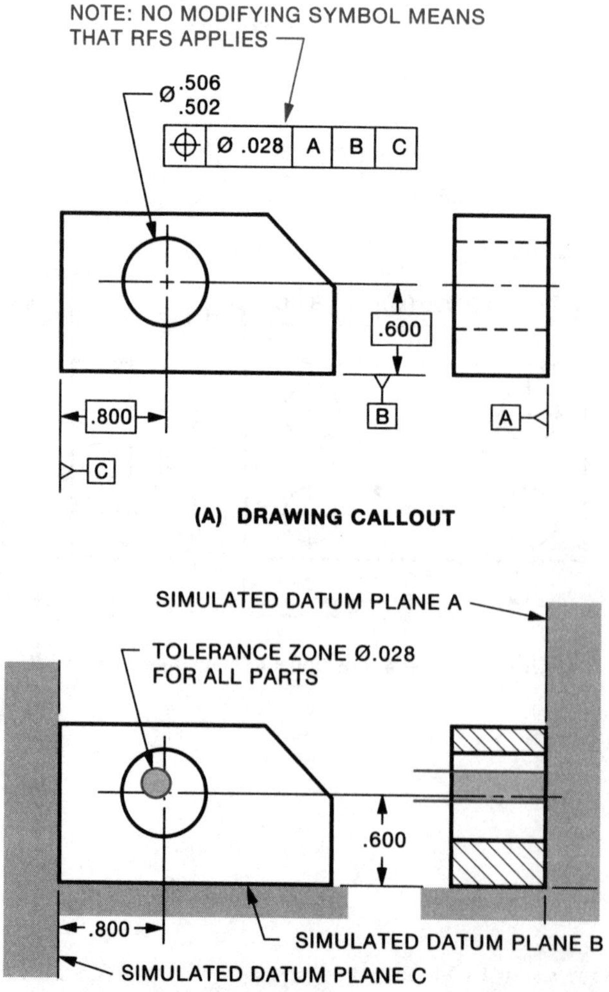

FIGURE 49–15 ■ Positional tolerancing—RFS

and evaluate them on a chart as shown in Figure 49–17. For example, the four parts shown in Figure 49–18 were rejected when the coordinate tolerances were applied to them.

If the parts had been toleranced using the positional tolerance—RFS method shown in Figure 49–15 and given a tolerance of Ø.028 in. (equal to the diagonal of the coordinate tolerance zone), three of the parts—A, B, and D—would not have been rejected.

If the parts shown in Figure 49–18 had been toleranced using the positional tolerance (MMC) method and given a tolerance of Ø.028 in. at MMC (Figure 49–12), part C, which was rejected using the RFS tolerancing method (Figure 49–15), would not have been rejected if it had been straight. The positional tolerance can be increased to Ø.034 in. for a part having a diameter of .508 in. (LMC) without jeopardizing the function of the part (Figure 49–13).

REFERENCES

CAN/CSA B78.2-M91 Dimensioning and Tolerancing of Technical Drawings
ASME Y14.5M-1994 Dimensioning and Tolerancing

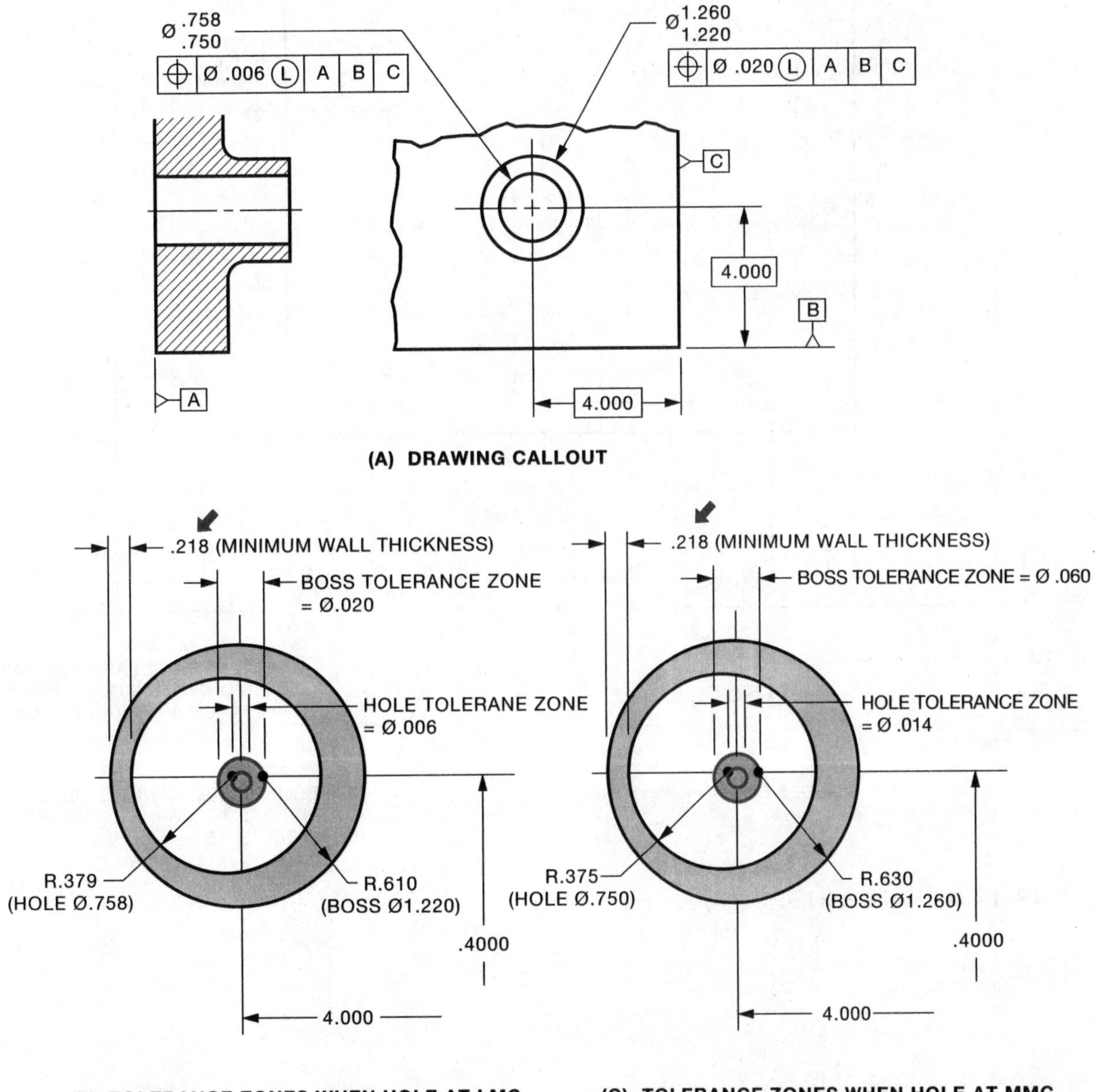

(A) DRAWING CALLOUT

(B) TOLERANCE ZONES WHEN HOLE AT LMC

(C) TOLERANCE ZONES WHEN HOLE AT MMC

FIGURE 49–16 ■ LMC applied to a boss and hole

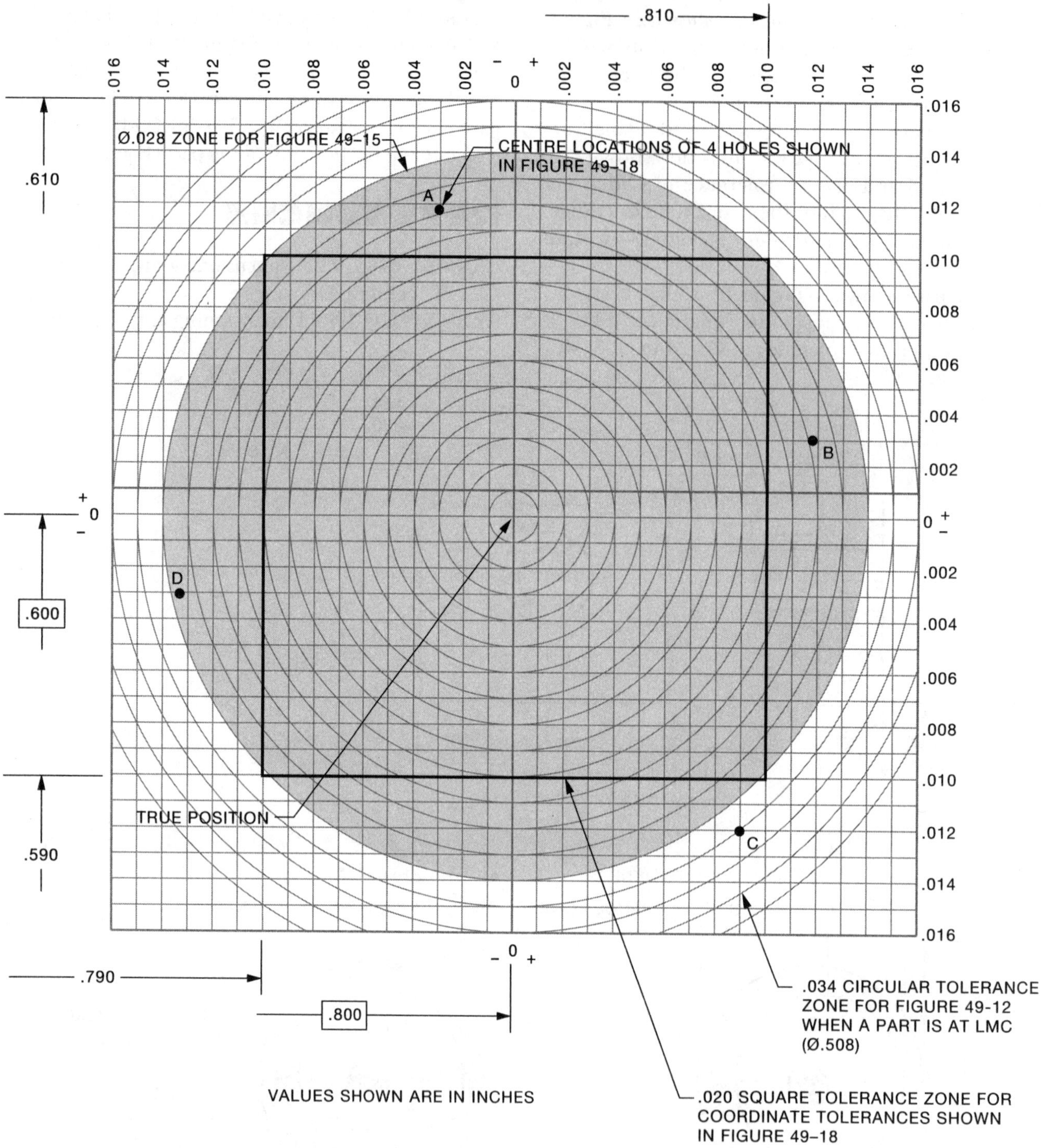

FIGURE 49–17 ■ Charts for evaluating positional tolerancing

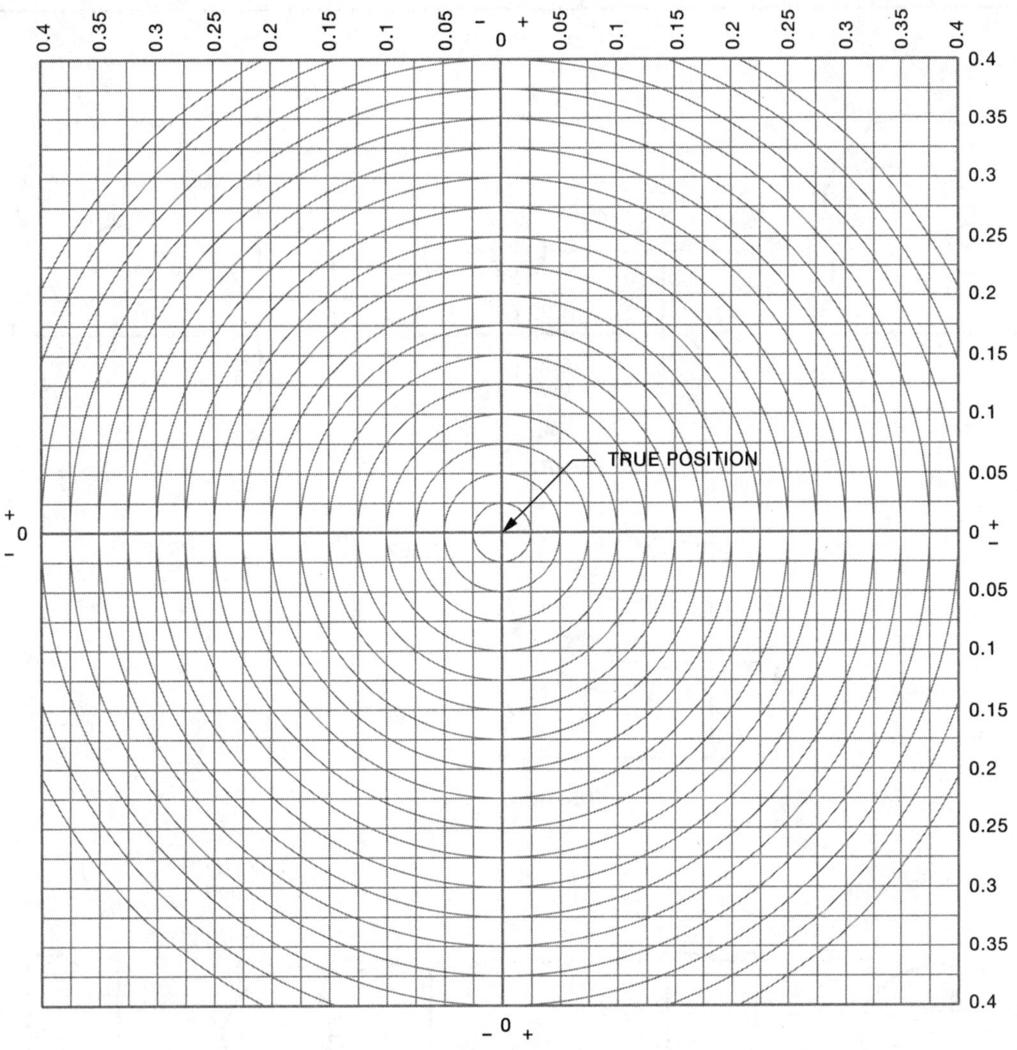

VALUES SHOWN ARE IN MILLIMETRES

FIGURE 49–17 CONT'D ■ Charts for evaluating positional tolerancing

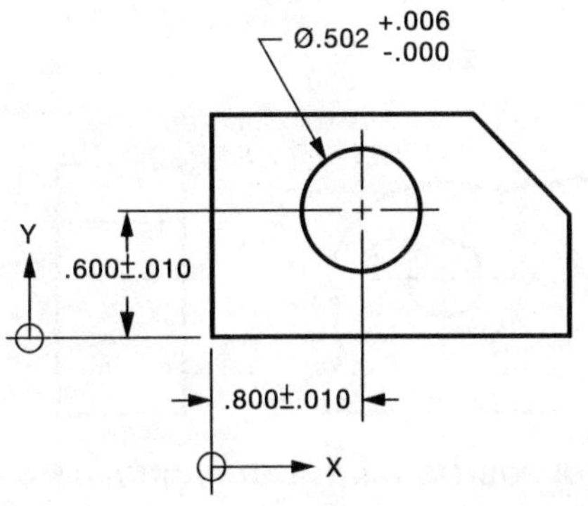

(A) DRAWING CALLOUT

PART	HOLE DIA	HOLE LOCATION X	HOLE LOCATION Y	COMMENT
A	.503	.797	.612	REJECTED
B	.504	.812	.603	REJECTED
C	.508	.809	.588	REJECTED
D	.506	.787	.597	REJECTED

REFER TO FIGURE 49–17 FOR LOCATION ON CHART

(B) LOCATION AND SIZE OF REJECTED PARTS

FIGURE 49–18 ■ Parts A to D rejected because hole centres do not lie within coordinate tolerance zone

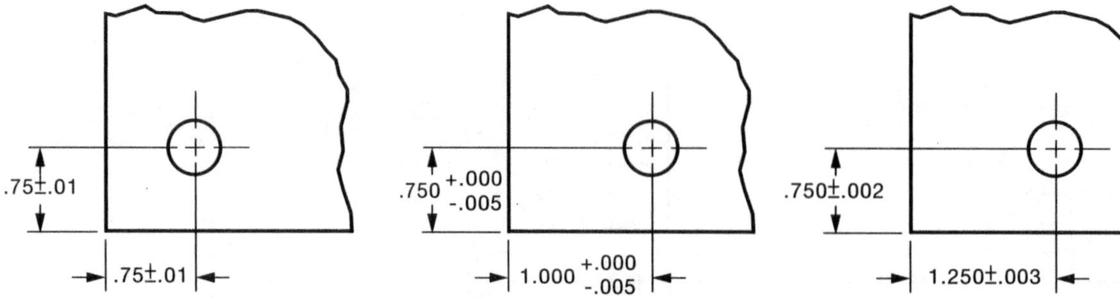
.75±.01
.75±.01
.750 +.000 -.005
1.000 +.000 -.005
.750±.002
1.250±.003

(A) (B) (C)

FIGURE 1

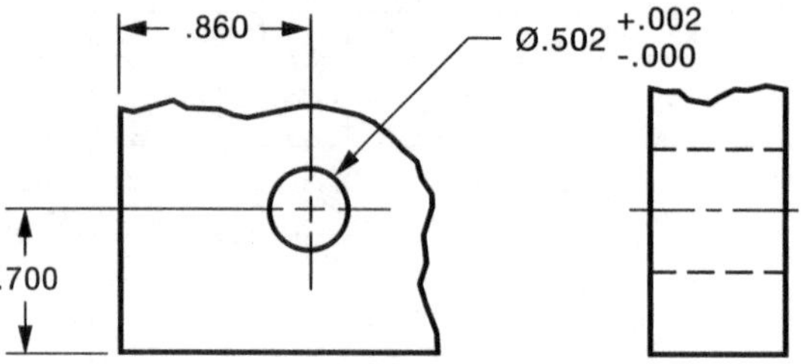
.860
Ø.502 +.002 -.000
.700

FIGURE 2

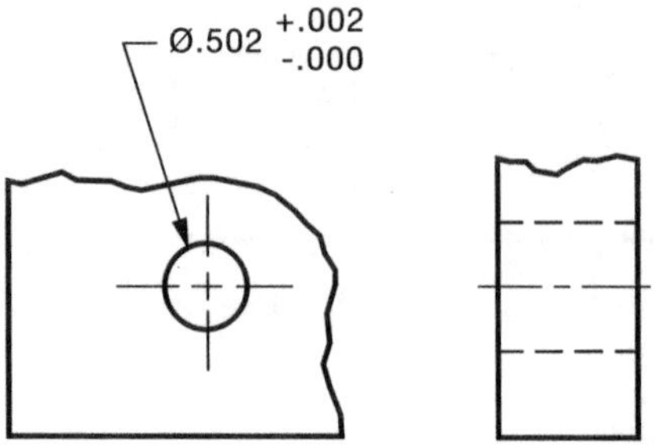
Ø.502 +.002 -.000

(A) COORDINATE TOLERANCING

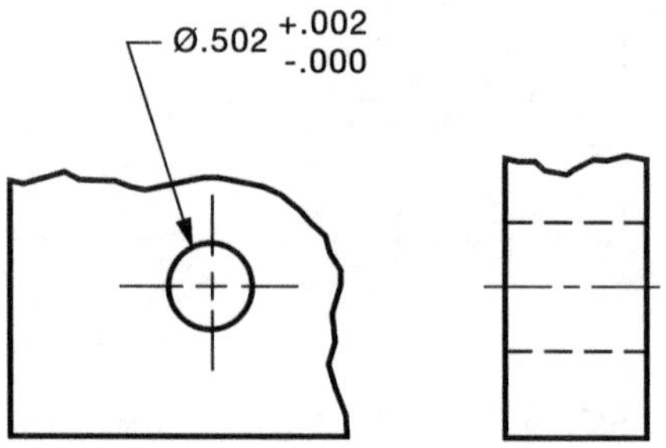
Ø.502 +.002 -.000

(B) POSITIONAL TOLERANCING—RFS

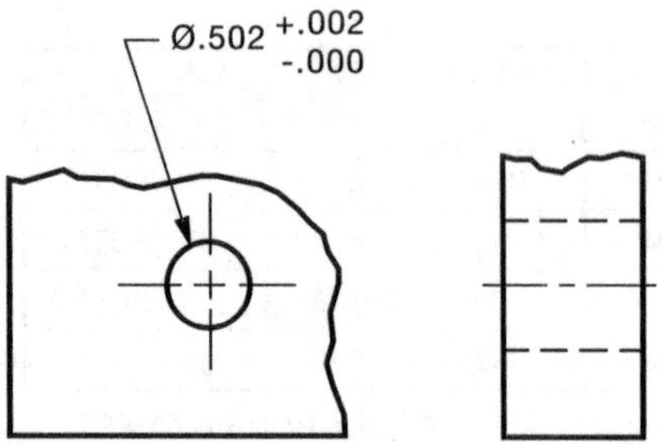
Ø.502 +.002 -.000

(C) POSITIONAL TOLERANCING—MMC

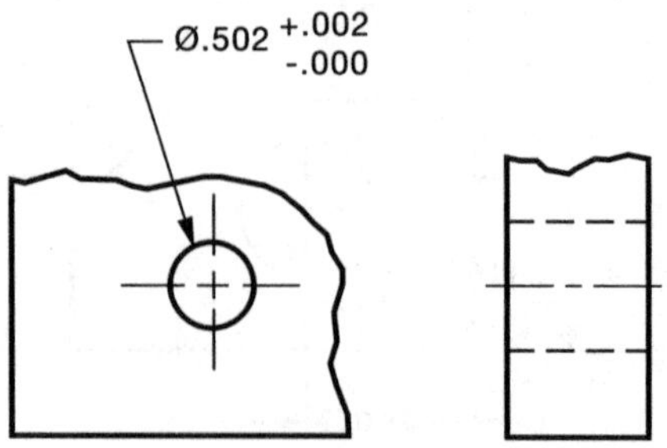
Ø.502 +.002 -.000

(D) POSITIONAL TOLERANCING—LMC

FIGURE 3

QUESTIONS

1. If coordinate tolerances as shown in Figure 1 are given, what is the maximum distance between centres of mating holes for parts made to these drawing callouts?

2. In order to assemble correctly, the hole shown in Figure 2 must not vary more than .0014 in. in any direction from its true position when the hole is at its smallest size. Show suitable tolerancing, dimensioning, and datums where required on the drawings in Figure 2 to achieve this by using
   (A) coordinate tolerancing
   (B) positional toleracing—RFS
   (C) positional tolerancing—MMC
   (D) positional tolerancing—LMC

3. With reference to question 2 and Figure 3, what would be the maximum permissible deviation from true position when the hole was at its largest size?

4. The part shown in Figure 4A is set on a revolving table, so adjusted that the part revolves about the true position centre of the Ø.316 in. hole. If the indicators give identical readings and the results in Figure 4(B) are obtained, which parts are acceptable?

5. What is the positional error for each part in Figure 4B?

6. If MMC instead of RFS had been shown in the feature control frame in Figure 4(A), what is the diameter of the mandrel that would be required to check the parts?

ANSWERS

1. A ____________
   B ____________
   C ____________
2. A SEE FIGURE 3A
   B SEE FIGURE 3B
   C SEE FIGURE 3C
   D SEE FIGURE 3D
3. A ____________
   B ____________
   C ____________
   D ____________
4. PT.1 ____________
   PT.2 ____________
   PT.3 ____________
   PT.4 ____________
   PT.5 ____________
   PT.6 ____________
5. PT.1 ____________
   PT.2 ____________
   PT.3 ____________
   PT.4 ____________
   PT.5 ____________
   PT.6 ____________
6. ____________

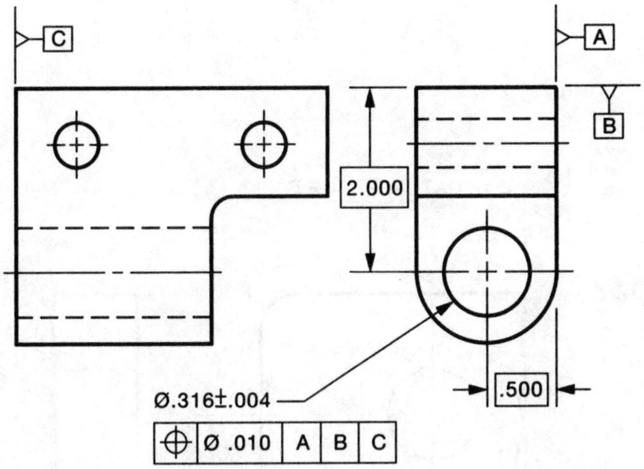

C
A
B
2.000
.500
Ø.316±.004
Ø .010 A B C

(A) DRAWING CALLOUT

PART NO.	SIZE OF MANDREL	HIGHEST READING	LOWEST READING
1	.316	.014	.008
2	.320	.008	-.004
3	.314	.026	.012
4	.312	.016	.006
5	.316	.015	.009
6	.318	.018	.010

(B) READINGS FOR PARTS

FIGURE 4

50 UNIT

SELECTION OF DATUM FEATURES FOR POSITIONAL TOLERANCING

When selecting datums for positional tolerancing, the first consideration is to select the primary datum feature. The usual course of action is to specify as the primary datum the surface in which the hole is produced. This will ensure that the true position of the axis is perpendicular to this surface or at a basic angle if other than 90°. This surface is resting on the gauging plane or surface plate for measuring purposes. Secondary and tertiary datum features are then selected and identified, if required, Figures 50–1 and 50–2.

Positional tolerancing is also useful for parts having holes not perpendicular to the primary surface. This principle is illustrated in Figure 50–3.

LONG HOLES

It is not always essential to have the true position of a hole perpendicular to the face into which the hole is produced. It may be functionally more important, especially with long holes, to have it parallel to one of the sides. Figure 50–4 is a case in point. In this example, the sides are designated as primary and secondary datums. Gauging

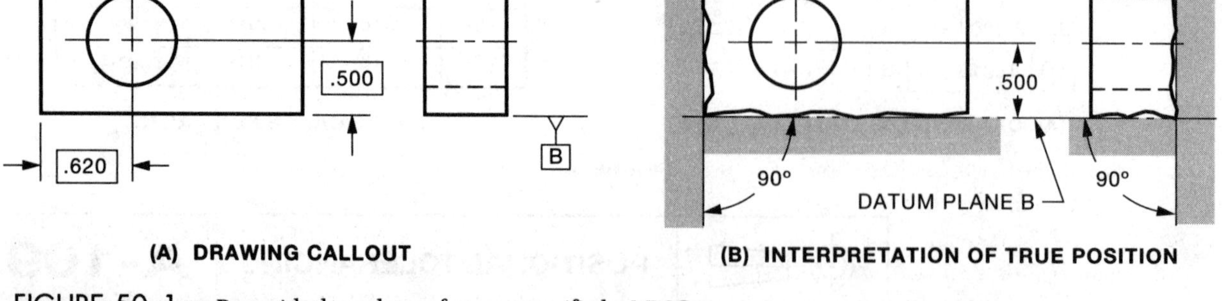

Ø.562 +.002 -.000
Ø .005 (M) A B C
C
A
.500
.620
B
(A) DRAWING CALLOUT
DATUM PLANE C
.620
DATUM PLANE A
.500
90°
DATUM PLANE B
90°
(B) INTERPRETATION OF TRUE POSITION

FIGURE 50–1 ■ Part with three datum features specified—MMC

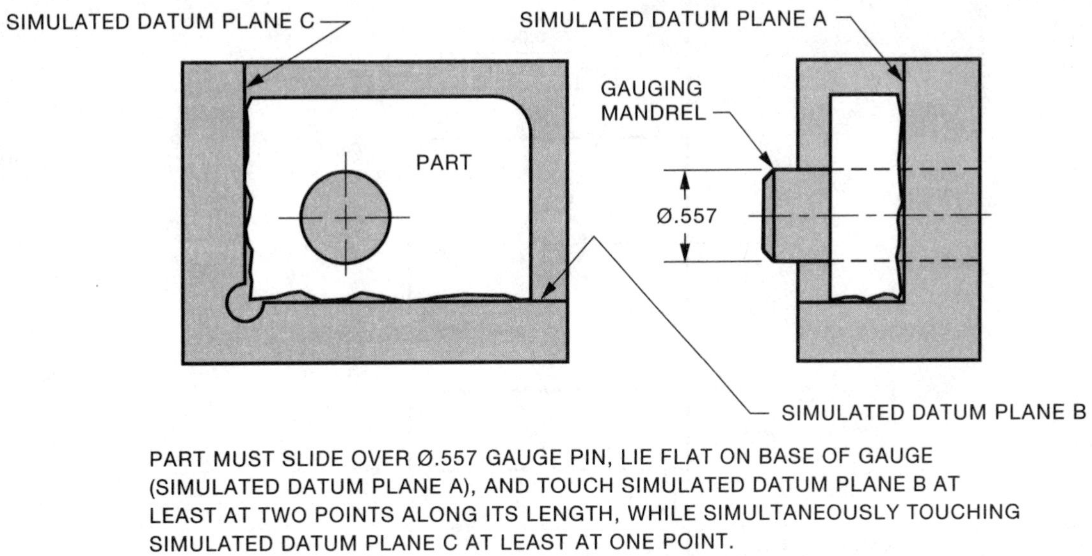
SIMULATED DATUM PLANE C
SIMULATED DATUM PLANE A
GAUGING MANDREL
PART
Ø.557
SIMULATED DATUM PLANE B
PART MUST SLIDE OVER Ø.557 GAUGE PIN, LIE FLAT ON BASE OF GAUGE (SIMULATED DATUM PLANE A), AND TOUCH SIMULATED DATUM PLANE B AT LEAST AT TWO POINTS ALONG ITS LENGTH, WHILE SIMULTANEOUSLY TOUCHING SIMULATED DATUM PLANE C AT LEAST AT ONE POINT.

FIGURE 50–2 ■ Gauge for the part in Figure 50–1

is facilitated if the positional tolerance is specified on an MMC basis.

CIRCULAR DATUMS

Example 1

Circular features, such as holes or external cylindrical features, can be used as datums just as readily as flat surfaces. In the simple part shown in Figure 50–5, the true position of the small hole is established from the flat surface, datum A, and the large hole, datum D. Specifying datum hole D on an MMC basis facilitates gauging.

Example 2

In other cases, such as that shown in Figure 50–6, the datum could either be the axis of the hole or the axis of the outside cylindrical surface. In such applications, a determination should be made as to whether the true position should be established perpendicular to the surface as shown or parallel with the datum axis. In the latter case, datum A would not be specified and it would not be necessary to ensure that the gauge made full contact with the surface.

In a group of holes, it may be desirable to indicate one of the holes as the datum from which all the other holes are located. This is described in succeeding units. All circular datums of this type may be specified on an MMC basis when required, and this is preferred for ease of gauging.

MULTIPLE HOLE DATUMS

On an MMC basis, any number of holes or similar features that form a group or pattern may be specified as a single datum. All features forming such a datum must be related with a positional tolerance on an MMC basis. The actual datum position is based on the virtual condition of all features in the group; that is, the collectible effect of the maximum material sizes of the features and the specified positional tolerance.

Thus, in the example shown in Figure 50–7, the gauging element that locates the datum position would have four ∅.240 pins located at true position with respect to one another. It should be noted that this setup automatically checks the positional tolerance specified for these four holes.

REFERENCES

CAN/CSA B78.2-M91 Dimensioning and Tolerancing of Technical Drawings
ASME Y14.5M-1994 Dimensioning and Tolerancing

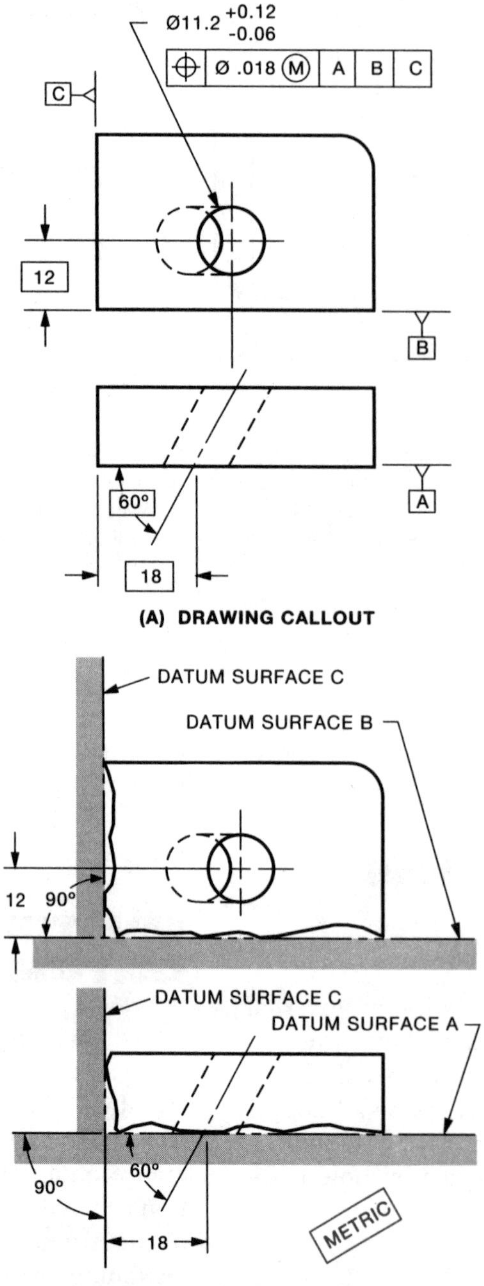
Ø11.2 +0.12 -0.06
Ø .018 (M) A B C
C
12
B
60°
A
18
(A) DRAWING CALLOUT
DATUM SURFACE C
DATUM SURFACE B
12 90°
DATUM SURFACE C
DATUM SURFACE A
90°
60°
18
METRIC
(B) INTERPRETATION OF TRUE POSITION

FIGURE 50–3 ■ Part with angular hole referred to a datum system—MMC

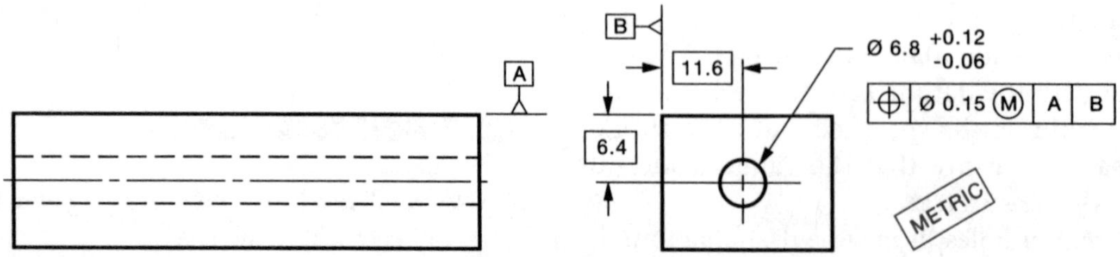
B
A
11.6
Ø 6.8 +0.12 -0.06
Ø 0.15 (M) A B
6.4
METRIC

FIGURE 50–4 ■ Datum system for a long hole—MMC

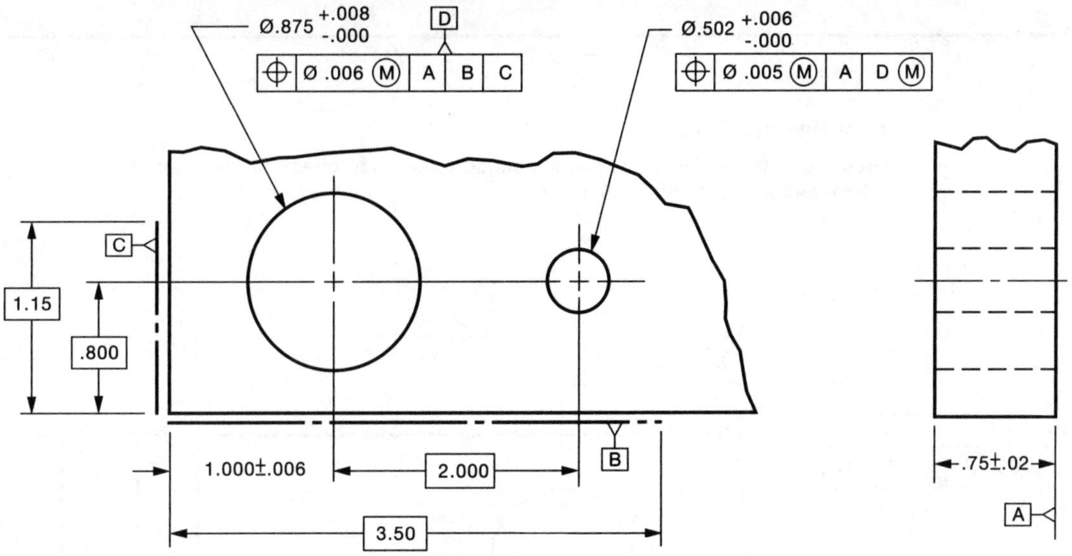

FIGURE 50–5 ■ Specifying an internal circular feature as a datum—MMC

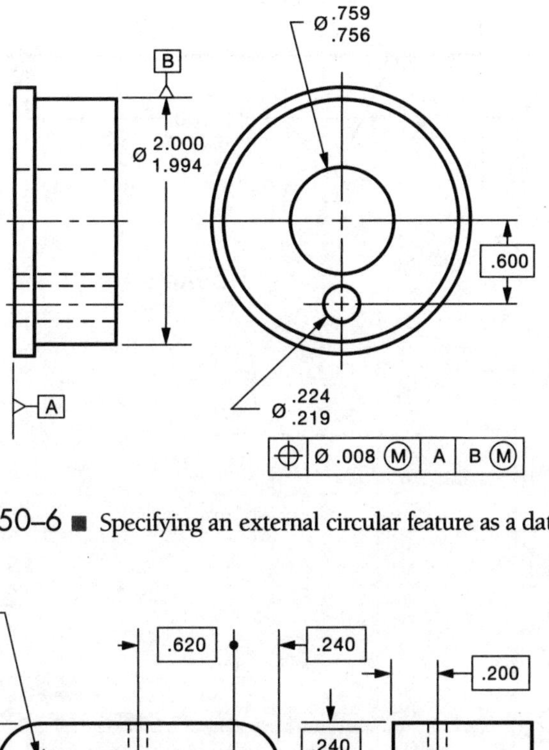

FIGURE 50–6 ■ Specifying an external circular feature as a datum—MMC

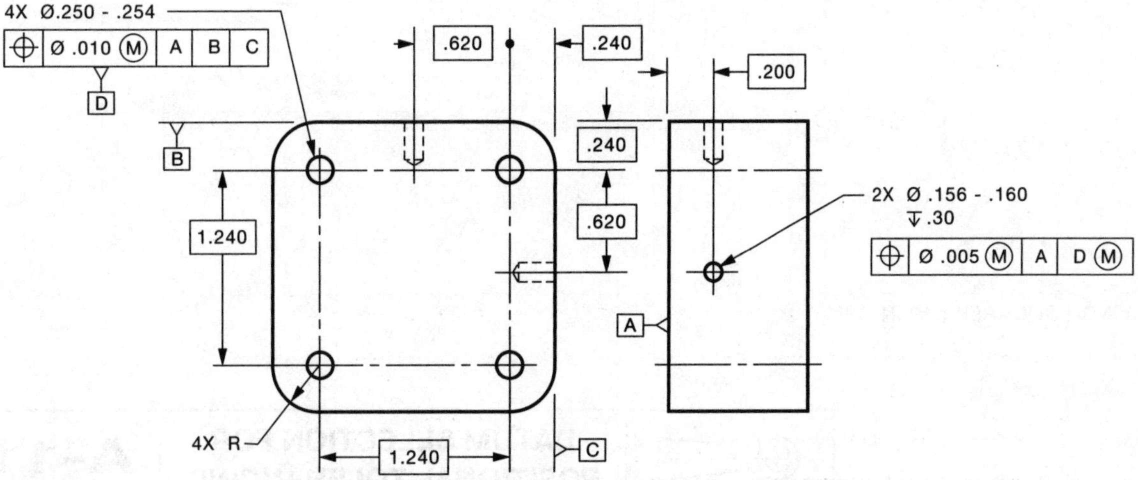

FIGURE 50–7 ■ Specifying a group of holes as a single datum—MMC

ASSIGNMENT:

On the grid below Figure 1, show a suitable gauge to check the positional tolerance for the Ø.750-.755 in. hole.

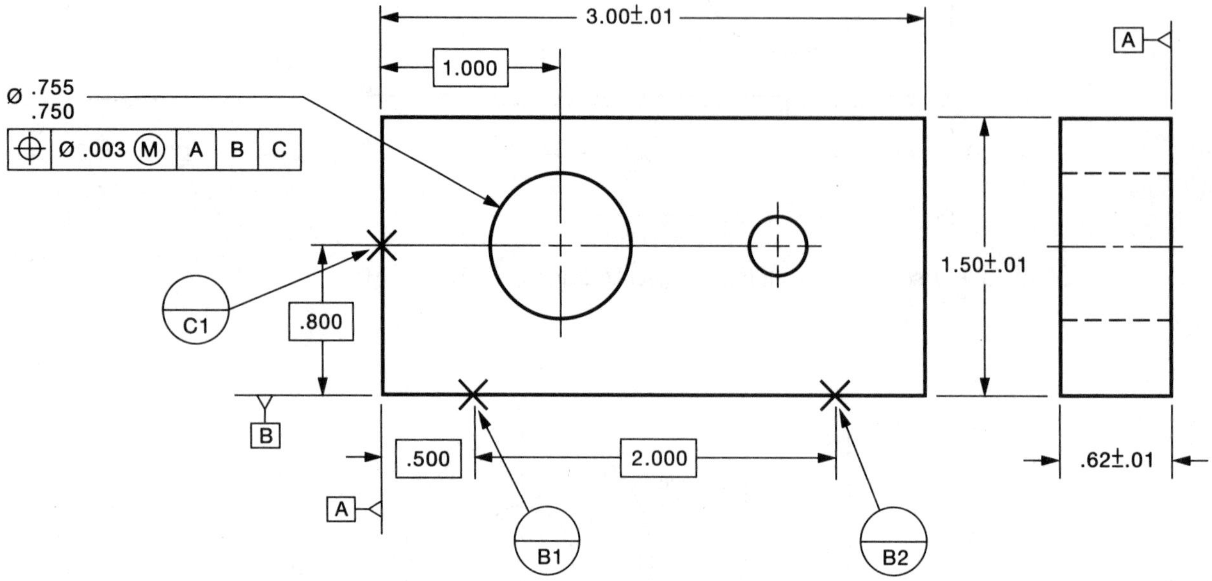

FIGURE 1

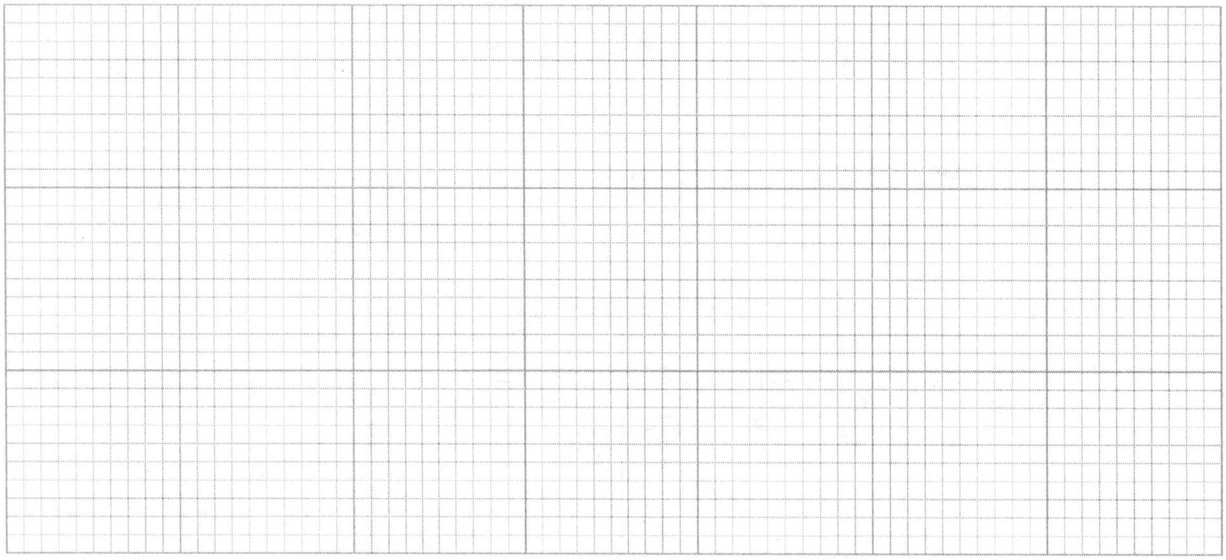

1.00 INCH SQUARES (.10 IN GRID)

	DATUM SELECTION FOR POSITIONAL TOLERANCING	A-110

UNIT 51

PROFILE TOLERANCES

A profile is the outline form or shape of a line or surface. A line profile may be the outline of a part or feature as depicted in a view on a drawing. It may represent the edge of a part or it may refer to line elements of a surface in a single direction, such as the outline of cross sections through the part. In contrast, a surface profile outlines the form or shape of a complete surface in three dimensions.

The elements of a line profile may be straight lines, arcs, or other curved lines. The elements of a surface profile may be flat surfaces, spherical surfaces, cylindrical surfaces, or surfaces composed of various line profiles in two or more directions.

A profile tolerance specifies a uniform boundary along the true profile within which the elements of the surface must lie. MMC is not applicable to profile tolerances. Where used as a refinement of size, the profile tolerance must be contained within the size limits.

Profile Symbols

There are two geometric characteristic symbols for profiles: one for lines and one for surfaces. Separate symbols are required because it is often necessary to distinguish between line elements of a surface and the complete surface itself.

The symbol for profile of a line consists of a semicircle with a diameter equal to twice the lettering size used on the drawing. The symbol for profile of a surface is identical except that the semicircle is closed by a straight line at the bottom, Figure 51–1. All other geometric tolerances of form and orientation are merely special cases of profile tolerancing.

Profile tolerances are used to control the position of lines and surfaces that are neither flat nor cylindrical.

PROFILE OF A LINE

A profile-of-a-line tolerance may be directed to a line of any length or shape. With a profile-of-a-line tolerance, datums may be used in some circumstances but would not be used when the only requirement is the profile shape taken cross section by cross section. Profile-of-a-line tolerancing is used where it is not desirable to control the entire surface of the feature as a single entity.

A profile-of-a-line tolerance is specified in the usual manner by including the symbol and tolerance in a feature control frame directed to the line to be controlled, Figure 51–2.

The tolerance zone established by the profile-of-a-line tolerance is two-dimensional, extending along the length of the considered feature.

If the line on the drawing to which the tolerance is directed represents a surface, the tolerance applies to all line elements of the surface parallel to the plane of the view on the drawing, unless otherwise specified.

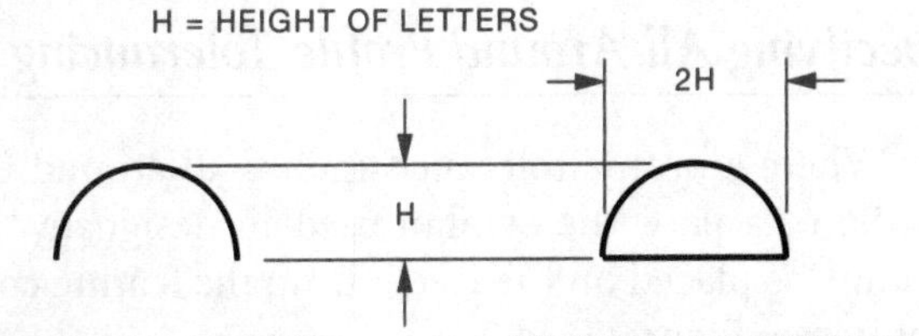

FIGURE 51–1 ■ Profile symbols

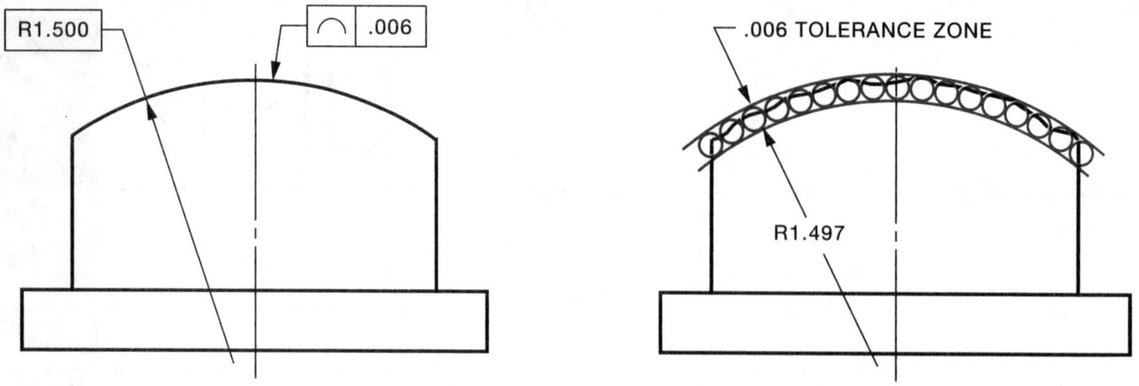

(A) DRAWING CALLOUT

(B) BILATERAL TOLERANCE ZONE

FIGURE 51–2 ■ Simple profile with a bilateral profile of a line tolerance zone

The tolerance indicates a tolerance zone consisting of the area between two parallel lines, separated by the specified tolerance, which are themselves parallel to the basic form of the line being toleranced.

Bilateral and Unilateral Tolerances

The profile tolerance zone, unless otherwise specified, is equally disposed about the basic profile in a form known as a bilateral tolerance zone. The width of this zone is always measured perpendicular to the profile surface. The tolerance zone may be considered to be bounded by two lines enveloping a series of circles, each having a diameter equal to the specified profile tolerance. Their centres are on the theoretical, basic profile as shown in Figure 51–2.

Occasionally, it is desirable to have the tolerance zone wholly on one side of the basic profile instead of equally divided on both sides. Such zones are called unilateral tolerance zones. They are specified by showing a phantom line drawn parallel and close to the profile surface. The tolerance is directed to this line, Figure 51–3. The zone line need extend only a sufficient distance to make its application clear.

Specifying All-Around Profile Tolerancing

Where a profile tolerance applies all around the profile of a part, the symbol used to designate "all around" is placed on the leader from the feature control frame, Figure 51–4.

Method of Dimensioning

The true profile is established by means of basic dimensions, each of which is enclosed in a rectan-

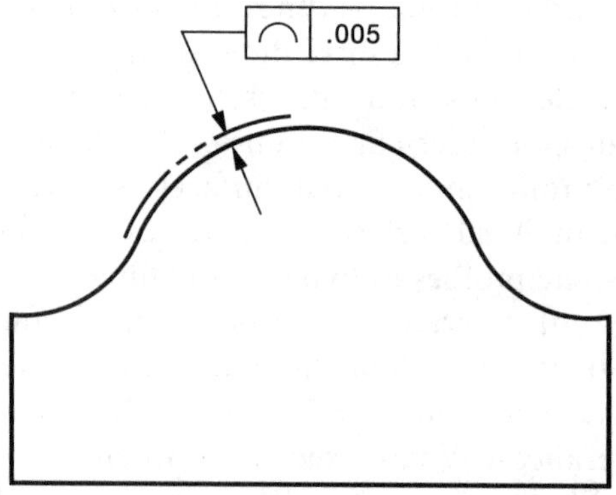

(A) TOLERANCE ZONE ON OUTSIDE OF TRUE PROFILE

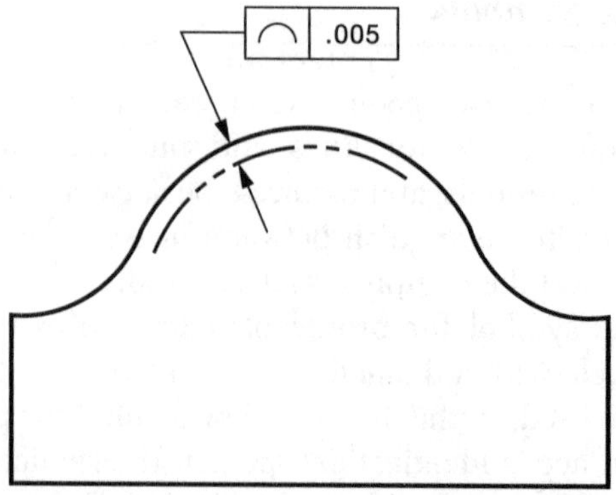

(B) TOLERANCE ZONE ON INSIDE OF TRUE PROFILE

FIGURE 51–3 ■ Unilateral tolerance zones

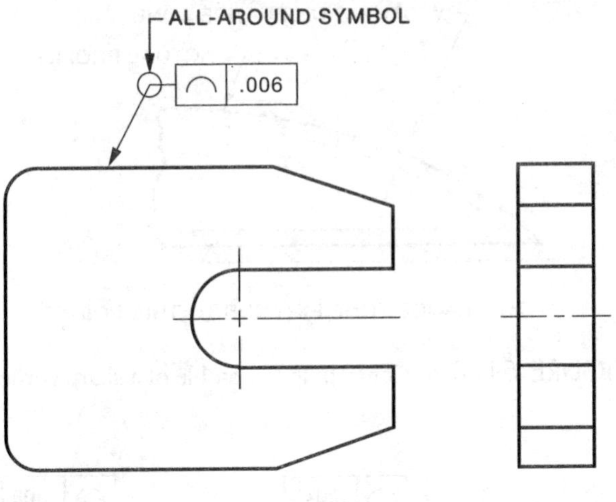

FIGURE 51–4 ■ Profile tolerance required for all around the surface

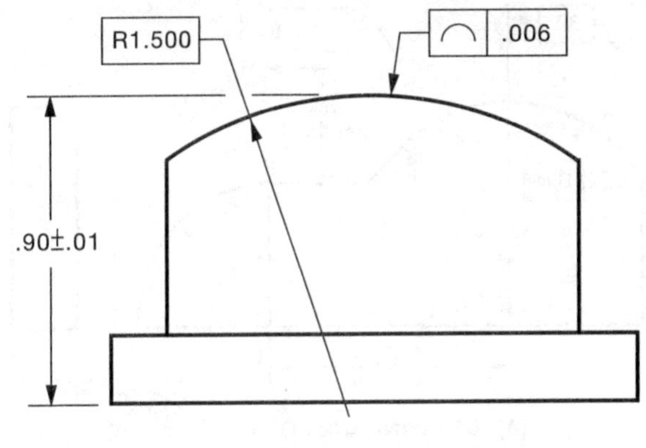

FIGURE 51–5 ■ Positional and form as separate requirements

gular frame to indicate that the tolerance in the general tolerance note does not apply.

When the profile tolerance is not intended to control the position of the profile, there must be clear distinction between dimensions that control the position of the profile and those that control the form or shape of the profile.

To illustrate, the simple part in Figure 51–5 shows a dimension of .90 ± .01 in. controlling the height of the profile. This dimension must be separately measured. The radius of 1.500 in. is a basic dimension and it becomes part of the profile. Therefore the profile tolerance zone has radii of 1.497 and 1.503 in., but is free to float in any direction within the limits of the positional tolerance zone in order to enclose the curved profile.

Figure 51–6 shows a more complex profile, where the profile is located by a single toleranced dimension. There are, however, four basic dimensions defining the true profile.

In this case, the tolerance on the height indicates a tolerance zone .06 in. wide, extending the full length of the profile. This is because the profile is established by basic dimensions. No other dimension exists to affect the orientation or height. The profile tolerance specifies a .008 in. wide tolerance zone, which may lie anywhere within the .06 in. tolerance zone.

Extent of Controlled Profile

The profile is generally intended to extend to the first abrupt change or sharp corner. For example, in Figure 51–6, it extends from the upper left- to the upper right-hand corners, unless otherwise specified. If the extent of the profile is not clearly identified by sharp corners or by basic profile dimensions, it must be indicated by a note under the feature

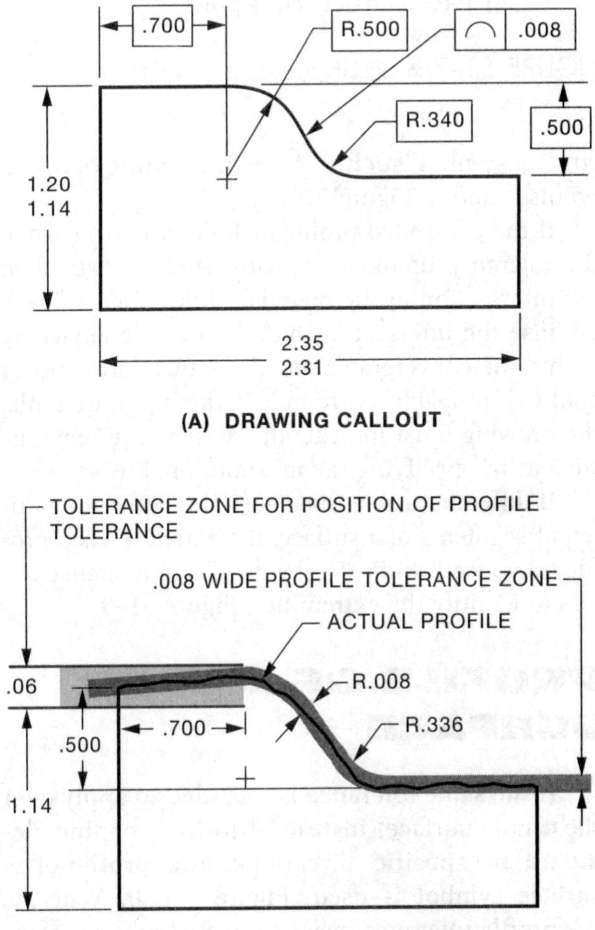

FIGURE 51–6 ■ Profile defined by basic dimensions

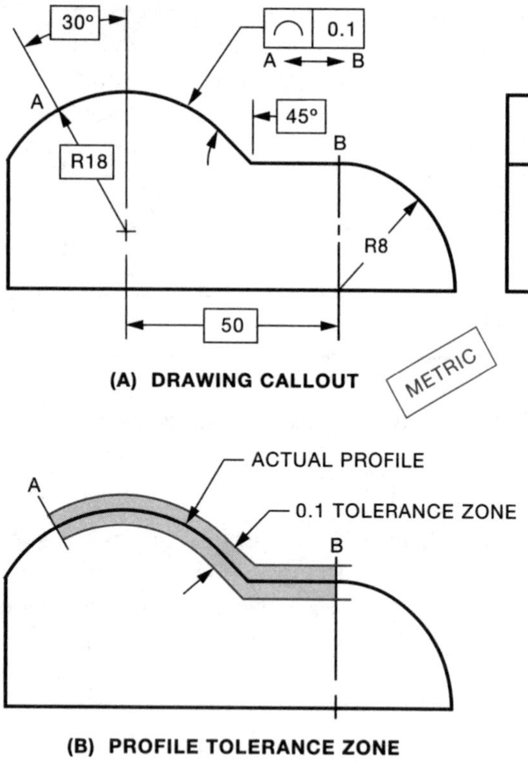

FIGURE 51–7 ■ Specifying extent of profile

control symbol, such as A↔B, meaning between points A and B, Figure 51–7.

If the controlled profile includes a sharp corner, the tolerance boundary is considered to extend to the intersection of the boundary lines, Figure 51–8. Because the intersecting surfaces may lie anywhere within the converging zone, the actual part contour could conceivably be round. If this is undesirable, the drawing must indicate the design requirements, such as by specifying the maximum radius.

If different profile tolerances are required on different segments of a surface, the extent of each profile tolerance is indicated by the use of reference letters to identify the extremities, Figure 51–9.

PROFILE OF A SURFACE

If the same tolerance is intended to apply over the whole surface, instead of to lines or line elements in specific directions, the profile-of-a-surface symbol is used, Figure 51–10. Whereas the profile tolerance may be directed to the surface in either view, it is usually directed to the view showing the shape of the profile.

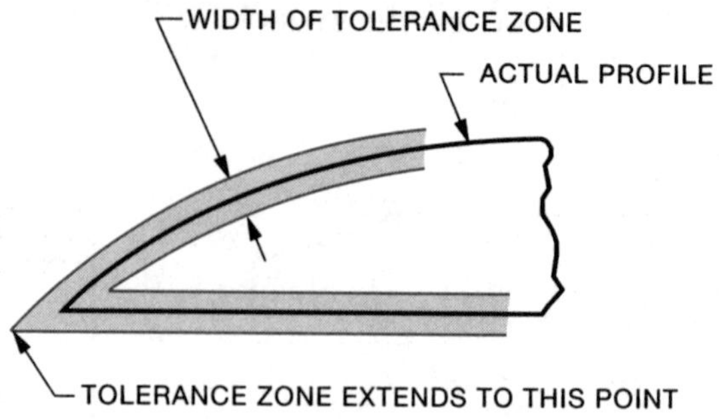

FIGURE 51–8 ■ Controlling the profile of a sharp corner

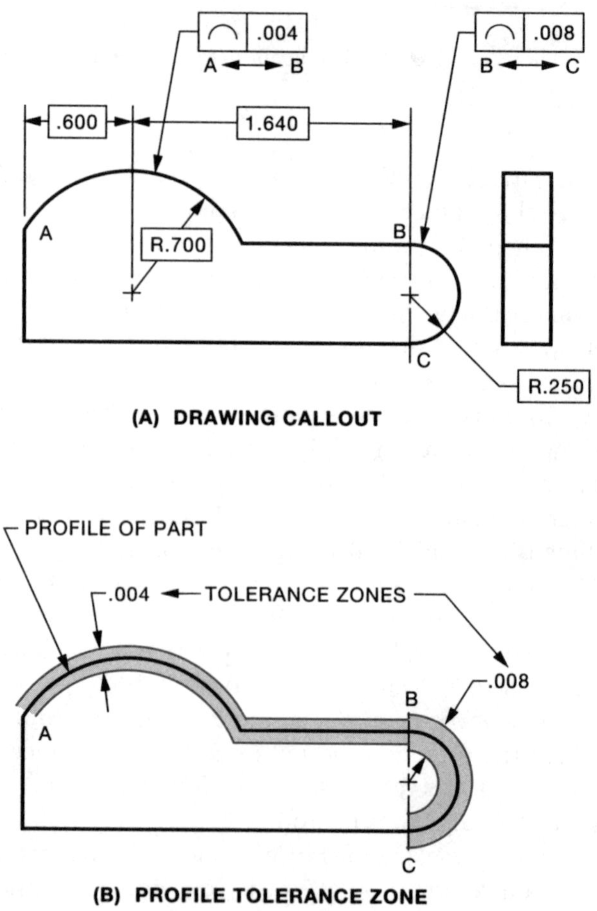

FIGURE 51–9 ■ Dual tolerance zones

The profile-of-a-surface tolerance indicates a tolerance zone having the same form as the basic surface, with a uniform width equal to the specified tolerance within which the entire surface must lie. It is used to control form or combinations of size, form, and orientation. Where used as a refinement of size, the profile tolerance must be contained within the size limits.

As previously mentioned, MMC is not applicable to profile tolerances.

The basic rules for profile-of-a-line tolerancing apply to profile-of-a-surface tolerancing except that, in most cases, profile-of-a-surface tolerance requires reference to datums in order to provide proper orientation of the profile. This is specified simply by indicating suitable datums. Figure 51–10 shows a simple part where two datums are designated.

The criterion that distinguishes a profile tolerance as applying to position or to orientation is whether the profile is related to the datum by a basic dimension or by a toleranced dimension.

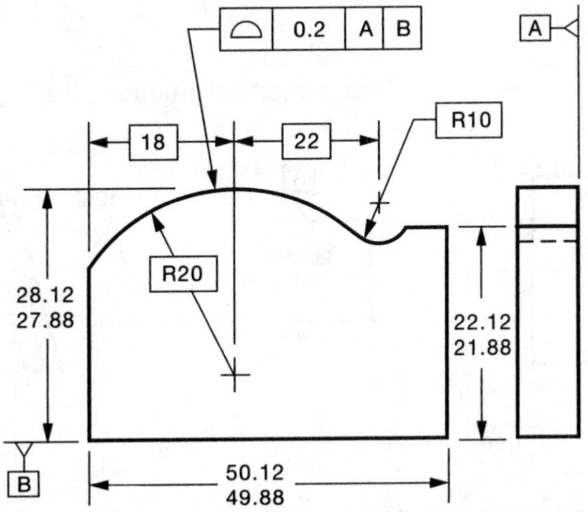

(A) PROFILE TOLERANCE CONTROLS FORM AND ORIENTATION OF A PROFILE

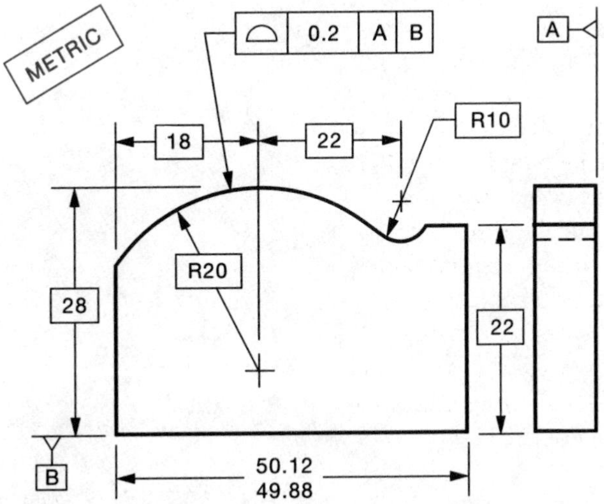

(B) PROFILE TOLERANCE CONTROLS FORM, ORIENTATION, AND POSITION OF A PROFILE

FIGURE 51–10 ■ Comparison of profile-of-a-surface tolerances

Profile tolerancing may be used to control the form and orientation of plane surfaces. In Figure 51–11, profile of a surface is used to control a plane surface inclined to a datum feature.

Where a profile-of-a-surface tolerance applies all around the profile of a part, the symbol used to designate "all around" is placed on the leader from the feature control frame, Figure 51–12.

REFERENCES

CAN/CSA-B78.2-M91 Dimensioning and Tolerancing of Technical Drawings

ASME Y14.5M-1994 Dimensioning and Tolerancing

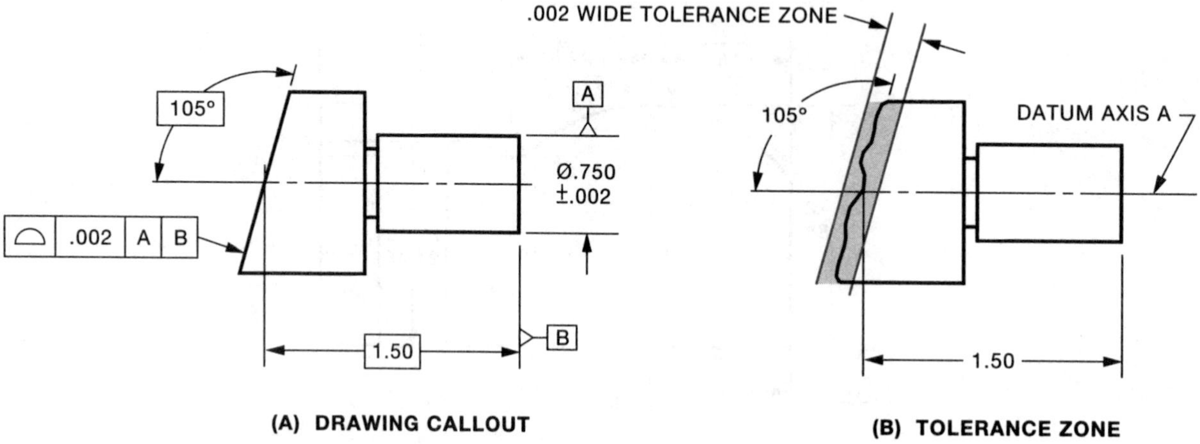

105°
A
Ø.750
±.002
.002
A
B
1.50
B
(A) DRAWING CALLOUT
.002 WIDE TOLERANCE ZONE
105°
DATUM AXIS A
1.50
(B) TOLERANCE ZONE

FIGURE 51–11 ■ Specifying profile-of-a-surface tolerance for a plane surface

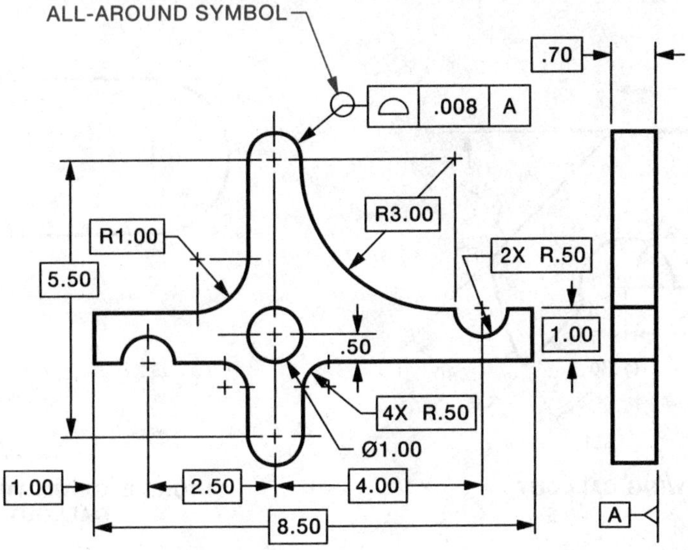

FIGURE 51–12 ■ Profile-of-a-surface tolerance required for all around the surface

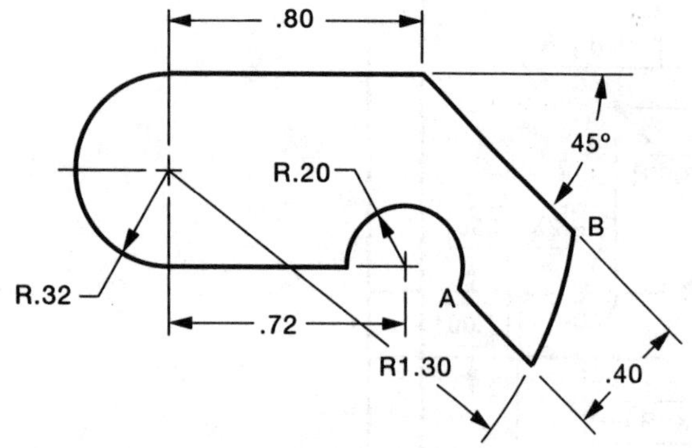

FIGURE 1 DRAWING CALLOUT

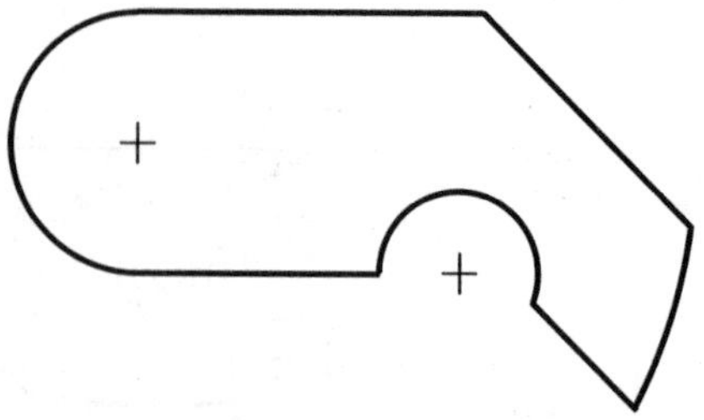

FIGURE 2 GEOMETRIC TOLERANCING CALLOUT FOR FIGURE 1

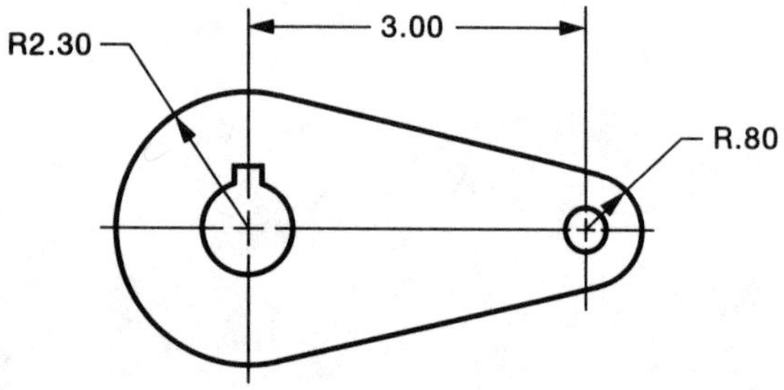

FIGURE 3 DRAWING CALLOUT

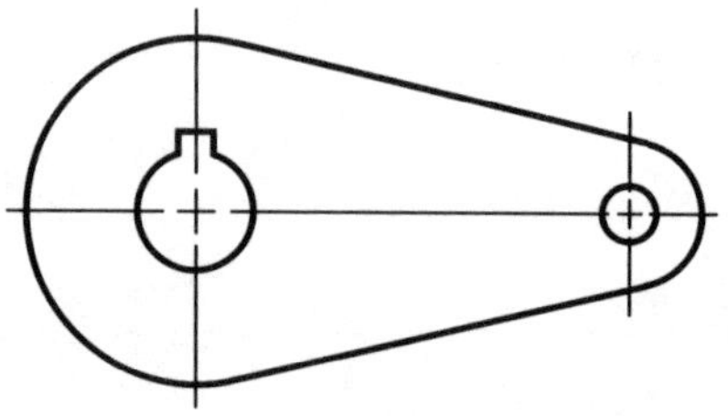

FIGURE 4 GEOMETRIC TOLERANCING CALLOUT FOR FIGURE 3

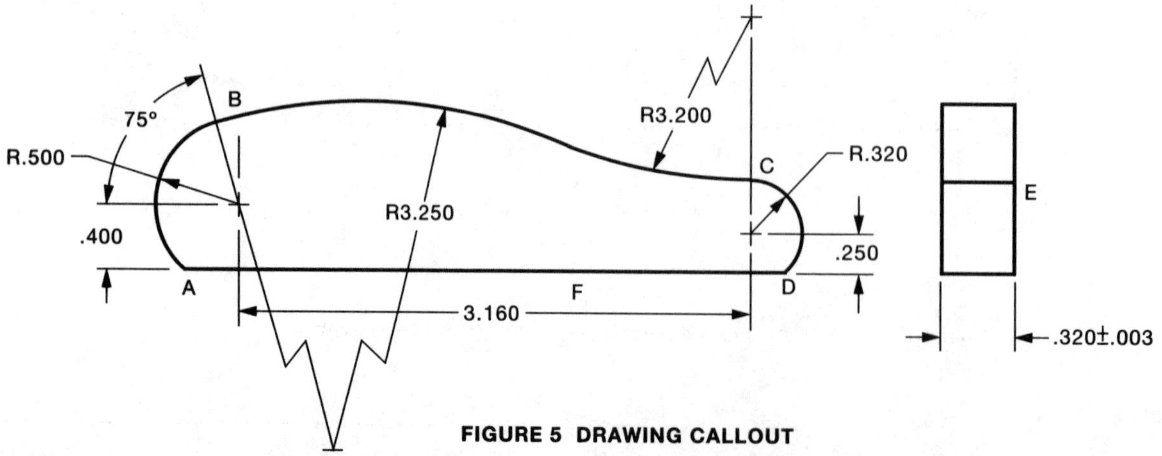

FIGURE 5 DRAWING CALLOUT

ASSIGNMENT:

1. The profile form B to A (clockwise) as shown in Figure 1 requires a profile-of-a-line tolerance of .004 in. It is essential that the point between B and A remain sharp, having a maximum .010-in. radius. The remainder of the profile requires a profile-of-a-line tolerance of .020 in. On Figure 2, show the geometric tolerance and basic dimensions to meet these requiirements.

2. The part shown in Figure 3 requires an all-around profile-of-a-line tolerance of .005 in. located on the outside of the true profile. On Figure 4, show the geometric tolerance and basic dimensions to meet these requirements.

3. With the information given below and that on Figure 5, dimension Figure 6 showing the geometric tolerances, datums, and basic dimensions. Profile-of-a-surface tolerances are to be applied to the part as follows:

   (A) between points A and B - .005 in.
   (B) between points B and C - .004 in.
   (C) between points C and D - .002 in.

   These tolerances are to be referenced to datum surfaces marked E and F, in that order.

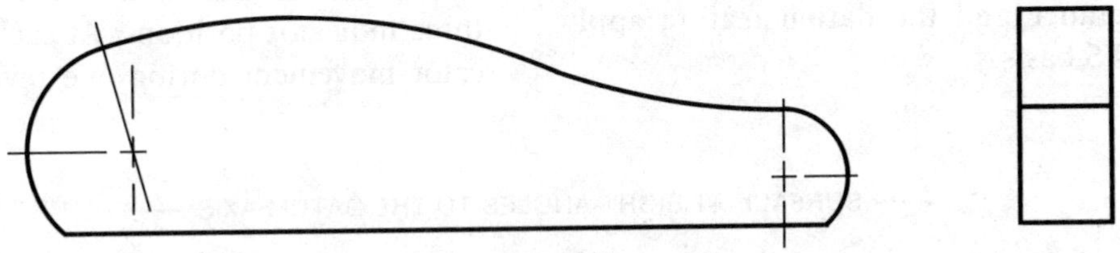

FIGURE 6 GEOMETRIC TOLERANCING CALLOUT FOR FIGURE 5

52 UNIT

RUNOUT TOLERANCES

Runout is a composite tolerance used to control the functional relationship of one or more features of a part to a datum axis. The types of features controlled by runout tolerances include those surfaces constructed around a datum axis and those constructed at right angles to a datum axis, Figure 52–1.

Each feature must be within its runout tolerance when rotated about the datum axis.

The datum axis is established by a diameter of sufficient length, two diameters having sufficient axial separation, or a diameter and a face at right angles to it. Features used as datums for establishing axes should be functional, such as mounting features that establish an axis of rotation.

The tolerance specified for a controlled surface is the total tolerance or full indicator movement (FIM) in inspection and international terminology. Both the tolerance and the datum feature apply only on an RFS basis.

There are two types of runout control: circular runout and total runout. The type used is dependent on design requirements and manufacturing considerations. The geometric characteristic symbols for runout are shown in Figure 52–2.

CIRCULAR RUNOUT

Circular runout provides control of circular elements of a surface. The tolerance is applied independently at any cross section as the part is rotated 360°. Where applied to surfaces constructed around a datum axis, circular runout controls variations such as circularity and coaxiality. Where applied to surfaces constructed at right angles to the datum axis, circular runout controls wobble at all diametral positions.

Thus, in Figure 52–3 the surface is measured at several positions along the surface, as shown by the three indicator positions. At each position the indicator movement during one revolution of the part

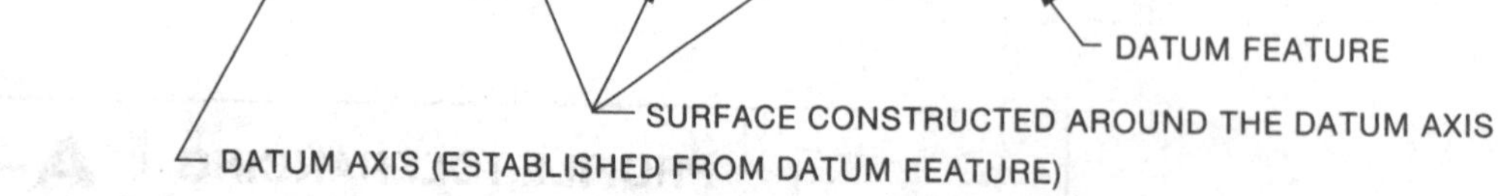
SURFACE AT RIGHT ANGLES TO THE DATUM AXIS
DATUM FEATURE
SURFACE CONSTRUCTED AROUND THE DATUM AXIS
DATUM AXIS (ESTABLISHED FROM DATUM FEATURE)

FIGURE 52–1 ■ Features applicable to runout tolerances

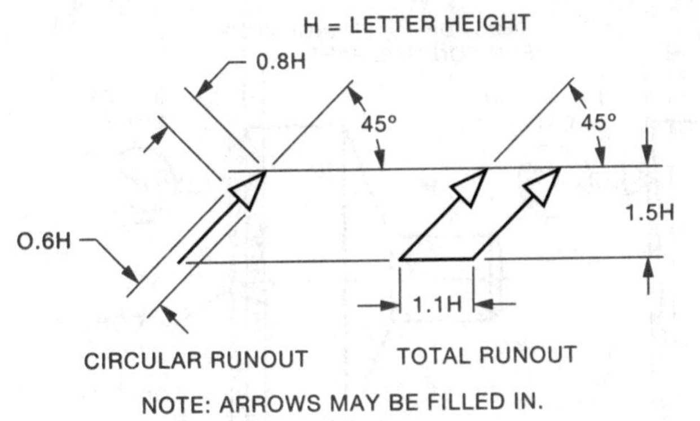

FIGURE 52–2 ■ Runout symbols

must not exceed the specified tolerance, in this case .005 inch. For a cylindrical feature such as this, runout error is caused by eccentricity and errors of roundness. It is not affected by taper (conicity) or errors of straightness of the straight line elements such as barrel shaping.

Figure 52–4 shows a part where the tolerance is applied to a surface that is at right angles to the axis. In this case, an error—generally referred to as wobble—will be shown if the surface is flat but not perpendicular to the axis, as shown at B. No error will be indicated if the surface is convex or concave but otherwise perfect, as shown at C.

Circular runout can also be applied to curved surfaces. Unless otherwise specified, measurement is always made normal to the surface.

A runout tolerance directed to a surface applies to the full length of the surface up to an abrupt change in direction.

If a control is intended to apply to more than one portion of a surface, additional leaders and arrowheads may be used where the same tolerance applies. If different tolerance values are required, separate tolerances must be specified.

Where a runout tolerance applies to a specific portion of a surface, a thick chain line is drawn adjacent to the surface profile to show the desired length. Basic dimensions are used to define the extent of the portion so indicated, Figure 52–5.

If only part of a surface or several consecutive portions require the same tolerance, the length to which the tolerance applies may be indicated as shown in Figure 52–6.

Circular runout can only be applied on an RFS basis.

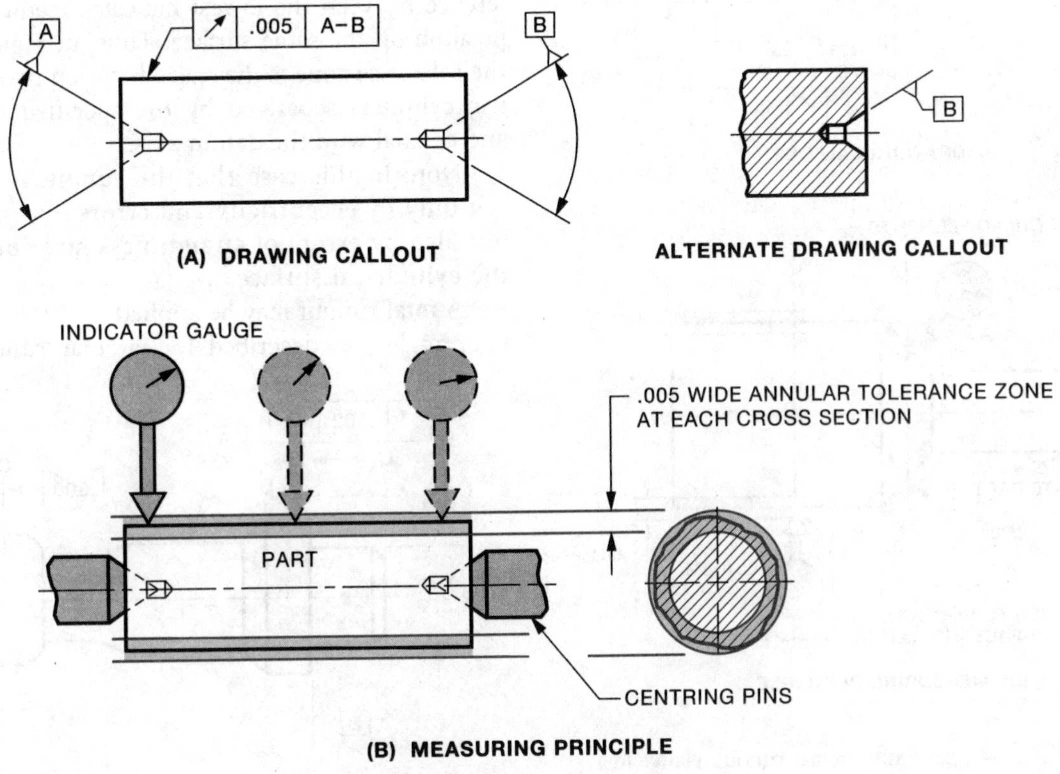

FIGURE 52–3 ■ Circular runout for cylindrical features

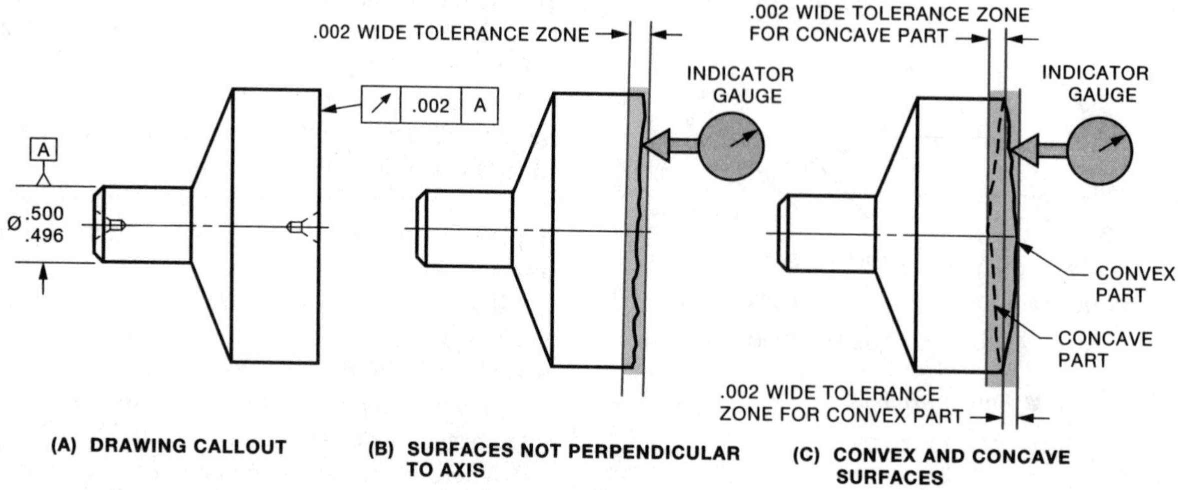

FIGURE 52–4 ■ Circular runout perpendicular to datum axis

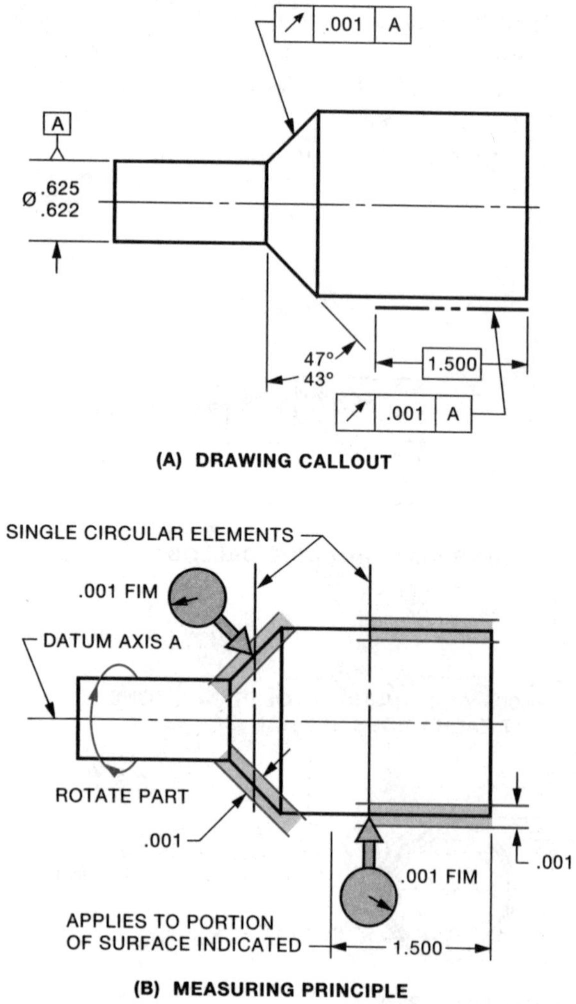

FIGURE 52–5 ■ Specifying circular runout relative to a datum diameter

TOTAL RUNOUT

Total runout concerns the runout of a complete surface, not merely the runout of each circular element. For measurement purposes, the checking indicator must traverse the full length or extent of the surface while the part is revolved about its datum axis. Measurements are made over the whole surface without resetting the indicator. Total runout is the difference between the lowest indicator reading in any position on the same surface. Thus, in Figure 52–7, the tolerance zone is the space between two concentric cylinders separated by the specified tolerance and coaxial with the datum axis.

Note in this case that the runout is affected not only by eccentricity and errors of roundness, but also by errors of straightness and conicity of the cylindrical surface.

A total runout may be applied to surfaces at various angles, as described for circular runout, and

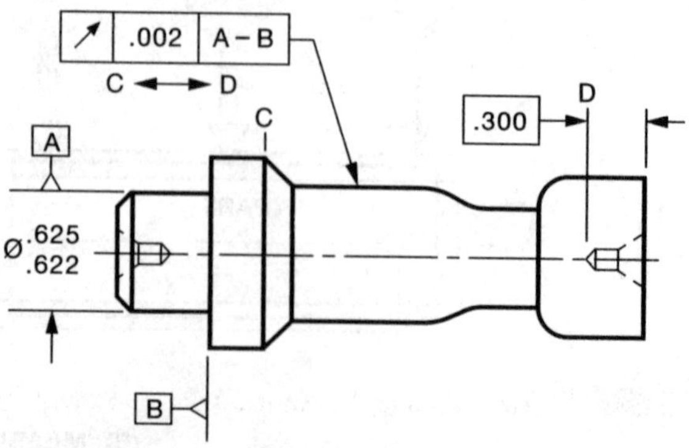

FIGURE 52–6 ■ Indication of length for a runout tolerance

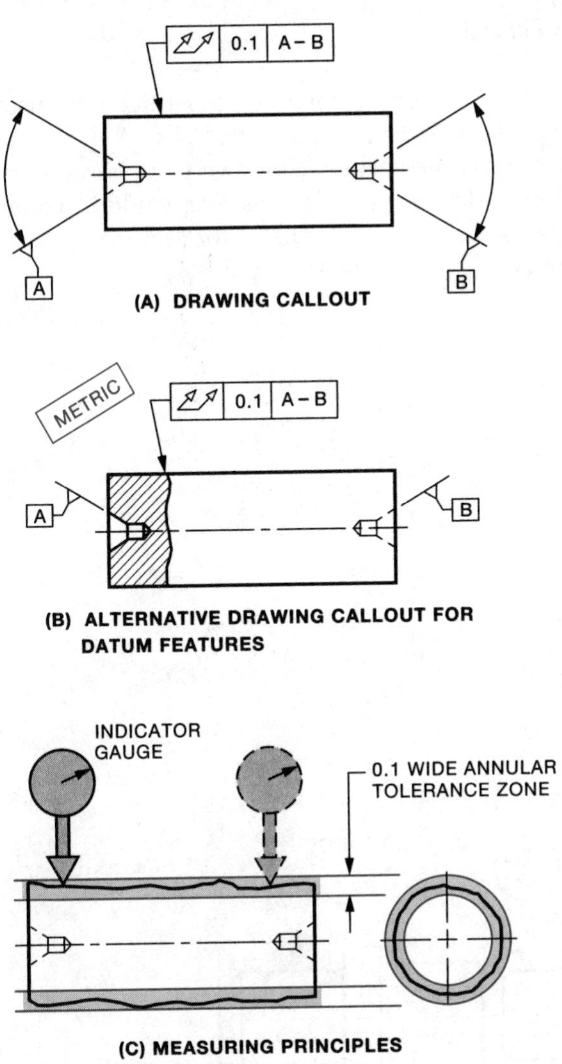

FIGURE 52–7 ■ Tolerance zones for total runout

may therefore control profile of the surface in addition to runout. However, for measurement purposes, the indicator gauge must be capable of following the true profile direction of the surface. This is comparatively simple for straight surfaces, such as cylindrical surfaces and flat faces. For conical surfaces, the datum axis can be tilted to the taper angle so that the measured surface becomes parallel to a surface plate.

ESTABLISHING DATUMS

In many examples the datum axis has been established from centres drilled in the two ends of the part, in which case the part is mounted between centres for measurement purposes. This is an ideal method of mounting and revolving the part when such centres have been provided for manufacturing purposes. When centres are not provided, any cylindrical or conical surface may be used to establish the datum axis if chosen on the basis of the functional requirements of the part. In some cases, a runout tolerance may also be applied to the datum feature. Some examples of suitable datum features and methods of establishing datum axes are discussed next.

Measuring Principles

Example 1

Figure 52–8 shows a simple external cylindrical feature specified as the datum feature.

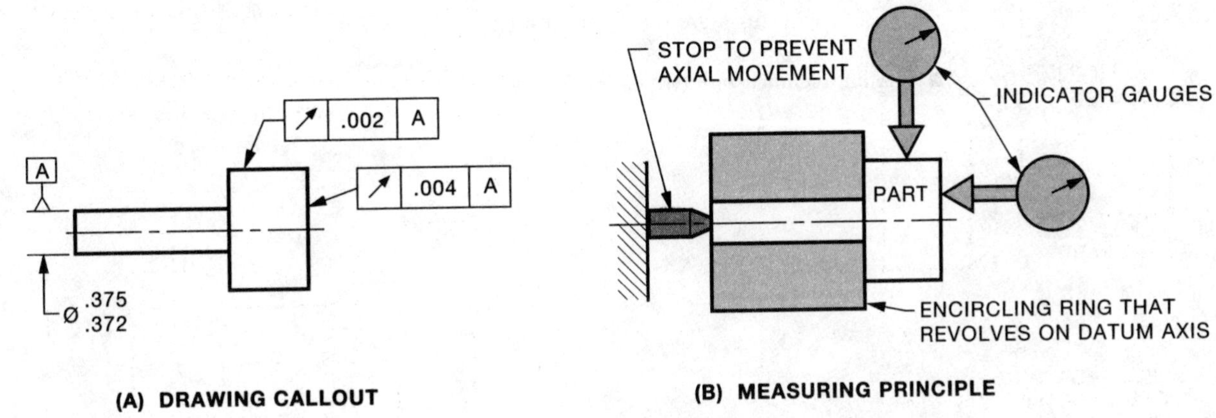

FIGURE 52–8 ■ External cylindrical datum feature for runout tolerance

Measurement would require the datum feature to be held in an encircling ring capable of being revolved about the datum axis. Parts with these types of datum features are sometimes mounted in a vee-block, although this practice permits precise measurements only if there are no significant roundness errors of the datum feature.

Example 2

The L-support method is particularly useful when two datum features are used, Figure 52–9. Measuring the part by using two L-supports is quite simple. Measurement for this part would be complicated were it necessary to fit the features into concentric encircling rings.

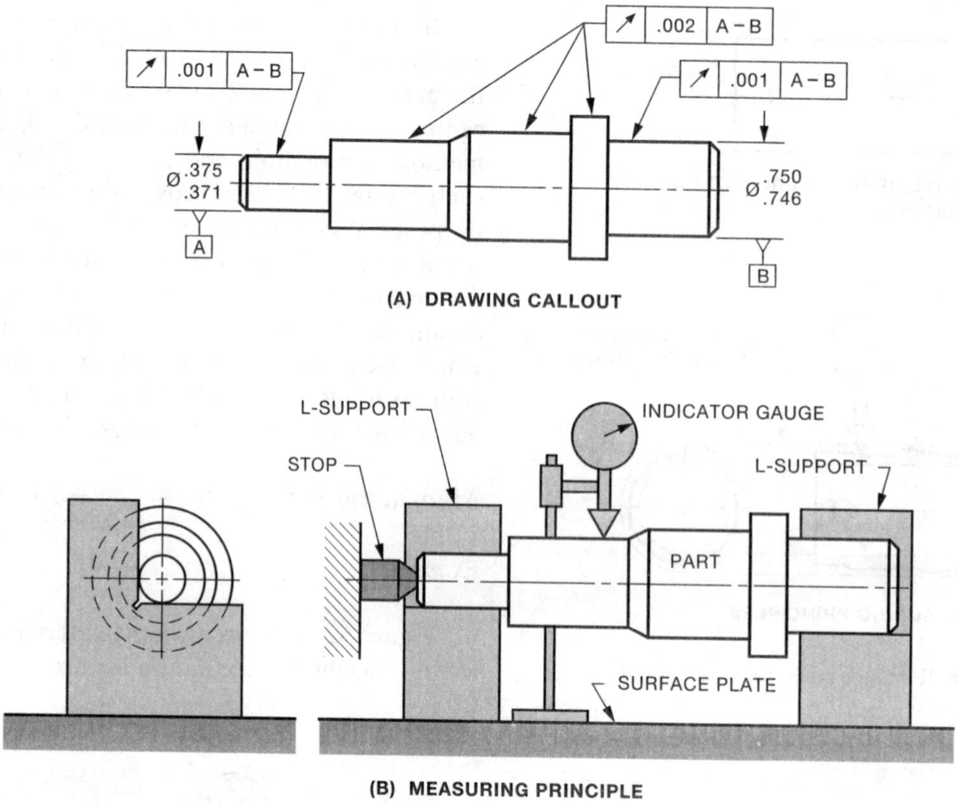

FIGURE 52–9 ■ Runout tolerance with two datum features

Example 3

Figure 52–10 illustrates the application of runout tolerances where two datum diameters act as a single datum axis to which the features are related. For measurement purposes, the part may be mounted on a mandrel having a diameter equal to the maximum size of the hole.

When required, runout tolerances may be referenced to a datum system, usually consisting of two datum features perpendicular to each other. For measuring purposes, the part is mounted on a flat surface capable of being rotated. Centring on the secondary datum requires some form of centralizing device, such as an expandable arbor.

Example 4

It may be necessary to control individual datum surface variations with respect to flatness, circularity, parallelism, straightness, or cylindricity. Where such control is required, the appropriate tolerances are specified. See Figure 52–11 for applying cylindricity to the datum.

REFERENCES

CAN/CSA-B78.2-M91 Dimensioning and Tolerancing of Technical Drawings
ASME Y14.5M-1994 Dimensioning and Tolerancing

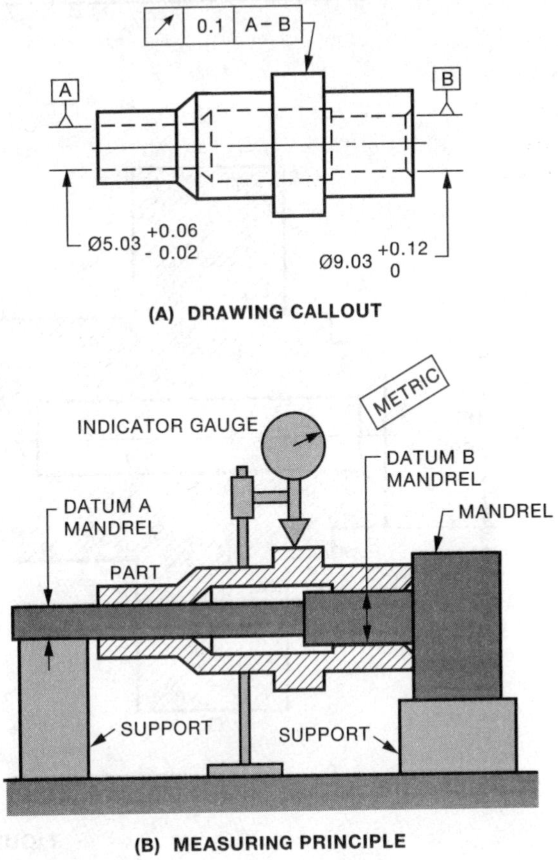

FIGURE 52–10 ■ Specifying runout relative to two datum diameters

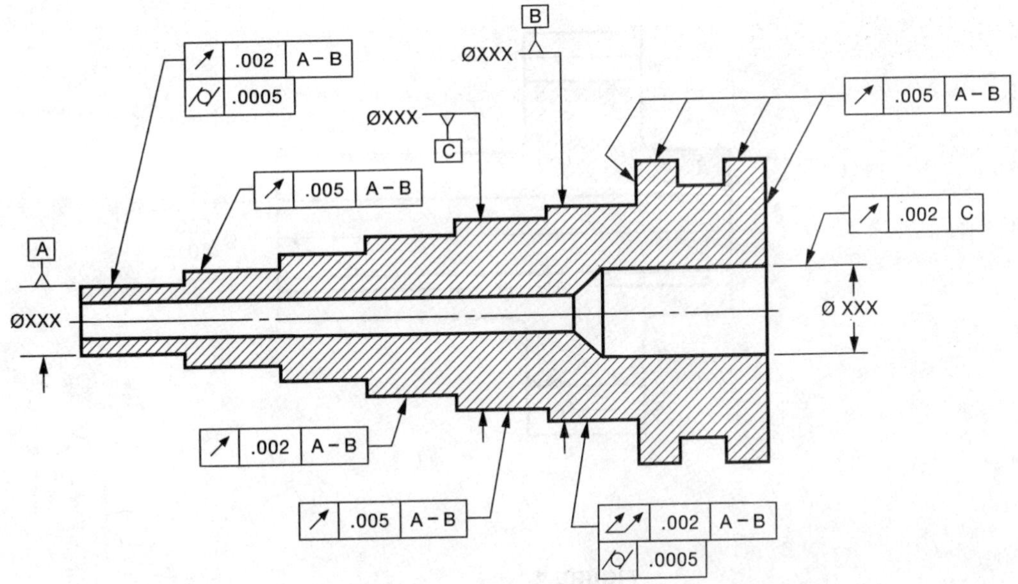

FIGURE 52–11 ■ Specifying runout relative to two datum diameters with form tolerances

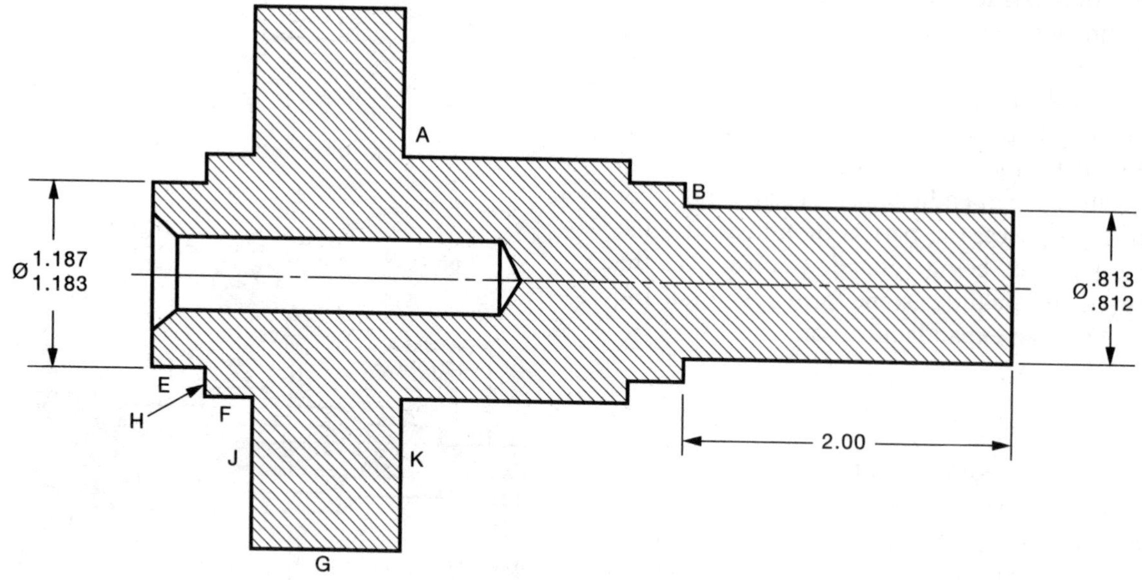

FIGURE 1

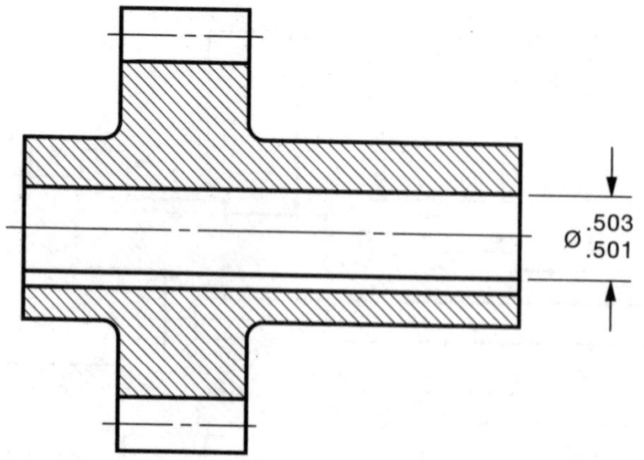

FIGURE 2

ASSIGNMENT:

1. The part shown in Figure 1 requires runout tolerances and datums as follows:
   (A) The Ø1.187 in. is to be datum C.
   (B) A 1.20-in. length starting .40 in. from the right end of the part is to be datum D.
   (C) Runout tolerances are related to the axis established by datums C and D.
   (D) A total runout tolerance of .005 in. between positions A and B.
   (E) A circular runout tolerance of .002 in. for diameters E and F.
   (F) A circular runout tolerance of .005 in. for diameter G.
   (G) A circular runout tolerance of .004 in. for surface H.
   (H) A circular runout tolerance of .003 in. for surfaces J and K.

2. The gear shown in Figure 2 requires circular runout tolerances referenced to datum A. Both side faces of the gear portion require a tolerance of .015 in. The two hub portions require a tolerance of .010 in. The hole is to be datum A. Add these requirements to the drawing.

3. The part shown in Figure 3 is intended to function by rotating with the two ends (datum diameters A and B) supported in bearings. These two datums collectively act as a coaxial datum for the larger diameters, which are required to have a total runout tolerance of .001 in. Add the above requirements to the drawing.

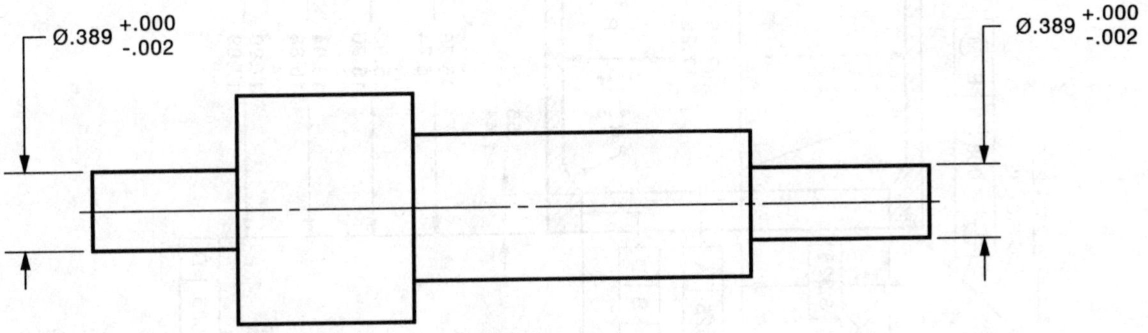
Ø.389 +.000 -.002
Ø.389 +.000 -.002

FIGURE 3

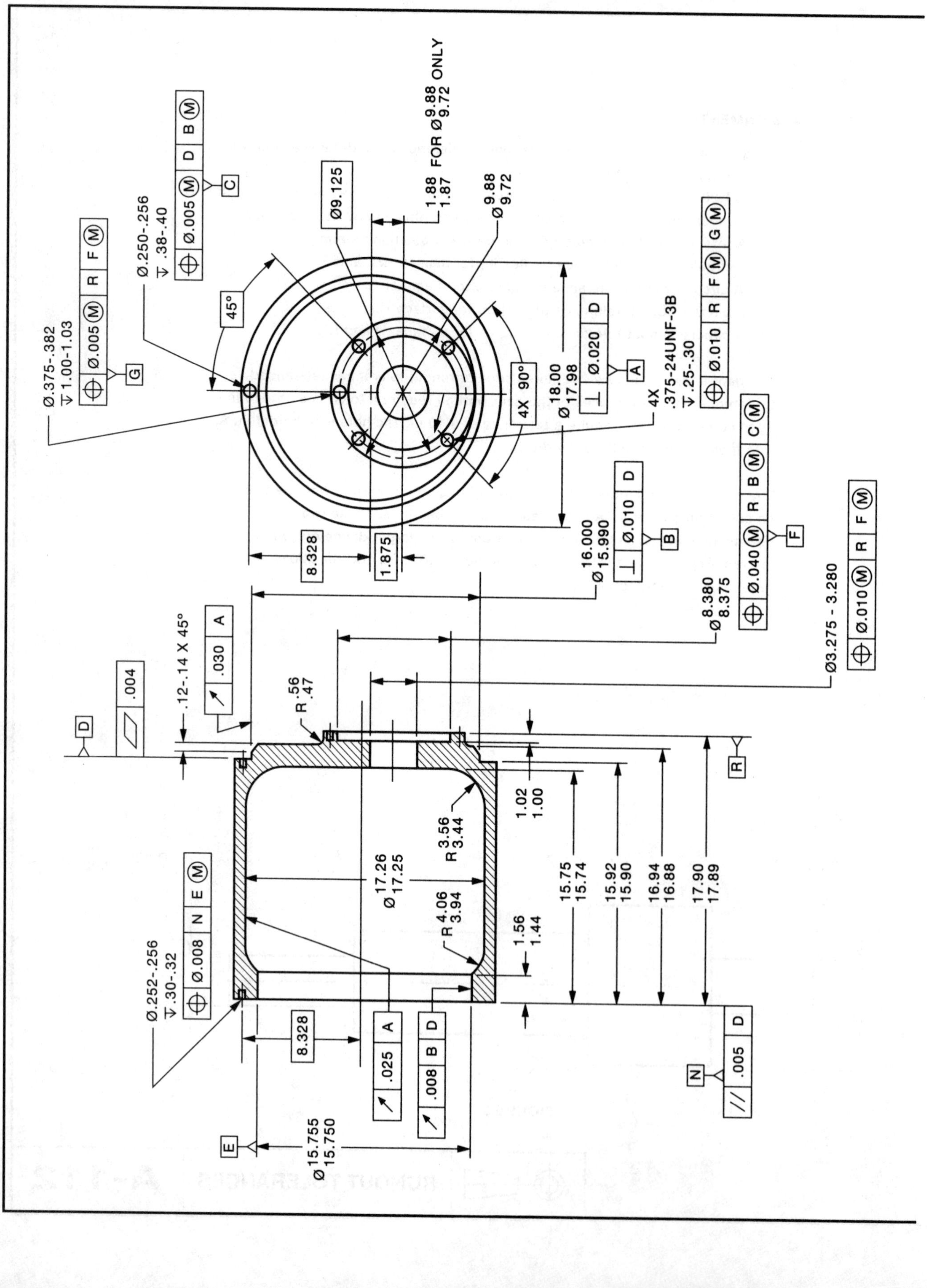
Ø.375-.382
↧ 1.00-1.03
Ø.250-.256
↧ .38-.40
Ø9.125
1.88
1.87
FOR Ø9.88
9.72
ONLY
Ø9.88
9.72
45°
4X 90°
Ø18.00
17.98
4X
.375-24UNF-3B
↧ .25-.30
8.328
1.875
Ø16.000
15.990
Ø8.380
8.375
Ø3.275 - 3.280
.12-.14 X 45°
.004
.030
R .56
.47
R 3.56
3.44
R 4.06
3.94
Ø17.26
17.25
1.02
1.00
1.56
1.44
15.75
15.74
15.92
15.90
16.94
16.88
17.90
17.89
Ø.252-.256
↧ .30-.32
Ø.008
.025
.008
.005
Ø15.755
15.750
Ø.005 Ⓜ
Ø.020
Ø.010
Ø.040 Ⓜ
Ø.010 Ⓜ

GRID SIZE TO SUIT

ASSIGNMENT:

1. Sketch a suitable gauge to check the Ø3.275-3.280 hole.
2. Make a sketch of datum surface D showing the permissible tolerance zone.
3. Make a sketch of datum surface N showing the permissible tolerance zone.

QUESTIONS

1. How many datum surfaces or points are indicated?
2. How many basic dimensions are indicated?
3. How many datum surfaces are flat?
4. How many datum surfaces are circular?
5. How many dimensions show positional tolerancing?
6. How many form tolerances are required?
7. How many orientation tolerances are shown?
8. How many features use datum A as a reference?
9. If the diameter of datum F was Ø8.375, what would be the maximum permissible positional tolerance?
10. What is the tertiary datum for the positional tolerance of the diameter shown as datum F?
11. The geometric tolerance placed on datum surface D controls______.
12. With reference to the Ø3.275-3.280 hole, what is the maximum deviation permitted from true position when the hole is (A) Ø3.275 and (B) Ø3.280?
13. With refenence to the Ø.252-.256 hole, what is the maximum deviation permitted from true position if the hole was (A) Ø.252 and (B) Ø.256?
14. With reference to the Ø.250-.256 hole, what is the maximum deviation permitted from true position if the hole was (A) Ø.250, (B) Ø.254, and (C) Ø.256?

ANSWERS

1. ______
2. ______
3. ______
4. ______
5. ______
6. ______
7. ______
8. ______
9. ______
10. ______
11. ______
______
12. A ______
B ______
13. A ______
B ______
14. A ______
B ______
C ______

	HOUSING	**A-113**

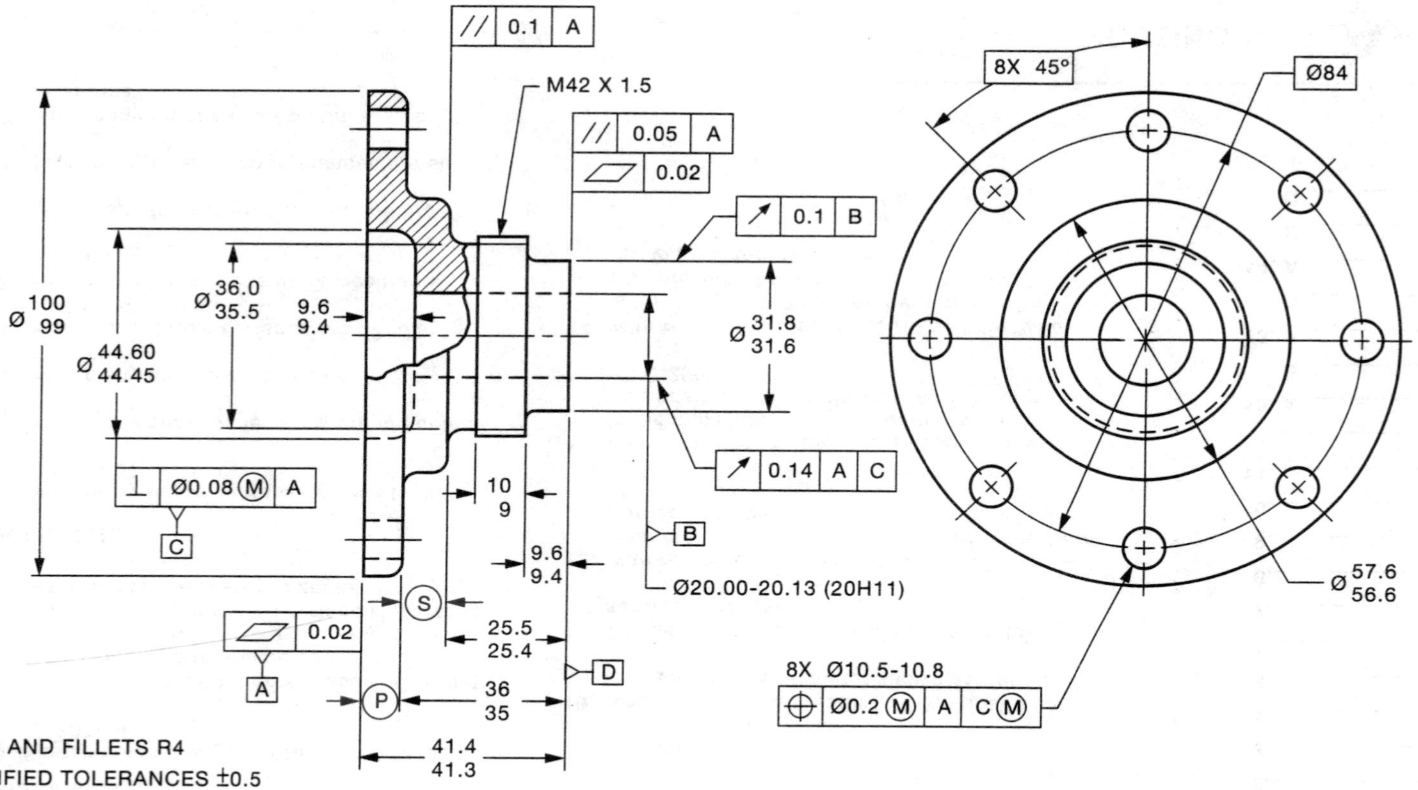

ROUNDS AND FILLETS R4
UNSPECIFIED TOLERANCES ±0.5

ASSIGNMENT:

1. Sketch a suitable gauge to check the eight Ø10.5-10.8 holes.
2. Make a sketch of datum surface C showing the permissible tolerance zone.
3. Make a sketch of datum surface D showing the permissible tolerance zone.

QUESTIONS

1. How many datum surfaces are indicated?
2. How many basic dimensions are shown?
3. How many different geometric tolerancing symbols are shown?
4. How many datum surfaces are circular?
5. How many features use datum A as a reference?
6. How many form tolerances are shown?
7. With reference to the Ø10.5-10.8 holes, what variation from the true position is permissible if the holes are (A) Ø10.5 and (B) Ø10.8?
8. Calculate the following dimensions: (A) P min., (B) P max., (C) S min., and (D) S max.

METRIC
DIMENSIONS ARE IN MILLIMETRES

END PLATE | **A-114M**

APPENDIX

Fraction	Decimal Inch		Millimetres	Fraction	Decimal Inch		Millimetres
	Two Place	Three Place			Two Place	Three Place	
1/64	.02	.016	.04	33/64	.52	.516	13.1
1/32	.03	.031	.08	17/32	.53	.531	13.5
3/64	.05	.047	1.2	35/64	.55	.547	13.9
1/16	.06	.062	1.6	9/16	.56	.562	14.3
5/64	.08	.078	2	37/64	.58	.578	14.7
3/32	.09	.094	2.4	19/32	.59	.594	15.1
7/64	.11	.109	2.8	39/64	.61	.609	15.5
1/8	.12	.125	3.2	5/8	.62	.625	15.9
9/64	.14	.141	3.6	41/64	.64	.641	16.3
5/32	.16	.156	4	21/32	.66	.656	16.7
11/64	.17	.172	4.4	43/64	.67	.672	17.1
3/16	.19	.188	4.8	11/16	.69	.688	17.5
13/64	.20	.203	5.2	45/64	.70	.703	17.9
7/32	.22	.219	5.6	23/32	.72	.719	18.3
15/64	.23	.234	6	47/64	.73	.734	18.7
1/4	.25	.250	6.4	3/4	.75	.750	19.1
17/64	.27	.266	6.8	49/64	.77	.766	19.5
9/32	.28	.281	7.1	25/32	.78	.781	19.9
19/64	.30	.297	7.5	51/64	.80	.797	20.2
5/16	.31	.312	7.9	13/16	.81	.812	20.6
21/64	.33	.328	8.3	53/64	.83	.828	21
11/32	.34	.344	8.7	27/32	.84	.844	21.4
23/64	.36	.359	9.1	55/64	.86	.859	21.8
3/8	.38	.375	9.5	7/8	.88	.875	22.2
25/64	.39	.391	9.9	57/64	.89	.891	22.6
13/32	.41	.406	10.3	29/32	.91	.906	23
27/64	.42	.422	10.7	59/64	.92	.922	23.4
7/16	.44	.438	11.1	15/16	.94	.938	23.8
29/64	.45	.453	11.5	61/64	.95	.953	24.2
15/32	.47	.469	11.9	31/32	.97	.969	24.6
31/64	.48	.484	12.3	63/64	.98	.984	25
1/2	.50	.500	12.7	1	1.00	1.000	25.4

TABLE 1 ■ Chart for Converting Inch Dimensions to Millimetres

Term	Abbreviation or Symbol
Across Flats	ACR FLT
And	&
Approximate	APPROX
Assembly	ASSY
Bill of Material	B/M
Bolt Circle	BC
Brass	BR
Bronze	BRZ
Brown and Sharpe Gauge	B & S GA
Carbon Steel	CS
Cast Iron	CI
Centimetre	cm
Centre Line	℄ or CL
Centre to Centre	C to C
Chamfer	CHAM
Circularity	CIR
Cold Rolled Steel	CRS
Concentric	CONC
Conical Taper	⌲
Copper	COP
Counterbore	CBORE or ⌴
Countersink	CSK or ⌵
Cubic Centimetre	cm^3
Cubic Metre	m^3
Datum	[A] over △
Deep or Depth	↧
Degree (Angle)	°
Diameter	Ø or DIA
Diametral Pitch	DP
Dimension	DIM
Dimension Origin	⌖
Drawing	DWG
Eccentric	ECC
Equally Spaced	EQL SP
Figure	FIG
Finish All Over	FAO
Gauge	GA
Grey Iron	GI
Head	HD
Heat Treat	HT TR
Hexagon	HEX
Inside Diameter	ID
International Organization for Standardization	ISO
International Pipe Standard	IPS
Kilogram	kg
Kilometre	km
Least Material Condition	LMC or Ⓛ
Left Hand	LH
Long	LG
Machined	✓
Machine Steel	MST
Malleable Iron	MI
Material	MATL
Maximum	MAX
Maximum Material Condition	MMC or Ⓜ
Metre	m
Metric Thread	M
Micrometre	μm
Mild Steel	MS
Millimetre	mm
Minimum	MIN
Minute (Angle)	(′)
Nominal	NOM
Not to Scale	XXX
Number	NO
Outside Diameter	OD
Parallel	PAR
Perpendicular	PERP
Pitch Circle Diameter	PCD
Pitch Diameter	PD
Projected Tolerance Zone	Ⓟ
Radius	R
Reference or Reference Dimension	( )
Regardless of Feature Size	RFS
Revolutions per Minute	R/MIN
Right Hand	RH
Second (Arc)	″
Section	SECT
Slope	⊿
Spherical Radius	SR
Spotface	SF or ⌴
Square	SQ or □
Square Centimetre	cm^2
Square Metre	m^2
Steel	STL
Symmetrical	SYM or ⌯
Symmetry	⌯
Taper Pipe Thread	NPT
Thick	THK
Through	THRU
Undercut	UCUT
United States Gauge	USG
Wrought Iron	WI
Wrought Steel	WS

TABLE 2 ■ Abbreviations and Symbols Used on Technical Drawings

Decimal Inch and Millimetre Equivalents of Number Size Drills						Decimal Inch and Millimetre Equivalents of Letter Size Drills		
No.	Decimal Inch	mm	No.	Decimal Inch	mm	Letter	Decimal Inch	mm
1	.2280	5.8	31	.1200	3.0	A	.234	5.9
2	.2210	5.6	32	.1160	2.9	B	.238	6.0
3	.2130	5.4	33	.1130	2.9	C	.242	6.1
4	.2090	5.3	34	.1110	2.8	D	.246	6.2
5	.2055	5.2	35	.1100	2.8	E	.250	6.4
6	.2040	5.2	36	.1065	2.7	F	.257	6.5
7	.2010	5.1	37	.1040	2.6	G	.261	6.6
8	.1990	5.1	38	.1015	2.6	H	.266	6.8
9	.1960	5.0	39	.0095	2.5	I	.272	6.9
10	.1935	4.9	40	.0980	2.5	J	.277	7.0
11	.1910	4.9	41	.0960	2.4	K	.281	7.1
12	.1890	4.8	42	.0935	2.4	L	.290	7.4
13	.1850	4.7	43	.0890	2.3	M	.295	7.5
14	.1820	4.6	44	.0860	2.2	N	.302	7.7
15	.1800	4.6	45	.0820	2.1	O	.316	8.0
16	.1770	4.5	46	.0810	2.1	P	.323	8.2
17	.1730	4.4	47	.0785	2.0	Q	.332	8.4
18	.1695	4.3	48	.0760	1.9	R	.339	8.6
19	.1660	4.2	49	.0730	1.9	S	.348	8.8
20	.1610	4.1	50	.0700	1.8	T	.358	9.1
21	.1590	4.0	51	.0670	1.7	U	.368	9.3
22	.1570	4.0	52	.0635	1.6	V	.377	9.6
23	.1540	3.9	53	.0595	1.5	W	.386	9.8
24	.1520	3.9	54	.0550	1.4	X	.397	10.1
25	.1495	3.8	55	.0520	1.3	Y	.404	10.3
26	.1470	3.7	56	.0465	1.2	Z	.413	10.5
27	.1440	3.7	57	.0430	1.1			
28	.1405	3.6	58	.0420	1.1			
29	.1360	3.5	59	.0410	1.0			
30	.1285	3.3	60	.0400	1.0			

TABLE 3 ■ Number and Letter Size Drills

Metric Drill Sizes (mm)		Reference Decimal Equivalent (Inches)	Metric Drill Sizes (mm)		Reference Decimal Equivalent (Inches)	Metric Drill Sizes (mm)		Reference Decimal Equivalent (Inches)
Preferred	Available		Preferred	Available		Preferred	Available	
–	0.40	.0157	2.2	–	.0866	10	–	.3937
–	0.42	.0165	–	2.3	.0906	–	10.3	.4055
–	0.45	.0177	2.4	–	.0945	10.5	–	.4134
–	0.48	.0189	2.5	–	.0984	–	10.8	.4252
0.5	–	.0197	2.6	–	.1024	11	–	.4331
–	0.52	.0205	–	2.7	.1063	–	11.5	.4528
0.55	–	.0217	2.8	–	.1102	12	–	.4724
–	0.58	.0228	–	2.9	.1142	12.5	–	.4921
0.6	–	.0236	3	–	.1181	13	–	.5118
–	0.62	.0244	–	3.1	.1220	–	13.5	.5315
0.65	–	.0256	3.2	–	.1260	14	–	.5512
–	0.68	.0268	–	3.3	.1299	–	14.5	.5709
0.7	–	.0276	3.4	–	.1339	15	–	.5906
–	0.72	.0283	–	3.5	.1378	–	15.5	.6102
0.75	–	.0295	3.6	–	.1417	16	–	.6299
–	0.78	.0307	–	3.7	.1457	–	16.5	.6496
0.8	–	.0315	3.8	–	.1496	17	–	.6693
–	0.82	.0323	–	3.9	.1535	–	17.5	.6890
0.85	–	.0335	4	–	.1575	18	–	.7087
–	0.88	.0346	–	4.1	.1614	–	18.5	.7283
0.9	–	.0354	4.2	–	.1654	19	–	.7480
–	0.92	.0362	–	4.4	.1732	–	19.5	.7677
0.95	–	.0374	4.5	–	.1772	20	–	.7874
–	0.98	.0386	–	4.6	.1811	–	20.5	.8071
1	–	.0394	4.8	–	.1890	21	–	.8268
–	1.03	.0406	5	–	.1969	–	21.5	.8465
1.05	–	.0413	–	5.2	.2047	22	–	.8661
–	1.08	.0425	5.3	–	.2087	–	23	.9055
1.1	–	.0433	–	5.4	.2126	24	–	.9449
–	1.15	.0453	5.6	–	.2205	25	–	.9843
1.2	–	.0472	–	5.8	.2283	26	–	1.0236
1.25	–	.0492	6	–	.2362	–	27	1.0630
1.3	–	.0512	–	6.2	.2441	28	–	1.1024
–	1.35	.0531	6.3	–	.2480	–	29	1.1417
1.4	–	.0551	–	6.5	.2559	30	–	1.1811
–	1.45	.0571	6.7	–	.2638	–	31	1.2205
1.5	–	.0591	–	6.8	.2677	32	–	1.2598
–	1.55	.0610	–	6.9	.2717	–	33	1.2992
1.6	–	.0630	7.1	–	.2795	34	–	1.3386
–	1.65	.0650	–	7.3	.2874	–	35	1.3780
1.7	–	.0669	7.5	–	.2953	36	–	1.4173
–	1.75	.0689	–	7.8	.3071	–	37	1.4567
1.8	–	.0709	8	–	.3150	38	–	1.4961
–	1.85	.0728	–	8.2	.3228	–	39	1.5354
1.9	–	.0748	8.5	–	.3346	40	–	1.5748
–	1.95	.0768	–	8.8	.3465	–	41	1.6142
2	–	.0787	9	–	.3543	42	–	1.6535
–	2.05	.0807	–	9.2	.3622	–	43.5	1.7126
2.1	–	.0827	9.5	–	.3740	45	–	1.7717
–	2.15	.0846	–	9.8	.3858	–	46.5	1.8307

TABLE 4 ■ Metric Twist Drill Sizes

Size		Coarse Thread Series UNC & NC		Fine Thread Series UNF & NF		Extra Fine Series UNEF & NEF		8-Pitch Thread Series 8 N		12-Pitch Thread Series 12 N		16-Pitch Thread Series 16 N	
Number or Fraction	Decimal	Threads Per Inch	Tap Drill	Threads Per Inch	Tap Drill	Threads Per Inch	Tap Drill	Threads Per Inch	Tap Drill	Threads Per Inch	Tap Drill	Threads Per Inch	Tap Drill
	.060			80	3/64								
1	.073	64	No. 53	72	No. 53								
2	.086	56	No. 50	64	No. 50								
3	.099	48	No. 47	56	No. 45								
4	.112	40	No. 43	48	No. 42								
5	.125	40	No. 38	44	No. 37								
6	.138	32	No. 36	40	No. 33								
8	.164	32	No. 29	36	No. 29								
10	.190	24	No. 25	32	No. 21								
12	.216	24	No. 16	28	No. 14	32	No. 13						
1/4	250	20	No. 7	28	No. 3	32	7/32						
5/16	.312	18	F	24	I	32	9/32						
3/8	.375	16	5/16	24	Q	32	11/32						
7/16	.438	14	U	20	25/64	28	13/32						
1/2	.500	13	27/64										
1/2	.500	12		20	29/64	28	15/32			12	27/64		
9/16	.562	12	31/64	18	33/64	24	33/64			12	31/64		
5/8	.625	11	17/32	18	37/64	24	37/64			12	35/64		
3/4	.750	10	21/32	16	11/16	20	45/64			12	43/64	16	11/16
7/8	.875	9	49/64	14	13/16	20	53/64			12	51/64	16	13/16
1	1.000	8	7/8	12	59/64	20	61/64	8	7/8	12	59/64	16	15/16
1 1/8	1.125	7	63/64	12	1 3/64	18	1 5/64	8	1	12	1 3/64	16	1 1/16
1 1/4	1.250	7	1 7/64	12	1 11/64	18	1 3/16	8	1 1/8	12	1 11/64	16	1 3/16
1 3/8	1.375	6	1 7/32	12	1 19/64	18	1 5/16	8	1 1/4	12	1 19/64	16	1 5/16
1 1/2	1.500	6	1 11/32	12	1 27/64	18	1 7/16	8	1 3/8	12	1 27/64	16	1 7/16
1 3/4	1.750	5	1 9/16			16	1 11/16	8	1 5/8	12	1 43/64	16	1 11/16
2	2.000	4 1/2	1 25/32			16	1 15/16	8	1 7/8	12	1 51/64	16	1 15/16
2 1/4	2.250	4 1/2	2 1/32					8	2 1/8	12	2 11/64	16	2 3/16
1 1/2	2.500	4	2 1/4					8	2 3/8	12	2 27/64	16	2 7/16
2 3/4	2.750	4	2 1/2					8	2 5/8	12	2 43/64	16	2 11/16
3	3.000	4	2 3/4					8	2 7/8	12	2 59/64	16	2 15/16

Colour shows unified thread

TABLE 5 ■ Unified and American (Inch) Threads

Nominal Size DIA (mm)		Series with Graded Pitches				Series with Constant Pitches																	
		Course		Fine		4		3		2		1.5		1.25		1		0.75		0.5		0.35	
Preferred		Thread Pitch	Tap Drill Size	Thread Pitch	Tap Drill Size	Thread Pitch	Tap Drill Size	Thread Pitch	Tap Drill Size	Thread Pitch	Tap Drill Size	Thread Pitch	Tap Drill Size	Thread Pitch	Tap Drill Size	Thread Pitch	Tap Drill Size	Thread Pitch	Tap Drill Size	Thread Pitch	Tap Drill Size	Thread Pitch	Tap Drill Size
1.6		0.35	1.25																				
	1.8	0.35	1.45																				
2		0.4	1.6																				
	2.2	0.45	1.75																				
2.5		0.45	2.05																			0.35	2.15
3		0.5	2.5																			0.35	2.65
	3.5	0.6	2.9																			0.35	3.15
4		0.7	3.3																	0.5	3.5		
	4.5	0.75	3.7																	0.5	4		
5		0.8	4.2																	0.5	4.5		
*6		1	5															0.75	5.2				
**6.3		1	5.3																				
8		1.25	6.7	1	7											1	7	0.75	7.2				
10		1.5	8.5	1.25	8.7											1	9	0.75	9.2				
12		1.75	10.2	1.25	10.8							1.5	10.5	1.25	8.7	1	11						
	14	2	12	1.5	12.5							1.5	12.5	1.25	10.7	1	13						
16		2	14	1.5	14.5							1.5	14.5	1.25	12.7	1	15						
	18	2.5	15.5	1.5	16.5					2	16	1.5	16.5			1	17						
20		2.5	17.5	1.5	18.5					2	18	1.5	18.5			1	19						
	22	2.5	19.5	1.5	20.5					2	20	1.5	20.5			1	21						
24		3	21	2	22					2	22	1.5	22.5			1	23						
	27	3	24	2	25					2	25	1.5	25.5			1	26						
30		3.5	26.5	2	28					2	28	1.5	28.5			1	29						
	33	3.5	29.5	2	31					2	31	1.5	31.5										
36		4	32	3	33					2	34	1.5	34.5										
	39	4	35	3	36					2	37	1.5	37.5										
42		4.5	37.5	3	39	4	38	3	39	2	40	1.5	40.5										
	45	4.5	39	3	42	4	41	3	42	2	43	1.5	43.5										
48		5	43	3	45	4	44	3	45	2	46	1.5	46.5										

* ISO thread size

** ASME thread size (to be discontinued)

TABLE 6 ■ Metric Threads

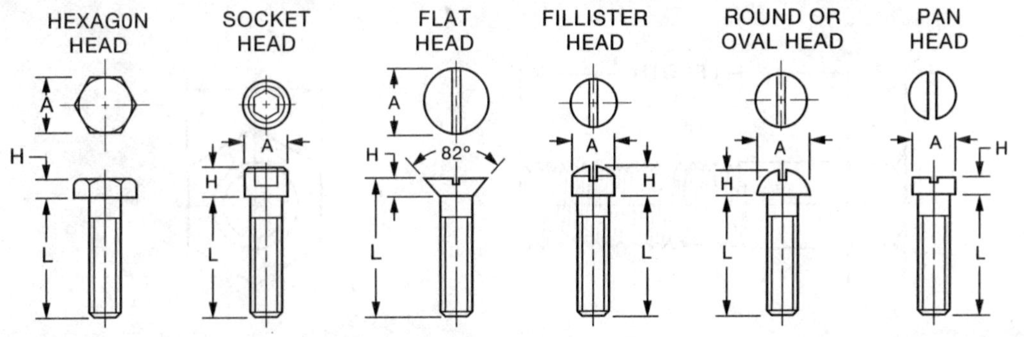

Imperial and U.S. Customary (Inches)

Nominal Size		Hexagon Head		Socket Head		Flat Head		Fillister Head		Round or Oval Head	
Fraction	Decimal	A	H	A	H	A	H	A	H	A	H
1/4	.250	.44	.17	.38	.25	.50	.14	.38	.22	.44	.19
5/16	.312	.50	.22	.47	.31	.62	.18	.44	.25	.56	.25
3/8	.375	.56	.25	.56	.38	.75	.21	.56	.31	.62	.27
7/16	.438	.62	.30	.66	.44	.81	.21	.62	.36	.75	.33
1/2	.500	.75	.34	.75	.50	.88	.21	.75	.41	.81	.35
5/8	.625	.94	.42	.94	.62	1.12	.28	.88	.50	1.00	.44
3/4	.750	1.12	.50	1.12	.75	1.38	.35	1.00	.59	1.25	.55
7/8	.875	1.31	.58	1.31	.88	1.62	.42	1.12	.69		
1	1.000	1.50	.67	1.50	1.00	1.88	.49	1.31	.78		
1 1/8	1.125	1.69	.75	1.69	1.12	2.06	.53				
1 1/4	1.250	1.88	.84	1.88	1.25	2.31	.60				
1 1/2	1.500	2.25	1.00	2.25	1.50	2.81	.74				

Metric (Millimetres)

Nominal Size	Hexagon Head		Socket Head			Flat Head		Fillister Head		Pan Head	
	A	H	A	H	Key Size	A	H	A	H	A	H
M3	5.5	2	5.5	3	2.5	5.6	1.6	6	2.4	5.6	1.9
4	7	2.8	7	4	3	7.5	2.2	8	3.1	7.5	2.5
5	8.5	3.5	9	5	4	9.2	2.5	10	3.8	9.2	3.1
6	10	4	10	6	5	11	3	12	4.6	11	3.8
8	13	5.5	13	8	6	14.5	4	16	6	14.5	5
10	17	7	16	10	8	18	5	20	7.5	18	6.2
12	19	8	18	12	10						
14	22	9	22	14	12						
16	24	10	24	16	14						
18	27	12	27	18	14						
20	30	13	30	20	17						
22	36	15	33	22	17						
24	36	15	36	24	19						
27	41	17	40	27	19						
30	46	19	45	30	22						

NOTE: Length sizes normally available in .25 inch and 10 mm increments

TABLE 7 ■ Common Cap Screws

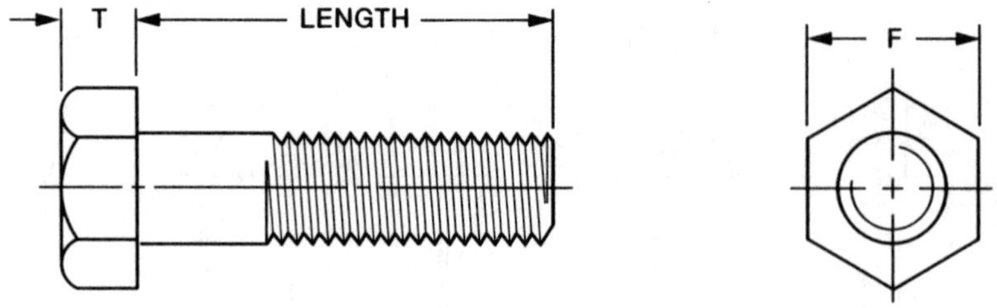

Imperial and U.S. Customary (Inches)			
Nominal Size Fraction	Decimal	Width across Flats	Thickness
1/4	.250	.44	.17
5/16	.312	.50	.22
3/8	.375	.56	.25
7/16	.438	.62	.30
1/2	.500	.75	.34
5/8	.625	.94	.42
3/4	.750	1.12	.50
7/8	.875	1.31	.58
1	1.000	1.50	.67
1 1/8	1.125	1.69	.75
1 1/4	1.250	1.88	.84
1 3/8	1.375	2.06	.91
1 1/2	1.500	2.25	1.00

Metric (Millimetres)		
Nominal Size (Millimetres)	Width across Flats	Thickness
4	7	2.8
5	8	3.5
6	10	4
8	13	5.5
10	17	7
12	19	8
14	22	9
16	24	10
18	27	12
20	30	13
22	32	14
24	36	15
27	41	17
30	46	19
33	50	21
36	55	23

NOTE: For bold and cap screw sizes below 7/16 inch and 8 mm length sizes normally available in .25 inch and 10 mm increments

TABLE 8 ■ Hexagon-Head Bolts and Cap Screws

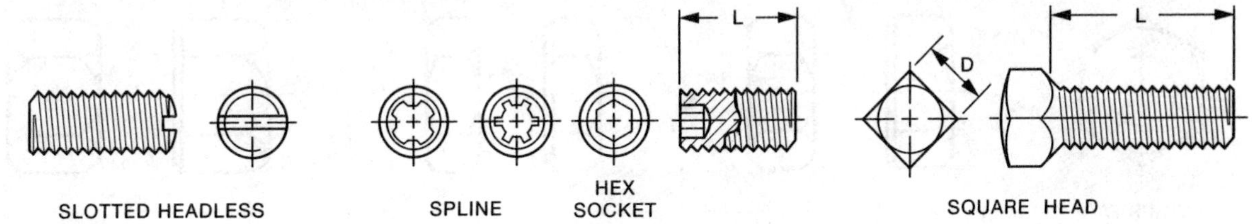

SETSCREW HEADS

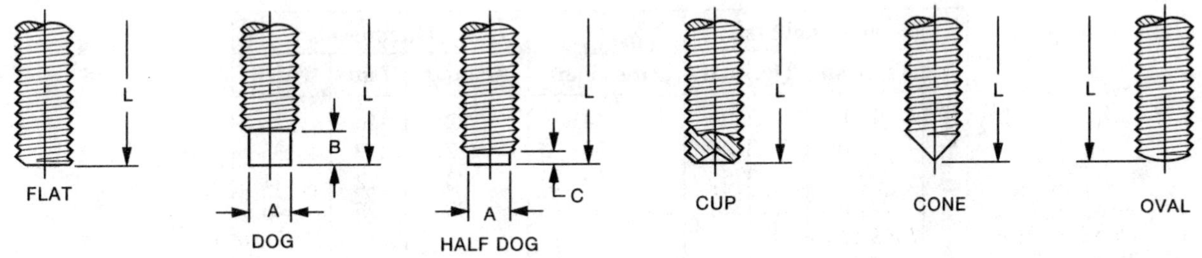

SETSCREW POINTS

Imperial and U.S. Customary (Inches)			Metric (Millimetres)	
Nominal Size		Key Size	Nominal Size	Key Size
Number	Decimal			
4	.112	.050	M 1.4	0.7
5	.125	.062	2	0.9
6	.138	.062	3	1.5
8	.164	.078	4	2
10	.190	.094	5	2.5
12	.216	.109	6	3
1/4	.250	.125	8	4
5/16	.312	.156	10	5
3/8	.375	.188	12	6
1/2	.500	.250	16	8

TABLE 9 ■ Setscrews

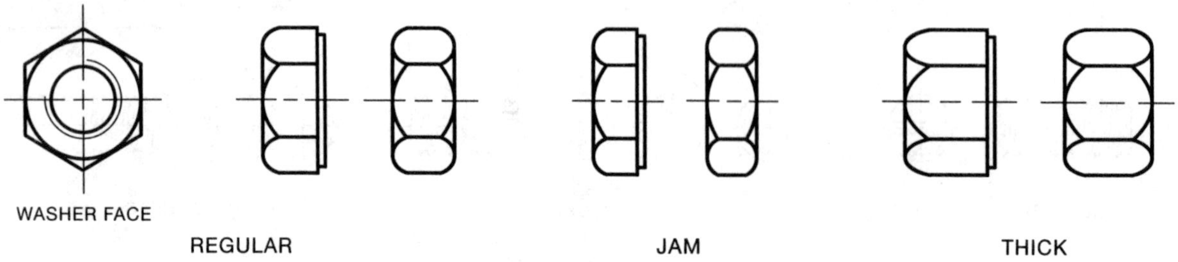
WASHER FACE
REGULAR
JAM
THICK

Imperial and U.S. Customary (Inches) Nominal Size Fraction	Nominal Size Decimal	Distance across Flats	Thickness Regular	Thickness Jam	Thickness Thick
1/4	.250	.44	.22	.16	.28
5/16	.312	.50	.27	.19	.33
3/8	.375	.56	.33	.22	.41
7/16	.438	.69	.38	.25	.45
1/2	.500	.75	.44	.31	.56
9/16	.562	.88	.48	.31	.61
5/8	.625	.94	.55	.38	.72
3/4	.750	1.12	.64	.42	.81
7/8	.875	1.31	.75	.48	.91
1	1.000	1.50	.86	.55	1.00
1 1/8	1.125	1.69	.97	.61	1.16
1 1/4	1.250	1.88	1.06	.72	1.25
1 3/8	1.375	2.06	1.17	.78	1.38
1 1/2	1.500	2.25	1.28	.84	1.50

Metric (Millimetres) Nominal Size (Millimetres)	Distance across Flats	Thickness Regular	Thickness Jam	Thickness Thick
4	7	3	2	5
5	8	4	2.5	5
6	10	5	3	6
8	13	6.5	5	8
10	17	8	6	10
12	19	10	7	12
14	22	11	8	14
16	24	13	8	16
18	27	15	9	18.5
20	30	16	9	20
22	32	18	10	22
24	36	19	10	24
27	41	22	12	27
30	46	24	12	30
33	50	26		
36	55	29		
39	60	31		

TABLE 10 ■ Hexagon-Head Nuts

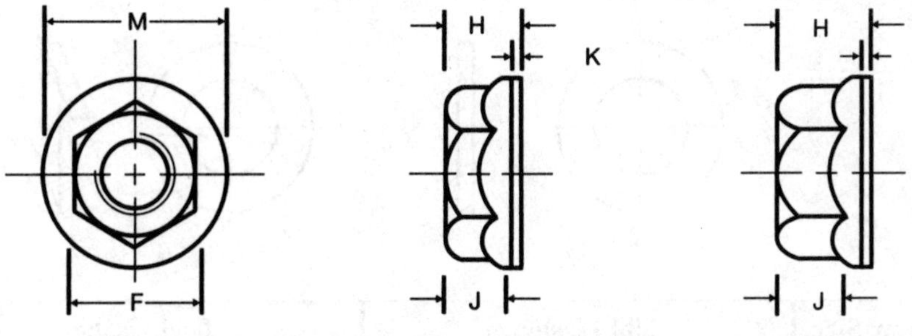

Metric (Millimetres)							
Nominal Nut Size and Thread Pitch	Width across Flats F	Style 1 H	Style 1 J	Style 1 K	Style 1 M	Style 2 H	Style 2 J
M6 × 1	10	5.8	3	1	14.2	6.7	3.7
M8 × 1.25	13	6.8	3.7	1.3	17.6	8	4.5
M10 × 1.5	15	9.6	5.5	1.5	21.5	11.2	6.7
M12 × 1.75	18	11.6	6.7	2	25.6	13.5	8.2
M14 × 2	21	13.4	7.8	2.3	29.6	15.7	9.6
M16 × 2	24	15.9	9.5	2.5	34.2	18.4	11.7
M20 × 2.5	30	19.2	11.1	2.8	42.3	22	12.6

TABLE 11 ■ Hex Flange Nuts

FLAT WASHER　　　　LOCKWASHER

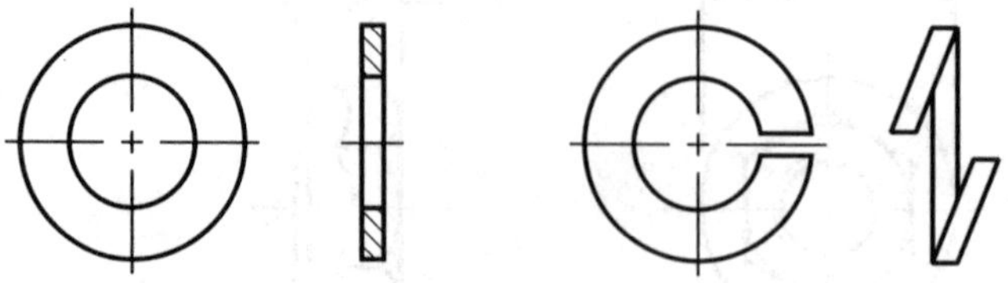

Nominal Screw Size		Flat Washer			Lockwasher		
Number or Fraction	Decimal	Inside Dia A	Outside Dia B	Thickness C	Inside Dia A	Outside Dia B	Thickness C
6	.138	.16	.38	.05	.14	.25	.03
8	.164	.19	.44	.05	.17	.29	.04
10	.190	.22	.50	.05	.19	.33	.05
12	.216	.25	.56	.07	.22	.38	.06
1/4	.250 N	.28	.63	.07	.26	.49	.06
1/4	.250 W	.31	.73	.07			
5/16	.312 N	.34	.69	.07	.32	.59	.08
5/16	.312 N	.38	.88	.08			
3/8	.375 W	.41	.81	.07	.38	.68	.09
3/8	.375 W	.44	1.00	.08			
7/16	.438 W	.47	.92	.07	.45	.78	.11
7/16	.438 W	.50	1.25	.08			
1/2	.500 N	.53	1.06	.10	.51	.87	.12
1/2	.500 W	.56	1.38	.11			
5/8	.625 N	.66	1.31	.10	.64	1.08	.16
5/8	.625 W	.69	1.75	.13			
3/4	.750 N	.81	1.47	.13	.76	1.27	.19
3/4	.750 W	.81	2.00	.15			
7/8	.875 N	.94	1.75	.13	.89	1.46	.22
7/8	.875 W	.94	2.25	.17			
1	1.000 N	1.06	2.00	.13	1.02	1.66	.25
1	1.000 W	1.06	2.50	.17			
1 1/8	1.125 N	1.25	2.25	.13	1.14	1.85	.28
1 1/8	1.125 W	1.25	2.75	.17			
1 1/4	1.250 N	1.38	2.50	.17	1.27	2.05	.31
1 1/4	1.250 W	1.38	3.00	.17			
1 3/8	1.375 N	1.50	2.75	.17	1.40	2.24	.34
1 3/8	1.375 W	1.50	3.25	.18			
1 1/2	1.500 N	1.62	3.00	.17	1.53	2.43	.38
1 1/2	1.500 W	1.62	3.50	.18			

N—SAE Sizes (Narrow)
W—Standard Plate (Wide)

INCH SIZES

TABLE 12 ■ Common Washer Sizes

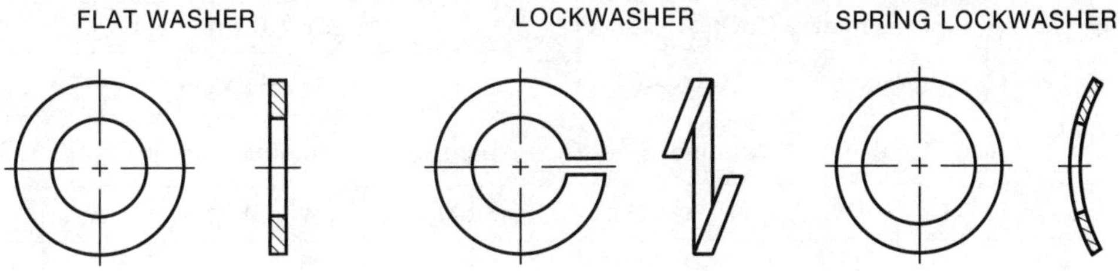

Bolt Size	Flat Washer			Lockwasher			Spring Lockwasher		
	ID	OD	Thickness	ID	OD	Thickness	ID	OD	Thickness
2	2.2	5.5	0.5	2.1	3.3	0.5			
3	3.2	7	0.5	3.1	5.7	0.8			
4	4.3	9	0.8	4.1	7.1	0.9	4.2	8	0.3 0.4
5	5.3	11	1	5.1	8.7	1.2	5.2	10	0.4 0.5
6	6.4	12	1.5	6.1	11.1	1.6	6.2	12.5	0.5 0.7
7	7.4	14	1.5	7.1	12.1	1.6	7.2	14	0.5 0.8
8	8.4	17	2	8.2	14.2	2	8.2	16	0.6 0.9
10	10.5	21	2.5	10.2	17.2	2.2	10.2	20	0.8 1.1
12	13	24	2.5	12.3	20.2	2.5	12.2	25	0.9 1.5
14	15	28	2.5	14.2	23.2	3	14.2	28	1 1.5
16	17	30	3	16.2	26.2	3.5	16.3	31.5	1.2 1.7
18	19	34	3	18.2	28.2	3.5	18.3	35.5	1.2 2
20	21	36	3	20.2	32.2	4	20.4	40	1.5 2.25
22	23	39	4	22.5	34.5	4	22.4	45	1.75 2.5
24	25	44	4	24.5	38.5	5			
27	28	50	4	27.5	41.5	5			
30	31	56	4	30.5	46.5	6			

MILLIMETRE SIZES

TABLE 12 (CONT'D) ■ Common Washer Sizes

Imperial and U.S. Customary (Inches)					Metric (Millimetres)					
Diameter of Shaft	Square Key		Flat Key		Diameter of Shaft (mm)		Square Key		Flat Key	
	Nominal Size		Nominal Size				Nominal Size		Nominal Size	
Inclusive	W	H	W	H	Over	Up To	W	H	W	H
.500 – .562	.125	.125	.125	.094	12	17	5	5		
.625 – .875	.188	.188	.188	.125	17	22	6	6		
.938 –1.250	.250	.250	.250	.188	22	30	7	7	8	7
1.312 –1.375	.312	.312	.312	.250	30	38	8	8	10	8
1.438 –1.750	.375	.375	.375	.250	38	44	9	9	12	8
1.812 –2.250	.500	.500	.500	.375	44	50	10	10	14	9
2.312 –2.750	.625	.625	.625	.438	50	58	12	12	16	10

TABLE 13 ■ Square and Flat Stock Keys

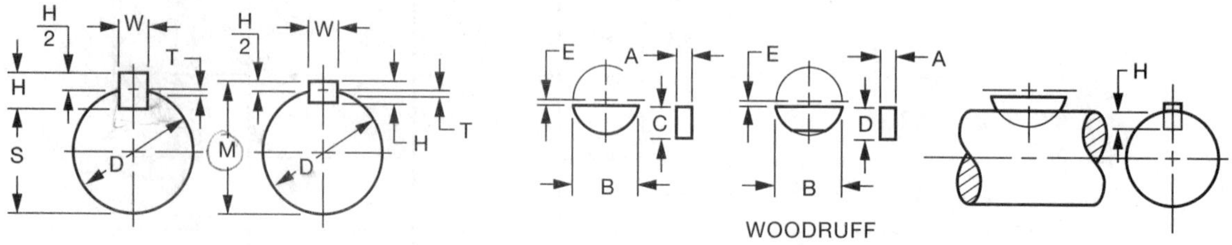

C = ALLOWANCE FOR PARALLEL KEYS = .005 IN. OR 0.12 MM

$$S = D - \frac{H}{2} - T = \frac{D - H + \sqrt{D^2 - W^2}}{2} \qquad T = \frac{D - \sqrt{D^2 - W^2}}{2}$$

W = NORMAL KEY WIDTH (INCHES OR MILLIMETRES)

$$M = D - T + \frac{H}{2} + C = \frac{D + H + \sqrt{D^2 - W^2} + C}{2}$$

Key No.	Nominal (A × B)		Imperial and U.S. Customary (Inches)				Metric (Millimetres)			
			Key			Keyseat	Key			Keyseat
	Millimetres	Inches	E	C	D	H	E	C	D	H
204	1.6 × 6.4	0.062 × 0.250	.05	.20	.19	.10	0.5	2.8	2.8	4.3
304	2.4 × 12.7	0.094 × 0.500	.05	.20	.19	.15	1.3	5.1	4.8	3.8
305	2.4 × 15.9	0.094 × 0.625	.06	.25	.24	.20	1.5	6.4	6.1	5.1
404	3.2 × 12.7	0.125 × 0.500	.05	.20	.19	.14	1.3	5.1	4.8	3.6
405	3.2 × 15.9	0.125 × 0.625	.06	.25	.24	.18	1.5	6.4	6.1	4.6
406	3.2 × 19.1	0.125 × 0.750	.06	.31	.30	.25	1.5	7.9	7.6	6.4
505	4.0 × 15.9	0.156 × 0.625	.06	.25	.24	.17	1.5	6.4	6.1	4.3
506	4.0 × 19.1	0.156 × 0.750	.06	.31	.30	.23	1.5	7.9	7.6	5.8
507	4.0 × 22.2	0.156 × 0.875	.06	.38	.36	.29	1.5	9.7	9.1	7.4
606	4.8 × 19.1	0.188 × 0.750	.06	.31	.30	.21	1.5	7.9	7.6	5.3
607	4.8 × 22.2	0.188 × 0.875	.06	.38	.36	.28	1.5	9.7	9.1	7.1
608	4.8 × 25.4	0.188 × 1.000	.06	.44	.43	.34	1.5	11.2	10.9	8.6
609	4.8 × 28.6	0.188 × 1.250	.08	.48	.47	.39	2.0	12.2	11.9	9.9
807	6.4 × 22.2	0.250 × 0.875	.06	.38	.36	.25	1.5	9.7	9.1	6.4
808	6.4 × 25.4	0.250 × 1.000	.06	.44	.43	.31	1.5	11.2	10.9	7.9

TABLE 14 ■ Woodruff Keys

	Imperial and U.S. Customary (Inches)				Metric (Millimetres)			
		Wall Thickness				Wall Thickness (Millimetres)		
Nominal Pipe Size	Outside Diameter	Schedule 40 Pipe *	Schedule 80 Pipe **	Schedule 160 Pipe	Outside Diameter (Millimetres)	Standard	Extra Strong	Double Extra Strong
.125 (1/8)	.405	.068	.095	–	10.29	1.75	2.44	—
.250 (1/4)	.540	.088	.119	–	13.72	2.29	3.15	—
.375 (3/8)	.675	.091	.126	–	17.15	2.36	3.28	—
.500 (1/2)	.840	.109	.147	.188	21.34	2.82	3.84	7.80
.750 (3/4)	1.050	.113	.154	.219	26.67	2.92	3.99	8.08
1.00	1.315	.133	.179	.250	33.4	3.45	4.65	9.37
1.25	1.660	.140	.191	.250	42.4	3.63	4.98	9.98
1.50	1.900	.145	.200	.281	48.3	3.76	5.18	10.44
2.00	2.375	.154	.218	.344	60.3	3.99	5.66	11.35
2.50	2.875	.203	.276	.375	73.0	5.26	7.16	14.40
3.00	3.500	.216	.300	.438	88.9	5.61	7.77	15.62
3.50	4.000	.226	.318	–	101.6	5.87	8.25	16.54
4.00	4.500	.237	.337	.531	114.3	6.15	8.74	17.53
5.00	5.563	.258	.375	.625	141.3	6.68	9.73	19.51
6.00	6.625	.280	.432	.719	168.3	7.26	11.20	22.45
8.00	8.625	.322	.500	.096	219.1	8.36	12.98	22.73
10.00	10.750	.365	.594	1.125	273.1	9.45	12.95	—
12.00	12.750	.406	.688	1.312	323.9	—	12.95	—
14.00	14.000	.438	.750	1.406	355.6	9.73	12.95	—
16.00	16.000	.500	.844	1.594	406.4	9.73	12.95	—

*Standard
**Extra Strong Pipe

Nominal pipe sizes are specified in inches.
Outside diameter and wall thickness are specified in millimetres.

TABLE 15 ■ American Standard Wrought Steel Pipe

North American Gauges								European Gauges			
Ferrous Metals, Such as Galvanized Steel, Tin Plate				Galvanized Steel, Tin Plate, Copper, Strip Steel and Steel, Copper, Aluminum Tubes				Nonferrous Metals, Such as Copper, Brass, Aluminum		Nonferrous	
U.S. Standard (USS)		U.S. Standard (Revised)		Birmingham (BWG)		New Birmingham (BG)		Browne and Sharpe (B & S)		Imperial Standard (SWG)	
Gauge	In.	Gauge	In.	Gauge	In.	Gauge	In.	Gauge	In.	Gauge	In.
		3	.239					3	.229		
4	.234	4	.224	4	.238	4	.250	4	.204	4	.232
5	.219	5	.209	5	.220	5	.223	5	.182	5	.212
6	.203	6	.194	6	.203	6	.198	6	.162	6	.192
7	.188	7	.179	7	.180	7	.176	7	.144	7	.176
8	.172	8	.164	8	.165	8	.157	8	.129	8	.160
9	.156	9	.149	9	.148	9	.140	9	.114	9	.144
10	.141	10	.135	10	.134	10	.125	10	.102	10	.128
11	.125	11	.120	11	.120	11	.111	11	.091	11	.116
12	.109	12	.105	12	.109	12	.099	12	.081	12	.104
13	.094	13	.090	13	.095	13	.088	13	.072	13	.092
14	.078	14	.075	14	.083	14	.079	14	.064	14	.080
15	.070	15	.067	15	.072	15	.070	15	.057	15	.072
16	.063	16	.060	16	.065	16	.063	16	.051	16	.064
17	.056	17	.054	17	.058	17	.056	17	.045	17	.056
18	.050	18	.048	18	.049	18	.050	18	.040	18	.048
19	.044	19	.042	19	.042	19	.044	19	.036	19	.040
20	.038	20	.036	20	.035	20	.039	20	.032	20	.036
21	.034	21	.033	21	.032	21	.035	21	.029	21	.032
22	.031	22	.030	22	.028	22	.031	22	.025	22	.028
23	.028	23	.027	23	.025	23	.028	23	.023	23	.024
24	.025	24	.024	24	.022	24	.025	24	.020	24	.022
25	.022	25	.021	25	.020	25	.022	25	.018	25	.020
26	.019	26	.018	26	.018	26	.020	26	.016	26	.018
27	.017	27	.016	27	.016	27	.017	27	.014	27	.016
28	.016	28	.015	28	.014	28	.016	28	.013	28	.015
29	.014	29	.014	29	.013	29	.014	29	.011	29	.014
30	.012	30	.012	30	.012	30	.012	30	.010	30	.012
31	.011	31	.011	31	.010	31	.011	31	.009		
32	.010	32	.010	32	.009			32	.008	32	.011
33	.009	33	.009	33	.008	33	.009	33	.007	33	.010
34	.008	34	.008	34	.007	34	.008	34	.006	34	.009
				35	.005	35	.007			35	.008
36	.007	36	.007	36	.004	36	.006	36	.005		

TABLE 16 ■ Sheet Metal Gauges and Thicknesses

EXAMPLE: RC2 SLIDING FIT FOR A Ø1.50 NOMINAL HOLE DIAMETER

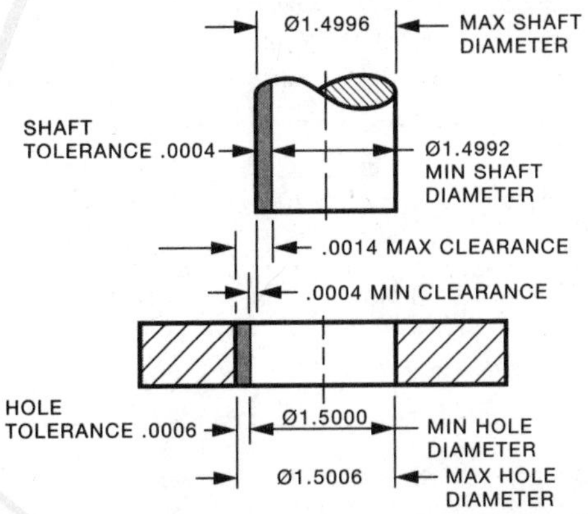

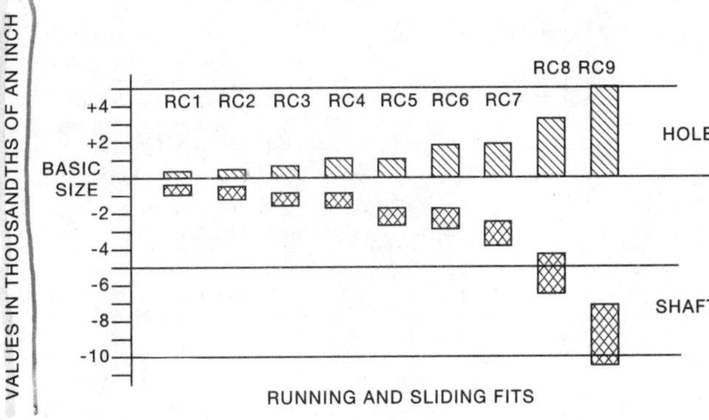

Nominal Size Range Inches		Class RC1 Precision Sliding			Class RC2 Sliding Fit			Class RC3 Precision Running			Class RC4 Close Running			Class RC5 Medium Running		
		Hole Tol. GR5	Minimum Clearance	Shaft Tol. GR4	Hole Tol. GR6	Minimum Clearance	Shaft Tol. GR5	Hole Tol. GR7	Minimum Clearance	Shaft Tol. GR6	Hole Tol. GR8	Minimum Clearance	Shaft Tol. GR7	Hole Tol. GR8	Minimum Clearance	Shaft Tol. GR7
Over	To	-0		+0	-0		+0	-0		+0	-0		+0	-0		+0
0	.12	+0.15	0.10	-0.12	+0.25	0.10	-0.15	+0.40	0.30	-0.25	+0.60	0.30	-0.40	+0.60	0.60	-0.40
.12	.24	+0.20	0.15	-0.15	+0.30	0.15	-0.20	+0.50	0.40	-0.30	+0.70	0.40	-0.50	+0.70	0.80	-0.50
.24	.40	+0.25	0.20	-0.15	+0.40	0.20	-0.25	+0.60	0.50	-0.40	+0.90	0.50	-0.60	+0.90	1.00	-0.60
.40	.71	+0.30	0.25	-0.20	+0.40	0.25	-0.30	+0.70	0.60	-0.40	+1.00	0.60	-0.70	+1.00	1.20	-0.70
.71	1.19	+0.40	0.30	-0.25	+0.50	0.30	-0.40	+0.80	0.80	-0.50	+1.20	0.80	-0.80	+1.20	1.60	-0.80
1.19	1.97	+0.40	0.40	-0.30	+0.60	0.40	-0.40	+1.00	1.00	-0.60	+1.60	1.00	-1.00	+1.60	2.00	-1.00
1.97	3.15	+0.50	0.40	-0.30	+0.70	0.40	-0.50	+1.20	1.20	-0.70	+1.80	1.20	-1.20	+1.80	2.50	-1.20
3.15	4.73	+0.60	0.50	-0.40	+0.90	0.50	-0.60	+1.40	1.40	-0.90	+2.20	1.40	-1.40	+2.20	3.00	-1.40
4.73	7.09	+0.70	0.60	-0.50	+1.00	0.60	-0.70	+1.60	1.60	-1.00	+2.50	1.60	-1.60	+2.50	3.50	-1.60
7.09	9.85	+0.80	0.60	-0.60	+1.20	0.60	-0.80	+1.80	2.00	-1.20	+2.80	2.00	-1.80	+2.80	4.50	-1.80
9.85	12.41	+0.90	0.80	-0.60	+1.20	0.80	-0.90	+2.00	2.50	-1.20	+3.00	2.50	-2.00	+3.00	5.00	-2.00
12.41	15.75	+1.00	1.00	-0.70	+1.40	1.00	-1.00	+2.20	3.00	-1.40	+3.50	3.00	-2.20	+3.50	6.00	-2.20

Nominal Size Range Inches		Class RC6 Precision Sliding			Class RC7 Sliding Fit			Class RC8 Precision Running			Class RC9 Close Running		
		Hole Tol. GR9	Minimum Clearance	Shaft Tol. GR8	Hole Tol. GR9	Minimum Clearance	Shaft Tol. GR8	Hole Tol. GR10	Minimum Clearance	Shaft Tol. GR9	Hole Tol. GR11	Minimum Clearance	Shaft Tol. GR10
Over	To	-0		+0	-0		+0	-0		+0	-0		+0
0	.12	+1.00	0.60	-0.60	+1.00	1.00	-0.60	+1.60	2.50	-1.00	+2.50	4.00	-1.60
.12	.24	+1.20	0.80	-0.70	+1.20	1.20	-0.70	+1.80	2.80	-1.20	+3.00	4.50	-1.80
.24	.40	+1.40	1.00	-0.90	+1.40	1.60	-0.90	+2.20	3.00	-1.40	+3.50	6.00	-2.20
.40	.71	+1.60	1.20	-1.00	+1.60	2.00	-1.00	+2.80	3.50	-1.60	+4.00	6.00	-2.80
.71	1.19	+2.00	1.60	-1.20	+2.00	2.50	-1.20	+3.50	4.50	-2.00	+5.00	7.00	-3.50
1.19	1.97	+2.50	2.00	-1.60	+2.50	3.00	-1.60	+4.00	5.00	-2.50	+6.00	8.00	-4.00
1.97	3.15	+3.00	2.50	-1.80	+3.00	4.00	-1.80	+4.50	6.00	-3.00	+7.00	9.00	-4.50
3.15	4.73	+3.50	3.00	-2.20	+3.50	5.00	-2.20	+5.00	7.00	-3.50	+9.00	10.00	-5.00
4.73	7.09	+4.00	3.50	-2.50	+4.00	6.00	-2.50	+6.00	8.00	-4.00	+10.00	12.00	-6.00
7.09	9.85	+4.50	4.00	-2.80	+4.50	7.00	-2.80	+7.00	10.00	-4.50	+12.00	15.00	-7.00
9.85	12.41	+5.00	5.00	-3.00	+5.00	8.00	-3.00	+8.00	12.00	-5.00	+12.00	18.00	-8.00
12.41	15.75	+6.00	6.00	-3.50	+6.00	10.00	-3.50	+9.00	14.00	-6.00	+14.00	22.00	-9.00

TABLE 17 ■ Running and Sliding Fits (Values in Thousandths of an Inch)

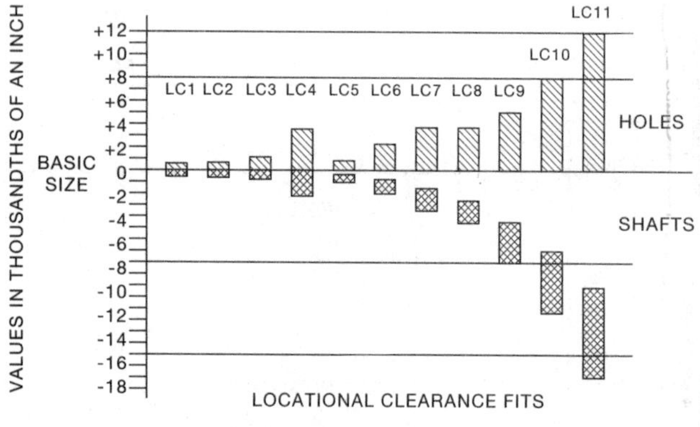

EXAMPLE: LC2 LOCATIONAL FIT FOR A Ø1.50 NOMINAL HOLE DIAMETER

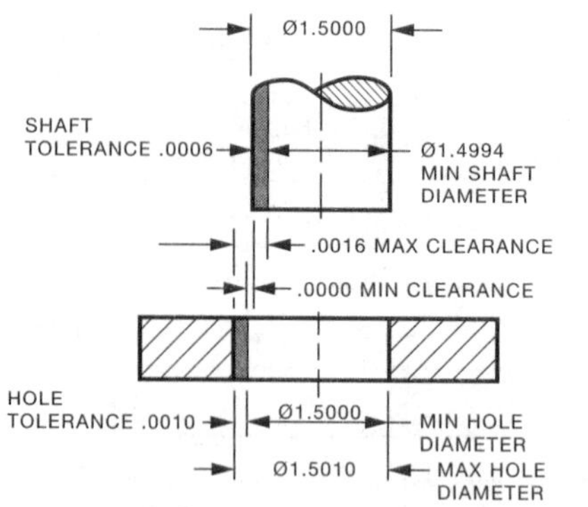

Nominal Size Range Inches		Class LC1			Class LC2			Class LC3			Class LC4			Class LC5			Class LC6		
		Hole Tol. GR6	Minimum Clearance	Shaft Tol. GR5	Hole Tol. GR8	Minimum Clearance	Shaft Tol. GR7	Hole Tol. GR10	Minimum Clearance	Shaft Tol. GR9	Hole Tol. GR7	Minimum Clearance	Shaft Tol. GR6	Hole Tol. GR9	Minimum Clearance	Shaft Tol. GR8	Hole Tol. GR9	Minimum Clearance	Shaft Tol. GR8
Over	To	-0		+0	-0		+0	-0		+0	-0		+0	-0		+0	-0		+0
0	.12	+0.25	0	-0.15	+0.4	0	-0.25	+0.6	0	-0.4	+1.6	0	-1.0	+0.4	0.10	-0.25	+1.0	0.3	-0.6
.12	.24	+0.30	0	-0.20	+0.5	0	-0.30	+0.7	0	-0.5	+1.8	0	-1.2	+0.5	0.15	-0.30	+1.2	0.4	-0.7
.24	.40	+0.40	0	-0.25	+0.6	0	-0.40	+0.9	0	-0.6	+2.2	0	-1.4	+0.6	0.20	-0.40	+1.4	0.5	-0.9
.40	.71	+0.40	0	-0.30	+0.7	0	-0.40	+1.0	0	-0.7	+2.8	0	-1.6	+0.7	0.25	-0.40	+1.6	0.6	-1.0
.71	1.19	+0.50	0	-0.40	+0.8	0	-0.50	+1.2	0	-0.8	+3.5	0	-2.0	+0.8	0.30	-0.50	+2.0	0.8	-1.2
1.19	1.97	+0.60	0	-0.40	+1.0	0	-0.60	+1.6	0	-1.0	+4.0	0	-2.5	+1.0	0.40	-0.60	+2.5	1.0	-1.6
1.97	3.15	+0.70	0	-0.50	+1.2	0	-0.70	+1.8	0	-1.2	+4.5	0	-3.0	+1.2	0.40	-0.70	+3.0	1.2	-1.8
3.15	4.73	+0.90	0	-0.60	+1.4	0	-0.90	+2.5	0	-1.4	+5.0	0	-3.5	+1.4	0.50	-0.90	+3.5	1.4	-2.2
4.73	7.09	+1.00	0	-0.70	+1.6	0	-1.00	+2.7	0	-1.6	+6.0	0	-4.0	+1.6	0.60	-1.00	+4.0	1.6	-2.5
7.09	9.85	+1.20	0	-0.80	+1.8	0	-1.20	+2.8	0	-1.8	+7.0	0	-4.5	+1.8	0.60	-1.20	+4.5	2.0	-2.8
9.85	12.41	+1.20	0	-0.90	+2.0	0	-1.20	+3.0	0	-2.0	+8.0	0	-5.0	+2.0	0.70	-1.20	+5.0	2.2	-3.0
12.41	15.75	+1.40	0	-1.00	+2.2	0	-1.40	+3.5	0	-2.2	+9.0	0	-6.0	+2.2	0.70	-1.40	+6.0	2.5	-3.5

Nominal Size Range Inches		Class LC7			Class LC8			Class LC9			Class LC10			Class LC11		
		Hole Tol. GR10	Minimum Clearance	Hole Tol. GR9	Hole Tol. GR10	Minimum Clearance	Hole Tol. GR9	Hole Tol. GR11	Minimum Clearance	Hole Tol. GR10	Hole Tol. GR12	Minimum Clearance	Hole Tol. GR11	Hole Tol. GR13	Minimum Clearance	Hole Tol. GR12
Over	To	-0		+0	-0		+0	-0		+0	-0		+0	-0		+0
0	.12	+1.6	0.6	-1.0	+1.6	1.0	-1.0	+2.5	2.5	-1.6	+1.0	4.0	-2.5	+6.0	5.0	-4.0
.12	.24	+1.8	0.8	-1.2	+1.8	1.2	-1.2	+3.0	2.8	-1.8	+5.0	4.5	-3.0	+7.0	6.0	-5.0
.24	.40	+2.2	1.0	-1.4	+2.2	1.6	-1.4	+3.5	3.0	-2.2	+6.0	5.0	-3.5	+9.0	7.0	-6.0
.40	.71	+2.8	1.2	-1.6	+2.8	2.0	-1.6	+4.0	3.5	-2.8	+7.0	6.0	-4.0	+10.0	8.0	-7.0
.71	1.19	+3.5	1.6	-2.0	+3.5	2.5	-2.0	+5.0	4.5	-3.5	+8.0	7.0	-5.0	+12.0	10.0	-8.0
1.19	1.97	+4.0	2.0	-2.5	+4.0	3.6	-2.5	+6.0	5.0	-4.0	+10.0	8.0	-6.0	+16.0	12.0	-10.0
1.97	3.15	+4.5	2.5	-3.0	+4.5	4.0	-3.0	+7.0	6.0	-4.5	+12.0	10.0	-7.0	+18.0	14.0	-12.0
3.15	4.73	+5.0	3.0	-3.5	+5.0	5.0	-3.5	+9.0	7.0	-5.0	+14.0	11.0	-9.0	+22.0	16.0	-14.0
4.73	7.09	+6.0	3.5	-4.0	+6.0	6.0	-4.0	+10.0	8.0	-6.0	+16.0	12.0	-10.0	+25.0	18.0	-16.0
7.09	9.85	+7.0	4.0	-4.5	+7.0	7.0	-4.5	+12.0	10.0	-7.0	+18.0	16.0	-12.0	+28.0	22.0	-18.0
9.85	12.41	+8.0	4.5	-5.0	+8.0	7.0	-5.0	+12.0	12.0	-8.0	+20.0	20.0	-12.0	+30.0	28.0	-20.0
12.41	15.75	+9.0	5.0	-6.0	+9.0	8.0	-6.0	+14.0	14.0	-9.0	+22.0	22.0	-14.0	+35.0	30.0	-22.0

TABLE 18 ■ Locational Clearance Fits (Values in Thousandths of an Inch)

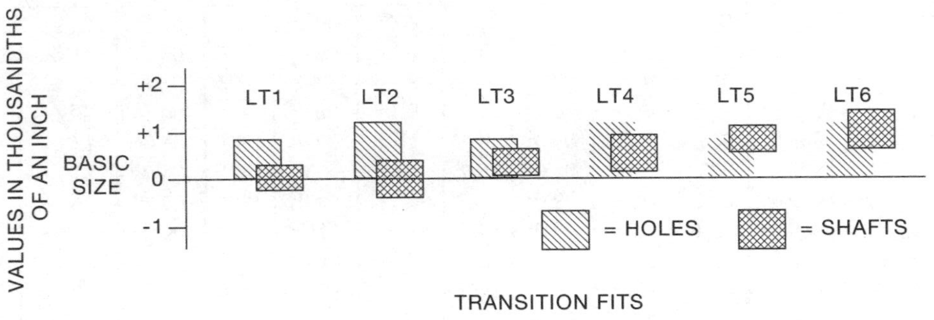
VALUES IN THOUSANDTHS OF AN INCH
+2
+1
0
-1
BASIC SIZE
LT1
LT2
LT3
LT4
LT5
LT6
= HOLES
= SHAFTS
TRANSITION FITS

EXAMPLE: LT2 TRANSITION FIT FOR A Ø1.50 NOMINAL HOLE DIAMETER

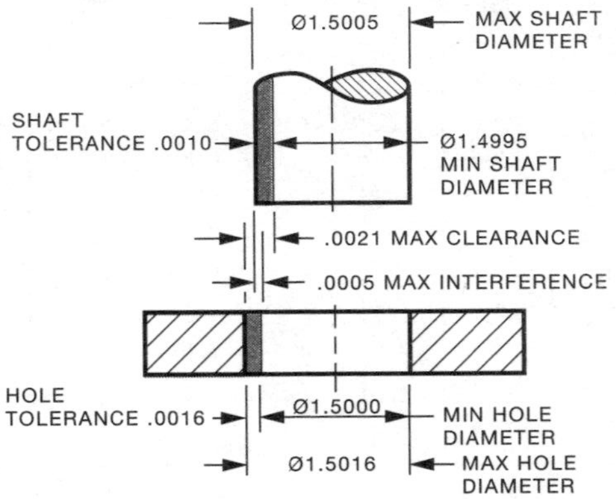
Ø1.5005
MAX SHAFT DIAMETER
SHAFT TOLERANCE .0010
Ø1.4995
MIN SHAFT DIAMETER
.0021 MAX CLEARANCE
.0005 MAX INTERFERENCE
HOLE TOLERANCE .0016
Ø1.5000
MIN HOLE DIAMETER
Ø1.5016
MAX HOLE DIAMETER

Nominal Size Range Inches		Class LT1			Class LT2			Class LT3			Class LT4			Class LT5			Class LT6		
		Hole Tol. GR7	Maximum Interference	Shaft Tol. GR6	Hole Tol. GR8	Maximum Interference	Shaft Tol. GR7	Hole Tol. GR7	Maximum Interference	Shaft Tol. GR6	Hole Tol. GR8	Maximum Interference	Shaft Tol. GR7	Hole Tol. GR7	Maximum Interference	Shaft Tol. GR6	Hole Tol. GR8	Maximum Interference	Shaft Tol. GR7
Over	To	-0		+0	-0		+0	-0		+0	-0		+0	-0		+0	-0		+0
0	.12	+0.4	0.10	-0.25	+0.6	0.20	-0.4	+0.4	0.25	-0.25	+0.6	0.4	-0.4	+0.4	0.5	-0.25	+0.6	0.65	-0.4
.12	.24	+0.5	0.15	-0.30	+0.7	0.25	-0.5	+0.5	0.40	-0.30	+0.7	0.6	-0.5	+0.5	0.6	-0.30	+0.7	0.80	-0.5
.24	.40	+0.6	0.20	-0.40	+0.9	0.30	-0.6	+0.6	0.50	-0.40	+0.9	0.7	-0.6	+0.6	0.8	-0.40	+0.9	1.00	-0.6
.40	.71	+0.7	0.20	-0.40	+1.0	0.30	-0.7	+0.7	0.50	-0.40	+1.0	0.8	-0.7	+0.7	0.9	-0.40	+1.0	1.20	-0.7
.71	1.19	+0.8	0.25	-0.50	+1.2	0.40	-0.8	+0.8	0.60	-0.50	+1.2	0.9	-0.8	+0.8	1.1	-0.50	+1.2	1.40	-0.8
1.19	1.97	+1.0	0.30	-0.60	+1.6	0.50	-1.0	+1.0	0.70	-0.60	+1.6	1.1	-1.0	+1.0	1.3	-0.60	+1.6	1.70	-1.0
1.97	3.15	+1.2	0.30	-0.70	+1.8	0.60	-1.2	+1.2	0.80	-0.70	+1.8	1.3	-1.2	+1.2	1.5	-0.70	+1.8	2.00	-1.2
3.15	4.73	+1.4	0.40	-0.90	+2.2	0.70	-1.4	+1.4	1.00	-0.90	+2.2	1.5	-1.4	+1.4	1.9	-0.90	+2.2	2.40	-1.4
4.73	7.09	+1.6	0.50	-1.00	+2.5	0.80	-1.6	+1.6	1.10	-1.00	+2.5	1.7	-1.6	+1.6	2.2	-1.00	+2.5	2.80	-1.6
7.09	9.85	+1.8	0.60	-1.20	+2.8	0.90	-1.8	+1.8	1.40	-1.20	+2.8	2.0	-1.8	+1.8	2.6	-1.20	+2.8	3.20	-1.8
9.85	12.41	+2.0	0.60	-1.20	+3.0	1.00	-2.0	+2.0	1.40	-1.20	+3.0	2.2	-2.0	+2.0	2.6	-1.20	+3.0	3.40	-2.0
12.41	15.75	+2.2	0.70	-1.40	+3.5	1.00	-2.2	+2.2	1.60	-1.40	+3.5	2.4	-2.2	+2.2	3.0	-1.40	+3.5	3.80	-2.2

TABLE 19 ■ Locational Transition Fits (Values in Thousandths of an Inch)

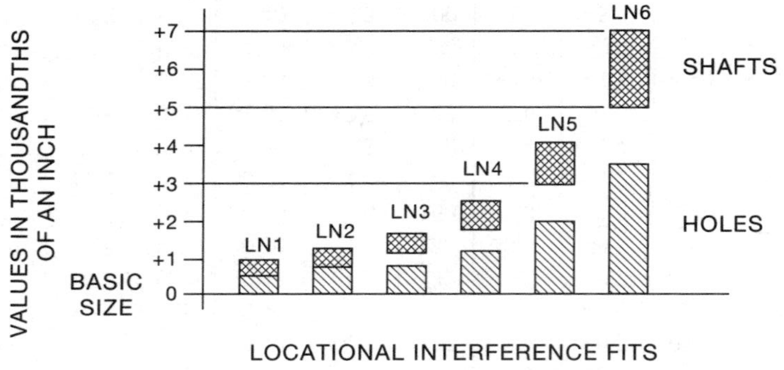
VALUES IN THOUSANDTHS OF AN INCH
+7
+6
+5
+4
+3
+2
+1
0
BASIC SIZE
LN1
LN2
LN3
LN4
LN5
LN6
SHAFTS
HOLES
LOCATIONAL INTERFERENCE FITS

EXAMPLE: LN2 LOCATIONAL INTERFERENCE FIT FOR A Ø1.50 NOMINAL HOLE DIAMETER

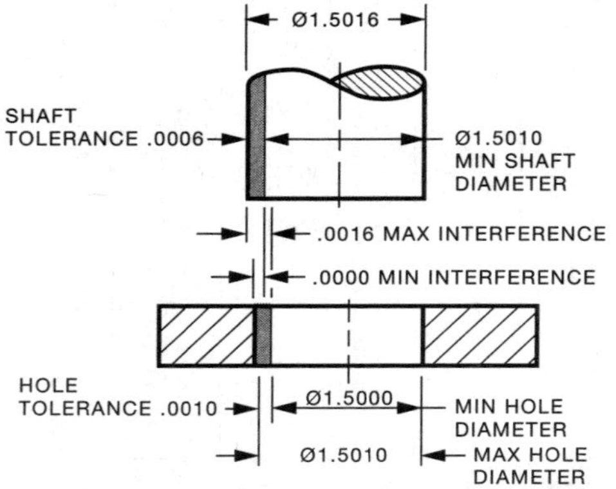
Ø1.5016
SHAFT TOLERANCE .0006
Ø1.5010 MIN SHAFT DIAMETER
.0016 MAX INTERFERENCE
.0000 MIN INTERFERENCE
HOLE TOLERANCE .0010
Ø1.5000
MIN HOLE DIAMETER
Ø1.5010
MAX HOLE DIAMETER

Nominal Size Range Inches		Class LN1 Light Press Fit			Class LN2 Medium Press Fit			Class LN3 Heavy Press Fit			Class LN4			Class LN5			Class LN6		
		Hole Tol. GR6	Maximum Interference	Shaft Tol. GR5	Hole Tol. GR7	Maximum Interference	Shaft Tol. GR6	Hole Tol. GR7	Maximum Interference	Shaft Tol. GR6	Hole Tol. GR8	Maximum Interference	Shaft Tol. GR7	Hole Tol. GR9	Maximum Interference	Shaft Tol. GR8	Hole Tol. GR10	Maximum Interference	Shaft Tol. GR9
Over	To	-0		+0	-0		+0	-0		+0	-0		+0	-0		+0	-0		+0
0	.12	+0.25	0.40	-0.15	+0.4	0.65	-0.25	+0.4	0.75	-0.25	+0.6	1.2	-0.4	+1.0	1.8	-0.6	+1.6	3.0	-1.0
.12	.24	+0.30	0.50	-0.20	+0.5	0.80	-0.30	+0.5	0.90	-0.30	+0.7	1.5	-0.5	+1.2	2.3	-0.7	+1.8	3.6	-1.2
.24	.40	+0.40	0.65	-0.25	+0.6	1.00	-0.40	+0.6	1.20	-0.40	+0.9	1.8	-0.6	+1.4	2.8	-0.9	+2.2	4.4	-1.4
.40	.71	+0.40	0.70	-0.30	+0.7	1.10	-0.40	+0.7	1.40	-0.40	+1.0	2.2	-0.7	+1.6	3.4	-1.0	+2.8	5.6	-1.6
.71	1.19	+0.50	0.90	-0.40	+0.8	1.30	-0.50	+0.8	1.70	-0.50	+1.2	2.6	-0.8	+2.0	4.2	-1.2	+3.5	7.0	-2.0
1.19	1.97	+0.60	1.00	-0.40	+1.0	1.60	-0.60	+1.0	2.00	-0.60	+1.6	3.4	-1.0	+2.5	5.3	-1.6	+4.0	8.5	-2.5
1.97	3.15	+0.70	1.30	-0.50	+1.2	2.10	-0.70	+1.2	2.30	-0.70	+1.8	4.0	-1.2	+3.0	6.3	-1.8	+4.5	10.0	-3.0
3.15	4.73	+0.90	1.60	-0.60	+1.4	2.50	-0.90	+1.4	2.90	-0.90	+2.2	4.8	-1.4	+4.0	7.7	-2.2	+5.0	11.5	-3.5
4.73	7.09	+1.00	1.90	-0.70	+1.6	2.80	-1.00	+1.6	3.50	-1.00	+2.5	5.6	-1.6	+4.5	8.7	-2.5	+6.0	13.5	-4.0
7.09	9.85	+1.20	2.20	-0.80	+1.8	3.20	-1.20	+1.8	4.20	-1.20	+2.8	6.6	-1.8	+5.0	10.3	-2.8	+7.0	16.5	-4.5
9.85	12.41	+1.20	2.30	-0.90	+2.0	3.40	-1.20	+2.0	4.70	-1.20	+3.0	7.5	-2.0	+6.0	12.0	-3.0	+8.0	19.0	-5.0
12.41	15.75	+1.40	2.60	-1.00	+2.2	3.90	-1.40	+2.2	5.90	-1.40	+3.5	8.7	-2.2	+6.0	14.5	-3.5	+9.0	23.0	-6.0

TABLE 20 ■ Locational Interference Fits (Values in Thousandths of an Inch)

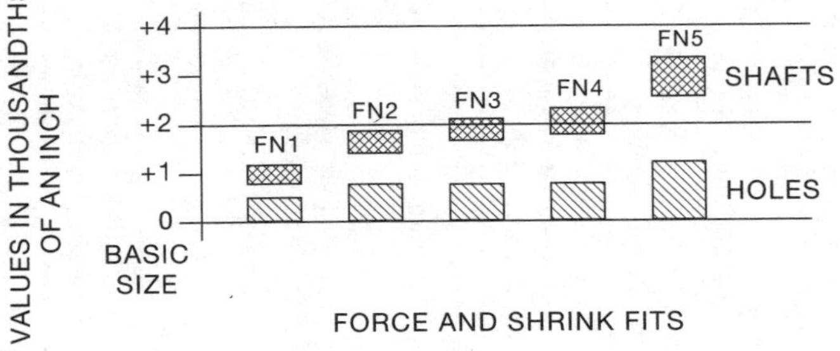
VALUES IN THOUSANDTHS OF AN INCH
+4
+3
+2
+1
0
BASIC SIZE
FN1
FN2
FN3
FN4
FN5
SHAFTS
HOLES

FORCE AND SHRINK FITS

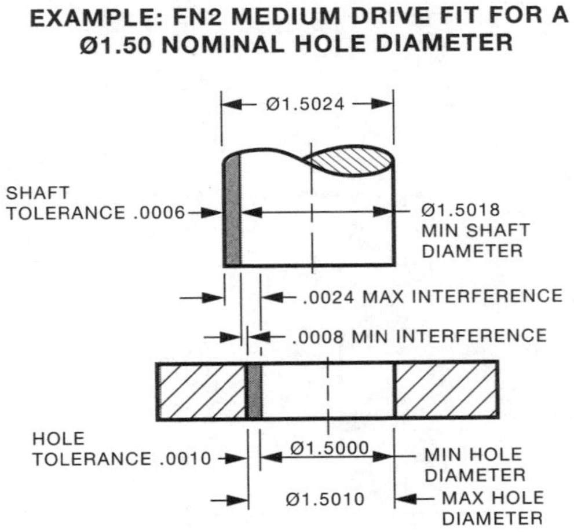
EXAMPLE: FN2 MEDIUM DRIVE FIT FOR A Ø1.50 NOMINAL HOLE DIAMETER
Ø1.5024
SHAFT TOLERANCE .0006
Ø1.5018 MIN SHAFT DIAMETER
.0024 MAX INTERFERENCE
.0008 MIN INTERFERENCE
HOLE TOLERANCE .0010
Ø1.5000
MIN HOLE DIAMETER
Ø1.5010
MAX HOLE DIAMETER

Nominal Size Range Inches		Class FN1 Light Drive Fit			Class FN2 Medium Drive Fit			Class FN3 Heavy Drive Fit			Class FN4 Shrink Fit			Class FN5 Heavy Shrink Fit		
		Hole Tol. GR6	Maximum Interference	Shaft Tol. GR5	Hole Tol. GR7	Maximum Interference	Shaft Tol. GR6	Hole Tol. GR7	Maximum Interference	Shaft Tol. GR6	Hole Tol. GR7	Maximum Interference	Shaft Tol. GR6	Hole Tol. GR8	Maximum Interference	Shaft Tol. GR7
Over	To	-0		+0	-0		+0	-0		+0	-0		+0	-0		+0
0	.12	+0.25	0.50	-0.15	+0.40	0.85	-0.25				+0.40	0.95	-0.25	+0.60	1.30	-0.40
.12	.24	+0.30	0.60	-0.20	+0.50	1.00	-0.30				+0.50	1.20	-0.30	+0.70	1.70	-0.50
.24	.40	+0.40	0.75	-0.25	+0.60	1.40	-0.40				+0.60	1.60	-0.40	+0.90	2.00	-0.60
.40	.56	+0.40	0.80	-0.30	+0.70	1.60	-0.40				+0.70	1.80	-0.40	+1.00	2.30	-0.70
.56	.71	+0.40	0.90	-0.30	+0.70	1.60	-0.40				+0.70	1.80	-0.40	+1.00	2.50	-0.70
.71	.95	+0.50	1.10	-0.40	+0.80	1.90	-0.50				+0.80	2.10	-0.50	+1.20	3.00	-0.80
.95	1.19	+0.50	1.20	-0.40	+0.80	1.90	-0.50	+0.80	2.10	-0.50	+0.80	2.30	-0.50	+1.20	3.30	-0.80
1.19	1.58	+0.60	1.30	-0.40	+1.00	2.40	-0.60	+1.00	2.60	-0.60	+1.00	3.10	-0.60	+1.60	4.00	-1.00
1.58	1.97	+0.60	1.40	-0.40	+1.00	2.40	-0.60	+1.00	2.80	-0.60	+1.00	3.40	-0.60	+1.60	5.00	-1.00
1.97	2.56	+0.70	1.80	-0.50	+1.20	2.70	-0.70	+1.20	3.20	-0.70	+1.20	4.20	-0.70	+1.80	6.20	-1.20
2.56	3.15	+0.70	1.90	-0.50	+1.20	2.90	-0.70	+1.20	3.70	-0.70	+1.20	4.70	-0.70	+1.80	7.20	-1.20
3.15	3.94	+0.90	2.40	-0.60	+1.40	3.70	-0.90	+1.40	4.40	-0.70	+1.40	5.90	-0.90	+2.20	8.40	-1.40

TABLE 21 ■ Force and Shrink Fits (Values in Thousandths of an Inch)

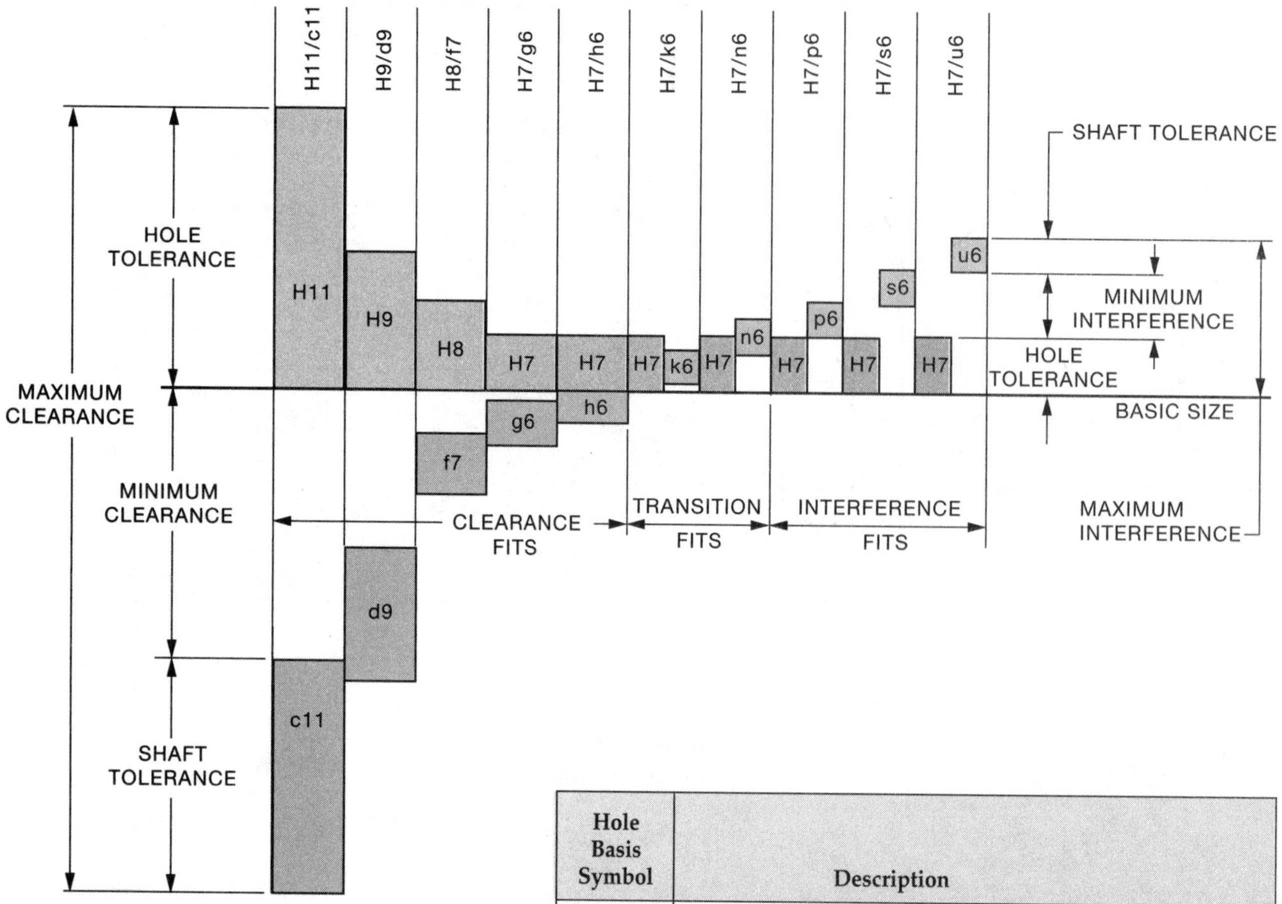

Hole Basis Symbol	Description
H11/c11 (RC9)	*Loose running* fit for wide commercial tolerances or allowances on external members.
H9/d9 (RC7)	*Free running* not fit for use where accuracy is essential, but good for large temperature variations, high running speeds, or heavy journal pressures.
H8/f7 (RC4)	*Close running* fit for running on accurate machines and for accurate location at moderate speeds and journal pressures.
H7/g6 (LC5)	*Sliding* fit not intended to run freely, but to move and turn freely and locate accurately.
H7/h6 (LC2)	*Locational clearance* fit provides snug fit for locating stationary parts, but can be freely assembled and disassembled.
H7/k6 (LT3)	*Locational transition* fit for accurate location, a compromise between clearance and interference.
H7/n6 (LT5)	*Locational transition* fit for more accurate location where greater interference is permissible.
H7/p6 (LN2)	*Locational interference* fit for parts requiring rigidity and alignment with prime accuracy of location but without special bore pressure requirements.
H7/s6 (FN2)	*Medium drive* fit for ordinary steel parts or shrink fits on light sections, the tightest fit usable with cast iron.
H7/u6 (FN4)	*Force* fit suitable for parts that can be highly stressed or for shrink fits where the heavy pressing forces required are impractical.

TABLE 22 ■ Preferred Hole Basis Metric Fits Description

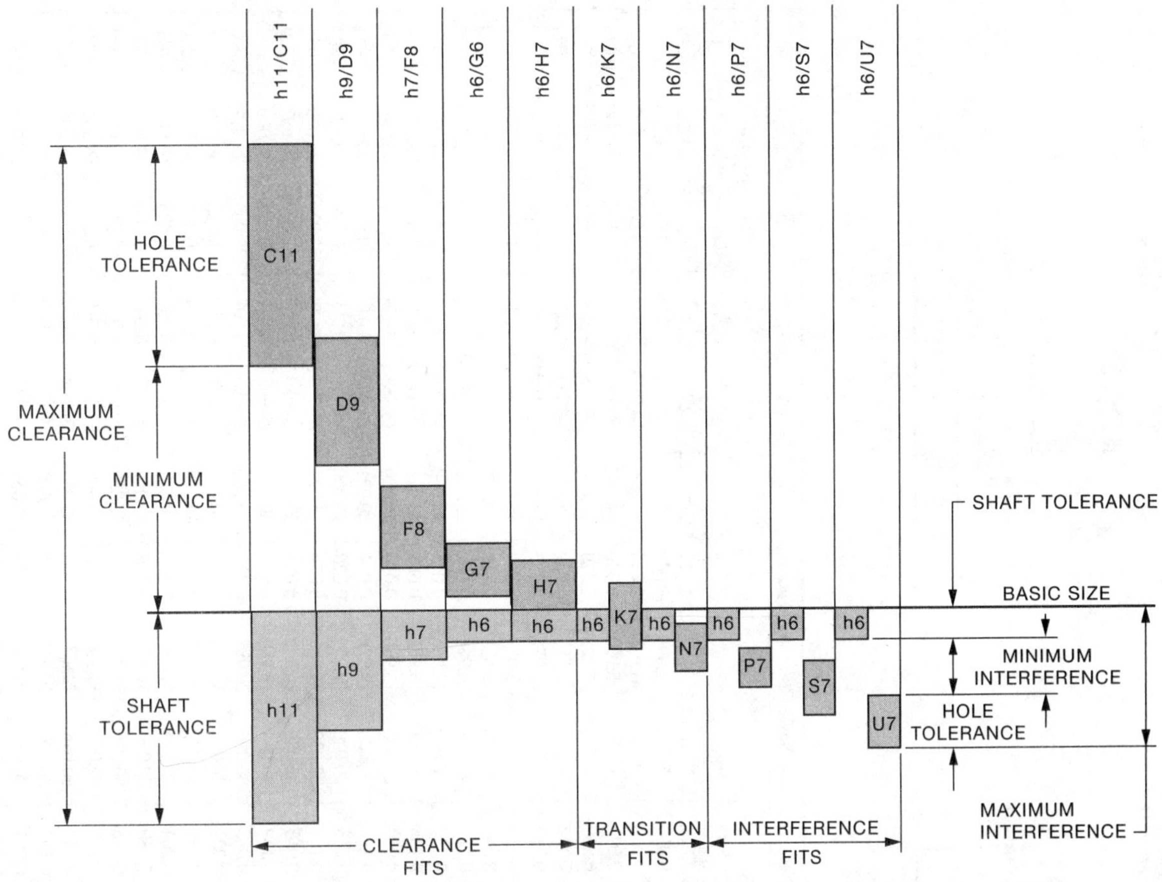

Shaft Basis Symbol	Description	Shaft Basis Symbol	Description
C11/h11	*Loose running* fit for wide commercial tolerances or allowances on external members.	K7/h6	*Locational transition* fit for accurate location, a compromise between clearance and interference.
D9/h9	*Free running* not fit for use where accuracy is essential, but good for large temperature variations, high running speeds, or heavy journal pressures.	N7/h6	*Locational transition* fit for more accurate location where greater interference is permissible.
F8/h7	*Close running* fit for running on accurate machines and for accurate location at moderate speeds and journal pressures.	P7/h6	*Locational interference* fit for parts requiring rigidity and alignment with prime accuracy of location but without special bore pressure requirements.
G7/h6	*Sliding* fit not intended to run freely, but to move and turn freely and locate accurately.	S7/h6	*Medium drive* fit for ordinary steel parts or shrink fits on light sections, the tightest fit usable with cast iron.
H7/h6	*Locational clearance* fit provides snug fit for locating stationary parts, but can be freely assembled and disassembled.	U7/h6	*Force* fit suitable for parts that can be highly stressed or for shrink fits where the heavy pressing forces required are impractical.

TABLE 23 ■ Preferred Shaft Basis Metric Fits Description

EXAMPLE: RC9 LOOSE RUNNING FIT FOR A Ø20 NOMINAL HOLE DIAMETER

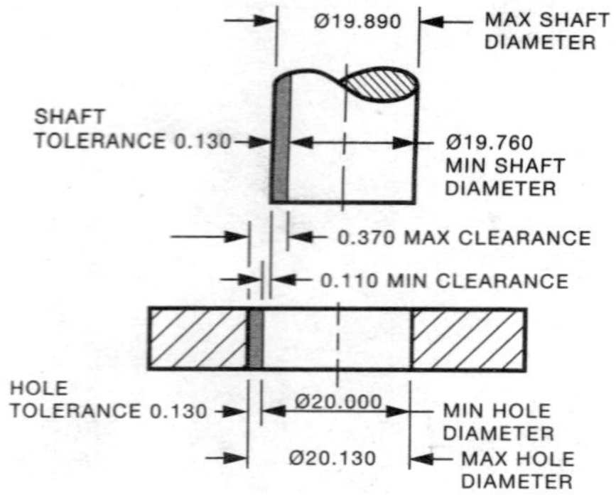

EXAMPLE: LC2 LOCATIONAL CLEARANCE FIT FOR A Ø40 NOMINAL HOLE DIAMETER

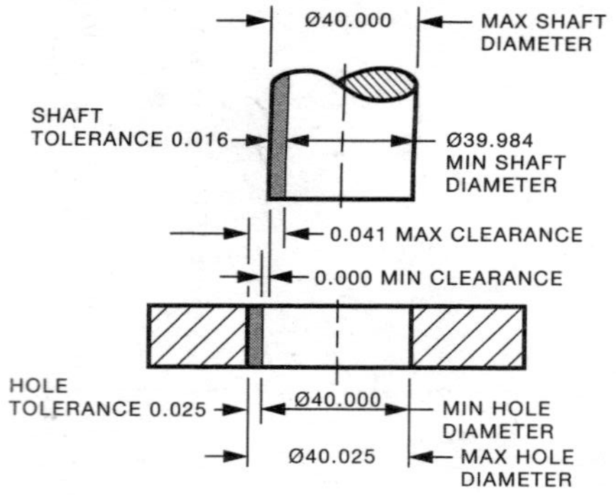

Preferred Hole Basis Clearance Fits															
	Loose Running			Free Running			Close Running			Sliding			Locational Clearance		
Basic Size	Hole H11	Shaft c11	Fit RC9	Hole H9	Shaft d9	Fit RC7	Hole H8	Shaft f7	Fit RC4	Hole H7	Shaft g6	Fit LC5	Hole H7	Shaft h6	Fit LC2
5 MAX	5.075	4.930	0.220	5.030	4.970	0.090	5.018	4.990	0.040	5.012	4.996	0.024	5.012	5.000	0.020
MIN	5.000	5.855	0.070	5.000	4.940	0.030	5.000	4.978	0.010	5.000	4.988	0.004	5.000	4.992	0.000
6 MAX	6.075	5.930	0.220	6.030	5.970	0.090	6.018	5.990	0.040	6.012	5.996	0.024	6.012	6.000	0.020
MIN	6.000	5.855	0.070	6.000	5.940	0.030	6.000	5.978	0.010	6.000	5.988	0.004	6.000	5.992	0.000
8 MAX	8.090	7.920	0.260	8.036	7.960	0.112	8.022	7.987	0.050	8.015	7.995	0.029	8.015	8.000	0.024
MIN	8.000	7.830	0.080	8.000	7.924	0.040	8.000	7.972	0.013	8.000	7.986	0.006	8.000	7.991	0.000
10 MAX	10.090	9.920	0.260	10.036	9.960	0.112	10.022	9.987	0.050	10.015	9.995	0.029	10.015	10.000	0.024
MIN	10.000	9.830	0.080	10.000	9.924	0.040	10.000	9.972	0.013	10.000	9.986	0.005	10.000	9.991	0.000
12 MAX	12.110	11.905	0.315	12.043	11.950	0.136	12.027	11.984	0.061	12.018	11.994	0.035	12.018	12.000	0.029
MIN	12.000	11.795	0.095	12.000	11.907	0.050	12.000	11.966	0.016	12.000	11.983	0.006	12.000	11.989	0.000
16 MAX	16.110	15.905	0.315	16.043	15.950	0.136	16.027	15.984	0.061	16.018	15.994	0.035	16.018	16.000	0.029
MIN	16.000	15.795	0.095	16.000	15.907	0.050	16.000	15.966	0.016	16.000	15.983	0.006	16.000	15.989	0.000
20 MAX	20.130	19.890	0.370	20.052	19.935	0.169	20.033	19.980	0.074	20.021	19.993	0.041	20.021	20.000	0.034
MIN	20.000	19.760	0.110	20.000	19.883	0.065	20.000	19.959	0.020	20.000	19.980	0.007	20.000	19.987	0.000
25 MAX	25.130	24.890	0.370	25.052	24.935	0.169	25.033	24.980	0.074	25.021	24.993	0.042	25.021	25.000	0.034
MIN	25.000	24.760	0.110	25.000	24.883	0.065	25.000	24.959	0.020	25.000	24.980	0.007	25.000	24.987	0.000
30 MAX	30.130	29.890	0.370	30.052	29.935	0.169	30.033	29.980	0.074	30.021	29.993	0.041	30.021	30.000	0.034
MIN	30.000	29.760	0.110	30.000	29.883	0.065	30.000	29.959	0.020	30.000	29.980	0.007	30.000	29.987	0.000
40 MAX	40.160	39.880	0.440	40.062	39.920	0.204	40.039	39.975	0.089	40.025	39.991	0.050	40.025	40.000	0.041
MIN	40.000	39.720	0.120	40.000	39.858	0.080	40.000	39.950	0.025	40.000	39.975	0.009	40.000	39.984	0.000
50 MAX	50.160	49.870	0.450	50.062	49.920	0.204	50.039	49.975	0.089	50.025	49.991	0.050	50.025	50.000	0.041
MIN	50.000	49.710	0.130	50.000	49.858	0.080	50.000	49.950	0.025	50.000	49.975	0.009	50.000	49.984	0.000
60 MAX	60.190	59.860	0.520	60.074	59.900	0.248	60.046	59.970	0.106	60.030	59.990	0.059	60.030	60.000	0.049
MIN	60.000	59.670	0.140	60.000	59.826	0.100	60.000	59.940	0.030	60.000	59.971	0.010	60.000	59.981	0.000
80 MAX	80.190	79.850	0.530	80.074	79.900	0.248	80.046	79.970	0.106	80.030	79.990	0.059	80.030	80.000	0.049
MIN	80.000	79.660	0.150	80.000	79.826	0.100	80.000	79.940	0.030	80.000	79.971	0.010	80.000	79.981	0.000
100 MAX	100.220	99.830	0.610	100.087	99.880	0.294	100.054	99.964	0.125	100.035	99.988	0.069	100.035	100.000	0.057
MIN	100.000	99.610	0.170	100.000	99.793	0.120	100.000	99.929	0.036	100.000	99.966	0.012	100.000	99.978	0.000

TABLE 24 ■ Preferred Hole Basis Metric Fits (Values in Millimetres)

EXAMPLE: LT5 LOCATIONAL TRANSITION FIT FOR A Ø50 NOMINAL HOLE DIAMETER

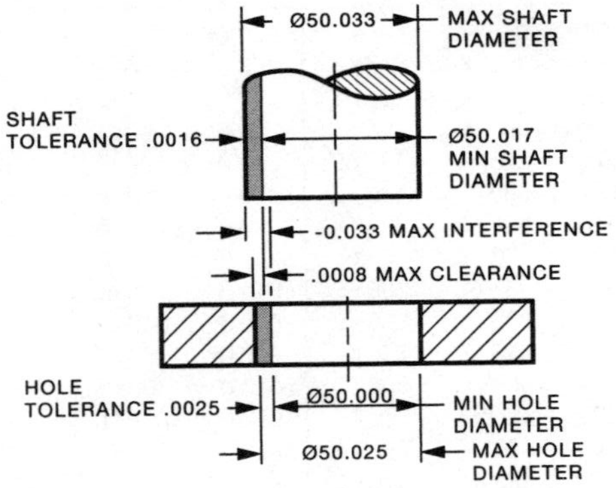
Ø50.033
MAX SHAFT DIAMETER
SHAFT TOLERANCE .0016
Ø50.017 MIN SHAFT DIAMETER
-0.033 MAX INTERFERENCE
.0008 MAX CLEARANCE
HOLE TOLERANCE .0025
Ø50.000
MIN HOLE DIAMETER
Ø50.025
MAX HOLE DIAMETER

EXAMPLE: FN4 FORCE FIT FOR A Ø30 NOMINAL HOLE DIAMETER

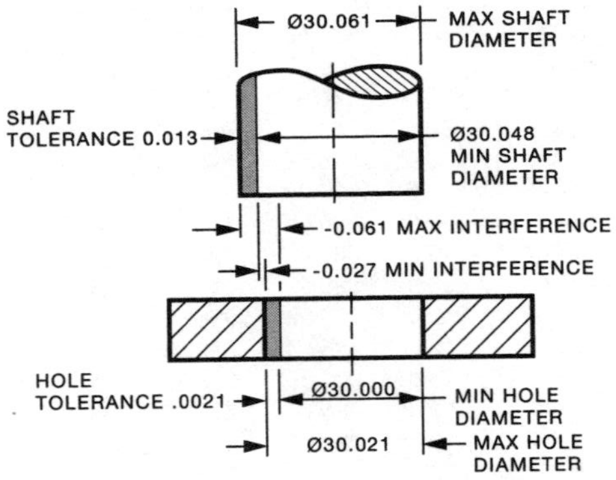
Ø30.061
MAX SHAFT DIAMETER
SHAFT TOLERANCE 0.013
Ø30.048 MIN SHAFT DIAMETER
-0.061 MAX INTERFERENCE
-0.027 MIN INTERFERENCE
HOLE TOLERANCE .0021
Ø30.000
MIN HOLE DIAMETER
Ø30.021
MAX HOLE DIAMETER

	Preferred Hole Basis Transition and Interference Fits														
Basic Size	Locational Transn.			Locational Transn.			Locational Interf.			Medium Drive			Force		
	Hole H7	Shaft k6	Fit LT3	Hole H7	Shaft n6	Fit LT5	Hole H7	Shaft p6	Fit LN2	Hole H7	Shaft s6	Fit FN2	Hole H7	Shaft u6	Fit FN4
5 MAX	5.012	5.009	0.011	5.012	5.016	0.004	5.012	5.020	0.000	5.012	5.027	-0.007	5.012	5.031	-0.011
MIN	5.000	5.001	-0.009	5.000	5.008	0.016	5.000	5.012	-0.020	5.000	5.019	-0.027	5.000	5.023	-0.031
6 MAX	6.012	6.009	0.011	6.012	6.016	0.004	6.012	6.020	0.000	6.012	6.027	-0.007	6.012	6.031	-0.011
MIN	6.000	6.001	-0.009	6.000	6.008	0.016	6.000	6.012	-0.020	6.000	6.019	-0.027	6.000	6.023	-0.031
8 MAX	8.015	8.010	0.014	8.015	8.019	0.005	8.015	8.024	0.000	8.015	8.032	-0.008	8.015	8.037	-0.013
MIN	8.000	8.001	-0.010	8.000	8.010	0.019	8.000	8.015	-0.024	8.000	8.023	-0.032	8.000	8.028	-0.037
10 MAX	10.015	10.010	0.014	10.015	10.019	0.005	10.015	10.024	0.000	10.015	10.032	-0.008	10.015	10.037	-0.013
MIN	10.000	10.001	-0.010	10.000	10.010	0.019	10.000	10.015	-0.024	10.000	10.023	-0.032	10.000	10.028	-0.037
12 MAX	12.018	12.012	0.017	12.018	12.023	0.006	12.018	12.029	0.000	12.018	12.039	-0.010	12.018	12.044	-0.015
MIN	12.000	12.001	-0.012	12.000	12.012	0.023	12.000	12.018	-0.029	12.000	12.028	-0.039	12.000	12.033	-0.044
16 MAX	16.018	16.012	0.017	16.018	16.023	0.006	16.018	16.029	0.000	16.018	16.039	-0.010	16.018	16.044	-0.015
MIN	16.000	16.001	-0.012	16.000	16.012	0.023	16.000	16.018	-0.029	16.000	16.028	-0.039	16.000	16.033	-0.044
20 MAX	20.021	20.015	0.019	20.021	20.028	0.006	20.021	20.035	0.001	20.021	20.048	-0.014	20.021	20.054	-0.020
MIN	20.000	20.002	-0.015	20.000	20.015	0.028	20.000	20.022	-0.035	20.000	20.035	-0.048	20.000	20.041	-0.054
25 MAX	25.021	25.014	0.019	25.021	25.028	0.006	25.021	25.035	0.001	25.021	25.048	-0.014	25.021	25.061	-0.027
MIN	25.000	25.002	-0.015	25.000	25.015	0.028	25.000	25.022	-0.035	25.000	25.035	-0.048	25.000	25.048	-0.061
30 MAX	30.021	30.015	0.019	30.021	30.028	0.006	30.021	30.035	0.001	30.021	30.048	-0.014	30.021	30.061	-0.027
MIN	30.000	30.002	-0.015	30.000	30.015	0.028	30.000	30.022	-0.035	30.000	30.035	-0.048	30.000	30.048	-0.061
40 MAX	40.025	40.018	0.023	40.025	40.033	0.008	40.025	40.042	-0.001	40.025	40.059	-0.018	40.025	40.076	-0.035
MIN	40.000	40.002	-0.018	40.000	40.017	0.033	40.000	40.026	-0.042	40.000	40.043	-0.059	40.000	40.060	-0.076
50 MAX	50.025	50.018	0.023	50.025	50.033	0.008	50.025	50.042	0.001	50.025	50.059	-0.018	50.025	50.086	-0.045
MIN	50.000	50.002	-0.018	50.000	50.017	0.033	50.000	50.026	-0.042	50.000	50.043	-0.059	50.000	50.070	-0.086
60 MAX	60.030	60.021	0.028	60.030	60.039	0.010	60.030	60.051	0.002	60.030	60.072	-0.023	60.030	60.106	-0.057
MIN	60.000	60.002	-0.021	60.000	60.020	0.039	60.000	60.032	-0.051	60.000	60.053	-0.072	60.000	60.087	-0.106
80 MAX	80.030	80.021	0.028	80.030	80.039	0.010	80.030	80.051	0.002	80.030	80.078	-0.029	80.030	80.121	-0.072
MIN	80.000	80.002	-0.021	80.000	80.020	0.039	80.000	80.032	-0.051	80.000	80.059	-0.078	80.000	80.102	-0.121
100 MAX	100.035	100.025	0.032	100.035	100.045	0.012	100.035	100.059	0.002	100.035	100.093	-0.036	100.035	100.146	-0.089
MIN	100.000	100.003	-0.025	100.000	100.023	0.045	100.000	100.037	-0.059	100.000	100.071	-0.093	100.000	100.124	-0.146

TABLE 24 (CONT'D) ■ Preferred Hole Basis Metric Fits (Values in Millimetres)

MAX. HOLE = 40.025
MIN. SHAFT = -40.026
-.001

EXAMPLE: RC9 LOOSE RUNNING FIT FOR A Ø20 NOMINAL SHAFT DIAMETER

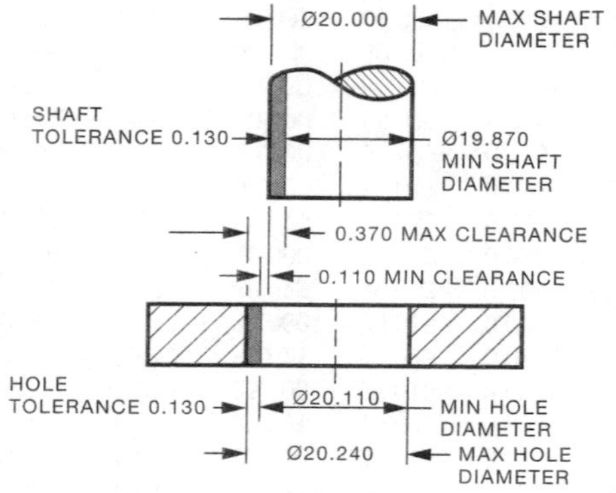
Ø20.000
MAX SHAFT DIAMETER
SHAFT TOLERANCE 0.130
Ø19.870 MIN SHAFT DIAMETER
0.370 MAX CLEARANCE
0.110 MIN CLEARANCE
HOLE TOLERANCE 0.130
Ø20.110
MIN HOLE DIAMETER
Ø20.240
MAX HOLE DIAMETER

EXAMPLE: LC2 LOCATIONAL CLEARANCE FIT FOR A Ø40 NOMINAL SHAFT DIAMETER

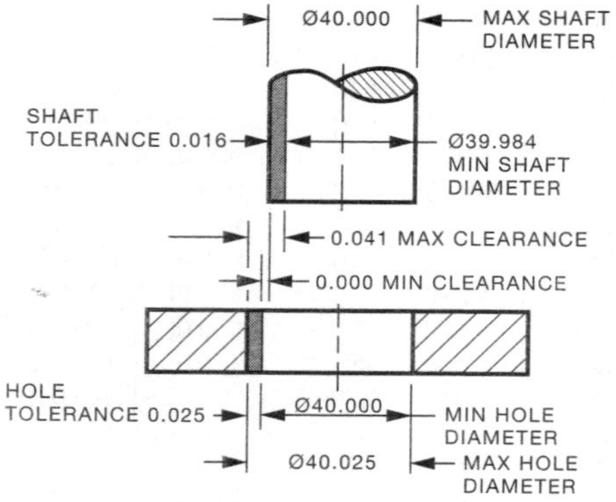
Ø40.000
MAX SHAFT DIAMETER
SHAFT TOLERANCE 0.016
Ø39.984 MIN SHAFT DIAMETER
0.041 MAX CLEARANCE
0.000 MIN CLEARANCE
HOLE TOLERANCE 0.025
Ø40.000
MIN HOLE DIAMETER
Ø40.025
MAX HOLE DIAMETER

Preferred Shaft Basis Transition and Interference Fits															
Basic Size	Locational Transn.			Locational Transn.			Locational Interf.			Medium Drive			Force		
	Hole K7	Shaft h6	Fit LT3	Hole N7	Shaft h6	Fit LT5	Hole F7	Shaft h6	Fit LN2	Hole S7	Shaft h6	Fit FN2	Hole U7	Shaft h6	Fit FN4
5 MAX	5.003	5.000	0.011	4.996	5.000	0.004	4.992	5.000	0.000	4.985	5.000	-0.007	4.981	5.000	-0.011
MIN	4.991	4.992	-0.009	4.984	4.992	-0.016	4.980	4.992	-0.020	4.973	4.992	-0.027	4.969	4.992	-0.031
6 MAX	6.003	6.000	0.011	5.996	6.000	0.004	5.992	6.000	0.000	5.985	6.000	-0.007	5.981	6.000	-0.011
MIN	5.991	5.992	-0.009	5.984	5.992	-0.016	5.980	5.992	-0.020	5.973	5.992	-0.027	5.969	5.992	-0.031
8 MAX	8.005	8.000	0.014	7.996	8.000	0.005	7.991	8.000	0.000	7.983	8.000	-0.008	7.978	8.000	-0.013
MIN	7.990	7.991	-0.010	7.981	7.991	-0.019	7.976	7.991	-0.024	7.968	7.991	-0.032	7.963	7.991	-0.037
10 MAX	10.005	10.000	0.014	9.996	10.000	0.005	9.991	10.000	0.000	9.983	10.000	-0.008	9.978	10.000	-0.013
MIN	9.990	9.991	-0.010	9.981	9.991	-0.019	9.976	9.991	-0.024	9.968	9.991	-0.032	9.963	9.991	-0.037
12 MAX	12.006	12.000	0.017	11.995	12.000	0.006	11.989	12.000	0.000	11.979	12.000	-0.010	11.974	12.000	-0.015
MIN	11.988	11.989	-0.012	11.977	11.989	-0.023	11.971	11.989	-0.029	11.961	11.989	-0.039	11.956	11.989	-0.044
16 MAX	16.006	16.000	0.017	15.955	16.000	0.006	15.989	16.000	0.000	15.979	16.000	-0.010	15.974	16.000	-0.015
MIN	15.988	15.989	-0.012	15.977	15.989	-0.023	15.971	15.989	-0.029	15.961	15.989	-0.039	15.956	15.989	-0.044
20 MAX	20.006	20.000	0.019	19.993	20.000	0.006	19.986	20.000	0.001	19.973	20.000	-0.014	19.967	20.000	-0.020
MIN	19.985	19.987	-0.015	19.972	19.987	-0.028	19.965	19.987	-0.035	19.952	19.987	-0.048	19.946	19.987	-0.054
25 MAX	25.006	25.000	0.019	24.993	25.000	0.006	24.986	25.000	0.001	24.973	25.000	-0.014	24.960	25.000	-0.027
MIN	24.985	24.987	-0.015	24.972	24.987	-0.028	24.965	24.987	-0.035	24.952	24.987	-0.048	24.939	24.987	-0.061
30 MAX	30.006	30.000	0.019	29.993	30.000	0.006	29.986	30.000	0.001	29.973	30.000	-0.014	29.960	30.000	-0.027
MIN	29.985	29.987	-0.015	29.972	29.987	-0.028	29.965	29.987	-0.035	29.952	29.987	-0.048	29.939	29.987	-0.061
40 MAX	40.007	40.000	0.023	39.992	40.000	0.008	39.983	40.000	0.001	39.966	40.000	-0.018	39.949	40.000	-0.035
MIN	39.982	39.984	-0.018	39.967	39.984	-0.033	39.958	39.984	-0.042	39.941	39.984	-0.059	39.924	39.984	-0.076
50 MAX	50.007	50.000	0.023	49.992	50.000	0.008	49.983	50.000	0.001	49.966	50.000	-0.018	49.939	50.000	-0.045
MIN	49.982	49.984	-0.018	49.967	49.984	-0.033	49.958	49.984	-0.042	49.941	49.984	-0.059	49.914	49.984	-0.086
60 MAX	60.009	60.000	0.028	59.991	60.000	0.010	59.979	60.000	0.002	59.958	60.000	-0.023	59.924	60.000	-0.057
MIN	59.979	59.981	-0.021	59.961	59.981	-0.039	59.949	59.981	-0.051	59.928	59.981	-0.072	59.894	59.981	-0.106
80 MAX	80.009	80.000	0.028	79.991	80.000	0.010	79.979	80.000	0.002	79.952	80.000	-0.029	79.909	80.000	-0.072
MIN	79.979	79.981	-0.021	79.961	79.981	-0.039	79.949	79.981	-0.051	79.922	79.981	-0.078	79.879	79.981	-0.121
100 MAX	100.010	100.000	0.032	99.990	100.000	0.012	99.976	100.000	0.002	99.942	100.000	-0.036	99.889	100.000	-0.089
MIN	99.975	99.978	-0.025	99.955	99.978	-0.045	99.941	99.978	-0.059	99.907	99.978	-0.093	99.854	99.978	-0.146

TABLE 25 ■ Preferred Shaft Basis Metric Fits (Values in Millimetres)

EXAMPLE: LT5 LOCATIONAL TRANSITION FIT FOR A Ø50 NOMINAL SHAFT DIAMETER

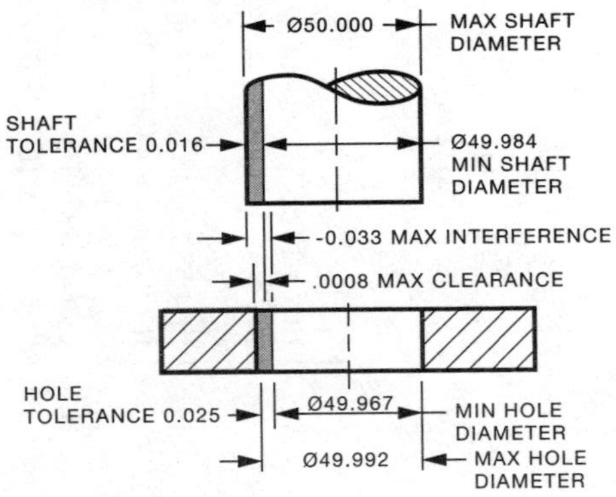
Ø50.000
MAX SHAFT DIAMETER
SHAFT TOLERANCE 0.016
Ø49.984 MIN SHAFT DIAMETER
-0.033 MAX INTERFERENCE
.0008 MAX CLEARANCE
HOLE TOLERANCE 0.025
Ø49.967
MIN HOLE DIAMETER
Ø49.992
MAX HOLE DIAMETER

EXAMPLE: FN4 FORCE FIT FOR A Ø30 NOMINAL SHAFT DIAMETER

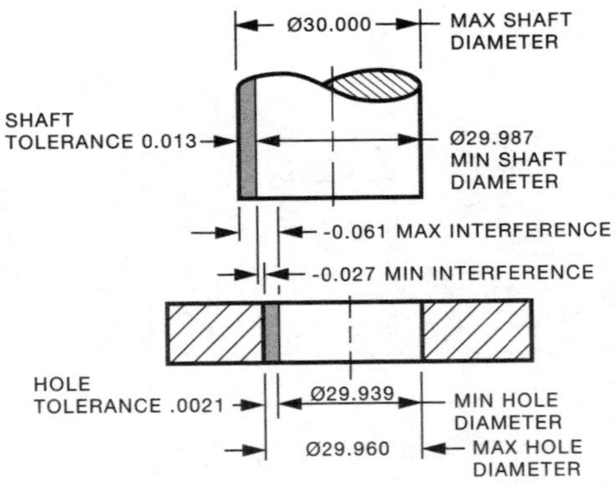
Ø30.000
MAX SHAFT DIAMETER
SHAFT TOLERANCE 0.013
Ø29.987 MIN SHAFT DIAMETER
-0.061 MAX INTERFERENCE
-0.027 MIN INTERFERENCE
HOLE TOLERANCE .0021
Ø29.939
MIN HOLE DIAMETER
Ø29.960
MAX HOLE DIAMETER

Preferred Shaft Basis Transition and Interference Fits															
Basic Size	Loose Running			Free Running			Close Running			Sliding			Locational Clearance		
	Hole C11	Shaft h11	Fit RC3	Hole D9	Shaft h9	Fit RC7	Hole F8	Shaft h7	Fit RC4	Hole G7	Shaft h6	Fit LC5	Hole H7	Shaft h6	Fit LC2
5 MAX	5.145	5.000	0.220	5.060	5.000	0.090	5.028	5.000	0.040	5.016	5.000	0.024	5.012	5.000	0.020
MIN	5.070	4.925	0.070	5.030	4.970	0.030	5.010	4.988	0.010	5.004	4.992	0.004	5.000	4.992	0.000
6 MAX	6.145	6.000	0.220	6.060	6.000	0.090	6.028	6.000	0.040	6.016	6.000	0.024	6.012	6.000	0.020
MIN	6.070	5.925	0.070	6.030	5.970	0.030	6.010	5.988	0.010	6.004	5.992	0.004	6.000	5.992	0.000
8 MAX	8.170	8.000	0.260	8.076	8.000	0.112	8.035	8.000	0.050	8.020	8.000	0.029	8.015	8.000	0.024
MIN	8.080	7.910	0.080	8.040	7.964	0.040	8.013	7.985	0.013	8.005	7.991	0.005	8.000	7.991	0.000
10 MAX	10.170	10.000	0.260	10.076	10.000	0.112	10.035	10.000	0.050	10.020	10.000	0.029	10.015	10.000	0.024
MIN	10.080	9.910	0.080	10.040	9.964	0.040	10.013	9.985	0.013	10.005	9.991	0.005	10.000	9.991	0.000
12 MAX	12.205	12.000	0.315	12.093	12.000	0.136	12.043	12.000	0.061	12.024	12.000	0.035	12.018	12.000	0.029
MIN	12.095	11.890	0.095	12.050	11.957	0.050	12.016	11.982	0.016	12.006	11.989	0.006	12.000	11.989	0.000
16 MAX	16.205	16.000	0.315	16.093	16.000	0.136	16.043	16.000	0.061	16.024	16.000	0.035	16.018	16.000	0.029
MIN	16.095	15.890	0.095	16.050	15.957	0.050	16.016	15.982	0.016	16.006	15.989	0.006	16.000	15.989	0.000
20 MAX	20.240	20.000	0.370	20.117	20.000	0.169	20.053	20.000	0.074	20.028	20.000	0.041	20.021	20.000	0.034
MIN	20.110	19.870	0.110	20.065	19.948	0.065	20.020	19.979	0.020	20.007	19.987	0.007	20.000	19.987	0.000
25 MAX	25.240	25.000	0.370	25.117	25.000	0.169	25.053	25.000	0.074	25.028	25.000	0.041	25.021	25.000	0.034
MIN	25.110	24.870	0.110	25.065	24.948	0.065	25.020	24.979	0.020	25.007	24.987	0.007	25.000	24.987	0.000
30 MAX	30.240	30.000	0.370	30.117	30.000	0.169	30.053	30.000	0.074	30.028	30.000	0.041	30.021	30.000	0.034
MIN	30.110	29.870	0.110	30.065	29.948	0.065	30.020	29.979	0.020	30.007	29.987	0.007	30.000	29.987	0.000
40 MAX	40.280	40.000	0.440	40.142	40.000	0.204	40.064	40.000	0.089	40.034	40.000	0.050	40.025	40.000	0.041
MIN	40.120	39.840	0.120	40.080	39.938	0.080	40.025	39.975	0.025	40.009	39.984	0.009	40.000	39.984	0.000
50 MAX	50.290	50.000	0.450	50.142	50.000	0.204	50.064	50.000	0.089	50.034	50.000	0.050	50.025	50.000	0.041
MIN	50.130	49.840	0.130	50.080	49.938	0.080	50.025	49.975	0.025	50.009	49.984	0.009	50.000	49.984	0.000
60 MAX	60.330	60.000	0.510	60.174	60.000	0.248	60.076	60.000	0.106	60.040	60.000	0.059	60.030	60.000	0.049
MIN	60.140	59.810	0.140	60.100	59.926	0.100	60.030	59.970	0.030	60.010	59.981	0.010	60.000	59.981	0.000
80 MAX	80.340	80.000	0.530	80.174	80.000	0.248	80.076	80.000	0.106	80.040	80.000	0.059	80.030	80.000	0.049
MIN	80.150	79.810	0.150	80.100	79.926	0.100	80.030	79.970	0.030	80.010	79.981	0.010	80.000	79.981	0.000
100 MAX	100.390	100.000	0.610	100.207	100.000	0.294	100.090	100.000	0.125	100.047	100.000	0.069	100.035	100.000	0.057
MIN	100.170	99.780	0.170	100.120	99.913	0.120	100.036	99.965	0.036	100.012	99.978	0.012	100.000	99.987	0.000

TABLE 25 (CONT'D) ■ Preferred Shaft Basis Metric Fits (Values in Millimetres)

Quality	Metric Unit	Symbol	Metric to Inch-Pound Unit	Inch-Pound to Metric Unit
Length	millimetre	mm	1 mm = 0.0394 in.	1 in. = 25.4 mm
	centimetre	cm	1 cm = 0.394	1 ft. = 30.5 cm
	metre	m	1 m = 39.37 in. = 3.28 ft.	1 yd. = 0.914 m = 914 mm
	kilometre	km	1 km = 0.62 mile	1 mile = 1.61 km
Area	square millimetre	mm^2	1 mm = 0.001 55 sq. in.	1 sq. in. = 6 452 mm^2
	square centimetre	cm^2	1 cm = 0.155 sq. in.	1 sq. ft. = 0.093 m^2
	square metre	m^2	1 m = 10.8 sq. ft. = 1.2 sq. yd.	1 sq. yd. = 0.836 m^2
Mass	milligram	mg	1 g = 0.035 oz.	1 oz. = 28.3 g
	gram	g	1 kg = 2.205 lb.	1 lb. = 0.454 kg
	kilogram	kg	1 tonne = 1.102 tons	1 ton = 907.2 kg = 0.907 tonnes
	tonne	t		
Volume	cubic centimetre	cm^3	1 mm^3 = 0.000 061 cu. in.	1 fl. oz. = 28.4 cm^3
	cubic metre	m^3	1 cm^3 = 0.061 cu. in.	1 cu. in. = 16.387 cm^3
	millilitre	m^3	1 m^3 = 35.3 cu. in. = 1.308 cu. yd.	1 cu. ft. = 0.028 m^3
			1 mL = 0.035 fl. oz.	1 cu. yd. = 0.756 m^3
Capacity	litre	L	U.S. Measure 1 pt. = 0.473 L 1 qt. = 0.946 L 1 gal. = 3.785 L Imperial Measure 1 pt. = 0.568 L 1 qt. = 1.137 L 1 gal. = 4.546 L	U.S. Measure 1 L = 2.113 pt. = 1.057 qt. = 0.264 gal. Imperial Measure 1 L = 1.76 pt. = 0.88 qt. = 0.22 gal.
Temperature	Celsius degree	°C	°C = $\frac{5}{9}$(°F-32)	°F = $\frac{5}{9}$ × °C + 32
Force	newton	N	1 N = 0.225 lb (f)	1 lb (f) = 4.45 N = 0.004 448 kN
	kilonewton	kN	1 kN = 0.225 kip (f) = 0.112 ton (f)	
Energy/Work	joule	J	1 J = 0.737 ft ∘ lb	1 ft ∘ lb = 1.355 J
	kilojoule	kJ	1 J = 0.948 Btu	1 Btu = 1.055 J
	megajoule	MJ	1 MJ = 0.278 kWh	1 kWh = 3.6 MJ
Power	kilowatt	kW	1 kW = 1.34 hp	1 hp (550 ft ∘ lb/s) = 0.746 kW
			1 W = 0.0226 ft ∘ lb/min.	1 ft ∘ lb/min = 44.2537 W
Pressure	kilopascal	kPa	1 kPa = 0.145 psi = 20.885 psf = 0.01 ton-force per sq. ft.	1 psi = 6.895 kPa 1 lb-force/sq. ft. = 47.88 Pa 1 ton-force/sq. ft. = 95.76 kPa
	*kilogram per square centimetre	kg/cm^2	1 kg/cm = 13.780 psi	
Torque	newton metre	N ∘ m	1 N ∘ m = 0.74 lb ∘ ft.	1 lb ∘ ft = 1.36 N ∘ m
	*kilogram metre	kg/m	1 Kg/m = 7.24 lb ∘ ft.	1 lb ∘ ft = 0.14 kg/m
	*kilogram per centimetre	kg/cm	1 Kg/cm = 0.86 lb ∘ in.	1 lb ∘ in = 1.2 kg/cm
Speed/Velocity	metres per second	m/s	1 m/s = 3.28 ft/s	1 ft/s = 0.305 m/s
	kilometres per hour	km/h	1 km/h = 0.62 mph	1 mph = 1.61 km/h

*Not SI units, but included here because they are employed on some of the gauges and indicators currently in use in industry.

TABLE 26 ■ Metric Conversion Tables

INDEX

A

Abbreviations, 25, 256–257
Absolute coordinate programming, 244
Addendum (ADD), 292
AISI (American Iron and Steel Institute), 188
Aligned system, 12
Alignment of parts and holes, 217
  foreshortened projection, 218
  holes revolved to show true center distance, 218
Allowances, 96
Angle dimensions, 31
Angularity, 370
Angularity tolerance, 370–371, 378
ANSI/AWS A2.4-86, 275, 285
Antifriction bearings, 183, 315
  ball bearings, 315, 317
  roller bearings, 317
Arrangement of views, 165
ASME (American Society of Mechanical Engineers), 1
ASME B18.8.2-1995, 236
ASME B27.7-1977 (R1999), 321
ASME Y14.24-1999, 250
ASME Y14.3M-1994, 131, 146, 152, 219, 226
ASME Y14.36M-1996, 59, 90
ASME Y14.5M-1994, 17, 42, 99, 211, 336, 349, 355, 365, 373, 386, 394, 409, 415, 424, 433
ASME Y14.6-1978 (R1998), 124
ASME Y14.7.1-1971 (R1998), 295
ASME Y14.7.2-1978 (R1999), 299
ASME Y14.8M-1996, 204
ASME Y32.2.3-1949 (R1999), 177
Assembly drawings, 12, 247
  bill of material, 249
  identifying parts of, 247
  subassembly drawings, 247
  swivels and universal joints, 249
Auxiliary views:
  primary, 146, 151
  secondary, 151–152

B

Back and backing weld symbol, 273–275
Ball bearings, 315, 317
Barrel-type cam, 309
Base line dimensioning, 211
Basic hole system, 108
Basic shaft system, 108
Basic size, 96
Bearings, 182
  plain, 182–183
  premounted, 184
Belt drive, 317, 320
Bevel gears, 290, 299
Bilateral tolerance, 98, 420
Bill of material, 249
Blank development formula, 161
Blind hole, 40
Boring, 42
Boron, 190
Bosses, 138
Break lines, 59
Broken-out sections, 224
Bushings, 321

C

Cams, 309
  displacement diagrams, 309
  drum (barrel-type), 309
  plate (outside diameter), 309
CAN3-B232-75 (R1996), 139
CAN3-B78.1-M83 (R1990), 124, 131, 146, 152, 219, 226
CAN3-B95-1962 (R1996), 59, 90
CAN-B97.3-M1982 (R1992), 112
CAN/CSA-B78.2-M91, 17, 42, 76, 99, 108, 139, 211, 336, 349, 355, 365, 373, 386, 394, 409, 415, 424, 433
Carbon, 190
Carbon steels, 188
Castings, 198
  cast irons, 200–201
  cored, 203
  design of, 201–203
  full mould, 200
  machining lugs, 203
  sand mould, 198
  surface coatings, 204
Cast iron pipe, 170
Cast irons, 200
  ductile, or nodular iron, 200–201
  grey iron, 200

malleable iron, 201
white iron, 201
Cellular rubber, 192
Centre lines, 39–40
Chain dimensioning, 211
Chamfer, 42, 75
Chamfering, 75
Check valves, 172
Chordal addendum, 292
Chordal thickness, 292
Chromium, 190
Circular features, 39
as datums, 415
Circularity, 353–354
of noncylindrical parts, 354
Circular pitch, 292
Circular runout, 428–429
Circular thickness of tooth, 292
Circular tolerance zones, 340
Civil engineer's scale, 49
Clearance, 292
Clearance fits, 104
Close running fit, 106
Clutches, 317
Coarse thread series, 121
Computer-aided drafting (CAD), 22–23
Conical tapers, 75
Conical washers, 258
Connections, 174
Coordinate tolerancing:
advantages of, 402
disadvantages of, 402
location of holes, 398
maximum permissible error, 399–402
Coped out, 202
Coping down, 202
Copper, 190
Copper pipe, 170
Copper tubing, 170
Cored castings, 203
Corrected addendum, 292
Cotter pins, 232, 234
Counterbores, 66
Countersinks, 66
Crest diameter, 122
Crossings, 174
CSA (Canadian Standards Association), 1
CSA-B97.3-1970 (R1992), 108
CSA Z85-1983, 25
Cutting-plane line, 62–63
Cylindrical features:
external, 384, 386
internal, 381–383
Cylindricity, 354–355

D

Datum, 211
establishing for runout tolerances, 431–433
establishing plane for uneven surfaces, 359, 361
feature, 358
primary, 358–359
secondary, 359
selecting for positional tolerancing, 414–415
tertiary, 359
Datum dimensioning, 211
Datum feature symbol:
association with geometric tolerances, 363–364
former ANSI symbol, 362–363
multiple datum features, 364
not subject to size variation, 361
partial surfaces as datums, 364
subject to size variation, 362
Datum targets, 390
datum-target areas, 392
datum-target lines, 391–392
datum-target points, 391
dimensioning for target location, 394
targets not in the same plane, 393–394
Datum-target symbol, 390–391
Decimal-inch scale, 49
Decimal-inch system, 14
Dedendum (DED), 292
Detail drawing, 12
Development drawings, 157
Diameter, 1
Diametral pitch, 292, 294
Dimensioning, 12, 14
base line, 211
basic rules for, 16–17
chain, 211
chamfers, 75
choice of, 16
cylindrical features, 40
cylindrical holes, 40
keyseats, 137
knurls, 76
for numerical control, 242
pipe and pipe fittings, 174
rectangular coordinate, 139
tapers, 75–76
for two-axis coordinate system, 242–244
undercuts, 75
Dimension lines, 12
Dimension origin symbol, 138
Dovetails, 49–50
Dowel pins, 232
Drafting office, 22
Drawing callout, 112
Drawing reproduction, 23–25
Drawing revisions, 58–59
Drawings for numerical control, 242
Drawing to scale, 47
Drilling, 40
Drill jigs, 232
Drill sizes, 219
Drive and force fits, 106
Drum cam, 309
Ductile, or nodular iron, 200–201

E

Edge, 157
Elastomers, 192
Engineering drawings, 1
Enlarged scale, 47
Extension lines, 12, 14
External cylindrical features:
perpendicularity for an axis
pin or boss at MMC, 384, 386
pin or boss RFS, 384
Extra-fine thread series, 121

F

Fastening devices, 119
Feature, 211
Feature control frame:
application to features of size, 332
application to surfaces, 331–332
Features of size, 340
definitions, 340–342

examples, 342–343
least material condition (LMC), 344
material contition symbols, 342
maximum material condition (MMC), 343–344
orientation tolerancing for, 378–386
regardless of feature size (RFS), 344
straightness, 345
with maximum value, 348
MMC basis, 346
per unit length, 348–349
RFS basis, 345
zero MMC, 346–347
Feet and inches system, 15
Field welds, 265
Fillets, 42
Fillet welds, 265–267
Fine thread series, 121
Finish, 85
FINISH ALL OVER (FAO), 56
First-angle projection, 3
Fit, 104
Fittings, 171
flanged, 172
reducing, 171
screwed, 171
welded, 171
Flange, 172
symbols, 177
welds, 284–285
Flat back patterns, 201
Flatness, 352
per unit area, 352
Flats, 138
Flat surfaces, orientation tolerancing for, 370–373
Flat tapers, 75–76
Flaws, 87–88
Follower, 309
Foot scales, 49
Force or shrink fit, 107–108
Forming, 160
Form tolerances, 333
circularity, 353–354
cylindricity, 354–355
flatness, 352
Fractional-inch scale, 49
Fractional-inch system, 15
Free running fit, 107
Full indicator movement (FIM), 428
Full mould casting, 200
Full scale, 47
Full sections, 64

G

Gate valves, 172
Gears, 290
bevel, 290, 299
spur, 291–294, 299
Gear tooth vernier, 294
Gear trains, 304
centre distance, 304
motor drive, 305
ratio of gears, 304–305
Geometric tolerancing, 328, 330. *See also* Features of size; Positional tolerancing
datums for, 358
feature control frame, 330–331
application to features of size, 332
application to surfaces, 331–332
points, lines, and surfaces, 330
Globe valves, 172
Grade 6 tolerances, 122
Grey iron, 200
Groove welds, 271–272
back and backing weld symbol, 273–275
melt-through symbol, 275

H

Half sections, 64
Heavy drive fit, 108
Height, 1
Hidden lines, 25
Hole basis fits system, 112
Hollow spring pins, 236

I

Inch fits:
description of, 104, 106
standard fits, 106–108
types of, 104
Inch scales, 49
Inch threads, 120–121
Classes 1A and 1B, 121–122
Classes 2A and 2B, 122
Classes 3A and 3B, 122
thread designation, 122
Inch tolerances, 98
Inch units of measurement, 14–15
Inclined surfaces, 31, 146
Interference fits, 104
Internal cylindrical features, 381–382
perpendicularity for a median plane, 382
perpendicularity for an axis both feature and datum RFS, 382
zero tolerance at MMC, 383
perpendicularity with a maximum tolerance specified, 383
specifying parallelism for an axis, 382
Intersection of unfinished surfaces, 67
Irregular castings, 201
Isometric projection, 174
ISO projection symbol, 6–7
Items list, 249

J

Joint, 157
Journal bearings, 182–183
Junctions, 174

K

Keys, 136–137
Keyseat dimensions, 137
Knurls, 76

L

Lay, 87
symbols, 88
Leaders, 14, 40
Least material condition (LMC), 341, 344
Left-handed threads, 122
Length, 1, 6
Lettering, 3

Light drive fit, 107–108
Limit dimensioning, 97
Limits of size, 96
Linear units of measurement, 14–15
Line profile, 419–422
Locational:
clearance fit, 107
fits, 104, 106
interference fit, 107
transition fit, 107
Long holes, 414–415
Loose running fit, 107

M

Machine pins, 232, 234
Machine slots, 49
Machining allowance, 57
Machining lugs, 203
Machining symbols, 56–57
Malleable iron, 201
Manganese, 190
Manufacturing materials, 188
plastics, 190–191
rubber, 191–192
steel, 188–190
Mass production, 16
Material condition symbols, 342
Maximum material condition (MMC), 340–341
application with maximum value, 343–344
symbol for, 343
Measurement of angles, 31
Mechanical advantage, 325
Mechanical rubber, 192
Medium drive fit, 108
Medium running fit, 106
Melt-through symbol, 275
Metric dimensioning, 15
Metric fits, 110
drawing callout, 112
fit symbol, 111–112
hole basis fits system, 112
shaft basis fits system, 112
tolerance symbol, 110–111
Metric threads, 122
thread designation, 124
Microfilm, 23
Microinch, 86
Micrometre, 15, 86
Millimetre, 15
Millimetre tolerances, 98–99
Mitre gear, 299
Module, 294
Molybdenum, 190
Multiple-detail drawings, 80
Multiple hole datums, 415

N

Naming of views for spark adjuster, 219
Necking, 75
Nickel, 190
Notes, 89
Not-to-scale dimensions, 57–58
NPT (National Pipe Thread), 171
Number of teeth (N), 292
Numerical control (NC):
dimensioning for, 242
drawings for, 242

O

Oblique surfaces, 151
Odd-shaped castings, 201
Offset sections, 64
One-view drawings, 80
Orientation tolerancing:
for features of size
angularity tolerance, 378
control in two directions, 381
control on an MMC basis, 381
external cylindrical features, 384, 386
internal cylindrical features, 381–383
parallelism tolerance, 380
perpendicularity tolerance, 378–379
for flat surfaces
angularity tolerance, 370–371
applying form and orientation tolerances to a feature, 373
control in two directions, 372
parallelism tolerance, 371
perpendicularity tolerance, 371
reference to a datum, 370
Origin (zero point), 243
O-rings, 317
Orthographic piping symbols, 174, 177
Orthographic projection, 2, 174
Outside diameter cam, 309
Outside diameter (OD), 292
Overrunning clutch, 317

P

Pads, 138
Parallelism, 370
Parallelism tolerance, 371, 380
Partial sections, 224
Partial views, 218
Pawls, 324
Perpendicularity, 370
Perpendicularity tolerance, 371, 378–379
Phantom drawings, 257–258
Phosphorus, 190
Photoreproduction, 23–25
Pictorial drawings, 2
Pin fasteners, 232
machine pins, 232, 234
radial-locking pins, 234–236
Pinion, 290
Piping, 170
cast iron, 170
copper tubing, 170
joints and fittings for, 171–172
plastic, 171
seamless brass and copper, 170
steel and wrought iron, 170
valves in, 172
Piping drawings, 172
drawing projection, 174
single-line, 172
symbols, 174, 177
Pitch circle, 291, 299
Pitch cone, 299
Pitch diameter (PD), 122, 291
Plain bearings, 182–183
Plain material, 256
Plastic pipe, 171
Plastics, 190
thermoplastics, 190–191
thermosetting plastics, 191
Plate cam, 309
Plug welds, 279–280
Plus and minus tolerancing, 97–98
Position, 1
Positional tolerancing, 402
advantages of, 408–409

for circular features, 404
on MMC basis, 404, 406
RFS, 408
at zero MMC, 406
datum feature selection for, 414–415
at LMC, 408
location of holes, 398
material condition basis, 402
Precision running fit, 106
Precision sliding fit, 106
Premounted bearings, 184
Pressure angle, 291
Primary auxiliary views, 146, 151
Primary datum, 358–359
Profile tolerances, 419
profile of a line, 419–420
all-around profile tolerancing, 420
bilateral and unilateral tolerances, 420
dimensioning method, 420–421
extent of controlled profile, 421–422
profile of a surface, 422–424
profile symbols, 419
Proportions, 1

Q

Quick release fasteners, 232

R

Radial-locking pins, 234–236
Radius, 42
Ratchet wheels, 324
Reaming, 42
Rectangular coordinate dimensioning:
in tabular form, 139
without dimension lines, 139
Red shortness, 190
Reduced scale, 47
Reducing fittings, 171
Reference dimensions, 50
Regardless of feature size (RFS), 341, 344
Relative coordinate (point-to-point) programming, 244
Removal of material prohibited, 57
Removed sections, 131
Repetitive features and dimensions, 40
Reproductions, 23–25
Retaining rings, 317
Revisions, 58–59
Revolved sections, 131
Ribs in section, 224, 226
Right-handed threads, 122
Roller-element bearings. *See* Antifriction bearings
Root diameter (RD), 292
Roughness, 86
average, 86, 88
sampling length ratings, 88
width, 86
width cutoff, 86
Rounds, 42
Rubber, 191
cellular, 192
elastomers, 192
mechanical, 192
Running and sliding fits, 104, 106–107
Runout, 67
Runout tolerances, 428
circular runout, 428–429
establishing datums, 431–433
total runout, 430–431

S

SAE (Society of Automotive Engineers), 188
Sand mould casting, 198
Scale ratios, 47
Screwed fittings, 171
Seam, 157
welds, 282–283
Seamless brass pipe, 170
Secondary auxiliary views, 151–152
Secondary datum, 359
Sectional views, 62–63
Section lining, 63
Sections, 62
full, 64
half, 64
offset, 64
Section through shafts, pins, and keys, 236
Semipermanent pin fasteners, 232
Set cores, 201–202
Setscrews, 137–138
Setup point, 243–244
Shaft basis fits system, 112
Shearing, 161
Sheaves, 321
Sheet metal sizes, 157
Shims, 183
Shrinkage allowance, 200
Silicon, 190
SI (metric scales), 49
SI (metric) units of measurement, 15
Similarly sized features, identifying, 42
Sketching, 3
Sleeve bearings, 182–183
Sliding fit, 106
Slot, 49
welds, 280–281
Smoothness, 85
Snap rings, 317
Solid pins with grooved surfaces, 235
Split:
bearings, 183
patterns, 202–203
Spokes in section, 226
Spotface, 66
Spot welds, 281–282
Spur gears, 290, 299
calculation examples, 294
chordal thickness and corrected addendum, 292, 294
terminology, 291–292
working drawings of, 294
Stampings, 160
forming, 160
shearing, 161
Standard inch fits, 106–108
Steel, 188
effect of alloys on, 190
SAE and AISI systems of

identification, 188–189
Steel pipe, 170
Straight line development, 157
Straightness, 333
of a feature of size, 345–349
Straightness tolerance, 333–336
Structural steel shapes, 256
abbreviations, 256–257
conical washers, 258
phantom drawings, 257–258
Subassembly drawings, 247
Sulphur, 190
Surface:
coatings, 204
finish control, 85
profile, 419, 422–424
Surface texture, 85
control requirements, 89–90
definitions, 85–88
ratings, 88
symbol, 88
Swivel, 249
Symmetrical outlines, 50

T

Taper pins, 232
Tapers, 75–76
Technical drawings, 1
Tertiary datum, 359
Thermoplastics, 190–191
Thickness, 1
Third-angle projection, 3–6
Threaded assemblies, 119
thread standards, 120
Threaded fasteners, 119
thread representation, 119
Threaded holes, 120
Three-plane datum system, 358
Thrust bearings, 183
Title block, 7
Tolerancing, 96
inch tolerances, 98
limit dimensioning, 97
millimetre tolerances, 98–99
plus and minus, 97–98
Total runout, 430–431
Transition fits, 104
T slots, 49
Twist drill sizes, 219
Two-axis coordinate system, 242–243
absolute coordinate programming, 244
origin (zero point), 243
relative coordinate programming, 244
setup point, 243–244
Two-view drawings, 80

U

Undercuts, 75
Unidirectional system, 12
Unilateral tolerance, 98, 420
Unit production, 16
Universal joint, 249

V

Valves, 172
globe, 172
symbols, 177
Vanadium, 190
V-belt drive, 317
sizes, 320
Virtual condition, 341
Visible lines, 3

W

Waviness, 86
height ratings, 88
spacing ratings, 88
Webs in section, 224
Welded fittings, 171
Welding drawings, 262
Welding symbols, 262–264
multiple reference lines, 265
tail of, 264
weld locations on, 265
Welds:
flange, 284–285
groove, 271–272
plug, 279–280
seam, 282–283
slot, 280–281
spot, 281–282
Weld symbol, 263–264
White iron, 201
Whole depth (WD), 292
Width, 1
Woodruff key, 136–137
Working drawing, 12
Worm gears, 290
Wrought iron pipe, 170

X

X axis, 242
XY relationships, 242

Y

Y axis, 242